THE WORLD OF THE ATOM

ooooooooooooooo

The WORLD
of the ATOM

ooooooooooooooo

VOLUME
II

EDITED WITH COMMENTARIES BY

Henry A. Boorse and Lloyd Motz

Foreword by I. I. Rabi

BASIC BOOKS, INC., PUBLISHERS

NEW YORK · LONDON

၀၀၀၀၀၀၀၀၀၀

CONTENTS

ၜၜၜၜၜၜၜၜၜၜၜ

PART II THE FOUNDATIONS OF ATOMIC CHEMISTRY

Volume II

PART

XI

ATOMIC THEORY DEVELOPS

○○○○○○○○○○

ATOMIC NUMBER

○○○○○○○○○○

Henry G. J. Moseley (1887-1915)

The Bohr-Rutherford model of the atom was not immediately accepted, even though Bohr had succeeded in deriving the formula for the Balmer lines of hydrogen, for there appeared to be some difficulties in correlating the Bohr theory with the periodic table of Mendeleev. It had occurred to Mendeleev that, if he arranged the chemical elements according to their atomic weights (their masses), he might discern some kind of regularity in their chemical properties. He then discovered that elements with similar chemical properties did occur in the table periodically according to their weights so that one could arrange them into definite families. This seems to imply that the mass of an atom is the decisive physical parameter that determines its structure and chemical behavior. Now this is in conflict with the Bohr-Rutherford model, as H. G. J. Moseley showed. In this model it is not the mass of the atom that is important as far as its chemical behavior is concerned, but rather the charge on the nucleus—that is, the atomic number—determined by the number of protons in the nucleus.

According to the Bohr-Rutherford model, a nucleus is composed of protons, and, as one passes from one element to the next higher element, the number of protons increases by one so that the charge on the nucleus, and hence the atomic number, increases by one. We should therefore expect to find the chemical properties arranging themselves in a pattern according to the atomic number. Such is the direction that H. G. J. Moseley imparted to atomic physics as the result of his epochal work on the high-frequency spectra of the elements.

Moseley's investigations were concerned with the spectral lines emitted by the heavy elements in the X-ray part of the electromagnetic spectrum.

To obtain an X-ray spectrum, Moseley had to excite heavy atoms. Only in such elements as iron, tin, and silver are the electrons close to the nucleus bound with sufficient energy to emit X-rays during excitation. In the case of light atoms, such as hydrogen and helium, the most energetic radiation is in the ultraviolet wavelengths, which fall far short of the X-ray region Moseley was interested in investigating. To obtain an X-ray spectrum one subjects a target composed of the heavy element to a stream of very energetic electrons. On colliding with the target, these electrons bring about some rearrangement of the deep-lying electrons of the target atoms. When a target atom readjusts itself and returns to its normal state, energy is emitted in the form of X-radiation.

Moseley thought that if the electrons were moving in orbits according to the Bohr theory, the X-ray spectrum of a heavy element should exhibit a line structure similar to that of the hydrogen spectrum. Moreover, it occurred to Moseley that the X-ray spectrum would change in a regular way according to the charge on the nucleus (the atomic number) as one went from one heavy atom to the next if the Bohr-Rutherford model of the atom were correct.

In conducting his experiment, Moseley first had to deal with the continuous part of the X-ray spectrum that is emitted by the bombarding electrons as they slow down in hitting the target. This part of the X-ray spectrum has nothing to do with the structure of the target atom and therefore must be eliminated. Moseley did this by properly arranging his crystal analyzer relative to the slit from which the X-rays were emitted. As he points out in his paper, by allowing the X-rays to strike the face of the crystal at large angles of incidence he was able to reduce the reflection of the continuous radiation to a very small intensity. He was then able to pick out any particular X-ray frequency coming from the slit and reflected from the crystal face by applying the Laue-Bragg law of diffraction to these reflected X-ray beams. According to this law, each particular wavelength is reflected from the face of the crystal at a definite angle which is characteristic of that wavelength and no other.

An examination of Moseley's work shows how simple and straightforward was his approach. His experimental arrangement for investigating and photographing X-ray spectra involved no complex devices, but was built around a crystal mounted in a simple way on a prism table so that it could be rotated to give any desired angle of incidence of the incident X-rays. A measurement of this angle then gave the wavelength of the X-radiation striking the photographic plate.

To understand the results obtained by Moseley in terms of the Bohr theory we must remember that the electrons inside an atom occupy orbits (K, L, M, and so on) at increasing distances from the nucleus; as we go from one element to the next in the atomic table, these orbits lie closer to the nucleus because the charge on the nucleus increases each time we go to the next higher element. This means that the K electrons in the element with atomic number $Z + 1$ are more tightly bound to the nucleus than are the K electrons in the element with atomic number Z.

If we now consider the X-ray lines resulting from the excitation of the K electrons, we should expect to find the frequencies of these lines increasing by a definite (although not always the same) amount as we go from one element to the next heavier one. This should also be true of the lines arising from the L, M electrons, and so on.

This is precisely what Moseley found from his investigations, in which he dealt with two distinct lines. The photograph of these lines for brass, copper, nickel, cobalt, shown in the paper, clearly indicates the step-by-step change in the frequencies of these lines as one progresses from the lighter to the heavier elements. But the significance of these findings is in the discovery that the change in frequency depends not on the change in mass, but rather on the increase in the charge on the nucleus, the atomic number.

Moseley stated this relationship in a simple empirical formula, which he was able to match with the data. This formula may be expressed as follows:

The frequency of a particular line in the X-ray spectrum of an atom is equal to a universal constant multiplied by the square of the charge on the nucleus reduced by one. This formula is really equivalent to the Bohr formula for the frequencies of the lines in the hydrogen optical spectrum. It shows that even when we are dealing with heavy atoms the electrons arrange themselves in discrete orbits around the nucleus of the atom.

As already mentioned, Moseley's formula is important because it shows that the atomic number and not the atomic weight is the decisive quantity in the arrangement of the elements in the periodic table. But another interesting fact of great importance emerged from this research; it should be mentioned in connection with Moseley's experimental proof of van der Broek's idea of atomic number. The fact that the chemical elements could be arranged in a step-by-step sequence, changing by one unit at a time, carries the implication that where the numerical sequence is unbroken *no unsuspected elements can be present*. Thus Moseley's research not only vindicated the idea of atomic number and pointed out the places of undiscovered elements in the periodic table, but it also showed that *no other elements could exist*. Nature had made the elements by adding positive charges one at a time to the nucleus. Since it was shown by Millikan's work that fractional electrical charges do not exist, it is clear from these X-ray experiments that the known and predicted elements in the periodic table form a closed system.

The following article by L. A. Redman provides a portrait of Moseley as he appeared to his contemporaries. It is followed by Moseley's famous paper on atomic number.

০০০০০০০

REDMAN

H. G. J. Moseley [1]

. . . HENRY GWYN JEFFREYS MOSELEY—HARRY to his friends—was born into the quiet security of Oxford academic circles on 23rd November, 1887. Both sides of his family were distinguished in scientific fields. His grandfather, the Rev. Henry Moseley, F.R.S., a canon of Bristol and rector of Olveston, near the river Severn, was the author of numerous works on applied mathematics. His father, H. N. Moseley, F.R.S., after training for a medical career became more interested in pure science. During the years 1872 to 1876 he was engaged as a naturalist aboard the *Challenger* on an expedition investigating oceanic life. In 1881 he married Amabel, the youngest daughter of Mr. J. Gwyn Jeffreys, F.R.S., himself a distinguished conchologist. And in the very same year Moseley's father became Professor of Human and Comparative Anatomy at Oxford. . . .

Little is at present known about Moseley's early life save that he soon took an interest in natural history. This undoubtedly came from his mother's interest and his late father's collection of material brought back from the voyages of the *Challenger*. His interest in natural history continued actively throughout his life. Indeed, when he was working at Manchester he said that when he was feeling fit he wanted to be out walking in the country and that it was only when he was feeling tired out that he felt inclined for laboratory work. During his early years I feel sure his mother gave every encouragement to his enquiring mind.

At thirteen he won a King's scholarship to Eton. A contemporary, who was a year older than Moseley, recollecting his schooldays of 60 years ago, recalled that Moseley was comparatively undistinguished. At that time the only science teaching at Eton amounted to a smattering of chemistry, although Moseley may have done some physics "out of school," i.e., by

[1] L. A. Redman, *Physics Teacher*, 3 (1965), 151–157.

extra payment. The emphasis was on Classics at which Moseley was very bad, as he also was at any English subject: his mathematics were pretty good, though not outstanding. He seems to have been boyishly untidy, one who got on reasonably well with other boys although his interests diverged from theirs to a large extent. In sport he took a normal part and played for "College" against the other houses at football and he also rowed. A "House" is the centre of community life for each group of boys, great rivalries between houses being fought out on the river and sports field. Moseley continued to row when he went up to Oxford.

He entered Trinity College, Oxford, on October 12, 1906, with a Millard Scholarship. There are few records of his life as an undergraduate that I have been able to find. He rowed every year in one or other of the college boats and worked hard at his studies. At the end of the first year he sat the Mathematical Moderations (first Public Examination for the B.A. degree) and his hard work was rewarded since he was placed in the First Class (those few students obtaining the highest marks). Although he was a member of the *Alembicke Club,* which met in various College rooms to discuss scientific topics, he rarely attended the meetings.

The year before he graduated Moseley visited Rutherford in Manchester with a view to working in the physical laboratory there. The impression he made on Rutherford must have been a good one, and Moseley became Lecturer and Demonstrator in the Physics Department at Manchester University immediately after he graduated. He wrote to Rutherford, ". . . It will be a great pleasure to me to work in your laboratory, and after my failure in 'schools' (*final degree examination—he must have aimed for a First and was disappointed when he was placed in the Second Class Honours list*) I consider myself very lucky to have got the opening which I coveted.

"I would like to be guided entirely by you on the subject which I attempt, since until I have had a year or two for reading of a different kind, from that useful for examinations, I cannot profitably choose for myself.

"I will spend August in Oxford, and will then read up Radioactivity in the hope that your suggestion may be in that direction. My present knowledge extends little way beyond your books."

At 23 Moseley was the youngest of Rutherford's brilliant team of young men. Two became heads of Cambridge Colleges and five were destined to become professors, Moseley himself would have certainly been elected a Fellow of the Royal Society and would have been a strong candidate for the Nobel Prize had he lived. Reports of that time indicate that Moseley was from the first recognized by his colleagues as the most original and gifted man on the regular staff after the professor himself.

Moseley's first work at Manchester was specially chosen by Rutherford to ". . . give him experience in accurate measurement and in methods of obtaining high vacua." This led to the publication of a paper "The Number of β-Particles Emitted in the Transformation of Radium" in which Moseley's experiments showed definitely that only one electron, on the average, was emitted during the transformation of one atom of radium B or of radium C. This involved a large amount of careful and accurate experimental work, and Moseley was congratulated by the President of the Royal Society on his clear presentation of a difficult topic when he gave the paper at one of their meetings.

[Working conditions at Manchester during this period were primitive by today's standards but were some of the best available at that time. Later when Moseley went to Oxford (1913) he wrote to Rutherford, "Things seem to move slowly here compared to Manchester . . . liquid air is only made apparently about once a month. However, I naturally do not expect such good conditions for doing work as obtained in Manchester; as I am sure that it is no use looking for the like in England." Those good conditions were maintained by Rutherford on a grant which averaged some £420 a year. This was equivalent to $2,250 at the then rate of exchange and even allowing for the higher purchasing power of such a sum it was still a pitifully small allowance. Never has so small an investment provided such magnificent returns.] Rutherford's enthusiastic team of young researchers included E. N. da C. Andrade, N. Bohr, J. Chadwick, C. G. Darwin, H. Geiger, E. Marsden, H. G. J. Moseley, H. R. Robinson and A. S. Russell. [It meant, inevitably, that much of the apparatus had to be improvised on the spot so that work could continue. In fact, nothing seems to have pleased Rutherford more than to see a young newcomer (Andrade) making a photographic plateholder out of a piece of cardboard so that the experiment wouldn't be held up. Salaries also were small, Moseley was paid £140 ($700) and the other demonstrators £125 ($625).]

Despite material privations the laboratory was a hive of enthusiastic activity, the whole world of physics was in ferment and new discoveries were being announced almost weekly.

This general atmosphere of adventure into the unknown set the background to Moseley's work. After his experiments on the emission of β-particles from radium Moseley next examined whether there was any limit to the positive potential which an insulated body containing radium would reach in a high vacuum. The radium, as was well known, became positively charged due to the loss of electrons. Moseley's good technique enabled him to hold a high vacuum for several weeks and he found that a silvered quartz sphere 9 mm in diameter was raised to a potential of 160,000 volts above that of its surroundings. He concluded: "We see then that a radioactive substance may by the emission of β-radiation charge itself positively to a potential difference of more than 150,000 volts from its surroundings.

This fact provides a striking direct proof of the large amount of energy involved in the expulsion of a β-particle."

Basically this experiment indicates the possibility of converting atomic energy directly into electrical energy. Experimental devices on this principle have been tried both in the U.S.S.R. and in America. . . .

One of Rutherford's great qualities was the enthusiasm he sparked off in those who worked with him. All those who worked at Manchester at that time write about Rutherford's cheerful presence bobbing into each room where experiments were being set up or in progress, exchanging a few words if all was well or drawing up a stool to discuss some difficulty. Then he would be off, singing a tuneless "Onward, Christian Soldiers" if all was well or an equally tuneless but unintelligible dirge if all was not well.

Rutherford's laboratory teas, where he "gingered up" his team by general discussions on a wide range of topics, scientific or otherwise, have become justly famous. Apparently Moseley did not take a very active part in these discussions, and Rutherford did not seem to be at ease with him on these occasions. Rutherford liked to amuse his audience by "talking big" and he felt that Moseley was rather critical of his high spirits.

Remembering those days A. S. Russell wrote, "Moseley was a quiet chap in the lab. Not in the least stuck-up . . . but the opposite of hail-fellow-well-met . . . an unsympathetic observer might deem him proud. He was essentially a good man who lived a quiet stainless life. In technical colloquia he spoke well, always short and to the point on his own field but said nothing much of interest on points a bit outside of it."

Rutherford himself wrote that "in private life Moseley was a pleasant and genial companion with wide interests. . . . He was a keen gardener and a student of natural history."

Moseley did *not* go to the Music Halls as many of his other colleagues did.

A. S. Russell: "I felt that he was so reserved that I could neither like him nor not like him. In the lab we did not realise that he was one of those colts, unrecognised even by his trainers, destined to outstrip the others on the racecourse."

The work which proved Moseley's oirginality and powers of thought beyond all doubt was his investigation of the X-ray spectra of the elements. The importance of the two papers he wrote on this subject can be partly judged by the number of times they have since been read by students. By simply looking at the edges of the closed volumes of the *Philosophical Magazine* for 1913 and 1914 the articles which have been read most stand out clearly by the dirty edges of the pages. The paper most used of all with its much-thumbed pages literally loose from constant use is "High-Frequency Spectra of the Elements" by H. G. J. Moseley.

Work at Manchester under Rutherford had naturally concentrated on aspects of radioactivity. How then did Moseley come to be working with X-rays?

In 1912 von Laue of Munich learned that in a crystal the atoms could be arranged in a space lattice. He immediately suggested to Friedrich an experiment to see if a crystal of copper sulphate (a large one happened to be handy) could diffract an X-ray beam backwards. Assisted by Knipping, Friedrich could find no such back diffraction. But Knipping then tried putting the plate behind the crystal (he actually surrounded it with plates) and the first picture of diffracted X-rays was obtained.

Hearing about this in Manchester and seeing the picture of the X-ray diffraction pattern immediately aroused Moseley's interest. He combined forces with a theoretical physicist C. G. Darwin (the late Sir Charles, grandson of the author of *The Origin of the Species*) who had made a special study of waves. They wanted to find out what X-rays really were. And in a series of experiments lasting some six to eight months they convinced themselves that X-rays behaved like light waves. They were helped in matters of technique by the experience of the late Sir William Bragg and his son, now Sir Lawrence Bragg, Director of the Royal Institution, who were working at Leeds and had become really expert in using X-rays. Sir Lawrence Braggs writes: "After I had shown that one could get specular reflection of X-rays from a crystal face, Moseley and Darwin looked for spectra by reflecting X-rays over a range of angles into an ionisation chamber. They missed the spectra because they made the slit so thin and by ill-luck they just did not happen to hit the angles at which the spectra were reflected (i.e. the line spectra, Moseley and Darwin only observed the continuous spectrum at first—L.A.R.). My father discovered the spectra because he had first used a wide slit in his X-ray spectrometer so he was bound to find the lines when he set the chamber at a series of angles." . . .

The behaviour of the X-rays was still not entirely clear cut. Moseley and Darwin writing to *Nature* on January 21, 1913, on the reflection of the X-rays conclude with a paragraph:

"As Prof. Bragg has shown, the behaviour of the X-rays in connection with ionisation strongly suggests that their energy is concentrated as if they were corpuscular. Since the rays are reflected, they must be some kind of pulse with an extended wave-front, yet after reflection they retain their corpuscular character. Thus the energy of the X-rays appears to show the contrary properties of extension over a wavefront and concentration in a point."

We can see the same sort of confusion which must have been in the minds of those early workers whenever one of our own students meets the wave/particle duality for the first time.

At this stage Moseley and Darwin decided to work independently. Darwin wanted to work out the mathematical theory and Moseley was now confident of his technique in X-ray experiments—he wanted to examine the X-ray line spectra of a sequence of the chemical elements.

At that time (1913) Rutherford's theory of the nuclear atom was established and alpha-particle scattering experiments indicated that the helium nucleus had two units of positive charge, and the nucleus of hydrogen only one. Van der Broek pointed out that these results fitted in with the idea that the nuclear charge is equal to the atomic number, i.e. to the number of the element when they are all arranged in order of increasing atomic weight. Bohr, who was then at Manchester, also adopted the idea of atomic number and used it in his theoretical work on the constitution and spectra of the elements. It seems that the idea of atomic number was fully accepted in the Manchester laboratory as a useful working hypothesis. There was, however, no convincing direct experimental support for it. In June 1913 Bohr discussed with Darwin and Moseley the question of the proper sequence for the arrangement of the elements according to their atomic number and learned then for the first time about Moseley's plans to settle this problem by the systematic measurement of the high-frequency spectra of the elements by the Laue-Bragg method.

Moseley's skill as an experimenter was such that the paper describing the first results of this work was *published* that December. His concentration and phenomenal powers of endurance were indeed remarkable. Darwin said "There were two rules for his work. First, when you start to set up the apparatus for an experiment you must not stop until it is set up. Second, when the apparatus is set up you must not stop work until the experiment is finished." In fact, Moseley was noted for working through the night, making liquid air at two or three in the morning, walking back to his lodgings to snatch a couple of hours' sleep before returning to lecture at 9:30 in the morning. He could be relied on to find somewhere to eat in Manchester—even at three in the morning.

In the first series of experiments Moseley perfected the photographic method of examining the spectra; this was far more accurate than the ionisation method he had used previously. . . .

While preparing this first paper on the high-frequency spectra for publication Moseley was awarded the John Harling Fellowship. This enabled him to stop lecturing and devote all his time to research. Despite all Rutherford's powers of persuasion to keep him at Manchester he went back home to Oxford to work in the Electrical Laboratories there (now part of the Clarendon Laboratory).

As already mentioned, things started slowly at Oxford and Moseley was impatient to examine more elements. On the 7th of December 1913 he wrote to Rutherford, with evident relief ". . . but now I think I shall really be able to get started again." Characteristically he worked fast and on the 18th of January he wrote again to Rutherford saying that he was getting the spectra from aluminium, silver and tin and also of the rare earths. "I do not doubt," said Moseley, "that it will be possible to put every rare earth element into its right pigeon hole and to settle whether any of them are complex and where to look for new ones."

The experiments had new and serious difficulties of their own to be overcome. At Manchester Moseley had been examining the K-radiations but could not obtain high enough voltages to investigate elements beyond silver (47). However, Bohr had also developed a theory for the softer L-radiations and so Moseley used these in his study of the heavier elements. These rays were so soft that they would not pass through aluminium or more than a few centimetres of air, so the system had to be evacuated.

. . . The resulting L-radiations were defined by a narrow vertical slit in an iron screen and then passed through a window of goldbeaters' skin. This skin joined the X-ray tube to the spectrometer and was used because it is extremely transparent to X-rays. The rays then went into the spectrometer, an exhausted iron box, where they were analysed by the crystal of potassium ferrocyanide and then photographed. . . .

During the experiments the pressure on the goldbeaters' skin was relieved every time the spectrometer was exhausted and so the skin was continually breaking. Also in some cases the X-rays were so weak that they could not even penetrate the paper that would shield the photographic plate from the light and so two sheets of black tissue paper were used instead.

Another problem was in obtaining specimens of the elements he wished to examine. In the case of the rare earths he was greatly helped by Professor Urbain of the University of Paris who had spent a lifetime studying them. Professor Urbain spent two days with Moseley at Oxford, in which time Moseley examined the specimens he had brought with him. Writing to Rutherford after Moseley's death, Urbain said "I was most surprised, on my visit to Oxford, to find a very young man capable of doing such remarkable work . . . Moseley's law, for the end as well as for the beginning of the group of rare earths, has established in a few days the conclusions of my efforts of 20 years of patient work. However, it is not only that which makes me admire Moseley's work. His law replaced the somewhat imaginative classification of Mendeléyev with one which was scientifically precise. It brought something definite into a period of hesitant research on the chemical elements. It ended one of the finest chapters in the history of science." . . .

Now the periodic classification of the elements according to Mendeléyev had three pairs of elements which did not fit in. These were potassium and argon, cobalt and nickel and tellurium and iodine. When arranged in order of atomic weights, potassium, a violently active metal, came in the middle of the group of inert gases. When arranged in terms of atomic number, argon comes before potassium and so takes up its rightful place amongst the inert gases. Moseley's new classification also removed the anomalies of the other two pairs of elements by reversing their order as well.

The gaps for which elements had not then been discovered were identified by Moseley as having atomic numbers 43, 61, and 75. It was also thought that there was a rare earth element celtium (72), but Moseley's experiments failed to reveal it. This element was discovered in 1923 by Coster and Hevesy and was named hafnium (72). In this case the method of X-ray analysis was all-important since hafnium is always found with zirconium, and these two are almost impossible to separate chemically. Masurium (43) and rhenium (75) were identified by Noddack, Tacke and Berg. Promethium (61) was finally identified by Marinski and Glendenin in their researches during 1938–42.

In June 1914 Moseley and his mother travelled to Canada and from there went on to attend the British Association Meetings in Australia. Moseley gave an account of his experiments, particularly his more recent ones on the rare earths, but no written record of his conclusions has yet been found.

But by this time War had been declared and as soon as he could Moseley returned to England. He became signals officer to the 38th Brigade of the First Army and on 13th June, 1915, the Brigade left for the Dardanelles. Although Rutherford tried to get him transferred to scientific work which would help the War effort Moseley had sailed before any action could be taken.

In August the Brigade, its men weak with dysentery and jaundice, had been ordered to extend its forward line. This required crossing unknown and extremely difficult country at night: it would have been no easy task for fully fit men in daylight. There seems to be no clear-cut account of what actually happened. They were led, apparently, by two guides in Allied uniforms, but were forced to detour. Finally, completely exhausted, the men slept. They were *in front* of the most forward British post and the guides had disappeared.

It was August 10th, 1915: in daylight, and too late, they realised their exposed position and were attacked by the Turks. Moseley, as signalling officer, tried desperately to telephone the Brigade's position to Headquarters. He was still at his post when, with the enemy only 200 yards away, a bullet smashed into his brain. He was almost 28.

Millikan wrote "In a research which is destined to rank as one of the dozen most brilliant in the history of science a young man twenty-six years old threw open the windows through which we can glimpse the sub-atomic world with a definiteness and certainty never dreamt of before. Had the

European War had no other result than the snuffing out of this young life, that alone would make it one of the most hideous and most irreparable crimes in history." . . .

ᴼᴼᴼᴼᴼᴼᴼᴼ

MOSELEY

The High-Frequency Spectra of the Elements [2]

IN THE ABSENCE OF ANY available method of spectrum analysis, the characteristic types of X radiation, which an atom emits if suitably excited, have hitherto been described in terms of their absorption in aluminum. The interference phenomena exhibited by X-rays when scattered by a crystal have now, however, made possible the accurate determination of the frequencies of the various types of radiation. This was shown by W. H. and W. L. Bragg, who by this method analysed the line spectrum emitted by the platinum target of an X-ray tube. C. G. Darwin and the author extended this analysis and also examined the continuous spectrum, which in this case constitutes the greater part of the radiation. Recently Prof. Bragg has also determined the wave-lengths of the strongest lines in the spectra of nickel, tungsten, and rhodium. The electrical methods which have hitherto been employed are, however, only successful where a constant source of radiation is available. The present paper contains a description of a method of photographing these spectra, which makes the analysis of the X-rays as simple as any other branch of spectroscopy. The author intends first to make a general survey of the principal types of high-frequency radiation, and then to examine the spectra of a few elements in greater detail and with greater accuracy. The results already obtained show that such data have an important bearing on the question of the internal structure of the atom, and strongly support the views of Rutherford and of Bohr.

Kaye has shown that an element excited by a stream of sufficiently fast cathode rays emits its characteristic X radiation. He used as targets a number of substances mounted on a truck inside an exhausted tube. A magnetic device enabled each target to be brought in turn into the line of

---

[2] Henry G. J. Moseley, *Philosophical Magazine,* 26 (1913), 1024–1034; 27 (1914) 703–713. The two papers are combined in this excerpt—Editors.

fire. This apparatus was modified to suit the present work. The cathode stream was concentrated on to a small area of the target, and a platinum plate furnished with a fine vertical slit placed immediately in front of the part bombarded. The tube was exhausted by a Gaede mercury pump, charcoal in liquid air being also sometimes used to remove water vapour. The X-rays, after passing through the slit marked S in [Fig. 54–1], emerged through an aluminium window ·02mm. thick. The rest of the radiation was shut off by a lead box which surrounded the tube. The rays fell on the cleavage face, C, of a crystal of potassium ferrocyanide which was mounted on the prism-table of a spectrometer. The surface of the crystal was vertical and contained the geometrical axis of the spectrometer.

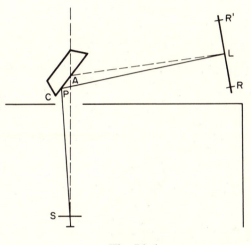

Fig. 54–1.

Now it is known that X-rays consist in general of two types, the heterogeneous radiation and characteristic radiations of definite frequency. The former of these is reflected from such a surface at all angles of incidence, but at the large angles used in the present work the reflexion is of very little intensity. The radiations of definite frequency, on the other hand, are reflected only when they strike the surface at definite angles, the glancing angle of incidence θ, the wave-length λ, and the "grating constant" d of the crystal being connected by the relation

$$n\lambda = 2d \sin \theta, \qquad\qquad (1)$$

where n, an integer, may be called the "order" in which the reflexion occurs. The particular crystal used, which was a fine specimen with face

6 cm. square, was known to give strong reflexions in the first three orders, the third order being the most prominent.

If then a radiation of definite wave-length happens to strike any part P of the crystal at a suitable angle, a small part of it is reflected. Assuming for the moment that the source of the radiation is a point, the locus of P is obviously the arc of a circle, and the reflected rays will travel along the generating lines of a cone with apex at the image of the source. The effect on a photographic plate L will take the form of the arc of an hyperbola, curving away from the direction of the direct beam. With a fine slit at S, the arc becomes a fine line which is slightly curved in the direction indicated.

The photographic plate was mounted on the spectrometer arm, and both the plate and the slit were 17 cm. from the axis. The importance of this arrangement lies in a geometrical property, for when these two distances are equal the point L at which a beam reflected at a definite angle strikes the plate is independent of the position of P on the crystal surface. The angle at which the crystal is set is then immaterial so long as a ray can strike some part of the surface at the required angle. The angle θ can be obtained from the relation $2\theta = 180° - SPL = 180° - SAL$.

The following method was used for measuring the angle SAL. Before taking a photograph a reference line R was made at both ends of the plate by replacing the crystal by a lead screen furnished with a fine slit which coincided with the axis of the spectrometer. A few seconds' exposure to the X-rays then gave a line R on the plate, and so defined on it the line joining S and A. A second line RQ was made in the same way after turning the spectrometer arm through a definite angle. The arm was then turned to the position required to catch the reflected beam and the angles LAP for any lines which were subsequently found on the plate deduced from the known value of RAP and the position of the lines on the plate. The angle LAR was measured with an error of not more than $0°\cdot1$, by superposing on the negative a plate on which reference lines had been marked in the same way at intervals of $1°$. In finding from this the glancing angle of reflexion two small corrections were necessary in practice, since neither the face of the crystal nor the lead slit coincided accurately with the axis of the spectrometer. Wave-lengths varying over a range of about 30 per cent. could be reflected for a given position of the crystal.

In almost all cases the time of exposure was five minutes. Ilford X-ray plates were used and were developed with rodinal. The plates were mounted in a plate-holder, the front of which was covered with black paper. In order to determine the wave-length from the reflexion angle θ it is necessary to know both the order n in which the reflexion occurs and the grating costant d. n was determined by photographing every spectrum both in the second order and the third. This also gave a useful check on the accuracy of the measurements; d cannot be calculated directly for the complicated crystal potassium ferrocyanide. The grating constant of this particular crystal had, however, previously been accurately compared with d', the constant of a specimen of rock-salt. It was found that

$$d = 3d' \frac{\cdot 1988}{\cdot 1985}.$$

Now W. L. Bragg has shown that the atoms in a rock-salt crystal are in simple cubical array. Hence the number of atoms per c.c.

$$2\frac{N\sigma}{M} = \frac{1}{(d')^3}:$$

N, the number of molecules in a gram-mol., $= 6\cdot05 \times 10^{23}$ assuming the charge (e) on an electron to be $4\cdot89 \times 10^{-10}$; σ, the density of this crystal of rock-salt was $2\cdot167$, and M the molecular weight $= 58\cdot46$.

This gives $d' = 2\cdot814 \times 10^{-8}$ and $d = 8\cdot454 \times 10^{-8}$ cm. It is seen that the determination of wave-length depends on $e^{1/3}$ so that the effect of uncertainty in the value of this quantity will not be serious. Lack of homogeneity in the crystal is a more likely source of error, as minute inclusions of water would make the density greater than that found experimentally.

Twelve elements have so far been examined. . . .

[Fig. 54–2] shows the spectra in the third order placed approximately in register. Those parts of the photographs which represent the same angle of reflexion are in the same vertical line. . . . It is to be seen that the spectrum of each element consists of two lines. Of these the stronger has been called α in the table, and the weaker β. The lines found on any of the plates besides α and β were almost certainly all due to impurities. Thus in both the second and third order the cobalt spectrum shows Niα very strongly and Feα faintly. In the third order the nickel spectrum shows Mnα_2 faintly. The brass spectra naturally show α and β both of Cu and of Zn, but Znβ has not yet been found. In the second order the ferro-vanadium and ferro-titanium spectra show very intense third-order Fe lines, and the former also shows Cuα_2 faintly. The Co contained Ni and $0\cdot8$ per cent. Fe, the Ni $2\cdot2$ per cent. Mn, and the V only a trace of Cu. No other lines have been found; but a search over a wide range of wave-lengths has been made only for one or two elements, and perhaps prolonged exposures, which have not yet been attempted, will show more complex spectra. The prevalence of lines due to impurities suggests that this may prove a powerful method of chemical analysis. Its advantage over ordinary spectroscopic methods lies in the simplicity of the spectra and the impossibility of one substance masking the radiation from another. It

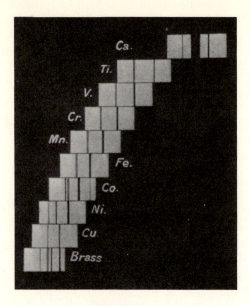

Fig. 54–2.

may even lead to the discovery of missing elements, as it will be possible to predict the position of their characteristic lines. . . .

A discussion will now be given of the meaning of the wave-lengths found for the principal spectrum-line α. In [Table 54–1] the values are of the quantity

$$Q = \sqrt{\frac{\nu}{\frac{3}{4}\nu_0}},$$

ν being the frequency of the radiation α, and ν_0 the fundamental frequency of ordinary line spectra. The latter is obtained from Rydberg's wave-number,

$$N_0 = \frac{\nu}{c} = 109,720.$$

The reason for introducing this particular constant will be given later. It is at once evident that Q increases as we pass from one element to the next, using the chemical order of the elements in the periodic system. While, however, Q increases uniformly the atomic weights vary in an apparently arbitrary manner, so that an exception in their order does not come as a surprise. We have here a proof that there is in the atom a

TABLE 54–1[3]

	α line. $\lambda \times 10^8$ cm.	Q_K.	N. Atomic Number.	β line. $\lambda \times 10^8$.
Aluminium	8·364	12·05	13	7·912
Silicon	7·142	13·04	14	6·729
Chlorine	4·750	16·00	17	
Potassium	3·759	17·98	19	3·463
Calcium	3·368	19·00	20	3·094
Titanium	2·758	20·99	22	2·524
Vanadium	2·519	21·96	23	2·297
Chromium	2·301	22·98	24	2·093
Manganese	2·111	23·99	25	1·818
Iron	1·946	24·99	26	1·765
Cobalt	1·798	26·00	27	1·629
Nickel	1·662	27·04	28	1·506
Copper	1·549	28·01	29	1·402
Zinc	1·445	29·01	30	1·306
Yttrium	0·838	38·1	39	
Zirconium	0·794	39·1	40	
Niobium	0·750	40·2	41	
Molybdenum	0·721	41·2	42	
Ruthenium	0·638	43·6	44	
Palladium	0·584	45·6	46	
Silver	0·560	46·6	47	

fundamental quantity, which increases by regular steps as we pass from one element to the next. This quantity can only be the charge on the central positive nucleus, of the existence of which we already have definite proof. Rutherford has shown, from the magnitude of the scattering of α particles by matter, that this nucleus carries a + charge approximately equal to that of $\frac{A}{2}$ electrons, where A is the atomic weight. Barkla, from the scattering of X rays by matter, has shown that the number of electrons in an atom is roughly $\frac{A}{2}$, which for an electrically neutral atom comes to the same thing. Now atomic weights increase on the average by about 2 units at a time, and this strongly suggests the view that N increases from

---

[3] This table is taken from the second of the two Moseley papers—Editors.

atom to atom always by a single electronic unit. We are therefore led by
experiment to the view that N is the same as the number of the place occupied by the element in the periodic system. This atomic number is then
for H 1 for He 2 for Li 3 . . . for Ca 20 . . . for Zn 30, &c. This theory
was originated by Broeck and since used by Bohr. We can confidently predict that in the few cases in which the order of the atomic weights A
clashes with the chemical order of the periodic system, the chemical properties are governed by N; while A is itself probably a complicated function of N. The very close similarity between the X-ray spectra of the different elements shows that these radiations originate inside the atom, and
have no direct connexion with the complicated light-spectra and chemical
properties which are governed by the structure of its surface.

TABLE 54–2

	α line. $\lambda \times 10^8$ cm.	Q_L.	N. Atomic Number.	β line. $\lambda \times 10^8$.	ϕ line. $\lambda \times 10^8$.	γ line. $\lambda \times 10^8$.
Zirconium	6·091	32·8	40			
Niobium	5·749	33·8	41	5·507		
Molybdenum	5·423	34·8	42	5·187		
Ruthenium	4·861	36·7	44	4·660		
Rhodium	4·622	37·7	45			
Palladium	4·385	38·7	46	4·168		3·928
Silver	4·170	39·6	47			
Tin	3·619	42·6	50			
Antimony	3·458	43·6	51	3·245		
Lanthanum	2·676	49·5	57	2·471	2·424	2·313
Cerium	2·567	50·6	58	2·360	2·315	2·209
Praseodymium	(2·471)	51·5	59	2·265		
Neodymium	2·382	52·5	60	2·175		
Samarium	2·208	54·5	62	2·008	1·972	1·893
Europium	2·130	55·5	63	1·925	1·888	1·814
Gadolinium	2·057	56·5	64	1·853	1·818	
Holmium	1·914	58·6	66	1·711		
Erbium	1·790	60·6	68	1·591	1·563	
Tantalum	1·525	65·6	73	1·330		1·287
Tungsten	1·486	66·5	74			
Osmium	1·397	68·5	76	1·201		1·172
Iridium	1·354	69·6	77	1·155		1·138
Platinum	1·316	70·6	78	1·121		1·104
Gold	1·287	71·4	79	1·092		1·078

The results obtained for the spectra of the L series are given in [Table 54–2] and plotted in [Fig. 54–3]. These spectra contain five lines, α, β, γ, δ, ϵ, reckoned in order of decreasing wave-length and decreasing intensity. There is also always a faint companion α' on the long wave-length side

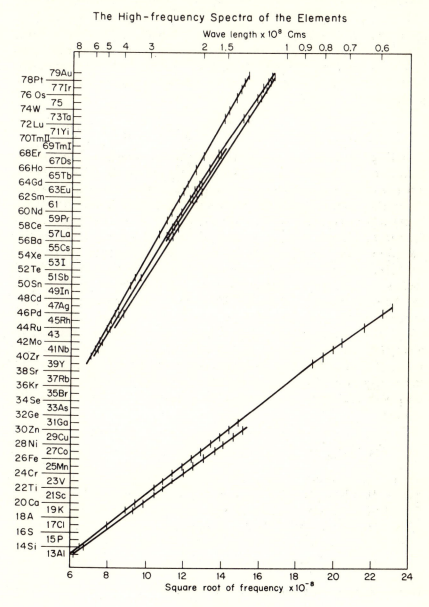

Fig. 54–3.

of α, a rather faint line ϕ between β and γ for the rare earth elements at least, and a number of very faint lines of wave-length greater than α. Of these, α, β, ϕ, and γ have been systematically measured with the object of finding out how the spectrum alters from one element to another. The fact that often values are not given for all these lines merely indicates the incompleteness of the work. The spectra, so far as they have been examined, are so entirely similar that without doubt α, β, and γ at least always exist. Often γ was not included in the limited range of wave-lengths which can be photographed on one plate. Sometimes lines have not been measured, either on account of faintness or of the confusing proximity of lines due to impurities. . . .

CONCLUSIONS

In [Fig. 54–3] the spectra of the elements are arranged on horizontal lines spaced at equal distances. The order chosen for the elements is the order of the atomic weights, except in the cases of A, Co, and Te, where this clashes with the order of the chemical properties. Vacant lines have been left for an element between Mo and Ru, an element between Nd and Sa, and an element between W and Os, none of which are yet known, while Tm, which Welsbach has separated into two constituents, is given two lines. This is equivalent to assigning to successive elements a series of successive characteristic integers. On this principle the integer N for Al, the thirteenth element, has been taken to be 13, and the values of N then assumed by the other elements are given on the left-hand side of [Fig. 54–3]. This proceeding is justified by the fact that it introduces perfect regularity into the X-ray spectra. Examination of [Fig. 54–3] shows that the values of $\nu^{\frac{1}{2}}$ for all the lines examined both in the K and the L series now fall on regular curves which approximate to straight lines. The same thing is shown more clearly by comparing the values of N in [Table 54–1] with those of

$$Q_K = \sqrt{\frac{\nu}{\frac{3}{4}\nu_0}},$$

ν being the frequency of the α line and ν_0 the fundamental Rydberg frequency. It is here plain that $Q_K = N - 1$ very approximately, except for the radiations of very short wave-length which gradually diverge from this relation. Again, in [Table 52–2], a comparison of N with

$$Q_L = \sqrt{\frac{\nu}{\frac{5}{36}\nu_0}},$$

where ν is the frequency of the L α line, shows that

$$Q_L = N - 7 \cdot 4$$

approximately, although a systematic deviation clearly shows that the relation is not accurately linear in this case.

Now if either the elements were not characterized by these integers, or any mistake had been made in the order chosen or in the number of places left for unknown elements, these regularities would at once disappear. We can therefore conclude from the evidence of the X-ray spectra alone, without using any theory of atomic structure, that these integers are really characteristic of the elements. Further, as it is improbable that two different stable elements should have the same integer, three, and only three, more elements are likely to exist between Al and Au. As the X-ray spectra of these elements can be confidently predicted, they should not be difficult to find. . . .

SUMMARY

1. Every element from aluminium to gold is characterized by an integer N which determines its X-ray spectrum. Every detail in the spectrum of an element can therefore be predicted from the spectra of its neighbours.

2. This integer N, the atomic number of the element, is identified with the number of positive units of electricity contained in the atomic nucleus.

3. The atomic numbers for all elements from Al to Au have been tabulated on the assumption that N for Al is 13.

4. The order of the atomic numbers is the same as that of the atomic weights, except where the latter disagrees with the order of the chemical properties.

5. Known elements correspond with all the numbers between 13 and 79 except three. There are here three possible elements still undiscovered.

6. The frequency of any line in the X-ray spectrum is approximately proportional to $A(N - b)^2$, where A and b are constants.

55

ooooooooooo

QUANTUM THEORY OF
RADIATION AND
ATOMIC PROCESSES

ooooooooooo

Albert Einstein (1879-1955)

Although the Bohr theory of atomic spectra and Moseley's work
on the X-ray spectra of heavy atoms had placed the nuclear atom in an
unassailable position, one more step had yet to be taken to complete the
picture and to give the nuclear atom a logically satisfying structure. This
was to show that the Planck radiation formula can be derived from the
Bohr theory and its stationary states. Einstein achieved this result in the
year 1917, when he wrote the last in his series of monumental papers
on the quantum nature of radiation. In some respects this is the most
penetrating of this group of papers, for in it he not only clearly establishes that the interaction between a radiation field and atoms (or
resonators, as he calls them) occurs via the emission and absorption of
quanta or photons, but he also derives the Planck radiation formula from
the most general principles, without making any assumptions about the
nature of the resonators. At the same time, Einstein clarifies the phenomena of emission and absorption of radiation by atoms and shows
that these processes are intimately related to the probabilities of an atom's
passing from one state to another. Finally, in this paper he emphasizes
the importance of taking into account the momentum of a quantum and
in a sense thus foresees the Compton effect. This is indicated in Einstein's

---

Note: The reader's attention is drawn to the similar appearance of the symbol ν
for the frequency and the italic vee, v, used to denote velocity.

statement that the emission and absorption of radiation by atoms are "fully directed events" and not spherically symmetric ones.

We recall that Planck derived his radiation formula by introducing harmonic oscillators (the Planck resonators) as the constituents of matter in equilibrium with the radiation. Bohr later used the quantum theory to explain the line spectrum of the elements by introducing his postulates about the absorption and emission of photons by individual atoms. However, up to that time (1913) nobody had shown that Planck's radiation law is independent of the type of resonators that one assumes and that the law can be derived without making any assumptions about the specific nature of the atomic systems. This Einstein did in the paper we are here discussing, by means of general statistical arguments in which the only assumptions are that the atoms (or molecules, as Einstein calls them) are in dynamic equilibrium with the radiation field and that each atom can be in only one of a set of discrete atomic states. The atom is then pictured as interacting with the radiation field by absorbing photons from and emitting photons into the field.

To make the analysis as simple as possible Einstein considers only two of the possible quantum states of the atom and investigates the condition for statistical equilibrium between these two states and the radiation field surrounding the atoms. He then considers three possible processes involving the emission and absorption of radiation by the atoms and assumes that these processes proceed at such rate that the total number of atoms in each of the two quantum states does not change with time (the condition of statistical equilibrium). Two of the processes involve the emission of photons by the atoms and one involves absorption, and we already find in the mere enumeration of these processes a departure from previous ideas. For in considering the emission of radiation, Einstein assumes not only that an atom can radiate a photon spontaneously, and thus pass from a higher to a lower state of energy, but also that the atom in the higher state can be induced or stimulated to emit a photon more readily than it would spontaneously. This can be achieved in the presence of electromagnetic radiation or photons of the same frequency as that of the emitted photons. Einstein called this "induced emission of radiation."

Einstein now introduces probability coefficients (the famous Einstein A and B coefficients) for each of these three processes, spontaneous emission, stimulated emission, and absorption. He assumes that the number of each of these processes occurring per unit time is proportional to the appropriate Einstein coefficient times the number of atoms in the given state. The spontaneous emission process is proportional only to the probability coefficient times this number of atoms, but the process of stimulated emission and the process of absorption are proportional to this number of atoms multiplied by the product of the appropriate coefficient for that process and the density of the radiation of frequency corresponding to the energy difference between the two quantum states.

Since statistical equilibrium requires that the number of processes per unit time involving transitions of atoms from the higher to the lower state (emission of photons) equal the number of processes per unit time involving transitions of atoms from the lower to the higher state (absorption), Einstein sets up an equation expressing this condition. This equation involves the three Einstein coefficients, the energy density of the radiation, and the numbers of atoms in the two quantum states at any moment.

To derive the Planck formula Einstein now sets up two relationships among his three probability coefficients and uses the general statistical law (the famous Boetzmann law) for the distribution of atoms among possible atomic states to eliminate from his equation the number of atoms in each state. This last relationship introduces the temperature of the equilibrium ensemble of atoms and radiation as well as the energy difference between the two states. To obtain the two relations among his three probability coefficients Einstein considers, first, the limiting case of the temperature going to infinity, and second, the limiting case for which the Wien law is valid. In this way he eliminates the probability coefficients from his equilibrium equation and obtains the Planck formula for the energy density of black-body radiation. At the same times he derives, as a necessary condition, Bohr's hypothesis that in going from one state to another an atom always emits one photon whose frequency is given by the energy difference between the two states divided by Planck's constant.

One of the remarkable things in Einstein's derivation of Planck's formula is the appearance of the stimulated emission process, which seems to play a rather mysterious role and which was considered until recently as a rather curious theoretical feature of the problem without any apparent practical application. But during the last two decades Einstein's hypothesis of stimulated emission of radiation has received its most dramatic experimental verification in the development of the Maser and the Laser by Charles Townes and his collaborators. The word maser is derived from the first letters of the phrase "microwave amplification by the stimulated emission of radiation" and the word laser is obtained from the phrase "light amplification by the stimulated emission of radiation."

In both of these devices radiation of a given frequency is greatly amplified by allowing the photons of the radiation to stimulate excited atoms to emit additional photons of the same kind. The remarkable property of the amplified beam thus obtained is its very high coherence: The amplified beam consists of photons that are all of very nearly the same frequency and there is hardly any spreading of the beam at all. This means that very energetic, monochromatic beams of radiation can be obtained and sent over great distances without attenuation. The basis for this is given very early in Einstein's paper when he points out that the emission and absorption of radiation is accompanied by a change in the momentum of the atom. Thus, when an atom is stimulated to emit a photon by a passing photon, the atom has momentum transferred to it whose direction is opposite to that of the passing photon. This means that the atom must emit another photon in the same direction as that of the passing photon. This is stated by Einstein as follows.

> If as a result of incident radiation the process $Z_n \rightarrow Z_m$ (absorption) occurs, then an amount of momentum $(E_n - E_m)/c$ is transferred to the molecule in the direction of propagation of the radiation. If we have the process $Z_m \rightarrow Z_n$ for the case of incident radiation (stimulated emission), the magnitude of the transferred momentum is the same, but it is in the opposite direction.

Einstein points out two other important consequences of his derivation of the Planck formula. The first concerns the direction of photons emitted. Whereas, according to the classical wave theory of radiation, the radiation leaves the atom in the form of a spherical wave (that is, the emission occurs symmetrically in all directions), Planck's formula can be derived only if one assumes that the emission process is a directed one. This, as Einstein points out, must be true whether the emission is due to stimulation by a beam of incident radiation or whether it is spontaneous.

The second consequence concerns the momentum of radiation. As Einstein states in the last paragraph of his paper, almost all of the previous work on the interaction of atoms and radiation dealt with the energy exchange between the atom and the radiation field but neglected the momentum exchange because the momentum of the radiation is very small, so that the momentum transferred to the atom is negligible as compared to the energy. Einstein correctly concludes, however, that for theoretical considerations this momentum transfer is of extreme importance and must be taken into account just as energy interchange is. He states:

> . . . But for theoretical considerations this small effect [momentum transfer] is on an equal footing with the energy transferred because momentum and energy are very intimately related to each other; a theory may therefore be considered correct only if it can be shown that the momentum transferred according to it from the radiation to the matter leads to the kind of motion that is demanded by thermodynamics.

This insight into the importance of the momentum of radiation was extremely prophetic for it contains in it the germ of the Compton effect. When Compton analyzed his experiments on the scattering of X-rays by electrons in 1923, he found that he could understand the results only if he took into account the conservation of both energy and momentum in the interaction between the electron and the X-ray photon.

৹৹৹৹৹৹৹৹

E I N S T E I N

The Quantum Theory of Radiation [1]

T H E   F O R M A L   S I M I L A R I T Y   O F   T H E   spectral distribution curve of temperature radiation to Maxwell's velocity distribution curve is too striking to have remained hidden very long. Indeed, in the important theoretical paper in which Wien derived his displacement law

$$\rho = v^3 f\left(\frac{v}{T}\right) \tag{1}$$

he was led by this similarity to a farther correspondence with the radiation formula. He discovered, as is known, the formula [Wien's radiation formula]

$$\rho = \alpha v^3 e^{-\frac{hv}{kT}} \tag{2}$$

which is recognized today as the correct limiting formula for large values of $\frac{v}{T}$. Today we know that no consideration which is based on classical mechanics and electrodynamics can lead to a useful radiation formula; rather that the classical theory leads to the Rayleigh formula.

$$\rho = \frac{k\alpha}{h} v^2 T \tag{3}$$

After Planck, in his ground-breaking investigation, established his radiation formula

$$\rho = \alpha v^3 \frac{1}{e^{\frac{hv}{kT}} - 1} \tag{4}$$

[1] Albert Einstein, *Physikalische Zeitschrift*, 18 (1917), 121–128—trans. Editors.

on the assumption that there are discrete elements of energy, from which quantum theory developed very rapidly, Wien's considerations, from which formula (2) evolved, quite naturally were forgotten.

A little while ago I obtained a derivation, related to Wien's original idea, of the Planck radiation formula which is based on the fundamental assumption of quantum theory and which makes use of the relationship of Maxwell's curve to the spectral distribution curve. This derivation deserves consideration not only because of its simplicity, but especially because it appears to clarify the processes of emission and absorption of radiation in matter, which is still in such darkness for us. In setting down certain fundamental hypotheses concerning the absorption and emission of radiation by molecules that are closely related to quantum theory, I showed that molecules with a distribution of states in the quantum theoretical sense for temperature equilibrium are in dynamical equilibrium with the Planck radiation; in this way, the Planck formula (4) was obtained in a surprisingly simple and general way. It was obtained from the condition that the quantum theoretic partition of states of the internal energy of the molecules is established only by the emission and absorption of radiation.

If the assumed hypotheses about the interaction of matter and radiation are correct, they will give us more than just the correct statistical partition or distribution of the internal energy of the molecules. During absorption and emission of radiation there is also present a transfer of momentum to the molecules; this means that just the interaction of radiation and molecules leads to a velocity distribution of the latter. This must clearly be the same as the velocity distribution which molecules acquire as the result of their mutual interaction by collisions, that is, it must coincide with the Maxwell distribution. We must require that the mean kinetic energy which a molecule (per degree of freedom) acquires in a Planck radiation field of temperature T be

$$\frac{kT}{2};$$

this must be valid regardless of the nature of the molecules and independent of frequencies which the molecules absorb and emit. In this paper we wish to verify that this far-reaching requirement is, indeed, satisfied quite generally; as a result of this our simple hypotheses about the emission and absorption of radiation acquire new supports.

In order to obtain this result, however, we must enlarge, in a definite way, the previous fundamental hypotheses which were related entirely to the exchange of energy. We are faced with this question: Does the molecule suffer a push, when it absorbs or emits the energy ϵ? As an example we consider, from the classical point of view, the emission of radiation. If a body emits the energy ϵ, it acquires a backward thrust [impulse] $\frac{\epsilon}{c}$ if all the radiation ϵ is radiated in the same direction. If, however, the radiation occurs through a spatially symmetric process, for example, spherical waves, there is then no recoil at all. This alternative also plays a role in the quantum theory of radiation. If a molecule, in going from one possible quantum theoretic state to another, absorbs or emits the energy ϵ in the form of radiation, such an elementary process can be looked upon as partly or fully directed in space, or also as a symmetric (non-directed) one. It turns out that we obtain a theory that is free of contradictions only if we consider the above elementary processes as being fully directed events; herein lies the principal result of the considerations that follow.

FUNDAMENTAL HYPOTHESES OF THE QUANTUM THEORY—CANONICAL DISTRIBUTION OF STATES

According to the quantum theory, a molecule of a definite kind may, aside from its orientation and its translational motion, be in one of only a discrete set of states $Z_1, Z_2, \ldots Z_n \ldots$ whose (internal) energies are $\epsilon_1, \epsilon_2, \ldots \epsilon_n \ldots$ If the molecules of this kind belong to a gas of temperature T, then the relative abundance W_n of the state Z_n is given by the statistical mechanical canonical partition function for states

$$W_n = p_n e^{-\frac{\epsilon_n}{kT}} \tag{5}$$

In this formula $k = \frac{R}{N}$ is the well-known Boltzmann constant, p_n a number that is independent of T and characteristic of the molecule and the state, which we may call the statistical "weight" of the state. Formula (5) can be derived from the Boltzmann principle or purely from thermodynamics. Equation (5) is the expression of the most far-reaching generalization of the Maxwellian distribution of velocities.

The latest important advances in quantum theory deal with the theoretical determination of the quantum theoretical possible states Z_n and their weights p_n. For the principal part of the present investigation, it is not necessary to have a more detailed determination of the quantum states.

HYPOTHESES ABOUT THE ENERGY EXCHANGE THROUGH RADIATION

Let Z_n and Z_m be two possible quantum theoretical states of a gas molecule whose energies ϵ_n and ϵ_m respectively, satisfy the inequality

$$\epsilon_m > \epsilon_n$$

Let the molecule be able to pass from the state Z_n to the state Z_m by absorbing the radiation energy $\epsilon_m - \epsilon_n$; similarly let the transition from state Z_n to the state Z_m be possible through the emission of this amount of energy. Let the radiation emitted or absorbed by the molecule for the given index and combination (m, n) have the characteristic frequency ν.

We now introduce certain hypotheses about the laws which are decisive for these transitions. These hypotheses are obtained by carrying over the known classical relations for a Planck resonator to the unknown quantum theoretical relations.

Emission

A Planck resonator that is vibrating radiates energy, according to Hertz, in a known way independently of whether it is stimulated by an external field or not. In accordance with this, let a molecule be able to pass from the state Z_m to the state Z_n with the emission of radiant energy $\epsilon_m - \epsilon_n$ of frequency ν without being excited by any external cause. Let the probability dW for this to happen in the time dt be

$$dW = A_m{}^n dt \qquad\qquad (A)$$

where $A_m{}^n$ is a characteristic constant for the given index combination.

The assumed statistical law corresponds to that of a radioactive reaction: that elementary process of such a reaction in which only γ-rays are emitted. We need not assume that this process requires no time; this time need only be negligible compared to the times which the molecule spends in the states Z_1, and so on.

Incident Radiation

If a Planck resonator is in a radiation field, the energy of the resonator changes because the electromagnetic field of the radiation does work on the resonator; this work can be positive or negative depending on the phases of the resonator and the oscillating field. In accordance with this, we introduce the following quantum theoretical hypothesis. Under the action of the radiation density ρ of the frequency ν a molecule in state Z_n can go over to state Z_m by absorbing the radiation energy $\epsilon_m - \epsilon_n$ in accordance with the probability law

$$dW = B_n{}^m \rho\, dt \qquad\qquad (B)$$

In the same way, let the transition $Z_m \to Z_n$ under the action of the radiation also be possible, whereby the radiation energy $\epsilon_m - \epsilon_n$ is emitted according to the probability law

$$dW = B_m{}^n \rho\, dt \qquad\qquad (B')$$

$B_n{}^m$ and $B_m{}^n$ are constants. We call both processes "changes of states through incident radiation."

The question presents itself now as to the momentum that is transferred to the molecule in these changes of state. We begin with the events associated with incident radiation. If a directed bundle of rays does work on a Planck resonator, then an equivalent amount of energy is removed from the bundle. This transfer of energy results, according to the law of momentum, to a momentum transfer from the beam to the resonator. The latter therefore experiences a force in the direction of the ray of the radiation beam. If the energy transferred is negative, the force acting on the resonator is opposite in direction. In the case of the quantum hypothesis, this clearly means the following. If, as the result of incident radiation, the process $Z_n \to Z_m$ occurs, then an amount of momentum

$$\frac{\epsilon_m - \epsilon_n}{c}$$

is transferred to the molecule in the direction of propagation of the bundle of radiation. If we have the process $Z_m \to Z_n$ for the case of incident radiation, the magnitude of the transferred momentum is the same, but it is in the opposite direction. If a molecule is simultaneously exposed to many bundles of radiation, we assume that the total energy $\epsilon_m - \epsilon_n$ is taken from or added to just one of these bundles, so that even in this case the momentum

$$\frac{\epsilon_m - \epsilon_n}{c}$$

is transferred to the molecule.

In the case of emission of energy by radiation by a Planck resonator, there is no net transfer of momentum to the resonator because, according to classical theory, the emission occurs as a spherical wave. However, we have already noted that we can arrive at a contradiction-free quantum theory only if we assume that the process of emission is a directed one. Every elementary process of emission $(Z_m \to Z_m)$ will then result in a transfer to the molecule of an amount of momentum

$$\frac{\epsilon_m - \epsilon_n}{c}.$$

If the molecule is isotropic, we must take every direction of emission as equally probable. If the molecule is not isotropic, we arrive at the same result if the orientation changes in a random way in the course of time. We must, in any case, make such an assumption also for the statistical laws

(B) and (B′) for incident radiation since otherwise the constants $B_n{}^m$ and $B_m{}^n$ would have to depend on direction, which we can avoid by assuming isotropy or pseudo-isotropy (through setting up temporal mean values).

DERIVATION OF THE PLANCK RADIATION LAW

We now enquire about those effective radiation densities ρ which must prevail in order that the energy exchange between molecules and radiation as a result of the statistical laws (A), (B) and (B′) shall not disturb the distribution of molecular states present as a consequence of equation (5). For this, it is necessary and sufficient that on the average, per unit time, as many elementary processes of type (B) take place as processes (A) and (B′) together. This condition gives as a result of (5), (A), (B), (B′), for the elementary processes corresponding to the index combination (m, n) the equation

$$p_n e^{-\frac{\epsilon_n}{kT}} B_n{}^m \rho = p_m e^{-\frac{\epsilon_m}{kT}} (B_m{}^n \rho + A_m{}^n)$$

If, further, ρ is to become infinite as T does, the constants $B_n{}^m$ and $B_m{}^n$ must satisfy the relation

$$p_n B_n{}^m = p_m B_m{}^n \tag{6}$$

We then obtain as the condition for dynamical equilibrium the equation

$$\rho = \frac{A_m{}^n / B_m{}^n}{e^{\frac{\epsilon_m - \epsilon_n}{kT}} - 1} \tag{7}$$

This is the dependence of the radiation density on the temperature that is given by the Planck law. From the Wien displacement law (1) it then follows immediately that

$$\frac{A_m{}^n}{B_m{}^n} = a\nu^3 \tag{8}$$

and

$$\epsilon_m - \epsilon_n = h\nu \tag{9}$$

where a and h are universal constants. To obtain the numerical values of α and h we must have an exact theory of electrodynamic and mechanical processes; we content ourselves for the moment with the Rayleigh law in the limit of high temperatures, where the classical theory is valid in the limit.

Equation (9) is, as we know, the second principal rule in Bohr's theory of spectra, about which we may assert, following upon Sommerfeld's and Epstein's completion of the theory, that it belongs to the most fully verified domain of our science. It also contains implicitly the photochemical equivalent law, as I have already shown.

METHOD FOR CALCULATING THE MOTION OF MOLECULES IN RADIATION FIELDS

We now turn our attention to the investigation of the motion imparted to our molecules by the radiation field. We make use in this of a method that is known to us from the theory of Brownian motion and which I have often used in investigating motions in a region containing radiation. To simplify the calculation, we shall carry it through for the case in which the motion occurs only along the X-direction of the coordinate system. We further content ourselves with calculating the mean value of the kinetic energy of the translational motion, and thus dispense with proof that these velocities v are distributed according to the Maxwell law. Let the mass M of the molecule be large enough so that higher powers of $\frac{v}{c}$ can be neglected relative to lower ones; we can then apply the usual mechanics to the molecule. Moreover, without any loss in generality, we may carry out the calculation as though the states with indices m and n were the only ones the molecule can be in.

The momentum Mv of a molecule undergoes two kinds of changes in the short time τ. Even though the radiation is the same in all directions, the molecule, because of its motion, will experience a resistance to its motion that stems from the radiation. Let this opposing force be Rv, where R is a constant to be determined later. This force would ultimately bring the molecule to rest if the randomness of the action of the radiation field were not such as to transfer to the molecule a momentum Δ of alternating sign and varying magnitude; this random effect will, in opposition to the previous one, sustain a certain amount of motion of the molecule. At the end of the given short time τ the momentum of the molecule will equal

$$Mv - Rv\tau + \Delta$$

Since the velocity distribution is to remain constant in time, the mean of the absolute value of the above quantity must equal that of the quantity

Mv; thus, the mean values of the squares of both quantities averaged over a long time or over a large number of molecules must be equal:

$$\overline{(Mv - Rv_\tau + \Delta)^2} = \overline{(Mv)^2}$$

Since we have taken into account the influence of v on the momentum of the molecule separately, we must discard the mean value $v\Delta$. On developing the left-hand side of the equation we thus obtain

$$\overline{\Delta^2} = \overline{2RMv^2\tau} \tag{10}$$

The mean value $\overline{v^2}$ which the radiation of temperature T by its interaction imparts to the molecule must just equal the mean value $\overline{v^2}$ which the gas molecule acquires at temperature T according to the gas law and the kinetic theory of gases. For otherwise the presence of our molecules would disturb the thermal equilibrium between thermal radiation and an arbitrary gas of the same temperature. We must therefore have

$$\frac{\overline{Mv^2}}{2} = \frac{kT}{2} \tag{11}$$

Equation (10) thus goes over into

$$\frac{\overline{\Delta^2}}{\tau} = 2RkT \tag{12}$$

The investigation is now to be carried through as follows. For a given radiation density $(\rho(v))$ we shall be able to compute $\overline{\Delta^2}$ and R by means of our hypotheses about the interaction between radiation and molecules. If we put this result into (12), this equation will have to be identically satisfied when ρ is expressed as a function of v and T by means of Planck's equation (4).

COMPUTING R

Let a molecule of the given kind be in uniform motion with speed v along the X-axis of the coordinate system K. We inquire about the momentum transferred on the average from the radiation to the molecule per unit time. To calculate this we must consider the radiation from a coordinate system K' that is at rest with respect to the given molecule. For we have formulated our hypotheses about emission and absorption only for molecules at rest. The transformation to the system K' has often been performed in the literature. Nevertheless, I shall repeat the simple considerations here for the sake of clarity.

Relative to K the radiation is isotropic, that is, the quantity of radiation in a solid angle $d\kappa$ in the direction of the radiation in a frequency range $d\nu$ is

$$\rho d\nu \, \frac{d\kappa}{4\pi} \tag{13}$$

where ρ depends only on the frequency ν but not on the direction of the radiation. This special beam corresponds to a special beam in the system K' which is also characterized by a frequency range $d\nu'$ and a solid angle $d\kappa'$. The volume density of this special beam is

$$\rho'(\nu',\phi')d\nu' \, \frac{d\kappa'}{4\pi} \tag{13'}$$

This defines ρ'. It depends on the direction of the radiation which, in the familiar manner, is defined by the angle ϕ' it makes with the X' axis and which its projection on the Y', Z' plane makes with the Y' axis. These angles correspond to the angles ϕ and ψ which in an analogous manner determine the direction of $d\kappa$ in K.

To begin with, it is clear that the same transformation law between (13) and (13') must hold as between the amplitudes A^2 and A'^2 of a plane wave moving in the corresponding direction. Hence, to our desired approximation we have

$$\frac{\rho'(\nu',\phi')d\nu'd\kappa'}{\rho(\nu)d\nu d\kappa} = 1 - 2\frac{\nu}{c}\cos\phi \tag{14}$$

or

$$\rho'(\nu',\phi') = \rho(\nu)\frac{d\nu}{d\nu'}\frac{d\kappa}{d\kappa'}\left(1 - 2\frac{\nu}{c}\cos\phi\right) \tag{14'}$$

The relativity theory further gives the formulae, valid to the desired approximation,

$$\nu' = \nu\left(1 - \frac{\nu}{c}\cos\phi\right) \tag{15}$$

$$\cos\phi' = \cos\phi - \frac{\nu}{c} + \frac{\nu}{c}\cos^2\phi \tag{16}$$

$$\psi' = \psi \tag{17}$$

From (15) it follows, to the same approximation, that

$$\nu = \nu'\left(1 + \frac{\nu}{c}\cos\phi'\right).$$

Hence, again to the desired approximation

$$\rho(\nu) = \rho\left(\nu' + \frac{\nu}{c}\nu'\cos\phi'\right)$$

or

$$\rho(\nu) = \rho(\nu') + \frac{\partial\rho(\nu')}{\partial\nu}\left(\frac{\nu}{c}\nu'\cos\phi'\right) \tag{18}$$

Further, according to (15), (16), and (17)

$$\frac{d\nu}{d\nu'} = \left(1 + \frac{\nu}{c}\cos\phi'\right)$$

$$\frac{d\kappa}{d\kappa'} = \frac{\sin\phi'\,d\phi'\,d\psi'}{\sin\phi\,d\phi\,d\psi} = \frac{d(\cos\phi)}{d(\cos\phi')} = 1 - 2\frac{\nu}{c}\cos\phi'$$

As a result of these two equations and equation (18), equation (14′) goes over into

$$\rho'(\nu', \phi') = \left[(\rho)_{\nu'} + \frac{\nu}{c}\nu'\cos\phi'\left(\frac{\partial\rho}{\partial\nu}\right)_{\nu'}\right]\left(1 - 3\frac{\nu}{c}\cos\phi'\right) \tag{19}$$

With the aid of (19) and our hypotheses about the radiation from and radiation onto molecules, we can easily calculate the average momentum transferred to the molecule per unit time. Before we can do this, however, we must say something to justify our procedure. It may be objected that equations (14), (15), (16) are based on Maxwell's theory of the electromagnetic field that is not consistent with the quantum theory. This objection deals, however, more with the form than with the substance of the problem. For, no matter how the theory of electromagnetic processes may be formulated, in any case the Doppler principle and the law of aberration still remain, and hence also the equations (15) and (16). Moreover, the validity of the energy relationship (14) certainly extends beyond that of the wave theory; this transformation law is also valid, for example, according to relativity theory, for the energy density of a mass of infinitesimally small rest density that is moving with the [quasi-] speed of light. We may therefore assert the validity of equation (19) for any theory of radiation.

The radiation belonging to the solid angle $d\kappa'$ would, according to (B), give rise to

$$B_n^m \rho'(\nu', \phi') \frac{d\kappa'}{4\pi}$$

elementary processes per second of radiation events of the type $Z_n \rightarrow Z_m$ if the molecule after each such process immediately returned to state

Z_n. Actually, however, the time of lingering in state Z_n, according to (5), is

$$\frac{1}{S} p_n e^{-\frac{\epsilon_n}{kT}}$$

where we have used the abbreviation

$$S = p_n e^{-\frac{\epsilon_n}{kT}} + p_m e^{-\frac{\epsilon_m}{kT}} \tag{20}$$

The number of these processes per second is therefore actually

$$\frac{1}{S} p_n e^{-\frac{\epsilon_n}{kT}} B_n{}^m \rho'(\nu', \phi') \frac{d\kappa'}{4\pi}.$$

In each of these elementary processes the momentum

$$\frac{\epsilon_m - \epsilon_n}{c} \cos \phi'$$

is transferred to the molecule in the direction of the X'-axis. In an analogous manner we find, based on (B') that the corresponding number of elementary processes of radiation events of type $Z_m \to Z_n$ per second is

$$\frac{1}{S} p_m e^{-\frac{\epsilon_m}{kT}} B_m{}^n \rho'(\nu', \phi') \frac{d\kappa'}{4\pi}$$

and in each such elementary process the momentum

$$-\frac{\epsilon_m - \epsilon_n}{c} \cos \phi'$$

is transferred to the molecule. The total momentum transferred to the molecule per unit time by incident radiation is, keeping in mind (6) and (9),

$$\frac{h\nu'}{cS} p_n B_n{}^m \left(e^{-\frac{\epsilon_n}{kT}} - e^{-\frac{\epsilon_m}{kT}} \right) \int \rho'(\nu', \phi') \cos \phi' \frac{d\kappa'}{4\pi}$$

where the integration is to be taken over all solid angles. Carry this out, and we obtain with the aid of (19) the value

$$-\frac{h\nu}{c^2 S} \left(\rho - (\tfrac{1}{3})\nu \frac{\partial \rho}{\partial \nu} \right) p_n B_n{}^m \left(e^{-\frac{\epsilon_n}{kT}} - e^{-\frac{\epsilon_m}{kT}} \right) \nu.$$

Here we have represented the effective frequency again with ν and not with ν'. This expression gives, however, the total momentum transferred on the average to a molecule moving with speed v. For it is clear that those elementary processes of emission of radiation not induced by the action of the radiation field have no preferred direction as seen from system K$'$ and hence, on the average, cannot transfer any momentum to the molecule. We thus obtain as the final result of our considerations

$$R = \frac{h\nu}{c^2 S}\left(\rho - \tfrac{1}{3}\nu\,\frac{\partial\rho}{\partial\nu}\right) p_n B_n{}^m e^{-\frac{\epsilon_n}{kT}}\left(1 - e^{-\frac{h\nu}{kT}}\right) \tag{21}$$

CALCULATING $\overline{\Delta^2}$

It is much easier to calculate the random effect of the elementary processes on the mechanical behavior of the molecule. For we can calculate this for a molecule at rest for which the approximation which we have been using applies.

Let some event cause the momentum λ to be transferred to a molecule in the X direction. This momentum is to be of varying magnitude and direction from moment to moment. However, let λ obey a statistical law such that its average value vanishes. Then let $\lambda_1, \lambda_2 \ldots$ be the momenta which are transferred to the molecule in the X-direction by various operating causes that are independent of each other so that the total momentum that is transferred is

$$\Delta = \Sigma\lambda_\nu$$

We then have (if for the individual λ_ν their mean values $\overline{\lambda_\nu}$ vanish)

$$\overline{\Delta^2} = \overline{\Sigma\lambda_\nu{}^2} \tag{22}$$

If the mean values $\overline{\lambda_\nu{}^2}$ of the individual momenta are all equal to each other $(= \overline{\lambda^2})$ and if l is the total number of processes giving rise to momenta, we have the relation

$$\overline{\Delta^2} = \overline{l\lambda^2} \tag{22a}$$

According to our hypothesis, in each process of incident radiation and outflowing radiation, the momentum

$$\lambda = \frac{h\nu}{c}\cos\phi$$

is transferred to the molecule. Here ϕ is the angle between the X-axis and some randomly chosen direction. Hence, we obtain

$$\bar{\lambda}^2 = \tfrac{1}{3} \left(\frac{h\nu}{c}\right)^2.$$

Since we assume that all the elementary processes that are present are to be considered as events that are independent of each other, we may apply (22a); l is then the number of all elementary processes that occur in the time τ. This is twice as large as the number of radiation-incident processes $Z_n \to Z_m$ in the time τ. We thus have

$$l = \frac{2}{S} p_n B_n{}^m e^{-\frac{\epsilon_n}{kT}} \rho \tau \tag{24}$$

From (23), (24) and (22) we thus obtain

$$\frac{\overline{\Delta^2}}{\tau} = \frac{2}{3S} \left(\frac{h\nu}{c}\right)^2 p_n B_n{}^m e^{-\frac{\epsilon_n}{kT}} \rho \tag{25}$$

RESULTS

In order now to show that the momenta transferred from the radiation to the molecule according to our basic hypotheses never disturb the thermodynamic equilibrium, we need only introduce the values for $\dfrac{\overline{\Delta^2}}{\tau}$ and R calculated in (25) and (21) respectively after the quantity

$$\left(\rho - (\tfrac{1}{3})\nu \frac{\partial \rho}{\partial \nu}\right)\left(1 - e^{-\frac{h\nu}{kT}}\right)$$

in (21) is replaced by

$$\frac{\rho h\nu}{3RT}$$

from (4). We then see that our fundamental equation (12) is satisfied identically.

The above consideration lends very strong support to the hypotheses introduced earlier for the interaction between matter and radiation by means of absorption and emission, and through incident and outgoing radiation. I was led to these hypotheses in trying to postulate in the simplest possible way a quantum behavior of molecules that is analogous to the Planck resonators of classical theory. We obtained, without effort, from the general quantum assumption for matter, the second Bohr rule (equation (9)) as well as Planck's radiation formula.

Most important, however, appears to me the result about the momentum transferred to the molecule by incoming and outgoing radiation. If one of our hypotheses were altered, the result would be a violation of equation (12); it appears hardly possible, except by way of our hypotheses, to be in agreement with this relationship which is demanded by thermodynamics. We may therefore consider the following as pretty well proven.

If a beam of radiation has the effect that a molecule on which it is incident absorbs or emits an amount of energy $h\nu$ in the form of radiation by means of an elementary process, then the momentum $h\nu/c$ is always transferred to the molecule, and, to be sure, in the case of absorption, in the direction of the moving beam and in the case of emission in the opposite direction. If the molecule is subject to the simultaneous action of beams moving in various directions, then only one of these takes part in any single elementary process of incident radiation; this beam alone then determines the direction of the momentum transferred to the molecule.

If, through an emission process, the molecule suffers a radiant loss of energy of magnitude $h\nu$ without the action of an outside agency, then this process, too, is a directed one. Emission in spherical waves does not occur. According to the present state of the theory, the molecule suffers a recoil of magnitude $h\nu/c$ in a particular direction only because of the chance emission in that direction.

This property of elementary processes as expressed by equation (12) makes a quantum theory of radiation almost unavoidable. The weakness of the theory lies, on the one hand, in its not bringing us closer to a union with the wave theory, and, on the other hand, that it leaves the time and direction of the elementary processes to chance; in spite of this, I have full confidence in the trustworthiness of this approach.

Only one more general remark. Almost all theories of thermal radiation rest on the considerations of the interaction between radiation and molecules. But, in general, one is satisfied with dealing only with the energy exchange, without taking into account the momentum exchange. One feels justified in this because the momentum transferred by radiation is so small that it always drops out as compared to that arising from other dynamical processes. But for the theoretical considerations, this small effect is on an equal footing with the energy transferred by radiation because energy and momentum are very intimately related to each other; a theory may therefore be considered correct only if it can be shown that the momentum transferred accordingly from the radiation to the matter leads to the kind of motion that is demanded by thermodynamics.

56

ooooooooooo

THE COMPTON EFFECT

ooooooooooo

Arthur H. Compton (1892-1962)

Although the Bohr theory had been remarkably successful early in its history in explaining the gross features of atomic spectra and in providing a model of the atom which appealed to one's sense of the unity in nature, it became clear in the 1920's that the more refined spectral features lay outside its domain. Most of the evidence for the inadequacy of the Bohr theory was derived from experimental work with atomic spectra. But other investigations involving scattering experiments also suggested that fundamental changes would have to be made in the Bohr theory before it could account for all observations. Of the many relevant experiments that were carried out during this period, the Compton experiment on the scattering of X-rays by electrons was the most revealing of the shortcomings of the Bohr theory and the most instructive as to the direction in which atomic theory would have to move.

Compton's experiment is a very simple one in principle. A beam of X-rays of known frequency emanating from a molybdenum anticathode is allowed to strike electrons that are weakly bound in atoms such as carbon; the X-rays leaving the atoms in a given direction are then carefully analyzed. In Compton's experiment, the primary X-ray beam was directed against a graphite target, and the rays coming away from the target at right angles to the direction of the primary incident beam were studied.

As Compton points out in the introductory paragraphs of his paper, his results were in sharp disagreement with J. J. Thomson's classical theory of X-ray scattering and could be accounted for only by a drastic departure from classical theory. What is essential in the experimental results is that the X-ray beam, after it is scattered by the electrons, suffers a definite reduction in frequency. In contrast, the Thompson theory predicts that the electrons are set vibrating by the incident X-rays with exactly the same frequency as the rays themselves, and should therefore reradiate X-rays of the same frequency.

Compton first attempted to explain his results by assuming that the electrons have a certain size and that X-rays emitted from different parts of the electron interfere with each other in such a way as to give the observed results. But he soon realized that this assumption was untenable because it necessitated introducing an electron size that depended on the wavelength of the X-rays that were employed in the scattering. He discarded this idea as too "difficult to defend," then proceeded to analyze the scattering data by means of the quantum hypothesis.

He first assumed that the incident beam of electrons consisted of quanta each with momentum $h\nu/c$ where ν is the frequency of the quantum, h is Planck's constant of action, and c is the speed of light. He then analyzed the scattering of each quantum by an electron as though the quantum and the electron were billiard balls colliding with each other. By applying the principles of conservation of momentum and energy to such a collision, and using the appropriate relativistic relationships, he showed that the scattered quantum would move off in some direction making an angle θ with the direction of the incident beam of X-ray quanta, and that the electron that did the scattering (the so-called "recoil electron") would move off at the appropriate angle given by the conservation principles. Compton demonstrated that the frequency of the scattered quantum is reduced by an amount in agreement with the Planck expression for the energy of a photon and the relativistic expression for the kinetic energy of the recoil electron. In other words, the energy of the photon, as given by its frequency, is reduced by the same amount that the kinetic energy of the recoil electron is increased.

Compton's analysis was completely confirmed by his experimental data. This experiment established the validity of the quantum structure of radiation more firmly than ever before. As Compton stated in his discussion of the experiment, "The experimental support of the theory indicates very convincingly that a radiation quantum carries with it directed momentum as well as energy." This was a striking verification of Einstein's analysis of the emission and absorption of radiation by an atom (discussed in the previous chapter). As we saw, it led him to the concept of the photon as a momentum-carrying corpuscle that can transfer its momentum in a given direction to an atom.

Compton's remarkable findings, however, had consequences that went well beyond the concept of the photon; they became the experimental basis for Heisenberg's uncertainty principle. To determine the position of an electron accurately we must irradiate it with photons of high frequency because a short wavelength (which is equivalent to high frequency) is necessary to minimize the error in measuring this position. One of these photons must then enter our observing microscope after hitting the electron, if we are to observe it. Because of the Compton effect, the electron receives a recoil of the order of magnitude of Planck's constant of action divided by the wavelength of the photon. But the full recoil of the electron cannot be exactly determined since we know only the approximate direction of the scattered photon. This is so because the photon can enter the objective of our observing microscope over a range of directions because of the comparatively broad aperture of the microscope lens. Because of the phenomenon known as the "Compton effect," therefore, we can know neither the precise recoil of the electron nor, as a consequence, its precise momentum if we attempt an accurate determination of its position.

The Compton effect also implies that the electron must be treated as a wave and not a particle. Let us consider the electron moving in one of the Bohr orbits inside an atom. To observe it in its orbit, we must again irradiate the electron with photons of a certain frequency; their wavelength should be about equal to, or smaller than, the radius of the orbit of the electron. However, the electron receives a Compton recoil; this may throw it into one of a series of higher orbits. Since we do not know the full recoil, we must allow this electron a whole series of orbits and treat it as though it were associated with all of them. Because each of these orbits has a definite frequency, we must discuss the electron as though it were characterized by an array of frequencies, not just the single one of the orbit, which the Bohr theory would assign. In other words, we must treat the electron not as a particle but as a kind of "wave packet."

There is still another consequence of the Compton effect whose full significance is not yet comprehended. It would seem that the Compton effect should lead not only to the uncertainty principle, as expressed by Heisenberg, but also to an uncertainty in the position of any single particle. No matter how small the wavelength of the initial, incident photon is in Compton's experiment, the wavelength of the scattered photon for a stationary electron is never smaller than Planck's constant h divided by mc, where m is the mass of the electron, and c is the speed of light. This remarkable quantity, h/mc, given in formula (5) of Compton's paper, is known as the Compton wavelength of the electron. Today we believe that the position of the electron cannot be determined without allowing for an error of at least the size of this quantity.

It appears from this that there is some kind of inner structure of the electron that begins to manifest itself at distances from the center of the electron equal to the Compton wavelength. Since physicists are more and more inclined to the belief that the electron has some complex structure, they may obtain insight into this presumed complexity by a more thorough analysis of the Compton effect.

Allison's reminiscences of Compton appear first in our selection of papers. Compton's account of two of his researches then follows.

○○○○○○○

ALLISON

Arthur Holly Compton, Research Physicist [1]

I FIRST MET ARTHUR COMPTON in 1924, in William Duane's x-ray research laboratory at Harvard University. Compton had come on a visit to attempt to discover why Duane and his associates could not confirm his discovery of the change of wavelength of x-rays on scattering, now known as the Compton effect. I do not know what Compton had been doing just before he arrived, but his appearance late that afternoon was completely nontypical. He was disheveled, unshaven, and obviously overtired. He returned to the laboratory the following morning looking like himself—a well-groomed, energetic, and clear-thinking physicist.

The situation was rather tense, with peculiar overtones. Compton was not the first to perform experiments which indicated that scattered x-rays and gamma rays were more absorbable—that is, of longer wavelength—than their primaries. As far back as 1912 Sadler and Mesham had observed such an effect in x-rays scattered from carbon, and Compton himself, in 1921, had followed others in experiments showing the softening of gamma rays on scattering. But, as has several times happened in physics, the experiment, the interpretation, and the audience were not simultaneously ready, and these prior results attracted little attention. Compton, however, had never completely laid aside those gamma-ray experiments he performed in Rutherford's laboratory, and he turned them over and over in his mind, finally reaching an interpretation based on the transfer of momentum from light quanta to free electrons. Again the "interpretation" was not new; the idea of photons or light quanta had long been in the minds of many physicists. Some had even worked out

[1] Samuel K. Allison, *Science,* 138 (1962), 794–797.

Compton's equations for the conservation of energy and momentum in the photon-electron collision, ending with the wry remark that this would be a beautifully simple theory of scattering but was of course untenable because everyone knew that scattered light and x-rays were unchanged in wavelength and coherent with the primary radiation. Compton solved the equations independently, however, and was the first to publish the results.

It took Compton to correlate theory and experiment and finally to clinch the matter with a demonstration in which the change in wavelength was precisely measured with a crystal spectrometer and shown to be h/mc or 0.024 angstrom units at 90 degrees, as the calculation had predicted. The audience was ready, because the apparent conflict between the corpuscular and the wave theories of light was in every physicist's mind. A Nobel-prize discovery had been made.

But here at Harvard in 1924, in the laboratory of a highly respected investigator of x-rays, the crystal spectrometer measurements seemed to give different results. The scattered radiation showed, as Compton had found, part of the radiation to be shifted to longer wavelengths, but Duane interpreted this as "tertiary radiation," of the bremsstrahlung type, caused by the deceleration of photoelectrons ejected from the scatterer by the primary radiation. Actually, the shift at 90 degrees, from carbon, of the K x-rays of molybdenum could be quantitatively accounted for by the energy loss in the ejection of carbon K-electrons. The crucial tests of the angular dependence of the shift, and of its independence of the atomic number of the scatterer, had not been decisively performed at Harvard.

A peculiar overtone to the situation was Duane's great resistance to accepting a photon theory of scattering. It was Duane and Hunt who, a few years previously, had quantitatively established the relation between the electron kinetic energy and the maximum frequency of the bremsstrahlung, which, in those pre-wavemechanical days, was considered one of the strongest evidences of a photon theory of light. And Duane himself was at the time working on a thought-provoking attempt to explain the crystalline diffraction of x-rays without recourse to wave theory, using photons only. The essential feature was the quantized transfer of momentum from photon to crystal lattice, in the amount h/d, d being the crystal lattice spacing.* Nevertheless, Duane had resisted Compton's idea from its first pronouncement and had written Sommerfeld, who was here in the United States at that time, of his doubts and his alternative explanation. Somerfeld's reply, which Duane duly reported to us, was that after a visit

---

* It is interesting to note the completely independent rebirth of this idea in the semiclassical interpretation of the angular distribution resulting from the Butler stripping process in nuclear reactions; the necessary length is supplied by the diameter of the target nucleus on whose surface the reaction is supposed to take place.

to Compton in his new laboratory at Chicago he remained convinced of the fundamental importance of Compton's discovery.

At the time of Compton's visit I was not working on the scattering problem but was working on some problems Duane had suggested, involving fluorescence radiation. All the excitement, however, was in the next room, and I often wandered in to hear the latest scattering news. Compton's visit did not resolve the difficulty, but his incisive questions and earnestness greatly impressed Duane and his scattering group. The Harvard experiments were continued, with more self-criticism, and Duane, who had been spending most of his time directing the Roentgenology Laboratory at Harvard Medical School, neglected those duties to take readings himself on scattered x-rays. Soon some spurious effects were discarded and the results showed clearly that Compton was correct in all respects. Duane quickly withdrew his objections, at a memorable meeting of the American Physical Society. There were some who injected notes of recrimination and personalities into the situation, but the principals involved, Compton and Duane, conducted themselves at the highest levels of scientific controversy.

At this time Compton had just moved from Washington University to a professorship of physics at the University of Chicago and was chairman of the National Research Council's committee on x-rays and radioactivity. He had used the *Bulletin* of the Council for his first announcement of a spectroscopic measurement of the shift in wavelength, and in the same year (1922) the *Bulletin* carried his announcement of the discovery of the total reflection of x-rays. This work alone, if it had not been overshadowed by the work of scattering, would have established him in the first rank of experimental physicists. The earlier work of Stenström in Sweden had indicated that the index of refraction for x-rays was less than unity; Compton realized that this meant there was total reflection from denser to lighter media if the interfacial glancing angle were small enough. He quickly selected monochromatic radiation with his crystal spectrometer and demonstrated that the beam was totally reflected from glass and silver mirrors, and that the effect disappeared if the glancing angle was more than a few minutes of arc. In the hands of subsequent experimenters this became an important method for measuring the refractive index.

In an outline autobiography written in 1935 Compton has listed what he considers to have been his principal contributions to physics up to that time. The total reflection of x-rays is not on the list, but in addition to the Compton effect he mentions the study of the distribution of electrons in atoms by diffraction methods. In writing his first book on x-rays,* Compton had worked out a method of calculating, from the intensities of diffrac-

---

* A. H. Compton, *X-Rays and Electrons* (New York: Van Nostrand, 1926).

tion in various orders, the linear density of diffracting material in a direction perpendicular to the set of crystal planes under investigation. The method was applied by Compton's associates and produced elegant electron distribution curves easily identified, in the case of rock salt, as the electron clusters around sodium and chlorine nuclei. Similar and independent investigations were under way in England, in W. L. Bragg's laboratory. Later, in an even more impressive manner, Compton extended the method to the study of scattering from gases, where the sharp crystalline diffraction maxima do not exist and the coherent and incoherent components of the scattering can only be separated by an experimenter with a basic understanding of the complexities of the scattering process. Compton and his associates measured electron distributions in helium, neon, argon, and mercury atoms by this method, which is now being revived in the study of electric charge distribution in nuclei, with ultra-high-energy x-rays.

In his modest résumé of his contributions to physics Compton fails to mention a fundamental contribution to the theory of ferromagnetism. By a very careful investigation of the intensity of x-rays diffracted by magnetized and unmagnetized magnetite and silicon steel, Compton and his associate, the late J. C. Stearns, showed conclusively that the magnetization of these substances could not be explained by a tilting of the planes of electronic orbits in their atoms. As he correctly surmised, this left orientation of the electron spins as the ultimate source of the ferromagnetic behavior.

In the early 1930's Compton began to shift his attention from x-rays to cosmic rays. He began building high-pressure ionization chambers and encouraged his associates to construct simple and rugged electrometers, such as had been developed by Millikan and his co-workers at Pasadena. During this period his fame as a physicist and lecturer was spreading rapidly, and he was eagerly sought as a guest professor by universities throughout the world. He enjoyed traveling (always accompanied by his wife), and he was now able to carry out experimental work on cosmic rays by taking readings on their intensity as he journeyed. Fortunately, his travels often took him to the Southern Hemisphere, and by intelligent evaluation of his intensity readings he discovered a latitude effect—namely, that cosmic ray intensities are less near the equator than at the poles. Again, such an effect had previously been discovered, by a Dutch physicist, Clay, who had measured the intensity as a function of latitude on his travels from Holland to Java, but the effect remained buried in Clay's notebooks and in obscure publications until Compton rediscovered it and at once saw its implication.

The other great name in cosmic rays at that time was R. A. Millikan, whose extensive observations had convinced him that the primary cosmic radiation, incident on the earth's outer atmosphere, was electromagnetic in nature. Compton realized that the probable explanation of his latitude effect was that a significant part, at least, of the primaries was made up of charged particles, kept away from the earth's equatorial regions by the shielding effect of the earth's magnetic field. Millikan was not the type of physicist who gracefully accepts correction of his results (witness the controversy over the quantitative value of the electronic charge, when the value derived in Millikan's beautiful oil-drop experiment was corrected upward by about 0.6 percent in later x-ray work, again initiated in Compton's laboratory), and a lively discussion over the nature of cosmic ray primaries arose. But the evidence of the latitude effect could not be refuted, and the explanation that charged particles play a predominant role in the influx from outer space is now accepted.

In the latter part of the 1930's Compton spent less and less time working with his own hands in the laboratory. It seemed difficult for him to refuse any of the multitudinous requests he received for lecturing, on both scientific and humanitarian topics. There was an intensely religious and idealistic side to his nature, coexisting in a truly remarkable way with his ability to reason in the rigorous and objective manner of physics. His early religious training, received from his mother and father and reinforced by association with his missionary relatives, had made a permanent impression. He was one of the few scientists of stature who could and would address religious groups, and Compton was in constant demand as an outstanding exponent of the compatibility of science and religion.

In the early 1940's he realized, and often mentioned to me, that he was turning over his experimental work to "younger men who could do it better" (!), and I remember a day in 1942 when he solemnly informed me that he was 50 years old. He obviously had been taking stock of his life and was on the point of making decisions on what to accomplish in his remaining years. But before he could retire from an active interest in physics, a great ordeal was in store for him.

When World War II began in Europe, and even after the fall of France, Compton seemed less affected by it than were many other physicists in the United States, who dropped their research projects and reported to Washington, or congregated at the radar laboratory at the Massachusetts Institute of Technology. Actually Compton, as a physicist, was less a product of continental European universities than were many physicists of his generation in this country. He did not join the pilgrimages of the 1920's to Göttingen or Copenhagen, merely stopping off incidentally on a European tour. He seemed less aware than others of the frightful danger to civilization represented by the psychopathic Hitler and his congerie of fanatics. He had led a comfortable, protected life and had, from youth, been shielded from evil incarnate by his optimistic religious faith, which taught good will toward all men and the expectation of good will in return. His cosmic ray research group lost some men to the defense effort but continued under his leadership until the winter of 1941, when we were at war and the extreme gravity of the situation became evident to everyone. He then turned over the project entirely to Marcel Schein, who continued it with a reduced staff.

In October 1940 I had been called away from Chicago to help with rocket research in Washington; Compton had begun to think about what the University of Chicago group could do to increase the military potential of the country and was becoming more and more interested in the uranium fission program. In December 1940 he wrote me in Washington and urged me to return to Chicago and begin a study of the possibilities of using beryllium as a neutron moderator, a project in which he gave me great support.

The story of Compton's involvement in the atomic bomb effort has been written by himself, in his book *Atomic Quest*. I can only record some glancing observations. On 6 November 1941 Compton, as chairman, presented the report of a National Academy Committee organized to review the military potentialities of atomic energy. This report was a masterpiece of scientific and technological prevision; it, as much as any other one item, precipitated the vast uranium project effort. It was Compton at his best, with his full attention and enthusiasm concentrated on one subject. I had seen this happen once before, when he essentially locked the doors of his office in Chicago and, in about 3 weeks, wrote the long and profound chapter on the scattering of x-rays for the book *X-rays in Theory and Experiment*.

As the effort which eventually became the Manhattan Project developed at an incredible rate, the strain on Compton became terrific. He was buffeted unmercifully by the internal frictions in the project, by the difficulties in splitting off men for the work in Tennessee, by distrust between the pure scientists and the commercial engineers, and by the great decisions regarding the role of heavy water and the relative efficacy of liquid cooling and gaseous cooling, to name but a few. In addition, he felt a gnawing doubt about the morality of the whole effort, which, if successful, could very well mean a horrible death for thousands of civilians in the enemy countries.

He presided at long conferences which seemed never to end and were called at all hours of the day and night, with no regard for meal times. He had the physique to endure this; I did not. After my session in the hospital he somehow learned that it was thought that part of my difficulty had been caused by long periods without food. Thereafter he always had tomato juice and sandwiches available for our longer sessions; this made me feel that too great regard was being paid to one man's digestive tract in the midst of a war.

The end of the war brought Compton's resignation as Charles H. Swift distinguished service professor of physics at Chicago and his acceptance of the chancellorship of Washington University at St. Louis, where his famous experiment on the Compton effect had been performed 24 years previously. His administrative position meant that his career as a research physicist was ended, as was my close association with him. The last time I saw him before his death on 15 March 1962 was in the autumn of 1961, at the dedication of the A. A. Michelson public school in Chicago. He gave the dedicatory address, recalling the achievements of his famous predecessor at Ryerson Physical Laboratory. I had known of his serious illness in the preceding years, from which he never fully recovered. At a little reception following the ceremony, however, he talked clearly and naturally as we reminisced about days gone by.

The honors heaped upon him are literally too numerous to mention. Probably the one he appreciated most was the degree of doctor of science awarded him in 1927 by Wooster College, in the town where he had been born and had lived as a child and young man, and where his father, Elias Compton, had been dean and professor of philosophy.

His place is secure as one of the great American physicists of the 20th century.

∘∘∘∘∘∘∘

COMPTON

A Quantum Theory of the Scattering of X-Rays by Light Elements [2]

...J. J. THOMSON'S CLASSICAL THEORY of the scattering of X-rays, though supported by the early experiments of Barkla and others, has been found incapable of explaining many of the more recent experiments. This theory, based upon the usual electrodynamics, leads to the result that the energy scattered by an electron traversed by an X-ray beam of unit intensity is the same whatever may be the wave-length of the incident rays. Moreover, when the X-rays traverse a thin layer of matter, the intensity of the scattered radiation on the two sides of the layer should be the same. Experiments on the scatter-

---

[2] From Arthur H. Compton, *Physical Review*, 21 (1923), 483–522.

ing of X-rays by light elements have shown that these predictions are correct when X-rays of moderate hardness are employed; but when very hard X-rays or γ-rays are employed, the scattered energy is found to be decidedly less than Thomson's theoretical value, and to be strongly concentrated on the emergent side of the scattering plate.

Several years ago the writer suggested that this reduced scattering of the very short wave-length X-rays might be the result of interference between the rays scattered by different parts of the electron, if the electron's diameter is comparable with the wave-length of the radiation. By assuming the proper radius for the electron, this hypothesis supplied a quantitative explanation of the scattering for any particular wave-length. But recent experiments have shown that the size of the electron which must thus be assumed increases with the wave-length of the X-rays employed, and the conception of an electron whose size varies with the wave-length of the incident rays is difficult to defend.

Recently an even more serious difficulty with the classical theory of X-ray scattering has appeared. It has long been known that secondary γ-rays are softer than the primary rays which excite them, and recent experiments have shown that this is also true of X-rays. By a spectroscopic examination of the secondary X-rays from graphite, I have, indeed, been able to show that only a small part, if any, of the secondary X-radiation is of the same wave-length as the primary.* While the energy of the secondary X-radiation is so nearly equal to that calculated from Thomson's classical theory that it is difficult to attribute it to anything other than true scattering, these results show that if there is any scattering comparable in magnitude with that predicted by Thomson, it is of a greater wave-length than the primary X-rays.

Such a change in wave-length is directly counter to Thomson's theory of scattering, for this demands that the scattering electrons, radiating as they do because of their forced vibrations when traversed by a primary X-ray, shall give rise to radiation of exactly the same frequency as that of the radiation falling upon them. Nor does any modification of the theory such as the hypothesis of a large electron suggest a way out of the difficulty. This failure makes it appear improbable that a satisfactory explanation of the scattering of X-rays can be reached on the basis of the classical electrodynamics.

---

* In previous papers I have defended the view that the softening of the secondary X-radiation was due to a considerable admixture of a form of fluorescent radiation. Gray, Frank, and Florance have considered that the evidence favored true scattering, and that the softening is in some way an accompaniment of the scattering process. The considerations brought forward in the present paper indicate that the latter view is the correct one.

THE QUANTUM HYPOTHESIS
OF SCATTERING

According to the classical theory, each X-ray affects every electron in the matter traversed, and the scattering observed is that due to the combined effects of all the electrons. From the point of view of the quantum theory, we may suppose that any particular quantum of X-rays is not scattered by all the electrons in the radiator, but spends all of its energy upon some particular electron. This electron will in turn scatter the ray in some definite direction, at an angle with the incident beam. This bending of the path of the quantum of radiation results in a change in its momentum. As a consequence, the scattering electron will recoil with a momentum equal to the change in momentum of the X-ray. The energy in the scattered ray will be equal to that in the incident ray minus the kinetic energy of the recoil of the scattering electron; and since the scattered ray must be a complete quantum, the frequency will be reduced in the same ratio as is the energy. Thus on the quantum theory we should expect the wave-length of the scattered X-rays to be greater than that of the incident rays.

The effect of the momentum of the X-ray quantum is to set the scattering electron in motion at an angle of less than 90° with the primary beam. But it is well known that the energy radiated by a moving body is greater in the direction of its motion. We should therefore expect, as is experimentally observed, that the intensity of the scattered radiation should be greater in the general direction of the primary X-rays than in the reverse direction.

The Change in Wave-Length Due to Scattering

Imagine, as in [Fig. 56–1A], that an X-ray quantum of frequency v_0 is scattered by an electron of mass m. The momentum of the incident ray will be hv_0/c, where c is the velocity of light and h is Planck's constant, and that of the scattered ray is hv_θ/c at an angle θ with the initial momentum. The principle of the conservation of momentum accordingly demands that the momentum of recoil of the scattering electron shall equal the vector difference between the momenta of these two rays, as in [Fig. 56–1B]. The momentum of the electron, $m\beta c/\sqrt{1-\beta^2}$, is thus given by the relation

$$\left(\frac{m\beta c}{\sqrt{1-\beta^2}}\right)^2 = \left(\frac{hv_\theta}{c}\right)^2 + \left(\frac{hv_0}{c}\right)^2 + 2\,\frac{hv_0}{c}\cdot\frac{hv_\theta}{c}\cos\theta, \qquad (1)$$

where β is the ratio of the velocity of recoil of the electron to the velocity of light. But the energy hv_0 in the scattered quantum is equal to that of

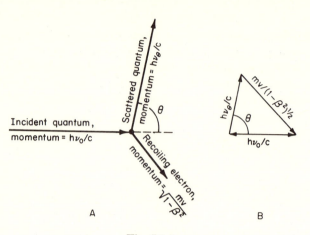

Fig. 56–1.

the incident quantum $h\nu_0$ less the kinetic energy of recoil of the scattering electron, *i.e.,*

$$h\nu_\theta = h\nu_0 - mc^2 \left(\frac{1}{\sqrt{1 - \beta^2}} - 1 \right). \tag{2}$$

We thus have two independent equations containing the two unknown quantities β and ν_θ. On solving the equations we find

$$\nu_\theta = \nu_0 / (1 + 2\alpha \sin^2 \tfrac{1}{2}\theta), \tag{3}$$

where

$$\alpha = h\nu_0/mc^2 = h/mc\lambda_0. \tag{4}$$

Or in terms of wave-length instead of frequency,

$$\lambda_\theta = \lambda_0 + (2h/mc) \sin^2 \tfrac{1}{2}\theta. \tag{5}$$

It follows from Eq. (2) that $1/(1 - \beta^2) = \{1 + \alpha[1 - (\nu_\theta/\nu_0)]\}^2$, or solving explicitly for β

$$\beta = 2\alpha \sin \tfrac{1}{2}\theta \, \frac{\sqrt{1 + (2\alpha + \alpha^2) \sin^2 \tfrac{1}{2}\theta}}{1 + 2(\alpha + \alpha^2) \sin^2 \tfrac{1}{2}\theta}. \tag{6}$$

Eq. (5) indicates an increase in wave-length due to the scattering process which varies from a few per cent in the case of ordinary X-rays to more than 200 per cent in the case of γ-rays scattered backward. At the same time the velocity of the recoil of the scattering electron, as calculated from Eq. (6), varies from zero when the ray is scattered directly forward to about 80 per cent of the speed of light when a γ-ray is scattered at a large angle.

It is of interest to notice that according to the classical theory, if an X-ray were scattered by an electron moving in the direction of propagation at a velocity $\beta'c$, the frequency of the ray scattered at an angle θ is given by the Doppler principle as

$$v_\theta = v_0 \left/ \left(1 + \frac{2\beta'}{1 - \beta'} \sin^2 \tfrac{1}{2}\theta\right)\right. . \tag{7}$$

It will be seen that this is of exactly the same form as Eq. (3), derived on the hypothesis of the recoil of the scattering electron. Indeed, if $\alpha = \beta'/(1 - \beta')$ or $\beta' = \alpha/(1 + \alpha)$, the two expressions become identical. It is clear, therefore, that so far as the effect on the wave-length is concerned, we may replace the recoiling electron by a scattering electron moving in the direction of the incident beam at a velocity such that

$$\bar{\beta} = \alpha/(1 + \alpha). \tag{8}$$

We shall call $\bar{\beta}c$ the "effective velocity" of the scattering electrons. . . . It is interesting to note that

$$I_\theta/I' = (v_\theta/v')^4. \tag{19}$$

This result may be obtained very simply for the total radiation from a black body, which is a special case of an isotropic radiator. For, suppose such a radiator is moving so that the frequency of maximum intensity which to a moving observer is v_m' appears to the stationary observer to be v_m. Then according to Wien's law, the apparent temperature T, as estimated by the stationary observer, is greater than the temperature T' for the moving observer by the ratio $T/T' = v_m/v_m'$. According to Stefan's law, however, the intensity of the total radiation from a black body is proportional to T^4; hence, if I and I' are the intensities of the radiation as measured by the stationary and the moving observers respectively,

$$I/I' = (T/T')^4 = (v_m/v_m')^4. \tag{20}$$

The agreement of this result with Eq. (19) may be taken as confirming the correctness of the latter expression.

The Intensity of Scattering from Recoiling Electrons

We have seen that the change in frequency of the radiation scattered by the recoiling electrons is the same as if the radiation were scattered by electrons moving in the direction of propagation with an effective velocity $\beta = \alpha/(1+\alpha)$, where $\alpha = h/mc\lambda_0$. It seems obvious that since these two methods of calculation result in the same change in wave-length, they must also result in the same change in intensity of the scattered beam. This assumption is supported by the fact that we find, as in Eq. (19), that the change in intensity is in certain special cases a function only of the change in frequency. I have not, however, succeeded in showing rigidly that if two methods of scattering result in the same relative wave-lengths at different angles, they will also result in the same relative intensity at different angles. Nevertheless, we shall assume that this proposition is true, and shall proceed to calculate the relative intensity of the scattered beam at different angles on the hypothesis that the scattering electrons are moving in the direction of the primary beam with a velocity $\beta = \alpha/(1+\alpha)$. If our assumption is correct, the results of the calculation will apply also to the scattering by recoiling electrons.

To an observer moving with the scattering electron, the intensity of the scattering at an angle θ', according to the usual electrodynamics, should be proportional to $(1 + \cos^2 \theta')$, if the primary beam is unpolarized. On the quantum theory, this means that the probability that a quantum will be emitted between the angles θ' and $\theta' + d\theta'$ is proportional to $(1 + \cos^2 \theta') \cdot \sin \theta' d\theta'$, since $2\pi \sin \theta' d\theta'$ is the solid angle included between θ' and $\theta' + d\theta'$. This may be written $P_{\theta'} d\theta' = k(1 + \cos^2 \theta') \sin \theta' d\theta'$. The factor of proportionality k may be determined by performing the integration

$$\int_0^\pi P_{\theta'} d\theta' = k \int_0^\pi (1 + \cos^2 \theta') \sin \theta' d\theta' = 1,$$

with the result that $k = \frac{3}{8}$. Thus

$$P_{\theta'} d\theta' = (\tfrac{3}{8})(1 + \cos^2 \theta') \sin \theta' d\theta' \qquad (21)$$

is the probability that a quantum will be emitted at the angle θ' as measured by an observer moving with the scattering electron.

To the stationary observer, however, the quantum ejected at an angle θ' appears to move at an angle θ with the direction of the primary beam, where $\sin \theta'$ and $d\theta'$ are given in Eqs. (12) and (13) [not included in this section]. Substituting these values in Eq. (21), we find for the probability that a given quantum will be scattered between the angles θ and $\theta + d\theta$,

$$P_\theta d\theta = \tfrac{3}{8} \sin \theta d\theta \frac{(1 - \beta^2)\{(1 + \beta^2)(1 + \cos^2 \theta) - 4\beta \cos \theta\}}{(1 - \beta \cos \theta)^4}. \quad (22)$$

Suppose the stationary observer notices that n quanta are scattered per second. In the case of the radiator emitting n'' quanta per second while approaching the observer, the n''th quantum was emitted when the radiator was nearer the observer, so that the interval between the receipt of the 1st and the n''th quantum was less than a second. That is, more quanta were received per second than were emitted in the same time. In the case of scattering, however, though we suppose that each scattering electron is moving forward, the nth quantum is scattered by an electron starting from the same position as the 1st quantum. Thus the number of quanta received per second is also n.

We have seen (Eq. 3) that the frequency of the quantum received at an angle θ is $v_\theta = v_0/(1 + 2\alpha \sin^2 \tfrac{1}{2}\theta) = v_0/\{1 + \alpha(1 - \cos \theta)\}$, where v_0, the frequency of the incident beam, is also the frequency of the ray scattered in the direction of the incident beam. The energy scattered per second at the angle θ is thus $nh v_\theta P_\theta d\theta$, and the intensity, or energy per second per unit area, of the ray scattered to a distance R is

$$I_\theta = \frac{nh v_\theta P_\theta d\theta}{2\pi R^2 \sin \theta d\theta}$$

$$= \frac{nh}{2\pi R^2} \cdot \frac{v_0}{1 + \alpha(1 - \cos \theta)} \cdot \frac{3}{8}$$

$$\cdot \frac{(1 - \beta^2)\{(1 + \beta^2)(1 + \cos^2 \theta) - 4\beta \cos \theta\}}{(1 - \beta \cos \theta)^4}.$$

Substituting for β its value $\alpha/(1 + \alpha)$, and reducing, this becomes

$$I_\theta = \frac{3nh v_0}{16\pi R} \frac{(1 + 2\alpha)\{1 + \cos^2 \theta + 2\alpha(1 + \alpha)(1 - \cos \theta)^2\}}{(1 + \alpha - \alpha \cos \theta)^5}. \quad (23)$$

In the forward direction, where $\theta = 0$, the intensity of the scattered beam is thus

$$I_0 = \frac{3}{8\pi} \frac{nh v_0}{R^2} (1 + 2\alpha). \quad (24)$$

Hence

$$\frac{I_\theta}{I_0} = \frac{1}{2} \frac{1 + \cos^2 \theta + 2\alpha(1 + \alpha)(1 - \cos \theta)^2}{\{1 + \alpha(1 - \cos \theta)\}^5}. \quad (25)$$

On the hypothesis of recoiling electrons, however, for a ray scattered directly forward, the velocity of recoil is zero (Eq. 6). Since in this case the scattering electron is at rest, the intensity of the scattered beam should be that calculated on the basis of the classical theory, namely,

$$I_0 = I(Ne^4/R^2m^2c^4), \tag{26}$$

where I is the intensity of the primary beam traversing the N electrons which are effective in scattering. On combining this result with Eq. (25), we find for the intensity of the X-rays scattered at an angle θ with the incident beam,

$$I_\theta = I \frac{Ne^4}{2R^2m^2c^4} \frac{1 + \cos^2\theta + 2\alpha(1 + \alpha)(1 - \cos\theta)^2}{\{1 + \alpha(1 - \cos\theta)\}^5}. \tag{27}$$

The calculation of the energy removed from the primary beam may now be made without difficulty. We have supposed that n quanta are scattered per second. But on comparing Eqs. (24) and (26), we find that

$$n = \frac{8\pi}{3} \frac{INe^4}{h\nu_0 m^2c^4(1 + 2\alpha)}.$$

The energy removed from the primary beam per second is $nh\nu_0$. If we define *the scattering absorption coefficient* as the fraction of the energy of the primary beam removed by the scattering process per unit length of path through the medium, it has the value

$$\sigma = \frac{nh\nu_0}{I} = \frac{8\pi}{3} \frac{Ne^4}{m^2c^4} \cdot \frac{1}{1 + 2\alpha} = \frac{\sigma_0}{1 + 2\alpha}, \tag{28}$$

where N is the number of scattering electrons per unit volume, and σ_0 is the scattering coefficient calculated on the basis of the classical theory.

In order to determine the total energy truly scattered, we must integrate the scattered intensity over the surface of a sphere surrounding the scattering material,

$$i.e., \quad \epsilon_s = \int_0^\pi I_\theta \cdot 2\pi R^2 \sin\theta d\theta.$$

On substituting the value of I_θ from Eq. (27), and integrating, this becomes

$$\epsilon_s = \frac{8\pi}{3} \frac{INe^4}{m^2c^4} \frac{1 + \alpha}{(1 + 2\alpha)^2}.$$

The *true scattering coefficient* is thus

$$\sigma_s = \frac{8\pi}{3} \frac{Ne^4}{m^2c^4} \frac{1+\alpha}{(1+2\alpha)^2} = \sigma_0 \frac{1+\alpha}{(1+2\alpha)^2}. \tag{29}$$

It is clear that the difference between the total energy removed from the primary beam and that which reappears as scattered radiation is the energy of recoil of the scattering electrons. This difference represents, therefore, a type of true absorption resulting from the scattering process. The corresponding *coefficient of true absorption due to scattering* is

$$\sigma_\alpha = \sigma - \sigma_s = \frac{8\pi}{3} \frac{Ne^4}{m^2c^4} \frac{\alpha}{(1+2\alpha)^2} = \sigma_0 \frac{\alpha}{(1+2\alpha)^2}. \tag{30}$$

EXPERIMENTAL TEST

Let us now investigate the agreement of these various formulas with experiments on the change of wave-length due to scattering, and on the magnitude of the scattering of X-rays and γ-rays by light elements.

Wave-Length of the Scattered Rays

If in Eq. (5) we substitute the accepted values of *h, m,* and *c,* we obtain

$$\lambda_\theta = \lambda_0 + 0.0484 \sin^2 \tfrac{1}{2}\theta, \tag{31}$$

if λ is expressed in angström units. It is perhaps surprising that the increase should be the same for all wave-lengths. Yet, as a result of an extensive experimental study of the change in wave-length on scattering, the writer has concluded that "over the range of primary rays from 0.7 to 0.025 A, the wave-length of the secondary X-rays at 90° with the incident beam is roughly 0.03 A greater than that of the primary beam which excites it." Thus the experiments support the theory in showing a wave-length increase which seems independent of the incident wave-length, and which also is of the proper order of magnitude.

A quantitative test of the accuracy of Eq. (31) is possible in the case of the characteristic K-rays from molybdenum when scattered by graphite. in [Fig. 56–2] is shown a spectrum of the X-rays scattered by graphite at right angles with the primary beam, when the graphite is traversed by X-rays from a molybdenum target. The solid line represents the spectrum of these scattered rays, and is to be compared with the broken line, which represents the spectrum of the primary rays, using the same slits and crystal, and the same potential on the tube. The primary spectrum is, of course, plotted on a much smaller scale than the secondary. The zero point

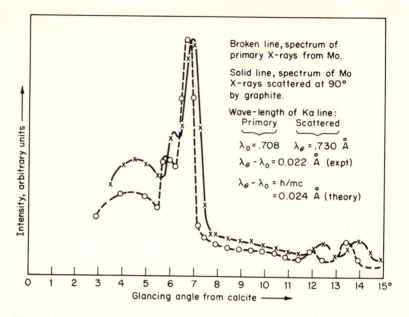

Fig. 56–2. Spectrum of molybdenum X-rays scattered by graphite, compared with the spectrum of the primary X-rays, showing an increase in wavelength on scattering.

for the spectrum of both the primary and secondary X-rays was determined by finding the position of the first order lines on both sides of the zero point.

It will be seen that the wave-length of the scattered rays is unquestionably greater than that of the primary rays which excite them. Thus the Kα line from molybdenum has a wave-length 0.708 A. The wavelength of this line in the scattered beam is found in these experiments, however, to be 0.730 A. That is,

$$\lambda_\theta - \lambda_0 = 0.022 \text{ A (experiment)}.$$

But according to the present theory (Eq. 5),

$$\lambda_\theta - \lambda_0 = 0.484 \sin^2 45° = 0.024 \text{ A (theory)},$$

which is a very satisfactory agreement.

The variation in wave-length of the scattered beam with the angle is illustrated in the case of γ-rays. The writer has measured the mass absorption coefficient in lead of the rays scattered at different angles when various substances are traversed by the hard γ-rays from RaC. The mean results for iron, aluminum, and paraffin are given in column 2 of [Table 56–1]. This variation in absorption coefficient corresponds to a difference in wave-length at the different angles. Using the value given by Hull and Rice for the mass absorption coefficient in lead for wave-length 0.122, 3.0, remembering that the characteristic fluorescent absorption τ/ρ is proportional to λ^3, and estimating the part of the absorption due to scattering by the method described below, I find for the wave-lengths corresponding to these absorption coefficients the values given in the fourth column of [Table 56–1]. That this extrapolation is very nearly correct is indicated by

TABLE 56–1   *Wave-Length of Primary and Scattered γ-Rays*

	Angle	μ/ρ	τ/ρ	λ obs.	λ calc.
Primary	0°	.076	.017	0.022 A	(0.022 A)
Scattered	45°	.10	.042	.030	0.029
"	90°	.21	.123	.043	0.047
"	135°	.59	.502	.068	0.063

the fact that it gives for the primary beam a wave-length 0.022 A. This is in good accord with the writer's value 0.025 A, calculated from the scattering of γ-rays by lead at small angles, and with Ellis' measurements from his β-ray spectra, showing lines of wave-length .045, .025, .021 and .020 A, with line .020 the strongest. Taking $\lambda_0 = 0.022$ A, the wavelengths at the other angles may be calculated from Eq. (31). The results, given in the last column of [Table 56–1], and shown graphically in [Fig. 56–3], are in satisfactory accord with the measured values. There is thus good reason for believing that Eq. (5) represents accurately the wavelength of the X-rays and γ-rays scattered by light elements.

Velocity of Recoil of the Scattering Electrons

The electrons which recoil in the process of the scattering of ordinary X-rays have not been observed. This is probably because their number and velocity is usually small compared with the number and velocity of the photoelectrons ejected as a result of the characteristic fluorescent absorption. I have pointed out elsewhere, however, that there is good reason for believing that most of the secondary β-rays excited in light elements by the action of γ-rays are such recoil electrons. According to Eq. (6), the velocity of these electrons should vary from 0, when the γ-ray is scattered forward, to $v_{max} = \beta_{max}c = 2c\alpha[(1+\alpha)/(1+2\alpha+2\alpha^2)]$, when the γ-ray quantum is scattered backward. If for the hard γ-rays from radium C, $\alpha = 1.09$, corresponding to $\lambda = 0.022$ A, we thus obtain $\beta_{max} = 0.82$. The effective velocity of the scattering electrons is, therefore (Eq. 8), $\beta = 0.52$.

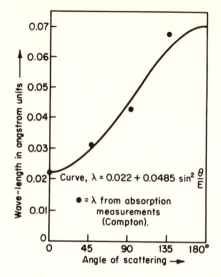

Fig. 56–3. The wavelength of scattered α-rays at different angles with the primary beam, showing an increase at large angles similar to a Doppler effect.

These results are in accord with the fact that the average velocity of the β-rays excited by the γ-rays from radium is somewhat greater than half that of light. . . .

The Relative Intensity of the X-Rays Scattered in Different Directions with the Primary Beam

Our Eq. (27) predicts a concentration of the energy in the forward direction. A large number of experiments on the scattering of X-rays have shown that, except for the excess scattering at small angles, the ionization due to the scattered beam is symmetrical on the emergence and incidence sides of a scattering plate. The difference in intensity on the two sides according to Eq. (27) should, however, be noticeable. Thus if the wavelength is 0.7 A, which is probably about that used by Barkla and Ayers in their experiments on the scattering by carbon, the ratio of the intensity of the rays scattered at 40° to that at 140° should be about 1.10. But their experimental ratio was 1.04, which differs from our theory by more than their probable experimental error.

It will be remembered, however, that our theory, and experiment also, indicates a difference in the wave-length of the X-rays scattered in different directions. The softer X-rays which are scattered backward are the more easily absorbed and, though of smaller intensity, may produce an ionization equal to that of the beam scattered forward. Indeed, if α is small compared with unity, as is the case for ordinary X-rays, Eq. (27) may be written approximately $I_\theta/I_\theta' = (\lambda_0/\lambda_\theta)^3$, where I_θ' is the intensity of the beam scattered at the angle θ according to the classical theory. The part of the absorption which results in ionization is however proportional to λ^3. Hence if, as is usually the case, only a small part of the X-rays entering the ionization chamber is absorbed by the gas in the chamber, the ionization is also proportional to λ^3. Thus if i_θ represents the ionization due to the beam scattered at the angle θ, and if i_θ' is the corresponding ionization on the classical theory, we have $i_\theta/i_\theta' = (I_\theta/I_\theta')(\lambda_\theta/\lambda_0)^3 = 1$, or $i_\theta = i_\theta'$. That is, to a first approximation, the ionization should be the same as that on the classical theory, though the energy in the scattered beam is less. This conclusion is in good accord with the experiments which have been performed on the scattering of ordinary X-rays, if correction is made for the excess scattering which appears at small angles.

In the case of very short wave-lengths, however, the case is different. The writer has measured the γ-rays scattered at different angles by iron,

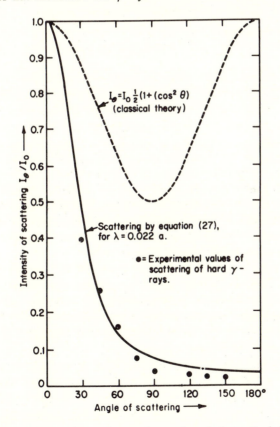

Fig. 56–4. Comparison of experimental and theoretical intensities of scattered α-rays.

using an ionization chamber so designed as to absorb the greater part of even the primary γ-ray beam. It is not clear just how the ionization due to the γ-rays will vary with the wave-length under the conditions of the experiment, but it appears probable that the variation will not be great. If we suppose accordingly that the ionization measures the intensity of the scattered γ-ray beam, these data for the intensity are represented by the circles in Fig. 56–4. The experiments showed that the intensity at 90° was 0.074 times that predicted by the classical theory, or 0.037 I_0, where I_0 is the intensity of the scattering at the angle $\theta = 0$ as calculated on either the classical or the quantum theory. The absolute intensities of the scattered beam are accordingly plotted using I_0 as the unit. The solid curve shows the intensity in the same units, calculated according to Eq. (27). As before, the wave-length of the γ-rays is taken as 0.022 A. The beautiful agreement between the theoretical and the experimental values of the scattering is the more striking when one notices that there is not a single adjustable constant connecting the two sets of values.

DISCUSSION

This remarkable agreement between our formulas and the experiments can leave but little doubt that the scattering of X-rays is a quantum phenomenon. The hypothesis of a large electron to explain these effects is accordingly superfluous, for all the experiments on X-ray scattering to which this hypothesis has been applied are now seen to be explicable from the point of view of the quantum theory without introducing any new hypotheses or constants. In addition, the present theory accounts satisfactorily for the change in wave-length due to scattering, which was left unaccounted for on the hypothesis of the large electron. From the standpoint of the scattering of X-rays and γ-rays, therefore, there is no longer any support for the hypothesis of an electron whose diameter is comparable with the wave-length of hard X-rays.

The present theory depends essentially upon the assumption that each electron which is effective in the scattering scatters a complete quantum. It involves also the hypothesis that the quanta of radiation are received from definite directions and are scattered in definite directions. The experimental support of the theory indicates very convincingly that a radiation quantum carries with it directed momentum as well as energy.

Emphasis has been laid upon the fact that in its present form the quantum theory of scattering applies only to light elements. The reason for this restriction is that we have tacitly assumed that there are no forces of constraint acting upon the scattering electrons. This assumption is probably legitimate in the case of the very light elements, but cannot be true for the heavy elements. For if the kinetic energy of recoil of an electron is less than the energy required to remove the electron from the atom, there is no chance for the electron to recoil in the manner we have supposed. The conditions of scattering in such a case remain to be investigated.

The manner in which interference occurs, as for example in the cases of excess scattering and X-ray reflection, is not yet clear. Perhaps if an electron is bound in the atom too firmly to recoil, the incident quantum of radiation may spread itself over a large number of electrons, distributing its energy and momentum among them, thus making interference possible. In any case, the problem of scattering is so closely allied with those of reflection and interference that a study of the problem may very possibly shed some light upon the difficult question of the relation between interference and the quantum theory.

Many of the ideas involved in this paper have been developed in discussion with Professor G. E. M. Jauncey of this department.

The Spectrum of Scattered X-Rays [3]

THE WRITER HAS RECENTLY PROPOSED a theory of the scattering of x-rays, based upon the postulate that each quantum of x-rays is scattered by an individual electron. The recoil of this scattering electron, due to the change in momentum of the x-ray quantum when its direction is altered, reduces the energy and hence also the frequency of the quantum of radiation. The corresponding increase in the wave-length of the x-rays due to scattering was shown to be

$$\lambda - \lambda_0 = \gamma(1 - \cos\theta) \qquad (1)$$

where λ is the wave-length of the ray scattered at an angle θ with the primary ray whose wave-length is λ_0, and

$$\gamma = h/mc = 0.0242 \text{ A}$$

where h is Planck's constant, m is the mass of the electron and c the velocity of light. It is the purpose of this paper to present more precise experimental data than has previously been given regarding this change in wave-length when x-rays are scattered.

APPARATUS AND METHOD

For the quantitative measurement of the change in wave-length it was clearly desirable to employ a spectroscopic method. In view of the com-

---

[3] Compton, *Physical Review*, 22 (1923), 409–413.

paratively low intensity of scattered x-rays, the apparatus had to be designed in such a manner as to secure the maximum intensity in the beam whose wave-length was measured. The arrangement of the apparatus is shown diagrammatically in Fig. 56–5. Rays proceeded from the molybdenum target T of an x-ray tube to the graphite scattering block R, which was placed in line with the slits 1 and 2. Lead diaphragms, suitably disposed, prevented stray radiation from leaving the lead box that surrounded the x-ray tube. Since the slit 1 and the diaphragms were mounted upon an insulating support, it was possible to place the x-ray tube close to the slit without danger of puncture. The x-rays, after passing through the slits, were measured by a Bragg spectrometer in the usual manner.

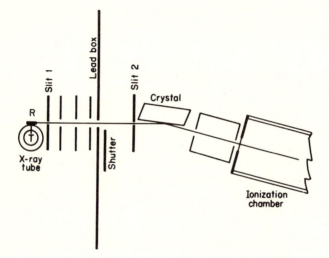

Fig. 56–5. Measuring the wavelength of scattered α-rays.

The x-ray tube was of special design. A water-cooled target was mounted in a narrow glass tube, so as to shorten as much as possible the distance between the target and the radiator. This distance in the experiments was about 2 cm. When 1.5 kw was dissipated in the x-ray tube, the intensity of the rays reaching the radiator was thus 125 times as great as it would have been if a standard Coolidge tube with a molybdenum target had been employed. The electrodes for this tube were very kindly supplied by the General Electric Company.

In the final experiments the distance between the slits was about 18 cm, their length about 2 cm, and their width about 0.01 cm. Using a crystal of calcite, this made possible a rather high resolving power even in the first order spectrum.

SPECTRA OF SCATTERED MOLYBDENUM RAYS

Results of the measurements, using slits of two different widths, are shown in [Fig. 56–6]. Curves A represent the spectrum of the Kα line, and curves B, C and D are the spectra of this line after being scattered at angles of 45°, 90° and 135° respectively with the primary beam. While in [the second column] the experimental points are a little

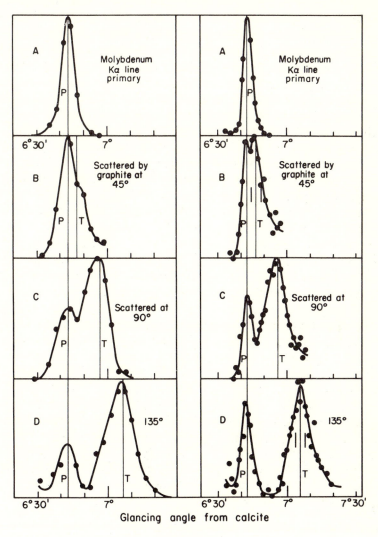

Fig. 56–6.

erratic, it may be noted that in this case the intensity of the x-rays is only about $\frac{1}{25,000}$ as great as if the spectrum of the primary beam were under examination, so that small variations produce a relatively large effect.

It is clear from these curves that when a homogeneous x-ray is scattered by graphite it is separated into two distinct parts, one of the same wave-length as the primary beam, and the other of increased wave-length. Let us call these the *modified* and the *unmodified* rays respectively. In each curve the line P is drawn through the peak of the curve representing the primary line, and the line T is drawn at the angle at which the scattered line should appear according to Eq. (1). In [the second column], in which the settings were made with the greater care, within an experimental error of less than 1 minute of arc, or about 0.001 A, the peak of the unmodified ray falls upon the line P and the peak of the modified ray falls upon the line T. The wave-length of the modified ray thus increases with the scattering angle as predicted by the quantum theory, while the wave-length of the unmodified ray is in accord with the classical theory.

There is a distinct difference between the widths of the unmodified and the modified lines. A part of the width of the modified line is due to the fact that the graphite radiator R subtends a rather large angle as viewed from the target T, so that the angles at which the rays are scattered to the spectrometer crystal vary over an appreciable range. As nearly as I can estimate, the width at the middle of the modified line due to this cause is that indicated in [the second column] Fig. 56–7 by the two short lines above the letter T. It does not appear, however, that this geometrical consideration is a sufficient explanation for the whole increased width of the modified line, at least for the rays scattered at 135°. It seems more probable that the modified line is heterogeneous, even in a ray scattered at a definite angle.

The unmodified ray is usually more prominent in a beam scattered at a small angle with the primary beam, and the modified ray more prominent when scattered at a large angle. A part of the unmodified ray is doubtless due to regular reflection from the minute crystals of which the graphite is composed. If this were the only source of the unmodified ray, however, we should expect its intensity to diminish more rapidly at large angles than is actually observed. The conditions which determine the distribution of energy between these two rays are those which determine whether an x-ray shall be scattered according to the simple quantum law or in some other manner. I have studied this distribution experimentally by another method, and shall discuss it in another paper; but the reasons underlying this distribution are puzzling.

EXPERIMENTS WITH SHORTER WAVE-LENGTHS

These experiments have been performed using a single wave-length, $\lambda = 0.711$ A. In this case we find for the modified ray a change in wave-length which increases with the angle of scattering exactly in the manner described by Eq. (1). While these experiments seem conclusive, the evidence would of course be more complete if similar experiments had been performed for other wave-lengths. Preliminary experiments similar to those here described have been performed using the K radiation from tungsten, of wave-length about 0.2 A. This work has shown a change in wave-length of the same order of magnitude as that observed using the molybdenum Kα line. Furthermore, as described in earlier papers, absorption measurements have confirmed these results as to order of magnitude over a very wide range of wave-lengths. This satisfactory agreement between the experiments and the theory gives confidence in the quantum formula (1) for the change in wave-length due to scattering. There is, indeed, no indication of any discrepancy whatever, for the range of wave-length investigated, when this formula is applied to the wave-length of the modified ray.

57

ooooooooooo

SPACE QUANTIZATION

ooooooooooo

Otto Stern (b. 1888)
Walter Gerlach (b. 1900)

The planetary theory of the atom as it had been first proposed by Bohr, with its discrete circular orbits for the electrons, was much too simple a model to account for all the observed details of the spectra of atoms, and it soon became clear that the theory itself would have to be refined and improved. The way this was to be done was first indicated by Arnold Sommerfeld, who showed that not only must the energy of the electron in the atom be quantitized, as Bohr requires, but also its angular momentum. Thus, not only must the sizes of the orbits be discrete but their shapes also. This new type of quantization enabled Sommerfeld to explain the fine structure of spectral lines. But the theory was still not complete because, even with Sommerfeld's improvement, it could not account for the Zeeman pattern of the spectral lines that appears when an atom is placed in a magnetic field. A new kind of quantization, called "space quantization," was needed. The following description will explain what is meant by this term.

One of the most remarkable concepts of the quantum theory is that the angular momentum, that is, the spin of a system, is "space-quantized." This means that if an arbitrary direction in space is chosen, let us say the z-direction of a rectangular coordinate system, we find experimentally that the angle between the direction of the angular momentum vector and this z-direction cannot assume continuous values ranging from zero degrees to 180 degrees, as one would expect from classical theory, but can have only a discrete number of values. Put somewhat differently, we find that if we measure the component of the angular momentum vector along the z-direction, this component can not take on all values between zero and the numerical value of the angular momentum, but only certain ones.

This restriction originally suggested by Pauli was demonstrated as a reality by the experiments of Stern and Gerlach. A few years later, when quantum mechanics was formulated, it was found to be a direct consequence of the Schroedinger wave equation and also of the Heisenberg matrix mechanics, developments discussed in subsequent sections of this book. From the classical point of view, space quantization is a baffling phenomenon and we need to see why, from a quantum mechanical point of view, it is not only reasonable but necessary. To do this we proceed to show how space quantization arises as a direct consequence of the procedure for measuring the angular momentum. To do this we must introduce some way of disturbing the system whose angular momentum we wish to measure; this disturbance must involve the angular momentum. In other words, we must see how the angular momentum interacts with some field that we can impose on the system. This interaction between the spin and the imposed field will, of course, change the energy of the system. By observing this change in energy we should be able to measure the angular momentum of the system and its quantized states.

We can easily guess what field we must impose for our purposes, for we note that our spinning system (in this case, an atom) is equivalent to a spinning magnet in that it consists of charges (electrons) that are moving around a nucleus. Now such revolving charges are equivalent to loops of electric current, and such loops carry a magnetic field. In general, there is associated with each atom a spin and a magnetic field and hence the atom behaves like a spinning magnet. We should then be able to observe the angular momentum of the atom by subjecting it to an external magnetic field, for such a field will disturb these magnetic loops in some way.

Suppose now that we place our atom in a magnetic field pointing in a given direction, let us say the z-direction in a rectangular coordinate system. By "pointing in a given direction," we simply mean that the lines of force of the magnetic field are parallel to the chosen direction. The introduction of such a magnetic field introduces a preferred direction—the direction of the field—and thus eliminates the implied paradox of having the angular momentum adjust itself to any arbitrary direction. Since the magnetic field is necessary for measuring the direction of the angular momentum (spin), the very process that we use for our measurement establishes a direction for us.

Now what happens when we turn on such a magnetic field? The field imparts to the atom additional energy, which—and this is a crucial point—

depends on the product of the strength of the magnetic field (if it is not too large) and the magnitude of the projection of the spin along the field. There is another factor in this expression, for the energy, which depends on the electric charge and the mass of the system, but this factor is not significant for our discussion. The important thing is that the energy depends on the spin component along the field. But we have seen that the spin can have only a discrete number of projections, in fact, just $2j + 1$ if j is the spin, along the field. We can look upon each of these as representing a different state of the atom, but if no magnetic field is present, all of these atomic states are equal. They coincide. In a magnetic field, however, the energy of each of these states is slightly different. This made it possible for Stern and Gerlach to carry out their experiment and demonstrate space quantization, since they were able to use this energy difference to separate one state from another. We shall elaborate on this point in a moment.

We note that the introduction of a magnetic field removes the seemingly paradoxical quality of space quantization because of the energy the field imparts to the atom. We know from the work of Planck, Einstein, and Bohr that energy in an atomic system is quantized; it therefore follows that the magnetic energy is also quantized. But the magnetic energy, as we have just seen, is proportional to the component of the spin along the field. Hence this component must be quantized and we have, in a sense, solved the mystery.

We may enquire into the nature of the magnetic energy. There is, of course, potential energy, which is measured by the work we would have to do to remove the atom from the magnetic field. But there is also kinetic energy, which arises as follows: When the magnetic field is turned on, it tries to turn the atom so that the atom's magnet is lined up with the field just as it would tend to turn an ordinary bar magnet; for example, the way a compass needle turns toward the north in the earth's magnetic field. The "little magnet" associated with an atom has an effective pole strength and length; the product of these is called the *magnetic moment* of the atom. The magnetic moment is a vector that is parallel to and proportional to the spin of the atom. We may therefore say that the magnetic field, when turned on, tries to turn the magnetic moment of the atom parallel to the field. But we must remember that the atom is spinning and therefore resists being turned, just the way a gyroscope does. Instead of turning parallel to the magnetic field, the spin vector of the atom therefore precesses around the magnetic field the way the axis of a spinning top precesses around the vertical. The atom thus acquires additional kinetic energy—the energy of precession—in the field.

We can see now why space quantization must exist. It is a consequence of the general rule that all periodic motion must be quantized, that action is discontinuous. Since the precession of the atom is periodic, it must be quantized, which means that only a discrete number of precessional states is allowed and that each of these states has a slightly different amount of energy. This is the basis of the Stern-Gerlach experiment which we now discuss.

To take a specific example, suppose we have an atom whose total spin, j, is $\frac{3}{2}$. There are then four spin states corresponding to the values $\frac{3}{2}$, $\frac{1}{2}$, $-\frac{1}{2}$, $-\frac{3}{2}$ of the z-component of the spin, where z is any direction in space. If a constant magnetic field is imposed, we obtain four different energy states, whose energies are proportional to $\frac{3}{2}$ B, $\frac{1}{2}$ B, $-\frac{1}{2}$ B, $-\frac{3}{2}$ B, where B is the strength or intensity of the magnetic field. This simply means that if a system of such atoms is placed in a magnetic field, these atoms are distributed randomly among these states, or almost so, since the energies of the four states are almost but not quite equal. In other words, there are about equal numbers of atoms precessing at four different angles about the magnetic field.

The purpose of the Stern-Gerlach experiment was in effect to show that the spin vectors of the atoms do, indeed, distribute themselves among these four states only (that is, along four different directions relative to the magnetic field), and to use the energy difference between any two of these states to demonstrate this. Now the energy of the atom in a magnetic field depends on the intensity of the field if the magnetic field is inhomogeneous, and the atom will experience a force. Depending on how the magnetic moment, or the spin, of the atom aligns itself with respect to this field, the atom is pulled toward the strong part of the field or pushed toward the weak part. Thus, in our example the atoms in the spin state $\frac{3}{2}$ are pulled most strongly toward the strongest part of the field; the atoms in spin state $\frac{1}{2}$ are pulled in the same direction but not so strongly; the atoms in the two negative spin states are pushed away from the strong part of the field toward the weak part. Hence, if a beam of such atoms is allowed to pass through an inhomogeneous magnetic field, it will be split into four different beams owing to the four different forces experienced by the atoms in the different spin states.

In 1922, Stern and Gerlach devised an experiment to demonstrate this with silver atoms. They obtained a beam of silver atoms by first evaporating the metal in a hot oven, then passing these gaseous atoms through a series of small holes arranged in a straight line. This beam passed between the two poles of a magnet designed to give a strongly inhomogeneous field at right angles to the motion of the atoms in the beam. Finally, after moving through the magnetic field, the atoms were collected on a photographic plate.

When these atoms left the oven they were distributed randomly among their various possible spin states. If Stern and Gerlach had used a homogeneous magnetic field, the atoms would have been subjected to no forces by the magnetic field. The beam of atoms would thus have passed right through the field unchanged. But instead, they used a magnet of which one pole was a flat surface, the other a sharp edge parallel to the flat surface and to the atomic beam. This gave an inhomogeneous field in which the magnetic lines of force were spread out at the flat pole but highly concentrated at the pole with the sharp edge. Consequently, atoms in the beam experienced strong forces perpendicular to their direction of motion. Had the spins of the silver atoms behaved classically, the beam of silver atoms would have been spread out uniformly since all possible spin orientations are allowed classically and each orientation would have resulted in a different force.

But Stern and Gerlach did not find this; they found just two spots on their photographic plate, showing that the magnetic field had *split,* not spread, the initial beam. This clearly demonstrated space quantization and showed that the spin or angular momentum of the silver atom is just $\frac{1}{2}$ unit. This means that the magnetic moment of the silver atom can align itself either parallel to the direction of magnetic field, or opposite to its direction. In other words, when the silver atoms passed between the poles of the Stern-Gerlach magnet, their spins either pointed toward the sharp-edged pole or toward the flat pole, and in about equal numbers. The atoms in the first group were pulled toward the flat pole and the others were pulled toward the sharp edge, so that two beams were formed, as predicted by space quantization.

Otto Stern was trained in theoretical physics, but went on to do even more significant work in experimental physics. Born in Sorau, Upper Silesia, Germany, on February 17, 1888, he moved to Breslau with his parents in 1892, where he completed his elementary and secondary schooling. After graduating from Gymnasium in 1906, he entered the University of Breslau to study physical chemistry. In 1912 he received his doctorate and came under the influence of Einstein, whom he joined at the University of Prague that same year; he later followed Einstein to the University of Zurich. In 1913 he was appointed *Privatdozent* (unpaid lecturer) of physical chemistry at the Eidgenössische Technische Hochschule of Zurich.

During this early period in his scientific career, Stern published important theoretical papers in statistical mechanics, thermodynamics, and quantum theory. In 1913, he derived the correct quantum theoretical expression for the entropy of a gas, using a step-by-step analysis of the changes taking place in a substance when it passes from the crystalline to the gaseous phase. To accomplish this, Stern applied Einstein's method of quantizing the vibrations of the crystal to introduce Planck's constant into the formula for the entropy. It was one of the earliest applications of the quantum theory to physical systems other than radiation, and occurred just about the time when Bohr was applying the quantum theory to the dynamics of the atom.

In 1914, Stern went to the University of Frankfurt am Main as lecturer in theoretical physics; there his attention turned more and more to problems of experimental physics. In 1919, he became particularly interested in experimental methods of proving the theoretical deductions of the kinetic theory of gases, and began to devise procedures for measuring the velocities of molecules in a gaseous phase. He finally hit on the method of molecular beams, which is one of the most powerful techniques in experimental physics for studying the behavior of individual molecules, atoms, and atomic nuclei. Stern began his experimental work by applying the molecular-beam technique to verify Maxwell's law of the distribution of molecular velocities in a gas.

It soon occurred to Stern that his molecular beam method was ideally suited for studying the magnetic properties of molecules and atoms; it was a simple matter to impose a magnetic field, of whatever nature might be desired, onto the molecular beam and examine the results. Thus, in 1922, working with Gerlach, he passed beams of silver atoms through an inhomogeneous magnetic field and proved experimentally—for the first time—that the direction of the magnetic moment of an atom is quantized in a magnetic field. At that time, Stern was associate professor of theoretical physics at the University of Rostock, to which he had come in 1921. As a result of his molecular-beam experiments, he was invited to become professor of physical chemistry and director of the laboratory at the University of Hamburg. He remained at Hamburg until Hitler came to power in 1933, then left Germany to become research professor of physics at the Carnegie Institute of Technlogy in Pittsburgh, Pennsylvania.

Just before he left Germany, Stern made one of the most important applications of the molecular beam method. In collaboration with Estermann and Frisch, he passed a beam of neutral hydrogen molecules through an inhomogeneous magnetic field and measured the magnetic moment of the proton, which, like the electron, is a small spinning magnet. The results of this experiment were quite surprising, for they showed that the magnetic moment of the proton is $2\frac{1}{2}$ times as large as one would expect if the proton were a simple particle governed, as is the electron, by the Dirac wave equation. This experiment indicates that the proton is some kind of composite particle, a finding that is borne out by the important experiments of Hofstadter.

The 1943 Nobel Prize in physics was awarded to Stern for developing the molecular beam method and for his measurement of the magnetic moment of the proton.

Stern remained at the Carnegie Institute of Technology until 1945, when he retired as professor emeritus. At the present time, he is living at Berkeley, California.

ͻͻͻͻͻͻͻ

GERLACH and STERN

Experimental Proof of Space Quantization in a Magnetic Field [1]

A SHORT TIME AGO A possible procedure was outlined in this journal for determining whether or not space quantization in a magnetic field exists. In a second communication it was shown that the normal silver atom has a magnetic moment. By continuing these investigations, on which we shall report in what follows, we have established *space quantization in a magnetic field* as a fact.

EXPERIMENTAL SETUP

The methods and apparatus were in general the same as in our earlier experiments. In certain details, however, essential improvements were introduced which we shall describe in this completion of our previous report.

The silver atom beam emanated from an electrically heated furnace with a steel insert, in the cover of which, at the exit point of the silver atom beam, a 1-mm² circular opening was found. The separation between the oven opening and the first beam aperture was increased to 2.5 cm which prevented the clogging of the aperture by the occasional spurting of drops of silver from the oven as well as by the too rapid growth of layers of silver through precipitation of the atomic beam itself. This first aperture is approximately circular and has an area of 3×10^{-3} cm²; 3.3 cm behind this circular aperture the silver beam passes through a slit-shaped aperture 0.8 mm long and 0.03 to 0.04 mm wide. Both apertures are made of sheet platinum. The slit-shaped stop is situated at the front end of the magnetic field. The opening of the slit stop lies directly over the

---

[1] Walter Gerlach and Otto Stern, *Zeitschrift für Physik*, 9 (1922), 349–352— trans. Editors.

cut S [see Fig. 57–1] and is so adjusted to the circular stop and to the oven opening that the silver beam runs parallel to the 3.5-cm long cut. Directly at the end of the cut the silver atomic beam strikes a glass plate onto which it is deposited.

The two stops, the two magnetic poles, and the glass plate sit in a brass housing having 1-cm thick walls, all rigidly connected so that any pressure of the magnetic pole of the electromagnet will not cause a deformation of the housing nor result in a change in the relative positions of the stops, the pole, and the glass plate.

Fig. 57–1.

Just as in the first experiments, the evacuation is carried out with two Volmer diffusion pumps and Gaede Hy-pumps as preliminary pumps. By means of continuous pumping and cooling with solid carbon dioxide, a vacuum of about 10^{-5} mm Hg was achieved and continuously maintained.

The "irradiation time" was stretched out to eight hours without interruption. But even after eight hours of vaporization the layer of silver deposited on the receiving plate was so thin because of the very narrow apertures and the great length of the beam that, just as previously reported, it had to be developed.

RESULTS

To begin with, [Fig. 57–2] shows a photograph after a $4\frac{1}{2}$ hour irradiation time without magnetic field; the enlargement is about 20-fold. The measurement of the original with a microscope having an ocular micrometer gave the following dimensions: length 1.1 mm., width at the narrowest point 0.06 mm., at the widest point 0.10 mm. We see that the slit is not exactly parallel. We must, however, note that the figure is a 40-fold enlargement of the slit since the "silver image" of the slit itself already had double the dimensions; it is difficult to make such a slit in a frame a few millimeters in size.

[Fig. 57–3] gives a photograph [after] eight hours irradiation with magnetic field, enlarged 20-fold (20 scale divisions of the imaged scale =1 mm). This is the most successful photograph. Two other photographs gave pretty much the same results in all essential points but not with this com-

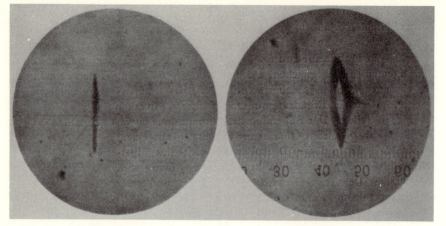

Fig. 57–2.   Fig. 57–3.

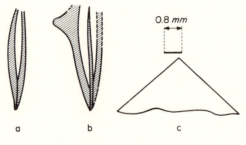

a   b   c

0.8 *mm*

Fig. 57–4.

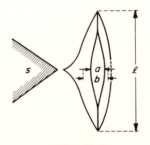

Fig. 57–5.

plete symmetry. We must point out here that a precise adjustment of such small stops by optical methods is very difficult; that to obtain such a completely symmetrical photograph as in [Fig. 57–3] is in part due to luck; an error of only a few hundredths of a millimeter in the position of a stop is sufficient to ruin a photograph completely.

The results of the other two experiments are shown schematically in [figs. 57–4a and b]. In [Fig. 57–4a] the silver beam was arranged intentionally to move at a slightly greater distance past the cut than in the experiment of [Fig. 57–3]. In this case the split aperture was not completely filled. In the case of [Fig. 57–4b] the same glass plate was used for a deposit with and without field; the beam passed very close to the cut, but it was displaced by about 0.3 mm in a direction at right angles to the field [Fig. 57–4c]. As far as clarity of the pictures, complete splitting, and all other details, these pictures are in no way inferior to these given in [Fig. 57–3].

The pictures show that the silver atom beam in an inhomogeneous magnetic field is split up into two beams in the direction of the inhomogeneity, one of which is attracted to the knife-edged pole and the other of which is repelled. The deposits show the following details (compare with the diagram of [Fig. 57–5]).

(a) The dimensions of the originals were measured in a microscope: length 1, 1.1 mm; width a, 0.11 mm; width b, 0.20 mm.

(b) The splitting of the atomic beam in the magnetic field occurs in two discrete beams. No undeviated atoms are found.

(c) The attraction is somewhat stronger than the repulsion. The attracted atoms come closer to the pole and hence into zones of larger inhomogeneity so that the deflection increases more and more during the flight. [Figs. 57–3 and 4b] show the quite appreciably increased deflection directly at the knife edge of the one magnetic pole. In the immediate vicinity of the edge the attraction becomes very large so that a bulge, shown by the sharp point toward the edge, arises.

(d) The width of the deflected strip is larger than that of the undeviated image. The latter is just the image of the slit B_2 projected onto the glass plate by the slit B_1. The deflected bands are broadened because of the velocity distribution of the silver atoms.

(e) This fact sharpens the evidence against the existence of undeflected atoms in any perceptible amounts (compare point (b)). For the evidence based on undeflected atoms falling together on a small surface is much more sensitive than that based on a dispersed beam of undeflected atoms falling on a wide area.

We view these results as direct experimental verifications of space quantization in a magnetic field.

58

ooooooooooo

ELECTRON SPIN

ooooooooooo

Samuel A. Goudsmit (b. 1902)
George E. Uhlenbeck (b. 1900)

When Niels Bohr applied Planck's quantum hypothesis to the structure of the hydrogen atom and succeeded in deriving the wavelengths of the Balmer lines in the hydrogen spectrum, he did so with the very simplest possible model. According to it the electron in the atom was pictured as moving around the proton in circular orbits of discrete radii. With this model Bohr could compute the frequencies of the various spectral lines by assigning to each orbit a very definite energy. As we know, he pictured the electron as emitting or absorbing a quantum of energy (a photon) every time it changed orbits. Since the energy of the electron in a circular orbit is determined solely by the radius of the orbit, and the radius, in this quantum picture of Bohr's is determined by one of the integers (the lowest orbit is assigned the integer 1, and so on), it follows that the energy of the electron depends on the value of the integer that is associated with its orbit. This integer n is called the principal quantum number of the orbit.

It soon became clear, however, that for the electron to jump from one orbit to any other orbit, the orbits could not be circles. For if the orbits were circular, the electron could jump from a given orbit only to the adjacent orbit lying either directly above or below according to certain rules —selection rules—that had to be introduced. Thus it was necessary to replace the circular orbits by elliptical orbits to allow for all possible jumps.

However, we know from planetary theory that associated with an orbit having a definite semimajor axis there is an infinitude of elliptical shapes ranging all the way from a circle to a straight line, and that an electron

940

in any of these orbits, regardless of shape, has the same energy. One might have been inclined therefore to picture an infinitude of possible elliptical orbits associated with an electron moving around a proton, all having the same size, that is, the same principal quantum number n and hence the same energy. Now this is not the case in the Bohr quantum picture of the atom, since the shape of the orbit is itself quantized (that is, associated with integers), as we shall see in Chapter 59 in our discussion of Pauli's work. Only certain shapes, equal in number to n, are permissible. If the principal quantum number of the orbit of the electron is 3, for instance, only three elliptical orbits are permissible.

When the elliptical orbits associated with a given principal quantum number were introduced into the theory, it was first thought that they should all be assigned the same energy. Hence, an electron jumping from any one of these orbits to any elliptical orbit of a set associated with some other principal quantum number would emit or absorb a photon of exactly the same frequency. In other words, it was thought that as far as the observed spectral lines of hydrogen were concerned it made no difference whether the orbits were circular or elliptical, except that in the latter case each spectral line was to be associated not with just two orbits, but with two sets of orbits. These sets of orbits were thought to be a convenient mathematical fiction without any bearing on the physics.

This simple picture was soon discarded. It was quickly shown by Arnold Sommerfeld that the different elliptical orbits associated with a given principal quantum number do not have the same energy. This arises from the relativistic variation in the mass of the electron as it moves about in an elliptical orbit, which causes the entire orbit to precess. This means that the electron will have slightly different energies if it is in different elliptical orbits of a given set. The energy of an electron, then, is determined by two quantum numbers: the previously discussed principal quantum number n and another, let us say l, called the azimuthal quantum number, which gives the shape and therefore the angular momentum of the electron in the given elliptical orbit. This means that instead of one spectral line associated with the jump of an electron when it changes its principal quantum number, there is a group of lines all lying very close together. Thus, each of the Balmer lines (the lines as predicted by the first Bohr theory) has a fine structure, so that each line is a multiplet of lines. In fact, each Balmer line consists of three closely spaced components. This is exactly what the spectroscopists discovered.

However, very careful analysis of the spectral lines shows that they are even more complex than this Sommerfeld relativistic theory indicates. Whereas the Sommerfeld theory predicts that each Balmer line should consist of three almost identical members, actual observations prove that each Balmer line consists of five close components. We shall come back

ATOMIC THEORY DEVELOPS

to this point presently in connection with the idea of electron spin as introduced by Goudsmit and Uhlenbeck.

Not only did the Bohr theory run into difficulty in trying to explain the fine structure of the hydrogen spectral lines under ordinary conditions, but there was also trouble (even with Sommerfeld's relativistic refinement superimposed) in connection with the multiplet structure of the lines when the atom emitting the radiation was placed in a magnetic field. We have already noted, with relativity taken into account, that two quantum numbers—the principal quantum number, giving the size of the orbit of the electron, and the azimuthal quantum number, giving the shape of the orbit—are required to specify the energy of the electron. However, it is clear that at least one other quantum number is also needed, since the orientation of the orbit in space must still be specified. As long as no magnetic field is present, the spatial orientation of the orbit has no influence on the energy of the orbiting electron; as already noted in our discussion of space quantization, the situation changes when the atom is in a magnetic field.

We must keep in mind that the electron circling around the nucleus behaves like a small magnet. As such, it will precess around a magnetic field with a frequency that depends on how the plane of its orbit is oriented with respect to the magnetic field. This magnetic precession will then contribute to the energy of the electron, so that the orientation of the atom must also be specified by a quantum number. Indeed, such a quantum number, the magnetic quantum number m, was introduced into the theory by Stern and Gerlach. To some extent it helped explain the complexity of the spectral lines when the atom is in a magnetic field.

That a magnetic field should bring about a splitting of the spectral lines was recognized as early as 1896, when the Dutch physicist Zeeman observed that each spectral line of an atom in a magnetic field breaks up into three lines. This is known as the normal Zeeman effect and was explained by Lorentz with the aid of his classical theory of the electron. Lorentz pictured an atom as a small magnet that can precess in a magnetic field. Since the magnetic precession (the so-called Larmor precession) can either be added to or subtracted from the electron's ordinary motion, we obtain two additional lines in the spectrum. This same result can be obtained from the Bohr theory, since the introduction of the magnetic quantum number gives rise to an additional term, which depends on the magnetic quantum number in the expression for the energy of the electron in any one of the Bohr orbits. When the electron jumps from one orbit to another the magnetic quantum number may either remain unaltered, or it may change by becoming one unit smaller or larger. We thus have the possibility for three lines arising in place of each ordinary line when no field is present.

This, of course, was all to the good. But it was not long before spectroscopists, with their ever-increasing refinements, observed that the Zeeman effect is considerably more complicated than had previously been imagined. Instead of a splitting of the lines always into sets of three, a magnetic field induces a splitting into three lines in some cases but into more than three lines in others. Although attempts were first made to explain these spectral complexities by picturing the atom as consisting of a core (the nucleus plus the inner electrons) and an external electron, the core possessing certain magnetic properties, Pauli showed that a model of this sort runs into other serious difficulties. Pauli then suggested that many points in connection with the multiple spectral lines and the Zeeman effect could be explained if one pictured the electron as having an additional degree of freedom, that is, a fourth quantum number.

As Pauli demonstrated, the assignment of a fourth quantum number to an electron would fall very nicely into the relativistic scheme, since four numbers according to relativity theory are, indeed, required to describe the electron: three-space coordinates and a time coordinate. Pauli, however, did not suggest just how this fourth quantum number was to be assigned to the electron nor what its physical significance was to be. This is where Goudsmit and Uhlenbeck came into the picture. In two communications, in the form of a note to *Naturwissenschaften* in November 1925, and in a letter to *Nature* the following month, which follows this discussion, they proposed a scheme to account for the fine structure in the lines of hydrogen-like atoms and at the same time for the complexities of the Zeeman spectral pattern. The essential feature of the scheme is that the electron is pictured as spinning (that is, as possessing an intrinsic angular momentum, and hence a magnetic moment). Since a spinning electron precesses when placed in a magnetic field and this precession can be quantized, the spinning hypothesis automatically introduces another quantum number.

To explain the multiplicity of the fine structure of the lines, Goudsmit and Uhlenbeck found it necessary to suppose that the angular momentum of the spinning electron is not an integral multiple of $h/2\pi$, which is the unit of angular momentum in quantum mechanics, but only half of this. This means that the spin of the electron can only be added to the angular momentum of the orbital motion or subtracted from it. Thus, there are possible suborbits associated with an orbit of given angular momentum, depending upon whether the electron spin adds to or subtracts from the orbital angular momentum.

Essentially this means the following: Before the introduction of the spinning electron, the electron was pictured in its orbit as being equivalent to a small magnet because of its motion around the nucleus. But if the electron is spinning, it must, in virtue of this spin, behave like a little magnet even if it is not going around in an orbit. Thus two magnets may be imagined associated with the motion of the electron in its orbit around a nucleus, and these two magnets can either align themselves so that they are parallel to each other (north pole next to north pole and south pole next to south) or align themselves so that they are antiparallel. Since these two alignments correspond to states of different energy two sub-orbits are associated with each orbit. This, therefore, gives rise to a doubling of the spectral lines for a single electron moving around a nucleus (a hydrogen-like atom).

Although the introduction for the electron of an intrinsic magnetic moment, that is, a spin, eliminated the spectroscopic difficulties, the idea of a spinning electron was repugnant to many prominent physicists. Indeed, Pauli himself presented apparently insurmountable objections to such an idea, and Ehrenfest the great Dutch theoretical physicist rejected the idea because he argued that the surface of the electron would have to be moving with a speed greater than the speed of light if the electron possessed an angular momentum equal to $\frac{1}{2}(h/2\pi)$. Other objections dealt with the fact that the electron has to be treated as a point from relativity considerations, and it is difficult to see how a point can be spinning. All of these oddities in connection with the spin of the electron show that it cannot be treated as one would treat ordinary classical angular momentum.

In spite of all the objections raised against the spin of the electron, it finally had to be fully accepted in light of the experimental evidence. A particularly strong point in its favor is the famous Stern-Gerlach experiment, which shows that a beam of atoms, which should show no magnetic effects if the electron had no spin, breaks up into two beams when passing through an inhomogeneous magnetic field as though the electron were a small magnet of the sort postulated by Goudsmit and Uhlenbeck. The final triumph of the spinning electron came with Dirac's discovery that the spin itself can be derived from the relativity theory.

The year 1924 to 1925 was one of the most remarkable in the entire history of physics: in that period Pauli published his paper on the exclusion principle, De Broglie announced his discovery of the wave nature of electrons, Heisenberg discovered the matrix mechanics, Dirac published his version of the quantum mechanics, Schroedinger was writing his paper on the wave mechanics, and Goudsmit and Uhlenbeck proposed their hypothesis of a spinning electron. It is interesting that this concept of spin should have originated in the Leiden school of physics since it was in the tradition of Lorentzian electron theory and, at first sight, somewhat out of step with the other rapidly occurring developments. Indeed, Pauli, whose exclusion principle, as applied to the arrangement of electrons inside the atom, requires a fourth quantum number—which the spin provides—

initially doubted the validity of this idea because of what he called its "classical-mechanical" character. But the spin was needed to clear up the difficulty with the Zeeman effect, and Zeeman's great influence on Dutch physics must have played its role in the Goudsmit-Uhlenbeck discovery.

When they wrote their first paper on the spinning electron, which appeared in 1925 in the German scientific journal *Naturwissenschaft,* Samuel A. Goudsmit and George E. Uhlenbeck were young graduate students at Leiden, still two years away from their Ph.D. degrees. Goudsmit was born in The Hague, Holland, on July 11, 1902; after attending elementary and secondary school there, he began his career in physics as an assistant at Amsterdam in 1923. After collaborating with Uhlenbeck at Leiden in 1925, Goudsmit spent a year at Tübingen as a fellow of the Institute of International Education and returned to Leiden in 1927 to receive his Ph.D.

At this time American universities were beginning to build up their science faculties, particularly in the field of theoretical physics, and they were looking for promising European physicists who were willing to come to the United States. The University of Michigan was in the forefront of this effort, and invited both Goudsmit and Uhlenbeck to come there as instructors in physics. Both men, newly married, came to Michigan in 1927 with their wives. After one year as an instructor, Goudsmit was promoted to an associate professorship in 1928; in 1932, at the age of thirty, he became professor of physics. He remained on the Michigan faculty until 1946, devoting his time to research and teaching. In 1938 he spent a year in Rome and Paris as a Guggenheim Fellow, and in 1941 he was a visiting lecturer at Harvard.

When the United States entered World War II, Goudsmit, like most of the other influential physicists, participated in military scientific research. He became a member of the staff of the Radiation Laboratory at the Massachusetts Institute of Technology and was also a consultant for the War Department. At the end of the war, in 1946, he went to Northwestern University as professor of physics, where he remained until 1948, when he became senior scientist at Brookhaven National Laboratories, Upton, Long Island. In 1952 he was appointed chairman of the physics department there and has held this post since then.

In 1951 Goudsmit became editor of *The Physical Review,* the outstanding journal of American physics. He is also editor of *Physical Review Letters,* which is issued weekly to permit physicists to quickly publish new and important discoveries.

In addition to a book on the theory of atomic spectra, published jointly with Pauling, and a book on German nuclear physics during the war, Goudsmit has published many papers on atomic structure, the theory of atomic spectra, nuclear spin, and statistical mechanics.

For his contributions in physics he has received the Order of the British Empire and the award of the Research Corporation. He is a member of the National Academy of Sciences, a fellow of the Physical Society, and a correspondent of the Royal Netherland Academy of Sciences.

That George E. Uhlenbeck should have collaborated with Goudsmit in the discovery of the spin of the electron was quite natural in view of their similar backgrounds. Although Uhlenbeck was born in Batavia, Java, on December 6, 1900—two years before Goudsmit—his training in physics paralleled that of Goudsmit. Like Goudsmit, he was a product of the Leiden school of physics, receiving his Ph.D. in 1927.

From 1925 to 1927 he was an assistant in physics at Leiden, but then went to Michigan with his wife to become an instructor at the university. A year later he was appointed assistant professor in the department of physics and, in 1930, associate professor. In 1935 he returned to Holland as professor of physics at the University of Utrecht, but remained there only until 1939, when he returned to the University of Michigan as the Henry S. Carhart professor of physics, retaining this post until 1960.

In the decade before World War II, the summer session of the University of Michigan became famous as a center of modern physics, graced, as it was for many summers, by Fermi. The emergence in the United States of the first international meeting ground of physicists—for it attracted such men as Heisenberg, Dirac, and Pauli—in large measure was due to the efforts of Uhlenbeck and Goudsmit. Unfortunately, the advent of war suspended this remarkable conclave. During the war, Uhlenbeck carried on military research as a member of the staff of the Radiation Laboratory at the Massachusetts Institute of Technology. Immediately after the war he returned to Michigan to resume his teaching duties and his own research. He left the University of Michigan in 1960 to become professor of physics and member of the Rockefeller Institute (now Rockefeller University) in New York.

Uhlenbeck has received many honors for his contributions to physics. He is a member of the National Academy of Sciences and has received honorary degrees of Doctor of Science from the University of Notre Dâme and from Case. He served as president of the American Physical Society in 1959 and is a member of the Dutch Physical Society.

Although Uhlenbeck has written numerous papers on atomic structure, quantum mechanics, and nuclear physics, his greatest love is statistical mechanics, of which he is one of the great masters. This proclivity stems from the early influence of Paul Ehrenfest at Leiden, who insisted on having his students pursue rigorous training in thermodynamics and statistical mechanics. Moreover, Uhlenbeck learned how to impart his knowledge to others; he is one of the great teachers of our time. Like Fermi, Uhlenbeck made the most difficult and obscure topic clear and understandable. Today, one finds his students in important academic posts in many American universities—living tributes to his greatness as a teacher.

୦୦୦୦୦୦୦

UHLENBECK and GOUDSMIT

SPINNING ELECTRONS AND THE STRUCTURE OF SPECTRA [1]

So far as we know, the idea of a quantised spinning of the electron was put forward for the first time by A. H. Compton, who pointed out the possible bearing of this idea on the origin of the natural unit of magnetism. Without being aware of Compton's suggestion, we have directed attention in a recent note to the possibility of applying the spinning electron to interpret a number of features of the quantum theory of the Zeeman effect, which were brought to light by the work especially of van Lohuizen, Sommerfeld, Landé, and Pauli and also of the analysis of complex spectra in general. In this letter we shall try to show how our hypothesis enables us to overcome certain fundamental difficulties which have hitherto hindered the interpretation of the results arrived at by those authors.

To start with, we shall consider the effect of the spin on the manifold of stationary states which corresponds to motion of an electron round a nucleus. On account of its magnetic moment, the electron will be acted on by a couple just as if it were placed at rest in a magnetic field of magnitude equal to the vector product of the nuclear electric field and the velocity of the electron relative to the nucleus divided by the velocity of light. This couple will cause a slow precession of the spin axis, the conservation of the angular momentum of the atom being ensured by a compensating precession of the orbital plane of the electron. This complexity of the motion requires that, corresponding to each stationary state of an imaginary atom, in which the electron has no spin, there shall in general exist a set of states which differ in the orientation of the spin axis relative to the orbital plane, the other characteristics of the motion remaining unchanged. If the spin corresponds to a one-quantum rotation there will be in general two such states. Further, the energy difference of these states will, as a simple calculation shows, be proportional to the fourth power of the nuclear charge. It will also depend on the quantum numbers which

---

[1] *Nature*, 117 (1926), 264 f.

define the state of motion of the non-spinning electron in a way very similar to the energy differences connected with the rotation of the orbit in its own plane arising from the relativity variation of the electronic mass. We are indebted to Dr. Heisenberg for a letter containing some calculations on the quantitative side of the problem.

This result suggests an essential modification of the explanation hitherto given of the fine structure of the hydrogen-like spectra. As an illustration we may consider the energy levels corresponding to electronic orbits for which the principal quantum number is equal to three. The scheme on the left side of the accompanying figure [Fig. 58–1] corresponds to the results

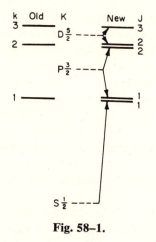

Fig. 58–1.

to be expected from Sommerfeld's theory. The so-called azimuthal quantum number k is defined by the quantity of moment of momentum [angular momentum] of the electron about the nucleus, $Kh/2\pi$, where k = 1, 2, 3. According to the new theory, depicted in the scheme * on the right, this moment of momentum is given by $Kh/2\pi$, where $K = \frac{1}{2}, \frac{3}{2}, \frac{5}{2}$. The total angular momentum of the atom is $Jh/2\pi$, where $J = 1, 2, 3$. The symbols K and J correspond to those used by Landé in his classification of the Zeeman effects of the optical multiplets. The letters S, P, D also relate to the analogy with the structure of optical spectra which we consider below. The dotted lines represent the position of the energy levels to be expected in the absence of the spin of the electron. As the arrows indicate, this

---

* Quite independently of the ideas discussed here, a scheme of levels corresponding to this figure has been previously proposed by the writers, on the ground of the formal analogy between spectral structures. From similar formal considerations, this scheme has recently also been arrived at by J. C. Slater.

spin now splits each level into two, with the exception of the level $K = \frac{1}{2}$, which is only displaced.

In order to account for the experimental facts, the resulting levels must fall in just the same places as the levels given by the older theory. Nevertheless, the two schemes differ fundamentally. In particular, the new theory explains at once the occurrence of certain components in the fine structure of the hydrogen spectrum and of the helium spark spectrum which according to the old scheme would correspond to transitions where K remains unchanged. Unless these transitions could be ascribed to the action of electric forces in the discharge which would perturb the electronic motion, their occurrence would be in disagreement with the correspondence principle, which only allows transitions in which the azimuthal quantum number changes by one unit. In the new scheme we see that, in the transitions in question, K will actually change by one unit and only J will remain unchanged. Their occurrence is, therefore, quite in conformity with the correspondence principle.

The modification proposed is specially important for explaining the structure of X-ray spectra. These spectra differ from the hydrogen-like spectra by the appearance of the so-called "screening" doublets, which are ascribed to the interaction of the electrons within the atom, effective mainly through reducing the effect of the nuclear attraction. In our view, these screening doublets correspond to pairs of levels which have the same angular momentum J but different azimuthal quantum numbers K. Consequently, the orbits will penetrate to different distances from the nucleus, so that the screening of the nuclear charge by the other electrons in the atom will have different effects. This screening effect will, however, be the same for a pair of levels which have the same K but different J's and correspond to the same orbital shape. Such pairs of levels were, on the older theory, labelled with values of K differing by one unit, and it was quite impossible to understand why these so-called "relativity" doublets should appear separately from the screening doublets. On our view, the doublets in question may more properly be termed "spin" doublets, since the sole reason for their appearance is the difference in orientation of the spin axis relative to the orbital plane. It should be emphasised that our interpretation is in complete accordance with the correspondence principle as regards the rules of combination of X-ray levels.

The assumption of the spinning electron leads to a new insight into the remarkable analogy between the multiplet structure of the optical spectra and the structure of X-ray spectra, which was emphasised especially by Landé and Millikan. While the attempt to refer this analogy to a relativity effect common to all the structures was most unsatisfactory, it obtains an immediate explanation on the hypothesis of the spin electron. If, for example, we consider the spectra of the alkaline type, we are led to recognise in the well-known doublets regular spin doublets of the character described above. In fact, this enables us to explain the dependence of the doublet width on the effective nuclear charge and the quantum numbers describing the orbit, as well as the rules of combination.

The simplicity of the alkaline spectra is due to the fact that the atom consists of an electron revolving round an atomic residue which contains only completed electronic groups, which are magnetically inert. When we pass to atoms in which several electrons revolve round a residue of this kind we meet with new features, since we have to take account of other directing influences on the spin axis of each electron besides the couple due to its own motion in the electric field. Not only does this enable us to account for the appearance of multiplets of higher complexity, but it also seems to throw light on the so-called "branching" of spectra, which usually accompanies the adding of a further electron to the atom, and for which hitherto no satisfactory explanation has been given. In fact, it seems that the introduction of the concept of the spinning electron makes it possible throughout to maintain the principle of the successive building up of atoms utilised by Bohr in his general discussion of the relations between spectra and the natural system of the elements. Above all, it may be possible to account for the important results arrived at by Pauli, without having to assume an unmechanical "duality" in the binding of the electrons.

So far we have not mentioned the Zeeman effect, although the introduction of the spinning electron was primarily suggested by the analysis of the anomalous Zeeman effects shown by the components of multiplet structures. From the point of view of the correspondence principle, this effect shows that the influence of a magnetic field on the motion of the atom differs considerably from that to be expected if the electron had no spin. In fact, from the well-known theorem of Larmor we would expect the effect on any spectral line to be of the simple Lorentz type, quite independently of the character of the multiplet structure. Therefore the appearance of the anomalous Zeeman effects has hitherto presented very grave difficulties. However, these difficulties disappear at once when, as assumed, the electron has a spin and the ratio between magnetic moment and angular momentum of this spin is different from that corresponding to the revolution of the electron in an orbit large compared with its own size. On this assumption the spin axis of an electron not affected by other forces would precess with a frequency different from the Larmor rotation. It is easily shown that the resultant motion of the atom for magnetic fields of small intensity will be of just the type revealed by Landé's analysis. If the field is so strong that its influence on the precession of the spin axis is comparable with that due to the orbital motion in the atom, this motion will be changed in a way which directly explains the gradual transformation of the multiplet structure for increasing fields known as the Paschen-Back effect.

It seems possible on these lines to develop a quantitative theory of the Zeeman effect, if it is assumed that the ratio between magnetic moment and angular momentum due to the spin is twice the ratio corresponding to an orbital revolution. At present, however, it seems difficult to reconcile this assumption with a quantitative analysis of our explanation of the fine structure of levels. In fact it leads, in a preliminary calculation, to widths of the spin doublets just twice as large as those required by observation. It must be remembered, however, that we are here dealing with problems which for their final solution require a closer study of quantum mechanics and perhaps also of questions concerning the structure of the electron.

In conclusion, we wish to acknowledge our indebtedness to Prof. Niels Bohr for an enlightening discussion, and for criticisms which helped us distinguish between the essential points and the more technical details of the new interpretation.

G. E. Uhlenbeck
S. Goudsmit

Having had the opportunity of reading this interesting letter by Mr. Goudsmit and Mr. Uhlenbeck, I am glad to add a few words which may be regarded as an addition to my article on atomic theory and mechanics, which was published as a supplement to Nature of December 5, 1925. As stated there, the attempts which have been made to account for the properties of the elements by applying the quantum theory to the nuclear atom have met with serious difficulties in the finer structure of spectra and the related problems. In my article expression was given to the view that these difficulties were inherently connected with the limited possibility of representing the stationary states of the atom by a mechanical model. The situation seems, however, to be somewhat altered by the introduction of the hypothesis of the spinning electron which, in spite of the incompleteness of the conclusions that can be derived from models, promises to be a very welcome supplement to our ideas of atomic structure. In fact, as Mr. Goudsmit and Mr. Uhlenbeck have described in their letter, this hypothesis throws new light on many of the difficulties which have puzzled the workers in this field during the last few years. Indeed, it opens up a very hopeful prospect of our being able to account more extensively for the properties of elements by means of mechanical models, at least in the qualitative way characteristic of applications of the correspondence principle. This possibility must be the more welcomed at the present time, when the prospect is held out of a quantitative treatment of atomic problems by the new quantum mechanics initiated by the work of Heisenberg, which aims at a precise formulation of the correspondence between classical mechanics and the quantum theory.

N. BOHR

59

OOOOOOOOOO

THE EXCLUSION PRINCIPLE

OOOOOOOOOO

Wolfgang Pauli (1900-1958)

In the early nineteen-twenties, just before the development of quantum mechanics, a serious difficulty arose in the interpretation of the spectra of complex atoms in which the Bohr theory appeared inadequate. This concerned the so-called "anomalous Zeeman effect," which, as Pauli stated in his Nobel address, "was hardly understandable from the standpoint of the mechanical model of the atom, since classical theory, as well as quantum theory, always led to the same triplet." To understand the nature of the difficulty and how its solution led Pauli to the discovery of one of the most profound and mysterious principles in nature, we must first consider a refinement of the Bohr theory introduced by Sommerfeld.

When Bohr propounded his theory, he made the simplest possible assumption about the orbits of the electron, namely, that they were circles. Therefore, according to this theory the electrons could have only one degree of freedom in their motion and hence just one periodicity. The energy corresponding to this motion would therefore depend on a single quantum number, the integer n, which determines the radius of the orbit. As we have already noted, this integer is called the principal quantum number of the electron. However, if one solves the general problem of an electron moving in the electric field of a positively charged nucleus, using the classical Newtonian laws of motion, one obtains elliptical Keplerian orbits; when an electron moves in such an orbit, a new degree of freedom, and a new periodicity of motion is introduced, as Sommerfeld suggested. He pointed out that because of the rapid motion of the electron in its orbit, its mass while in motion is not equal to its rest mass: it increases because of the relativistic change of mass with speed. If the orbit of the electron were circular, this increase in mass would be of constant size, because in a circular orbit the speed is constant. Hence, the somewhat larger, but still constant, mass of the electron would not affect its regular motion.

For an elliptical orbit, however, the situation is quite different; the mass of the electron changes continuously because the speed of the electron moving in an ellipse changes continuously. Because of this continuous change of mass, the electron cannot move in a closed ellipse, it describes a kind of rosette figure. This phenomenon can best be imagined by picturing the electron as moving in a closed ellipse, which is itself rotating with a definite period in the same direction as the electron is moving in its ellipse. Since the period of this precessional motion is independent of the period of the motion of the electron in the ellipse, we have two degrees of freedom of motion of the electron and thus have two energy modes associated with the orbit of an electron. Sommerfeld suggested that to describe this motion in accordance with the quantum theory a second quantum number, the orbital or azimuthal quantum number, be introduced.

This number, which is designated by the letter l, is also an integer, but its value is governed by the value of the principal quantum number n. The azimuthal quantum number can take on all integral values (starting with zero) up to and including $n - 1$. We see from this that associated with each Bohr orbit there are n suborbits corresponding to the n orbital quantum numbers l. These suborbits give rise to spectral lines that lie close together, so that each of the spectral lines, as predicted by the original Bohr theory, is really a combination of closely packed lines. Consequently, each of the Balmer lines should show a "fine structure." This is precisely what spectroscopists found. In fact, they discovered a somewhat more complex structure than the Sommerfeld theory predicts.

We should consider the physical significance of the new quantum number before we examine Pauli's discovery of the exclusion principle. The principal quantum number n is a measure of the size of the ellipse in which the electron moves and, hence, the total energy of the electron in its orbit. But we know that for a given-size ellipse we can have different shapes; from the roundest, a circle, to the narrowest, a straight line with the electron oscillating back and forth along it. The new quantum number l is related to the shape of the orbit; but since, as we know from planetary theory, the shape of the orbit determines the angular momentum of a planet in its orbit, the azimuthal quantum number really is a measure of the angular momentum of the electron.

We see, then, that just as the energy of the electron is quantized, so too is the shape of its orbit, or its angular momentum. We may illustrate this by considering an electron in the third Bohr orbit so that its principal quantum number is 3. Associated with this we have the three azimuthal quantum numbers, 0, 1, and 2, which determine the eccentricity—that is, the flatness—of the suborbits. The angular momentum is zero for value 0

of the azimuthal quantum number (when the orbital ellipse most resembles a straight line, or is flattest), and is largest for value 2 of the
azimuthal quantum number (when the orbit is circular). The electron
has a slightly different energy in each of these states because of the precession of the orbit. Hence, the third Bohr level actually corresponds to a
combination of three closely spaced sublevels. If the energy of the electron in each of these sublevels were the same, the three energy sublevels
would coincide to form a single level; we would then say that this state or
level is *degenerate*. We may note that the unit of angular momentum in
this theory is $h/2\pi$ and that the quantization rule always involves the
product of the quantum number, in this case l, and Planck's constant
divided by 2π.

In connection with the angular momentum, we must take up one final
point. The azimuthal quantum number is a measure only of the magnitude
of the angular momentum, which is a vector quantity. Hence we must also
introduce some way of taking into account the direction of this vector.
We may understand this if we consider the electron moving in one of the
elliptical suborbits discussed in the previous paragraph. If we want to
specify this orbit completely we should give not only its size and shape
but also its orientation in space. The question that naturally arises is
whether the specification of the orientation of the orbit in space involves
a quantum number the way the size and shape do, or whether the axis of
the electron's orbit can take on any direction and change continuously
from one direction to another. As we have seen in our discussion of the
Stern-Gerlach experiment in Chapter 57, we do, indeed, have to assign a
quantum number to the direction of the angular momentum. Thus, an
additional type of quantization, *space quantization,* must be introduced.
This phenomenon, first proved experimentally by Stern and Gerlach, plays
an important role in the Zeeman effect, which so puzzled Pauli and finally
led him to the discovery of the exclusion principle.

We may infer that a third quantum number has to be introduced in
the description of the motion of the electron, because each of the other
two quantum numbers is associated with one of the degrees of freedom
of the motion of the electron. Since the electron has three degrees of
freedom, it should have three quantum numbers attached to it. The
orientation of the orbit gives us this third degree of freedom, but it is a
bit puzzling to see just how a quantum number is to be assigned to this
degree of freedom because it is not clear how we are to associate
periodicity or energy with orientation. If there were no energy assigned to
this degree of freedom (in other words, if there were no orbital motion
of any kind related to the orientation of the axis of the orbit of the electron) there could be no sublevels associated with it and therefore we
would be dealing with a case of degeneracy.

To understand this we note we can assign a quantum number, and hence energy, to the orientation of the angular momentum vector only if certain directions in space are physically more meaningful than any other directions. At first it may seem that this is untenable, that all directions in space are equivalent. But all directions are not equivalent if there is a physical phenomenon in the neighborhood of the electron that establishes some preferred direction. It is precisely in establishing such a preferred direction that we can assign energy to this third degree of freedom and thus eliminate the degeneracy. For instance, the spectral lines can be made to take on an additional pattern of complexity, the Zeeman effect, if a preferred direction is obtained by means of a magnetic field.

We can easily see why a magnetic field, in some particular direction in the neighborhood of the electron, introduces additional states of energy. For as the electron moves around in its elliptical orbit, it is tantamount to an electric current, and therefore is accompanied by a magnetic field whose direction is parallel to the direction of the angular momentum of the electron. In other words the atom behaves like a very small magnet. If now, we have an external magnetic field pointing in some fixed direction, the angular momentum vector of the electron is not free to point in any direction whatsoever but has to adjust itself to this field.

If the atom were no more than a small magnet, and there were no angular momentum associated with it, its axis (or, as it is called in physics, the axis of the magnetic moment) would line up in the direction of the magnetic field, and we still could assign neither energy nor a quantum number to this direction. But we must recall that, in addition to behaving like a small magnet, the atom behaves like a spinning top, because the electron is revolving in its orbit; a spinning top has one very important property which gives it an additional motion and therefore an additional sublevel of energy. To see this we need only consider an ordinary top that is set spinning on the ground. If its axis of spin is perfectly upright, the only motion of the top is the one of spinning. But if the axis is tilted, not only does the top continue to spin, but its axis points in changing directions: it precesses around the vertical direction. This motion of precession is an additional state of energy of the top; we have a similar situation when a spinning magnet is placed in a magnetic field.

The rate at which this magnet precesses was first calculated on the basis of classical electrodynamic theory by Larmor, so that this frequency of precession is called the Larmor frequency. It is equal to the magnetic moment of the magnet (that is the length of the magnet multiplied by the pole strength of the magnet) multiplied by the strength of the magnetic field, with this product then divided by the angular momentum of the spinning magnet.

We can apply this calculation to the motion of the electron inside an atom, for example, to the hydrogen atom. As the electron revolves in its orbit, it imparts to the atom two properties: It gives the atom the propererties of a magnet and it also makes the atom behave like a top. This means that the atom must precess in a magnetic field; the Larmor frequency of this precession is obtained by multiplying the electric charge on the electron by the strength of the magnetic field and by dividing this by 4π times the mass of the electron and the speed of light. Hence, when an atom is in a magnetic field, the energy levels are not the same as in the absence of a field, since the Larmor precession takes place. Additional energy is associated with the additional periodicity of the Larmor precession. We must therefore introduce a third quantum number, since the periodicity of the Larmor precession is quite unrelated to the periodicities of the other two motions we have already discussed. This third number is called the magnetic quantum number and is designated by the letter m.

The magnetic quantum number m cannot be chosen arbitrarily but must be related to the azimuthal quantum number in a definite way; it is an integer that can range in unitary steps from $-l$ to $+l$. In the case of an electron in the third Bohr orbit, for example, with principal quantum number 3, and with the three possible azimuthal quantum numbers 0, 1, 2, there are nine possible magnetic quantum numbers. Thus for $l = 0$, m can only be 0; for $l = 1$, m can take on the three values, -1, 0, $+1$; for $l = 2$, m can have the values -2, -1, 0, $+1$, $+2$.

The significance of these magnetic quantum numbers is that the electron orbit (or the angular momentum vector) cannot orient itself in any direction with respect to the magnetic field, but is limited to a finite number of directions. Thus, if we consider the elliptical orbit for which the azimuthal quantum number in the above example is 2, there are only five possible orientations for it in a magnetic field. Of course, if no magnetic field is present there is no restriction as to the way in which the plane of the orbit of the electron can be tilted in space.

Even before Bohr had introduced his theory of the atom, it was known that the energy of an atom in a magnetic field is different from what it is in empty space, and the spectroscope gave evidence of this in the form of the Zeeman effect: When an atom is placed in a magnetic field, the usual lines in its spectrum are no longer simple but break up into multiplets. In the case of the hydrogen atom (and also of the atoms of the alkali metals like lithium and sodium), each line is replaced by a triplet, with the central component of this triplet having the same frequency as when no magnetic field is present; the frequency of the other components differs from that of the central component by the amount expressed by the Larmor frequency. This result had already been predicted by Lorentz on the basis of his classical theory of the electron. His argument was very simple, for it was clear to him that a vibrating electron in a magnetic field would suffer a perturbation that would give rise to new vibration frequencies. The electron would vibrate not only with its original frequency, but also with two new frequencies: one obtained by adding the Larmor precession frequency to the original frequency of the electron, and the other obtained by subtracting the Larmor precession frequency from the original frequency. In other words, when an atom is in a magnetic field, each of the spectral lines should break up into three lines. This is called the normal Zeeman effect.

Although the Lorentz theory gives the correct result for the Zeeman effect for the hydrogen atom, it does not account for the much more complicated magnetic splitting of spectral lines for the heavier atoms, the so-called anomalous Zeeman effect. If we now use the Bohr theory of the atom, we find that it gives us exactly the same results for the normal Zeeman effect as the classical Lorentz theory; but the Bohr theory can also explain the anomalous Zeeman effect for the heavier atoms.

At the time these investigations into the Zeeman effect were being pursued, another complication arose—a multiplicity of spectral lines was observed when the atom was not subjected to external magnetism. This added fine structure, which appeared in addition to the relativistic effect explained by Sommerfeld as the result of orbital precession, emphasized the need for still another quantum number. Sommerfeld attempted to provide it; he demonstrated that he could account for the observed multiplicities by introducing a quantum number that could have but two values.

To justify the introduction of this new quantum number, Landé suggested the core + electron model of the atom, in which the electron that is responsible for the spectral lines is pictured as moving all alone in an external orbit. At the center of the orbit is the core of the atom, which consists of the nucleus surrounded by the inner electrons. If this core is visualized as spinning, we are able to postulate the generation of a magnetic field. What follows is a kind of internal Zeeman effect that in turn gives rise to an internal, magnetic quantum number. Although this model appeared promising upon its introduction, it soon was discarded. Pauli demonstrated its inaccuracy for heavy atoms if one took into account the relativistic change in mass of the core electrons.

In his Nobel address, Pauli noted that he became interested in the anomalous Zeeman effect in 1922, and soon became convinced of the necessity of still another approach. But there was a twofold difficulty in attempting to discover a new scheme. On the one hand, he needed to find a suitable mechanical or classical model for heavy atoms; on the other hand, there was the necessity for incorporating such a model into the quantum picture. Pauli was well aware that the Bohr model and its correspondence principle were inadequate for his purposes.

Pauli was also aware that the anomalous Zeeman effect was associated with the problem of the closed electron shells. In analyzing this phase of the problem, Pauli "definitely rejected as incorrect" the "core + electron" model of the atom and replaced it with the concept of a new, nonclassical, twofold property of the electron. This actually amounts to assigning another quantum number to the electron, as Sommerfeld had attempted to do. Consequently, the electron is pictured as having a fourth quantum number, in addition to the three already discussed. This fourth quantum number, as Sommerfeld suggested, can take on only two values, which is what Pauli meant when he spoke of the "classically non-describable two-valuedness" of the electron. By "classically non-describable" Pauli simply meant that there was no classical model he could adopt to explain this fourth quantum number.

We have seen that a quantum number carries with it the idea of a classical-type periodic motion of the electron. Landé, in his "core + electron" model, had tried to incorporate this additional periodic motion by assigning it to the core of the atom. In contrast, Pauli assigned the additional periodic motion to the outer electrons, and in fact to every electron. The most difficult aspect of the conundrum, as far as Pauli was concerned, was determining just what classical periodic motion corresponded to this fourth degree of freedom, or fourth quantum number. This difficulty was partially overcome by Goudsmit's and Uhlenbeck's concept of electron spin, which was discussed in Chapter 58. However, Pauli was reluctant at first to accept without reservations the spinning electron model on the grounds that it was too mechanical an explanation for what he considered to be an essentially nonclassical, or nonmechanical effect. However, he finally accepted the spin phenomenon when Bohr pointed out that a spinning electron may differ considerably from classical analogs.

Having concluded that there are four and not three quantum numbers associated with the motion of each electron, Pauli was led to the exclusion principle by his study of the classification of spectral lines of an atom in a strong magnetic field, and by a disclosure made by E. C. Stoner. Stoner had pointed out that in a magnetic field the electron most distant from the nucleus of an atom like lithium, sodium, or potassium—the so-called optical electron—has as many energy states as there are electrons in the closed shell of the first inert gas (neon, argon, and so on) that follows this particular alkali metal in the atomic periodic chart.

Pauli's interpretation of this, which is the heart of the exclusion principle, takes the following course. Picture the optical electron moving all by itself in the second Bohr orbit of the lithium atom; if this atom is in a magnetic field, the electron is subject to the four independent periodic motions that are associated with its four quantum numbers, since the magnetic field removes all the degeneracies of the electronic motion. The

actual energy of the electron corresponds to some particular combination
of all of these periodic motions. Stoner stated that in the case of lithium
the total number of possible combinations of motions for this electron is
equal to the number of electrons in the closed shell of neon. The total
number of such electrons turns out to be eight, and therefore, according
to Stoner, there are eight energy levels for this optical electron.

Pauli proceeded by picturing each combination of the four periodic
motions, or of the quantum numbers, as defining a sublevel of the electron; he stated that each sublevel of any particular Bohr level can accommodate but one electron, so that every sublevel is closed as soon as it contains one electron. This means that, within a given atom, no two electrons
can have identical full sets of quantum numbers. If we assign one set of
quantum numbers to one electron and another set to another electron, the
two sets must differ by at least one number.

Let us consider the second Bohr level, for which the principal quantum
number is $n = 2$; we have in association with n the two azimuthal quantum numbers 0 and 1. Now associated with the azimuthal quantum number 0 there is only one magnetic quantum number, 0; in addition, the
azimuthal quantum number 1 carries with it the three magnetic quantum
numbers -1, 0, and $+1$. By this scheme, any electron in the second Bohr
orbit is assigned just four sets of combinations of azimuthal and magnetic
quantum numbers, namely: $(0, 0)$, $(1, -1)$, $(1, 0)$, and $(1, 1)$. If we take
into account Pauli's assumption that in addition to these three quantum
numbers the electron has a fourth degree of freedom because of its spin,
and that this fourth degree of freedom, or quantum number, can have
only two distinct values (regardless of what combination of the other
three quantum numbers is assigned to the electron) we see that we can
have twice the number of distinct quantum-number combinations that
we have listed above, or, all together, eight, the number of electrons in
the closed shell of neon. It can be shown that if the principal quantum
number is n, then the shell having this principal quantum number is closed
when it is occupied by exactly $2n^2$ electrons, since there exists just this
number of distinct combinations of the four quantum numbers.

Conversely, by using the same factors, we may arrive at an understanding of the "freedom of action" of the single optical electron of
lithium. A grossly simplified analogy may help. One person in a room has
a wide range of possible activities; likewise, the optical electron's solitude
makes lithium very active chemically. In the case of the element neon, the
room is full, and there is little freedom of activity. Hence, the gas, with
eight electrons completely filling this shell, is inert.

The importance of the Pauli exclusion principle extends far beyond its
application to atomic spectra and to the distribution of electrons in the
various closed shells of complex atoms. The full implications of this

principle became evident, as Pauli points out, only after the introduction of wave mechanics to describe the properties of particles. Since the description of a particular state of an atom is given by its wave function (a mathematical expression involving the positions and the spins of the electrons in the atom), one must look to this wave function for information about the atom. The wave functions that are found in nature have definite symmetry properties, and one finds wave functions that are either completely symmetrical (that is, if two particles are interchanged the wave function is unaffected) or wave functions that are antisymmetrical (if two particles are interchanged the wave function changes its sign, becoming negative if originally it was positive, or vice versa). We find that a given type of particle is described by either symmetrical or antisymmetrical wave functions, and that these two symmetries are never mixed.

Because electrons are described only by antisymmetrical wave functions, they are governed by the exclusion principle. Electrons, protons, and neutrons, in fact all particles that have a spin, or intrinsic angular momentum equal to that of the electron, are described only by antisymmetrical wave functions, wave functions that change sign when two particles are interchanged. All such particles, whether they are inside atoms or not, must obey the Pauli exclusion principle. Particles such as the photons, and certain mesons that are described by symmetrical wave functions, are not governed by this Pauli exclusion principle. As Pauli points out in his Nobel address, which follows this commentary, this leads to two types of statistical mechanics to explain the complexity of spectral lines.

In the investigation that finally led to the formulation of the exclusion principle Pauli first suggested that the complexity of spectral lines (the so-called hyperfine structure) might be caused by the spinning of the nucleus of the atom. Although this hypothesis was unable to account for the fine structure of the spectral lines, it led Goudsmit and Uhlenbeck to the hypothesis of the spinning electron. Subsequently, Pauli's picture of a spinning nucleus was found to be correct, and it was shown that the hyperfine structure of the spectral lines can be explained by this phenomenon.

As Pauli indicates in his discussion, the numerical value of the spin of a nucleus—and hence its symmetry class and the kind of statistics that it obeys—can be found by studying the molecular spectra of molecules composed of two similar atoms such as H_2 or O_2. Such molecules rotate the way a dumbbell does when it is thrown through the air; the transition of the molecule from one such rotational state to another gives rise to a line in the spectrum of the molecule. Since the rotational energy levels of such a molecule lie very close together, all the lines that arise from a given set of transitions are so closely packed that they form a bright band in the spectrum of the molecule. By studying the intensities of bands arising from transitions involving either only even or only odd rotational quantum numbers we can identify the spin of the nucleus of the atom in the two-atom molecule.

It was in connection with the symmetry properties of the rotational energy levels of molecules that the concept of the parity of the wave function was introduced. Transitions in any system occur either between states in which the wave function is symmetric or between states in which the function is antisymmetric. Transitions seldom occur (in principle never, if one neglects the effect of the spin of the nuclei on their motions within the molecule) between a state defined by a symmetric wave function and one described by an antisymmetric wave function. The states described by symmetric wave functions are called states of even parity and the antisymmetric ones, states of odd parity. It was assumed, as a general principle throughout nature, that only those processes can occur for which parity is conserved. This assumption, which is called the *principle of the conservation of parity,* proved to be incorrect under certain conditions, as was shown in 1957 by Lee and Yang.

Pauli in his Nobel address points out how important the exclusion principle is for the determination of the spin properties of nuclei and for such particles as the proton, the neutron, and the deuteron. From studies of the spectral bands emitted by the ortho and para types of hydrogen, the spins of the proton and electron were found to be the same. Since the spin of the proton is $\frac{1}{2}$ (the same as that of the electron), protons are also governed by the exclusion principle. From this it follows that a nucleus cannot contain electrons in addition to protons because the symmetry properties of any system composed of a number of particles is determined by the number of these particles that obey the exclusion principle. If this is an odd number, the system must obey the exclusion principle and must be governed by the antisymmetric type of statistics; but if this number is even, the system is described by symmetric wave functions and it obeys the same type of statistics that governs the photon.

We know from experiment that the nitrogen nucleus, for example, does not obey the exclusion principle. But if there were electrons in this nucleus, the total number of antisymmetric type particles in it (electrons and protons together) would be 21, an odd number, so that it would have to obey the exclusion principle. Hence it follows that there can be no electrons in this or any other nucleus. The number 21 for nitrogen is arrived at as follows: The nucleus is known to have an atomic weight of 14 so that it must consist of 14 particles, each with the mass of the proton (14 units of mass). If all of these particles were protons, there would have to be 7 electrons present as well, in order to compensate for the 7 positive electric charges and to leave a residue of 7 positive charges in agreement with the observed charge on the nitrogen nucleus.

We would thus have a total of 21 particles (7 electrons and 14 protons) each of spin $\frac{1}{2}$ in the nucleus. This same analysis can be applied to all nuclei. With the discovery of the neutron the mystery of the particles in the nuclei of atoms was cleared up, since if one assigns a spin $\frac{1}{2}$ to the neutron, imparting to it the same statistical properties as those of the electron (it is governed by the exclusion principle), one can explain all the spin and symmetry properties of the nuclei. The importance of this is indicated by the absence in nature of a nucleus consisting of two protons only. Such a nucleus would be a helium nucleus having the same weight as deuterium. However, because hydrogen obeys the exclusion principle, two protons, which are identical particles, cannot combine with their spins parallel to form a nucleus the way a neutron and a proton can.

The second part of Pauli's lecture is devoted to the questions relating to the classical and quantum-mechanical properties of fields arising from particles, and how the exclusion principle ultimately determines the way in which these fields are to be quantized. If one is dealing with classical fields, such as those obtained from the solution of Maxwell's equations, where quantization has no part, the exclusion principle plays no role. But all fields are governed by quantum principles (for example, the uncertainty principle in the case of the electromagnetic field), and therefore they should be treated from a quantum-mechanical point of view. Then the fields break up into two kinds: those, such as the electromagnetic field, that are generated by particles like photons, which do not obey the exclusion principle; those, such as the de Broglie fields, that are generated by particles like electrons, which do obey the exclusion principle. In these two cases, the algebras that govern the behavior of the fields are different, as expressed in the form of the commutation relations for these fields.

Pauli ends his lecture with a statement of his strong dislike for the current theories of elementary particles that endow the vacuum with what he considers artificial properties. Such a criticism could be leveled at the Dirac theory of the electron, which is really not a theory of a single particle, but rather of an infinite number of particles. In Dirac's theory, we have, in addition to the "perceived" electron, an infinitude of electrons in negative-energy states in the vacuum. This is what Pauli means when he refers to the "infinite zero charge," since these electrons contribute nothing to the electric field surrounding the electron being studied. He finally expresses his opinion that such theories must be faulty because they use "mathematical tricks" and "mathematical fictions" "to formulate the correct interpretation of the actual physical world."

We may note that although Pauli was one of the ablest mathematicians in the family of physicists, he was always highly critical and suspicious of a purely formalistic approach to physics. He, more than any other physicist, was able to draw the greatest content from the mathematics of the current theories. By means of very keen mathematical analysis, he was able to subject these theories to the most severe tests. In connection with this, it may be noted that his article on the theory of relativity, which he wrote in 1921 at the age of twenty, is still the most penetrating analysis of that theory that is available.

Wolfgang Pauli was one of the giants of twentieth-century theoretical physics. He was born in Vienna in 1900, the very year that Planck discovered the quantum of action, which was to play so important a role in Pauli's life. It was the theory to which he, in turn, was to contribute so much.

Pauli was the son of a physician, who himself was a university professor of chemistry. Young Pauli was raised in a scientific atmosphere, and this certainly must have contributed to his unusually rapid intellectual development. By the time he was nineteen he had already mastered enough physics and mathematics to be invited by A. Sommerfeld, his professor of theoretical physics at the University of Munich, to write the article on the theory of relativity for the *Encyclopädie der Mathematischen Wissenschaft*.

When Einstein read this article, which is still the leading text on relativity, it is said that he felt that perhaps Pauli knew more about relativity than he himself did. In reviewing this article, Einstein wrote:

> Whoever studies this mature, and grandly conceived work, can hardly believe that the author is a twenty-one-year-old man. One hardly knows what to admire and wonder at most, the psychological understanding of the development of the ideas, the sureness of the mathematical deductions, the deep physical insight, the capacity for a systematic, clear exposition, the knowledge of the literature, the completeness of the treatment, the sureness of the critical appraisal.[1]

Pauli's article on relativity was the first in a long series of scientific papers, each of which maintained the same high level of excellence set in the relativity article. All of these papers have been issued in two volumes under the joint editorship of R. Kronig and V. F. Weisskopf.

After graduating from a local gymnasium in 1918, Pauli enrolled in the University of Munich where he concentrated on theoretical physics for six semesters; here he was greatly influenced by Arnold Sommerfeld and by W. Lenz. Although he began his scientific career in the field of

---

[1] Albert Einstein, *Die Naturwissenschaften,* 10 (1922), 184.

relativity, he soon shifted to quantum theory and to quantum mechanics, which was just beginning its magnificent growth. Indeed, Pauli's scientific life may be said to recapitulate or mirror the developments in this subject, for he made essential contributions to every phase of it. He was numbered in the famous group of physicists, directed from Niels Bohr's headquarters at Copenhagen, who created quantum mechanics.

Although all of Pauli's contributions were of the first magnitude, his greatest achievement was the discovery of the exclusion principle for which he received the Nobel Prize in 1945; it is, as we indicate in our commentary, one of the pillars on which modern physics and the quantum mechanical understanding of the structure of matter rest.

Not content with having discovered the exclusion principle, Pauli sought continuously to explain it in terms of more basic principles; he finally succeeded in showing that the exclusion principle is the result of the symmetry properties of nature.

After writing his Ph.D. dissertation in 1921 (a paper on a special type of molecular model), Pauli went to the University of Göttingen where he served as Professor Born's assistant. From there he went to Copenhagen to spend a year with Niels Bohr and then to accept an assistant professorship at the University of Hamburg. Finally, in 1928, he accepted the chair of theoretical physics at the Federal Institute of Technology in Zurich, where he remained until he died, a victim of cancer, in 1958.

He influenced the development of physics not only by his papers but by his critical discussions and his voluminous correspondence with physicists all over the world. Kronig and Weisskopf describe Pauli's influence as follows:

> Pauli stimulated the thoughts and ideas of many leading theorists by letters and critical discussions, by suggestions and inspiration. He was a profuse letter writer. His correspondence reflects the development of modern physics in the most intimate way, and will some day serve as a fertile source for the historians of science. His sharp criticism by mouth and pen is part of the legend of modern physics. He could not tolerate vagueness or half-truth and his biting wit found devastating formulations for his contempt of ideas that did not measure up to his high standards. "Der Fürchterliche Pauli," so Ehrenfest called him, or, "Die Geissel Gottes." [2]

Many considered him the conscience of theoretical physics. His death has left a gap which still remains to be filled.

---

[2] R. Kronig and V. F. Weisskopf, *Pauli's Collected Works* (New York: Interscience, 1964).

၀၀၀၀၀၀၀၀

CONDON and MACK

An Interpretation of Pauli's Exclusion Principle [3]

PROBABLY THE MOST IMPORTANT TREND in current physics is that toward the recognition of the fact that our science gives no information about an objective reality wholly independent of ourselves. We are becoming increasingly impressed by the subjectivity of our knowledge. We owe much of this to the work of Bridgman with his emphasis on the unprofitableness of dallying over meaningless questions and his operational formulation of the reality of physical concepts. The rôle played by our subjective limitations on observation of the world about us has been discussed in detail by Heisenberg and by Bohr. We refer to the train of ideas known as Heisenberg's uncertainty principle.

Let us consider what the uncertainty principle did for physics. It came after the fairly complete formulation of the laws of quantum mechanics as we know them to-day. Before the principle the laws were quite definitely stated by Heisenberg, Born, Dirac, Jordan, Schrödinger, Pauli and others. They were stated so definitely that the method of treating special problems was recognised and applied with a good deal of success by a large number of physicists. Therefore, they were valid laws of science, since they met the test of being workable in the hands of physicists in general, and did not rest purely on the genius of the individuals who discovered them. Even without the principle they probably could have attained a universal applicability but we cannot say how that would have been, since, owing to the slowness of diffusion of scientific knowledge, the formal laws were still in the process of becoming the common property of professional physicists when Heisenberg enunciated the principle.

But before he did, even among those who had found the new methods workable and who had contributed to the many successes of the theory, there was a feeling of dissatisfaction, a feeling that the new theory was not understood, perhaps even not understandable. These were disturbing times

---

[3] E. U. Condon and J. E. Mack, *Physical Review*, 35 (1930), 579–582.

for we did not know why we felt dissatisfied (or perhaps unsatisfied) and so were quite helpless in attempting to remedy the situation. The remedy was provided by Heisenberg in his uncertainty principle. In a sense his famous paper in *Zeitschrift für Physik* has nothing new in it. For it does not alter or add to the formal statement of the laws of quantum mechanics. Nor does it apply them to any specific problem and produce calculations about some aspect of nature which are triumphantly in agreement with somebody's quantitative measurements. What it did do was to relieve that feeling of dissatisfaction. Many a physicist who had been working with the formalism of quantum mechanics felt that he understood it for the first time after he read that paper. Subsequently this satisfaction of understanding was considerably enhanced by the appearance of Bohr's Como lecture simultaneously in *Nature* and *Die Naturwissenschaften*. The title of Heisenberg's paper is significant: he called it the "anschaulich Inhalt" of the new quantum mechanics. It was just that: it was the intuitive, clear, evident content of the theory.

The important feature of this clear and intuitive part of the theory is the deflation of the lords-of-creation attitude of physicists. Wholly rational, detached fellows we thought ourselves (in our naïve way), studying objectively the true laws of the external world. We had no concern with unfruitful stuff like metaphysics. Now we know otherwise and are healthily aware of our own organic relation to the traditionally inorganic subject matter of our science.

At present there is another law of nature (empirical, like all laws of nature) intimately connected with quantum mechanics, which we feel that we do not understand. This is Pauli's exclusion principle. We refer to the same feeling of dissatisfaction which was felt about quantum mechanics in general before Heisenberg's paper.

Pauli's principle grew out of empirical spectroscopy and was stated in the form that no two electrons in an atom can have the same set of quantum numbers. A formal place was found for this in the equations of quantum mechanics by Heisenberg, Dirac, Wigner and others. The equations of quantum mechanics showed a remarkable property when applied to the description of a dynamical system consisting of several dynamically similar particles. Such properties are naturally of fundamental importance because of the belief that all electrons are dynamically similar and that they are the fundamental stuff of which all substance is built. This remarkable property may be described by saying that such dynamical systems may exist in $N!$ different classes of states such that if the system exists now in one of these classes then it must exist for all time to come in this same class of states. (N is the number of similar particles in the system.) In other words, quantum mechanics provides, when applied to the dynamical system which is the entire universe, not just one solution but $N!$ possible solutions, which we may call worlds, where N is the total number of electrons in the universe. Since it is an exact conclusion from the postulated exact similarity of all the particles that the universe cannot change from one of these classes of states to another, our universe must represent a selection from among these possible worlds. Which one? There is one which has the property that it has no possible states characterized by two of the particles having the same quantum numbers. That one agrees with the world that we know.

That is fine but it leaves us with a lack of understanding of the matter which is, perhaps, akin to the unsatisfied feeling toward quantum mechanics which preceded the discovery of its "anschaulich Inhalt" by Heisenberg. What of the other $N!-1$ possible worlds?

Now we come to our main thesis: The restriction to a world built in accordance with Pauli's principle can be understood as another and extreme instance of the subjectivity of our knowledge. We, physicists, humans, are creatures who are built out of, and therefore are capable of reacting with and having sense perceptions of, only a particular world constructed according to a particular one of the non-combining patterns possible under the laws of quantum mechanics. Because of our own nature we are aware of, or conscious of, only that part of possible reality that is built on our pattern.

Do worlds really exist that are built (of the same electrons as ours) on one of the other patterns but nevertheless according to the laws of quantum mechanics? The question is meaningless in a sense because of our subjective incapacity to be aware of them. It is meaningless for the same reason as is the question (sometimes asked after an individual has heard, for the first time, an exposition of Heisenberg's uncertainty principle), "Does a particle really have precise position and momentum simultaneously even though we cannot be experimentally aware of precise values for them?"

The situation turns on the meaning to be ascribed to the word "really" in the two questions. We prefer to associate with it the connotation, within the power of human sense perceptions. In that case the answer to both of them is no, as the "even though" clause makes ridiculously self-evident in the case of the second one. But we are reluctant to dismiss the other possible worlds quite so readily as we do simultaneous position and momentum. This is because the other worlds correspond to solutions of the equations of quantum mechanics, whereas there is no place in the structure of the mathematical formalism of quantum mechanics for simultaneous exact position and momentum.

Objective reality these other worlds cannot have, because of our subjective inability to react to them. (Remember that all objective reality is colored by important subjective elements!) This we feel is the simple, evident substratum of the Pauli exclusion principle which provides us with the right to say we "understand" it.

The foregoing shows that we can be conscious of only one of the possible worlds. But it throws no light on a possible reason why the real one is the one which obeys Pauli's exclusion principle.

One feels that the type of symmetry represented in our world is especially simple and that there must be some reason for it. It is another instance of an ancient paradox: out of $N!$ possibilities the chance of the Pauli principle world being the real one seems vanishingly small. But in the matter of building the real world the dice are cast but once and in that one throw the antisymmetric pattern has an equal chance with the others.

Dirac's recent theory of the proton published in the *Proceedings of the Royal Society* for January, 1930, throws new light on the matter, however. When we spoke . . . of there being $N!$ different possible worlds according to quantum mechanics, we were speaking of the non-relativistic theory. But the relativistic theory of the electron must represent a surer foundation on which to build cosmologic hypotheses. According to it, electrons can exist in states of negative energy (less than—mc^2), as well as in usual states of positive energy (of the order $+mc^2$). We have no experimental evidence of electrons of this sort and so the prediction of such negative energy electrons was regarded as a blemish in the theory. But now the solution to the difficulty is seen in the fact that Pauli's principle governs our world.

We can do no better than quote the crucial paragraph of Dirac's paper:

"The most stable states for an electron (i.e. the states of lowest energy) are those with negative energy and very high velocity. All the electrons in the world will tend to fall into these states with emission of radiation. The Pauli exclusion principle, however, will come into play and prevent more than one electron going into any one state. Let us assume that there are so many electrons in the world that all the most stable states are occupied, or, more accurately, that *all the states of negative energy are occupied except perhaps a few of small velocity*. Any electrons with positive energy will now have very little chance of jumping into negative-energy states and will therefore behave as electrons are observed to behave in the laboratory. We shall have an infinite number of electrons in negative-energy states, and indeed an infinite number per unit volume all over the world, but if their distribution is exactly uniform we should expect them to be completely unobservable. Only the small departures from exact uniformity, brought about by some of the negative-energy states being unoccupied, can we hope to observe."

And now we see why it is that the Pauli principle world is the only one which can be built out of Dirac's relativistic electrons. For it is the only one in which the available states can be filled up. For the others there is no limit to the number of electrons that can occupy a state. The antisymmetric one is the only pattern that has a "bottom." For the others all the electrons in the universe would be drained off into states of indefinitely great negative energy.

○○○○○○○

PAULI

Exclusion Principle and Quantum Mechanics [4]

THE HISTORY OF THE DISCOVERY of the exclusion principle, for which I have received the honor of the Nobel Prize award in the year 1945, goes back to my student days in Munich. While, in school in Vienna, I had already obtained some knowledge of classical physics and the then-new Einstein's relativity theory, it was at the University of Munich that I was introduced by Sommerfeld to the structure of the atom —somewhat strange from the point of view of classical physics. I was not spared the shock which every physicist, accustomed to the classical way of thinking, experienced when he came to know of Bohr's "Basic postulate of quantum theory" for the first time. At that time there were two approaches to the difficult problems connected with the quantum of action. One was an effort to bring abstract order to the new ideas by looking for a key to translate classical mechanics and electrodynamics into quantum language which would form a logical generalization of these. This was the direction which was taken by Bohr's Correspondence Principle. Sommerfeld, however, preferred, in view of the difficulties which blocked the use of the concepts of kinematical models, a direct interpretation, as independent of models as possible, of the laws of spectra in terms of integral numbers, following, as Kepler once did in his investigation of the planetary system, an inner feeling for harmony. Both methods, which did not appear to me irreconcilable, influenced me. The series of whole numbers 2, 8, 18, 32 . . . , giving the lengths of the periods in the natural system of chemical elements, was zealously discussed in Munich, in-

---

[4] Wolfgang Pauli, Nobel Prize Address, Stockholm, 1945.

cluding the remark of the Swedish physicist, Rydberg, that these numbers are of the simple form 2 n^2, if "n" takes on all integer values. Sommerfeld tried especially to connect the number 8 with the number of corners of a cube.

A new phase of my scientific life began when I met Niels Bohr personally for the first time. This was in 1922, when he gave a series of guest lectures at Göttingen, in which he reported on his theoretical investigations on the periodic system of elements. I shall recall only briefly that the essential progress made by Bohr's considerations at that time was the explaining by means of the spherically symmetric atomic model the formation of the intermediate shells of the atom and the general properties of the rare earths. The question as to why all electrons for an atom in its ground state were not bound in the innermost shell had already been emphasized by Bohr as a fundamental problem in his earlier works. In his Göttingen lectures he treated particularly the closing of this innermost K shell in the helium atom and its essential connection with the two noncombining spectra of helium, the ortho- and parahelium spectra. However, no convincing explanation for this phenomenon could be given on the basis of classical mechanics. It made a strong impression on me that Bohr at that time and in later discussions was looking for a *general* explanation which should hold for the closing of *every* electron shell and in which the number 2 was considered to be as essential as 8, in contrast to Sommerfeld's approach.

Following Bohr's invitation, I went to Copenhagen in the autumn of 1922, where I made a serious effort to explain the so-called "anomalous Zeeman effect," as the spectroscopists called a type of splitting of the spectral lines in a magnetic field which is different from the normal triplet. On the one hand the anomalous type of splitting exhibited beautiful and simple laws and Landé had already succeeded in finding the simpler splitting of the spectroscopic terms from the observed splitting of the lines. The most fundamental of his results thereby was the use of half-integers as magnetic quantum numbers for the doublet-spectra of the alkali metals. On the other hand the anomalous splitting was hardly understandable from the standpoint of the mechanical model of the atom, since very general assumptions concerning the electron, using classical theory as well as quantum theory, always led to the same triplet. A closer investigation of this problem left me with the feeling that it was even more unapproachable. We know now that, at that time, one was confronted with two logically different difficulties simultaneously. One of them was the absence of a general key to translate a given mechanical model into quantum theory which one tried in vain, by using classical mechanics, to describe the stationary quantum states themselves. The other difficulty was our ignorance concerning the proper classical model itself which could be suited to derive at all an anomalous splitting of spectral lines emitted by an atom in an external magnetic field. It is therefore not surprising that I could not find a satisfactory solution of the problem at that time. I succeeded, however, in generalizing Landé's term analysis for very strong magnetic fields, a case which, as a result of the magnetooptic transformation (Paschen-Back-effect), is in many respects simpler. This early work was of decisive importance for the finding of the exclusion principle.

Very soon after my return to the University of Hamburg, in 1923, I gave there my inaugural lecture as Privatdozent on the periodic system of elements. The contents of this lecture appeared very unsatisfactory to me, since the problem of the closing of the electronic shells had been clarified no further. The only thing that was clear was that there must exist a closer relation of this problem to the theory of multiplet structure. I therefore tried to examine again critically the simplest case, the doublet structure of the alkali spectra. According to the point of view then orthodox, which was also taken over by Bohr in his already mentioned lectures in Göttingen, a nonvanishing angular momentum of the atomic core was supposed to be the cause of this doublet structure.

In the autumn of 1924 I published some arguments against this point of view, which I definitely rejected as incorrect and proposed instead of it the assumption of a new quantum theoretic property of the electron, which I called a "classically non-describable two-valuedness." At this time a paper of the English physicist, Stoner, appeared which contained, besides improvements in the classification of electrons in subgroups, the following essential remark: "For a given value of the principal quantum number the number of energy levels of a single electron in the alkali metal spectra in an external magnetic field is the same as the number of electrons in the closed shell of the rare gases which corresponds to this principal quantum number." On the basis of my earlier results on the classification of spectral terms in a strong magnetic field the general formulation of the exclusion principle became clear to me. The fundamental idea can be stated in the following way: The complicated numbers of electrons in closed subgroups are reduced to the simple number *one* if the division of the groups by giving the values of the 4 quantum numbers of an electron is carried so far that every degeneracy is removed. An entirely non-degenerate energy level is already "closed," if it is occupied by a single electron; states in contradiction with this postulate have to be excluded. The exposition of this general formulation of the exclusion principle was made in Hamburg in the spring of 1925, after I had been able to verify some additional conclusions concerning the anomalous Zeeman effect of more complicated atoms during a visit to Tübingen with the help of the spectroscopic material assembled there.

With the exception of experts on the classification of spectral terms, the physicists found it difficult to understand the exclusion principle, since no meaning in terms of a model was given to the fourth degree of freedom of the electron. The gap was filled up by Uhlenbeck and Goudsmit's idea of electron spin which made it possible to understand the anomalous Zeeman effect simply by assuming that the spin quantum number of one electron is equal to $\frac{1}{2}$ and that the quotient of the magnetic moment to the mechanical angular moment has for the spin a value twice as large as for the ordinary orbit of the electron. Since that time, the exclusion principle has been closely connected with the idea of spin. Although at first I strongly doubted the correctness of this idea because of its classical mechanical character, I was finally converted to it by Thomas' calculations on the magnitude of doublet splitting. On the other hand, my earlier doubts as well as the cautious expression "classically non-describable two-valuedness" experienced a certain verification during later developments, as Bohr was able to show on the basis of wave mechanics that the electron spin cannot be measured by classically describable experiments (as, for instance, deflection of molecular beams in external electromagnetic fields) and must therefore be considered as an essentially quantum mechanical property of the electron.

The subsequent developments were determined by the occurrence of the new quantum mechanics. In 1925, the same year in which I published my paper on the exclusion-principle, de Broglie formulated his idea of matter waves and Heisenberg the new matrix-mechanics, after which in the next year Schrödinger's wave mechanics quickly followed. It is at present unnecessary to stress the importance and the fundamental character of these discoveries, all the more as these physicists themselves have explained here in Stockholm the meaning of their leading ideas. Nor does time permit me to illustrate in detail the general epistemological significance of the new discipline of quantum-mechanics, what has been done, among others, in a number of articles by Bohr, using hereby the idea of "complementarity" as a new central concept. I shall only recall that the statements of quantum mechanics are dealing only with possibilities, not with actualities. They have the form, "This is not possible" or, "Either this or that is possible," but they can never say, "that will actually happen then and there." The actual observation appears as an event outside the range of a description by physical laws and brings forth, in general, a discontinuous selection out of the several possibilities foreseen by the statistical laws of the new theory. Only this renouncement concerning the old claims for an objective descriptive of the physical phenomena, independent of the way in which they are observed, made it possible to reach again the self-consistency of quantum theory, which actually had been lost since

Planck's discovery of the quantum of action. Without discussing further the change of the attitude of modern physics to such concepts as "causality" and "physical reality" in comparison with the older classical physics, I shall discuss more particularly in the following the position of the exclusion principle in the new quantum mechanics.

As it was first shown by Heisenberg, wave mechanics leads to qualitatively different conclusions for particles of the same kind (for instance for electrons) than for particles of different kinds. As a consequence of the impossibility to distinguish one of several like particles from the other, the wave functions describing an ensemble of a given number of like particles in the configuration space are sharply separated into different classes of symmetry which can never be transformed into each other by external perturbations. In the term "configuration space" we are including here the spin degree of freedom, which is described in the wave function of a single particle by an index with only a finite number of possible values. For electrons this number is equal to two; the configuration space of N electrons has therefore 3 N space dimensions and N indices of "two-valuedness." Among the different classes of symmetry, the most important ones (which moreover for two particles are the only ones) are the symmetrical class, in which the wave function does not change its value when space and spin coordinates of two particles are permuted, and the antisymmetrical class, in which for such a permutation the wave function changes its sign. At this stage of the theory three different hypotheses concerning the actual ensemble of several like particles in nature, turned out to be logically possible.

I. This ensemble is a mixture of all symmetry classes.
II. Only the symmetrical class occurs.
III. Only the antisymmetrical class occurs.

As we shall see, the first assumption is never realized in nature. Moreover, it is only the third assumption that is in accordance with the exclusion principle, since an antisymmetrical function containing two particles in the same state is identically zero. The assumption III can therefore be considered as the correct and general wave mechanical formulation of the exclusion principle. It is this possibility which actually holds for electrons.

This situation appeared to me as disappointing in an important respect. Already in my original paper I stressed the circumstance that I was unable to give a logical reason for the exclusion principle or to deduce it from more general assumptions. I had always the feeling, and I still have it today, that this is a deficiency. Of course, in the beginning I hoped that the new quantum mechanics, with the help of which it was possible to deduce so many half-empirical formal rules in use at that time, will also rigorously deduce the exclusion principle. Instead of it there was for electrons still an exclusion: not of particular states any longer, but of whole classes of states, namely the exclusion of all classes different from the antisymmetrical one. The impression that the shadow of some incompleteness fell here on the bright light of success of the new quantum mechanics seems to me unavoidable. We shall resume this problem when we shall discuss relativistic quantum mechanics but I wish to give first an account of further results of the application of wave mechanics to systems of several like particles.

In the paper of Heisenberg, which we are discussing, he was also able to give a simple explanation of the existence of the two noncombining spectra of helium which I mentioned in the beginning of this lecture. Indeed, besides the rigorous separation of the wave-functions into symmetry classes with respect to space-coordinates and spin indices together, there exists an approximate separation into symmetry classes with respect to space-coordinates alone. The latter holds only so long as an interaction between the spin and the orbital motion of the electron can be neglected. In this way the para- and ortho-helium spectra could be interpreted as belonging to the class of symmetrical and antisymmetrical wave functions, respectively in the space-coordinates alone. It became clear that the energy difference between corresponding levels of the two classes has nothing to do with magnetic interactions but is of a new type of much larger order of magnitude, which one called exchange energy.

Of more fundamental significance is the connection of the symmetry classes with general problems of the statistical theory of heat. As it is well known this theory leads to the result that the entropy of a system is (apart from a constant factor) given by the logarithm of the number of quantum states of the whole system on a so-called energy shell. One might first expect that this number should be equal to the corresponding volume of the multidimensional phase space divided by hf, where h is Planck's constant and f the number of degrees of freedom of the whole system. However, it turned out that for a system of N like particles one had still to divide this quotient by N! in order to get a value for the entropy in accordance with the usual postulate of homogeneity that the entropy has to be proportional to the mass for a given inner state of the substance. In this way a qualitative distinction between like and unlike particles was already preconceived in the general statistical mechanics, a distinction which Gibbs tried to express with his concepts of a generic and a specific phase. In the light of the result of wave mechanics concerning the symmetry classes, this division by N!, which had caused already much discussion, can easily be interpreted by accepting one of our assumptions II and III, according to both of which only *one* class of symmetry occurs in nature. Then the density of quantum states of the whole system really becomes smaller by a factor N! in comparison with the density which had to be expected according to an assumption of the type I admitting all symmetry classes.

Even for an ideal gas, in which the interaction energy between molecules can be neglected, deviations from the ordinary equation of state have to be expected for the reason that only *one* class of symmetry is possible as soon as the mean de Broglie's wave length of a gas molecule becomes of an order of magnitude comparable with the average distance between two molecules, that is for small temperatures and large densities. For the antisymmetrical class the statistical consequences have been derived by Fermi and Dirac, for the symmetrical class the same had been done already before the discovery of the new quantum mechanics by Einstein and Bose. The former case could be applied to the electrons in a metal and could be used for the interpretation of magnetic and other properties of metals.

As soon as the symmetry classes for electrons were cleared, the question arose as to which are the symmetry classes for other particles. One example for particles with symmetrical wave-functions only (assumption II) was already known long ago, namely the photons. This is not only an immediate consequence of Planck's derivation of the spectral distribution of the radiation energy in the thermodynamical equilibrium, but it is also necessary for the applicability of the classical field concepts to light waves in the limit where a large and not accurately fixed number of photons is present in a single quantum state. We note that the symmetrical class for photons occurs together with the integer value 1 for their spin, while the antisymmetrical class for the electron occurs together with the half-integer value ½ for the spin.

The important question of the symmetry classes for nuclei, however, had still to be investigated. Of course, the symmetry class refers here also to the permutation of both the space coordinates and the spin-indices of two like nuclei. The spin-index can assume $2 I + 1$ values if I is the spin-quantum number of the nucleus which can be either an integer or a half-integer. I may include the historical remark that I proposed already in 1924, before the electron spin was discovered, to use the assumption of a nuclear spin to interpret the hyperfine structure of spectral lines. This proposal met on the one hand strong opposition from many sides, but on the other hand influenced Goudsmit and Uhlenbeck in their claim of an electron spin. It was only some years later that my attempt to interpret the hyperfine-structure could be definitely confirmed experimentally by investigations in which also Zeeman himself participated and which showed the existence of a magnetooptic transformation of the hyperfine structure as I had predicted it. Since that time the hyperfine structure of spectral lines became a general method of determining the nuclear spin.

In order to determine experimentally also the symmetry class of the nuclei, other methods were necessary. The most convenient, although not the only one, consists in the investigation of band spectra due to a molecule with two like atoms. It could easily be derived that in the ground state of the electron configuration of such a molecule, the states with even and odd values of the rotational quantum number are symmetric and antisymmetric respectively for a permutation of the space-coordinates of the two nuclei. Further there exist among the $(2I+1)^2$ spin states of the pair of nuclei, $(2I+1)(I+1)$ states symmetrical and $(2I+1)I$ states antisymmetrical in the spins, since the $(2I+1)$ states with two spins in the same direction are necessarily symmetrical. Therefore the conclusion was reached: If the total wave-function of space-coordinates and spin-indices of the nuclei is symmetrical, the ratio of the weights of states with an even rotational quantum number to the weight of states with an odd rational quantum number is given by $(I+1):I$. In the reverse case of an antisymmetrical total wave function of the nuclei the same ratio is $I:(I+1)$. Transitions between one state with an even and another state with an odd rotational quantum number will be extremely rare as they can only be caused by an interaction between the orbital motions and the spins of the nuclei. Therefore the ratio of the weights of the rotational states with different parity will give rise to two different systems of band spectra with different intensities, the lines of which are alternating.

The first application of this method was the result that the protons have the spin ½ and fulfil the exclusion principle just as electrons. The initial difficulties to understand quantitatively the specific heat of hydrogen molecules at low temperatures were removed by Dennison's hypothesis that at this low temperature the thermal equilibrium between the two modifications of the hydrogen molecule (ortho-H_2: odd rotational quantum numbers, parallel proton spins; para-H_2: even rotational quantum numbers, antiparallel spins) was not yet reached. As you know, this hypothesis was later confirmed by the experiments of Bonhoeffer and Harteck and of Eucken, which showed the theoretically predicted slow transformation of one modification into the other.

Among the symmetry classes for other nuclei those with a different parity of their mass numbers M and their charge number Z are of a particular interest. If we consider a compound system consisting of numbers A_1, A_2, . . . of different constituents, each of which is fulfilling the exclusion principle, and a number S of constituents with symmetrical states, one has to expect symmetrical or antisymmetrical states if the sum $A_1 + A_2 + . . .$ is even or odd. This holds regardless of the parity of S. Earlier one tried the assumption that nuclei consist of protons and electrons, so that M is the number of protons, $M-Z$ the number of electrons in the nucleus. It had to be expected then that the parity of Z determines the symmetry class of the whole nucleus. Already for some time the counter-example of nitrogen has been known to have the spin 1 and symmetrical states. After the discovery of the neutron, the nuclei have been considered, however, as composed of protons and neutrons in such a way that a nucleus with mass number M and charge number Z should consist of Z protons and M−Z neutrons. In case the neutrons would have symmetrical states, one should again expect that the parity of the charge number Z determines the symmetry class of the nuclei. If, however, the neutrons fulfil the exclusion principle, it has to be expected that the parity of M determines the symmetry class: For an even M, one should always have symmetrical states, for an odd M, antisymmetrical ones. It was the latter rule that was confirmed by experiment without exception, thus proving that the neutrons fulfil the exclusion principle.

The most important and simple crucial example for a nucleus with a different parity of M and Z is the heavy hydrogen or deuteron with $M = 2$ and $Z = 1$ which has symmetrical states and the spin $I = 1$, as could be proved by the investigation of the band spectra of a molecule with two deuterons. From the spin value 1 of the deuteron can be concluded, that the neutron must have a half-integer spin. The simplest possible assumption, that this spin of the neutron is equal to $\frac{1}{2}$, just as the spin of the proton and of the electron, turned out to be correct.

There is hope, that further experiments with light nuclei, especially with protons, neutrons and deuterons, will give us further information about the nature of the forces between the constituents of the nuclei, which, at present, is not yet sufficiently clear. Already now we can say, however, that these interactions are fundamentally different from electromagnetic interactions. The comparison between neutron-proton scattering and proton-proton scattering showed even that the forces between these particles are in good approximation the same, that means independent of their electric charge. If one had to take into account only the magnitude of the interaction energy, one should therefore expect a stable diproton or He_2^2 ($M = 2$, $Z = 2$) with nearly the same binding energy as the deuteron. Such a state is, however, forbidden by the exclusion principle in accordance with experience, because this state would acquire a wave-function symmetric with respect to the two protons. This is only the simplest example of the application of the exclusion principle to the structure of compound nuclei for the understanding of which this principle is indispensable, because the constituents of these heavier nuclei, the protons and the neutrons, fulfil it.

In order to prepare for the discussion of more fundamental questions, we want to stress here a law of nature which is generally valid, namely the connection between spin and symmetry class. *A half-integer value of the spin quantum number is always connected with antisymmetrical states (exclusion principle), an integer spin with symmetrical states.* This law holds not only for protons and neutrons but also for photons and electrons. Moreover, it holds for compound systems, if it holds for all of its constituents. If we search for a theoretical explanation of this law, we must pass to the discussion of relativistic wave mechanics, since we saw that it can certainly not be explained by nonrelativistic wave mechanics.

We first consider classical fields, which, like scalars, vectors and tensors, transform with respect to rotations in the ordinary space, according to a one-valued representation of the rotation group. We may, in the following, call such fields briefly "one-valued" fields. So long as interactions of different kinds of field are not taken into account, we can assume that all field components will satisfy a second order wave equation, permitting a superposition of plane waves as a general solution. Frequency and wavenumber of these plane waves are connected by a law which, in accordance with de Broglie's fundamental assumption, can be obtained from the relation between energy and momentum of a particle claimed in relativistic mechanics by division with the constant factor $\hbar$ equal to Planck's constant divided by 2π. There will appear, therefore, in the classical field equations, in general, a new constant μ with the dimension of a reciprocal length, with which the rest mass m in the particle picture is connected by $m = \dfrac{\hbar\mu}{c}$, where c is the vacuum-velocity of light. From the assumed property of one-valuedness of the field it can be concluded that the number of possible plane waves for a given frequency, wave number and direction of propagation, is for a non-vanishing μ always odd. Without going into details of the general definition of spin, we can consider this property of the polarization of plane waves as characteristic for fields which, as a result of their quantization, give rise to integer spin values.

The simplest cases of one-valued fields are the scalar fields and a field consisting of a four-vector and an antisymmetric tensor like the potentials and field strengths in Maxwell's theory. While the scalar field is simply fulfilling the usual wave equation of the second order in which the term proportional to μ^2 has to be included, the other field has to fulfil equations due to Proca which are a generalization of Maxwell's equations which they become in the particular case $\mu = 0$. It is satisfactory that for these simplest cases of one valued fields the energy density is a positive definite quadratic form of the field-quantities and their first derivatives at a certain point. For the general case of one-valued fields it can at least be achieved that the total energy after integration over space is always positive.

The field components can be assumed to be either real or complex. For a complex field, in addition to energy and momentum of the field a four-vector can be defined which satisfies the continuity equation and can be interpreted as the four-vector of the electric current. Its fourth component determines the electric charge density and can assume both positive and negative values. It is possible, that the charged mesons observed in cosmic rays have integer spins and thus can be described by such a complex field. In the particular case of real fields, this four-vector of current vanishes identically.

Especially, in view of the properties of the radiation in the thermodynamical equilibrium in which specific properties of the field sources do not play any role, it seemed to be justified at first, to disregard in the formal process of field quantization the interaction of the field with the sources. Dealing with this problem, one tried, indeed, to apply the same mathematical method of passing from a classical system to a corresponding system governed by the laws of quantum mechanics which has been so successful in passing from classical point mechanics to wave mechanics. It should not be forgotten, however, that a field can only be observed with help of its interaction with test bodies which are themselves again sources of the field.

The results of the formal process of field quantization were partly very encouraging. The quantized wave fields can be characterized by a wavefunction which depends on an infinite sequence of (non-negative) integers as variables. As the total energy and the total momentum of the field and, in case of complex fields, also its total electric charge turn out to be linear functions of these numbers, they can be interpreted as the number of particles present in a specified state of a single particle. By using a sequence of configuration spaces with a different number of dimensions corresponding to the different possible values of the total number of particles present, it could easily be shown that this description of our system by a wave function depending on integers is equivalent to an ensemble of particles with wave functions symmetrical in their configuration spaces.

Moreover, Bohr and Rosenfeld proved in the case of the electromagnetic field that the uncertainty relations which result for the average values of the field strengths over finite space-time regions from the formal commutation rules of this theory, have a direct physical meaning so long as the sources can be treated classically and their atomistic structure can be disregarded. We emphasize the following property of these commutation rules: All physical quantities in two world points, for which the four vector of their joining straight line is space-like, commute with each other. This is indeed necessary for physical reasons, because any disturbance by measurements in a world point P_1, can only reach such points P_2 for which the vector P_1P_2 is time-like, that is for which $c(t_1 - t_2) > r_{12}$. The points P_2 with a space-like vector P_1P_2, for which $c(t_1 - t_2) < r_{12}$, cannot be reached by this disturbance and measurements in P_1 and P_2 can then never influence each other.

This consequence made it possible to investigate the logical possibility of particles with integer spin which would obey the exclusion principle. Such particles could be described by a sequence of configuration spaces with different dimensions and wave-functions antisymmetrical in the co-ordinates of these spaces or also by a wave-function depending on integers again to be interpreted as the number of particles present in specified states which now can only assume the values 0 or 1. Wigner and Jordan proved that also in this case operators can be defined which are functions of the ordinary space-time coordinates and which can be applied to such a wave-function. These operators do not fulfil any longer commutation rules: instead of the difference the *sum* of the two possible products of two operators, which are distinguished by the different order of its factors, is now fixed by the mathematical conditions the operators have to satisfy. The simple change of the sign in these conditions changes entirely the physical meaning of the formalism. In the case of the exclusion principle there can never exist a limiting case where such operators can be replaced by a classical field. Using this formalism of Wigner and Jordan, I could prove under very general assumptions that a relativistic invariant theory, describing systems of like particles with integer spin obeying the exclusion principle, would always lead to the non-commutability of physical quantities joined by a space-like vector. This would violate a reasonable physical principle which holds good for particles with symmetrical states. In this way, by combination of the claims of relativistic invariance and the properties of field quantization, one step in the direction of an understanding of the connection of spin and symmetry class could be made.

The quantization of one-valued complex fields with a non-vanishing four-vector of the electric current gives the further result that particles both with positive and negative electric charge should exist and that they can be annihilated and generated in external electromagnetic fields. This pair generation and annihilation claimed by the theory makes it necessary to distinguish clearly the concept of charge density and of particle density. The latter concept does not occur in a relativistic wave theory either for fields carrying an electric charge or for neutral fields. This is satisfactory, since the use of the particle picture and the uncertainty relations (for instance, by analyzing imaginative experiments of the type of the γ-ray microscope) gives also the result that a localization of the particle is only possible with limited accuracy. This holds both, for the particles with integer and with half-integer spins. In a state with a mean value E of its energy, described by a wave packet with a mean frequency $v = E/h$, a particle can only be localized with an error $\Delta x > hc/E$ or $\Delta x > c/v$.

For photons it follows that the limit for the localization is the wave length; for a particle with a finite rest-mass m and a characteristic length $\mu^{-1} =$ h/mc. This limit is in the rest system of the center of the wave packet which describes the state of the particles given by $\Delta x > \hbar/mc$ or $\Delta x < \mu^{-1}$.

Until now I have mentioned only these results of the application of quantum mechanics to classical fields which are satisfactory. We saw that the statements of this theory about averages of field-strength over finite space-time regions have a direct meaning, while this is not so for the values of the field-strength at a certain point. Unfortunately, in the classical expression of the energy of the field, there enter averages of the squares of the field-strengths over such regions which cannot be expressed by the averages of the field-strengths themselves. This has the consequence that the zero-point energy of the vacuum, derived from the quantized field, becomes infinite, a result which is directly connected with the fact that the system considered has an infinite number of degrees of freedom. It is clear that this zero-point energy has no physical reality, for instance it is not the source of a gravitational field. Formally, it is easy to subtract constant infinite terms which are independent of the state considered and never change; nevertheless, it seems to me that already this result is an indication that a fundamental change in the concepts underlying the present theory of quantized fields will be necessary.

In order to clarify certain aspects of relativistic quantum theory, I have discussed here, different from the historical order of events, the one-valued fields first. Already earlier Dirac had formulated his relativistic wave equations corresponding to material particles with spin ½ using a pair of so-called spinors with two components each. He applied these equations to the problem of one electron in an electromagnetic field. In spite of the great success of this theory in the quantitative explanation of the fine structure of the energy-levels of the hydrogen atom and in the computation of the scattering cross section of one photon by a free electron, there was one consequence of this theory which was obviously in contradiction with experience. The energy of the electron can have, according to the theory, both positive and negative values and in external electromagnetic fields, transitions should occur from states with one sign of energy to states with the other sign. On the other hand there exists in this theory a four-vector satisfying the continuity equation with a fourth component corresponding to a density which is definitely positive.

It can be shown that there is a similar situation for all fields, which, like the spinors, transform for rotations in ordinary space, according to two-valued representations, thus changing their sign for a full rotation. We shall call briefly such quantities "two-valued." From the relativistic wave equations of such quantities one can always derive a four-vector bilinear in the field components which satisfies the continuity equation and for which the fourth component, at least after integration over the space, gives an essentially positive quantity. On the other hand, the expression for the total energy can have both the positive and the negative sign.

Is there any means to shift the minus sign from the energy back to the density of the four-vector? Then the latter could again be interpreted as charge density in contrast to particle density and the energy would become positive as it ought to be. You know that Dirac's answer was that this could actually be achieved by application of the exclusion principle. In his lecture delivered here in Stockholm he himself explained his proposal of a new interpretation of his theory, according to which in the actual vacuum all the states of negative energy should be occupied and only deviations of this state of smallest energy, namely holes in the sea of these occupied states, are assumed to be observable. It is the exclusion principle which guarantees the stability of the vacuum, in which all states of negative energy are occupied. Furthermore the holes have all properties of particles with positive energy and positive electric charge, which in external electromagnetic fields can be produced and annihilated in pairs. These predicted positions, the exact mirror images of the electrons, have been actually discovered experimentally.

The new interpretation of the theory obviously abandons in principle the standpoint of the one-body problem and considers a many-bodied problem from the beginning. It cannot any longer be claimed that Dirac's relativistic wave equations are the only possible ones, but if one wants to have relativistic field equations corresponding to particles, for which the value $\frac{1}{2}$ of their spin is known, one has certainly to assume the Dirac equations. Although it is logically possible to quantize these equations like classical fields, which would give symmetrical states of a system consisting of many such particles, this would be in contradiction with the postulate that the energy of the system has actually to be positive. This postulate is fulfilled on the other hand if we apply the exclusion principle and Dirac's interpretation of the vacuum and the holes, which at the same time substitutes the physical concept of charge density with values of both signs for the mathematical fiction of a positive particle density. A similar conclusion holds for all relativistic wave equations with two-valued quantities as field components. This is the other step (historically the earlier one) in the direction of an understanding of the connection between spin and symmetry class.

I can only shortly note that Dirac's new interpretation of empty and occupied states of negative energy can be formulated very elegantly with help of the formalism of Jordan and Wigner mentioned before. The transition from the old to the new interpretation of the theory can indeed be carried through simply by interchanging the meaning of one of the operators with that of its hermitian conjugate if they are applied to states originally of negative energy. The infinite "zero charge" of the occupied states of negative energy is then formally analogous to the infinite zero point energy of the quantized one-valued fields. The former has no physical reality either and is not the source of an electromagnetic field.

In spite of the formal analogy between the quantization of the one-valued fields leading to ensembles of like particles with symmetrical states and to particles fulfilling the exclusion principle described by two-valued operator quantities, depending on space and time coordinates, there is, of course, the fundamental difference that for the latter there is no limiting case, where the mathematical operators can be treated like classical fields. On the other hand, we can expect that the possibilities and the limitations for the applications of the concepts of space and time, which find their expression in the different concepts of charge density and particle density, will be the same for charged particles with integer and with half-integer spins.

The difficulties of the present theory become much worse, if the inter-action of the electromagnetic field with matter is taken into consideration, since the well-known infinities regarding the energy of an electron in its own field, the so-called self-energy, then occur as a result of the application of the usual perturbation formalism to this problem. The root of this difficulty seems to be the circumstance that the formalism of field quantization has only a direct meaning so long as the sources of the field can be treated as continuously distributed, obeying the laws of classical physics, and so long as only averages of field quantities over finite space-time regions are used. The electrons themselves, however, are essentially non-classical field sources.

At the end of this lecture I may express my critical opinion, that a correct theory should neither lead to infinite zero point energies nor to infinite zero charges, that it should not use mathematical tricks to sub-tract infinities or singularities, nor should it invent a "hypothetical world" which is only a mathematical fiction before it is able to formulate the correct interpretation of the actual world of physics.

From the point of view of logic, my report on "Exclusion Principle and Quantum Mechanics" has no conclusion. I believe that it will only be possible to write the conclusion if a theory will be established which will determine the value of the fine-structure constant and will thus explain the atomistic structure of electricity, which is such an essential quality of all atomic sources of electric fields actually occurring in nature.

60

ooooooooooo

SECONDARY RADIATION

oooooooooooo

Chandrasekhara Venkata Raman (b. 1888)

The scattering or diffusion of light is a well-known phenomenon that has been observed and studied for hundreds of years, but only within a relatively short time—since the advent of the quantum mechanics—has it been fully understood, and certain of its strange features such as the Raman effect have been explained. The simplest example of this phenomenon is the effect produced in the path of a beam of light by extremely fine dust. The eye cannot perceive light unless the light enters it; nevertheless, we can see a beam of light traversing a dust-filled room even though the beam itself is not moving toward the eye. The reason for this is that each particle of dust scatters the light, striking it so that the dust particle behaves as though it itself were a center of radiation, sending out rays in all directions. Thus observers standing anywhere in relation to the beam receive scattered light.

A brief discussion of how a dust particle does this will be useful for what we shall state later. We know that light is an oscillatory phenomenon consisting of rapidly oscillating electric and magnetic fields. As the light passes through the dust-laden air, each dust particle is pulled back and forth by the vibrating electric field of the light, and, as a result, emits electromagnetic radiation in all directions, thus scattering the incident light. This happens because the incident electric field pulls the negative electric charges in the dust particle to one side and the positive charges to the other side, forming a small electric dipole of the dust particle. As this dipole vibrates, it emits radiation. But the dipole vibrates with the same frequency as that of the incident light, so that the scattered light is of the same frequency as the incident light, at least according to this simple

985

analysis. That is, the color of the scattered light is the same as that of the incident light.

Here one more point must be mentioned. The response of a dust particle to light striking it is not the same for all colors. The shorter the wavelength, that is, the bluer the light, the more violently the dust particle responds and the more intense is the scattering. Thus, if white light (a fairly uniform mixture of all colors) passes through a dusty medium, the blue and green colors are scattered more readily than the red and yellow, and the dust, for example, smoke in a room, appears bluish. This is known as the Tyndall effect.

The question naturally arises as to whether or not molecules themselves scatter light. At first it may seem that they do not, since pure air appears perfectly clear, but a little thought and more careful observation show us that molecules do, indeed, scatter light. The best evidence for this is the blueness of the sky, which was first investigated by the British physicist, Lord Rayleigh, who suggested that it was caused by molecular scattering. When we look at the sky in a direction away from the sun, our eyes receive the scattered rays of sunlight; since these are mostly blue in color, the sky appears blue. When we look toward the sun at sunset, our eyes receive the rays of light coming through the atmosphere—the unscattered rays—and these are the red rays. Therefore, the sun appears red.

That molecules should also scatter light follows, in principle, from the same general analysis as in the case of dust particles. The molecule in the electromagnetic field of the light becomes a small electric dipole which vibrates with the oscillating electromagnetic field and emits light in all directions. In terms of the simple picture of a molecule vibrating with the same frequency as the incident light, we should expect to find the scattered light to be of the same frequency as the incident light. This is, indeed, what one generally finds, but a careful investigation of the scattered light shows that in addition to light of the same frequency as the incident light, weak components, different in frequency from that of the incident light, are present in the scattered radiation. Raman discovered this surprising and completely unexpected effect in 1928, which is now known as the Raman effect.

To study this phenomenon more thoroughly, Raman used incident light of a definite frequency instead of white light. He isolated the light of a definite spectral line from a mercury arc lamp and used this line as the primary radiation. When this light was sent into a homogeneous medium, Raman found that the scattered light contained not only this primary spectral line but also other faint lines on either side of the given line. In other words, the scattered light contained frequencies equal to, smaller than, and larger than the frequency of primary light, that is, of the mercury line. Raman found that this effect was present no matter which mercury line was used for the incident light. In other words, a "Raman spectrum" is present in the scattered radiation of any spectral line and the lines of this Raman spectrum in the scattered light lie symmetrically on either side of the incident line.

The problem associated with the Raman spectrum is the following: Because of the discrete orbits permitted to an electron in an atom or the discrete states that a molecule can have, an atom or a molecule can absorb or emit photons of a definite frequency. But the lines in the Raman spectrum of the scattered light are not those that are found either in the emission or absorption spectrum of the atom or the molecule. How, then, do the Raman lines arise?

We may get an idea of how this happens by first considering a simple classical argument. Consider a molecule in an electric field. This field displaces the negative and positive charges with respect to each other, so that the molecule becomes a dipole. Now this dipole has its own natural frequencies, and if the dipole were set vibrating, it would vibrate with its natural frequencies, like the strings of a violin, and emit light of these frequencies. If light of a given frequency—different from any one of the natural frequencies of the dipole—strikes the molecule, it oscillates under the influence of the oscillating electric field of this light. One can now show mathematically that the molecule, that is, our dipole, oscillates not only with its own natural frequencies, but with additional frequencies that are obtained by adding and subtracting the frequency of the incident light from the natural frequency. In other words, if v_n is one of the natural frequencies of the molecule and v is the frequency of the incident light, then the light scattered by the molecule contains not only the frequency v but also the neighboring frequencies $v + v_n$ and $v - v_n$, lying at equal intervals to the left and to the right of the incident line.

Although this simple classical analysis shows why we can expect to find frequencies in the scattered light different from those of the incident radiation, we can obtain a complete understanding of the Raman effect only by using the quantum theory. To see how the quantum theory is applied to the explanation of the Raman effect, we consider the discrete energy states of a molecule. Under ordinary conditions, the only photons that the molecule can absorb or emit are those associated with transitions of the molecule from one of these discrete states to another. But the spectral lines arising from all such transitions are not present because there are certain rules, called selection rules, that prohibit certain transitions and the spectral lines associated with these transitions do not occur in the spectrum of the molecule. However, these lines and others may appear in the Raman spectrum under the following conditions.

Consider a photon that has a frequency different from that which the atom or molecule can emit under ordinary conditions. Such a photon will, in general, not be absorbed by the molecule because this would bring the molecule to a state of energy that does not correspond to any of its possible energy levels. But suppose the molecule absorbs this photon, and immediately re-emits another one whose frequency is such (let us say smaller than that of the incident photon) that the molecule ends up in one of its possible excited states above the state from which it started. The energy of the emitted photon is clearly the difference between the energy of the incident photon and the energy of a photon that the molecule would have had to absorb to bring it from its initial to its final state. Thus, a line is present in the Raman spectrum of frequency smaller than that of the incident photon.

Suppose, now, that immediately on absorbing the incident photon, the molecule emits a photon of greater frequency than that of the one it absorbed. It can do this provided it ends up in a state lower in energy than the one from which it started. The emitted photon in this case has an energy equal to the energy of the incident photon, plus the energy of the photon that the molecule would emit if it jumped directly from its initial to this final state. Thus, a line is present in the Raman spectrum whose frequency is higher than that of the incident photon.

For Raman lines to appear both to the left and to the right of the incident line, that is, for larger and smaller frequencies to appear in the scattered light, the molecule does not have to be in its ground state. If it were always in its ground state, only frequencies lower than the frequency of the incident photon could appear, since the end state of the molecule would then have to lie above the initial state (because the initial state in this case is the ground state, and hence the lowest possible state). Under ordinary conditions, the thermal motions of the molecules bring about collisions between them, which cause the molecules to spin and to vibrate. Hence the molecules are initially in rotational and vibrational states that lie above the ground state and hence the final state of the molecule can be lower than the initial state.

We would therefore expect to find a difference between the intensity of the Raman lines below (in frequency) the incident line and the intensity of the lines above, depending on the temperature of the medium. As the temperature gets lower and lower, the number of molecules in excited rotational or vibrational states gets smaller and smaller, and there are thus fewer and fewer molecules available to emit photons of frequency higher than that of the incident photon. This is, indeed, observed.

One more point is of interest in connection with the Raman spectrum. The lines in this spectrum are associated with transitions of the molecule between rotational (or, to a lesser extent, vibrational) energy levels. The energies associated with such transitions, excited by the thermal motion, are quite small and correspond to photons in the infrared part of the molecular spectrum. Thus, in a sense, the Raman spectrum gives a picture of the infrared !ines of the molecule.

In the papers that follow this commentary, Raman and Krishnan discuss only the Raman effect in gases. But since this early work was done, the Raman spectrum in crystals has also been studied extensively. Since the fundamental vibrations of a crystal are difficult to analyze under ordinary conditions, the Raman lines arising when a crystal is excited by photons of a definite frequency are a source of information of the structure of the crystal.

Chandrasekhara Venkata Raman, whose father was a lecturer in mathematics and physics, was raised in an academic atmosphere. From the time of his birth at Trichonopoly in Southern India on November 7, 1888, Raman lived in a world of ideas and quickly absorbed advanced concepts of mathematics and physics. He was so precocious and showed such a grasp of science that he was admitted to the Presidency College, Madras, in 1902 at the age of fourteen and passed his B.A. examinations two years later. He placed first in this examination and won the gold medal in physics. In 1907 he received his M.A. degree with highest distinction.

From the time he began his graduate studies, Raman devoted himself to optics and acoustics. In the early years of his career, he had to do research on a part-time basis because he took a job in the Indian Finance Department to support himself. He carried on his scientific work at every spare moment in the laboratories of the Indian Association for the Cultivation of Science in Calcutta.

He was very successful in this part-time research career and soon acquired a reputation as an excellent experimentalist. When a newly endowed Palit chair of physics was established at Calcutta University in 1917 it was offered to Raman, who accepted it. During his stay at Calcutta, he performed the experiments that led to his discovery in 1928 of what is now called the Raman effect, for which he received the Nobel Prize in 1930. Raman's curiosity about the blue opalescence of the sea, which he had observed in the Mediterranean on a trip to Europe in the summer of 1921, started the chain of events that led to his final discovery. In thinking about this strange glow of the sea, Raman stated in his Nobel address, "It seemed not unlikely that the phenomenon owed its origins to the scattering of sunlight by the molecules of the water."

Raman decided to test this hypothesis by investigating the laws that govern the diffusion of light in liquids; he started experiments immediately on his return to Calcutta in September 1921. This entailed a much greater effort than he had originally anticipated, since it very quickly broadened into a general investigation of the molecular scattering of light. A critical review of the entire subject and the results of Raman's initial experiments were published as an essay by the Calcutta University Press in February 1922. From 1922 until 1927, Raman, with various collaborators, investigated as many facets of optical scattering as possible. In one of these experiments in April 1923, a collaborator, Ramanathan, discovered that in addition to the usual type of scattered light, which is similar in wavelength to the incident light, there was present a very weak secondary radiation differing in wavelength from that of the incidental light.

Raman became greatly interested in this secondary radiation and devised various experiments to increase its intensity so that it might be studied spectroscopically. Finally, on February 18, 1928, he found that if he used a mercury arc lamp as his incident light source, the spectra of the scattered light from a variety of liquids and solids include a number of lines and bands not present in the spectrum of the mercury arc light. The production of these lines by the scattering molecules is called the Raman effect.

After receiving the Nobel Prize for this discovery, Raman became professor of physics at the Indian Institute of Science at Bangalore, where he continued his work in optics. He remained there until 1948 when he became director of the Raman Institute of Research at Bangalore, which he himself established and endowed. Raman has remained very active in research; he has also inspired many of his countrymen to go into physics and has done a great deal to further physical research in India. Thus, in 1926, he founded the *Indian Journal of Physics,* of which he is editor, and initiated the establishment of the Indian Academy of Sciences, serving ever since as its president. He has also begun publishing the *Proceedings* of that academy, and is now president of the Current Science Association of Bangalore, which publishes *Current Science (India).*

Besides his research into the scattering of light, Raman has done a considerable amount of study in acoustical vibrations, X-ray diffraction by crystals, crystal dynamics, crystal structure, optics of colloids, electric and magnetic anisotropy, and the physiology of human vision. His interests in acoustics led him to study the manner in which the violin maintains its vibrations, and he has published on the subject of the string and other musical instruments.

Raman has received his share of laurels, among them many honorary doctorates, and honorary memberships in scientific societies in several countries. He was elected a fellow of the Royal Society in 1924 and was knighted in 1929.

The paper announcing his discovery of the Raman effect is reproduced in its entirety. It is followed by excerpts from a subsequent article, co-authored with K. S. Krishnan, that substantiates experimentally the scientific expectations expressed in the first paper.

००००००००

RAMAN

A New Radiation [1]

INTRODUCTION

I PROPOSE THIS EVENING TO speak to you on a new kind of radiation or light-emission from atoms and molecules. To make the significance of the discovery clear, I propose to place before you the history of the investigations made at Calcutta which led up to it. Before doing so, however, a few preliminary remarks regarding radiation from atoms and molecules will not be out of place.

Various ways are known to the physicist by which atoms or molecules may be caused to emit light, as for instance, heating a substance or bombarding it with a stream of electrons. The light thus emitted is usually characteristic of the atoms or molecules and is referred to as *primary* radiation. It is also possible to induce radiation from atoms and molecules by illuminating them strongly. Such light-emission is referred to as *secondary* radiation. The familiar diffusion of light by rough surfaces may be cited as an example of secondary radiation, but strictly speaking, it hardly deserves the name, being an effect occurring at the boundaries between media of different refractive indices and not a true volume-effect in which all the atoms and molecules of the substance take part. The first case discovered of secondary radiation really worthy of the name was the phenomenon of fluorescence whose laws were elucidated by the investigations of Sir George Stokes. This is a familiar effect which is exhibited in a very conspicuous manner in the visible region of the spectrum by various organic dye-stuffs. I have here a bottle of water in which an extremely small quantity of fluorescein is dissolved. You notice that when placed in the beam of light from the lantern, it shines with a vivid green light, and that the colour of the emission is not altered, though its brightness is changed, by placing filters of various colours between the bottle and the lantern. A violet filter excites the green fluorescence strongly, while a red filter has but little effect.

Another kind of secondary radiation whose existence has been experi-

---

[1] C. V. Raman, *Indian Journal of Physics,* 2 (1928), 387–398.

mentally recognized more recently is the scattering of light by atoms and molecules. It is this scattering that gives us the light of the sky, the blue colour of the deep sea and the delicate opalescence of large masses of clear ice. I have here a large bottle of a very clear and transparent liquid, toluene, which as you notice contains hardly any dust-particles, but the track of the beam from the lantern passing through it is visible as a brilliant blue cone of light. This internal opalescence continues to be visible even after the most careful purification of the liquid by repeated distillation in vacuo. A similar opalescence is shown, though much less brightly, by dust-free gases and vapours, and also by solids. A large clear block of ice shows a blue colour in the track of the beam when sunlight passes through it. The blue opalescence of blocks of clear optical glass is also readily demonstrable. The molecular scattering of light is thus a phenomenon common to all states of matter.

During the past seven years, the scattering of light in transparent media has been the subject of intensive experimental and theoretical investigation at Calcutta, and it is the researches made on this subject that have led to the discovery which I shall lay before you this evening. One important outcome of our researches has been to show that while light-scattering is in one sense a molecular phenomenon, in another sense it is a bulk-effect having a thermal origin. It is the thermal agitation of the molecules which causes them to be distributed and orientated in space with incomplete regularity, and it is the local fluctuations in the properties of the medium thus arising which give rise to optical heterogeneity and consequent diffusion of light. The subject of light-scattering is thus a meeting ground for thermodynamics, molecular physics and the wave-theory of radiation. That the combination of theories in such diverse fields of physics gives us predictions which have been experimentally verified, is one of the triumphs of modern physics.

A NEW PHENOMENON

While the quantitative investigations made at Calcutta have in the main substantiated the thermodynamic-wave-optical theory of light-scattering, indications appeared even in our earliest studies of a new phenomenon which refused to fit in with our pre-conceived notions. Thus, in some observations made by me with the assistance of Mr. Seshagiri Rao in December, 1921, it was found that the depolarisation of the light transversely scattered by distilled water measured with a double-image prism and Nicol increased very markedly when a violet filter was placed in the path of the incident light. More careful investigations made with dust-free liquids in 1922 confirmed this effect and showed it to exist also in methyl and ethyl alcohols, and to a lesser degree in ether. It was also noticed that the colours of the scattered light from the different liquids studied did not match perfectly. An important advance was made when Dr. Ramanathan, working at Calcutta in the summer of 1923, investigated the phenomenon more closely and discovered that it was not a true dependance of the depolarisation on the wave-length of the scattering radiation but was due to the presence in the scattered light of what he described as "a trace of fluorescence." This was shown by the fact that the measured depolarisation depended on whether the blue filter used was placed in the path of the incident beam or of the scattered light, being smaller in the latter case. Accepting the explanation of the effect as "weak fluorescence," it naturally became important to discover whether it was due to some impurity present in the substance. Dr. Ramanathan tested this by careful chemical purification followed by repeated slow distillation of the liquid at the temperature of melting ice. He found that the effect persisted undiminished.

The investigation of this species of "weak fluorescence" has ever since 1923 been on our programme of research at Calcutta. Krishnan, who investigated 60 liquids for light-scattering in the spring and summer of 1924, made systematic studies of the phenomenon, and found that it was shown markedly by water, ether, all the monohydric alcohols and a few other compounds. He pointed out that the liquids which exhibit the effect have certain family relationships amongst themselves, and that they are also substances whose molecules are known to be polar. The chemical importance of the subject led to Mr. S. Venkateswaran attempting to make a fuller study of it in the summer of 1925, but without any special success. The research was discontinued at the time but was resumed by him later in the current year (January, 1928). The remarkable observation was made that the visible radiation which is excited in pure dry glycerine by ultra-violet radiation (sunlight filtered through Corning glass G. 586) *is strongly polarised.*

The possibility of a similar effect in gases and vapours was also borne in mind and repeatedly looked for by the workers at Calcutta. The feebleness of the scattering in gases and vapours, and the infructuousness of the earlier efforts in this direction, however, discouraged progress.

ITS UNIVERSALITY

Though the phenomenon was described in the paper of Dr. Ramanathan and Mr. Krishnan as a "feeble fluorescence," the impression left on my mind at the time was that we had here an entirely new type of secondary radiation distinct from what is usually described as fluorescence. The publication of the idea was however discouraged by the belief then entertained that only a few liquids exhibited the effect and by the supposition that it was unpolarised in the same way as ordinary fluorescence in liquids. Indeed, a chemical critic might even have asserted that the effect was in each case due to a trace of dissolved fluorescent impurity present in the substance which our efforts at purification had failed to remove. Early this year, however, a powerful impetus to further research was provided when I conceived the idea that the effect was some kind of optical analogue to the type of X-ray scattering discovered by Prof. Compton, for which he recently received the Nobel Prize in Physics. I immediately undertook an experimental re-examination of the subject in collaboration with Mr. K. S. Krishnan and this has proved very fruitful in results. The first step taken in the research was to find whether the effect is shown by all liquids. The method of investigation was to use a powerful beam of sunlight from a heliostat concentrated by a 7″ telescope objective combined with a short focus lens. This was passed through a blue-violet filter and then through the liquid under examination contained in an evacuated bulb and purified by repeated distillation in vacuo. A second filter of green glass was used which was complementary in colour to the blue-violet filter. If it were placed in the track of the incident light, all illumination disappears, while, if it be placed between the bulb and the observer's eye, the opalescent track within the liquid continued to be visible, though less brightly. All the liquids examined (and they were some 80 in number) showed the effect in a striking manner. There was therefore no longer any doubt that the phenomenon was universal in character; with the bulb of toluene on the lantern, you see that the effect is readily demonstrable. The cone of light vanishes when I place the violet and green filters together, but it appears when I transfer the latter to a place between my audience and the observation bulb.

Now the test with the complementary filters is precisely that ordinarily used for detecting fluorescence and indeed was first suggested by Stokes in his investigations on the subject. You may therefore rightly ask me the question how does this phenomenon differ from fluorescence? The answer to the question is, firstly, that it is of an entirely different order of intensity. A more satisfactory proof was however forthcoming when Mr. Krishnan and myself examined the polarisation of this new type of radiation and found that it was nearly as strong as that of the ordinary light scattering in many cases, and is thus quite distinct from ordinary fluorescence which is usually unpolarised.

This is shown for the case of toluene in [figs 60–1 and 60–2]. [Fig. 60–1] is a photograph of the scattering by toluene of sunlight filtered through a blue-violet glass. It was taken through a double-image prism of iceland spar with an exposure of 3 seconds. [Fig. 60–2] is a picture with an additional complementary filter of green glass interposed in front of the camera lens. The exposure necessary is now increased greatly by the insensitiveness of the plate to green light, and had to be as much as 25 minutes. It will be noticed that the polarisation of the track as shown by the difference in brightness of the two polarised images is quite as prominent in [Fig. 60–2] as in [Fig. 60–1].

I may also mention that Mr. Krishnan and myself have succeeded in detecting the new radiation and observing its partial polarisation in a number of organic vapours and also in the gases CO_2 and N_2O. The problem in these cases is one of securing sufficient intensity of scattering for the effect to be detectable through the complementary filter. This can be secured by heating up the substance in a sealed bulb or by using steel observation-vessels for containing the compressed gases, so as to obtain sufficient density of the scattering molecules. The question of the background against which the track is observed is also of great importance.

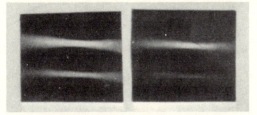

Fig. 60–1 (Left). Polarization of scattering—unmodified. Fig. 60–2 (Right). Polarization of scattering—modified.

The new type of secondary radiation is also observable in crystals such as ice, and in amorphous solids. It is thus a phenomenon whose universal nature has to be recognised.

LINE-SPECTRUM OF NEW RADIATION

That the secondary radiation passes the complementary filter and yet is strongly polarised to an extent comparable with the ordinary molecular scattering, is clear evidence that we have in it an entirely new type of secondary radiation which is distinct from either the ordinary scattering or the usual type of fluorescence. A striking and even startling confirmation of this view is furnished by an examination of its spectrum. Preliminary observations with sunlight filtered through a combination which passes a narrow range of wave-lengths, showed the spectrum of the new radiation to consist mainly of a narrow range of wave-lengths clearly separated from the incident spectrum by a dark space. This encouraged me to take up observations with a monochromatic source of light. A quartz mercury lamp with a filter which completely cuts out all the visible lines of longer wave-length than the indigo line 4,358. A. U. was found to be very effective. When the light from such a lamp was passed through the bulb containing a dust-free liquid, and the spectrum of the scattered light was observed through a direct-vision spectroscope, it was found to exhibit two or more sharp bright lines in the blue and green regions of the spectrum. These lines are not present in the spectrum of the incident light or in the unfiltered light of the mercury arc and are thus manufactured by the molecules of the liquid.

[Figs. 60–3 and 60–4] show the phenomenon. They are spectrograms taken with a small Hilger quartz instrument of the scattering by *liquid* benzene. [Fig. 60–3] was taken with the light from the quartz mercury arc filtered through a blue glass which allows the wave-lengths from about 3,500 A. U. to 4,400 A. U. to pass through. [Fig. 60–3, top] represents the incident-spectrum and [Fig. 60–3, bottom] the scattered spectrum, and the latter shows the number of sharp lines not present in [Fig. 60–3, top]. These are indicated in the figure. [Fig. 60–4] similarly represents the incident and scattered spectra with benzene liquid, the filter used being a potassium permanganate solution. Here again the new lines which appear are indicated in the figure. Visual observations were also made using a quinine sulphate solution together with the blue glass as a filter and thus cutting off all the radiations except 4,358 A. U. from the incident spectrum. Some of the modified lines then disappear, leaving only those of longer wave-length. It is thus clear that each line in the incident spectrum gives rise to at least two lines in the scattered spectrum, one in the original or unmodified position, and a second in a shifted position of longer wave-length. There is thus a striking analogy with the Compton effect in the X-ray region.

There has, as yet, not been sufficient time for photographing the spectra from a large number of liquids, or even for measuring the photographs already obtained. Visual observations have however been made with a large number of liquids. There is an astonishing similarity between the spectra obtained with different liquids. When only the 4,358 line was used, most liquids showed in the spectrum of the scattered light, a bright line in the blue-green region of the spectrum (about 5,000 A. U.), whose position was practically the same for chemically similar liquids such as pentane, hexane and octane for instance. There was, however, a recognizable difference in the position of the modified line when other liquids such as benzene or water were used. When the 4,047 line of the mercury arc was let in by removing the quinine sulphate solution, a second modified line in the blue region of the spectrum was seen with most liquids.

Photographs obtained so far with benzene and toluene suggest that there may be several modified lines, and that each modified line may be a doublet in some cases. In many liquids, the scattered spectrum shows in addition to sharp lines also an unmistakable continuous spectrum accompanying it. Carbon disulphide behaves in an exceptional manner, showing a diffuse band.

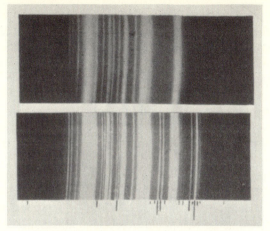

Fig. 60–3. Top: Incident spectrum. Bottom: Scattered spectrum with liquid benzene.

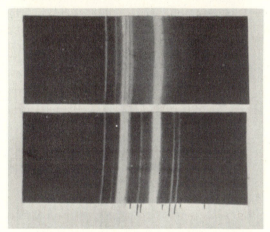

Fig. 60–4. Top: Incident spectrum with different filters than those used in achieving the top photograph in Fig. 60–3. Bottom: Scattered spectrum with liquid benzene; filters are the same as in above photograph.

Observations already made show that the new lines in the scattered spectrum are usually markedly polarised; they also suggest that a continuous spectrum, when present, is less markedly polarised.

NATURE OF THE NEW RADIATION

The discovery set out above naturally opens up an array of problems for investigation. The most pressing question is, how is the modified scattered radiation, as we may call it, generated by the molecules of the liquid?

As a tentative explanation, we may adopt the language of the quantum theory, and say that the incident quantum of radiation is partially absorbed by the molecule, and that the unabsorbed part is scattered. The suggestion does not seem to be altogether absurd and indeed such a possibility is already contemplated in the Kramers-Heisenberg theory of dispersion. If we accept the idea indicated above, then the difference between the incident and scattered quanta would correspond to a quantum of absorption by the molecule. The measurement of the frequencies of the new spectral lines thus opens a new pathway of research into molecular spectra, particularly those in the infra-red region.

If a molecule can take up part of the incident quantum of radiation and scatter the remaining part, then it might also be capable of adding a quantum of its own characteristic frequency to the incident radiation when scattering it. In such a case we should expect a modified line of *increased* frequency. Such a result appears to be shown in [Fig. 60–3, bottom] as a solitary line in the extreme left of the photograph [marked but not visible in plate—Editors]. This result, however, requires to be confirmed by more photographs and with other liquids. So far it would appear that a degradation of frequency is more probable than an enhancement. It is too early to speculate at present on the origin of the continuous radiation observed in some cases, whether it is due to changes in the molecule itself, or whether it arises from inelastic collisions of the second kind within the liquid resulting in *partial* transformation of the incident quantum of radiation into translatory kinetic energy of the molecules. When further data are obtained, it should be possible to express a definite opinion on this point, and also on the role played by the solvent in the explanation of ordinary fluorescence.

RELATION TO THERMODYNAMICS

As explained in the introduction, the ordinary scattering of light can be regarded equally well as a molecular effect, and as a bulk effect arising from the thermodynamic fluctuations of the whole medium. The question arises whether the effect depends on the solution temperature. Quantitative observations are necessary to decide the very fundamental question here raised.

POSSIBLE X-RAY ANALOGIES

If a quantum of radiation can be absorbed in part and scattered in part in the optical region of the spectrum, should not similar phenomena also occur in X-ray scattering? The type of scattering discovered by Prof. Compton may possibly be only one of numerous other types of scattering with modified frequencies, some with a line spectrum and some in the nature of continuous radiation. The extreme ultra-violet region of the spectrum may also furnish us with numerous examples of the new type of radiation, which clearly occupies a position intermediate between scattering and fluorescence.

CONCLUSION

We are obviously only at the fringe of a fascinating new region of experimental research which promises to throw light on diverse problems relating to radiation and wave-theory, X-ray optics, atomic and molecular spectra, fluorescence and scattering, thermodynamics and chemistry. It all remains to be worked out.

I have to add in conclusion that I owe much to the valuable cooperation in this research of Mr. K. S. Krishnan, and the assistance of Mr. S. Venkateswaran and other workers in my laboratory.

The line spectrum of the new radiation was first seen on the 28th February, 1928. The observation was given publicity the following day.

ೲೲೲೲ

R A M A N   and   *K R I S H N A N*

A New Class of Spectra Due to
Secondary Radiation [2]

INTRODUCTION

THE DISCOVERY OF A NEW type of secondary radiation, distinct from either the classical scattering or ordinary fluorescence, has been recorded in an address delivered recently by one of us and published in the previous issue of this journal. Whenever light is diffused by the molecules of a transparent medium, the scattered radiations contain not only the wave-lengths present in the incident light but also radiations of modified frequency. The effect is most striking when the scattering medium is a dust-free liquid, and the incident radiations consist of sharply defined spectral lines, *e.g.,* the light of a quartz mercury lamp. It is then found that in the spectrum of the scattered light we have besides the inci-

[2] C. V. Raman and K. S. Krishnan, *Indian Journal of Physics,* 2 (1928), 399–416.

dent lines also other new lines which are usually quite sharp. A continuous spectrum may also be observed and is specially noticeable in certain liquids. The scattered radiation of altered wave-lengths is partially polarised. Though the effects mentioned above are most readily studied with liquids, other media such as vapours, crystals and even amorphous solids exhibit the modified scattering, which is thus a universal phenomenon. The explanation was tentatively put forward that the new type of secondary radiation is produced when the incident quantum of radiation is partly absorbed by the molecule, shifting it to a higher level of energy, and is partly scattered. The difference between the frequencies of the incident and scattered radiations would thus correspond to a characteristic frequency of the molecule. Accepting this explanation it follows that corresponding to a given frequency of the incident radiation, we should expect a new line in the spectrum of the scattered radiation for each one of the characteristic frequencies of the molecule, that is to say, for each incident frequency we should expect as many lines of modified frequency as the molecule has characteristic electronic frequencies. Further, when the incident radiation contains several spectral lines, we should expect several sets of such modified lines in the scattered spectrum. The new type of secondary radiation should thus create for us a whole new class of spectra, and indeed as many new spectra as there are chemical substances suitable for study, multiplied by the number of spectral lines available in the light-source used.

The discovery of the new radiation thus opens up a wonderful avenue of research in spectroscopy. During the past few weeks we have succeeded in obtaining a number of spectrograms of the scattered radiation with the following liquids selected for their importance, namely, benzene, toluene, pentane, ether, methyl alcohol and water. The spectrograms obtained with benzene have been measured. It is proposed in this paper to detail the highly significant results which have emerged from the detailed study of the spectrograms for benzene, and from a qualitative study of the spectra obtained with the other liquids. . . .

[The details of the experiments have been omitted—Editors.]

INTERPRETATION OF RESULTS

. . . From the analysis of the measurements . . . several striking results emerge.

The first and most significant result is that the shift of the modified line with respect to the exciting line (measured in wave-numbers) is independent of the frequency of the exciting line. This is shown by the fact that the shift is the same for all exciting lines, within the limits of error in measurement.

The second most significant result is that very similar groups of lines are generated by each incident line in the spectrum. This is shown by the fact that for each incident line, modified lines are to be found in known positions relative to it, or else, if they are absent, an adequate explanation is forthcoming, *e.g.,* insufficient intensity of the incident line, or of the modified line, or of both, or else the obscuration of a modified line by strong lines in the incident spectrum.

Thirdly, the order of the relative intensities within each group of modified lines appears to depend but little on the frequency of the line which excites the group. The shifts of +990 and of 3059 in wave-number give rise to the brightest modified lines in every case.

A fourth and most interesting result is that while most of the modified lines are *degraded* in frequency relatively to the exciting lines, an *enhancement* of frequency is also possible, though such modified line of enhanced frequency is usually of extremely low intensity. Further the *enhancement* of frequency of such line is equal to the *degradation* of frequency of another modified line.

A fifth and rather curious result, which is probably not an accident, is that one of the shifts in wave-number (1591) is approximately the sum of two others (606 + 990 = 1596). It may be significant to note that the modified lines showing this shift appear distinctly more diffuse on the plate than other modified lines.

ORIGIN OF THE MODIFIED SPECTRUM

The results set out above definitely prove the correctness of the explanation of the new type of secondary radiation advanced by one of us previously, namely, that the incident quantum of radiation is partly absorbed and partly scattered by the molecule. The shift of frequency would then correspond to some characteristic frequency of the molecule and would therefore be independent of the frequency of the exciting radiation. The latter is, with the liquids under study, far removed from either the characteristic ultra-violet or infra-red frequencies of the molecule, and hence the phenomenon we are studying is a pure scattering effect and does not partake of the nature of resonance radiation. The great differences in the brightness of the different modified lines produced by a given incident line must presumably be ascribed to the differences in the "Einsteinian coefficients of probability" of the transitions induced by the incident radiation.

The existence of lines of enhanced frequency referred to above may be regarded as a definite experimental proof that *negative* transitions may be induced by incident radiation, that is to say, that a molecule may pass to a state of *lower* energy as the result of radiation falling upon it. This of course will be possible only if it be initially in a state of higher energy than the normal. As the number of molecules in a liquid in the state of higher energy at any instant would be only a fraction of the number present in the normal state, the feebleness of the modified line corresponding to such negative transition is readily understood. The fact that the negative shift of frequency is equal to the positive shift of frequency for some other modified line is also intelligible if we assume that the initial state of higher energy is identical with one of those to which the molecule might be raised from the normal state by the incident radiation. As the result of the existence of thermal agitation within the fluid, a certain fraction of the molecules (which may be taken as $e^{-\frac{w}{kT}}$, where w is the increase of energy) exist in the higher level of energy under consideration and tend under the action of the incident radiation to return to the normal state. Multiplying the observed shift of frequency by Planck's constant, the energy difference w is readily calculated. Thus corresponding to a shift of wave number equal to 900, $e^{-\frac{w}{kT}}$ comes out as about $\frac{1}{120}$ at room temperature (*viz.* 30° *c.*), which is of the same order of magnitude as the relative intensities of the two modified lines with positive and negative shift of frequency. . . .

61

ooooooooooo

STATISTICAL MECHANICS

ooooooooooo

S. N. Bose (b. 1894)

One of the most powerful techniques the physicist has for the solution of problems dealing with ensembles, such as groups of electrons, molecules, or photons, is statistical mechanics. It had its beginnings in the kinetic theory of gases, as formulated by Maxwell and Boltzmann. This discipline was later developed more fully and applied to the equilibrium of chemical systems by the famous American physical chemist, Willard Gibbs. In fact, the form in which Gibbs developed this branch of physics is what finally came to be known as statistical mechanics. The procedures of Maxwell and Boltzmann are generally referred to as kinetic theory.

The real power of statistical mechanics did not become fully apparent until Einstein redeveloped it and applied it to all types of phenomenon from Brownian motion to the behavior of photons. In all of these applications of statistical mechanics, the type of statistics used is called Boltzmann statistics or classical statistics. No one doubted the validity of this type of statistics, since there was then no reason to question the validity of classical physics. But as the quantum theory developed from its early stages to its more complex phases, the question of the validity of Boltzmann statistics began to intrude into the discussions of physicists.

To understand the problem involved in the application of statistical mechanics to an ensemble of identical particles (e.g., the molecules of a gas), we must first define the "state of a system." There are various ways of doing this. One is by considering the microscopic measurable properties of the ensemble. Thus, the state of a gas can be represented macroscopically by specifying its pressure, its volume, and its temperature. Actually, we need specify only two of these three quantities since an equation exists that connects these three quantities; therefore, we can obtain the

1003

third quantity if we know any two. This equation is called "the equation of state of the gas." This macroscopic way of representing the state of an ensemble gives us no insight into the way this state depends on the motion of the individual particles in the system. It is clear that the gross or macroscopic condition of the ensemble is determined by how the individual particles are moving about and how they happen to be distributed throughout the volume. We should thus be able to define the macroscopic state of the ensemble by specifying the distribution of the particles in the ensemble and giving their motions. We may refer to this as the "microscopic" specification of the state. Statistical mechanics is the branch of physics that deals with the microscopic representation of the states of a system.

To define the microscopic state of the ensemble we first consider a single particle. As we follow this particle, we note that its position and its motion, that is, its velocity or its momentum, change continuously. At each moment, therefore, we can, on the basis of classical physics, assign to this particle a position and a velocity. Suppose we did this for every particle in our ensemble. We would then, at each moment, have a detailed microscopic picture of the state of the system—the position and velocity of each of its particles.

If we think about this for a moment, we realize that we do not have to go into such detail to define the state of the ensemble. It is not really necessary to know where each particle is and how it is moving at each moment, because, since all the particles are identical, it does not matter—insofar as the state of the system goes—whether a given particle or some other one is at a particular point, moving with a particular velocity. It is clear that the only thing that counts here is how many particles in a given neighborhood are moving in a given way.

In considering groups of particles instead of individual particles to describe the state of our system, we run into a certain arbitrariness that becomes apparent when we speak of the positions of the particles in the group. We clearly cannot speak of the particles in a group as occupying the same position, since no two particles can be in the same place at the same time. We must therefore consider a small region of space in our ensemble, and ask how many particles at any moment are in this small region. Clearly, the smallness of this region is arbitrary, but we can select a region so small that all points in it may be considered identical insofar as defining the state of the system is concerned. How small this volume must be cannot be precisely specified in classical physics. All that can be said is that it must be so small that any change of position of a particle within this restricted volume leaves the state of the ensemble unaltered.

We can now picture the entire volume of the ensemble broken up into these small volume elements and consider the number of particles in each. But the knowledge of the number of particles in each such element of volume is not enough to give us the microscopic state of the ensemble. We must also know in what manner the particles in each volume element are moving. To see what this means, we single out a given element of volume, which, though small, contains many particles moving with various velocities. We now separate these particles into groups such that all the particles in a given group have the same velocities (the same speed in the same direction). Here again we must introduce an arbitrary feature, because it is impossible to group particles with precisely the same velocities. We must consider a particular velocity and then assign all particles to the same group if they have velocities close enough to the chosen velocity. The arbitrariness arises because the expression "close enough" is not precisely defined. All that can be said about this in classical physics is that no appreciable change in the state of the system is said to occur if a particle changes its velocity by an amount which keeps it within the range of velocity defined as "close enough."

We have now laid the basis for defining the microscopic state of an ensemble, at least classically. Consider all the particles of our ensemble—let us say N in number—and suppose that at a certain moment we distribute them so that a definite number—let us say N_1—lie in a given volume element and have velocities lying in the neighborhood of some given velocity, and another group—say N_2—lies in another element volume with velocities lying close to some other velocity, and so on, until we have exhausted all N molecules. Notice that in doing this we differentiate between two groups if either the volume element, or the velocity value (or both) differs for the two groups.

A distribution of the N particles of our ensemble into the subgroups N_1, N_2, and so on, defines the microscopic state of the system. But this same microscopic state has a corresponding macroscopic state, that is, a description in terms of pressure, volume, and temperature. What alterations in the distribution of particles can change either or both of these pictures? We first note that there are many more ways of changing the microscopic than the macroscopic state. The macroscopic state is affected only if we change the number of particles within groups. For example, the macroscopic state is changed if the number of particles in N_1 is decreased or increased (which implies an increase or loss in one or more of the other groups of particles, since the total number of gas molecules in the system is conserved). But the microscopic state is altered if we merely interchange particles between groups, neither adding to nor subtracting from the numbers within the groups. In other words, if a particle from one group is interchanged with a particle from another, the macroscopic state is unaffected; the microscopic state, on the other hand, does change, even though this change is not measurable in terms of the volume, pressure, and temperature of the gas.

A simple numerical example should illustrate this. Suppose our ensemble consists of ten molecules of a gas distributed in five groups. A possible macroscopic state might be defined by the distribution of these particles into groups of 3, 1, 3, 1, and 2 particles. Another macroscopic state would be given by the groups 1, 3, 0, 4, 2, another by 1, 1, 1, 1, 6, and so on, until the various combinations of ten particles arranged in five groups are exhausted.

Now, corresponding to the macroscopic state that consists of the groups 3, 1, 3, 1, and 2 of particles, there are many related states at the microscopic level, because of the numerous ways of assigning the ten molecules to places within these groups. We may choose any of the ten molecules to occupy position one in the first group. After filling this first opening, we have nine remaining particles from which to assign position two. Similarly, after this choice is made, we are left with eight particles from which to assign the third and final position in this group. Altogether, in assigning particles to this first group with its three places, we have had $10 \times 9 \times 8$ possible orders of selection. Not all of these denote different microscopic states, because we may discount the order in which we arrange particles within a group. Since interchanging particles within a group has no effect even on the microscopic state, we divide the product $10 \times 9 \times 8$ by the possible combinations of arranging the three particles among themselves within this group, in this case $3 \times 2 \times 1$, or 6. We thus arrive at the number of microscopic states arising from the assignment of particles to the first group: $\frac{10 \times 9 \times 8}{3 \times 2 \times 1}$. We now carry out the same calculations for the remaining groups 1, 3, 1 and 2, and get a similar product for each of them. In carrying out this procedure for each remaining group, we must, in each instance, subtract from the total number of particles the number we have already arranged in groups, since these are no longer available for forming others. Thus, in the example being considered, only seven particles are left to form the remaining groups because three have been used for the first group.

From this we see that the total number of microscopic states corresponding to the first macroscopic state is the product of all of these choices or

$$\frac{10 \times 9 \times 8}{3 \times 2 \times 1} \times \frac{7}{1} \times \frac{6 \times 5 \times 4}{3 \times 2 \times 1} \times \frac{3}{1} \times \frac{2 \times 1}{2 \times 1}$$

We may write this as

$$\frac{10 \times 9 \times 8 \times 7 \times 6 \times 5 \times 4 \times 3 \times 2 \times 1}{(3 \times 2 \times 1)(1)(3 \times 2 \times 1)(1)(2 \times 1)}$$

It is convenient to introduce a shorthand notation here. The product of successively decreasing numbers like $4 \times 3 \times 2 \times 1$ is written as 4! and in general $N(N-1)(N-2) \ldots$ is written as N! Thus the number of ways we can distribute the N particles of an ensemble so that there are N_1 particles in the first group, N_2 in the second, N_3 in the third, and so on, until all N particles have been exhausted is

$$\frac{N!}{N_1! \, N_2! \, N_3! \, \ldots}$$

This, then, is the number of microscopic states that correspond to the macroscopic state given by the distribution $N_1, N_2, N_3. \ldots$

How does one use this combinatorial procedure in the analysis of the ensemble? In other words, how can this approach lead to the laws that govern the ensemble? We note, first, that the more microscopic states there are that give a particular macroscopic state, the greater is the chance for that macroscopic state to occur. That is, the probability for finding our ensemble in a particular macroscopic state is proportional to the expression we wrote above for the number of microscopic states that correspond to the given macroscopic state. Second, we note that if the ensemble is left to itself, it will ultimately reach that particular macroscopic state with the maximum probability of occurrence. Put differently, the populations N_1, N_2, N_3 of the various groups will ultimately be such that the expression

$$\frac{N!}{N_1! \, N_2! \, N_3! \, \ldots}$$

is a maximum.

We now see how to go about solving our problem. We examine all possible values of the group populations $N_1, N_2, N_3 \ldots$ and find that particular set for which the expression for the number of microscopic states is a maximum. This, then, gives us the distribution law for the group populations, that is, the N_1, N_2, and so on, and from these the macroscopic properties of the ensemble can be derived. In doing this, we must observe two conditions: First, in considering all possible group populations we must make sure that the sum of the group populations is always equal to N, the total number of particles. Clearly, in playing this combinatorial game, we must abide by the rule that the total number of particles is a constant; particles can neither be created nor destroyed. Second, we must impose the restriction that the total energy of our ensemble must remain constant. In other words, if we add the energies of all the particles in all the groups, no matter how we vary the composition of the groups, the answer must always be the same. Any microscopic state for which this is not true (that is, any set of group populations for which this does not hold) must not be considered in seeking the maximum probability.

With this understood, one can apply well-known mathematical techniques for finding the maximum probability, or the most probable macroscopic state, and this leads to what is known as the Boltzmann statistics, or the Boltzmann distribution. When we apply this procedure to a gas, we obtain the Maxwell-Boltzmann distribution of velocities, discussed in our commentary on Maxwell. This, in turn, leads to the equation of state of a perfect gas—the law of Charles and Gay-Lussac.

Since the entire discussion above is based on classical physics, we must re-examine the concepts of the macroscopic and microscopic states of a system in the light of the quantum laws. These laws introduce two very important changes in our outlook. To begin with, the arbitrariness associated with choosing an element of volume and the values of the velocity near a given velocity is removed. This follows from the uncertainty principle (see commentary on Heisenberg, Chapter 66), which says that the product of the position and the momentum of a particle cannot be known with an accuracy greater than a value related to Planck's constant of action. This means that we may not make the volume elements of our ensemble, multiplied by the momenta of the particles, smaller than this value.

The second modification introduced by the quantum theory is related to the identity of the particles in our ensemble. One of the basic tenets of quantum mechanics is that we must not introduce into our theory any concept that cannot be verified experimentally. Consider now, in the light of this statement, a system of identical particles. Since there is no observational way of distinguishing one particle from another, we must not differentiate in our theory between two microscopic states that differ simply by the interchange of two particles, since there is no way, in practice, of telling the difference between such distributions. We now see that this alters the relationship between microscopic and macroscopic states introduced in our discussion of the Boltzmann statistics. We saw that for a given distribution of our N particles into groups N_1, N_2, and so on, which defines a macroscopic state, there are as many microscopic states as there are ways of interchanging particles among the groups. But this is not true in quantum statistics. All of these microscopic states are identical, so that there is just one microscopic state associated with the given macroscopic state. In fact, a microscopic state in the quantum theory coincides with the classical macroscopic state.

But if this is, indeed, the case, how are we to calculate the most probable macroscopic state? It appears from what we have just stated that all macroscopic states are equally probable, since just one microscopic state is associated with each of them. How, then, are we to proceed? We must alter our definition of a macroscopic state in such a way that we obtain macroscopic states of different probability. The easiest way to do this is to arrange the particles into groups according to the energies of the particles. Thus, suppose that N_1 is the number of particles in our ensemble, regardless of where in the ensemble they may be, with energies ranging from 0 to a certain small value, and suppose that N_2 is the number of particles with energies lying between this small value and twice this value, N_3 is the number with energies between twice and three times this value, and so on. We see that such a grouping, which we now define as a macroscopic state, consists of many of our previously defined macroscopic states and hence many quantum-mechanical microscopic states.

To calculate the most probable distribution now we must do one more thing. The way in which we have grouped the particles of our ensemble still does not describe the state of the ensemble completely, for in quantum mechanics there are discrete energy levels. Thus, in assigning N_1 particles to the energy range from 0 to some small value, we must take into account the presence within this energy range of a certain number, let us say Z_1, of energy levels. Any two distributions of the N_1 particles among these Z_1 levels must be treated as distinct microscopic states in the quantum sense if they differ in the actual numbers of particles assigned to the different Z_1 levels. In other words, two distributions of the N_1 particles among the Z_1 energy levels are to be counted as one if they differ only by an interchange of particles, with the numbers remaining the same.

Thus the difference between classical and quantum statistics lies in the definition of microscopic states: classically these states are defined without taking into account the identity of the particles; the quantum definition takes identity into account. Bose was the first physicist to consider this difference and to set up what we now call the Bose-Einstein statistics. He used this to derive Planck's formula for black-body radiation without reference to any classical ideas or the introduction of oscillators in equilibrium with the radiation. He simply pictured an ensemble of photons of all frequencies in a state of equilibrium at a given temperature T and then determined the most probable distribution of these photons among all energy states—that is, the number of photons of each frequency—by using the combinatorial analysis outlined above, in which the exact identity of all photons is taken into account.

When Bose did this in 1924 and communicated his paper to Einstein, who translated it into German and submitted it to the *Zeitschrift für Physik*, quantum mechanics had not yet been invented, and the only justification for what Bose did lay in the correctness of his results. Even without quantum mechanics Einstein saw at once the importance of Bose's work; indeed, as he remarked in the translator's note at the end of the

Bose paper, he was, himself, at that very time, applying the Bose-type statistics to a gas of molecules. The importance of Einstein's work is that it shows clearly that the Bose-Einstein statistics is not limited to photons but can be applied to material particles (molecules) as well, and leads to a distribution different from the Maxwell-Boltzmann distribution, and hence to a different equation of state for a perfect gas. Boyle's law does not hold for such a gas and the departure from Boyle's law becomes greater and greater as the temperature decreases.

Shortly after Bose did his work, Fermi presented another type of quantum statistics, which we discuss in some detail in our commentary on Fermi (Chapter 75). However, it is worth noting here the distinction between Fermi's and Bose's statistics. Although both of these statistics start from the assumption that, because of the identity of the particles, no distinction must be made between two group distributions of the particles that differ only in an interchange of two particles, they differ from one another in counting the number of microscopic states that must be assigned to a macroscopic state. The difference arises for the following reason: In the Bose statistics no restriction is placed on the number of particles that can be in a given group, that is, be in approximately the same position and have the same momentum (the same velocity in magnitude and direction). In other words, the numbers N_1, N_2, N_3, and so on, in the Bose statistics are not restricted. This is not the case in the Fermi statistics, for Fermi assumed that his particles obeyed the Pauli exclusion principle (see commentary on Pauli in Chapter 59). He therefore introduced the restriction that no two particles can occupy approximately the same position and have the same momentum. This leads to Fermi's statistics, later discovered independently by Dirac, and now known as the Fermi-Dirac statistics.

The difference between the way microscopic states are counted in the Boltzmann, Bose, and Fermi statistics can best be illustrated by a simple example. Suppose we have two identical particles that must be distributed among three energy levels, which we may represent as three boxes, shown as square brackets in Table 61–1. Since, in the Boltzmann statistics, each particle is considered as a distinct individual, we label the two particles a and b. However, in the Bose and in the Fermi counting of states we label each particle a since they are not to be distinguished. Let us first distribute the particles among the three energy levels, on the basis of the numerical possibilities for these levels. We would then have the following distributions: (2,0,0), (0,2,0), (0,0,2), (0,1,1), (1,0,1) and (1,1,0). Each of these groupings corresponds to a macroscopic state according to the Boltzmann reckoning. We must now see how the microscopic states are to be counted. This is shown in Table 61–1.

We see from the table that while there are nine microscopic states in the Boltzmann statistics, there are just six in the Bose and three in the Fermi statistics. Thus there are two microscopic states in the Boltzmann statistics for the grouping (0,1,1) but only one for the Bose statistics and only one for the Fermi statistics. There is no microscopic state at all in the Fermi case for the first three groups since they have two identical particles in the same energy box and that is forbidden by the Pauli principle.

TABLE   61–1

Macroscopic grouping	Boltzmann			Bose-Einstein			Fermi-Dirac		
[2,0,0]	[ab]	[ ]	[ ]	[aa]	[ ]	[ ]	—		
[0,2,0]	[ ]	[ab]	[ ]	[ ]	[aa]	[ ]	—		
[0,0,2]	[ ]	[ ]	[ab]	[ ]	[ ]	[aa]	—		
[0,1,1]	[ ] [ ]	[a] [b]	[b] [a]	[ ]	[a]	[a]	[ ]	[a]	[a]
[1,0,1]	[a] [b]	[ ] [ ]	[b] [a]	[a]	[ ]	[a]	[a]	[ ]	[a]
[1,1,0]	[a] [b]	[b] [a]	[ ] [ ]	[a]	[a]	[ ]	[a]	[a]	[ ]

To complete this discussion, we must give some criterion for distinguishing between particles that obey the Bose statistics and those that obey the Fermi statistics. From what we have said above, we see that this is the same as distinguishing between particles that are governed by the Pauli exclusion principle and those that are not. The general rule is this: Particles such as electrons, protons, neutrons, neutrinos, and so on, which have a half unit of spin, obey the Pauli principle and hence are governed by the Fermi-Dirac statistics. Particles that have zero spin, such as α particles, or an integral number of spin units, are not governed by the Pauli principle and hence obey the Bose statistics.

One other criterion can be used, based upon "wave mechanics," the subject of Part XII. The state of an ensemble of particles is given by a particular wave function. Those particles for which the wave function is antisymmetric (that is, its sign changes when any two particles are interchanged) are governed by the Pauli principle. Those particles for which the wave function is symmetric (with no change of sign when two particles are interchanged) obey the Bose statistics. Thus the two different kinds of quantum statistics are a direct consequence of the wave nature of particles and the laws of quantum mechanics. See Pauli's Nobel address in Chapter 59.

Although the great schools of physics, during the first two and a half decades of this century, grew up around the dominant European physicists, such as Bohr, Born, and Fermi, and most of the contributions to physics in this period came from the disciples of these schools, a number of important discoveries were made by men who were outside the mainstream of events and, in a sense, were self-taught. This was true of the physicists of India, who, although to some extent under the influence of British physics, developed an excellent school of their own. This was primarily owing to the work of such men as Raman, M. N. Saha, who derived the equations of thermal ionization, and S. N. Bose, who developed one branch of quantum statistics.

Bose was born in 1894 and studied physics at Calcutta University, where he received his M.Sc. degree just at the time when the Bohr theory of the atom was enjoying its greatest triumphs and European physicists were busily applying this theory to all phases of atomic dynamics. It was partly because of this feverish concern with the consequences of the Bohr theory, particularly in its relation to spectroscopy, that a physicist like Bose, rather than one of the Europeans, discovered the relationship between quantum theory and statistical mechanics.

Bose was well acquainted with European scientific literature and in 1924, arriving in Germany, fortunately came under the influence of Einstein, who was concerned predominantly with the general concepts of physics rather than with the specific consequences of the Bohr theory. Einstein was one of the few physicists who, early in the development of the quantum theory, insisted on the importance of applying quantum principles to all branches of physics, and not just to phenomena involving the emission and absorption of radiation. It is curious that Einstein, at the first Solvay Conference of Physics in 1911, stood alone in his insistence on the reality of the photon as a particle; at that time Planck himself, the founder of the quantum theory, was reluctant to accept this particulate consequence. Einstein had already applied quantum ideas to the vibrations of atoms in crystals and had thereby cleared up the difficulty associated with the specific heats of solids; he thus had ample evidence of the power of quantum concepts.

When Bose came to Germany, Einstein was greatly interested in obtaining as general a derivation of the Planck black-body radiation formula as possible, and as free of classical ideas. He had already taken a big step in that direction in his 1917 paper, in which he had used only the Bohr concepts of discrete states and the emission and absorption of photons to derive this formula. Since, in both Einstein's 1917 paper and in his work on specific heats, the approach is a statistical one, he undoubtedly was convinced that all of statistical mechanics should be reformulated in terms of quantum ideas.

In addition to the stimulation derived from his contacts with Einstein, three other developments influenced Bose. First was the discovery of the third law of thermodynamics by Nernst, which states that the entropy of a system goes to zero when the absolute temperature goes to zero. Nernst showed that this entropy principle is a direct consequence of the application of quantum theory to thermodynamics. The second was Stern's derivation of the expression for the entropy of a gas, again using quantum principles. The third was Planck's suggestion, in 1921, that the size of a cell in phase space—a fictitious six-dimensional space (constructed by combining the three dimensions of ordinary space and the three components of momentum), which plays an important role in statistical mechanics—must be placed equal to the cube of Planck's constant. This was one of the decisive points in Bose's derivation of his quantum statistics.

It is interesting that Bose derived his quantum statistics just when De Broglie was discovering the wave properties of particles. Since one can show that the Bose quantum statistics can be derived as a consequence of the wave nature of particles, it may well be that Bose would have discovered electron waves had not De Broglie done so first.

From 1924 to 1927 Bose was reader in physics at Dacca University. He then became professor and head of the physics department and remained at Dacca until 1946. He was then appointed Khaira professor of physics at Calcutta University and held this position until 1956. In addition to his academic posts, he was chairman of the National Institute of Science of India from 1948 to 1950. In 1958 he was elected a fellow of the Royal Society of London, and was also appointed professor and vice-chancellor of Visva-Bharati University.

ooooooo

B O S E

Planck's Law and Light Quantum Hypothesis [1]

PLANCK'S FORMULA FOR THE DISTRIBUTION of energy in the radiation from a black body was the starting point of the quantum theory, which has been developed during the last 20 years and

---

[1] S. N. Bose, trans. into German, A. Einstein; trans. from German, Eds., *Zeitschrift für Physik,* 26 (1924).

has borne a wealth of fruit in every domain of physics. Since its publication in 1901 many methods for deriving this law have been proposed. It is recognized that the basic assumptions of the quantum theory are irreconcilable with the laws of classical electrodynamics. All derivations up to now use the relation

$$\rho_\nu d\nu = \frac{8\pi\nu^2 d\nu}{c^3}\, E,$$

that is, the relation between the radiation density and the mean energy of an oscillator, and they make assumptions about the number of degrees of freedom of the ether, which appear in the above formula (the first factor on the right-hand side). This factor, however, can be derived only from classical theory. This is the unsatisfactory feature in all derivations and it is therefore no wonder that attempts are being made to obtain a derivation that is free of this logical flaw.

Einstein has given a remarkably elegant derivation. He recognized the logical defect of all previous derivations and tried to deduce the formula independently of classical theory. From very simple assumptions about the energy exchange between molecules and a radiation field he found the relation

$$\rho_\nu = \frac{\alpha_{mn}}{e^{\frac{\epsilon_m - \epsilon_n}{kT}} - 1}.$$

To make this formula agree with Planck's he had to use Wien's displacement law and Bohr's correspondence principle. Wien's law is based on classical theory and the correspondence principle assumes that the quantum theory and the classical theory coincide in certain limits.

In all cases it appears to me that the derivations have not been sufficiently justified from a logical point of view. As opposed to these the light quantum hypothesis combined with statistical mechanics (as it was formulated to meet the needs of the quantum theory) appears sufficient for the derivation of the law independent of classical theory. In the following I shall sketch the method briefly.

Let the radiation be enclosed in the volume V and let its total energy be E. Let various types of quanta be present of abundances N_s and energy $h\nu_s$ ($s = 0$ to $s = \infty$). The total energy is then

$$E = \sum_s N_s h\nu_s = V \int \rho_\nu \, d\nu. \tag{1}$$

The solution of the problem therefore requires the determination of the N_s, which, in turn, determine ρ_ν. If we can give the probability for each distribution characterized by arbitrary values of N_s, then the solution is given by the condition that this probability is to be a maximum, keeping in mind the condition (1) which is a constraint on the problem. We now seek this probability.

The quantum has the momentum $\dfrac{h\nu_s}{c}$ in the direction of its motion. The momentary state of the quantum is characterized by its coordinates x, y, z and the corresponding components of the momentum p_x, p_y, p_z. These six quantities can be considered as point coordinates in a six-dimensional space, where we have the relation

$$p_x^2 + p_y^2 + p_z^2 = \frac{h^2 \nu^2}{c^2},$$

in virtue of which the point representing the quantum in our six-dimensional space is forced to lie on a cylindrical surface determined by the frequency. To the frequency range $d\nu_s$ there belongs in this sense the phase space

$$\int dx\, dy\, dz\, dp_x\, dp_y\, dp_z = V \cdot 4\pi (h\nu/c)^2\, h d\nu/c$$
$$= 4\pi \cdot h^3\nu^3/c^3 \cdot V\, d\nu$$

If we divide the total phase volume into cells of size h^3, there are then $4\pi V \cdot \nu^2/c^3 \cdot d\nu$ cells in the frequency range $d\nu$. Nothing definite can be said about the method of dividing the phase space in this manner. However, the total number of cells must be considered as equal to the number of possible ways of placing a quantum in this volume. To take into account polarization it appears necessary to multiply this number by 2 so that we obtain $8\pi V\, \nu^2 d\nu/c^3$ as the number of cells belonging to $d\nu$.

It is now easy to calculate the thermodynamic probability of a (macroscopically defined) state. Let N^s be the number of quanta belonging to the frequency range $d\nu^s$. In how many ways can these be distributed among the cells that belong to $d\nu^s$? Let p_0^s be the number of empty cells, p_1^s the number containing 1 quantum, p_2^s the number containing 2 quanta, and so on. The number of possible distributions is then

$$\frac{A^s!}{p_0^s!\, p_1^s! \, \cdots} \qquad \text{where } A^s = \frac{8\pi\nu^2}{c^3} V d\nu^s$$

and where

$$N^s = 0 \cdot p_0^s + 1 \cdot p_1^s + 2p_2^s + \cdots$$

is the number of quanta belonging to $d\nu^s$.

The probability W of the state defined by all p_r^s is clearly

$$\Pi_s \frac{A^s!}{p_0^s! \, p_1^s! \, \cdots}$$

Taking into account that the p_r^s are large numbers we have

$$\log W = \sum_s A^s \log A^s - \sum_s \sum_r p_r^s \log p_r^s$$

where

$$A^s = \sum_r p_r^s.$$

This expression must be a maximum under the constraints

$$E = \sum_s N^s h \nu^s; \quad N^s = \sum_r r p_r^s.$$

Carrying through the variations we obtain the conditions

$$\sum_s \sum_r \delta \, p_r^s (1 + \log p_r^s) = 0, \quad \sum \delta \, N^s h \nu^s = 0$$

$$\sum_r \delta \, p_r^s = 0 \qquad\qquad\qquad \delta N^s = \sum_r r \delta p_r^s.$$

From this we obtain

$$\sum_r \sum_s \delta \, p_r^s (1 + \log p_r^s + \lambda^s) + \frac{1}{\beta} \sum_s r \delta p_r^s = 0.$$

From this we first see that

$$p_r^s = B^s e^{-\frac{r h \nu^s}{\beta}}.$$

Since, however,

$$A^s = \sum_r B^s e^{-\frac{r h \nu^s}{\beta}} = B^s \left(1 - e^{-\frac{h \nu^s}{\beta}}\right)^{-1}$$

then

$$B^s = A^s \left(1 - e^{-\frac{h \nu^s}{\beta}}\right).$$

We further have

$$N^s = \sum_r r\, p_r^s = \sum_r r A^s \left(1 - e^{-\frac{h\nu s}{\beta}}\right) e^{-\frac{r h \nu s}{\beta}}$$

$$= \frac{A^s e^{-\frac{h\nu s}{\beta}}}{1 - e^{-\frac{h\nu s}{\beta}}}.$$

Taking into account the value of A^s found above, we have

$$E = \sum_s \frac{8\pi h \nu^{s3}\, d\nu^s}{c^3}\, V\, \frac{e^{-\frac{h\nu s}{\beta}}}{1 - e^{-h\nu s/\beta}}$$

Using the result obtained previously

$$S = k \left[\frac{E}{\beta} - \sum_s A^s \log\left(1 - e^{h\nu s/\beta}\right) \right]$$

and noting that

$$\frac{\partial S}{\partial E} = \frac{1}{T}$$

we obtain

$$\beta = kT$$

Hence

$$E = \sum_s \frac{8\pi h \nu^{s3}}{c^3}\, V\, \frac{1}{e^{h\nu s/kT} - 1}\, d\nu^s$$

which is Planck's formula.

Comment of translator. Bose's derivation of Planck's formula appears to me to be an important step forward. The method used here gives also the quantum theory of an ideal gas, as I shall show elsewhere. [A. Einstein]

PART

XII

WAVE MECHANICS

ooooooooooo

THE PRINCIPLE OF
LEAST ACTION

ooooooooooo

William Rowan Hamilton
(1805-1865)

To understand how De Broglie was led to the wave theory of matter, the subject of the next chapter, we must begin by considering the behavior of light, which can be treated from two different points of view. Suppose that a beam of light is moving between two points in a homogeneous medium, a medium in which the index of refraction, and therefore the speed of light, are constant. The light then travels in a straight line between the two points. This fact, borne out by experiment, was the starting point of an important principle developed by the famous seventeenth-century French mathematician Fermat; it describes the propagation of a beam of light when the index of refraction of the medium is *not* constant. If the light is traveling in an inhomogeneous medium, its speed changes from point to point because of the variation of the index of refraction. In general, it does not travel in a straight line.

Fermat described the motion of the light correctly by introducing the principle that light always travels between any two points in the shortest possible time. In other words, if we consider all the possible paths in the medium connecting the two points, the light chooses that particular path along which it has to spend the least time. This is called Fermat's principle of least or minimum time and leads to what we now call geometrical optics, since it treats light as though it were composed of geometrical rays that travel along geometrical lines. The path along which the light travels may be geometrically longer than some other path connecting the two points, but the time along the chosen path is always the shortest.

1021

Fermat's principle of least time accounts for the gross behavior of light, including such phenomena as reflection and refraction (the bending of a ray of light when it passes from a rarer medium such as air to a denser medium such as glass). Thus, this principle can be used to explain the formation of images by lenses and mirrors, but it cannot explain the refined details in the behavior of light, such as interference and diffraction (the bending of light around corners). To explain these properties we must use physical optics, which takes into account the wave structure of light.

As long as we are dealing with phenomena in which the wavelength of the light is not important, geometrical optics (that is, Fermat's principle of least time) gives an adequate description of the optical events, but as soon as the wavelength of the light becomes an important factor, geometrical optics gives wrong results and physical optics must be used. This is the case when light rays pass through tiny openings or around very small bodies. Since such openings, through which the light must move, and such tiny bodies, in the paths of the rays, are comparable in size to the wavelength of the light, the wave properties of the light play an essential role in the phenomena. We may state this differently by saying that the laws of geometrical optics approach those of physical optics when the wavelength of the light approaches zero or when it is very small. Thus, geometrical optics, in general, gives a much better description of ordinary light than it does of radio waves.

There is another important distinction between these two points of view that has a bearing on the corpuscular theory of light and on the trajectories of particles. Since the Newtonian corpuscles must also be described in terms of well-defined trajectories, and since well-defined ray trajectories are the hallmark of geometrical optics, it follows that geometrical optics is really a corpuscular theory of light, whereas physical optics is a wave theory. As the wavelength of the light gets smaller and smaller, the corpuscular theory becomes more and more applicable, but the wave theory becomes more and more important as the wavelength of light gets larger. This at once suggests an important analogy between the behavior of light of very short wavelength and the behavior of ordinary particles of matter, such as atoms, molecules, and electrons, for we know, according to Newton's laws of motion, that such particles, at least in classical physics, travel along geometrical trajectories. This analogy between geometrical optics and the trajectories of particles of matter is further strengthened when we consider that the classical laws of mechanics can also be formulated in terms of a minimum principle (referred to as a stationary or variational principle by physicists) similar, in its mathematical form, to Fermat's principle.

The great Irish mathematician and astronomer Sir William Rowan

Hamilton was the first to recognize the importance of such a formulation of the laws of mechanics; he developed the necessary mathematical scheme for handling problems in Newtonian mechanics in a manner similar to that of geometrical optics. To do this he first redeveloped the laws of geometrical optics, starting from Fermat's principle, and thus showed that the path of light rays can be computed from a single mathematical quantity, the *characteristic function,* whose properties are quite similar to those of the action function that had been used for a long time to study the dynamics of a particle. In this formulation of geometrical optics, with the emphasis on the trajectories of the rays, one sees the parallel to mechanics.

This similarity between the ray trajectories of geometrical optics and the Newtonian paths of particles suggested to Hamilton that it should be possible to express the laws of mechanics in a mathematical form closely resembling that of geometrical optics. He was further encouraged in this project by his knowledge that the Newtonian laws of motion of a particle can be derived from a minimum principle similar to Fermat's principle.

As Hamilton saw it, one merely had to start from this minimum principle in mechanics and transform it in such a way that it resembled the Fermat principle as closely as possible; the analogy between mechanics and optics would then be complete, at least as far as the formal aspects of these two branches of physics go. Hamilton therefore started from the principle of least action that was discovered and introduced into mechanics by Maupertuis. This principle states that a particle or any system of particles in a force field, for example, a gravitational field, moves between any two points in such a way that the total action of the system taken along its path between the two points is a minimum.

To understand this more fully we consider the momentum of a particle —its velocity multiplied by its mass. As the particle moves along its path under the action of the force, its momentum changes continuously. Now consider the particle for a very short time interval during which its momentum does not change appreciably. We can always make the time interval short enough for this to be true. During this interval the particle describes a small section of its path. If we multiply the length of this "element of path" by the momentum, we obtain what Maupertuis called the "element of action." We can now formulate Maupertuis' principle of least action by stating that of all possible paths a particle can take in going from some point A to another point B, the path that it actually takes is the one for which the sum of all the "elements of action" along the path is minimal.

But this statement is not a correct description of the behavior of a mechanical system at all times, although Maupertuis was so convinced of its universal validity that he considered it to manifest divine efficiency in the guidance of the world: [1]

> Here then is this principle, so wise, so worthy of the Supreme Being: Whenever any change takes place in Nature, the amount of action expended in this change is always the smallest possible.

Hamilton started from Maupertuis' principle, in his great work on dynamics, and generalized it into what is called the principle of stationary action: the path chosen by a particle or a system of particles in going from one point to another is such that the action, measured along any path that differs only infinitesimally from the actual path, does not differ from the action measured along the actual path. This means that the action is "stationary" in terms of its near neighbors: either a maximum or a minimum, but not necessarily the minimum imposed by Maupertuis.

Hamilton states this as follows in the paper that follows this commentary:

> In mathematical language, the integral called action, instead of being always a minimum, is often a maximum; and often it is neither one nor the other; though it has always a certain *stationary* property. . . . We cannot therefore suppose the economy of this quantity to have been designed in the divine idea of the universe; though a simplicity of some kind may be believed to be included in that idea. And though we may retain the name of *action* to denote the stationary integral to which it has become appropriate—which we may do without adopting either the metaphysical or (in optics) the physical opinions that first suggested the name—yet we ought not (I think) to retain the epithet *least:* but rather to adopt the alteration proposed above, and to speak, in mechanics and in optics, of the *Law of Stationary Action.*

Hamilton did not introduce the action directly, but rather used a related quantity called the "Lagrangian" of the system, or the kinetic-potential. This quantity is obtained by subtracting the potential energy from the kinetic energy of the system, for example, of a particle, at each point, along its path. If we now observe a particle for a very short time interval and multiply this interval by the momentary value of the particle's kinetic energy minus its potential energy, we obtain the element of Hamiltonian action, which is related to, but not always the same as, the element of action defined by Maupertuis. The Hamiltonian action can be obtained from the Maupertuis action by subtracting from the latter the total energy (the sum of the kinetic and the potential energies) multiplied by the small time interval during which we are observing the system.

---

[1] Pierre Louis Moreau de Maupertuis, W. Yourgrou, and S. Mandelstam, *Variational Principles* (New York: Pitman Pub., 1960).

Restating the Hamilton principle of action:

If a particle is allowed to move from some point A to another point B in a field of force, and if the mechanical energy of the particle is always conserved, or remains constant, then the path actually followed by the particle is the one for which its total action is stationary. Let us suppose that we consider a large number of possible paths connecting points A and B, and that we compute the total Hamiltonian action along each one of these paths. If these paths do not differ very much from one another, all the Hamiltonian actions lie close to the same value, but we find that there is one path among the many for which there is practically no change in action as we go to a very nearby path on either side of it. This path is then called the stationary path.

By using this principle of least or stationary action, Hamilton was able to express the Newtonian dynamical equations in a form appropriate, not only for describing the motions of a particle or a collection of individual particles, but also for the description of the motion of rigid bodies. To see how Hamilton did this we may note that if we want to describe in complete detail the motion of a system of particles rigidly connected to each other, it is not necessary to consider the position and the motion of each particle in the system separately. Since they are all connected, it is evident that the complete description of the system can be given by introducing six quantities (six generalized coordinates) which we may consider as giving the "position" of the system and the six "velocities" associated with these generalized coordinates. This procedure of working with generalized coordinates was first introduced by Lagrange. Hamilton took over the Lagrangian idea of generalized coordinates and in addition introduced generalized momenta corresponding to these coordinates. These momenta can be obtained from the Lagrangian, that is, the kinetic-potential, by introducing the generalized coordinates and the generalized velocities and then differentiating the Lagrangian with respect to each of the generalized velocities in turn.

By using generalized coordinates and generalized momenta Hamilton was able to transform the Newtonian equations of motion for any complex system into a set of simple and symmetrical equations—one set for each pair of generalized coordinates and momenta. A still greater simplification was achieved by Jacobi, who was able to show that one could replace the system of Hamilton's equations by a single partial differential equation for a single mathematical quantity, the total action of the system. The knowledge of this function enables one to determine completely the trajectory of the particle and thus to solve the dynamical problem. This procedure is closely analogous to the treatment of geometrical optics by Hamilton who derived the paths of rays by solving an equation, similar to the one introduced by Jacobi, for a single optical quantity called the characteristic function. According to this point of view the dynamical problem may be solved by considering the motion of a system as though it were a gradual unfolding of a series of states, each one derived from the preceding one by an infinitesimal transformation similar to what we have when a ray of light advances from one wave front to the next.

From considerations of the similarity between the principle of Fermat for geometrical optics and the Maupertuis principle of least action for dynamical systems, Hamilton was thus led to the idea that the behavior of particles might be described by a kind of wave mechanics. He showed that the trajectories of particles having the same total amount of energy are identical with the paths of rays of light in a medium having the proper index of refraction. In other words, it is possible, according to Hamilton, to find an index of refraction such that the trajectory of any particle can be described by the path of some ray of light in a medium having the given index of refraction. Since, however, rays are only an approximation (which becomes more accurate as the wavelength gets smaller) to the correct wave description of light, it follows that the Newtonian trajectories are only an approximation to a wave description of the motion of particles. Just as in optics, the rays of light are orthogonal to the wave fronts (which are surfaces of equal phase), so in mechanics the trajectories of particles are orthogonal to another kind of wave front (the surfaces of equal action). In other words, in particle wave mechanics the action would play the role of the phase in optics. This Hamiltonian formalism is just what was needed to go from the classical mechanics of a particle to the quantum and wave mechanics; it was taken over bodily by Schroedinger.

We may now summarize Hamilton's great contribution to classical dynamics: Suppose we have a particle that is moving in a force field. We may now, in accordance with Hamilton's procedure, describe the path of the particle as though the particle were a ray of light moving through an optical medium having an index of refraction that is related in a definite way to the force field through which the particle is moving. One may therefore surmise from this (which Hamilton did not, but which Schroedinger did) that just as ray optics, that is, geometrical optics, gives only an approximate description of light, so classical dynamics gives only an approximate description of the motion of a particle. And just as ray optics has its wave-optical supplement, so particle dynamics has its wave-dynamical aspect.

It is not often that a great mathematician leaves his abstract world to contribute to another field, as Hamilton did. Mathematics is so vast, and one problem leads so naturally to another, that the mathematician often works quite unaware of the mathematical needs of other disciplines.

But every now and then this does happen, and the results are quite remarkable, for it seems that only the very greatest minds can create important mathematics at the same time as they master enough of another field, like physics, to do creative work there also. Thus in this select group we have men like Lagrange, Laplace, Bernoulli, Gauss; more recently, Hilbert, Von Neumann, and Weyl. Near the very top of the first group is Sir William Rowan Hamilton, who reshaped Newtonian mechanics into a mathematical form from which its extension to quantum mechanics is a very simple and natural step. This was just one of the many domains of physics to which Hamilton contributed. One volume of his collected works, consisting of 460 pages, deals only with his work in geometrical optics, so that we have here, indeed, one of the mathematical giants of the world of physics.

Hamilton was born in August 1805 in Dublin, and displayed his precocity and unusual powers at a very early age. His father therefore decided to let his brother, the Reverend James Hamilton, a member of the Royal Irish Academy, direct young William's education. From the age of three until Hamilton entered Trinity College in 1823, his uncle carefully nurtured the youngster and introduced him to the subjects that were calculated to stimulate his intellectual powers to their fullest capacity.

At the age of thirteen, five years before entering college, Hamilton had already begun to think very deeply about optics, and at the age of seventeen he began to write on this subject. While carrying on his first-year college studies, at the age of nineteen, he completed his first paper, "On Caustics" (a branch of geometrical optics) which he submitted for publication to the Royal Irish Academy.

The committee to whom the paper was referred did not quite know what to do with it, for it was in such an abstract mathematical form that they did not really understand it. They therefore asked that Hamilton explain his presentation more fully.

Hamilton accepted this advice. While still an undergraduate, he completed the project and presented it to the Academy in 1827 as a paper entitled "Theory of Systems of Rays." It is one of the great classics in theoretical physics and has remained the basis of most treatises on geometrical optics. Moreover, it contains the germ of the idea which was to lead Hamilton to his famous formulation of dynamics. In this paper Hamilton introduces the characteristic function of a system of rays from which all the properties of the system can be deduced by simple mathematical operations such as differentiation. The importance of this function is that it is directly related to the action integral, which plays the dominant role in Hamiltonian dynamics and which was the starting point of Schroedinger's derivations of his wave equation.

The importance of the characteristic function for optics is that it can be used as a starting point to develop either a corpuscular theory of propagation or a wave theory. In the corpuscular theory the characteristic function is related to the principle of least action. In the wave theory the characteristic function is related to the Huygens' wave front.

Hamilton surmised that the concept of the characteristic function would also be of great importance in dynamics, since dynamics can be derived from a principle of least action. He indicates this extension in his essay on the relationship between the path of light and the path of a planet, a portion of which follows this commentary.

With the publication of his paper on the theory of rays Hamilton's genius was universally recognized; his reputation was further enhanced when the phenomenon of conical refraction, which he had discovered theoretically, was observed experimentally.

When Dr. Brinkley was promoted to the Bishopric of Cloyne in 1827 the professorship of astronomy in Trinity College became vacant and Hamilton, then only twenty-one and still an undergraduate, was offered the post—perhaps the most remarkable example of foresight in the history of university administration. Hamilton accepted the chair and devoted himself not only to his researches into mathematics, mathematical physics, and astronomy, but also to the practical problems of teaching and supervising the observatory.

In 1834 Hamilton was awarded the Cunningham medal of the Royal Irish Academy and the Royal medal of the Royal Society for his discovery of conical refraction, which was then considered one of the wonders of mathematical physics and a most remarkable prediction, attesting to the great usefulness of mathematical analysis.

On the death of the president of the Irish Academy in 1837 Hamilton was elected to that position, which he held for eight years. This was one of his most fruitful periods, during which he developed his dynamical theories in a famous paper "General Methods in Dynamics." In this paper he applied the concept of the characteristic function to the motion of a system of particles in a force field and developed the equations of motion in the form now universally known as Hamilton's equations. The concept of the "Hamiltonian function," so useful today in quantum mechanics, is the basis of these equations.

The basic idea is as follows: Suppose we have a system, say a particle, moving in a field of force. We may then write down the total energy of this system (kinetic plus potential) in terms of the components of the momentum and the coordinates. This expression is called the Hamiltonian of the system and the equation describing the motion of the system can be obtained from this quantity by certain mathematical operations. The advantage of such a formulation of dynamics is that it can be applied to very complex systems by a judicious choice of coordinates.

While developing his theory of dynamics Hamilton also did extensive work in many branches of mathematics. He published papers on algebra, theory of functions, calculus of probability, theory of equations, and so on. During the last twenty-two years of his life he invented and extensively developed the calculus of quaternions, which is an extension of vector analysis.

In spite of his great skill in abstract analysis and profound intuition, Hamilton never shied away from extended and tedious calculations that he felt were necessary to prove a point. Often he would reach a result by a series of involved computations and then, having established the truth of a theorem for a special case, he would generalize it and formulate it in its most elegant mathematical form. As the Very Reverend Charles Graves, president of the Irish Academy, stated in his eulogy of Hamilton on the latter's death:

> He engaged in exercises of this kind [extensive numerical calculations] sometimes from a wish to strengthen his intellectual hold in general propositions by scrutinizing results obtained by applying them in a number of particular cases; and sometimes from a wish to mature and keep in exercise those powers of calculation upon the exactitude and prompt operation of which so much depends in difficult mathematical investigations.[2]

In spite of his deep involvement in the most abstract problems, Hamilton was very much aware of the people about him and was as much concerned with the least learned as with the most learned. He was a kind and patient man who could spend hours convincing some "half-crazed squarer of the circle that his proposed construction was inaccurate" or answering with gentle good nature the most elementary questions of students and visitors.

Hamilton was a deeply religious man and he devoted a great deal of his time to establishing a metaphysical basis for his discoveries. For example, his paper "Algebra Considered as a Science of Pure Time" was a metaphysical attempt to derive algebra from the elements of space and time and establish it as a science rather than as a branch of mathematics. He undoubtedly was attracted to the principle of least action by his predisposition to metaphysics, which he studied extensively. He considered himself a disciple of Bishop Berkeley's, and studied Berkeley's writings avidly, although he was also devoted to Kant, whose works he had mastered when he learned German. Finally, he was greatly influenced by Descartes as well as Francis Bacon and Newton. He indicated his intellectual and spiritual preferences in assigning religion to the highest place

---

[2] Charles Graves in W. R. Hamilton, *Collected Mathematical Papers* (Cambridge, Eng.: Cambridge University Press, 1931), Vol. I.

in man's activities, followed by metaphysics. Next in order was mathematics and then poetry. Finally physics and general literature.

Early in his life Hamilton began to master various languages and was soon reading the classics in the original Greek and Latin. He was generally familiar with the literature of the world, and was on friendly terms with Wordsworth, Southey, Coleridge, and others. He might, indeed, have become a great poet had science not captured him; on a few occasions he won prizes for English poetry. To him mathematics and poetry were closely related for they both expressed the essence of beauty in different forms.

Hamilton was very much of a humanist. Like John Donne he felt that "no man is an island entire in itself," but that all humanity is interrelated and every person is diminished when any single individual is.

At the time of his death in September 2, 1865, he was Andrews professor of astronomy and Astronomer Royal of Ireland, and had completed sixty volumes of carefully written manuscripts, all chronologically arranged and carefully dated, showing the day-to-day progress of his work. In addition to the unpublished manuscripts there are more than two hundred of his notebooks deposited in the Library of Trinity College, Dublin.

Hamilton was unquestionably the most outstanding man of science Ireland has produced. His equations brought the science of dynamics to the peak of its development.

ooooooo

HAMILTON

On a General Method of Expressing the Paths of Light, and of the Planets, by the Coefficients of a Characteristic Function [3]

THE LAW OF SEEING IN straight lines was known from the infancy of optics, being in a manner forced upon men's notice by the most familiar and constant experience. It could not fail to be observed that when a man looked at any object, he had it in his power to

---

[3] W. R. Hamilton, *Dublin University Review* (1833), 795–826.

interrupt his vision of that object, and hide it at pleasure from his view, by interposing his hand between his eyes and it; and that then, by withdrawing his hand, he could see the object as before: and thus the notion of straight lines or rays of communication, between a visible object and a seeing eye, must very easily and early have arisen. This notion of straight lines of vision was of course confirmed by the obvious remark that objects can usually be seen on looking through a straight but not through a bent tube; and the most familiar facts of perspective supplied, we may suppose, new confirmations and new uses of the principle. A globe, for example, from whatever point it may be viewed, appears to have a circular outline; while a plate, or a round table, seems oval when viewed obliquely: and these facts may have been explained, and reduced to mathematical reasoning, by shewing that the straight rays or lines of vision, which touch any one given globe and pass through any one given point, are arranged in a hollow cone of a perfectly circular shape; but that the straight rays, which connect an eye with the round edge of a plate or table, compose, when they are oblique, an elliptical or oval cone. The same principle, of seeing in straight lines, must have been continually employed from the earliest times in the explanation of other familiar appearances, and in interpreting the testimony of sight respecting the places of visible bodies. It was, for example, an essential element in ancient as in modern astronomy.

The shapes and sizes of shadows, again, could not fail to suggest the notion of straight illuminating rays: although opinions, now rejected, respecting the nature of light and vision, led some of the ancients to distinguish the lines of luminous from those of visual communication, and to regard the latter as a kind of feelers by which the eye became aware of the presence of visible objects. It appears, however, that many persons held, even in the infancy of optics, the modern view of the subject, and attributed vision, as well as illumination, to an influence proceeding from the visible or luminous body. But what finally established this view, and along with it the belief of a finite velocity of progress of the luminous influence, was the discovery made by Roemer, of the gradual propagation of light from objects to the eye, in the instance of the satellites of Jupiter; of which we have good reason to believe, from astronomical observation, that the eclipses are never seen by us, till more than half an hour after they have happened; the interval, besides, being found to be so much the greater, as Jupiter is more distant from the Earth. Galileo had indeed proposed terrestrial experiments to measure the velocity of light, which he believed to be finite; and Descartes, who held that the communication of light was instantaneous, had perceived that astronomical consequences ought to follow, if the propagation of light were gradual: but experiments such as Galileo proposed were not, and could not, be made on a scale sufficient for the purpose; and the state of astronomical observation in the time of Descartes did not permit him to verify the consequences which he perceived, and seemed rather to justify the use that he made of their non-verification, as an argument against the opinion with which he had shown them to be logically connected. But when astronomers had actually observed appearances, which seemed and still seem explicable only by this opinion of the gradual propagation of light from objects to the eye, the opinion itself became required, and was adopted, in the legitimate progress of induction.

By such steps, then, it has become an established theorem, fundamental in optical science, that the communication, whether between an illuminating body and a body illuminated, or between an object seen and a beholding eye, is effected by the gradual but very rapid passage of some thing, or influence, or state, called light, from the luminous or visible body, along mathematical or physical lines, called usually *rays,* and found to be, under the most common circumstances, exactly or nearly straight.

Again, it was very early perceived that in appearances connected with mirrors, flat or curved, the luminous or visual communication is effected in bent lines. When we look into a flat mirror, and seem to see an object, such as a candle, behind it, we should err if we were to extend to this new case the rules of our more familiar experience. We should not now come to touch the candle by continuing the straight line from the eye to a hand or other obstacle, so placed between the eye and the mirror as to hide the candle; this line continued would meet the mirror in a certain place from which it would be necessary to draw a new and different straight line, if we wished to reach the real or tangible candle: and the whole bent line, made up of these two straight parts, is found to be now the line of visual communication, and is to be regarded now as the linear path of the light. An opaque obstacle, placed any where on either part of this bent line, is found to hide the reflected candle from the eye; but an obstacle, placed any where else, produces no such interruption. And the law was very early discovered, that for every such bent line of luminous or visual communication, the angle between any two successive straight parts is bisected by the normal, or perpendicular, to the mirror at the point of bending.

Another early and important observation was that of the broken or refracted lines of communication, between an object in water and an eye in air, and generally between a point in one ordinary medium and a point in another. A valuable series of experiments on such refraction was made and recorded by Ptolemy; but it was not till long afterwards that the law was discovered by Snellius. He found that if two lengths, in a certain ratio or proportion determined by the natures of the two media, be measured, from the point of breaking, or of bending, on the refracted ray and on the incident ray prolonged, these lengths have one common projection on the refracting surface, or on its tangent plane. This law of ordinary refraction has since been improved by Newton's discovery of the different refrangibility of the differently coloured rays; and has been applied to explain and to calculate the apparent elevation of the stars, produced by the atmosphere of the earth.

The phenomena presented by the passage of light through crystals were not observed until more lately. Bartolinus seems to have been the first to notice the double refraction of Iceland spar; and Huygens first discovered the laws of this refraction. The more complicated double refraction produced by biaxal crystals was not observed until the present century; and the discovery of conical refraction in such crystals is still more recent, the experiments of Professor Lloyd on arragonite (undertaken at my request) having been only made last year.

For the explanation of the laws of the linear propagation of light, two principal theories have been proposed, which still divide the suffrages of scientific men.

The theory of Newton is well known. He compared the propagation of light to the motion of projectiles; and as, according to that First Law of Motion, of which he had himself established the truth by so extensive and beautiful an induction, an ordinary projectile continues in rectilinear and uniform progress, except so far as its course is retarded or disturbed by the influence of some foreign body; so, he thought, do luminous and visible objects shoot off little luminous or light-making projectiles, which then, until they are accelerated or retarded, or deflected one way or another, by the attractions or repulsions of some refraction or reflecting medium, continue to move uniformly in straight lines, either because they are not acted on at all by foreign bodies, or because the foreign actions are nearly equal on all sides, and thus destroy or neutralise each other. This theory was very generally received by mathematicians during the last century, and still has numerous supporters.

Another theory, however, proposed about the same time by another great philosopher, has appeared to derive some strong confirmations from modern inductive discoveries. This other is the theory of Huygens, who compared the gradual propagation of light, not to the motion of a projectile, but to the spreading of sound through air, or of waves through water. It was, according to him, no *thing,* in the ordinary sense, no *body,* which moved from the sun to the earth, or from a visible object to the eye; but a *state,* a *motion,* a *disturbance,* was first in one place, and afterwards in another. As, when we hear a cannon which has been fired at a distance, no bullet, no particle even of air, makes its way from the cannon to our ears; but only the aerial motion spreads, the air near the cannon is disturbed first, then that which is a little farther, and last of all the air that touches us. Or like the waves that spread and grow upon some peaceful lake, when a pebble has stirred its surface; the floating water-lilies rise and fall, but scarcely quit their place, while the enlarging wave passes on and moves them in succession. So that great ocean of ether which bathes the farthest stars is ever newly stirred, by waves that spread and grow, from every source of light, till they move and agitate the whole with their minute vibrations: yet like sounds through air, or waves on water, these multitudinous disturbances make no confusion, but freely mix and cross, while each retains its identity, and keeps the impress of its proper origin. Such is the view of Light which Huygens adopted, and which justly bears his name; because, whatever kindred thoughts occurred to others before, he first shewed clearly how this view conducted to the laws of optics, by combining it with that essential principle of the undulatory theory which was first discovered by himself, the principle of accumulated disturbance.

According to this principle, the minute vibrations of the elastic luminous ether cannot perceptibly affect our eyes, cannot produce any sensible light, unless they combine and concur in a great and, as it were, infinite multitude; and on the other hand, such combination is possible, because particular or secondary waves are supposed in this theory to spread from every vibrating particle, as from a separate centre, with a rapidity of propagation determined by the nature of the medium. And hence it comes, thought Huygens, that light in any one uniform medium diffuses itself only in straight lines, so as only to reach those parts of space to which a straight path lies open from its origin; because an opaque obstacle, obstructing such straight progress, though it does not hinder the spreading of weak particular waves into the space behind it, yet prevents their accumulation within that space into one grand general wave, of strength enough to generate light. This want of accumulation of separate vibrations behind an obstacle was elegantly proved by Huygens: the mutual destruction of such vibrations by interference is an important addition to the theory, which has been made by Young and by Fresnel. Analogous explanations have been offered for the laws of reflexion and refraction.

Whether we adopt the Newtonian or the Huygenian, or any other physical theory, for the explanation of the laws that regulate the lines of luminous or visual communication, we may regard these laws themselves, and the properties and relations of these linear paths of light, as an important separate study, and as constituting a separate science, called often *mathematical optics*. This science of the laws and relations of luminous rays is, however, itself a branch of another more general science, which may perhaps be called the *Theory of Systems of Rays*. I have published . . . a series of investigations in that theory; and have attempted to introduce a new principle and method for the study of optical systems. . . . Having been requested to resume the subject here, and to offer briefly some new illustrations of my view, I shall make some preliminary remarks on the state of deductive optics, and on the importance of a general method.

The science of optics, like every other physical science, has two different directions of progress, which have been called the ascending and the descending scale, the inductive and the deductive method, the way of analysis and of synthesis. In every physical science, we must ascend from facts to laws, by the way of induction and analysis; and must descend from laws to consequences, by the deductive and synthetic way. We must gather and group appearances, until the scientific imagination discerns their hidden law, and unity arises from variety: and then from unity must re-deduce variety, and force the discovered law to utter its revelations of the future.

It was with such convictions that Newton, when approaching to the close of his optical labours, and looking back on his own work, remarked, in the spirit of Bacon, that "As in Mathematics, so in Natural Philosophy, the investigation of difficult things by the method of Analysis ought ever to precede the method of Composition. This analysis consists in making experiments and observations, and in drawing general conclusions from them by induction, and admitting of no objections against the conclusions but such as are drawn from experiments or other certain truths." "And although the arguing from experiments and observations by induction be no demonstration of general conclusions; yet it is the best way of arguing which the nature of things admits of, and may be looked upon as so much the stronger, by how much the induction is more general. And if no exception occur from phenomena, the conclusion may be pronounced generally. But if at any time afterwards any exception shall occur from experiments, it may then begin to be pronounced with such exceptions as occur. By this way of analysis, we may proceed from compounds to ingredients, and from motions to the forces producing them; and, in general, from effects to their causes, and from particular causes to more general ones, till the argument end in the most general. This is the method of analysis: and the synthesis consists in assuming the causes discovered, and established as principles, and by them explaining the phenomena proceeding from them, and proving the explanations." "And if Natural Philosophy in all its parts, by pursuing this method, shall at length be perfected, the bounds of Moral Philosophy will also be enlarged. For, so far as we can know by Natural Philosophy, what is the First Cause, what power He has over us, and what benefits we receive from Him, so far our duty towards Him, as well as that towards one another, will appear to us by the light of nature."

In the science of optics, which has engaged the attention of almost every mathematician for the last two thousand years, many great discoveries have been attained by both these ways. It is, however, remarkable that, while the laws of this science admit of being stated in at least as purely mathematical a form as any other physical results, their mathematical consequences have been far less fully traced than the consequences of many other laws; and that while modern experiments have added so much to the *inductive* progress of optics, the *deductive* has profited so little in proportion from the power of the modern algebra.

It was known to Euclid and to Ptolemy, that the communication between visible objects and a beholding eye is usually effected in straight lines; and that when the line of communication is bent, by reflexion, at any point of a plane or of a spheric mirror, the angle of bending at this point, between the two straight parts of the bent line, is bisected by the normal to the mirror. It was known also that this law extends to successive reflexions. Optical induction was therefore sufficiently advanced two thousand years ago to have enabled a mathematician to understand, and, so far as depended on the knowledge of physical laws, to resolve the following problem: to determine the arrangement of the final straight rays, or lines of vision, along which a shifting eye should look, in order to see a given luminous point, reflected by a combination of two given spherical mirrors. Yet, of two capital deductions respecting this arrangement, without which its theory must be regarded as very far from perfect—namely, that the final rays are in general *tangents to a pair,* and that they are *perpendicular to a series* of surfaces—the one is a theorem new and little known, and the other is still under dispute. For Malus, who first discovered that the rays of an ordinary reflected or refracted system are in general tangents to a pair of caustic surfaces, was led, by the complexity of his calculations, to deny the general existence (discovered by Huygens) of surfaces perpendicular to such rays; and the objection of Malus has been lately revived by an eminent analyst of Italy, in a valuable memoir on caustics, which was published last year in the correspondence of the observatory of Brussels.

To multiply such instances of the existing imperfection of mathematical or deductive optics would be an unpleasant task, and might appear an attempt to depreciate the merit of living mathematicians. It is better to ascend to the source of the imperfection, the want of a general method, a presiding idea, to guide and assist the deduction. For although the deductive, as opposed to the inductive process, may be called itself a *method,* yet so wide and varied is its range, that it needs the guidance of some one central principle, to give it continuity and power.

Those who have meditated on the beauty and utility, in theoretical mechanics, of the general method of Lagrange—who have felt the power and dignity of that central dynamical theorem which he deduced, in the *Mécanique Analytique,* from a combination of the principle of virtual velocities with the principle of D'Alembert—and who have appreciated the simplicity and harmony which he introduced into the research of the planetary perturbations, by the idea of the variation of parameters, and the differentials of the disturbing function, must feel that mathematical optics can only *then* attain a coordinate rank with mathematical mechanics, or with dynamical astronomy, in beauty, power, and harmony, when it shall possess an appropriate method, and become the unfolding of a central idea.

This fundamental want forced itself long ago on my attention; and I have long been in possession of a method, by which it seems to me to be removed. But in thinking so, I am conscious of the danger of a bias. It may happen to me, as to others, that a meditation which has long been dwelt on shall assume an unreal importance; and that a method which has for a long time been practised shall acquire an only seeming facility. It must remain for others to judge how far my attempts have been successful, and how far they require to be completed, or set aside, in the future progress of the science.

Meanwhile it appears that if a general method in deductive optics can be attained at all, it must flow from some law or principle, itself of the highest generality, and among the highest results of induction. What, then, may we consider as the highest and most general axiom (in the Baconian sense) to which optical induction has attained, respecting the rules and conditions of the lines of visual and luminous communication? The answer, I think, must be, the principle or law, called usually the Law of Least Action; suggested by questionable views, but established on the widest induction, and embracing every known combination of media, and every straight, or bent, or curved line, ordinary or extraordinary, along which light (whatever light may be) extends its influence successively in space and time: namely, that this linear path of light, from one point to another, is always found to be such, that if it be compared with the other infinitely various lines by which in thought and in geometry the same two points might be connected, a certain integral or sum, called often *Action,* and depending by fixed rules on the length, and shape, and position of the path, and on the media which are traversed by it, is less than all the similar integrals for the other neighbouring lines, or, at least, possesses, with respect to them, a certain *stationary* property. From this Law, then, which may, perhaps, be named the Law of Stationary Action, it seems that we may most fitly and with best hope set out, in the synthetic or deductive process, and in the search of a mathematical method.

Accordingly, from this known law of least or stationary action, I deduced (long since) another connected and coextensive principle, which may be called, by analogy, the Law of Varying Action, and which seems to offer naturally a method such as we are seeking: the one law being as it were the last step in the ascending scale of induction, respecting linear paths of light, while the other law may usefully be made the first in the descending and deductive way. And my chief purpose, in the present paper, is to offer a few illustrations and consequences of these two coordinate laws.

The former of these two laws was discovered in the following manner. The elementary principle of straight rays shewed that light, under the most simple and usual circumstances, employs the direct, and, therefore, the shortest course to pass from one point to another. Again, it was a very early discovery (attributed by Laplace to Ptolemy) that in the case of a plane mirror, the bent line formed by the incident and reflected rays is shorter than any other bent line, having the same extremities, and having its point of bending on the mirror. These facts were thought by some to be instances and results of the simplicity and economy of nature; and Fermat, whose researches on maxima and minima are claimed by the continental mathematicians as the germ of the differential calculus, sought anxiously to trace some similar economy in the more complex case of refraction. He believed that by a metaphysical or cosmological necessity, arising from the simplicity of the universe, light always takes the course which it can traverse in the shortest time. To reconcile this metaphysical opinion with the law of refraction, discovered experimentally by Snellius, Fermat was led to suppose that the two lengths, or *indices,* which Snellius had measured on the incident ray prolonged and on the refracted ray, and had observed to have one common projection on a refracting plane, are inversely proportional to the two successive velocities of the light before and after refraction, and therefore that the velocity of light is diminished on entering those denser media in which it is observed to approach the perpendicular: for Fermat believed that the time of propagation of light along a line bent by refraction was represented by the sum of the two products, of the incident portion multiplied by the index of the first medium, and of the refracted portion multiplied by the index of the second medium; because he found, by his mathematical method, that this sum was less, in the case of a plane refractor, than if light went by any other than its actual path from one given point to another; and because he perceived that the supposition of a velocity inversely as the index, reconciled his mathematical discovery of the minimum of the foregoing sum with his cosmological principle of least time. Descartes attacked Fermat's opinions respecting light, but Leibnitz zealously defended them; and Huygens was led, by reasonings of a very different kind, to adopt Fermat's conclusions of a velocity inversely as the index, and of a *minimum time* of propagation of light, in passing from one given point to another through an ordinary refracting plane. Newton, however, by his theory of emission and attraction, was led to conclude that the velocity of light was *directly,* not *inversely,* as the index, and that it was *increased* instead of being *diminished* on entering a denser medium; a result incompatible with the theorem of shortest time in refraction. This theorem of shortest time was accordingly abandoned by many, and among the rest by Maupertuis, who, however, proposed in its stead, as a new cosmological principle, that celebrated *law of least action* which has since acquired so high a rank in mathematical physics, by the improvements of Euler and Lagrange. Maupertuis gave the name of *action* to the product of space and velocity, or rather to the sum of all such products for the various elements of any motion; conceiving that the more space has been traversed and the less time it has been traversed in, the more action may be considered to have been expended: and by combining this idea of action with Newton's estimate of the velocity of light, as increased by a denser medium, and as proportional to the refracting index, and with Fermat's mathematical theorem of the minimum sum of the products of paths and indices in ordinary refraction at a plane, he concluded that the course chosen by light corresponded always to the *least possible action,* though not always to the least possible time. He proposed this view as reconciling physical and metaphysical principles, which the results of Newton had seemed to put in opposition to each other; and he soon proceeded to extend his law of least action to the phenomena of the shock of bodies. Euler, attached to Maupertuis, and pleased with these novel results, employed his own great mathematical powers to prove that the law of least action extends to all the curves described by points under the influence of central forces; or, to speak more precisely, that if any such curve be compared with any other curve between the same extremities, which differs from it indefinitely little in shape and in position, and may be imagined to be described by a neighbouring point with the same law of velocity, and if we give the name of *action* to the integral of the product of the velocity and element of a curve, the difference of the two neighbouring values of this action will be indefinitely less than the greatest linear distance (itself indefinitely small) between the two near curves; a theorem which I think may be advantageously expressed by saying that the action is *stationary.* Lagrange extended this theorem of Euler to the motion of a system of points or bodies which act in any manner on each other; the action being in this case the sum of the masses by the foregoing integrals. Laplace has also extended the use of the principle in optics, by applying it to the refraction of crystals; and has pointed out an analogous principle in mechanics, for all imaginable connexions between force and velocity. But although the law of least action has thus attained a rank among the highest theorems of physics, yet its pretensions to a cosmological necessity, on the ground of economy in the universe, are now generally rejected. And the rejection appears just, for this, among other reasons, that the quantity pretended to be economised is in fact often lavishly expended. In optics, for example, though the sum of the incident and reflected portions of the path of light, in a single ordinary reflexion at a plane, is always the shortest of any yet in reflexion at a curved mirror this economy is often violated. If an eye be placed in the interior but not at the centre of a reflecting hollow sphere, it may see itself reflected in two opposite points, of which one indeed is the nearest to it, but the other on the contrary is the furthest; so that of the two different paths of light, corresponding to these two opposite points, the one indeed is the shortest, but the other is the longest of any. In mathematical language, the integral called action, instead of being always a minimum, is often a maximum; and often it is neither the one nor the other: though it has always a certain *stationary* property, of a kind which has been already alluded to, and which will soon be more fully explained. We cannot, therefore, suppose the economy of this quantity to have been designed in the divine idea of the universe: though a simplicity of some high kind may be believed to be included in that idea. And though we may retain the name of *action* to denote the stationary integral to which it has become appropriated—which we may do without adopting either the metaphysical or (in optics) the physical opinions that first suggested the name—yet we ought not (I think) to retain the epithet *least:* but rather to adopt the alteration proposed above, and to speak, in mechanics and in optics, of the *Law of Stationary Action.* . . .

63

THE WAVELENGTHS
OF PARTICLES

Prince Louis V. de Broglie (b. 1892)

Although the Bohr model of the atom proved successful in account-ing for the spectral series in hydrogen and in helium, it was clear from its inception that the Bohr theory was something of a hybrid and not based upon logically sound axioms. Bohr himself in his fundamental paper had already indicated that the theory was a mixture of classical Newtonian dynamics and nonclassical electrodynamics. On the one hand, the motion of the electron in its equilibrium orbit, that is, in a stationary state, is described by Newtonian dynamics, but the transition of the electron from one stationary state to the other is described by a new kind of electro-dynamics, which allows the electron to emit and absorb radiation in bundles (quanta) rather than continuously.

As the Bohr model was applied to more and more atomic processes it became increasingly evident that it suffered from basic inconsistencies, and that it gave wrong answers, in some instances failing to provide any answers at all. It was unable to account for the differential intensities of the spectral lines of atoms and gave no reason for the absence of certain lines that should have been present on the basis of the model.

By the beginning of the 1920's, so many difficulties faced the Bohr theory that every physicist was aware that changes of a fundamental na-ture in all our physical concepts would have to be made before a com-pletely consistent theory could emerge. The Bohr theory would then be but an approximation of the correct theory. But where was this new theory to come from? The solution to this problem came from three sep-arate investigations, each of which began from a different point, but all of which ended with essentially the same result.

1041

Prince Louis V. de Broglie was the first of the investigators to see where the difficulty lay in the Bohr theory and what had to be done to establish the foundations of a correct theory. De Broglie began his study of the problem in 1920; within a three-year period he had formulated the basis of our contemporary understanding of the behavior of matter. De Broglie first considered the fundamental duality of nature (matter and energy), assuming that these two aspects must have some common meeting ground.

Until 1900, physicists believed that matter and energy were two distinct realms in nature governed by different laws. Pure energy, manifesting itself as radiation, was thought of entirely in terms of waves, whereas matter was considered to be entirely corpuscular in nature. The first important departure from this concept occurred in 1900 when Planck showed that radiation cannot be described entirely in terms of waves; it also possesses corpuscular properties. The final destruction of the classical notion of energy as waves and matter as corpuscles was accomplished by De Broglie, whose chain of reasoning started from Einstein's famous mass-energy relationship.

De Broglie's basis for a new picture of matter is set forth in his Nobel Prize address, which is reproduced at the end of this chapter. His reasoning is based upon the concept of symmetry in nature and stems from the special theory of relativity. He was prompted in his discovery of the wave nature of particles by what at first appeared to be a serious contradiction in the quantum picture of radiation; namely, that one must speak of a radiant corpuscle—that is, a photon—as having a frequency and a wavelength, as did Planck when he introduced the quantum of energy. Since the assumption of these dual properties—that is, wave and corpuscle—was necessary for the correct description of radiation, why, then, on the basis of symmetry, should not material particles also have wave properties?

Once De Broglie had convinced himself that there was nothing wrong, however strange, in assigning a frequency and a wavelength to particles —even material ones like electrons and protons—he hit upon the method for determining the relationship between the mechanical and wave properties of all particles. He used the fundamental equations of relativity. These equations already contained a relationship between radiant energy and matter, and therefore between matter and frequency, which is a property of radiation.

In the discussion of his procedure, De Broglie introduced concepts that require some prior explanation. One is the idea of the "proper" time of a particle, a concept that is derived from the special theory of relativity. In the theory of relativity one has to distinguish between the time as measured by a clock moving along with a particle, and the time as measured by a clock relative to which the particle is moving. The "proper" time of the particle is measured by the clock that is moving along with the particle. It is related to the time given by the clock relative to which the particle is moving by the simple transformation formula that De Broglie gives in his address. It is the factor that gives the amount by which a moving clock slows down.

He also finds it necessary to introduce the concepts of group velocity and wave or phase velocity. It is the group velocity that must be related to the speed of the particle. This is what De Broglie succeeded in doing, thereby establishing the wave properties of electrons. His approach owes much to the investigations of Lord Rayleigh, who demonstrated that the speed of a group of waves—each of which varies slightly in wavelength and frequency from its neighbors—is not just equal to the speeds of the component, individual waves. If we had just a single wave in the group, that is, a wave extending infinitely far in both directions, the group and phase velocities would be identical and would be the value obtained by multiplying the wavelength by the frequency of the wave. But if many waves are present, each with its own phase velocity, the over-all velocity, or group velocity, results from the interference of the component waves with one another. One can actually see this with water waves by dropping a pebble into the water. The main wave is seen to advance with a definite speed while tiny wavelets move up to the main wave front and then disappear.

In his analysis of the behavior of the electron, the concept of the group velocity was very helpful to De Broglie. For he realized that if he assigned a wavelength and a frequency to an electron, using the equations of relativity theory, the number obtained by multiplying these two quantities would not equal the velocity of the particle. Indeed, this number is always larger than the speed of light. In fact, it is the phase velocity, and it shows us that the particle is really compounded of a group of waves.

In a sense the work of De Broglie established an amalgamation of special relativity theory and quantum theory by relating Planck's constant to the momentum-energy concept of relativity theory. That a relationship between waves and particles should exist on the basis of the theory of relativity is clear from a consideration of the invariant properties of waves and particles. One of the most important concepts derived from the theory of relativity is that of invariance: physical systems are characterized by certain quantities that appear as constants to observers moving with uniform speed with respect to one another. For example, consider a train of waves of radiation moving in a certain direction and suppose that we have only a single frequency and wavelength associated with this train. What is the invariant property of this train? What physical quantity associated with this wave train would all observers moving with uniform speed with respect to one another find the same?

This constant quantity is, of course, the number of waves that the observers would tally, starting from a given wave and counting for the same period of time. This can be shown to be equal to what is called the phase of the wave, so that the phase is invariant when one goes from one coordinate system to another. Now the phase of a wave is obtained as follows: Divide the distance a wave has moved in a given time interval by its wavelength. Multiply the frequency of the wave by this time interval and subtract this quantity from the previous one. We may picture this invariant of a wave somewhat differently. Since the distance a wave moves and the time during which it is moving may be defined as the space-time interval of the wave, we can say that the invariant of the wave is obtained by properly combining (usually multiplying) the space-time interval of the wave and its wavelength-frequency interval.

Let us now look at the invariant properties of a moving particle such as an electron. A particle has momentum and energy associated with it; it can be shown that if one properly combines (in fact, in the same mathematical way as in the case of the light wave above) the space-time interval of the particle with its momentum-energy one also gets an invariant property of the particle. It thus appears from considerations of symmetry that the momentum-energy of a particle plays a role in its motion similar to the role played by the wavelength-frequency in the motion of a wave. It is, therefore, quite natural to seek a correspondence between momentum-energy and wavelength-frequency. Planck had already established the fact that frequency is related to energy for waves, and De Broglie completed the work by showing that wavelength is related to momentum. This means that wherever energy is present we must have a frequency and wherever momentum is present we must have a wavelength, and vice versa. From this it follows that waves must have momentum and therefore particle properties and particles must have wavelengths and therefore wave characteristics.

De Broglie considers one more important point: the relationship between his wave theory of the electron and the discrete orbits introduced by Bohr. Why does an electron move in special orbits inside an atom?

De Broglie answers this simply by writing down the expression for the wavelength of a particle: Planck's constant divided by the momentum of the particle. In other words, the faster a particle moves, the shorter is the wavelength that must be assigned to it. If one now considers a particle moving in a closed orbit (that is, always retracing the same path like the electron inside a hydrogen atom) this orbit can be closed only if the waves in the wave packet associated with the circling electron do not destroy each other as they move around. Such waves move with the phase velocity we described above, whereas the electron moves with the group velocity; thus the waves move faster than the electron does and catch up with the electron time and again.

Let us now consider a wave that has left the electron, gone around the orbit, and caught up with the electron again. At that moment another wave will be leaving the electron. If the motion of the electron is stable, the crest of the wave that has caught up with the electron must just match the crest of the wave that is leaving the electron; otherwise these two waves would cancel and the motion would be disturbed. This means that the circumference of the path of the electron must be equal in length to an integral number of wavelengths. But this turns out to be equivalent, as De Broglie shows, to the condition that Bohr imposed on the motion of the electron.

In developing his theory, De Broglie made another significant contribution that clarified a puzzling point concerning the quantum picture. Classical physics is based on the concept of continuity, which apparently is fundamental for an understanding of the properties of wave motion, whereas the quantum theory departs radically from classical physics in introducing discrete discontinuous processes. However, it still retains the ideas of frequency and wavelength that were derived from the continuous wave picture. How, one might naturally ask, is it possible to describe something as discrete and as continuous at the same time?

De Broglie pointed out that the notion of discreteness is not foreign even to the classical wave theory. For when two waves meet, an interference pattern is formed that can be described only by a discrete set of numbers, since one sees a discrete set of interference fringes (light and dark spots). In other words, whenever one is dealing with collections of waves, a discrete pattern becomes evident. The same thing happens when we set a membrane vibrating. If one first scatters particles of sand on such a membrane and then sets the membrane vibrating, the sand rearranges itself in *definite patterns* on the membrane. These patterns may be pictured as similar to the stationary states of the electron in the Bohr theory of the atom.

Finally, we might compare the De Broglie picture with the wave mechanics developed by Hamilton (see Chapter 62). Hamilton had shown that a formal similarity exists between the laws of classical mechanics and the laws of geometrical optics: both sets of laws can be obtained from minimum, or stationary, principles.

In a sense, then, we might say that Hamilton had foreshadowed De Broglie. But this is not really the case, for Hamilton's work never went beyond pure formal analogy. Although the Hamiltonian formulation is of great importance in modern wave mechanics, at no point in his work did he consider the possibility that particles might have wave characteristics associated with them. De Broglie used the formal relationship between geometrical optics and Newtonian mechanics to establish a relationship between wave optics and a new kind of mechanics, wave mechanics. Since geometrical optics is wholly inadequate to describe such optical phenomena as interference and diffraction—that is, phenomena in which the wavelength of the light becomes apparent—so, too, the Newtonian mechanics is wholly inadequate to describe the behavior of particles in atoms where phenomena involving discrete processes and whole numbers occur (in this respect similar to diffraction and interference in optics). As De Broglie says: "This suggests the idea that the older Mechanics too may be no more than an approximation as compared with a more comprehensive mechanics of an undulatory character."

It should be noted that the waves associated with particles in this theory of De Broglie's are not to be considered merely as a fictitious, useful device for describing an electron, but as real. As he points out, the dualism of waves and particles is real and the wavelength associated with a particle is as concrete a physical quantity as the mass of the particle. It is on this idea of the dualism in nature between waves and corpuscles, expressed in more or less abstract form, that the entire recent development of theoretical physics has been built and that its immediate future development appears likely to be erected.

In 1911, when Louis de Broglie was still a young student, his brother Maurice, who was then a well-known physicist, attended the first of the famous Solvay conferences on physics. This must have been a very exciting conference, indeed, for the quantum theory was just beginning to make itself felt, primarily because of Einstein's remarkable success in applying it to various phenomena; Einstein's relativity theory had, to some extent, been accepted. H. A. Lorentz, recognized by all as the leading physicist presided, and Planck, Einstein, Nernst, and other top scientists were present. Most of the discussion was devoted to the photon; Einstein insisted that it be recognized as a real physical particle, but the majority was willing to accept it only as an artificial device for clarifying certain radiation phenomena. Maurice de Broglie carried a description of these events back to Louis, who was deeply stirred by the account and decided that he, too, was going to participate in this exciting search for the laws of nature.

Except for the fact that his brother was a physicist, no one would have thought that Louis would become a physicist and win the Nobel Prize for his remarkable synthesis of waves and particles into a wave-particle dualism. For De Broglie was born a prince, the son of Victor, Duc de Broglie, and Paulini d'Armaillé, and very few of the royalty adopted science as a career. Indeed, Louis was almost lost to science, for he first devoted himself to literary studies and actually took a degree in history in 1910, a year after he had graduated from the Lycée Janson of Sailly. He was born on August 15, 1892, at Dieppe and living in an ancestral manor, with its emphasis on tradition and duty to one's family, must have experienced little to bring him in contact with science. Nevertheless, after completing his history degree, he went over completely to science and took his degree in physics in 1913.

Then World War I intervened; he was conscripted for military service and spent 1914–1918 with the wireless section of the army at the Eiffel Tower. Although the technical problems associated with wireless were of some interest, he could not keep his mind off the problem of the photon. Immediately after the war he threw himself into this phase of physics with great vigor and passion. Experimental problems interested him to some extent, but theoretical physics dominated his life.

In 1920 De Broglie became interested in the apparent contradictions that seemed to stem from the quantum theory of radiation, for it appeared then that if the corpuscular theory (Einstein's photons) were accepted, one could not explain interference and diffraction, which are essentially wave phenomena. On the other hand, if the wave picture were accepted, there would be no way to account for black-body radiation. After thinking about this for many days, De Broglie finally saw the solution. There was no need to accept *either* the wave theory *or* the photon theory exclusively, because both theories were correct and light consisted of both waves and corpuscles. Indeed, Planck's basic concept, that a photon (or quantum) has an amount of energy proportional to its frequency (the famous $E = h\nu$ relation, where E is energy, h is Planck's constant and ν is frequency), shows that particles and waves go together—one cannot have one without the other. In his Nobel address, De Broglie stated this revelation as follows:

> I thus arrived at the following overall concept which guided my studies: For both matter and radiations, light in particular, it is necessary to introduce the corpuscle concept and the wave concept at the same time. In other words, the existence of corpuscles accompanied by waves has to be assumed in all cases.

Here one sees De Broglie's generalization: If corpuscles (photons) are associated with waves, then waves must be associated with corpuscles. From this assumption the derivation of De Broglie's famous equation relating the wavelength of a particle to its momentum and Planck's constant was a matter of straightforward algebra applied to the relativistic kinematics of a particle. Thus began wave mechanics, which has so drastically altered our concepts of matter.

De Broglie presented the essential ideas of this theory in a thesis entitled "Recherches sur la Théorie des Quanta" ("Researches on the Quantum Theory") to the faculty of sciences at Paris University in 1924. It aroused considerable astonishment at first because of the strangeness of its ideas and was not fully accepted until the experiments of Davisson and Germer proved it to be correct.

Soon after presenting his thesis, De Broglie began teaching, first as a free lecturer at the Sorbonne and then as professor of theoretical physics at the Henri Poincaré Institute, which had just been built. In 1932 he occupied the chair of theoretical physics of the science faculty of the University of Paris.

During the last two decades De Broglie has tried to obtain a causal interpretation of the wave mechanics to replace the probabilistic theories of Born, Bohr, and Heisenberg. Thus far he has had little success in this endeavor—the uncertainty principle and the wave-particle dualism still dominate modern physics.

De Broglie's work has brought him international honors of all kinds. In addition to the Nobel Prize he has received awards from almost every country in the world.

ooooooo

DE BROGLIE

The Undulatory Aspects of the Electron [1]

WHEN, IN 1920, I RESUMED my investigations in theoretical Physics after a long interruption through circumstances out of my own control, I was far from imagining that this research would within a few years be rewarded by the lofty and coveted distinction given each year by the Swedish Academy of Sciences: the Nobel Prize in Physics. At that time what drew me towards theoretical Physics was not the hope that so high a distinction would ever crown my labours: what attracted me was the mystery which was coming to envelop more and more deeply the structure of Matter and of radiation in proportion as the strange concept of the quantum, introduced by Planck about 1900 during his research on black body radiation, came to extend over the entire field of Physics.

But to explain the way in which my research came to develop I must first outline the critical period through which Physics had for the last twenty years been passing.

---

[1] Prince Louis V. de Broglie, Nobel Prize Address, Stockholm, 1929.

Physicists had for long been wondering whether Light did not consist of minute corpuscles in rapid motion, an idea going back to the philosophers of antiquity, and sustained in the eighteenth century by Newton. After interference phenomena had been discovered by Thomas Young, however, and Augustin Fresnel had completed his important investigation, the assumption that Light had a granular structure was entirely disregarded, and the Wave Theory was unanimously adopted. In this way the physicists of last century came to abandon completely the idea that Light had an atomic structure. But the Atomic Theory, being thus banished from optics, began to achieve great success, not only in Chemistry, where it provided a simple explanation of the laws of definite proportions, but also in pure Physics, where it enabled a fair number of the properties of solids, liquids and gases to be interpreted. Among other things it allowed the great kinetic theory of gases to be formulated, which, in the generalized form of statistical Mechanics, has enabled clear significance to be given to the abstract concepts of thermodynamics. We have seen how decisive evidence in favour of the atomic structure of electricity was also provided by experiments. Thanks to Sir J. J. Thomson, the notion of the corpuscle of electricity was introduced; and the way in which H. A. Lorentz has exploited this idea in his electron Theory is well known.

Some thirty years ago, then, Physics was divided into two camps. On the one hand there was the Physics of Matter, based on the concepts of corpuscles and atoms which were assumed to obey the classical laws of Newtonian Mechanics; on the other hand there was the Physics of radiation, based on the idea of wave propagation in a hypothetical continuous medium: the ether of Light and of electromagnetism. But these two systems of Physics could not remain alien to each other: an amalgamation had to be effected; and this was done by means of a theory of the exchange of energy between Matter and radiation. It was at this point, however, that the difficulties began; for in the attempt to render the two systems of Physics compatible with each other, incorrect and even impossible conclusions were reached with regard to the energy equilibrium between Matter and radiation in an enclosed and thermally isolated region: some investigators even going so far as to say that Matter would transfer all its energy to radiation, and hence tend towards the temperature of absolute zero. This absurd conclusion had to be avoided at all costs; and by a brilliant piece of intuition Planck succeeded in doing so. Instead of assuming, as did the classical Wave Theory, that a light-source emits its radiation continuously, he assumed that it emits it in equal and finite quantities —in quanta. The energy of each quantum, still further, was supposed to be proportional to the frequency of the radiation, v, and to be equal to hv, where h is the universal constant since known as Planck's Constant.

The success of Planck's ideas brought with it some serious consequences.

For if Light is emitted in quanta, then surely, once radiated, it ought to have a granular structure. Consequently the existence of quanta of radiation brings us back to the corpuscular conception of Light. On the other hand, it can be shown—as has in fact been done by Jeans and H. Poincaré—that if the motion of the material particles in a light-source obeyed the laws of classical Mechanics, we could never obtain the correct Law of black body radiation—Planck's Law. It must therefore be admitted that the older dynamics, even as modified by Einstein's Theory of Relativity, cannot explain motion on a very minute scale.

The existence of a corpuscular structure of Light and of other types of radiation has been confirmed by the discovery of the photo-electric effect which, as I have already observed, is easily explained by the assumption that the radiation consists of quanta—hv—capable of transferring their entire energy to an electron in the irradiated substance; and in this way we are brought to the theory of light-quanta which, as we have seen, was advanced in 1905 by Einstein—a theory which amounts to a return to Newton's corpuscular hypothesis, supplemented by the proportionality subsisting between the energy of the corpuscles and the frequency. A number of arguments were adduced by Einstein in support of his view, which was confirmed by Compton's discovery in 1922 of the scattering of X-rays, a phenomenon named after him. At the same time it still remained necessary to retain the Wave Theory to explain the phenomena of diffraction and interference, and no means was apparent to reconcile this Theory with the existence of light-corpuscles.

I have pointed out that in the course of investigation some doubt had been thrown on the validity of small-scale Mechanics. Let us imagine a material point describing a small closed orbit—an orbit returning on itself; then according to classical dynamics there in an infinity of possible movements of this type in accordance with the initial conditions, and the possible values of the energy of the moving material point form a continuous series. Planck, on the other hand, was compelled to assume that only certain privileged movements—*quantized* motion—are possible, or at any rate stable, so that the available values of the energy form a discontinuous series. At first this seemed a very strange idea; soon, however, its truth had to be admitted, because it was by its means that Planck arrived at the correct Law of black body radiation and because its usefulness has since been proved in many other spheres. Finally, Bohr founded his famous atomic Theory on this idea of the quantization of atomic motion—a theory so familiar to scientists that I will refrain from summing it up here.

Thus we see once again it had become necessary to assume two contradictory theories of Light, in terms of waves, and of corpuscles, respectively; while it was impossible to understand why, among the infinite number of paths which an electron ought to be able to follow in the atom according to classical ideas, there was only a restricted number which it could pursue in fact. Such were the problems facing physicists at the time when I returned to my studies.

When I began to consider these difficulties I was chiefly struck by two facts. On the one hand the Quantum Theory of Light cannot be considered satisfactory, since it defines the energy of a light-corpuscle by the equation $W = hv$, containing the frequency v. Now a purely corpuscular theory contains nothing that enables us to define a frequency; for this reason alone, therefore, we are compelled, in the case of Light, to introduce the idea of a corpuscle and that of periodicity simultaneously.

On the other hand, determination of the stable motion of electrons in the atom introduces integers; and up to this point the only phenomena involving integers in Physics were those of interference and of normal modes of vibration. This fact suggested to me the idea that electrons too could not be regarded simply as corpuscles, but that periodicity must be assigned to them also.

In this way, then, I obtained the following general idea, in accordance with which I pursued my investigations:—that it is necessary in the case of Matter, as well as of radiation generally and of Light in particular, to introduce the idea of the corpuscle and of the wave simultaneously: or in other words, in the one case as well as in the other, we must assume the existence of corpuscles accompanied by waves. But corpuscles and waves cannot be independent of each other: in Bohr's terms, they are two complementary aspects of Reality: and it must consequently be possible to establish a certain parallelism between the motion of a corpuscle and the propagation of its associated wave. The first object at which to aim, therefore, was to establish the existence of this parallelism.

With this in view, I began by considering the simplest case: that of an isolated corpuscle, i.e. one removed from all external influence; with this we wish to associate a wave. Let us therefore consider first of all a reference system O $x_0 y_0 z_0$ in which the corpuscle is at rest: this is the "proper" system for the corpuscle according to the Theory of Relativity. Within such a system the wave will be stationary, since the corpuscle is at rest; its phase will be the same at every point, and it will be represented by an expression of the form $\sin 2\pi v_0 (t_0 - \tau_0)$, t_0 being the "proper" time of the corpuscle, and τ_0 a constant.

According to the principle of inertia the corpuscle will be in uniform rectilinear motion in every Galilean system. Let us consider such a Galilean system, and let v be the velocity of the corpuscle in this system. Without loss of generality, we may take the direction of motion to be the axis of x. According to the Lorentz transformation, the time t employed by an observer in this new system is linked with the proper time t_o by the relation:

$$t_o = \frac{t - \dfrac{\beta x}{c}}{\sqrt{1 - \beta^2}}$$

where $\beta = v/c$.

Hence for such an observer the phase of the wave will be given by

$$\sin 2\pi \frac{v_o}{\sqrt{1 - \beta^2}} \left(t - \frac{\beta x}{c} - \tau_o \right).$$

Consequently the wave will have for him a frequency

$$v = \frac{v_o}{\sqrt{1 - \beta^2}}$$

and will move along the axis of x with the phase-velocity

$$V = \frac{c}{\beta} = \frac{c^2}{v}.$$

If we eliminate β from the two preceding formulae we shall easily find the following relation, which gives the index of refraction of free space, n, for the waves under consideration

$$n = \sqrt{1 - \frac{v_o{}^2}{v^2}}$$

To this "law of dispersion" there corresponds a "group velocity." You are aware that the group velocity is the velocity with which the resultant amplitude of a group of waves, with almost equal frequencies, is propagated. Lord Rayleigh has shown that this velocity U satisfies the equation

$$\frac{1}{U} = \frac{1}{c} \frac{d(nv)}{dv}$$

Here we find that $U = v$, which means that the velocity of the group of waves in the system $x\, y\, z\, t$ is equal to the velocity of the corpuscle in this system. This relation is of the greatest importance for the development of the Theory.

Accordingly, in the system $x\, y\, z\, t$ the corpuscle is defined by the frequency v and by the phase-velocity V of its associated wave. In order to establish the parallelism mentioned above, we must try to connect these magnitudes to the mechanical magnitudes—to energy and momentum. The ratio between energy and frequency is one of the most characteristic relations of the Quantum Theory; and since, still further, energy and frequency are transformed when the Galilean system of reference is changed, it is natural to establish the equation

$$\text{Energy} = h \times \text{frequency, or } W = h\nu$$

where h is Planck's constant. This relation must apply to all Galilean systems; and in the proper system of the corpuscle where, according to Einstein, the energy of the corpuscle is reduced to its internal energy $m_o c^2$ (where m_o is its proper mass) we have $h\nu_o = m_o c^2$.

This relation gives the frequency ν_o as a function of the proper mass m_o, or inversely.

The momentum is a vector $\mathbf{p}$ equal to $\dfrac{m_o \mathbf{v}}{\sqrt{1 - \beta^2}}$, where $|\mathbf{v}| = v$, and then we have

$$p = |\mathbf{p}| = \frac{m_o v}{\sqrt{1 - \beta^2}} = \frac{Wv}{c^2} = \frac{h\nu}{V} = \frac{h}{\lambda}.$$

The quantity λ is the wave-length—the distance between two consecutive wave-crests, hence

$$\lambda = \frac{h}{p}.$$

This is a fundamental relation of the Theory.

All that has been said refers to the very simple case where there is no field of force acting on the corpuscle. I shall now indicate very briefly how the Theory can be generalized for the case of a corpuscle moving in a field of force not varying with time derived from a potential energy function $F(x,y,z)$. Arguments into which I shall not enter here lead us in such a case to assume that the propagation of the wave corresponds to an index of refraction varying from point to point in space in accordance with the formula

$$n(x,y,z) = \sqrt{\left[1 - \frac{F(x,y,z)}{h\nu}\right]^2 - \frac{\nu_o^2}{v^2}}$$

or, as a first approximation, if we neglect the corrections introduced by the Theory of Relativity

$$n(x,y,z) = \sqrt{\frac{2(E - F)}{m_o c^2}} \quad \text{with} \quad E = W - m_0 c^2.$$

The constant energy W of the corpuscle is further connected with the constant frequency v of the wave by the relation

$$W = hv$$

while the wave-length λ, which varies from one point to the other in the field of force, is connected with the momentum p (which is also variable) by the relation

$$\lambda(x,y,z) = \frac{h}{p(x,y,z)}.$$

Here again we show that the velocity of the wave-group is equal to the velocity of the corpuscle. The parallelism thus established between the corpuscle and its wave enables us to identify Fermat's Principle in the case of waves and the Principle of Least Action in that of corpuscles, for constant fields. Fermat's Principle states that the ray in the optical sense passing between two points A and B in a medium whose index is $n(x,y,z)$, variable from one point to the other but constant in time, is such that the integral $\int_A^B n\,dl$, taken along this ray, shall be an *extremum*. On the other hand, Maupertuis' Principle of Least Action asserts that the trajectory of a corpuscle passing through two points A and B is such that the integral $\int_A^B p\,dl$ taken along the trajectory shall be an *extremum*, it being understood that we are considering only the motion corresponding to a given value of energy. According to the relations already established between the mechanical and the wave magnitudes, we have

$$n = \frac{c}{V} = \frac{c}{v} \cdot \frac{1}{\lambda} = \frac{c}{hv} \cdot \frac{h}{\lambda} = \frac{c}{W} p = \text{constant} \times p$$

since W is constant in a constant field. Hence it follows that Fermat's Principle and Maupertuis' Principle are each a rendering of the other: the possible trajectories of the corpuscle are identical with the possible rays of its wave.

These ideas lead to an interpretation of the conditions of stability introduced by the Quantum Theory. If we consider a closed trajectory C [in] a constant field, it is quite natural to assume that the phase of the associated wave should be a uniform function along this trajectory. This leads us to write

$$\int_c \frac{dl}{\lambda} = \int_c \frac{1}{h} p\,dl = \text{an integer.}$$

Now this is exactly the condition of the stability of atomic periodic motion, according to Planck. Thus the quantum conditions of stability appear as analogous to resonance phenomena, and the appearance of integers here becomes as natural as in the theory of vibrating cords and discs.

The general formulae establishing the parallelism between waves and corpuscles can be applied to light-corpuscles if we assume that in that case the rest-mass m_o is infinitely small. If then for any given value of the energy W we make m_o tend to zero, we find that both v and V tend to c, and in the limit we obtain the two fundamental formulae on which Einstein erected his Theory of Light-quanta

$$W = hv \quad p = \frac{hv}{c}.$$

Such were the principal ideas which I had developed during my earlier researches. They showed clearly that it was possible to establish a correspondence between waves and corpuscles of such a kind that the Laws of Mechanics correspond to those of geometrical optics. But we know that in the Wave Theory geometrical optics is only an approximation: there are limits to the validity of this approximation, and especially when the phenomena of interference and of diffraction are concerned it is wholly inadequate. This suggests the idea that the older Mechanics too may be no more than an approximation as compared with a more comprehensive Mechanics of an undulatory character. This was what I expressed at the beginning of my researches when I said that a new Mechanics must be formulated, standing in the same relation to the older Mechanics as that in which wave optics stands to geometrical optics. This new Mechanics has since been developed, thanks in particular to the fine work done by Schrödinger. It starts from the equations of wave propagation, which are taken as the basis, and rigorously determines the temporal changes of the wave associated with a corpuscle. More particularly, it has succeeded in giving a new and more satisfactory form to the conditions governing the quantization of intra-atomic motion: for, as we have seen, the older conditions of quantization are encountered again if we apply geometrical optics to the waves associated with intra-atomic corpuscles; and there is strictly no justification for this application.

I cannot here trace even briefly the development of the new Mechanics. All that I wish to say is that on examination it has shown itself to be identical with a Mechanics developed independently, first by Heisenberg and later by Born, Jordan, Pauli, Dirac and others. This latter Mechanics—Quantum Mechanics—and Wave Mechanics are, from the mathematical point of view, equivalent to each other.

Here we must confine ourselves to a general consideration of the results obtained. To sum up the significance of Wave Mechanics, we can say that a wave must be associated with each particle, and that a study of the propagation of the wave alone can tell us anything about the successive localizations of the corpuscle in space. In the usual large-scale mechanical phenomena, the localizations predicted lie along a curve which is the trajectory in the classical sense of the term. What, however, happens if the wave is not propagated according to the laws of geometrical optics; if, for example, interference or diffraction occurs? In such a case we can no longer assign to the corpuscle motion in accordance with classical dynamics. So much is certain. But a further question arises: Can we even suppose that at any given moment the corpuscle has an exactly determined position within the wave, and that in the course of its propagation the wave carries the corpuscle with it, as a wave of water would carry a cork? These are difficult questions, and their discussion would carry us too far and actually to the borderland of Philosophy. All that I shall say here is that the general modern tendency is to assume that it is not always possible to assign an exactly defined position within the wave to the corpuscle, that whenever an observation is made enabling us to localize the corpuscle, we are invariably led to attribute to it a position inside the wave, and that the probability that this position is at a given point, M, within the wave is proportional to the square of the amplitude, or the intensity, at M.

What has just been said can also be expressed in the following way. If we take a cloud of corpuscles all associated with the same wave, then the intensity of the wave at any given point is proportional to the density of the cloud of corpuscles at that point, i.e. to the number of corpuscles per unit of volume around that point. This assumption must be made in order to explain how it is that in the case of interference the luminous energy is found concentrated at those points where the intensity of the wave is at a maximum: if it is assumed that the luminous energy is transferred by light-corpuscles, or photons, then it follows that the density of the photons in the wave is proportional to this intensity.

This rule by itself enables us to understand the way in which the undulatory theory of the electron has been verified experimentally.

For let us imagine an indefinite cloud of electrons, all having the same velocity and moving in the same direction. According to the fundamental ideas of Wave Mechanics, we must associate with this cloud an infinite plane wave having the form

$$a \exp. 2\pi i \left[\frac{W}{h} t - \frac{\alpha x + \beta y + \gamma z}{\lambda} \right]$$

where α, β, γ are the direction cosines of the direction of propagation, and where the wave-length λ is equal to $\dfrac{h}{p}$. If the electrons have no extremely high velocity, we may say

$$p = m_o v$$

and hence

$$\lambda = \frac{h}{m_o v}$$

m_o being the rest-mass of the electron.

In practice, to obtain electrons having the same velocity they are subjected to the same potential difference P. We then have

$$\frac{1}{2} m_o v^2 = e P$$

Consequently

$$\lambda = \frac{h}{\sqrt{2 m_o e \, P}}$$

Numerically, this gives

$$\lambda = \frac{12 \cdot 24}{\sqrt{P}} \cdot 10^{-8} \text{ cm. } (P \text{ in volts}).$$

As we can only use electrons that have fallen through a potential difference of at least some tens of volts, it follows that the wave-length λ, assumed by the Theory, is at most of the order of 10^{-8} cm., i.e. of the order of the Ångström unit. This is also the order of magnitude of the wave-lengths of X-rays.

The length of the electron wave being thus of the same order as that of X-rays, we may fairly expect to be able to obtain a scattering of this wave by crystals, in complete analogy to the Laue phenomenon in which, in a natural crystal like rock salt, the atoms of the substances composing the crystal are arranged at regular intervals of the order of one Ångström, and thus act as scattering centres for the waves. If a wave having a length of one Ångström encounters the crystal, then the waves scattered agree in phase in certain definite directions. In these directions the total intensity scattered exhibits a strong maximum. The location of these maxima of scattering is given by the well known mathematical Theory elaborated by Laue and Bragg, which gives the position of the maxima in terms of the distance between the atomic arrangements in the crystal and of the length of the incident wave. For X-rays the Theory has been triumphantly substantiated by Laue, Friedrich and Knipping, and today the diffraction of X-rays by crystals has become a quite commonplace experiment. The exact measurement of the wave-lengths of X-rays is based on this diffraction, as I need hardly recall in a country where Siegbahn and his collaborators are pursuing their successful labours.

In the case of X-rays, the phenomenon of diffraction by crystals was a natural consequence of the idea that these rays are undulations analogous to Light, and differ from Light only by their shorter wave-length. But for electrons no such view could be entertained, so long as the latter were looked upon as being merely minute corpuscles. If, on the other hand, we assume that the electron is associated with a wave, and that the density of a cloud of electrons is measured by the intensity of the associated wave, we may then expect that there will be effects in the case of electrons similar to the Laue effect. In that event, the electron wave will be scattered with an intensity in certain directions which the Laue-Bragg Theory enables us to calculate, on the assumption that the wave-length is $\lambda = \dfrac{h}{mv}$, a length corresponding to the known velocity v of the electrons falling on the crystal. According to our general principle, the intensity of the scattered wave measures the density of the cloud of scattered electrons, so that we may expect to find large numbers of scattered electrons in the directions of the maxima. If this effect actually occurs, it would provide a crucial experimental proof of the existence of a wave associated with the electron, its length being $\dfrac{h}{mv}$. In this way the fundamental idea of Wave Mechanics would be provided with a firm experimental foundation.

Now experiment—which is the last Court of Appeal of theories—has shown that the diffraction of electrons by crystals actually occurs, and that it follows the Laws of Wave Mechanics exactly and quantitatively. It is (as we have seen already) to Davisson and Germer, working at the Bell Laboratories in New York, that the credit belongs of having been the first to observe this phenomenon by a method similar to that used by Laue for X-rays. Following up the same experiments, but substituting for the single crystal a crystalline powder, in accordance with the method introduced for X-rays by Debye and Scherrer, Professor G. P. Thomson, of Aberdeen, the son of the great Cambridge physicist, Sir J. J. Thomson, has discovered the same phenomena. At a later stage Rupp in Germany, Kikuchi in Japan and Ponte in France have also reproduced them under varying experimental conditions. Today the existence of the effect is no longer subject to doubt, and the minor difficulties of interpretation which Davisson's and Germer's earlier experiments had raised have been resolved in a satisfactory manner. Rupp has actually succeeded in obtaining the diffraction of electrons in a particularly striking form. A grating is employed—a metal or glass surface, either plane or slightly curved, on which equidistant lines have been mechanically drawn, the interval between them being of an order of magnitude comparable to that of the wave-lengths of Light. Between the waves diffracted by these lines there will be interference, and the interference will give rise to maxima of diffracted Light in certain directions depending on the distance between the lines, on the direction of the Light falling on the grating and on the wave-lengths. For a long time it remained impossible to obtain similar effects with gratings of this kind produced by human workmanship when X-rays were used instead of Light. The reason for this was that the wave-length of X-rays is a great deal shorter than that of Light, and that there is no instrument capable of drawing lines on any surface at intervals of the order of X-ray wave-lengths. Ingenious physicists, however (Compton and Thibaud), succeeded in overcoming the difficulty. Let us take an ordinary optical grating and let us look at it more or less at a tangent. The lines of the grating will then seem to be much closer together than they actually are. For X-rays falling on the grating at this grazing angle, the conditions will be the same as though the lines were extremely close together, and diffraction effects like those of Light will be produced. The physicists just mentioned have proved that such was in fact the case. But now—since the electron wave-lengths are of the same order as those of X-rays—we should also be able to obtain these diffraction phenomena by causing a beam of electrons to fall on such an optical grating at a very small grazing angle. Rupp succeeded in doing this. He was thus enabled to measure the length of electron waves by comparing it directly with the distance between the lines drawn mechanically on the grating.

We thus find that in order to describe the properties of Matter, as well as those of Light, we must employ waves and corpuscles simultaneously. We can no longer imagine the electron as being just a minute corpuscle of electricity: we must associate a wave with it. And this wave is not just a fiction: its length can be measured and its interferences calculated in advance. In fact, a whole group of phenomena was in this way predicted before being actually discovered. It is, therefore, on this idea of the dualism in Nature between waves and corpuscles, expressed in a more or less abstract form, that the entire recent development of theoretical Physics has been built up, and that its immediate future development appears likely to be erected.

64

ooooooooooo

A WAVE EQUATION
FOR PARTICLES

ooooooooooo

Erwin Schroedinger (1887-1961)

Almost at the very moment that Heisenberg and his collaborators were developing the matrix phase of quantum mechanics (presented in Chapter 66), and with its aid deriving the frequencies of the lines of the normal hydrogen spectrum, an entirely different approach to the same problem was being taken by Erwin Schroedinger, a Viennese physicist who was then working at the University of Zurich.

Schroedinger's starting point was De Broglie's discovery of the wave nature of particles and his conviction that it should be possible to describe this wave pattern by a wave equation, just as it is possible to describe the propagation of light by a wave equation. This conviction was greatly strengthened by Schroedinger's knowledge that under certain conditions the motion of a system described by a wave equation (for example, vibrating strings or a vibrating metal plate) can be represented by integers. Here, then, was the kernel of an exciting idea and possibly the source of a new theory of the atom. For if waves are associated with particles and waves are described by wave equations, the solutions of which, in turn, involve integers, then it should be possible to introduce quantum numbers quite naturally into the description of the motion of an electron inside an atom by using a wave equation to describe this motion. With this approach, the solution of atomic problems would become fairly simple, as opposed to the complex processes of matrix mechanics.

To obtain his wave equation, Schroedinger went back to the work of Hamilton, aware that this great mathematician had established an analogy between the Newtonian mechanics of a particle and the geometrical optics

1060

of a ray. As already noted in Chapter 62, Hamilton had shown that we can duplicate the path of a particle in a given force field (for example, of a freely falling body in a gravitational field) by the path of a ray of light in a given medium—provided we choose the correct index of refraction of the medium.

We remember that the equations of wave optics become identical to those of geometrical optics if the wavelength in the former is placed equal to zero. Schroedinger suggested, then, that since classical geometrical optics is the limiting case of wave optics, when the wavelength is infinitesimally small, classical, Newtonian mechanics is nothing more than the limiting case of a more general wave mechanics, which invests particles with wavelengths and wave properties. If, indeed, this were so, one should be able to obtain a wave equation that would describe the motion of a particle, and obtain it by a method similar to the one used in going from geometrical optics to wave optics. This was Schroedinger's plan.

The excerpt that we have included in this volume is the first in a series of four lectures that Schroedinger gave shortly after he had discovered his wave equation for the electron and had used it to obtain the correct energy levels of an electron inside an atom (that is, the frequencies of the spectral lines), and to explain the motion of the electron in these levels. He begins by restating the Hamiltonian theory in the form of a variational principle, which involves the kinetic energy, or the difference between the total and potential energies of a particle moving in a force field. This is the content of equation (2) of the Schroedinger excerpt.

To understand this equation, consider a particle, for example, a planet, falling freely in a gravitational field. If this planet is to move from some point A to another point B, it is clear that, with a given velocity, that is with a given speed and direction of motion at point A, it can reach point B along only one possible path (this path is, of course, a segment of the actual orbit of the planet). What distinguishes this path from all other lines that can be drawn between A and B? Hamilton's principle, as contained in equation (2) tells us: If we divide the actual path of the particle into infinitesimal segments, we note that in each of these segments the particle has a kinetic, a potential, and a total energy—this last being the sum of the first two. If for any segment we represent the kinetic energy as the difference between the total energy E of the particle and its potential energy V, multiply this by twice the mass of the particle, take the square root of the result, and multiply this by the length of the segment of the path (ds in the equation), we obtain an element of Maupertuis action. If we now sum all of these elements of action along the true path of the particle from point A to point B by integrating along the path, the sum we obtain is smaller than that for any nearby—but of course, not permissible

—path connecting these two points; or, more generally, it differs only slightly from that of any neighboring path.

The analogy with a ray of light in geometric optics is obtained by considering Fermat's principle: A ray of light in an inhomogeneous medium moves from A to B along a path that requires the shortest time. We see that the two situations are similar because in each case the actual path is described in terms of a minimum or stationary principle. The analogy between the two situations is even more striking if we divide the path of the ray into infinitesimal segments, as we did that of the particle. If we then divide the length of each of these segments by the speed of the ray along that segment, we obtain a series of infinitesimal time intervals; the sum of these intervals is smaller along the actual path of the ray than it is along any nearby path.

If we compare these two minimum principles, we see that the particle moves in the force field as though it were a ray of light moving in a special optical medium in which the speed depends on the wavelength or frequency of the light (that is, on the energy of the particle) so that the medium is dispersive. This is the content of equation (4) of Schroedinger's lecture.

With this important first step, Schroedinger obtained a wave equation for a particle (for example, an electron moving in the electric field of a proton, as in the case of the hydrogen atom) by starting from the usual equation for the propagation of a wave disturbance in some medium, equation (10). Since the speed of propagation of this disturbance, called the phase velocity of the wave, appears in this equation, Schroedinger saw that it should be possible to obtain a wave equation for a particle by replacing the phase velocity in equation (10) with the expression from equation (8) for the phase velocity of a particle. He had already obtained such an expression for the phase velocity of a particle from his analogy between geometrical optics and the motion of a particle. To complete the derivation, one more step was necessary: the introduction of Planck's fundamental hypothesis. Therefore, Schroedinger, like De Broglie, assumed that the frequency of a particle-wave is equal to the total energy of the particle divided by the Planck constant of action.

When we consider the derivation of the Schroedinger equation in this series of steps, we realize that few of his procedures were based on anything more than analogy. Nothing in Schroedinger's analysis can be taken as a proof for any step in his reasoning, and yet the result of his inexact and rather amorphous method was the discovery of one of the most powerful equations in all of physics. It may be noted that when Schroedinger introduced his wave equation, he had no idea of the physical significance of the wave function (the quantity ψ) that his equation governs. He remarked that "in the case of waves which are to replace in our thought the motion of the electron, there must also be some quantity p subject to a wave equation like equation (10), though we cannot yet tell the physical meaning of p." It is all the more remarkable that this reasoning by analogy guided Schroedinger to a correct wave equation when we consider the complexity of the problem involved and that the ultimate correct interpretation of the wave function brought into consideration some of the most subtle concepts of modern physics. Furthermore, the complex nature of the wave function (consisting of both a real and an imaginary part) must at first have been somewhat puzzling, if not disturbing.

Schroedinger's derivation of his wave equation must have appeared very much like pulling rabbits out of a hat to the physicists of his day. It is doubtful that his equation would have been accepted had it come at a time when events did not demand a radical break with the past. Even so, physicists found it extremely difficult to reconcile the Schroedinger equation with their understanding of quantum theory, for it was known that quantum phenomena are essentially of a discontinuous, discrete nature, whereas his equation describes the behavior of a continuously propagated wave. The wave-particle dualism (Bohr's complementarity) was then unknown.

Most physicists continued to believe that the only correct approach to the quantum mechanics of the atom was the use of the Heisenberg matrix mechanics. Matrices, being arrays of discrete numbers, seemed perfectly suited for the description of the motion of an electron inside an atom with its discrete orbits. They therefore accepted the Schroedinger picture only with the greatest reservations, as a sort of mathematical trick that could be used to solve problems easily, but without any true physical content. It remained for Dirac, Born, and Jordan to show finally that the Schroedinger equation and wave function are related to the probability of finding an electron at a given point and that the Schroedinger wave mechanics and the matrix mechanics are two sides of the same coin, although Schroedinger himself had already shown how wave mechanics and matrix mechanics were to be reconciled in terms of operators.

Erwin Schroedinger's personality was much more complex than that of any one of the other physicists who created the quantum mechanics; except for Born, he approached the subject with much deeper roots in classical physics and traditional philosophy than the others. Moreover, again with the exception of Born, he was a good deal older than the others and less inclined to accept revolutionary solutions to problems. Indeed, we shall see that that very revolutionary creation of his own—the famous Schroedinger wave equation—was, to some extent, an attempt to escape from the discontinuity of quantum physics as represented by Bohr's quantum jumps.

He was born August 12, 1887, in Vienna, the only child of Rudolf

Schroedinger and of the daughter of Alexander Bauer, professor of chemistry at the Vienna Institute of Technology. Erwin spent his childhood in the delightful atmosphere of the academic circles of late nineteenth-century Vienna; he was raised in a household devoted to learning and culture. His father, who came from a Bavarian family that had settled in Vienna generations before Erwin was born, was an intellectually gifted man with a broad educational background, who studied chemistry at the Vienna Institute under Professor Bauer. He did not become a professional chemist but devoted himself to Italian painting and, later, to botany. This led to a series of papers on plant phylogeny. There is no doubt that these activities of his father greatly influenced Erwin, for he had a profound interest in the arts and in the origin and nature of life.

Schroedinger attended the Gymnasium at Vienna and there developed a wide range of interests in addition to his scientific work. He was particularly fond of the grammatical structures of ancient languages and was devoted to literature in general and to poetry in particular. Like most creative people he was repelled by rote learning and the need to follow a rigid curriculum.

In 1906 Schroedinger entered the University of Vienna and began his studies of classical physics under Fritz Hasenöhrl, who had succeeded Boltzmann. He greatly influenced Schroedinger and steered him into the kind of work that ultimately led him to the idea of a wave equation for the atom. This work dealt with the physics of "continuous media," which means media that are assumed to have no granular structure, like a smooth jelly. The vibrations of such media are classified as *eigenvalue* problems; Schroedinger thus became a master of these problems.

We may illustrate an *eigenvalue* problem in a simple way by considering a violin string. The vibrations of such a string can be described by a "differential equation" that contains a constant, which can be chosen at will. However, it turns out that only those vibrations of the string are actually observed (that is, are possible) for which this constant is an integer. These integers are called the *eigenvalues* of the problem. Thus, although the string is continuous, its vibrations are governed by integers. We shall see presently how Schroedinger used this idea.

After receiving his degree in physics in 1910, Schroedinger remained at the university as an assistant in physics, setting up elementary experiments in physics, from which, as he said, he never learned what experimental work really was. His academic career was interrupted by World War I and he spent the war years as an artillery officer.

In 1920 he became assistant to Willy Wien and from that position went to the University of Stuttgart as assistant professor and then to Breslau as full professor. When Max von Laue left the University of Zurich in the early 1920's, Schroedinger was invited to replace him as full professor of physics. The six years that he remained there were the most fruitful of his life and years of great happiness. He had married Annemarie Bertel in 1920 and life was very pleasant and exciting. It was during this period that he developed the wave equation.

In the early years of his residence at Zurich, Schroedinger published theoretical papers in the field of the specific heats of solids, thermodynamics, statistical mechanics, and atomic spectra. He also investigated various problems in the physiology of color.

The idea of a wave equation that would describe the motion of an electron inside an atom and would, at the same time, give the spectral lines, was very appealing to him, for he was unhappy about, and unreconciled to, the idea of quantum jumps. He therefore sought to return to some kind of continuous classical description by treating the spectrum as the solution of an *eigenvalue* problem. His reasoning was that if the discrete modes of vibration of a classical system like a violin string could be obtained as the solution of an *eigenvalue* problem, so could the Bohr stationary states. One could thus eliminate, so he thought, the idea of quantum jumps and replace it by the concept of transitions from one mode of vibration (*eigenvalue*) to another.

Schroedinger did not quite see how to do this before 1926, but toward the end of 1925 he learned about De Broglie's wave theory of the electron through some words of praise written by Einstein. This was all that Schroedinger needed, for if De Broglie was right and electrons were indeed waves, this meant vibrations, and vibrations in turn meant *eigenvalue* problems, and *eigenvalues* meant integers, and these, finally, meant the discrete spectral lines like the Balmer series. In a masterful display of creativity, Schroedinger grafted De Broglie's wave ideas onto Hamilton's formulation of Newtonian dynamics, and in a few months developed a wave equation that answered all the questions about the atom. He presented it to the scientific world without revealing how he had come to this remarkable invention. Only in later papers did he outline his derivation and show how his wave equation follows naturally from De Broglie and Hamilton. He shared the 1933 Nobel Prize in physics with Dirac for this discovery.

The Schroedinger wave equation was and still is the wonder of atomic physics for it presents a well-known and easily handled mathematical procedure for solving any imaginable problem without using the cumbersome matrix algebra of Born and his group. After discovering the wave equation, Schroedinger took the first step in unifying all the different approaches to quantum mechanics—Heisenberg's matrices, Dirac's non-commuting algebra and his own wave mechanics—by showing that if one solved the Schroedinger wave equation, the solution itself, which is called the Schroedinger wave function, could be used to obtain the Heisenberg matrices. This unification of quantum mechanics was later generalized and stated in its complete form by Dirac.

Schroedinger parted company with most physicists (particularly Born) when it came to the interpretation of the Schroedinger wave function. He proposed to treat the electron not as a particle but as a real wave spread throughout all of space in varying concentrations. He rejected the wave-particle dualism. In this he differed radically from Born's probability interpretation. This led to many private and public debates between Born and Schroedinger. In one letter to Born, Schroedinger wrote, "You, Maxel, you know that I am very fond of you, and nothing can change that, but I must once and for all give you a basic scolding . . ." and then followed an admonition taking Born to task for the "boldness" with which he constantly asserts that the "Copenhagen interpretation" of the quantum mechanics is generally accepted, when he knows well enough that Einstein, Planck, De Broglie, von Laue, and Schroedinger himself are not satisfied with it. When Born replied, giving a list of good physicists who did not agree with the group mentioned by Schroedinger, Schroedinger in turn answered, "Since when, moreover, is a scientific thesis determined by a majority? (You could perhaps answer: at least since Newton's time)." And so it went between these two warm friends and intellectual opponents.

After Schroedinger's great success with his wave equation, he was invited to Berlin as Planck's successor in 1927 and remained there until 1933, taking an active part in the vigorous exchange of ideas among the great physicists that occurred at the weekly colloquia. When Hitler came to power in 1933, Schroedinger, racially acceptable to the Nazis, who would have showered him with wealth and honors had he collaborated with them, decided to leave immediately. As Born, who was forced to leave Germany because of the racial laws, put it, "He did it, and we admired him. For it is no small matter to be uprooted in one's middle age and to live in a foreign land. But he would have it no other way."

Schroedinger left Berlin to hold a fellowship at Oxford, but in 1936 he accepted a position at the University of Graz, Austria. He did this only after a great deal of thought, for he was well aware of the Nazi danger. But his love for Austria outweighed his caution. In 1938, when Austria was annexed, Schroedinger escaped to Italy and from there he came to Princeton. De Valera then founded the Institute of Advanced Studies in Dublin, primarily for Schroedinger, who became the director of its School for Theoretical Physics. He remained in Dublin until his retirement in 1955.

During this period, Schroedinger did active research in numerous fields and published many papers on topics ranging from the unification of gravitation and electromagnetism to the problems of life. In 1944 he published a small book, *What Is Life?*, and this question continued to interest him until his death. In an article "Are There Quantum Jumps?" published in two parts in the *British Journal for the Philosophy of Science* in 1952, he challenged the whole statistical concept of the Born school. A public debate between him and Born, who was then at Edinburgh, was arranged, but Schroedinger could not attend because of illness.

After his retirement, Schroedinger returned to Vienna as a highly honored citizen; he died there on January 4, 1961.

More than any of his contemporaries, Schroedinger was a lone worker, finding it very difficult to collaborate with anyone else. He was very reserved in his personal life, sharing his experiences with only a few of his very intimate friends.

Wanting to be free at all times to wander off at a moment's notice he always carried his belongings in a rucksack on his back. He generally was last to arrive at the hotel reserved for participants of a conference, for he always walked to the hotel from the station, lost in his own thoughts.

The name of this many-sided genius, who contributed so profoundly to our understanding of nature, will never be forgotten. Just as we cannot today speak of the motion of an electron without mentioning the Schroedinger wave equation or the Schroedinger wave function so will it be with physicists for ages to come.

ဝဝဝဝဝဝဝ

SCHROEDINGER

Wave Mechanics [1]

DERIVATION OF THE FUNDAMENTAL IDEA OF WAVE MECHANICS FROM HAMILTON'S ANALOGY BETWEEN ORDINARY MECHANICS AND GEOMETRICAL OPTICS

WHEN A MASS-POINT M MOVES in a conservative field of force, described by the potential energy $V(x, y, z)$, then, if you let it start from a given point A with a given velocity, i.e. with a given energy E, you will be able to get it into another arbitrarily chosen point B by suitably "aiming," i.e. by letting it start in a quite definitely chosen *direction*. There is in general *one* definite dynamical orbit which leads from A to B *with a given energy*. This orbit possesses the property that

$$\delta \int_A^B 2T dt = 0, \qquad (1)$$

---

[1] Erwin Schroedinger, *Four Lectures on Wave Mechanics* (London: Blackie & Sons, Ltd., 1928), pp. 1–12.

and is defined by this property (Hamilton's principle in the form given to it by Maupertuis). Here T means the kinetic energy of the mass-point, and the equation means: consider the manifold of *all* orbits leading from A to B and subject to the law of conservation of energy $(T + V = E)$; among them the actual dynamical orbit is distinguished by the fact that, *for it* and for all infinitely adjacent orbits of the manifold, the $\int_A^B$ has the *same* value up to small quantities of the *second* order (the words "infinitely adjacent" being taken to define the *first* order of smallness).

Calling $w = \dfrac{ds}{dt}$ the velocity of the mass-point, we have

$$2T = mw^2 = m\left(\frac{ds}{dt}\right)^2 = 2(E - V) = \frac{ds}{dt}\sqrt{2m(E - V)},$$

by means of which equation (1) can be transformed into

$$\delta\int_A^B \sqrt{2m(E - V)}\,ds = 0. \tag{2}$$

This form has the advantage that the variational principle is applied to a purely geometrical integral, which does not contain the time-variable, and further, that the condition of constant energy is automatically taken care of.

Hamilton found it useful to compare equation (2) with *Fermat's* principle, which tells us that in an optically non-homogeneous medium the actual light rays, i.e. the tracks along which energy is propagated, are determined by the "law of minimum time" (as it is usually called). Let [Fig. 64–1] *now* refer to an optical medium of arbitrary non-homogeneity,

Fig. 64–1.

e.g. the earth's atmosphere; then, if you have a searchlight at A, furnishing a well-defined beam, it will in general be possible to illuminate an arbitrarily chosen point B by suitably *aiming* at it with the searchlight. There is one definite light-path leading from A to B, which obeys, and is uniquely defined by, the law

$$\delta\int_A^B \frac{ds}{u} = 0. \tag{3}$$

Here *ds,* as before, means the element of the path, and *u* is the velocity of light, a function of the co-ordinates *x, y, z.*

The two laws contained in equations (2) and (3) respectively become identical, if we postulate that

$$u = \frac{C}{\sqrt{2m(E - V)}},\tag{4}$$

where *C* must be independent of *x, y, z* but may depend on *E.* Thus we have made a mental picture of an optical medium, in which the manifold of possible light-rays coincides with the manifold of dynamical orbits of a mass-point *m* moving *with given energy E* in a field of force *V(x, y, z).* The fact that *u,* the velocity of light, depends not only on the co-ordinates but also on *E,* the total energy of the mass-point, is of the utmost importance.

This fact enables us to push the analogy a step farther by picturing the dependence on *E* as dispersion, i.e. as a dependence on *frequency.* For this purpose we must attribute to our light-rays a definite frequency *v,* depending on *E.* We will (arbitrarily) put

$$E = hv\tag{5}$$

(*h* being Planck's constant), without dwelling much on this assumption, which is very suggestive to modern physicists. Then this non-homogeneous and dispersive medium provides in its *rays* a picture of *all* the dynamical orbits of our particle. Now we can proceed a stage farther, putting the question: can we make a small "point-like" *light-signal* move *exactly* like our mass-point? (Hitherto we have only secured the geometrical identity of *orbits,* quite neglecting the question of time-rate.) At first sight this seems impossible, since the velocity of the mass-point,

$$w = \frac{1}{m} \sqrt{2m(E - V)},\tag{6}$$

is (along the path, i.e. with constant *E*) *inversely* proportional to the light-velocity *u* (see equation (4); *C* depends on *E* only). But we must remember that *u* is of course the ordinary *phase*-velocity, whereas a small light-signal moves with the so-called *group-velocity,* say *g,* which is given by

$$\frac{1}{g} = \frac{d}{dv}\left(\frac{v}{u}\right),$$

or, in our case, following equation (5), by

$$\frac{1}{g} = \frac{d}{dE}\left(\frac{E}{u}\right).\tag{7}$$

We will try to make g = w. The only means we have at our disposal for this purpose is a suitable choice of C, the arbitrary function of E that appeared in equation (4). From (4), (6), and (7), the postulate $g = w$ becomes

$$\frac{d}{dE}\left(\frac{E\sqrt{2m(E-V)}}{C}\right) = \frac{m}{\sqrt{2m(E-V)}} \equiv \frac{d}{dE}\left(\sqrt{2m(E-V)}\right);$$

hence

$$\left(\frac{E}{C}-1\right)\sqrt{2m(E-V)}$$

is constant with respect to E. Since V contains the co-ordinates and C must be a function of E only, this relation can obviously be secured in a general way only by making the first factor vanish. Hence

$$\frac{E}{C}-1 = 0, \quad \text{or} \quad C = E,$$

which gives equation (4) the special form

$$u = \frac{E}{\sqrt{2m(E-V)}} \tag{8}$$

This assumption about phase-velocity is the only one which will secure absolute coincidence between the dynamical laws of motion of the mass-point and the optical laws of motion of light-signals in our imagined light-propagation. It is worth while mentioning that, according to (8),

$$u = \frac{\text{energy}}{\text{momentum}} \tag{8'}$$

There is still *one* arbitrariness in the definition of u, viz.: E may obviously be changed by an arbitrary additive constant, if the same constant is added to $V(x, y, z)$. This arbitrariness cannot be overcome in the non-relativistic treatment and we are not going to deal with the relativistic one in the present lectures.

Now the fundamental idea of wave-mechanics is the following. The phenomenon, of which we believed we had given an adequate description in the old mechanics by describing the motion of a mass-point, i.e. by giving its co-ordinates x, y, z as functions of the time variable t, is to be described correctly—according to the new ideas—by describing a definite wave-motion, which takes place among waves of the type considered, i.e. of the definite frequency and velocity (and hence of the definite wave-length) which we ascribed to what we called "light" in the preceding. The mathematical description of a wave-motion will be furnished not by a limited number of functions of the one variable t, but by a continuous manifold, so to speak, of such functions, viz. by a function (or possibly by several functions) of x, y, z, and t. These functions will be subject to a *partial* differential equation, viz. to some sort of *wave equation*.

The statement that what *really* happens is correctly described by describing a wave-motion does not necessarily mean exactly the same thing as: what really *exists* is the wave-motion. We shall see later on that in generalizing to an *arbitrary* mechanical system we are led to describe what really happens in such a system by a wave-motion in the generalized space of its co-ordinates (q-space). Though the latter has quite a definite physical meaning, it cannot very well be said to "exist"; hence a wave-motion in this space cannot be said to "exist" in the ordinary sense of the word either. It is merely an adequate mathematical description of what happens. It may be that also in the case of one single mass-point, with which we are now dealing, the wave-motion must not be taken to "exist" in *too* literal a sense, although the configuration space happens to coincide with ordinary space in this particularly simple case.

ORDINARY MECHANICS ONLY AN APPROXIMATION, WHICH NO LONGER HOLDS FOR VERY SMALL SYSTEMS

In replacing the ordinary mechanical description by a wave-mechanical description our object is to obtain a theory which comprises both ordinary mechanical phenomena, in which quantum conditions play no appreciable part, and, on the other hand, typical quantum phenomena. The hope of reaching this object resides in the following analogy. Hamilton's wave-picture, worked out in the way discussed above, contains *something* that corresponds to ordinary mechanics, viz. the *rays* correspond to the mechanical *paths*, and *signals* move like *mass-points*. But the description of a wave-motion in terms of *rays* is merely an approximation (called "geometrical optics" in the case of light-waves). It only holds if the structure of the wave phenomenon that we happen to be dealing with is coarse compared with the wave-length, and as long as we are only interested in its "coarse structure." The detailed fine structure of a wave phenomenon can never be revealed by a treatment in terms of rays ("geometrical optics"), and there always exist wave-phenomena which are altogether so minute that the ray-method is of no use and furnishes no information whatever. Hence in replacing ordinary mechanics by wave mechanics we may hope on the one hand to retain ordinary mechanics as an approximation which is valid for the coarse "macro-mechanical" phenomena, and on the other hand to get an explanation of those minute "micro-mechanical" phenomena (motion of the electrons in the atom), about which ordinary mechanics was quite unable to give any information. At least it was unable to do so without making very artificial accessory assumptions, which really formed a much more important part of the theory than the mechanical treatment itself.*

The step which leads from ordinary mechanics to wave mechanics is an advance similar in kind to Huygens' theory of light, which replaced Newton's theory. We might form the symbolic proportion:

Ordinary mechanics : Wave mechanics
   = Geometrical optics : Undulatory optics.

Typical quantum phenomena are analogous to typical wave phenomena like diffraction and interference.

For the conception of this analogy it is of considerable importance that the failure of ordinary mechanics does occur in dealing with very *tiny* systems. We can immediately control the order of magnitude at which complete failure is to be expected, and we shall see that it is exactly the right one. The wave-length, say λ, of our waves is (see equations (5) and (8))

$$\lambda = \frac{u}{v} = \frac{h}{\sqrt{2m(E-V)}} = \frac{h}{mw}, \tag{9}$$

i.e. Planck's constant divided by the momentum of the mass-point. Now take, for the sake of simplicity, a circular orbit of the hydrogen-model, of radius a, but not necessarily a "quantized" one. Then we have by ordinary mechanics (without applying quantum rules):

$$mwa = n\frac{h}{2\pi},$$

where n is any real positive number (which for Bohr's quantized circles would be 1, 2, 3 . . . ; the occurrence of h in the latter equation is for the moment only a convenient way of expressing the order of magnitude).

---

* To give an example: the actual application of the rules for quantization to the several-electron problem was, strange to say, not hindered by the fact that nobody in the world ever knew how to *enunciate* them for a non-conditionally periodic system! We simply *took* the problem of several bodies to be conditionally periodic, though it was perfectly well known that it was not. This shows, I think, that ordinary mechanics was not made use of in a very serious manner, otherwise the said application would have been as impossible as the application of penal law to the motion of the planets.

Combining the last two equations, we get

$$\frac{\lambda}{a} = \frac{2\pi}{n}.$$

Now in order that we may be justified in the application of ordinary mechanics it is necessary that the dimensions of the path calculated in this way should turn out to be large compared with the wave-length. This is seen to be the case as long as the "quantum number" n is large compared with unity. As n becomes smaller and smaller, the ratio of λ to a becomes less and less favourable. A complete failure of ordinary mechanics is to be expected precisely in the region where we actually meet with it, viz. where n is of the order of unity, as it would be for orbits of the normal size of an atom (10^{-8} cm.).

BOHR'S STATIONARY ENERGY-LEVELS DERIVED AS THE FREQUENCIES OF PROPER VIBRATIONS OF THE WAVES

Let us now consider the wave-mechanical treatment of a case which is inaccessible to ordinary mechanics; say, to fix our ideas, the wave-mechanical treatment of what in ordinary mechanics is called the motion of the electron in the hydrogen atom.

In what way are we to attack this problem?

Well, in very much the same way as we would attack the problem of finding the possible movements (vibrations) of an elastic body. Only, in the latter case the problem is complicated by the existence of *two* types of waves, longitudinal and transverse. To avoid this complication, let us consider an elastic fluid contained in a given enclosure. For the pressure, p, say, we should have a wave equation

$$\nabla^2 p - \frac{1}{u^2}\ddot{p} = 0, \tag{10}$$

u being the *constant* velocity of propagation of longitudinal waves, the only waves possible in the case of a fluid. We should have to try to find the most general solution of this partial differential equation that satisfies certain boundary conditions at the surface of the vessel. The standard way of solving is to try

$$p(x, y, z, t) = \psi(x, y, z)e^{2\pi i \nu t},$$

which gives for ψ the equation

$$\nabla^2 \psi + \frac{4\pi^2 \nu^2}{u^2}\psi = 0, \tag{10'}$$

ψ being subject to the same boundary conditions as p. We then meet with the well-known fact that a regular solution ψ satisfying the equation and the boundary conditions cannot be obtained for *all* values of the co-efficient of ψ, i.e. for *all* frequencies ν, but only for an infinite set of discrete frequencies ν_1, ν_2, ν_3, . . . , ν_k, . . . , which are called the characteristic or proper frequencies (*Eigenfrequenzen*) of the problem or of the body. Call ψ_k the solution (ordinarily unique apart from a multiplying constant) that belongs to ν_k, then—since the equation and the boundary conditions are homogeneous—

$$p = \sum_k c_k \psi_k e^{2\pi i (\nu_k t + \theta_k)} \tag{11}$$

will, with arbitrary constants c_k, θ_k, be a more general solution and will indeed be *the* general solution, if the set of quantities (ψ_k, ν_k) is complete. (For physical applications we shall of course have to use the real part of the expression (11).)

In the case of the waves which are to replace in our thought the motion of the electron, there must also be some quantity p, subject to a wave equation like equation (10), though we cannot yet tell the physical meaning of p. Let us put this question aside for the moment. In equation (10) we shall have to put (see above)

$$u = \frac{E}{\sqrt{2m(E - V)}} \tag{8}$$

This is not a constant; it depends (1) on E, that is, essentially on the frequency $\nu(= E/h)$; (2) on the co-ordinates x, y, z, which are contained in the potential energy V. These are the two complications as compared with the simple case of a vibrating fluid body considered above. Neither of them is serious. By the first, the dependence on E, we are restricted in that we can apply the wave equation only to a function p whose dependence on the time is given by

$$p \sim e^{\frac{2\pi i E t}{h}},$$

whence

$$\ddot{p} = -\frac{4\pi^2 E^2}{h^2} p \tag{12}$$

We need not mind that, since it is precisely the same assumption (*Ansatz*) as would be made in any case in the standard method of solution. Substituting from (12) and (8) in (10) and replacing the letter p by ψ (to remind us that now, just as before, we are investigating a function of the co-ordinates only), we obtain

$$\Delta^2\psi + \frac{8\pi^2 m}{h^2}(E - V)\psi = 0 \qquad (13)$$

We now see that the *second* complication (the dependence of u on V, i.e. on the co-ordinates) merely results in a somewhat more interesting form of equation (13) as compared with (10′), the quantity multiplying ψ being no longer a *constant,* but depending on the co-ordinates. This was really to be expected, since an equation that is to embody the mechanical problem cannot very well help containing the potential energy of the problem. A simplification in the problem of the "mechanical" waves (as compared with the fluid problem) consists in the absence of boundary conditions.

I thought the latter simplification fatal when I first attacked these questions. Being sufficiently versed in mathematics, I could not imagine how proper vibration frequencies could appear *without* boundary conditions. Later on I recognized that the more complicated form of the coefficients (i.e. the appearance of $V(x, y, z)$) takes charge, so to speak, of what is ordinarily brought about by boundary conditions, namely, the selection of definite values of E.

I cannot enter into this rather lengthy mathematical discussion here, nor into the detailed process of finding the solutions, though the method is practically the same as in ordinary vibration problems, namely: introducing an appropriate set of co-ordinates (e.g. spherical or elliptical, according to the form of the function V) and putting ψ equal to a *product* of functions, each of which contains one co-ordinate only. I will state the result straightforwardly for the case of the hydrogen atom. Here we have to put

$$V = -\frac{e^2}{r} + \text{const.,} \qquad (14)$$

r being the distance from the nucleus. Then it is found that not for all, but only for the following values of E, is it possible to find regular, one-valued, and finite solutions ψ:

$$\left.\begin{array}{l} \text{(A)} \quad E_n = \text{const.} - \dfrac{2\pi^2 m e^4}{h^2 n^2} \; ; n = 1, 2, 3, 4 \\[2mm] \text{(B)} \quad E > \text{const.} \end{array}\right\} \qquad (14')$$

The constant is the same as in (14) and is (in non-relativistic wave mechanics) meaningless, except that we cannot very well give it the value which is usually adopted for the sake of simplicity, viz. zero. For then all the values (A) would become negative. And a negative frequency, if it means anything at all, means the same as the positive frequency of the same absolute value. Then it would be mysterious why all positive frequencies should be allowed, but only a discrete set of negative ones. But the question of this constant is of no importance here.

You see that our differential equation automatically selects as the allowed E-values (A) the energy-levels of the elliptic orbits quantized according to Bohr's theory; (B) all energy-levels belonging to hyperbolic orbits. This is very remarkable. It shows that, whatever the waves may mean physically, the theory furnishes a method of quantization which is absolutely free from arbitrary postulates that this or that quantity must be an integer. Just to give an idea *how* the integers occur here: if e.g. ϕ is an azimuthal angle and the wave amplitude turns out to contain a factor $\cos m\phi$, m being an arbitrary constant, then m must *necessarily* be chosen integral, since otherwise the wave function would not be *single-valued*.

You will be interested in the form of the wave functions ψ which belong to the E-values mentioned above, and will inquire whether any observable facts can be explained by them. This *is* the case, but the matter is rather intricate.

ooooooooooo

STATISTICS AND WAVES

ooooooooooo

Max Born (b. 1882)

As we have seen, the Schroedinger wave mechanics gave physicists a complete mathematical procedure (the Schroedinger wave equation) for solving the dynamic problems associated with the motion of electrons in the atom. Moreover, De Broglie and Schroedinger had succeeded in relating the quantum conditions introduced by Bohr to the wave properties of electrons; the various stationary states were to be considered as similar to the nodes in the vibration of a metal plate. With his wave equation, Schroedinger solved the problem of deriving from the De Broglie wave picture the Bohr stationary states, or energy levels of the electron. One had only to solve the appropriate Schroedinger wave equation, using the proper boundary conditions, and the energy levels of the electron came out automatically.

In spite of this great achievement there were still some difficulties associated with the interpretation of the Schroedinger wave mechanics that gave the entire theory an appearance of unreality. For although the solutions of the Schroedinger equation gave the correct energy levels of the electrons inside an atom, still it was difficult to see just what physical meaning one could give to the waves that the Schroedinger equation assigned to the motion of an electron.

De Broglie considered his waves as real properties of the electron and therefore as representing physical vibrations of the electron itself. However, Schroedinger's development of the wave equation cast some serious doubts on the reality of these waves. The amplitudes of the waves that one obtains from a solution of the Schroedinger equation are complex mathematical quantities composed of real and imaginary parts. Now we know that although complex quantities appear very often in the mathematical description of physical systems, the only physical interpretation that can have any meaning must involve only the real parts of these mathematical expressions, and in all theories up to the time of Schroedinger's, all physical quantities such as the amplitudes of physical waves (sound waves, waves of light, etc.) always appeared as real mathematical quantities even though complex and imaginary mathematical quantities (to simplify the mathematics) were used to obtain these physical quantities. In the case of the Schroedinger theory, however, the amplitudes of the waves describing the electrons are not real quantities and one obtains incorrect results if one works only with the real parts of these waves.

Just like De Broglie, Schroedinger believed in the physical reality of his waves and assumed that electrons were not particles at all but vibrating clouds extending in all directions in space. He thought that the particle picture of the electron was completely untenable and that physical reality existed only in the waves. He pictured the radiation from an electron as resulting from the vibrations associated with the waves of the electron.

Aside from the purely formal difficulty of describing real things with imaginary mathematical quantities, a more serious objection to the Schroedinger interpretation was pointed out by Max Born, who finally gave the correct interpretation of the wave functions associated with the motion of an electron. As Born notes in the article taken from his book *Atomic Physics* and reproduced in this chapter, the wave packet interpretation of the electron (that is, the notion that the electron is a vibrating cloud of charge) is incorrect because such a cloud, on the basis of the elementary properties of wave packets, could not retain its structure, and would spread until it became thoroughly dissipated. To overcome these difficulties, Born proposed an interpretation of the wave function in terms of probabilities. As he states in the excerpt that follows this commentary:

> According to this view, the whole course of events is determined by the laws of probability; to a state in space there corresponds a definite probability, which is given by the de Broglie wave associated with the state.[1]

This means that the waves do not represent physical vibrations but rather the unfolding of the probabilities of future events from a given initial state. In arriving at this interpretation, Born was guided by the behavior of waves and particles that are scattered by some body or field of force. In such scattering processes involving light, the intensity of the scattered beam is determined by the square of the amplitude of the wave associated with the light, and therefore this must be a measure of the number of photons that are present in the scattered wave. But the num-

---

[1] Max Born, *Atomic Physics* (7th ed.; New York: Hafner, 1962), Chapter IV.

ber of photons in a scattered beam is a measure of the probability of finding a photon in that beam. In other words, the probability for finding a particular state of scattering, or a beam scattered in a given direction, is determined by the amplitude of the scattered wave.

Born assumed that the De Broglie wave associated with a scattered beam of electrons would be a measure of the probability for that particular state of scattering. In general, therefore, the square of the amplitude of the De Broglie wave of an electron determines the probability of finding the electron in a given region of space.

We may illustrate this point by drawing an analogy between the De Broglie waves of a collection of particles and the water waves on the ocean. If we watch the ocean, we observe that the surface is in constant agitation. The disturbances range from small ripples to large waves. The greater the amplitude of a wave, that is, the higher above the surface of the ocean is the crest of the wave, the more intense is the disturbance of the water at that point. Where there is no disturbance at all, the water is perfectly smooth and the amplitude of the wave is zero. We now picture the space surrounding an electron or a swarm of electrons as being similar to the surface of the ocean. But the waves with which we are now concerned are not physical ones, but rather probability waves, or waves that are a measure of the probability for finding the electron, or groups of electrons, at particular points in space. The greater the intensity of a De Broglie wave at a point, the greater is the probability for finding the electron there; should the amplitude of the De Broglie wave vanish at any point, the probability for finding the electron there is zero.

Suppose we consider an electron in a region of space in which the De Broglie wave is spread out uniformly, so that the amplitude of the wave is everywhere the same. This means that there is an equal probability of finding the electron at any point in this region. What happens, then, if we perform an experiment in which we look for the electron and locate it at a given point in this region? For example, we can place a fluorescent screen in some position and if the electron happens to strike it, we observe a scintillation at the point where it hits the screen. Since we know that the electron is precisely at this point of scintillation on the screen, the probability of finding the electron there is one and the probability of finding the electron elsewhere at this time is zero. This means that we may think of the De Broglie wave describing the electron, which originally was spread out uniformly, as now concentrated in a tiny packet. Thus, by performing an experiment we have altered the nature of the wave describing the electron and therefore the future unfolding of the probability.

In this connection, it is interesting to consider a very penetrating objection by Einstein to the interpretation that the De Broglie waves are real. If a beam of light is allowed to fall on a surface such as glass, part of the beam is reflected and part is transmitted. If we attribute this to the wave character of light, the same thing must then be true of the electron wave packet. If we allow an electron, represented by a De Broglie wave packet, to impinge upon a surface or to pass into an electric field, which is the same thing, part of the packet should pass through the surface and part should be reflected. If we place a fluorescent screen in such a position as to intercept these two packets, a scintillation occurs where one, but not both of these packets strikes the screen. The reason for this is that the electron is not divisible. If we look for it, we find it in either one or the other of the paths but never in both. Of course, if we do not look for the electron, we must consider the electron as being simultaneously in both the transmitted and reflected beams; then the probability of finding the electron in either beam is given by the square of the amplitude of the De Broglie wave of the respective beam. However, by looking for the electron and finding it in a particular beam we immediately destroy the wave packet in the other beam so that a mere increase in our knowledge of the electron's position has altered the structure of the wave describing the electron after its interaction with the reflecting surface.

The remarkable part about this type of phenomena is that by finding the electron in one of the beams, we destroy the wave packet in the other beam regardless of how far apart in space the two packets were at the moment we looked for the electron. This occurs instantaneously, and, according to Einstein, this means that the waves defining the packets cannot be physical quantities; for if they were, we should be faced with a situation in which a causal action is transmitted from one packet to the other with a speed greater than the speed of light.

In spite of Einstein's important observation, one cannot get away entirely from the physical reality of the waves. We may understand the nature of this difficulty better if we consider the interference of waves. We know that if we allow a beam of light to fall on an opaque surface in which two small holes have been punched fairly close together, two trains of waves leave the holes on the other side of the screen. If we now permit these two trains of waves to fall upon another screen, we discover that the light is not distributed uniformly in two small regions where the two wave trains hit, but rather that the light is distributed in a series of light and dark bands over a single region of the screen. In other words, the two wave trains interfere with each other, giving rise to bands of maximum intensity alternating with bands of zero intensity. The same is true if a stream of electrons falls on a surface with two small holes in it. When the electrons leave the other side of the surface, there are two interfering De Broglie wave trains, and in accordance with the principles of the interference of such wave trains, a scintillating screen shows that the electrons are not distributed uniformly over two small regions but instead are found in the regions of maximum intensity of the interfering waves, which are spread over a large area.

But now we come to one of the strange paradoxes that beset this theory. If we allow just one electron at a time to hit the surface, we find that the pattern left on the scintillating screen after many such electrons have passed through the two holes is precisely the same as when the electrons move together in a stream. What does this mean? It is clear that the interference pattern could not have been caused by the interference of two or more electrons, since each electron arrived at the scintillating screen alone. How then do we account for the interference pattern? Only by assuming that each electron interferes with itself by passing through both holes! Or, put differently, that the wave train representing the electron passes through both holes, and the resulting two wave trains representing the electron after it has passed through the holes interfere with each other. But this must imply that both wave trains have a physical reality because there could be no interference otherwise.

According to the views of Heisenberg and Niels Bohr, we must assume that the electron is simultaneously in both beams, and, in a sense, that the electron has passed through both holes simultaneously. It is in this very sense that a particle, like the electron, loses its particle properties and becomes a wave diffused over an extended region of space. As Bohr here pointed out, the wave and the particle pictures are complementary aspects of the same physical entity and one must exist at the expense of the other. The electron has this diffused wave character so long as we do not try to observe it, for as soon as we look for it and find it as a particle, we immediately condense it into a small wave packet concentrated in a small region of space. The more accurately we observe its position, the less diffuse its wavelike character becomes and the more do its corpuscular properties manifest themselves. This duality is intimately related to the Heisenberg uncertainty principle, which is discussed by Born in his article included in this chapter and which is considered in more detail in connection with Heisenberg's work in Chapter 66.

In the year 1901, Max Born, studying mathematics at the University of Breslau, his place of birth, was determined to become a professional mathematician. Attending the lectures in algebra given by Rosanes, a student of the famous algebraist Frobenius, he was thus introduced to the theory of matrices. At the time, he could not know that this course in algebra, with its emphasis on matrices, would give him the clue to the meaning of Heisenberg's strange rule for multiplying the coordinates and momenta of a particle, and lead to the quantum mechanics. Still intent on becoming a mathematician, Born continued his studies in mathematics at Heidelberg and at Zurich under Hurwitz, whose lectures on higher analysis were a great delight to him.

Probably the greatest influence on Born's future development came while he was at Göttingen where he attended the lectures of the outstanding mathematicians of the time—Felix Klein, David Hilbert, and Herman Minkowski. These men must have directed his attention to physical problems, for their mathematics had many applications to physics. Undoubtedly, Born's contact with Minkowski, who had developed the elegant four-dimensional mathematics for treating the theory of relativity, gave Born his abiding interest in this theory; no one can read Minkowski's work without experiencing a sense of great wonder and beauty. At that time Born was also studying with Runge, one of the pioneers in modern numerical methods, and pursuing courses in astronomy with K. Schwarzschild, who, more than a decade later, was to give the first solution of Einstein's famous gravitational field equations. Born's budding interest in physics was further heightened by work with Voigt, who was the expert in the elastic properties of matter. This work in physics must have made a very great impression on Born; his first venture into physics dealt with the elastic properties of wires and tapes and he later became an authority on crystal structure. In 1906 he was awarded the prize of the philosophical faculty of the University of Göttingen for his work on the stability of elastic wires and tapes, and from that time on his devotion to physics never faltered.

Like many another great physicist in our roster, Born came from a highly cultured family, steeped in the finest traditions of German humanism. He was born on December 11, 1882, to Professor Gustav Born, an anatomist and embryologist; his mother was Margarete Kauffmann, a member of a Silesian family of industrialists. With this background it was quite natural for Born to retain his interest in the humanities and literature while pursuing his research in physics; one finds in all of his writings a recognition and deep understanding of the unity of all knowledge. In particular, Born always wrote with a profound sense of the history of physics and the evolution of modern concepts from classical physics.

While still at Göttingen, he decided to continue with physics. Born subsequently studied at Cambridge under Larmor and J. J. Thomson, and still later worked with Lummer and Pringsheim at Breslau, where he acquired his ever-abiding interest in optics, which years later led him to write outstanding textbooks in optics. During this period he also studied relativity theory intensively and wrote his first paper on one phase of the theory; as a consequence, Minkowski invited Born to Göttingen. Minkowski died shortly after Born returned to Göttingen, but Born remained to prepare some of Minkowski's unfinished papers for publication. He later accepted a position as lecturer at Göttingen and published several papers on the relativity theory of the electron. Albert Michelson, then the outstanding physicist in the United States, recognized the importance of this work, and in 1912 invited Born to lecture on relativity at the University of Chicago.

Although appointed assistant professor at the University of Berlin in 1915 to assist Planck, Born entered the German Army where he worked on military technical problems. During this period he did considerable work on the theory of crystals and published his first book, *The Dynamics of Crystal Lattices*. This was the first in a series of papers, books, and monographs on crystal structure that spanned all of Born's creative life.

After the war Born, in 1919, accepted a professorship at the University of Frankfurt am Main, where his assistant was Otto Stern, who was later to win the Nobel Prize for the famous Stern-Gerlach experiment for measuring the spin and magnetic moment of an atom. In fact, Stern began these experiments under Born's direction.

By 1921 Born had attained a maturity and mastery of physics that clearly gave promise of great creative work. At this stage of his life he was contributing to almost every phase of physics; he had the ability to handle diverse problems with equal skill. In addition to his remarkable grasp of physics, he was an excellent mathematician who could apply the most powerful type of mathematical analysis to physical problems. With such an array of intellectual skills it is small wonder that, in 1921, he was offered the chair of theoretical physics at Göttingen, one of the most coveted posts in the German university system.

Born came to Göttingen at the same time as James Franck; these top-ranking physicists made the university the outstanding center of atomic research in Germany, surpassed in world-wide renown only by Bohr's Copenhagen Institute. So powerful was Born's influence that no serious student of physics considered his education complete without spending at least a year at Göttingen; among some of the outstanding physicists who worked with him were Pauli, Heisenberg, Jordan, Fermi, Von Neumann, Wigner, Weisskopf, Oppenheimer, Dirac, and Maria Goeppert-Mayer.

From 1921 to 1933, when Born was forced to leave Germany, he did his greatest work. With Heisenberg and Jordan he discovered the quantum mechanics. At the same time he extended and improved his theory of crystal structure and modernized his early book on the subject. He also wrote two books on atomic theory: one in the early twenties, based on the Bohr theory; later, one with Jordan, using the newly discovered quantum mechanics. This was the period during which Born discovered the correct interpretation of the wave function and assigned to quantum mechanics the statistical interpretation that has been its principal feature since then. It was for this work that he received the Nobel Prize in 1954, about fifteen years later than it should have been awarded. He also found the correct mathematical interpretation of Heisenberg's multiplication rule for physical quantities, which was the beginning of matrix mechanics.

This was a remarkable period in the history of physics, for during this time, while Born, Heisenberg, and Jordan were developing matrix mechanics, Paul Dirac was publishing his paper on noncommuting dynamic operators, and Schroedinger was preparing his famous paper on wave mechanics. Born declared in his Nobel address:

> The result [his collaboration with Heisenberg and Jordan] was a three-author paper which brought the formal side of the investigation to a definite conclusion. Before this paper appeared, came the first dramatic surprise: Paul Dirac's paper on the same subject . . . he did not resort to the known matrix theory of the mathematicians, but discovered the tool for himself and worked out the theory of such non-commuting symbols. . . .
>
> What this formalism really signified, was, however, by no means clear. Mathematics, as often happens, was cleverer than interpretative thought. While we were still discussing this point, there came the second dramatic surprise, the appearance of Schroedinger's famous paper. He took up quite a different line of thought which originated from Louis de Broglie.[2]

Interestingly enough, in 1925, Born received a letter from Davisson about the peculiar results that he had found in the reflection of electrons from metallic surfaces. Both Born and Franck suspected that Davisson's patterns were diffraction patterns of the De Broglie electron waves. On investigating this further they found that Davisson's results did, indeed, confirm De Broglie's theory and that De Broglie's formula for the wavelength of an electron moving with a particular speed agreed perfectly with the wavelength as measured from the diffraction pattern.

With the various aspects of work in quantum mechanics that was going on at that time, there was considerable confusion about the significance of many of the results. In particular, nobody knew exactly what the physical meaning of Schroedinger's wave function was. Schroedinger proposed that the particle concept be entirely discarded and his concept of wave function be given all the physical reality, which meant that the electron was to be pictured as spread out continuously over all of space. On the other hand, the Göttingen group, led by Born, refused to accept this interpretation, for they could not see how to reconcile such a concept with distinct particle counts in Geiger counters, cloud chambers, and so on. It was at this point that Born discovered the correct statistical interpretation of the wave function, which has been used in all atomic processes ever since. It is of historical interest to note that Born reached his conclusions by analogy with a suggestion of Einstein's concerning photons.

---

[2] Max Born, *Nobel Lecture—Physics: 1942–1962* (Amsterdam: Elsevier Pub. Co., 1964), p. 266.

Again an idea of Einstein's gave me the lead. He had tried to make the duality of particles—light quanta or photons—and waves comprehensible by interpreting the square of the optical wave amplitudes as probability density for the occurrence of photons. This concept could at once be carried over to the [Schroedinger] ψ-function: $|\psi|^2$ ought to represent the probability density for electrons (or other particles). It was easy to assert this, but how could it be proved? [3]

Born finally did prove it and firmly established the statistical interpretation of quantum mechanics. It may be explained as follows: If ψ_E is the wave function that describes the electron in a state of energy E, then the probability of finding the electron in the element of volume dV is given by $\psi_E \psi_E^*$ where ψ_E^* is the complex conjugate of ψ_E. This concept has been extremely fruitful and, as we shall see in Chapter 67, is the basis of the explanation of radioactivity of nuclei by Gamow, and that by Condon and Gurney.

After leaving Germany in 1933, Born went to Cambridge, where he remained for three years as Stokes lecturer. During this period he proposed, in a series of papers published with L. Infeld, a new type of electrodynamics to replace Maxwell's theory. His idea was to incorporate the structure of the electron into the electromagnetic field. Although this theory has many attractive features, it has not been generally accepted because of its mathematical complexity.

After spending some time at the Indian Institute of Science in Bangalore, in 1936, Born went to the University of Edinburgh as Tait professor of natural philosophy, where he remained until his retirement. During his career, Born received numerous awards, medals, prizes, fellowships, and honorary doctorates from many countries and universities, such as Bristol, Bordeaux, Oxford, Edinburgh, Oslo and Brussels, to name but a few. He holds the Stokes medal of Cambridge, the Max Planck medal of Germany, the Hughes medal of the Royal Society of London, and the Hugo Grotius medal for international law. In 1953 he was made Honorary Citizen of Göttingen and in 1959 was awarded the Grand Cross of Merit with Star of the Order of Merit of the German Federal Republic.

Born is not only a great scientist and scholar who has made significant contributions to all aspects of physics, he is also a great human being who is as much concerned with humanity as he is with science. For years he has been in the forefront of those who, like Einstein, have sought and are still seeking to make this a peaceful, more beautiful world. He has never divorced his science from the broad field of human knowledge and philosophy, but has attempted to relate all the recent discoveries in physics to basic philosophical principles.

---

[3] *Loc. cit.*

ooooooo

B O R N

Wave Corpuscles [4]

. . . To BEGIN WITH, SCHRÖDINGER ATTEMPTED
to interpret corpuscles, and particularly electrons, as *wave packets*. Although his formulæ are entirely correct, his interpretation cannot be maintained, since on the one hand, as we have already explained above, the
wave packets must in course of time become dissipated, and on the other
hand the description of the interaction of two electrons as a collision of
two wave packets in ordinary three-dimensional space lands us in grave
difficulties.

The interpretation generally accepted at present goes back to the present
writer. According to this view, the whole course of events is determined
by the laws of probability; to a state in space there corresponds a definite
probability, which is given by the de Broglie wave associated with the
state. A mechanical process is therefore accompanied by a wave process,
the guiding wave, described by Schrödinger's equation, the significance
of which is that it gives the probability of a definite course of the mechanical process. If, for example, the amplitude of the guiding wave is
zero at a certain point in space, this means that the probability of finding
the electron at this point is vanishingly small.

The physical justification for this hypothesis is derived from the consideration of scattering processes from the two points of view, the corpuscular and the undulatory. The problem of the scattering of light by
small particles of dust or by molecules, from the standpoint of the
classical wave theory, was worked out long ago. If the idea of light quanta
is to be applied, we see at once that the number of incident light quanta
must be put proportional to the intensity of the light at the place concerned, as calculated by the wave theory. This suggests that we should
attempt to calculate the scattering of electrons by atoms, by means of
wave mechanics. We think of an incident beam of electrons as having a
de Broglie wave associated with it. When it passes over the atom this

---

[4] Max Born, *Atomic Physics* (7th ed.; New York: Hafner, 1962), Chapter IV.

wave generates a secondary spherical wave; and analogy with optics suggests that a certain quadratic expression formed from the wave amplitude should be interpreted as the current strength, or as the number of scattered electrons. On carrying out the calculation it has been found that for scattering by a nucleus we get exactly Rutherford's formula. Many other scattering processes were afterwards subjected to calculation in this way, and the results found in good agreement with observation. These are the grounds for the conviction of the correctness of the principle of associating wave amplitude with number of particles (or probability).

In this picture the particles are regarded as independent of one another. If we take their mutual action into account, the pictorial view is to some extent lost again. We have then two possibilities. Either we use waves in spaces of more than three dimensions (with two interacting particles we would have $2 \times 3 = 6$ co-ordinates), or we remain in three-dimensional space, but give up the simple picture of the wave amplitude as an ordinary physical magnitude, and replace it by a purely abstract mathematical concept (the second quantisation of Dirac, Jordan) into which we cannot enter. Neither can we discuss the extensive formalism of the quantum theory which has arisen from this theory of scattering processes, and has been developed so far that every problem with physical meaning can in principle be solved by the theory. What, then, is a problem with physical meaning? This is for us the really important question, for clearly enough the corpuscular and wave ideas cannot be fitted together in a homogeneous theoretical formalism, without giving up some fundamental principles of the classical theory. The unifying concept is that of probability; this is here much more closely interwoven with physical principles than in the older physics. The elucidation of these relationships we owe to Heisenberg and Bohr (1927). According to them we must ask ourselves what after all it means when we speak of the description of a process in terms of corpuscles or in terms of waves. Hitherto we have always spoken of waves and corpuscles as given facts, without giving any consideration at all to the question whether we are justified in assuming that such things actually exist. The position has some similarity to that which existed at the time the theory of relativity was brought forward. Before Einstein, no one ever hesitated to speak of the *simultaneous* occurrence of two events, or ever stopped to consider whether the assertion of the simultaneity of two events at different places can be established physically, or whether the concept of simultaneity has any meaning at all. In point of fact Einstein proved that this concept must be "relativized," since two events may be simultaneous in one system of reference, but take place at different times in another. In a similar way, according to Heisenberg, the concepts corpuscle and wave must also be subjected to close scrutiny. With the concept of corpuscle, the idea is necessarily bound up that the thing in question possesses a perfectly definite momentum, and that it is at a definite place at the time considered. But the question arises: can we actually determine exactly both the position and the velocity of the "particle" at a given moment? If we cannot do so—and as a matter of fact we cannot—i.e. if we can never actually determine more than one of the two properties (possession of a definite position and of a definite momentum), and if when one is determined we can make no assertion at all about the other property for the same moment, so far as our experiment goes, then we are not justified in concluding that the "thing" under examination can actually be described as a particle in the usual sense of the term. We are equally unjustified in drawing this conclusion even if we can determine both properties simultaneously, if neither can then be determined exactly, that is to say, if from our experiment we can only infer that this "thing" is somewhere within a certain definite volume and is moving in some way with a velocity which lies within a certain definite interval. We shall show later by means of examples that the simultaneous determination of position and velocity is actually impossible, being inconsistent with quantum laws securely founded on experiment.

The ultimate origin of the difficulty lies in the fact (or philosophical principle) that we are compelled to use the words of common language when we wish to describe a phenomenon, not by logical or mathematical analysis, but by a picture appealing to the imagination. Common language has grown by everyday experience and can never surpass these limits. Classical physics has restricted itself to the use of concepts of this kind; by analysing visible motions it has developed two ways of representing them by elementary processes: moving particles and waves. There is no other way of giving a pictorial description of motions—we have to apply it even in the region of atomic processes, where classical physics breaks down.

Every process can be interpreted either in terms of corpuscles or in terms of waves, but on the other hand it is beyond our power to produce proof that it is actually corpuscles or waves with which we are dealing, for we cannot simultaneously determine all the other properties which are distinctive of a corpuscle or of a wave, as the case may be. We can therefore say that the wave and corpuscular descriptions are only to be regarded as complementary ways of viewing one and the same objective process, a process which only in definite limiting cases admits of complete pictorial interpretation. It is just the limited feasibility of measurements that defines the boundaries between our concepts of a particle and a wave. The corpuscular description means at bottom that we carry out the measurements with the object of getting exact information about momentum and energy relations (e.g. in the Compton effect), while experiments which amount to determinations of place and time we can always picture to ourselves in terms of the wave representation (e.g. passage of electrons through thin foils and observations of the deflected beam).

We shall now give the proof of the assertion that position and momentum (of an electron, for instance) cannot be exactly determined simultaneously. We illustrate this by the example of diffraction through a slit [Fig. 65–1]. If we propose to regard the passage of an electron through a slit and the observation of the diffraction pattern as simultaneous measurement of position and momentum from the standpoint of the corpuscle concept, then the breadth of the slit gives the "uncertainty" Δx, in the specification of position perpendicular to the direction of flight.

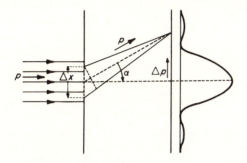

Fig. 65–1. Diffraction of electrons at a slit.

The fact that a diffraction pattern appears merely allows us to assert that the electron has passed through the slit; at what place in the slit the passage took place remains quite indefinite. Again, from the standpoint of the corpuscular theory, the occurrence of the diffraction pattern on the screen must be understood in the sense that the individual electron suffers deflection at the slit, upwards or downwards. It acquires a component of momentum perpendicular to its original direction of flight, of amount Δp (the resultant momentum p remaining constant). The mean value of Δp, [see Fig. 65–1], is given by $\Delta p \sim p \sin \alpha$, if α is the mean angle of deflection. We know that the experimental results can be explained satisfactorily on the basis of the wave representation, according to which α is connected with the slit-width Δx and the wave-length $\lambda = h/p$ by the equation $\Delta x \sin \alpha \sim \lambda = h/p$. Thus the mean added momentum in the direction parallel to the slit is given by the relation

$$\Delta p \sim p \, \lambda / \Delta x = h/\Delta x,$$

or

$$\Delta x \Delta p \sim h.$$

This relation is called *Heisenberg's uncertainty relation.* In our example, therefore, it signifies that, as the result of the definition of the electron's position by means of the slit, which involves the uncertainty (or possible error) Δx, the particle acquires momentum parallel to the slit of the order of magnitude stated (i.e. with the indicated degree of uncertainty). Only subject to this uncertainty is its momentum known from the diffraction pattern. According to the uncertainty relation, therefore, *h represents an absolute limit to the simultaneous measurement of co-ordinate and momentum,* a limit which in the most favourable case we may get down to, but which we can never get beneath. In quantum mechanics, moreover, the uncertainty relation holds generally for any arbitrary pair of "conjugated variables."

Fig. 65–2. Determination of the position of an electron by means of the γ-ray microscope.

A second example of the uncertainty relation is the definition of position by a microscope [Fig. 65–2]. Here the order of ideas is as follows. If we wish to determine the position of an electron in the optical way by illuminating it and observing the scattered light, then it is clear, and known as a general rule in optics, that the wave-length of the light employed forms a lower limit to the resolution and accordingly to the exactness of the determination of position. If we wish to define the position as accurately as possible, we will employ light of the shortest possible wave-length (γ-rays). The employment of short-wave radiation implies, however, the occurrence of a Compton scattering process when the electron is irradiated, so that the electron experiences a recoil, which to a certain extent is indeterminate. We may investigate the circumstances mathematically. Let the electron under the microscope be irradiated in any direction with light of frequency v. Then by the rules of optics (resolving power of the microscope) its position can only be determined subject to the possible error

$$\Delta x \sim \frac{\lambda}{\sin \alpha},$$

where α is the angular aperture. Now, according to the corpuscular view, the particle in the radiation process suffers a Compton recoil of the order of magnitude hv/c, the direction of which is undetermined to the same extent as is the direction in which the light quantum flies off after the process. Since the light quantum is actually observed in the microscope, this indeterminateness of direction is given by the angular aperture α. The component momentum of the electron perpendicular to the axis of the microscope is therefore after the process undetermined to the extent Δp, where approximately

$$\Delta p \sim \frac{hv}{c} \sin \alpha.$$

Thus the order of magnitude relation

$$\Delta x \Delta p \sim h$$

holds good here also.

Just as every determination of position carries with it an uncertainty in the momentum, and every determination of time an uncertainty in the energy (although we have not yet proved the latter statement), so the converse is also true. The more accurately we determine momentum and energy, the more latitude we introduce into the position of the particle and the time of an event. We give an example of this also, viz. the so-called *resonance fluorescence*. We have seen [earlier] that the atoms of a gas which is irradiated with light of frequency v_{10}, corresponding to the energy difference between the ground state and the first excited state, are raised to the latter state. They then fall back again to the lower state, at the same time emitting the frequency v_{10}; and if the pressure of the gas is sufficiently low, so that the number of gas-kinetic collisions which occur while the atom remains in the excited state is negligible, then the whole energy which was absorbed will again be emitted. Thus the atom behaves like a classical resonator which is in resonance with the incident light wave, and we speak of resonance fluorescence.

But the energy of excitation of the atoms can also be utilized, not for re-emission of light, but for other actions, by introducing another gas as an indicator. If the latter consists, say, of not too rigidly bound diatomic molecules, the energy transferred in collisions with the excited atoms of the first gas can be utilized for dissociation (Franck, 1922). Again, if the added gas is monatomic, and has a lower excitation level than the first gas, it is itself caused to radiate by the collisions; this is called sensitized fluorescence (Franck). In any case we see that a fraction of the atoms of the first gas is certainly thrown into the excited state by the exciting light. We may take the following view of the matter. Excitation by monochromatic light means communication of exact quanta hv_{10} to the atom.

We therefore know the energy of the excited atoms exactly. Consequently, by Heisenberg's relation $\Delta E \Delta t \sim h$, the time at which the absorption takes place must be absolutely indeterminate. We can satisfy ourselves that this is so, by considering that any experiment to determine the moment in question would necessarily require a mark in the original wave train—an interruption of the train, for example. But that means disturbing the monochromatic character of the light wave, and so contradicts the hypothesis. A rigorous discussion of the circumstances shows that, if the light is kept monochromatic, the moment at which the elementary act happens does actually altogether elude observation.

The uncertainty relation can also be deduced from the following *general idea*. If we propose to build up a wave packet, extending for a finite distance in the *x*-direction, from separate wave trains, we need for the purpose a definite finite frequency-range in the monochromatic waves, i.e., since $\lambda = h/p$, a finite momentum-range in the particles. But it can be proved generally that the length of the wave packet is connected with the requisite range of momenta by the relation

$$\Delta p \Delta x \sim h.$$

The analogous relation

$$\Delta E \Delta t \sim h$$

can be derived in a similar way.

Consider, say, *Young's interference experiment* with the two slits; then we have on the screen a system of interference fringes. By replacing the screen by a photoelectric cell, we can demonstrate the corpuscular character of the light even in the fringes. It therefore appears as if we had here an experiment in which waves and particles are demonstrated simultaneously. Really, however, it is not so; for, to speak of a particle means nothing unless at least two points of its path can be specified experimentally; and similarly with a wave, unless at least two interference maxima are observed. If then we propose to carry out the "demonstration of a corpuscle," we must settle the question whether its path has gone through the upper or the lower of the two slits to the receiver. We therefore repeat the experiment, not only setting up a photoelectrically sensitive instrument as receiver, but also providing some contrivance which shows whether the light has passed through the upper slit (say a thin photographic film or the like). This contrivance in the slit, however, necessarily throws the light quantum out of its undisturbed path; the probability of getting it in the receiver (the screen) is therefore not the same as it was originally, i.e. the preliminary calculation by wave theory of the interference phenomenon is illusory. Thus, if pure interference is to be observed, we are necessarily precluded from making an observation of any point of the path of the light quantum before it strikes the screen.

We add in conclusion a few general remarks on the philosophical side of the question. In the first place it is clear that the dualism, wave-corpuscle, and the indeterminateness essentially involved therein, compel us to abandon any attempt to set up a *deterministic theory*. The *law of causation*, according to which the course of events in an isolated system is completely determined by the state of the system at time $t = 0$, loses its validity, at any rate in the sense of classical physics. In reply to the question whether a law of causation still holds good in the new theory, two standpoints are possible. Either we may look upon processes from the pictorial side, holding fast to the wave-corpuscle picture—in this case the law of causation certainly ceases to hold; or, as is done in the further development of the theory, we describe the instantaneous state of the system by a (complex) quantity ψ, which satisfies a differential equation, and therefore changes with the time in a way which is completely determined by its form at time $t = 0$, so that its behaviour is rigorously causal. Since, however, physical significance is confined to the quantity $|\psi|^2$ (the square of the amplitude), and to other similarly constructed quadratic expressions (matrix elements), which only partially define ψ, it follows that, even when the physically determinable quantities are completely known at time $t = 0$, the initial value of the ψ-function is necessarily not completely definable. This view of the matter is equivalent to the assertion that events happen indeed in a strictly causal way, but that we do not know the initial state exactly. In this sense the law of causation is therefore empty; physics is in the nature of the case indeterminate, and therefore the affair of statistics.

66

ooooooooooo

THE UNCERTAINTY
PRINCIPLE

ooooooooooo

Werner Karl Heisenberg (b. 1901)

As noted in preceding chapters, the serious discrepancies between observation and the Bohr model of the atom did not give way immediately to a single unified theory that led to an unambiguous picture of the atom or to a description of the behavior of the electron inside the atom. Instead, the new developments stemmed from a series of different approaches that at first seemed quite irreconcilable if not actually contradictory. On the one hand, De Broglie's theoretical discoveries seemed to indicate that the difficulty with the Bohr theory lay in an inadequate picture of the physical nature of the electron; instead of treating the electron as a particle one should consider its wave characteristics to understand its behavior. This approach, which dealt primarily with the nature of the electron and not with the relationship of the observer to the electron, reached its final development in the discovery of the Schroedinger wave equation.

Against these discoveries, which indicated that the electron could no longer be treated as a particle, Heisenberg, Born, and Jordan propounded a new theory in 1925. This theory, called matrix mechanics, was the first complete form of quantum mechanics presented to the world as a technique for solving atomic problems. The starting point was an investigation carried out by Heisenberg and the Dutch physicist H. A. Kramers into the nature of the dispersion of light passing through a gas. Since the use of the Bohr theory in this analysis gave incorrect results, it was clear that a new approach was necessary. Instead of introducing a change in the concept of the particle nature of the electron, Heisenberg rejected the classical concept of the relationship of the observer to the phenomenon being observed. Just as Einstein had been led to a revolutionary picture of space and time by analyzing the manner in which the physicist performs measurements of time and distance, so Heisenberg was now led to a radically different picture of the atom. He subjected accepted concepts, such as the orbit of an electron, the position of an electron inside an atom, and the momentum of an electron, to profound criticism.

At first sight, it may appear highly improbable that an approach of this sort could lead to results identical with those obtained by ascribing wave-like properties to the electron, and, indeed, to all particles. Yet this is exactly what happened. For soon after the discovery of the Schroedinger wave equation, Schroedinger, Dirac and others demonstrated that the two apparently unrelated prescriptions for discovering what is going on inside an atom are different ways of looking at the same thing.

To physicists, this was especially puzzling since the two theories appeared to be contraries. One theory (Schroedinger-De Broglie) introduced a revolutionary picture of the intrinsic nature of a particle, the electron. The other (Born, Heisenberg, and Jordan) seemed to assume nothing about the nature of matter, but rather about the way we go about making our measurements and recordings of material things and events. But the basic agreement between the two theories should not have been altogether surprising, because something of a precedent had been established in the theory of relativity. As Einstein had demonstrated, a revision of our methods of measuring space and time intervals led to a change in our concepts of the very nature of matter.

Heisenberg's great contribution was to show that in analyzing physical systems it is not permissible to use concepts that cannot be measured directly. Only those quantities should enter into our calculations that have meaning in terms of experiment—that is, which *have* been measured. By analyzing this requirement, Heisenberg discovered the uncertainty principle—the foundation of quantum mechanics. This principle forms a bridge between the wave picture and matrix mechanics.

There is, however, a fundamental difference between the relativity approach to the measurement of space and time and the Heisenberg approach to the measurement of physical quantities. The theory of relativity starts by placing an upper limit on a physical quantity, namely, the speed of a body. This arises from the observation that the speed of light is the same for all observers moving with uniform speed with respect to each other, regardless of how fast they may be moving. Thus, the point of departure of the theory of relativity is a statement about the intrinsic nature of a physical quantity. The quantum mechanics of Heisenberg also begins by introducing a limit, but it is not a limit on the value of an intrinsic physical quantity; rather, it is a limit on the accuracy with which we can measure certain pairs of quantities simultaneously.

As we have noted, the matrix form of quantum mechanics grew out of an attempt by Kramers and Heisenberg to calculate the dispersion of polarized light by atoms by means of the Bohr quantum theory. In this investigation, which appeared as a paper in the *Zeitschrift für Physik* (1925), the authors applied the Bohr theory to the interaction of radiation with an atom, assuming the atom to be in a particular energy state, or the electron in the atom to be in a particular Bohr orbit as described by the concepts of classical mechanics applied to an electron moving under the action of a Coulomb force. To perform a calculation of this sort, it was necessary to use what Bohr called the correspondence principle, since the Bohr theory without this empirical device lacks completeness. To explain this we must consider briefly how the Bohr and the classical theories separately describe the emission of radiation by an electron circling the nucleus in an atom.

The classical approach is quite straightforward. Imagine an electron moving with periodic motion in some orbit inside an atom. To describe its position inside the atom at any time we draw a vector from the nucleus to the electron. The length and the direction of this arrow at any moment give us the position of the electron. If the motion of the electron (like that of the earth around the sun) is periodic, then this vector has certain sets of regularly recurring lengths and directions. The same set recurs at intervals equal to the fundamental period of the motion, just as the earth comes back to its same position relative to the sun and the stars every year. Mathematically speaking, if $q(t)$ represents the position of an electron at time t, then $q(t)$ will always be the same for values of t that differ from each other by some integer multiplied by t_0, where t_0 is the period of the motion. We may express this as $q(t) = q(t \pm nt_0)$ where n is an integer.

We note that although the motion of the electron is periodic, it is generally also quite complicated, just the way a sound can be a complex mixture of simple tones, even though it is constantly repeated, like a bird call. Consider now the difference between the sound of a pure note and that of the same note obtained by sounding some complex instrument. We can get the pure note by striking a tuning fork that is allowed to vibrate only in its fundamental tone, or by plucking a string that vibrates only as a whole. Such vibrations are said to be simple harmonic vibrations and the frequency of such a vibration is also the frequency or pitch of the note that is produced. Such vibrations are the simplest kind known and are represented mathematically by sine and cosine formulas.

If we now produce the same note in an impure form—that is, not by inducing a simple harmonic vibration of the string, but by inducing complex vibrations so that the string oscillates not only in its fundamental mode but also in various higher modes, the resulting sound is complex. If this complex sound is analyzed with a harmonic analyzer, we find that in addition to the fundamental frequency of the pure note, corresponding to the simple harmonic vibration, many higher frequencies are present. All of these higher frequencies are simple integer multiples of the fundamental frequency.

We now assume that we know at each instant of time the position of each point of the vibrating string, or, as the mathematician would express it, that we know the shape of the vibrating string as a function of the time. We can then do mathematically what the harmonic analyzer does for us: analyze the vibration of the string into its component simple harmonic vibrations.

This mathematical analysis of a complex vibration into simple vibrations was discovered by the nineteenth-century French mathematician Fourier and is known as a Fourier analysis. Such an analysis, which can be applied to any periodic function of the time, leads to a representation of the function as an infinite series of sine and cosine terms, each one with a different frequency. But only those frequencies appear that are integral multiples of the fundamental frequency of the vibrating string.

Thus, if the fundamental frequency is v, the function representing the distortion of the string at any moment is given as a sum of terms of the form $\sin 2\pi n v t$ and $\cos 2\pi n v t$, where n is an integer that takes on all the values 1, 2, 3, and so on. Each term in this series appears multiplied by an appropriate coefficient, which is a measure of the amplitude of that particular harmonic in the complete vibration of the string. Or put somewhat differently, if the sound issuing from the vibrating string is analyzed mechanically into its component frequencies—or into its various harmonics—the intensity of a harmonic having a particular frequency is given by the coefficient multiplying the sine or cosine term of that particular frequency in the Fourier expansion of the function representing the periodic distortion of the vibrating string.

We may draw an analogy between this and the description of the motion of a planet as given by Ptolemy in the pre-Copernican geocentric theory of the solar system. The observed motion of a planet, with the earth assumed to be fixed, is quite complex, so that it cannot be represented by a *single* circular orbit around the earth. Ptolemy therefore assigned an entire series of circular orbits of smaller and smaller radii to each planet, with each succeeding circle having its center on the circumference of the preceding one. These small circles were called "epicycles," and it is easy to see that if one uses enough epicycles, one can describe the most complicated type of periodic motion. The epicycles are equivalent to a Fourier analysis into pure vibrations.

What has all this to do with the matrix mechanics of Heisenberg? The relationship becomes apparent if we consider how one might attack the problem of the radiation of a vibrating electron inside an atom from the classical point of view. According to this point of view, an electron is pictured as moving around the nucleus in an orbit similar to that of a planet around the sun; therefore, the motion is periodic, and, in a sense, similar to that of our vibrating string. Since the position of the electron in its orbit can be represented by a vector from the nucleus to the electron, this quantity, which we have called $q(t)$, can be represented by a Fourier series.

We must note that the orbit of the electron is, in general, quite complicated, even though it is periodic. Thus various overtones are present. In other words, the Fourier analysis of the orbit shows that the electron is really vibrating about the nucleus with a whole series of frequencies, each of which is an integral multiple of some fundamental frequency.

According to classical theory an electron that moves in this fashion must radiate energy, consisting of light having all the frequencies that are present in the Fourier analysis of the motion of the electron. But it is precisely here that the classical theory disagrees with observation. A spectral breakdown or harmonic analysis of the light emitted by an atom shows that the frequencies of the component radiation, the lines in the spectrum, are not associated with a single fundamental frequency of an orbit and its overtones. Rather, the frequency of any spectral line is expressed in terms of the differences of two numbers, as though two different orbits were associated with each line in the spectrum. This is known as the Ritz combination principle.

We have seen, in the discussion of Bohr's work, how Bohr treated this difficulty. He discarded the idea of classical frequencies associated with classical orbits of the electron. Although he retained the idea of a classical orbit, he did not associate the classical frequencies that could be obtained by a Fourier analysis of this orbit with the frequencies of the spectral lines. Nevertheless, it was still necessary for Bohr to retain the classical Fourier analysis to complete his picture of the atom. His theory of stationary states, with the emission of radiation from the electron occurring during jumps from a higher stationary state, or orbit, to a lower one, predicts which lines are found in the spectrum of an atom, but it does not predict the intensities of these lines. Indeed, it predicts that all the lines associated with all the possible jumps of the electron should be present with equal intensity. This is not the case; in fact, certain lines are not present at all, as though the electron were forbidden to make the jumps that would produce these lines.

Bohr managed to get around this difficulty by introducing his famous correspondence principle, which is the subject of our present discussion. The origin of this principle was his observation that the classical theory and his quantum theory of the atom merge if the electron is moving in an orbit that is at a great distance from the nucleus—that is, if the principal quantum number *n* of the orbit is very large. The reason for this is that for orbits of this sort the energy differences are extremely small, so that in going from one such orbit to another the electron does not behave as though it were jumping, but rather as though it were moving continuously —in other words, classically. Bohr assumed that for these outer orbits the classical Fourier analysis gives the correct picture of the spectral lines and their frequencies. If a particular term in the Fourier analysis were not present, the particular spectral line associated with that frequency would not be present in the spectrum.

The content of the correspondence principle is the extension of this idea to all the orbits of the electron, not only to the outer orbits with their very large quantum numbers. Consequently, one must use the Fourier analysis of the motion of an electron not in order to determine the frequencies of the spectral lines in the radiation, but rather to determine which lines are present in the spectrum. This means that the Fourier analysis gives incorrect answers if used to determine the *frequencies* of the spectral lines, but correct answers in the determination of the *intensities* of various spectral lines. It is the use of this classical Fourier analytical procedure for determining which lines are present and their intensities that is the essence of the correspondence principle. That it works for the intensities, even though it does not give the correct frequencies of the spectral lines, is a tribute to the great genius of Bohr and an indication of how deep was his insight.

We come now to the work of Heisenberg and Kramers, who used the correspondence principle and the Bohr theory to analyze the dispersion of light by an atom. If we consider an atom with its optically active electron in a particular Bohr orbit, we can solve the problem of the scattering of a monochromatic beam of light (a beam of definite frequency) classically by first analyzing the motion of the electron into a Fourier series, and then applying the usual rules for the interaction of a monochromatic beam of radiation with an electron moving in this way. The formula thus obtained is the classical formula for the scattering of light by an electron moving in a bound orbit. It involves the fundamental frequency and the various harmonics of the electron's orbit. Since this formula is based on classical dynamics, it is incorrect. However, Heisenberg and Kramers found that it is possible to start from this formula and obtain one that is in agreement with the quantum theory by using the correspondence principle.

Their first step was to replace the frequencies that appear in the Fourier analysis, which refer to the classical orbit, with proper quantum theoretical frequencies as given by the Planck relationship. When this is done, each frequency that appears in the revised Fourier expansions refers to two electronic states and not to one particular orbit. In mathematical terms, the frequencies appear in the form ν_{ik} where i and k refer to the states i and k of the electron. These are just the observed frequencies of the spectral lines. (The frequency of the scattered radiation can be represented as a square array since both i and k can take on all the integer values.) The next and final step in the application of the correspondence principle is to replace the coefficients in the Fourier expansion by coefficients that have quantum theoretic significance. This requires the Bohr quantization rule that relates the motion of the orbiting electron to Planck's constant.

When the classical dispersion formula was thus modified, it led Heisenberg to a very profound deduction that was the first step in the development of his matrix mechanics, and finally to the quantum mechanics as we know it today. To follow Heisenberg's reasoning, we consider an electron moving in a classical Bohr orbit and note how it would scatter light if it interacted with radiation according to the classical theory. The scattered radiation would contain as many different frequencies, all multiples of a fundamental frequency, as there are terms in the particular Fourier series that represents the position of the electron with respect to the nucleus. The intensity of each such component in the scattered radiation would be given by the coefficient of that particular term in the Fourier analysis. According to classical theory, then, the scattered radiation, in its frequencies and amplitude, refers to one particular orbit of the electron. In other words, it is the result of the electron's moving in some particular orbit.

But what does the correspondence principle tell us? First, that the component harmonic frequencies are not those associated with a definite orbit. They are, instead, associated with two orbits, or suborbits. Moreover, they are associated not with the frequencies of the electrons in these orbits, but with the energies of the electrons in these orbits. Second —and this is the important result of the Heisenberg-Kramers calculation —the amplitudes of the various components of the radiation do not refer to one particular orbit; instead, each amplitude is associated with the quantum numbers of two orbits or suborbits. Thus, the amplitudes and therefore the quantities that describe the motion of an electron (its position at any moment and its momentum or velocity) appear as square arrays. These quantities always have two numbers associated with them (the quantum numbers) that can take on integer values. This observation was the starting point of Heisenberg's remarkable development. We may get a still better insight if we take a special example.

We return to the electron moving in its Bohr orbit and consider its position $q(t)$ at any moment. Since the motion of the electron is periodic in its orbit, we may, from the classical point of view, replace $q(t)$ by its

Fourier analysis, and we can then say that the orbit of the electron is represented by the complete collection of coefficients in this Fourier expansion. This means the following: if these Fourier coefficients are A_0, A_1, A_2, and so on, then we can picture the electron as moving simultaneously in a collection of circles with radii A_0, A_1, A_2, etc., and all of these circles, taken together, give the effect of the actual orbit of the electron. This, of course, is purely a mathematical fiction, and from the classical point of view the orbit of the electron is the only real thing.

What happens when we pass over to the quantum theory using the correspondence principle? The quantities A_0, A_1, A_2, and so on, are now replaced by quantities referring to two orbits, so that we must write them as $q_{1,2}$, $q_{4,5}$, $q_{1,3}$, and so on. That is, as q_{ik}, where i and k refer to orbits i and k and can run through all the integers. If we want to replace $q(t)$ in quantum theory by the equivalent of a Fourier series, using the correspondence principle, we must use a square array of numbers each of which refers to two different orbits. But, what is more important, and what struck Heisenberg so forcefully, is that when such a square array is used in studying some atomic process (the scattering of light, for example), all the numbers of this square array must be taken into consideration and not just those that refer to two special orbits.

To Heisenberg this meant that it is not permissible to treat the electron inside the atom as though it were moving in a definite orbit; it is precisely in this denial of the possibility of assigning anything like a Bohr orbit to an electron that Heisenberg departed from the Bohr theory. Bohr had developed his quantum theory of the atom by discarding the idea of a classical frequency associated with the orbit of an electron, but he still retained the concept of the classical orbit. Heisenberg went one step further and discarded the concept of the orbit itself. Instead of the classical idea of the position and the motion, or momentum of the electron at each instant of time, Heisenberg introduced his square arrays or matrices, which depict the electron as existing simultaneously in all possible Bohr orbits. After Heisenberg's discovery, the classical concept of the electron as a particle was no longer tenable.

He was led to these revolutionary ideas for the description of the motion of an electron by his insistence on utilizing only those quantities in a theory which are directly observable. Since the orbit of an electron within the atom is not observable, it can have no place in a theory. Only the spectral lines are observed and since these involve pairs of orbits, all quantities that are used to describe the electron inside the atom should be associated with such pairs.

Such thinking led directly to Heisenberg's matrices. Once these square arrays or matrices were introduced to represent the position and the momentum of an electron, it was necessary to use a different kind of algebra to study these quantities. For if we have two such arrays that have to be multiplied, how are we to perform the multiplication? Certainly not in the way we usually multiply two numbers since we are here dealing with arrays containing many ordinary numbers.

Heisenberg discovered the correct way of multiplying such arrays to obtain results that agreed with observation. Born then pointed out that this multiplication rule had been known to mathematicians for many years and was, indeed, the rule for the multiplication of matrices. One of the important features of this rule is that it is not commutative. That is, if the array representing the position of an electron is q and the array representing its momentum is p, then the product pq is not the same as the product qp.

This is of great importance, for it showed Heisenberg that the uncertainty relationship is purely an algebraic consequence of his matrix theory. To see this we may picture the product pq as representing a measurement first of the position of the electron followed by a measurement of its momentum; qp, on the other hand, represents the measurement of the momentum of a particle followed by the measurement of its position. That these two sets of measurements give different results simply means that the measurement of the momentum of a particle destroys our knowledge of its position, and vice versa. From this it follows that it is impossible simultaneously to obtain or to have precise knowledge of the position and the momentum of a particle; this is the essence of the uncertainty principle.

Its significance for the structure of the atom (or our knowledge of this structure) is that we have no way of determining the orbit of an electron inside the atom observationally. For, as Heisenberg points out in his analysis of the "Copenhagen Interpretation of Quantum Theory," an electron can be observed inside an atom only with a γ-ray microscope which, because of the short wavelength of γ-rays, has a high resolving power. This microscope shows us where the electron is at any moment, but to do that at least one γ-ray photon must be reflected from the electron. In this very process the electron is knocked out of the atom and it is senseless then to speak of its orbit.

We can see now the connection between the De Broglie-Schroedinger picture, which assigns wave properties to particles, and the Heisenberg picture with its emphasis on the measurement process that destroys (by altering the behavior of the electron in the process of observing it) one bit of knowledge in the very act of supplying us with another. To say that a particle has wave properties implies that its motion and its position cannot be known simultaneously. We can, indeed, locate the particle-wave as accurately as we wish but only if in so doing we forego the opportunity to discern its wave character. On the other hand, this same particle-wave entity will lose all of its particlelike properties if our measurement gives us precise information about its motion.

Although the uncertainty relations can be derived purely mathematically from the formalism of the theory, it is much more instructive to derive them from the physical picture, and this Heisenberg does in Chapter II of his *Principles of Quantum Theory,* a selection from which follows this commentary. The importance of this method of deducing the uncertainty relations is that it shows clearly the interrelationship between the wave and the particle picture. In fact, it is clear from Heisenberg's analysis that wave and particle are complementary concepts just as position and momentum are. It was from considerations such as these that Bohr was led to his theory of complementarity which is essential for an understanding of modern atomic theories.

The uncertainty relations completely change our ideas of causality, for if we cannot determine the position and the momentum of a particle simultaneously to any desired degree of accuracy, we cannot determine its future course. Even though we can solve the equations of motion of the particle, these solutions can tell us the future history of the particle only if at some moment in the past or at the present instant we know the position and the momentum of the particle. The farther we try to peer into the future, the less accurate our predictions become, for our present uncertainty, however small it may be, leads to greater and greater deviations from the predicted pattern of the motion as time increases.

We can understand the situation by considering the lunar missile probes carried out by the United States and the USSR. To hit a target as far away as the moon involves extreme accuracy in aiming the rocket and giving it the correct initial momentum; if we wish to hit targets at greater distances, our accuracy will have to be increased considerably, for the further the distance, the greater the multiplication of any initial error.

By a happy coincidence, the first two years of the twentieth century witnessed the birth of several individuals who were destined to make important contributions to the development of modern physics. In those two years were born Fermi, Pauli, Dirac, Jordan, and Heisenberg. Heisenberg, in particular, played a dominant role in the third decade of this century with his introduction of matrix mechanics (as distinguished from Schroedinger's wave mechanics).

Today we use the term quantum mechanics (the term then applied to Heisenberg's work) for the entire mathematical scheme (i.e., the algebra of noncommutative operators) that is used to treat problems in atomic, nuclear, elementary-particle, and field physics. The mathematics of quantum mechanics stems directly from Heisenberg's matrix mechanics and is a consequence of his uncertainty principle.

Werner Karl Heisenberg was born in Würzburg, Germany, on December 5, 1901, and grew up in academic surroundings, in a household devoted to the humanities and steeped in culture. His father was a professor of the University of Munich when Werner began his schooling and undoubtedly greatly influenced the young Werner, who was a student at the Maximilian Gymnasium. This influence was apparent in Heisenberg's intense interest in the classics, especially in early Greek science to which he devoted himself in his high-school years. During his free time, while at the Gymnasium, Werner could usually be found deeply engrossed in Plato's dialogue "Timaeus," in the atomic theory of Democritus, in the writings of Thales of Miletus, or in some other ancient philosopher, all in the original Greek. This interest in the philosophy and history of science has remained with Heisenberg right up to the present and, in fact, has increased, for he has himself written critically on the relationship of Greek science to modern science.[1]

When not engrossed in physics and Greek philosophy, young Heisenberg divided his time between music and tennis, as well as climbing a mountain whenever one was available. He probably could have gone far in music, for he had an excellent ear and became a fairly good pianist, but his passion for theoretical physics dominated his life. When he graduated from the Gymnasium early in 1920 he immediately presented himself to Professor Arnold Sommerfeld (the dean of German atomic physicists and the greatest teacher and developer of new talent) and asked to be allowed to study theoretical physics. Sommerfeld, somewhat taken aback by so bold an approach by so young a man, proposed that Heisenberg first pursue the standard course of study in physics, including laboratory work, before thinking of specializing in theoretical physics. Nevertheless, Sommerfeld, who himself was a great theoretical physicist, allowed Heisenberg to attend his seminars during Heisenberg's first semester at the University of Munich. In 1923, six semesters later, and not yet twenty-three years old, Heisenberg took his doctoral examination and received his Ph.D. Like many of the brilliant young physicists of that period he decided to go the University of Göttingen, which, under Max Born's direction, was rapidly becoming the center of theoretical research in physics. He became Born's assistant in 1923 and two years later, in 1925, placed a revolutionary manuscript on Born's desk; this marked the beginning of quantum mechanics. He had then been appointed a lecturer (that is, *Privatdozent*) at the university.

Born quickly recognized the revolutionary significance of Heisenberg's work and sent the manuscript to the *Zeitschrift für Physik,* one of the two top German journals of physics, for publication. Following this, Heisen-

---

[1] Werner K. Heisenberg, *Physics and Philosophy* (New York: Harper, 1958).

berg's ideas were developed more fully in a series of papers published jointly with Born and Pascual Jordan, Born's other brilliant assistant.

Heisenberg's discovery stemmed from work he had done previously with the Dutch physicist H. A. Kramers on the dispersion of light by gaseous atoms, which clearly showed that the Bohr theory breaks down when pushed too far. When Heisenberg looked for the cause of this breakdown, he realized that the concepts that are introduced in the Bohr theory, such as the orbits of an electron and the electron's position and motion inside the atom, cannot be observed directly and therefore have no place in a self-consistent theory. He therefore decided to reformulate the theory solely in terms of observables and found that this could be done only by using noncommutative algebra.

This insistence on freeing atomic theory from unobservable quantities finally led Heisenberg to his famous uncertainty principle. It was clear to him that if the theory was to deal only with physical quantities that can be observed directly, it would have to be cast in a form in which it could not speak of the exact position and momentum of a particle simultaneously, since measuring either one of these quantities would affect the other and hence our knowledge of it.

Although matrix mechanics, as we know it today, finally evolved from Heisenberg's theory, it was not present as such in Heisenberg's first paper. In that paper Heisenberg had simply introduced a multiplication rule for the momentum and the position of an electron, which indicated that a special kind of algebra would have to be used in dealing with these quantities.

When Born saw this type of multiplication in Heisenberg's paper, certain memories stirred in him. He describes this "remembrance of things past" in his Nobel address as follows:

> Heisenberg's multiplication rule left no peace, and after eight days of intense reflection and probing, I suddenly recalled an algebraic theory that I learned from my teacher in Breslau. I applied this quadratic, algebraic scheme, called matrices, to Heisenberg's quantum condition.[2]

Thus, the actual mathematical scheme of matrix mechanics stems from Born.

One may conclude from this that even outstanding theoretical physicists in the early days were not too well equipped in advanced mathematics, particularly if this mathematics did not have an immediate bearing on physics. This is in contrast with conditions today, when no theoretical

---

[2] Max Born, Nobel Prize Address, Stockholm, 1954.

physicist who wishes to contribute significantly to physics can afford to be ignorant of any of the branches of modern mathematics.

By this time Heisenberg had left Göttingen to work at Bohr's institute in Copenhagen; consequently, Born and Jordan had to communicate by mail. Born describes that remarkable period in these words:

> With this result [his discovery of the matrix character of the Heisenberg law of multiplication] I felt like a seafarer, who after a good deal of wandering about sees the desired land, and I greatly regretted that Heisenberg was not there.
>
> A hectic period of collaboration among the three of us, made more difficult by Heisenberg's absence, followed. There occurred a lively exchange of letters. The result was a triple-authored paper which brought the formal part of the affair to a certain conclusion.[3]

After Heisenberg had spent three years at Copenhagen, he was offered the chair of theoretical physics at the University of Leipzig, where he remained until 1941. This was a period of great productivity, for not only did he publish many papers on the technical aspects of the new quantum mechanics but he applied it to diverse problems. Thus, he collaborated with Pauli to lay the foundations of quantum electrodynamics and quantum field theory in general, and he also applied quantum mechanics to the study of magnetic phenomena. During this period he also became interested in nuclear physics and introduced one of its most useful ideas— that of "isotopic-spin" in which both the neutron and the proton are considered as two different energy states of the same basic particle, the nucleon. While at Leipzig Heisenberg also made fundamental contributions to cosmic ray theory.

In 1934 he was awarded the Nobel Prize in physics for having discovered the quantum mechanics.

After World War II began, Heisenberg left Leipzig, and from 1942 to 1945 was director of the Max Planck Institute of Physics at Berlin. There is no doubt that this was a very unhappy period for him, since he was strongly opposed to the Nazi regime and remained in his academic post only because he felt that someone had to hold up the "torch of culture" against the barbarians. Before the war he had strongly defended his Jewish assistant, Guido Beck, against scurrilous racist attacks.

After the war Heisenberg continued with his research as director of the Max Planck Institute at Göttingen. He then became interested in high-energy particle physics and introduced the technique of what is now called the S-matrix theory (the so-called scattering matrix), which at-

---

[3] *Loc. cit.*

tempts to describe events only in terms of what one sees initially before two systems are brought together (two nuclei, for example, or two protons) and what one sees finally, after they have interacted and have separated. One does not try to describe the actual mechanism of the interaction (since one cannot observe this) but only the products of it. This S-matrix procedure has become very fashionable today in particle physics.

Today Heisenberg is trying to derive the properties of such elementary properties as electrons, protons, and so on, from a departure from quantum field theory by having the field itself construct its own particles. This leads to a very complex mathematical formulation, which spoils the great beauty of quantum mechanics.

In spite of his great concern with research Heisenberg is also greatly interested in the exposition and the philosophy of physics. Thus, such books as *The Principles of the Quantum Theory*, *Cosmic Rays,* and *Nuclear Physics* are models of clarity and excellent introductions to these subjects, and his *Physics and Philosophy* is one of the best books on the philosophy of modern physics.

 oooooooo

HEISENBERG

Critique of the Physical Concepts of the Corpuscular Theory of Matter [4]

THE UNCERTAINTY RELATIONS

THE CONCEPTS OF VELOCITY, ENERGY, etc., have been developed from simple experiments with common objects, in which the mechanical behavior of macroscopic bodies can be described by the use of such words. These same concepts have then been carried over to the electron, since in certain fundamental experiments electrons show a mechanical behavior like that of the objects of common experience. Since it is known, however, that this similarity exists only in a certain limited region of phenomena, the applicability of the corpuscular theory must be limited in a corresponding way. According to Bohr, this

[4] Werner K. Heisenberg, trans. Eckart and Hoyt, *Principles of the Quantum Theory* (Chicago: University of Chicago Press, 1930), pp. 13–25.

restriction may be deduced from the principle that the processes of atomic physics can be visualized equally well in terms of waves or particles. Thus the statement that the position * of an electron is known to within a certain accuracy Δx at the time t can be visualized by the picture of a wave packet in the proper position with an approximate extension Δx. By "wave packet" is meant a wavelike disturbance whose amplitude is appreciably different from zero only in a bounded region. This region is, in general, in motion, and also changes its size and shape, i.e., the disturbance spreads. The velocity of the electron corresponds to that of the wave packet, but this latter cannot be exactly defined, because of the diffusion which takes place. This indeterminateness is to be considered as an essential characteristic of the electron, and not as evidence of the inapplicability of the wave picture. Defining momentum as $p_x = \mu v_x$ (where $\mu =$ mass of electron, $v_x = x$-component of velocity), this uncertainty in the velocity causes an uncertainty in p_x of amount Δp_x; from the simplest laws of optics, together with the empirically established law $\lambda = h/p$, it can readily be shown that

$$\Delta x \Delta p_x \gtrsim h. \tag{1}$$

Suppose the wave packet made up by superposition of plane sinusoidal waves, all with wave-lengths near λ_0. Then, roughly speaking, $n = \Delta x/\lambda_0$ crests or troughs fall within the boundary of the packet. Outside the boundary the component plane waves must cancel by interference; this is possible if, and only if, the set of component waves contains some for which at least $n + 1$ waves fall in the critical range. This gives

$$\frac{\Delta x}{\lambda_0 - \Delta \lambda} \gtrsim n + 1,$$

where $\Delta \lambda$ is the approximate range of wave-lengths necessary to represent the packet. Consequently

$$\frac{\Delta x \Delta \lambda}{\lambda_0^2} \gtrsim 1. \tag{2}$$

On the other hand, the group velocity of the waves (i.e., the velocity of the packet) is . . .

$$v_g = \frac{h}{\mu \lambda_0}, \tag{3}$$

---

* The following considerations apply equally to any of the three space co-ordinates of the electron, therefore only one is treated explicitly.

so that the spreading of the packet is characterized by the range of velocities

$$\Delta v_g = \frac{h}{\mu \lambda_0^2} \Delta \lambda.$$

By definition $\Delta p_x = \mu \Delta v_g$ and therefore by equation (2),

$$\Delta x \Delta p_x \gtrsim h.$$

This uncertainty relation specifies the limits within which the particle picture can be applied. Any use of the words "position" and "velocity" with an accuracy exceeding that given by equation (1) is just as meaningless as the use of words whose sense is not defined.* . . .

ILLUSTRATIONS OF THE UNCERTAINTY RELATIONS

The uncertainty principle refers to the degree of indeterminateness in the possible present knowledge of the simultaneous values of various quantities with which the quantum theory deals; it does not restrict, for example, the exactness of a position measurement alone or a velocity measurement alone. Thus suppose that the velocity of a free electron is precisely known, while the position is completely unknown. Then the principle states that every subsequent observation of the position will alter the momentum by an unknown and undeterminable amount such that after carrying out the experiment our knowledge of the electronic motion is restricted by the uncertainty relation. This may be expressed in concise and general terms by saying that every experiment destroys some of the knowledge of the system which was obtained by previous experiments. This formulation makes it clear that the uncertainty relation does not refer to the past; if the velocity of the electron is at first known and the position then exactly measured, the position for times previous to the measurement may be calculated. Then for these past times $\Delta p \Delta q$ is smaller than the usual limiting value, but this knowledge of the past is of a purely speculative character, since it can never (because of the un-

---

* In this connection one should particularly remember that the human language permits the construction of sentences which do not involve any consequences and which therefore have no content at all—in spite of the fact that these sentences produce some kind of picture in our imagination; e.g., the statement that besides our world there exists another world, with which any connection is impossible in principle, does not lead to any experimental consequence, but does produce a kind of picture in the mind. Obviously such a statement can neither be proved nor disproved. One should be especially careful in using the words "reality," "actually," etc., since these words very often lead to statements of the type just mentioned.

known change in momentum caused by the position measurement) be used as an initial condition in any calculation of the future progress of the electron and thus cannot be subjected to experimental verification. It is a matter of personal belief whether such a calculation concerning the past history of the electron can be ascribed any physical reality or not.

Determination of the Position of a Free Particle

As a first example of the destruction of the knowledge of a particle's momentum by an apparatus determining its position, we consider the use of a microscope. Let the particle be moving at such a distance from the microscope that the cone of rays scattered from it through the ob-

Fig. 66–1.

jective has an angular opening ϵ. If λ is the wave-length of the light il-luminating it, then the uncertainty in the measurement of the x-co-ordinate [see Fig. 66–1] according to the laws of optics governing the resolving power of any instrument is:

$$\Delta x = \frac{\lambda}{\sin \epsilon}. \qquad (16)$$

But, for any measurement to be possible at least one photon must be scat-tered from the electron and pass through the microscope to the eye of the observer. From this photon the electron receives a Compton recoil of order of magnitude h/λ. The recoil cannot be exactly known, since the direction of the scattered photon is undetermined within the bundle of rays entering the microscope. Thus there is an uncertainty of the recoil in the x-direction of amount

$$\Delta p_x \sim \frac{h}{\lambda} \sin \epsilon, \qquad (17)$$

and it follows that for the motion after the experiment

$$\Delta p_x \Delta x \sim h. \qquad (18)$$

Objections may be raised to this consideration; the indeterminateness of the recoil is due to the uncertain path of the light quantum within the bundle of rays, and we might seek to determine the path by making the microscope movable and measuring the recoil it receives from the light quantum. But this does not circumvent the uncertainty relation, for it immediately raises the question of the position of the microscope, and its position and momentum will also be found to be subject to equation (18). The position of the microscope need not be considered if the electron and a fixed scale be simultaneously observed through the moving microscope, and this seems to afford an escape from the uncertainty principle. But an observation then requires the simultaneous passage of at least two light quanta through the microscope to the observer—one from the electron and one from the scale—and a measurement of the recoil of the microscope is no longer sufficient to determine the direction of the light scattered by the electron. And so on *ad infinitum*.

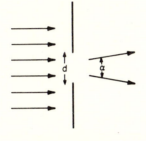

Fig. 66–2.

One might also try to improve the accuracy by measuring the maximum of the diffraction pattern produced by the microscope. This is only possible when many photons co-operate, and a calculation shows that the error in measurement of x is reduced to $\Delta x = \lambda/\sqrt{m}\ \sin \epsilon$ when m photons produce the pattern. On the other hand, each photon contributes to the unknown change in the electron's momentum, the result being $\Delta p_x = \sqrt{m}\ h \sin \epsilon/\lambda$ (addition of independent errors). The relation (18) is thus not avoided.

It is characteristic of the foregoing discussion that simultaneous use is made of deductions from the corpuscular and wave theories of light, for, on the one hand, we speak of resolving power, and, on the other hand, of photons and the recoils resulting from their collision with the particle under consideration. This is avoided, in so far as the theory of light is concerned, in the following considerations.

If electrons are made to pass through a slit of width d [Fig. 66–2], then their co-ordinates in the direction of this width are known at the moment after having passed it with the accuracy $\Delta x = d$. If we assume the momentum in this direction to have been zero before passing through the slit (normal incidence), it would appear that the uncertainty relation is not fulfilled. But the electron may also be considered to be a plane de Broglie wave, and it is at once apparent that diffraction phenomena are necessarily produced by the slit. The emergent beam has a finite angle of divergence α, which is, by the simplest laws of optics,

$$\sin \alpha \sim \frac{\lambda}{d}, \tag{19}$$

where λ is the wave-length of the de Broglie waves. Thus the momentum of the electron parallel to the screen is uncertain, after passing through the slit, by an amount

$$\Delta p = \frac{h}{\lambda} \sin \alpha \tag{20}$$

since h/λ is the momentum of the electron in the direction of the beam. Then, since $\Delta x = d$,

$$\Delta x \Delta p \sim h.$$

In this discussion we have avoided the dual character of light, but have made extensive use of the two theories of the electron.

As a last method of determining position we discuss the well-known method of observing scintillations produced by α-rays when they are received on a fluorescent screen or of observing their tracks in a Wilson chamber. The essential point of these methods is that the position of the particle is indicated by the ionization of an atom; it is obvious that the lower limit to the accuracy of such a measurement is given by the linear dimension Δq_s of the atom, and also that the momentum of the impinging particle is changed during the act of ionization. Since the momentum of the electron ejected from the atom is measurable, the uncertainty in the change of momentum of the impinging particle is equal to the range Δp_s within which the momentum of this electron varies while moving in its un-ionized orbit. This variation in momentum is again related to the size of the atom by the inequality

$$\Delta p_s \Delta q_s \gtrsim h.$$

Later discussion will show, in fact, that quite generally

$$\Delta p_s \Delta q_s \sim nh,$$

where n is the quantum number of the stationary state concerned. Thus the uncertainty relation also governs this type of position measurement; here the dualism of treatment is relegated to the background, and the uncertainty relation appears rather to be the result of the Bohr quantum conditions determining the stationary state, but naturally the quantum conditions are themselves manifestations of the duality.

Measurement of the Velocity or Momentum of a Free Particle

The simplest and most fundamental method of measuring velocity depends on the determination of position at two different times. If the time interval elapsing between the position measurements is sufficiently large, it is possible to determine the velocity before the second was made with any desired accuracy, but it is the velocity after this measurement which alone is of importance to the physicist, and this cannot be determined with exactness. The change in momentum which is necessarily produced by the last observation is subject to such an indeterminateness that the uncertainty relation is again fulfilled, as has been shown in the last section.

The Copenhagen Interpretation of Quantum Theory [5]

THE COPENHAGEN INTERPRETATION OF QUANtum theory starts from a paradox. Any experiment in physics, whether it refers to the phenomena of daily life or to atomic events, is to be described in the terms of classical physics. The concepts of classical physics form the language by which we describe the arrangement of our experiments and state the results. We cannot and should not replace these concepts by any others. Still the application of these concepts is limited by the relations of uncertainty. We must keep in mind this limited range of applicability of the classical concepts while using them, but we cannot and should not try to improve them.

For a better understanding of this paradox it is useful to compare the procedure for the theoretical interpretation of an experiment in classical physics and in quantum theory. In Newton's mechanics, for instance, we may start by measuring the position and the velocity of the planet whose motion we are going to study. The result of the observation is translated into mathematics by deriving numbers for the co-ordinates and the

---

[5] Heisenberg, *Physics and Philosophy* (New York: Harper, 1958), pp. 44–58.

momenta of the planet from the observation. Then the equations of motion are used to derive from these values of the co-ordinates and momenta at a given time the values of these co-ordinates or any other properties of the system at a later time, and in this way the astronomer can predict the properties of the system at a later time. He can, for instance, predict the exact time for an eclipse of the moon.

In quantum theory the procedure is slightly different. We could for instance be interested in the motion of an electron through a cloud chamber and could determine by some kind of observation the initial position and velocity of the electron. But this determination will not be accurate; it will at least contain the inaccuracies following from the uncertainty relations and will probably contain still larger errors due to the difficulty of the experiment. It is the first of these inaccuracies which allows us to translate the result of the observation into the mathematical scheme of quantum theory. A probability function is written down which represents the experimental situation at the time of the measurement, including even the possible errors of the measurement.

This probability function represents a mixture of two things, partly a fact and partly our knowledge of a fact. It represents a fact in so far as it assigns at the initial time the probability unity (i.e., complete certainty) to the initial situation: the electron moving with the observed velocity at the observed position; "observed" means observed within the accuracy of the experiment. It represents our knowledge in so far as another observer could perhaps know the position of the electron more accurately. The error in the experiment does—at least to some extent—not represent a property of the electron but a deficiency in our knowledge of the electron. Also this deficiency of knowledge is expressed in the probability function.

In classical physics one should in a careful investigation also consider the error of the observation. As a result one would get a probability distribution for the initial values of the co-ordinates and velocities and therefore something very similar to the probability function in quantum mechanics. Only the necessary uncertainty due to the uncertainty relations is lacking in classical physics.

When the probability function in quantum theory has been determined at the initial time from the observation, one can from the laws of quantum theory calculate the probability function at any later time and can thereby determine the probability for a measurement giving a specified value of the measured quantity. We can, for instance, predict the probability for finding the electron at a later time at a given point in the cloud chamber. It should be emphasized, however, that the probability function does not in itself represent a course of events in the course of time. It represents a tendency for events and our knowledge of events. The probability function can be connected with reality only if one essential condition is fulfilled: if a new measurement is made to determine a certain property of the system. Only then does the probability function allow us to calculate the probable result of the new measurement. The result of the measurement again will be stated in terms of classical physics.

Therefore, the theoretical interpretation of an experiment requires three distinct steps: (1) the translation of the initial experimental situation into a probability function; (2) the following up of this function in the course of time; (3) the statement of a new measurement to be made of the system, the result of which can then be calculated from the probability function. For the first step the fulfillment of the uncertainty relations is a necessary condition. The second step cannot be described in terms of the classical concepts; there is no description of what happens to the system between the initial observation and the next measurement. It is only in the third step that we change over again from the "possible" to the "actual."

Let us illustrate these three steps in a simple ideal experiment. It has been said that the atom consists of a nucleus and electrons moving around the nucleus; it has also been stated that the concept of an electronic orbit is doubtful. One could argue that it should at least in principle be possible to observe the electron in its orbit. One should simply look at the atom through a microscope of a very high resolving power, then one would see the electron moving in its orbit. Such a high resolving power could to be sure not be obtained by a microscope using ordinary light, since the inaccuracy of the measurement of the position can never be smaller than the wave length of the light. But a microscope using γ-rays with a wave length smaller than the size of the atom would do. Such a microscope has not yet been constructed but that should not prevent us from discussing the ideal experiment.

Is the first step, the translation of the result of the observation into a probability function, possible? It is possible only if the uncertainty relation is fulfilled after the observation. The position of the electron will be known with an accuracy given by the wave length of the γ-ray. The electron may have been practically at rest before the observation. But in the act of observation at least one light quantum of the γ-ray must have passed the microscope and must first have been deflected by the electron. Therefore, the electron has been pushed by the light quantum, it has changed its momentum and its velocity, and one can show that the uncertainty of this change is just big enough to guarantee the validity of the uncertainty relations. Therefore, there is no difficulty with the first step.

At the same time one can easily see that there is no way of observing the orbit of the electron around the nucleus. The second step shows a wave packet moving not around the nucleus but away from the atom, because the first light quantum will have knocked the electron out from the atom. The momentum of light quantum of the γ-ray is much bigger than the original momentum of the electron if the wave length of the γ-ray is much smaller than the size of the atom. Therefore, the first light quantum is sufficient to knock the electron out of the atom and one can never observe more than one point in the orbit of the electron; therefore, there is no orbit in the ordinary sense. The next observation—the third step—will show the electron on its path from the atom. Quite generally there is no way of describing what happens between two consecutive observations. It is of course tempting to say that the electron must have been somewhere between the two observations and that therefore the electron must have described some kind of path or orbit even if it may be impossible to know which path. This would be a reasonable argument in classical physics. But in quantum theory it would be a misuse of the language which, as we will see later, cannot be justified. We can leave it open for the moment, whether this warning is a statement about the way in which we should talk about atomic events or a statement about the events themselves, whether it refers to epistemology or to ontology. In any case we have to be very cautious about the wording of any statement concerning the behavior of atomic particles.

Actually we need not speak of particles at all. For many experiments it is more convenient to speak of matter waves; for instance, of stationary matter waves around the atomic nucleus. Such a description would directly contradict the other description if one does not pay attention to the limitations given by the uncertainty relations. Through the limitations the contradiction is avoided. The use of "matter waves" is convenient, for example, when dealing with the radiation emitted by the atom. By means of its frequencies and intensities the radiation gives information about the oscillating charge distribution in the atom, and there the wave picture comes much nearer to the truth than the particle picture. Therefore, Bohr advocated the use of both pictures, which he called "complementary" to each other. The two pictures are of course mutually exclusive, because a certain thing cannot at the same time be a particle (i.e., substance confined to a very small volume) and a wave (i.e., a field spread out over a large space), but the two complement each other. By playing with both pictures, by going from the one picture to the other and back again, we finally get the right impression of the strange kind of reality behind our atomic experiments. Bohr uses the concept of "complementarity" at several places in the interpretation of quantum theory. The knowledge of the position of a particle is complementary to the knowledge of its velocity or momentum. If we know the one with high accuracy we cannot know the other with high accuracy; still we must know both for determining the behavior of the system. The space-time description of the atomic events is complementary to their deterministic description. The probability function obeys an equation of motion as the co-ordinates did in Newtonian mechanics; its change in the course of time is completely determined by the quantum mechanical equation, but it does not allow a description in space and time. The observation, on the other hand, enforces the description in space and time but breaks the determined continuity of the probability function by changing our knowledge of the system.

Generally the dualism between two different descriptions of the same reality is no longer a difficulty since we know from the mathematical formulation of the theory that contradictions cannot arise. The dualism between the two complementary pictures—waves and particles—is also clearly brought out in the flexibility of the mathematical scheme. The formalism is normally written to resemble Newtonian mechanics, with equations of motion for the co-ordinates and the momenta of the particles. But by a simple transformation it can be rewritten to resemble a wave equation for an ordinary three-dimensional matter wave. Therefore, this possibility of playing with different complementary pictures has its analogy in the different transformations of the mathematical scheme; it does not lead to any difficulties in the Copenhagen interpretation of quantum theory.

A real difficulty in the understanding of this interpretation arises, however, when one asks the famous question: But what happens "really" in an atomic event? It has been said before that the mechanism and the results of an observation can always be stated in terms of the classical concepts. But what one deduces from an observation is a probability function, a mathematical expression that combines statements about possibilities or tendencies with statements about our knowledge of facts. So we cannot completely objectify the result of an observation, we cannot describe what "happens" between this observation and the next. This looks as if we had introduced an element of subjectivism into the theory, as if we meant to say: what happens depends on our way of observing it or on the fact that we observe it. Before discussing this problem of subjectivism it is necessary to explain quite clearly why one would get into hopeless difficulties if one tried to describe what happens between two consecutive observations.

For this purpose it is convenient to discuss the following ideal experiment: We assume that a small source of monochromatic light radiates toward a black screen with two small holes in it. The diameter of the holes may be not much bigger than the wave length of the light, but their distance will be very much bigger. At some distance behind the screen a photographic plate registers the incident light. If one describes this experiment in terms of the wave picture, one says that the primary wave penetrates through the two holes; there will be secondary spherical waves starting from the holes that interfere with one another, and the interference will produce a pattern of varying intensity on the photographic plate.

The blackening of the photographic plate is a quantum process, a chemical reaction produced by single light quanta. Therefore, it must also be possible to describe the experiment in terms of light quanta. If it would be permissible to say what happens to the single light quantum between its emission from the light source and its absorption in the photographic plate, one could argue as follows: The single light quantum can come through the first hole or through the second one. If it goes through the first hole and is scattered there, its probability for being absorbed at a certain point of the photographic plate cannot depend upon whether the second hole is closed or open. The probability distribution on the plate will be the same as if only the first hole was open. If the experiment is repeated many times and one takes together all cases in which the light quantum has gone through the first hole, the blackening of the plate due to these cases will correspond to this probability distribution. If one considers only those light quanta that go through the second hole, the blackening should correspond to a probability distribution derived from the assumption that only the second hole is open. The total blackening, therefore, should just be the sum of the blackenings in the two cases; in other words, there should be no interference pattern. But we know this is not correct, and the experiment will show the interference pattern. Therefore, the statement that any light quantum must have gone *either* through the first *or* through the second hole is problematic and leads to contradictions. This example shows clearly that the concept of the probability function does not allow a description of what happens between two observations. Any attempt to find such a description would lead to contradictions; this must mean that the term "happens" is restricted to the observation.

Now, this is a very strange result, since it seems to indicate that the observation plays a decisive role in the event and that the reality varies, depending upon whether we observe it or not. To make this point clearer we have to analyze the process of observation more closely.

To begin with, it is important to remember that in natural science we are not interested in the universe as a whole, including ourselves, but we direct our attention to some part of the universe and make that the object of our studies. In atomic physics this part is usually a very small object, an atomic particle or a group of such particles, sometimes much larger— the size does not matter; but it is important that a large part of the universe, including ourselves, does *not* belong to the object.

Now, the theoretical interpretation of an experiment starts with the two steps that have been discussed. In the first step we have to describe the arrangement of the experiment, eventually combined with a first observation, in terms of classical physics and translate this description into a probability function. This probability function follows the laws of quantum theory, and its change in the course of time, which is continuous, can be calculated from the initial conditions; this is the second step. The probability function combines objective and subjective elements. It contains statements about possibilities or better tendencies ("potentia" in Aristotelian philosophy), and these statements are completely objective, they do not depend on any observer; and it contains statements about our knowledge of the system, which of course are subjective in so far as they may be different for different observers. In ideal cases the subjective element in the probability function may be practically negligible as compared with the objective one. The physicists then speak of a "pure case."

When we now come to the next observation, the result of which should be predicted from the theory, it is very important to realize that our object has to be in contact with the other part of the world, namely, the experimental arrangement, the measuring rod, etc., before or at least at the moment of observation. This means that the equation of motion for the probability function does now contain the influence of the interaction with the measuring device. This influence introduces a new element of uncertainty, since the measuring device is necessarily described in the terms of classical physics; such a description contains all the uncertainties concerning the microscopic structure of the device which we know from thermodynamics, and since the device is connected with the rest of the world, it contains in fact the uncertainties of the microscopic structure of the whole world. These uncertainties may be called objective in so far as they are simply a consequence of the description in the terms of classical physics and do not depend on any observer. They may be called subjective in so far as they refer to our incomplete knowledge of the world.

After this interaction has taken place, the probability function contains the objective element of tendency and the subjective element of incomplete knowledge, even if it has been a "pure case" before. It is for this reason that the result of the observation cannot generally be predicted with certainty; what can be predicted is the probability of a certain result of the observation, and this statement about the probability can be checked by repeating the experiment many times. The probability function does—unlike the common procedure in Newtonian mechanics—not describe a certain event but, at least during the process of observation, a whole ensemble of possible events.

The observation itself changes the probability function discontinuously; it selects of all possible events the actual one that has taken place. Since through the observation our knowledge of the system has changed discontinuously, its mathematical representation also has undergone the discontinuous change and we speak of a "quantum jump." When the old adage "Natura non facit saltus" is used as a basis for criticism of quantum theory, we can reply that certainly our knowledge can change suddenly and that this fact justifies the use of the term "quantum jump."

Therefore, the transition from the "possible" to the "actual" takes place during the act of observation. If we want to describe what happens in an atomic event, we have to realize that the word "happens" can apply only to the observation, not to the state of affairs between two observations. It applies to the physical, not the psychical act of observation, and we may say that the transition from the "possible" to the "actual" takes place as soon as the interaction of the object with the measuring device, and thereby with the rest of the world, has come into play; it is not connected with the act of registration of the result by the mind of the observer. The discontinuous change in the probability function, however, takes place with the act of registration, because it is the discontinuous change of our knowledge in the instant of registration that has its image in the discontinuous change of the probability function.

To what extent, then, have we finally come to an objective description of the world, especially of the atomic world? In classical physics science started from the belief—or should one say from the illusion?—that we could describe the world or at least parts of the world without any reference to ourselves. This is actually possible to a large extent. We know that the city of London exists whether we see it or not. It may be said that classical physics is just that idealization in which we can speak about parts of the world without any reference to ourselves. Its success has led to the general ideal of an objective description of the world. Objectivity has become the first criterion for the value of any scientific result. Does the Copenhagen interpretation of quantum theory still comply with this ideal? One may perhaps say that quantum theory corresponds to this ideal as far as possible. Certainly quantum theory does not contain genuine subjective features, it does not introduce the mind of the physicist as a part of the atomic event. But it starts from the division of the world into the "object" and the rest of the world, and from the fact that at least for the rest of the world we use the classical concepts in our description. This division is arbitrary and historically a direct consequence of our scientific method; the use of the classical concepts is finally a consequence of the general human way of thinking. But this is already a reference to ourselves and in so far our description is not completely objective.

It has been stated in the beginning that the Copenhagen interpretation of quantum theory starts with a paradox. It starts from the fact that we describe our experiments in the terms of classical physics and at the same time from the knowledge that these concepts do not fit nature accurately. The tension between these two starting points is the root of the statistical character of quantum theory. Therefore, it has sometimes been suggested that one should depart from the classical concepts altogether and that a radical change in the concepts used for describing the experiments might possibly lead back to a nonstatical, completely objective description of nature.

This suggestion, however, rests upon a misunderstanding. The concepts of classical physics are just a refinement of the concepts of daily life and are an essential part of the language which forms the basis of all natural science. Our actual situation in science is such that we *do* use the classical concepts for the description of the experiments, and it was the problem of quantum theory to find theoretical interpretation of the experiments on this basis. There is no use in discussing what could be done if we were other beings than we are. At this point we have to realize, as von Weizsäcker has put it, that "Nature is earlier than man, but man is earlier than natural science." The first part of the sentence justifies classical physics, with its ideal of complete objectivity. The second part tells us why we cannot escape the paradox of quantum theory, namely, the necessity of using the classical concepts.

We have to add some comments on the actual procedure in the quantum-theoretical interpretation of atomic events. It has been said that we always start with a division of the world into an object, which we are going to study, and the rest of the world, and that this division is to some extent arbitrary. It should indeed not make any difference in the final result if we, e.g., add some part of the measuring device or the whole device to the object and apply the laws of quantum theory to this more complicated object. It can be shown that such an alteration of the theoretical treatment would not alter the predictions concerning a given experiment. This follows mathematically from the fact that the laws of quantum theory are for the phenomena in which Planck's constant can be considered as a very small quantity, approximately identical with the classical laws. But it would be a mistake to believe that this application of the quantum-theoretical laws to the measuring device could help to avoid the fundamental paradox of quantum theory.

The measuring device deserves this name only if it is in close contact with the rest of the world, if there is an interaction between the device and the observer. Therefore, the uncertainty with respect to the microscopic behavior of the world will enter into the quantum-theoretical system here just as well as in the first interpretation. If the measuring device would be isolated from the rest of the world, it would be neither a measuring device nor could it be described in the terms of classical physics at all.

With regard to this situation Bohr has emphasized that it is more realistic to state that the division into the object and the rest of the world is not arbitrary. Our actual situation in research work in atomic physics is usually this: we wish to understand a certain phenomenon, we wish to recognize how this phenomenon follows from the general laws of nature. Therefore, that part of matter or radiation which takes part in the phenomenon is the natural "object" in the theoretical treatment and should be separated in this respect from the tools used to study the phenomenon. This again emphasizes a subjective element in the description of atomic events, since the measuring device has been constructed by the observer, and we have to remember that what we observe is not nature in itself but nature exposed to our method of questioning. Our scientific work in physics consists in asking questions about nature in the language that we possess and trying to get an answer from experiment by the means that are at our disposal. In this way quantum theory reminds us, as Bohr has put it, of the old wisdom that when searching for harmony in life one must never forget that in the drama of existence we are ourselves both players and spectators. It is understandable that in our scientific relation to nature our own activity becomes very important when we have to deal with parts of nature into which we can penetrate only by using the most elaborate tools.

67

ooooooooooo

THE BARRIER AROUND THE
NUCLEUS

ooooooooooo

George Gamow (b. 1904)

Shortly after the discovery of quantum mechanics and the wave properties of particles, the new physical ideas that stemmed from these theories were given further support and extended to larger domains by George Gamow's brilliant application of wave mechanics to the analysis of the radioactivity of nuclei. The wave mechanics had been remarkably successful in accounting for the behavior of electrons both inside and outside atoms, and in explaining correctly the origin of atomic spectra. But it was not known, before the work of Gamow (and of Condon and Gurney, who did a similar analysis independently of Gamow), that wave mechanics is applicable to α particles and in regions such as the interior of the nucleus. Gamow's paper, which is reprinted in translation following this commentary, is thus an important step in the development of a complete quantum-mechanical picture of nature.

Although Gamow's prime purpose in this paper is to explain the spontaneous emission of α particles (α decay) from radioactive nuclei, such as uranium, and to deduce decay lifetimes theoretically (which he does very successfully), his paper also shows that the quantum mechanics is valid inside nuclei and that α particles obey the same kind of wave equation (the Schroedinger equation) as do electrons. In addition, he demonstrates the correctness of Born's concept that the Schroedinger wave function is the probability amplitude for finding a particle in a given small neighborhood of space. Gamow's paper also throws into sharp relief the essential difference between the classical dynamics of Newton and the modern wave picture of matter.

Until the work of Gamow and of Condon and Gurney the radioactivity of nuclei resulting in the emission of α particles was a complete mystery, senseless in terms of classical physics. To see why this is so, we need only consider the kinetic energy with which α particles are emitted from radioactive nuclei. This energy is considerably less than what it would be if an α particle were placed at the surface of a nucleus such as uranium and allowed to move away from this nucleus under the action of the Coulomb repulsion, resulting from the positive charges on the nucleus and on the α particle. Since we know the size of the uranium nucleus, and that Coulomb's law of electrostatic force between charged particles holds down to distances of the size of the nucleus, we can easily compute the kinetic energy the α particle would acquire in this way and compare it with the kinetic energy of observed α particles. We find that the kinetic energy of these particles is much smaller than would be expected from this classical picture. The observed α particles behave as though they came from a point quite distant from the nucleus, instead of from within it. Thus, classical theory is in complete disagreement with observation.

To account for the observations, and simultaneously to obtain an expression for the lifetime of a radioactive nucleus—that is, how long, on the average, a nucleus remains intact—Gamow applied quantum mechanics (more specifically the Schroedinger wave equation) to spontaneous α-particle emission. In 1928, little was known about nuclear forces (and we do not know very much even now). Thus, the prospects for a wave-mechanical treatment of the problem did not seem hopeful. However, as it turned out, because of the very short range of the attractive nuclear forces (the forces that oppose the Coulomb repulsive forces and thus keep the nucleus together), it was not necessary to have a detailed picture of those forces to obtain a quantum mechanical model of α-particle emission.

Gamow sensed this and went boldly ahead with his analysis. Although he had no precise knowledge of the nature of nuclear forces, he constructed an approximate force model of the nucleus that was good enough to allow him to solve the problem quantum-mechanically. This model consists first of a repulsive barrier (the Coulomb repulsive force or, more precisely, the Coulomb repulsive potential) that surrounds the nucleus like a hill and prevents positively charged particles from coming close to the nucleus—unless they are moving fast enough (with enough kinetic energy) to "break through" this barrier. In addition, the model includes a deep well in which the particles in the nucleus are pictured as moving about.

Classically, according to this picture, no particle (e.g., α particle) could leave the well, that is, the nucleus, unless its kinetic energy inside the well were greater than the potential energy represented by the height of the

Coulumb barrier, the "repulsive hill." But if that were the case, the particle would then have to leave the nucleus with kinetic energy much greater than that observed. For a particle to leave the well with the observed kinetic energy, it has to tunnel right through the repulsive hill; this is impossible classically because while it is in the tunnel, its kinetic energy (its total energy less its potential energy) is negative, a meaningless concept in classical physics. However, this offers no difficulty in quantum mechanics, since the only thing that one must be concerned with, in the sense of its being possible in nature, is what one can observe at the end of a process. Quantum mechanics allows a particle to pass through an intermediate state with negative kinetic energy as long as the final state of the particle is in agreement with correct principles.

If we keep this in mind the quantum-mechanical analysis of α particle emission is quite straightforward. It falls into a class of problems known as "potential barrier" problems which may be described briefly in terms of an optical model. Consider a particle that is moving along a straight line and impinges on a barrier of a certain height. Classically it would bounce right off this barrier unless it had enough energy to rise above it and roll over. But we must now take into account the wave properties of the particle and note that a wave spreads out into all regions and can penetrate barriers. Thus if a wave of light, moving along a straight line, strikes a barrier, for example, a glass surface, part of the light is reflected from the barrier and part of it passes right through. The amount of light that is reflected and the amount that is transmitted depend on the nature of the barrier, and can be expressed in terms of what is called the "index of refraction of the barrier," which depends on the density of the barrier and how the molecules in it are arranged.

In the case of a charged particle such as an electron or an α particle, the barriers with which we have to deal in treating the particle as a wave consist of electric and magnetic fields, for which one can introduce the equivalent of an index of refraction. This index of refraction depends on the field strengths that determine the height of the barrier, and just as in the case of an optical wave, the material De Broglie wave suffers both reflection and refraction when it strikes the barrier. Part of the wave passes right through the barrier, even though the particle counterpart of the wave does not have enough energy to get over the barrier.

Thus we can show by solving Schroedinger's wave equation for a particle surrounded by a potential barrier of finite height that the wave that describes the particle has two parts to it. One part lies inside the barrier; the other lies outside the barrier even if the particle is moving about inside the barrier with a kinetic energy that is less than the height of the barrier. This is the significant difference between classical and quantum physics.

We can further see what this involves by taking into account Born's interpretation of the Schroedinger wave function. According to Born, the probability of finding a particle in a small region of space is arrived at by multiplying the volume of this small region by the square of the absolute value of the particle's wave function in this region. This tells us at once that wherever the wave function of the particle is not zero, there is a finite probability for finding the particle. Thus in the case of the particle inside the potential barrier, the existence of a part of its wave function outside the barrier tells us that the particle has a finite probability of penetrating the barrier and being found outside it.

Gamow applied these very subtle ideas to the emission of α particles from radioactive nuclei. An α particle inside the nucleus is described by a wave (the solution of the Schroedinger equation for the particle); part of the wave lies inside the nucleus but part extends beyond the nucleus into the outside world. This means that there is a finite probability for finding the α particle on the outward side of the barrier, that is, outside the nucleus. We may put this differently by saying that as the α particle oscillates back and forth inside the nucleus, it has a finite chance of penetrating the barrier every time it comes near the surface of the nucleus. This probability or chance becomes larger the larger is the amplitude of its wave outside the nucleus.

One can now calculate the lifetime of a radioactive nucleus as opposed to its decay by α-particle emission. One first solves the Schroedinger wave equation for an α particle in the nucleus and then seeks among all the possible solutions that particular wave function that describes an α particle having the observed energy when it is emitted from the nucleus. The sum of the squares of the absolute values of this function taken over all regions of space outside the nucleus gives the total probability for finding the α particle outside the nucleus. If this is multiplied by the number of times per second that the α particle oscillates back and forth inside the nucleus, we obtain the probability per unit time that the α particle will escape from the nucleus. The reciprocal of this probability is the lifetime of the nucleus. Gamow carried through these calculations and showed that the theory agrees with the observations.

Gamow's theory has important applications far beyond those associated only with radioactive decay. The same analysis that Gamow used to analyze the radioactive emissions of α particles from nuclei can be reversed to analyze the capture of particles such as protons, α particles, and other particles by nuclei. This is of great importance in astrophysics, for we know today that the energy released by stars like the sun comes from the fusion of nuclei. The growth, evolution, and death of stars are governed by thermonuclear fusion in their deep interiors, and to understand such nuclear processes we must consider the penetration of potential barriers by interacting nuclei. The analysis of such thermonuclear processes is carried out by using Gamow's results for the penetration of the potential barriers that surround all nuclei.

George Gamow was born in Odessa, Russia, on March 4, 1904, and received his doctorate in physics from the University of Leningrad in 1928. This was a fortunate time for him to have completed his graduate studies, for quantum mechanics had just been discovered and many exciting problems were on the verge of solution. Gamow had the further good fortune of receiving a fellowship to spend a year at the Niels Bohr Theoretical Institute of Physics in Copenhagen, just when Born had proposed his statistical interpretation of the Schroedinger wave function.

Before Gamow tackled the problem of the emission of α particles from radioactive nuclei, the only way of testing Born's interpretation of the wave function was by analyzing collision phenomena. Gamow's paper on the structure of nuclei, published in 1928, showed that the Born statistical interpretation of the wave function gives a correct picture of radioactive decay processes. This paper was also important because it demonstrated clearly that quantum mechanics is valid inside the nucleus of an atom.

From Copenhagen, Gamow went to the University of Cambridge as a fellow of the Rockefeller Foundation and was there from 1929 to 1930. He then returned to Copenhagen for another year. In 1930 he returned to Leningrad as professor of theoretical physics and remained there until 1933. He left Leningrad to spend a year as visiting professor at the University of Paris.

In 1934 Gamow came to the United States as professor of theoretical physics at George Washington University in Washington, D.C., and remained at this post until 1956. During this period, Gamow's research interests shifted from pure physics to astrophysics and cosmology. While still continuing his research work in nuclear physics, he began a series of investigations into the evolution of stars. It was, of course, natural for him to become involved in the problem of stellar interiors, for the theoretical technique he used in analyzing the emission of α particles by radioactive nuclei is just what was needed to study thermonuclear reactions in stars. In fact, one of the factors that enter into the formula for the energy generation in stars is referred to as the Gamow reflection factor.

In one of his investigations during this period, Gamow discovered a process that can play a very important role in the life history of a star. This is the rapid emission of neutrinos, which allows a star to collapse to very high densities. In collaboration with Edward Teller, Gamow also studied the thermonuclear reactions in the early stages of a star's life.

After these investigations into stellar structure, Gamow became interested in cosmological problems and proposed the "big-bang" theory of the origin of the universe. As part of this theory, Gamow argued that all the heavy elements now present in the universe were built up from protons and neutrons in the first half hour after the big bang. This view of the formation of the heavy elements is no longer accepted, since we now know that the heavy elements are built up in the very hot interiors of stars during certain stages of their evolution.

As Gamow has become less and less active in research, he has become more and more active as a science writer. Besides his book on nuclear structure, which is a technical treatise, he has written numerous popular books, beginning with his famous *The Life and Death of a Sun,* which has gone through many printings. All of his books are brilliantly written, with emphasis on clarity, simplicity, and reader interest.

Since 1956, Gamow has been professor of physics at the University of Colorado in Boulder. He is a member of the National Academy of Science, and of the Royal Danish Academy of Sciences.

ଡ଼ଡ଼ଡ଼ଡ଼ଡ଼ଡ଼ଡ଼ଡ଼

GAMOW

Quantum Theory of the Atomic Nucleus [1]

IT HAS OFTEN BEEN SUGGESTED that non-Coulomb attractive forces play a very important role inside atomic nuclei. We can make many hypotheses concerning the nature of these forces. They can be the attractions between the magnetic moments of the individual constituents of the nucleus or the forces engendered by electric and magnetic polarization.

In any case, these forces diminish very rapidly with increasing distance from the nucleus, and only in the immediate vicinity of the nucleus do they outweigh the Coulomb force.

From the scattering of α-particles we may conclude that for heavy elements the forces of attraction are still not measurable down to a distance of $\sim 10^{-12}$ cm. We may therefore take the potential energy as being correctly represented by the curve in [Fig. 67–1].

Here r'' gives the distance down to which it has been shown experi-

---

[1] George Gamow, *Zeitschrift für Physik,* 51 (1928), 204–212—trans. Editors.

mentally that the Coulomb repulsion alone exists. From r' down the deviation (r' is unknown and perhaps much smaller than r'') from the Coulomb force is pronounced and the U-curve has a maximum at r_0. For $r < r_0$ the attractive forces dominate; in this region, the particle circles around the rest of the nucleus like a satellite.

This motion, however, is not stable since the particle's energy is positive, and, after some time, the α-particle will fly out (α-emission). Here, however, we meet a fundamental difficulty.

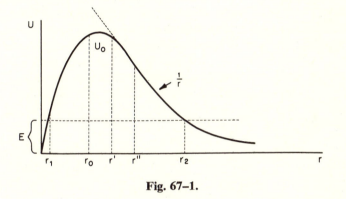

Fig. 67–1.

To fly off, the α-particle must overcome a potential barrier of height U_0 [Fig. 67–1]; its energy may not be less than U_0. But the energy of the emitted α-particle, as verified experimentally, is much less. For example, we find on analyzing the scattering of Ra-c'-α-particles by uranium that for the uranium nucleus the Coulomb law is valid down to distances of 3.2×10^{-12} cm. On the other hand, the α-particles emitted by uranium itself have an energy which represents a distance of 6.3×10^{-12} cm (r_2 in [Fig. 67–1]) on the repulsive curve. If an α-particle, coming from the interior of the nucleus, is to fly away, it must pass through the region r_1 and r_2 where its kinetic energy would be negative, which, naturally, is impossible classically.

To overcome this difficulty, Rutherford assumed that the α-particles in the nucleus are neutral, since they are assumed to have two electrons there. Only at a certain distance from the nucleus, on the other side of the potential barrier's maximum, do they, according to Rutherford, lose their two electrons, which fall back into the nucleus while the α-particles fly on impelled by the Coulomb repulsion. But this assumption seems very unnatural, and can hardly be a true picture.

If we consider the problem from the wave mechanical point of view, the above difficulties disappear by themselves. In wave mechanics a particle always has a finite probability, different from zero, of going from one region to another region of the same energy, even though the two regions are separated by an arbitrarily large but finite potential barrier.

As we shall see further, the probability for such a transition, all things considered, is very small and, in fact, is smaller the higher the potential barrier is. To clarify this point, we shall analyze a simple case [see Fig. 67–2].

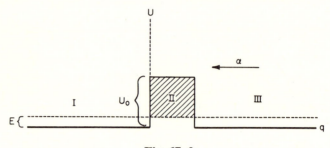

Fig. 67–2.

We have a rectangular potential barrier and we wish to find the solution of Schroedinger's equation which represents the penetration of the particle from right to left. For the energy E we write the wave function ψ in the following form:

$$\psi = \Psi(q)e^{(2\pi i/h)Et},$$

where $\Psi(q)$ satisfies the amplitude equation

$$\frac{\partial^2 \Psi}{\partial q^2} + \frac{8\pi^2 m}{h^2}(E - U)\Psi = 0 \tag{1}$$

For the region I we have the solution

$$\Psi_{\mathrm{I}} = A \cos(kq + \alpha)$$

where A and α are two arbitrary constants and

$$k = \frac{2\pi\sqrt{2m}}{h} \cdot \sqrt{E} \tag{2a}$$

In the region II the solution reads

$$\Psi_{\mathrm{II}} = B_1 e^{-k'q} + B_2 e^{k'q}$$

where

$$k' = \frac{2\pi\sqrt{2m}}{h}\sqrt{U_0 - E} \tag{2b}$$

At the boundary $q = 0$ the following conditions apply:

$$\Psi_\mathrm{I}(0) = \Psi_\mathrm{II}(0) \text{ and } \left[\frac{\partial\Psi_\mathrm{I}}{\partial q}\right]_{q=0} = \left[\frac{\partial\Psi_\mathrm{II}}{\partial q}\right]_{q=0},$$

from which we easily obtain

$$B_1 = \frac{A}{2\sin\theta}\sin(\alpha+\theta); B_2 = -\frac{A}{2\sin\theta}\sin(\alpha-\theta),$$

where

$$\sin\theta = \frac{1}{\sqrt{1+\left(\frac{k}{k'}\right)^2}}$$

The solution in region II therefore reads

$$\Psi_\mathrm{II} = \frac{A}{2\sin\theta}[\sin(\alpha+\theta)e^{-k'q} - \sin(\alpha-\theta)e^{k'q}].$$

In III we again have

$$\Psi_\mathrm{III} = C\cos(kq+\beta)$$

At the boundary $q = l$ we have from the boundary conditions

$$\frac{A}{2\sin\theta}[\sin(\alpha+\theta)e^{-lk'} - \sin(\alpha-\theta)e^{+lk'}] = C\cos(kl+\beta)$$

and

$$\frac{A}{2\sin\theta}k'[-\sin(\alpha+\theta)e^{-lk'} - \sin(\alpha-\theta)e^{+lk'}]$$
$$= -kC\sin(kl+\beta).$$

Hence

$$C^2 = \frac{A^2}{4\sin^2\theta}\left\{\left[1+\left(\frac{k'}{k}\right)^2\right]\sin^2(\alpha-\theta)\cdot e^{2lk'}\right.$$

$$-\left[1-\left(\frac{k'}{k}\right)^2\right]2\sin(\alpha-\theta)\sin(\alpha+\theta)$$

$$\left.+\left[1+\left(\frac{k'}{k}\right)^2\right]\sin^2(\alpha+\theta)e^{-2lk'}\right\}. \qquad (3)$$

The calculation of β is of no interest to us. We are interested only in the case in which lk' is very large so that we need consider only the first term in (3).

We thus have the following solution:

left: right:

$$A \cos (kq + \alpha) \ . \ . \ . \ A \frac{\sin (\alpha - \theta)}{2 \sin \theta} \left[1 + \left(\frac{k'}{k} \right)^2 \right]^{\frac{1}{2}} . \quad e^{+ lk'} \cos (kq + \beta).$$

If we now write $\alpha - \frac{\pi}{2}$ instead of α, multiply the obtained solution by i, and then add the two solutions, we obtain on the left

$$\Psi = A e^{i(kq + \alpha)}, \tag{4a}$$

on the right, however,

$$\Psi = \frac{A}{2 \sin \theta} \left[1 + \left(\frac{k'}{k} \right)^2 \right]^{\frac{1}{2}} . e^{+ lk'} \{ \sin (\alpha - \theta) \cos (kq + \beta)$$
$$- i \cos (\alpha + \theta) \cos (kq + \beta') \}, \tag{4b}$$

where β' is the new phase.

If we multiply this solution by $e^{2 \pi i \frac{E}{h} t}$, we obtain for Ψ on the left the (from right to left) advancing wave; on the right, however, the complex oscillatory phenomenon with a very large amplitude ($e^{lk'}$) that departs only slightly from a standing wave. This means nothing other than that the wave coming from the right is partly reflected and partly transmitted.

We thus see that the amplitude of the transmitted wave is smaller the smaller is the total energy E, and in fact the factor

$$e^{- lk'} = e^{\frac{2 \pi . \sqrt{2m}}{h} \sqrt{U_0 - E} . l}$$

plays an important role in this connection.

We can now solve the problem for two symmetrical potential barriers [Fig. 67–3]. We shall seek two solution.

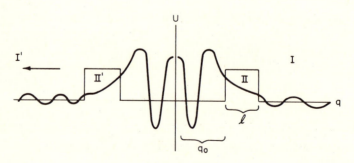

Fig. 67–3.

One solution is to be valid for positive q, and for $q > q_0 + l$ is to give the wave:

$$Ae^{i\left(\frac{2\pi E}{h}t - kq + \alpha\right)}$$

The other solution is valid for negative q, and for $q < -(q_0 + l)$ gives the wave

$$Ae^{i\left(\frac{2\pi Et}{h} + qk' - \alpha\right)}.$$

We cannot attach the two solutions to each other continuously at $q = 0$ since we have here two boundary conditions to fulfill and only one arbitrary constant α to adjust. The physical reason for this impossibility is that the Ψ-function constructed from these two solutions does not satisfy the conservation law

$$\frac{\partial}{\partial t} \int_{-(q_0 + l)}^{+(q_0 + l)} \psi\bar{\psi}dq = 2 \cdot \frac{-h}{4\pi i m} [\psi \ \text{grad} \ \bar{\psi} - \bar{\psi} \ \text{grad} \ \psi]_{\mathrm{I}}$$

To overcome these difficulties we must assume that the vibrations are damped and make E complex

$$E = E_0 + i\frac{h\lambda}{4\pi}$$

where E_0 is the usual energy and λ is the damping decrement (decay constant). We then see from the relations (2a) and (2b) that k and k' are complex, that is, that the amplitude of our wave also depends exponentially on the coordinate q. For example, for the running wave the amplitude in the direction of the diverging wave will increase. This means nothing more than that if the vibrations are damped at the source of the wave, the amplitude of the wave segment that left earlier must be larger. We can now determine α so that the boundary conditions are fulfilled. But the exact solution does not interest us. If λ is small compared to $\frac{E}{h}$ (for Ra-c' $\frac{E}{h} \cong \frac{10^{-5}}{10^{-27}}$ sec^{-1} = 10^{22} sec^{-1} and $\lambda = 10^5$ sec^{-1}) the change in $\Psi(q)$ is very small and we can simply multiply the old solution with $e^{-\frac{\alpha}{2}t}$.

The conservation principle then reads

$$\frac{\partial}{\partial t} e^{-\lambda t} \int_{-(q_0 + l)}^{+(q_0 + l)} \Psi^{(q)}_{\mathrm{II, III}} \cdot \Psi^{(q)}_{\mathrm{II, III}} \ dq = -2 \cdot \frac{A^2 h}{4\pi i m} \cdot 2 i k \cdot e^{-\lambda t},$$

from which we obtain

$$\lambda = \frac{4\,h\,k\,\sin^2\theta}{\pi\,m\left[1+\left(\dfrac{k'}{k^0}\right)^2\right]2(l+q_0)\kappa} \cdot e^{-\frac{4\pi l\sqrt{2m}}{h}\sqrt{U_0-E}}, \tag{5}$$

where κ is a number of order of magnitude one.

This formula gives the dependence of the decay constant on the decay energy for our simple nuclear model.

Now we can go over to the case of the actual nucleus.

We cannot solve the corresponding wave equation because we do not know the exact formula for the potential in the neighborhood of the nucleus. But even without an exact knowledge of the potential we can carry over to the actual nucleus results obtained from our simple model.

As usual, in the case of a central force, we seek the solution in polar coordinates and, in fact, in the form

$$\Psi = u(\theta, \phi)\chi(r).$$

For u we obtain the spherical harmonics, and χ must satisfy the differential equation

$$\frac{d^2\chi}{dr^2} + \frac{2}{r}\frac{d\chi}{dr} + \frac{8\pi^2 m}{h^2}\left[E - U - \frac{h^2}{8\pi^2\,m} \cdot \frac{n(n+1)}{r^2}\right]\chi = 0,$$

where n is the order of the spherical harmonic. We can place $n = 0$, since if $n > 0$, this would really be just as though the potential energy were enlarged, and because of this the damping for these oscillations is much smaller. The particle must first pass over to the state $n = 0$ and can only then fly away.

It is quite possible that such transitions are the cause of the γ rays which always accompany α-emission. The probable shape of U is shown in [Fig. 67–4].

For large values of r, we shall take for χ the solution

$$\chi_{\mathrm{I}} = \frac{A}{r}\,e^{i\left(\frac{2\pi E}{h}t - kr\right)}$$

Even though we cannot obtain the exact solution of the problem in this case, we can still say that on the average in the regions I and I', χ does not decrease very rapidly (in the three dimensional case like $1/r$).

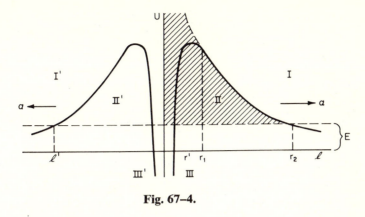

Fig. 67–4.

In the region III, however, χ decreases exponentially, and in analogy with our simple case we may state that the relation between the amplitude decrease and E is given by the factor

$$e^{-\frac{2\pi\sqrt{2m}}{h}\int_{r_1}^{r_2}\sqrt{U-E}\,dr}$$

If we use the conservation principle we can again write down the formula

$$\lambda = D \cdot e^{-\frac{2\pi\sqrt{2\,m}}{h}\int_{r_1}^{r_2}\sqrt{U-E}\,dr} \qquad (6)$$

where D depends on the particular properties of the nuclear model. We can neglect the dependence of D on E as compared to its exponential dependence.

We may also replace the integral

$$\int_{r_1}^{r_2}\sqrt{U-E}\,dr$$

by the approximate integral

$$\int_{0}^{\frac{2\,Z\,e^2}{E}}\sqrt{\frac{2\,Z\,e^2}{r}-E}\cdot dr$$

The relative error we introduce in this way is of the order of $\sqrt{\dfrac{r_1}{r_2}}$. Since r_1/r_2 is small, this error is not very large. Since E does not differ much for different radioactive elements, we write as an approximation

$$\log \lambda = \mathrm{const}_E + B_E \cdot \Delta E,$$

. . . where

$$B_E = \frac{\pi^2 \sqrt{2\,m} \cdot 2\,Ze^2}{h\,E^{3/2}}. \qquad (7)$$

We wish to compare this formula with the experimental results. It is known that if we plot the logarithm of the decay constant against the energy of the emitted α-particle, all the points for a definite radioactive family fall on a straight line. For different families we obtain different parallel lines. The empirical formula reads

$$\log \lambda = \mathrm{const} + bE$$

where b is a constant that is common to all radioactive families.

The experimental value of b is $b_{\exp} = 1.02 \times 10^7$ (calculated from Ra-A and Ra).

If we put the energy value for Ra-A into our formula, we get

$$b_{\mathrm{theoretical}} = 0.7 \times 10^7$$

This order of magnitude agreement shows that the basic assumptions of our theory must be correct. . . .

ELECTRON WAVES

ooooooooooo

Clinton J. Davisson (1881-1958)

George Paget Thomson (b. 1892)

When De Broglie first published his wave theory of the electron (and of matter in general) there was no experimental evidence at all to support his bold hypothesis since no one, before De Broglie announced his theory, had any reason to think that electrons might have wave in addition to corpuscular properties. De Broglie reasoned that since light exhibits both wave and corpuscular properties, this dualism might also extend to electrons.

As we know, De Broglie did more than present the basic ideas of his wave theory. He also clothed it in a complete and consistent mathematical formulation. From it, one can predict the behavior of the waves and, in particular, the wavelength of an electron moving with a given velocity. It is easy to find the wavelength of an electron moving with speed v or with momentum mv, where m is its mass, by analogy with a photon. The energy of a photon equals $h\nu$, where h is Planck's constant of action and ν is the frequency of the photon. Now one can show from the theory of relativity, as pointed out by Einstein, that the momentum of a photon equals its energy divided by its speed c. Hence the momentum of a photon equals $\dfrac{h\nu}{c}$. But $c = \lambda\nu$ where λ is the wavelength of the photon. Thus we find that the momentum of the photon equals Planck's constant divided by the wavelength, h/λ. It follows that wavelength = h/momentum.

This is the expression for the wavelength of an electron as derived by De Broglie. We see that the wavelength depends on the momentum and hence on the speed of the electron, so that one can obtain various wave-lengths for the same electron by altering the energy of the electron. This is important for experimental purposes: For electron speeds well below the speed of light (let us say less than one tenth of the speed of light) we may place the momentum equal to mv; for speeds closer to that of light this expression must be replaced by

$$\frac{mv}{\sqrt{1 - v^2/c^2}} .$$

From this we see that even for speeds of only a few thousand kilometers per second, the wavelength of an electron is about equal to that of X-rays. As the speed goes up the wavelength decreases. This was demonstrated by the experiments of G. P. Thomson and of Davisson and Germer. Just as crystals reflect and diffract X-rays, they should also reflect and diffract electron waves, if indeed electrons have wave properties.

Before describing the work of Thomson, and Davisson and Germer, we must discuss a classical phase of the particle aspect of an electron that would make the results of their experiments completely incomprehensible. If we suppose that the electric charge e of an electron is spread over the surface of a small sphere of radius a (which we may take as the classical radius of the electron) we obtain the electrostatic energy e^2/a. This gives us a particle picture that is very much at variance with the wave picture, since it indicates that the electron is an extremely tiny particle concentrated in a very small volume. To illustrate this, we note that the energy e^2/a must equal the energy mc^2 (obtained from Einstein's mass-energy formula). This means that the classical radius a of the electron is of the order of e^2/mc^2, which is about one ten-trillionth of a centimeter.

We may now consider the experiments of Davisson, who, with the assistance of Germer, first observed the wave properties of electrons. To begin with, we note that if electrons were particles in the classical sense (as described above), there would be no regular pattern in the reflection of electrons from the surfaces of crystals. The reason for this is that an electron, pictured as a classical particle, is thousands of times smaller than the spacings between the atoms in a crystal. Hence its behavior when it enters the crystal should depend only on whether or not it happens to pass close to some atom, which, in general, would not be very probable. Of course, as the electron pushes into the crystal, it is bound to meet some atom, but its behavior depends only on this single interaction, since all the other atoms are so far away that they do not affect the electron.

But this is not what Davisson and Germer found in 1928, when they scattered electrons from a nickel surface. Their discovery stemmed from a happy accident. Although they had designed an experiment to study the scattering of slowly moving electrons from smooth metal surfaces, they had no idea of looking for a wave pattern in the scattered electrons. Indeed, they were unaware of De Broglie's work, which had been done three years earlier. In any case, their experiment as it had first been set up would not have revealed the wave structure of the electron since, under ordinary conditions, the atoms in a metal are not arranged in an ordered scheme but are arranged haphazardly in small crystalline groups. In other words, the nickel strip that Davisson and Germer first used was not one large crystal and therefore it would not have scattered the incident electrons in a regular pattern. No diffraction patterns, the hallmark of a wave, should have been observable.

But the vacuum tube in which they had placed the nickel strip accidentally burst. They found it necessary to heat the nickel, then to cool it slowly before it could be put into another tube for the resumption of the experiments. The heating and slow cooling caused the atoms to arrange themselves into a regular crystalline pattern, which is precisely what is needed to obtain the diffraction they observed when they sent the electron beam against the nickel surface. The Davisson paper that follows expresses amazement at this discovery. Instead of finding electrons reflected at random from the face of the nickel, they observed a regular pattern, similar in every respect to that of a reflected wave. This is remarkable because such a pattern can arise only if the reflection of the electron is caused by its simultaneous interaction with many atoms, rather than with one. The reflection of each electron seemed to be a collective phenomenon, which is precisely what would be found if the electron were accompanied by a wave.

When a wave, for example, an X-ray wave, strikes a crystal surface, this entire wave is reflected not only from the face of the crystal, but also from different layers within the crystal. We must keep in mind that the atoms in a crystal are arranged in a definite formation, row after row, starting from the face of the crystal and going toward the interior. We may picture these rows as parallel to the face of the crystal, spaced at equal distances. A wave striking the face of the crystal at a given angle will, in part, be reflected from the first row of atoms, but parts of it will also be reflected from the second, third, and fourth rows, and so on, each in succession contributing less to the final reflected wave. The intensity of the reflected wave will depend on how all these partial waves, reflected in a given direction from the various layers, combine. Thus, if the reflected waves from the various layers are in phase when they leave the surface of the crystal (that is, if all their crests coincide) the intensity of the reflected wave will be maximum. If they are out of phase, however (crest coinciding with trough), the intensity of the reflected wave will be zero.

Using their crystalline nickel surface, Davisson and Germer found that if the speed of electrons in a beam is constant, the intensity of the reflected beam is a maximum for only one angle of incidence; if the speed is varied, however, this angle of maximum intensity changes inversely with the speed of the electrons, just as it does with the wavelength of a reflected wave. They found that the relationship between the angle of maximum intensity, the speed of the electrons, and the lattice spacing in the crystal are the same as that for a wave, provided one assigns to the electrons a wavelength given by the De Broglie formula. This observation definitely established the wave-particle dualism of the electron and set the study of wave mechanics on a sound experimental foundation.

Clinton J. Davisson began his experimental work on the scattering of electrons by crystals and by metallic surfaces at a most opportune time, for it was just before De Broglie and Schroedinger had introduced their wave picture of the electron. By the time the De Broglie-Schroedinger wave theory had been introduced, Davisson was ready to perform the experiments that were to establish the wave theory on a sound basis. Yet he had not undertaken his study to show that electrons have wave properties; he began in 1919 simply to inquire how electrons are scattered in various directions from metallic surfaces.

Davisson exhibited proficiency in physics and mathematics while still in high school, which he attended at a somewhat older age than is normal, graduating at twenty-one. He was born in Bloomington, Illinois, on October 22, 1881. His father Joseph was an artisan and a descendant of the early Dutch and French settlers of Virginia; his mother was Mary Calvert, a Pennsylvania schoolteacher of English and Scotch parentage. After attending the Bloomington grammar and high schools, he was given a scholarship at the University of Chicago for his high-school achievements in mathematics and physics. While at the university he came under the influence of Robert Millikan. After a year, he had to leave the university for lack of funds, and he went to work for the telephone company in Bloomington. In 1904, at the recommendation of Millikan, he was appointed an assistant in physics at Purdue University, although still without an undergraduate degree. From Purdue, again with Millikan's help, he went to Princeton University as a part-time instructor in physics. While holding this post he studied under Professors James J. Jeans and O. W. Richardson, returning to the University of Chicago to attend summer sessions in order to complete his undergraduate studies; in 1908 he received a B.S. degree from that university.

Princeton awarded him a fellowship in physics for the year 1910–1911, which allowed him to devote all of his time to his graduate studies and to complete his requirements for the Ph.D. He wrote his doctoral thesis, under Richardson, on *Thermal Emission of Positive Ions from Alkaline*

Earth Salts. Richardson himself was to go on and develop this field of thermionic phenomena and discover its basic laws, for which he received the Nobel Prize in 1929. From Princeton, Davisson went to the Carnegie Institute of Technology. For a short time he also worked at the Cavendish Laboratory for J. J. Thomson. During World War I he joined the engineering division of the Western Electric Company, and after the war continued as a member of the Bell Telephone Laboratory research staff.

The work which Davisson began in 1919 had a fairly obvious purpose; at first sight, his research had no unusual facets or hidden meanings. Its purpose was simply to find how the energies of the electrons reflected from a metallic surface are related to the energies of the incident electrons. But, on obtaining some unexpected results, Davisson investigated the scattering from crystals placed at various angles to the incident beam, and found, "purely by accident," he says, that the intensity of the scattered beam depends on the orientation of the crystal. This was the beginning of the crucial experiment, for Davisson sent his results to Born, asking for his interpretation. Born and Franck, on the basis of calculations made by Elsasser, one of their students, suggested that Davisson's results stemmed from the De Broglie wave character of the electrons and advised Davisson to perform an experiment designed specifically to look for De Broglie diffraction patterns. This experiment was begun in 1926 and completely verified the De Broglie-Schroedinger theory. In 1937, he shared the Nobel Prize in physics with G. P. Thomson for this work.

Davisson continued his work on electron scattering after completing his basic research, but he became more and more interested in electron optics than in fundamental questions relating to the structure of matter. During World War II he contributed to the development of electronic devices and to crystal physics.

After retiring from Bell Telephone Laboratories in 1946, he became visiting professor of physics at the University of Virginia in Charlottesville, where he died on February 1, 1958, at the age of seventy-six. In his lifetime he received honorary degrees from various universities, as well as numerous medals and prizes.

George Paget Thomson was born on May 3, 1892, at Cambridge, England. The only son of Sir J. J. Thomson, he was educated at Trinity College, Cambridge, where he achieved the distinction of winning first class honors in the mathematical and natural sciences tripos in 1913. In World War I, young Thomson was commissioned in the Queen's Regiment and served in France from 1914 to 1915; he was then assigned to the Royal Flying Corps for experimental work on aerodynamic problems. In 1918, he came to the United States as a member of the British War Mission.

After the war, Thomson returned to Cambridge and carried out various researches in the Cavendish Laboratory. In 1922, he became professor of natural philosophy at the University of Aberdeen, where he carried out independent experiments on the diffraction of electrons in thin films, for which he received the Nobel Prize, along with Davisson, in 1937. In 1930, he was appointed professor of physics at the Imperial College of Science and Technology, University of London, a chair which he held until 1952, when he was elected master of Corpus Christi College, Cambridge. He retired from this position in 1962. During World War II, Thomson was chairman of the British Atomic Energy Commission (1940–1941) and served as scientific adviser to the Air Ministry (1943–1944), during which period he received a knighthood. In 1946 and 1947, he was scientific adviser to the British Delegation on Atomic Energy to the United Nations Commission. He was elected a fellow of the Royal Society of London in 1929 and has been honored by numerous universities and scientific societies.

Thomson's demonstration of the wave nature of electrons was executed in a manner significantly different from the experiments of Davisson and Germer. In his first experiment with A. Reid, he directed a beam of cathode rays at a thin film of celluloid and examined the effect of the transmitted rays on a photographic plate placed behind this film. On developing the plate, a central spot made by the undeflected rays was found to be surrounded by diffuse rings. By means of densitometer measurements of the exposed plate, the rings were discovered to be clearly defined. Thus, with 13,000 volt-electrons, two rings were found inside the one apparent on visual inspection. These represented diffraction halos in the same way that Debye-Sherrer halos are obtained with X-rays reflected from powdered crystals. The rings arising from the diffraction of waves disclosed the wave properties of the electron. The fact that the rings show a radius roughly inversely proportional to the velocity of the electrons provided evidence supporting the De Broglie equation

$$\lambda = \frac{h}{mv}$$

relating the wavelength of the electron waves to the velocity of the electrons themselves. Subsequent experiments in which thin platinum films replaced the celluloid ones completely confirmed the De Broglie relation. Thomson and Reid's original paper is presented before the article by Davisson.

Since the original experiments of Thomson and of Davisson and Germer, numerous other types of experiments have been performed to demonstrate the interference of electron waves. All such experiments have shown that electron waves interfere with one another in accordance with the De Broglie theory.

ooooooo

T H O M S O N and *R E I D*

Diffraction of Cathode Rays by a Thin Film [1]

I F A F I N E B E A M O F homogeneous cathode rays is
sent nearly normally through a thin celluloid film (of the order 3×10^{-6}
cm. thick) and then received on a photographic plate 10 cm. away and
parallel to the film, we find that the central spot formed by the undeflected
rays is surrounded by rings, recalling in appearance the haloes formed
by mist round the sun. . . . If the density of the plate is measured by
a photometer at a number of points along a radius, and the intensity of
the rays at these points found by using the characteristic blackening curve
of the plate, the rings appear as humps on the intensity-distance curves.
In this way rings can be detected which may not be obvious to direct
inspection. With rays of about 13,000 volts two rings have been found
inside the obvious one. Traces have been found of a fourth ring in other
photographs, but not more than three have been found on any one exposure. This is probably due to the limited range of intensity within
which photometric measurements are feasible.

The size of the rings decreases with increasing energy of the rays, the
radius of any given ring being roughly inversely proportional to the velocity, but as the rings are rather wide the measurements so far made are
not very accurate. The energy of the rays, as measured by their electrostatic deflexion, varied from 3900 volts to 16,500 volts. The rings are
sharpest at the higher energies and were indistinguishable at about 2500
volts. In one photograph the radii of the rings were approximately 3, 5,
and 6·7 mm. for an energy of 13,800 volts.

It is natural to regard this phenomenon as allied to the effect found by
Dymond for the scattering of electrons in helium, though the angles are
of course much smaller than he found. This would be due partly to the
greater speed of the rays giving them a smaller wave-length. Using the
formula $\lambda = h/mv$ the wave-length in the above-quoted case would be
$\lambda = 1 \cdot 0 \times 10^{-9}$ cm. It is quite possible that there are other rings inside
or outside those observed at present, and no opinion is advanced as to

[1] G. P. Thomson and A. Reid, *Nature,* 119 (1927), 890.

whether the diffracting systems are atoms or molecules. The disappearance of the rays at low speeds is probably due to the increased total amount of scattering which occurs. In all, about fifteen plates have been taken showing the effect, including some using a slit, instead of a pin hole, to limit the beam of rays. It is hoped to make further experiments with rays of greater energy and to obtain more accurate measurements of the size of the rings.

ooooooo

DAVISSON

Are Electrons Waves? [2]

. . . THE TITLE WHICH I HAVE chosen for my address, "Are electrons waves?," suggests that some doubt has arisen in regard to the nature of electrons. And this is true. The fact is that circumstances have been found in which electrons try to make out that they are not particles at all, but are instead waves.

As an example of this perverseness I shall describe a simple type of experiment that Dr. Germer and I have been making for the past several months. We direct a narrow stream of electrons against the face of a nickel crystal, and observe that under certain conditions a sharply defined stream of electrons leaves the crystal in the direction of regular reflection—angle of reflection equal to angle of incidence.

At first thought there may seem to be nothing so very strange in this. Why should not electrons be regularly reflected from a metal surface? We know that Newton and other adherents of the corpuscular theory of light were not embarrassed by the fact that light is regularly reflected from a plane mirror. The phenomenon is one that they could explain quite easily. It is well known that in an elastic encounter between a particle and a plane surface the particle rebounds from the surface in the direction of regular reflection—hence the regular reflections of light on the corpuscular theory, and why not also the regular reflection of electrons?

---

[2] Clinton J. Davisson, *Franklin Institute Journal*, 205 (1928), 597-623; Davisson is the sole author. Germer assisted with the experiments—Editors.

Well, the adherents of the corpuscular theory of light had certain advantages over us in picturing reflection in this way. They had not committed themselves in regard to the size of the light corpuscle, and they knew nothing about the structure of metallic surfaces. We have reasons for believing that the electron is about 10^{-13} cm. in diameter. We know that atoms have diameters of the order 10^{-8} cm. and we know also that the least distance between atoms in the nickel crystal is 2.48×10^{-8} cm. If we take 10^{-13} cm. as a unit of length, then the diameter of the electron is one of these units, the diameter of the nickel atom is one hundred thousand, and the least distance between atoms in the nickel crystal is nearly 250,000.

The difficulty of picturing the regular reflection of particles as small as electrons from a surface made up of bodies as large as atoms is at once evident. If we were to fire a load of bird shot against a pyramid of cannon balls, we should not expect to find a little cloud of shot moving off in the direction of the regular reflection from the face of the pyramid. A surface made up of cannon balls is much too coarse grained to serve as a regular reflector for particles as small as bird shot.

The analogy is not such a good one really, for we do not think of electrons rebounding from the surface of an atom in the way that shot rebound from a cannon ball. We have been accustomed to think of the atom as rather like the solar system—a massive nuclear sun surrounded by planetary electrons moving in closed orbits. On this view the electron which strikes into a metal surface is like a comet plunging into a region rather densely packed with solar systems.

There is a certain small probability, or at least there might seem to be, that the electron will strike into an atom in or near the surface of the metal, be swung about comet-wise, and sent flying out of the metal without loss of energy. The direction taken by such an electron as it leaves the metal should be a matter of private treaty between the electron and the individual atom. One does not see how the neighboring atoms could have any voice in the matter. And yet we find that the high-speed scattered electrons have a preference for moving off in the direction of regular reflection, a direction which is related to the plane of the surface. Three atoms at least are required to fix this plane, so that the direction taken by the electron is determined not by one atom, but by three atoms at least.

One may say without qualification that in terms of atoms and electrons and their interaction as we have been accustomed to picture them the regular reflection of electrons from a metal surface is quite incomprehensible.

Of course, if electrons were waves there would be no difficulty. We think we understand the regular reflection of light and of x-rays—and we should understand the reflection of electrons as well if electrons were only waves instead of particles. This observation though true does not seem a particularly valuable one. It is rather as if one were to see a rabbit climbing a tree, and were to say, "Well, that is rather a strange thing for a rabbit to be doing, but after all there is really nothing to get excited about. Cats climb trees—so that, if the rabbit were only a cat, we would understand its behavior perfectly." Of course, the explanation might be that what we took to be a rabbit was not a rabbit at all, but was actually a cat. Is it possible that we are mistaken about electrons? Is it possible that we have been wrong all this time in supposing that they are particles, and that actually they are waves? Well, I do not need to enumerate to you the many reasons we have for believing—I may say for knowing—that electrons are actually particles

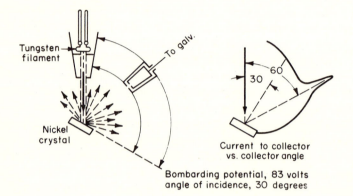

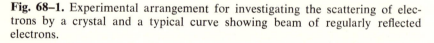

Fig. 68–1. Experimental arrangement for investigating the scattering of electrons by a crystal and a typical curve showing beam of regularly reflected electrons.

As if these reasons were not numerous enough—the very method by which we detect the regular reflected beam supplies still another. The regularly reflected beam is found by moving a small bucket about in front of the crystal and observing that more electrons are caught when the bucket stands in the direction of regular reflection than in any other.

A diagram of the experimental arrangement is shown in [Fig. 68–1].

This arrangement of filament and box is an electron gun which supplies us with a steady stream of electrons. The speed of the electrons is under our control and can be given any desired value by maintaining a suitable potential difference between the filament and the box.. This stream is directed against the crystal, and electrons of various speeds move off in all directions from the bombarded area.

To find how many are moving off in different directions we move the collector, which is really a bucket, and find how many electrons we catch in different positions. To get into the inner box an electron must pass through the opening in the outer box. Those that succeed in doing this flow off through a galvanometer, and the deflection of the galvanometer is a measure of the rate at which they are being caught.

The method is one which with some slight modification might be used to find how bird shot are scattered by a pile of cannon balls. It is not in principle a method we would employ to investigate the scattering of light or of x-rays.

In making observations the collector is moved about in front of the crystal, and curves are constructed showing the current received by the collector as a function of angle.

Such a curve for angle of incidence 30 degrees and for bombarding potential 83 volts is shown on the right, and you see the sharp spur protruding from the curve exactly in the direction of regular reflection. You will want to know about the electrons leaving the crystal in other directions. Well, those are, almost all of them, low-speed secondary electrons —while the electrons responsible for this spur have, most of them, the same speed as the incident electrons.

There is no doubt that the incident electrons recognize the surface of the crystal, and prefer to move off in the direction of regular reflection.

The next experiment I shall describe is more simple even than the first. We direct a stream of electrons against a target of ordinary nickel— a target made up of many small crystals instead of one large one—and we never under any circumstances find any indication of regular reflection. Electrons are not regularly reflected from a target of ordinary polycrystalline nickel.

It seems curious that electrons should be reflected only from a crystal-face—and then we remember that this is true also of x-rays. X-rays may be regularly reflected from the face of a crystal, but not from a polycrystalline mirror. The difference between light and x-rays in this respect is due, as we know, to a difference in order of wave-lengths. The lengths of light waves are great compared to the distance between atoms in solids while the x-ray wave-lengths are comparable with these distances.

We may say then that both of these results—the regular reflection of electrons from a crystal-face and the absence of such reflections from a polycrystalline surface—would be comprehensible if electrons were trains of waves of wave-lengths comparable to distances between atoms in solids.

Now it will be remembered that x-ray reflection is characterized by a marked selectivity. If a beam of monochromatic x-rays is directed against a crystal face, the intensity of the beam reflected at a certain angle is very nearly zero unless the wave-length of the beam happens to lie at, or very near to, one or another of a series of discrete values. It is as if we had a mirror which would reflect red light of a certain wave-length and also blue light of a certain wave-length, but which would not reflect light of any of the intermediate wave-lengths.

This suggests an interesting experiment. If electrons resemble x-rays in being reflected from a crystal, but not from a polycrystalline surface, do they also resemble x-rays in exhibiting selective reflection? We might expect, for example, that if electron reflection is really like x-ray reflection it would be selective in speed of bombardment. Well, the astonishing thing is that it *is* selective in speed. When we measure the intensity of the reflected beam as a function of speed of bombardment, we find that it passes through one maximum after another as the speed is increased. A curve exhibiting this behavior is shown in [Fig. 68–2].

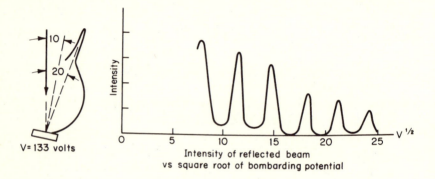

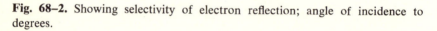

Fig. 68–2. Showing selectivity of electron reflection; angle of incidence to degrees.

The ordinate is the intensity of the reflected beam, and the abscissa is the square root of the bombarding potential, which is proportional to the speed of the electrons in the incident beam. These observations are for [an] angle [of] incidence of ten degrees, and the curve on the left shows the reflected beam at the second maximum of the intensity curve.

Now the selective reflection of x-rays is a phenomenon which is very thoroughly understood. In explaining it we make very definite and explicit use of the idea that x-rays are waves. In fact, the phenomenon supplies us with our most reliable means of measuring x-ray wave-lengths. It is very significant indeed that electron reflection resembles x-ray reflection in this particular respect.

I shall take just a few minutes to review with you the theory of x-ray crystal reflection and the explanation of the selectivity.

When a beam of x-rays is incident upon a single layer of atoms as illustrated on the left in [Fig. 68–3], the beam passes through the layer with only very slight diminution in its intensity. It does, however, set up forced vibrations in the atoms which it irradiates, and these send forth trains of spherical waves which are related in phase, and which combine to form a beam of waves moving off from the plane in the direction of regular reflection. The reflection of x-rays from a single layer of atoms is not selective.

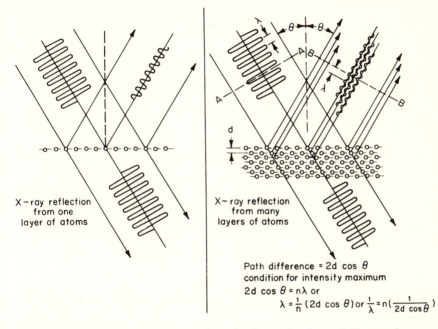

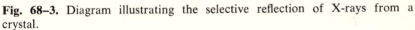

Path difference = 2d cos θ
condition for intensity maximum
2d cos θ = nλ or
$$\lambda = \frac{1}{n}(2d \cos \theta) \text{ or } \frac{1}{\lambda} = n(\frac{1}{2d \cos\theta})$$

Fig. 68–3. Diagram illustrating the selective reflection of X-rays from a crystal.

Selectivity develops when reflection occurs from a number of parallel layers of atoms such as we have in a crystal. The case is illustrated in the figure on the right. The reflection beams proceeding from the different layers are superposed and the resultant beam exhibits a strong intensity maximum when the elementary wave trains proceed from the crystal in phase as they do in the figure. The condition for such a maximum is clearly that the path-lengths from a plane AA to a plane BB via successive atom layers shall differ by a whole number of wave-lengths. This path difference is given by twice the distance between successive atom layers multiplied by the cosine of the angle of incidence, so that the intensity of the reflected beam is at a maximum when

$$2d \cos \theta = n\lambda.$$

The condition may be stated this way: The intensity of the reflected beam will be at a maximum when the wave-length of the incident beam has any one of the values

$$\lambda = \frac{1}{n}(2d \cos \theta),$$

or when the reciprocal of the wave-length has any one of the values

$$\frac{1}{\lambda} = n\,\frac{1}{2d \cos \theta}.$$

Thus, if we plot the intensity of the reflected beam against the reciprocal of the wave-length, we should obtain a curve characterized by a series of equally spaced maxima. What we should find is illustrated by the curve at the top of [Fig. 68–4].

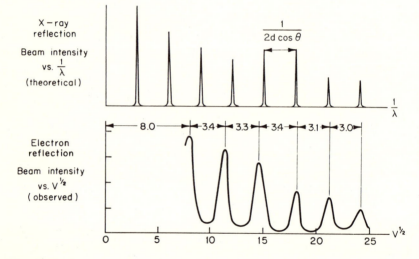

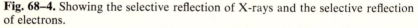

Fig. 68–4. Showing the selective reflection of X-rays and the selective reflection of electrons.

In the lower half of the figure I show again, for comparison, the intensity of the electron reflection beam as a function of $V^{1/2}$, the square root of the bombarding potential.

The maxima in the electron curve fall, as you see, at almost equal intervals. We may say, in fact, that we could understand electron reflection fairly well, including its selectivity, if electrons were waves of wavelength inversely proportional to the square root of the bombarding potential—inversely proportional, that is, to their speed. Apparently this would not be a perfect interpretation, for the maxima in the electron curve do not fall at exactly equal intervals. But it would do fairly well.

Well, here we are almost on the point of calculating electron wavelengths—knowing perfectly well that electrons are particles. It is time for us to take some definite stand in regard to this matter, and I propose that we hold to our knowledge that electrons are particles, but admit that they are behaving as if they were waves—at least, that we can describe what we observe by pretending that they are waves, and that we do not see how the observations can be described in terms of particles. We take this point of view, and see how long it can be maintained.

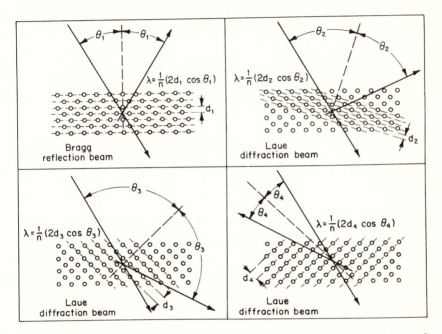

Fig. 68–5. Reflection of X-rays from various planes of atoms in a crystal, illustrating the formation of Laue diffraction beams.

Now, when x-rays are scattered by a crystal, beams issue from the crystal not only in the direction of regular reflection, but in other directions as well. One way of understanding this is that the atoms in the crystal may be regarded as arranged in planes parallel to the surface of the crystal, but that they may also be regarded as arranged in planes that are not parallel to the surface—and that as far as the x-rays are concerned one set of atom planes is just as good as another. The situation is illustrated in [Fig. 68–5].

If a beam of x-rays is incident upon a crystal face at angle θ_1, a regularly reflected beam issues from the crystal when the wave-length has any of the values

$$\lambda = \frac{1}{n} (2d_1 \cos \theta_1).$$

This beam is due to regular reflection from atom planes parallel to the surface and is ordinarily referred to as the Bragg reflection beam. But the atoms may also be regarded as arranged in other sets of planes as indicated in the other figures, and these also give rise to reflected beams. We find, for example, a beam issuing from the crystal in the direction of regular reflection from the atom planes shown in the second figure at the top when the wave-length has any of the values

$$\lambda = \frac{1}{n} (2d_2 \cos \theta_2).$$

Such beams are ordinarily known as Laue diffraction beams.

We have seen that electrons resemble x-rays in being regularly reflected from the face of a crystal and in exhibiting selectivity. The question now is, do they also resemble x-rays in giving rise to diffraction beams. Well, as it happens, we observed these diffraction beams first—more than a year before we got around to looking for the reflection beams.

It is not going to be so easy to describe these diffraction beams as it has been to describe the reflection beams; there are differences between the characteristics of the x-ray and electron diffraction beams from which one might think that after all electrons are really not so very good at passing themselves off as waves. And yet we will find that these differences can be explained in a reasonable way, and that the diffraction data lead to quite definite values of electron wave-lengths. In describing these experiments I shall try first to give you a clear idea of the conditions under which the observations were made, next what would have been observed had the experiments been made with x-rays, and finally what was actually observed with electrons.

To begin with we shall need to understand the arrangement of atoms in the nickel crystal. Nickel forms crystals of the face-centered cubic type. The unit of structure is a cube—3.51 Å. on the edge—with an atom at each corner and one in the center of each face. The large cube on the left in [Fig. 68–6] is built up of 27 of these unit cubes. The only atoms shown are those in the surface of the large cube. Henceforth I shall use this large cube as a symbol to represent the nickel crystal with which we began our experiments. We first cut through this structure at right angles to one of the cube diagonals, forming the triangular faces shown in the central figure. A beam of electrons was then directed against this face at normal incidence, as indicated in the figure on the right, and measurements were made of the number of electrons leaving the crystal as a function of direction and of speed of bombardment.

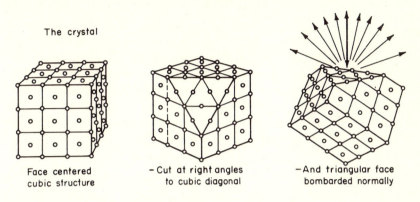

The crystal

Face centered
cubic structure

– Cut at right angles
to cubic diagonal

– And triangular face
bombarded normally

Fig. 68–6. Schematic representations of the face-centered cubic crystal of nickel.

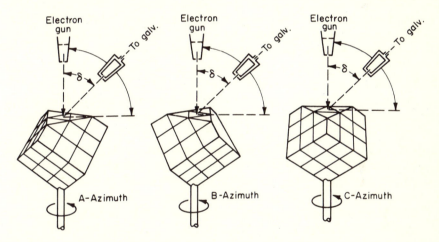

Electron gun — To galv.

Electron gun — To galv.

Electron gun — To galv.

A-Azimuth

B-Azimuth

C-Azimuth

Fig. 68–7. Schematic representations of experimental arrangement or investigating electron diffraction.

The experimental arrangements for making these measurements are indicated in [Fig. 68–7]. The collector could be moved about in a single plane—the plane of the drawing and the crystal could be rotated about a vertical axis so that any azimuth of the crystal could be brought into the plane of rotation of the collector.

It is clear that the crystal has a three-fold symmetry. If we find a beam issuing from the crystal when one of the apexes of the triangle is in the plane of the collector, we will expect, of course, to find a similar beam when the crystal has been turned through 120° to bring another of the apexes into the collector plane, and again when it has been turned through 240 degrees. We will call the azimuths of the crystal that include the apexes of the triangle the *A*-azimuths; those including the midpoints of the sides of the triangles the *B*-azimuths; and those parallel to the sides of the triangle the *C*-azimuths.

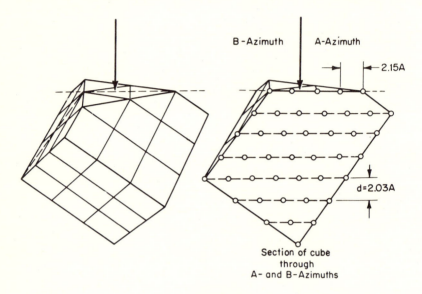

Section of cube
through
A- and B-Azimuths

Fig. 68–8.

In [Fig. 68–8] we show a cross section of the crystal through the plane of the *A–B*-azimuths. The circles represent lines of atoms extending through the crystal at right angles to this plane. The crystal may be regarded as built up of planes of atoms lying parallel to the surface of the crystal. The distance between these planes is 2.03 Å., and the distance between the lines of atoms in each plane is 2.15 Å. It will be noticed that the lines of atoms in a given plane are not directly below the lines of atoms in the next higher plane, but are shifted to the right by an amount equal to one-third of the distance between lines.

The crystal is now sufficiently specified to enable us to calculate the wave-lengths and positions of all the x-ray diffraction beams that can appear in the *A*- and *B*-azimuths. Thus, the atoms may be regarded as arranged in planes as shown in the upper left-hand diagram in [Fig. 68–9]. The distance between the successive atom planes is 1.24 Å. The angle of incidence is 35 degrees, and an x-ray diffraction beam will issue from the

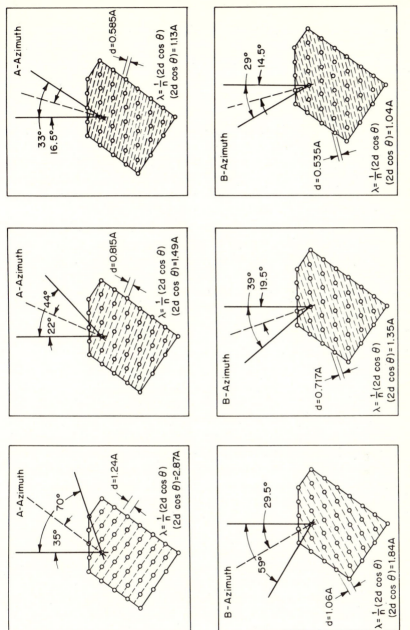

Fig. 68–9. The principal diffraction beams that would appear in the A- and B-azimuths if the incident beam were a beam of X-rays.

crystal in the direction $\theta' = 70$ degrees when the wave-length has any of the values

$$\frac{1}{n}\,(2d\cos\theta) = \frac{1}{n}\,(2 \times 1.24 \times \cos 35°) = \frac{2.87}{n}\,\text{Å}.$$

The three A-azimuth beams shown in the upper diagrams are the three for which the modulus ($2d \cos \theta$) has the greatest values, that is, they are the three A-azimuth beams of longest wave-length. Those shown below are the three B-azimuth beams of longest wave-length. What we need to get from this figure particularly is that as the wave-length of the incident x-ray beam is decreased from some large value diffraction beams appear in the following order: first, a beam at 70 degrees in the A-azimuth; next, a beam at 59 degrees in the B-azimuth; then, a beam at 44 degrees in the A-azimuth, followed by a B-azimuth beam at 39 degrees.

This is what would occur if the incident beam were a beam of x-rays —and from what we have seen of the regular reflection of electrons from the atom planes lying parallel to the surface it seems not unreasonable to expect that at particular speeds of bombardment electron beams will be found issuing from the crystal in these same directions. Well, electron beams issue from the crystal in its principal azimuths at certain critical speeds of bombardment, but they do not coincide in directions with any of these principal Laue beams. They appear not to be regularly reflected from any of the principal planes of atoms.

As the speed of bombardment is increased from zero the first of these beams appears in the A-azimuth, not however at 70 deg. or at 44 deg. but at 50 deg.; and the second appears in the B-azimuth, not at 59 deg. or at 39 deg. but at 44 deg. Curves for the first of these beams are shown in [Fig. 68–10]. The beam first appears at about 40 volts; it disappears at 70 volts, and is most intense when the bombarding potential is 54 volts. In [Fig. 68–11] we have the same beam in a weakened condition owing to gas adsorbed onto the surface of the crystal. The curve in the lower dia-

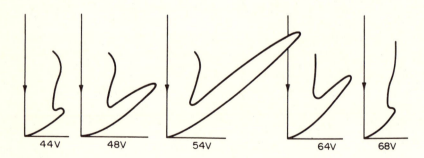

Fig. 68–10. Showing the growth and decay of the "54-volt" electron diffraction beam in the A-azimuth; surface of crystal clean.

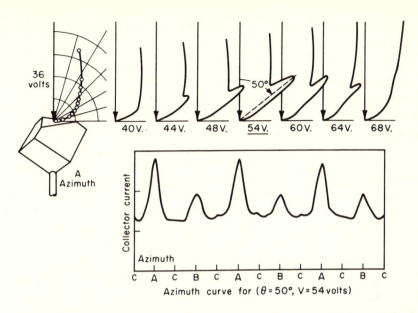

Fig. 68–11. Showing "54-volt" diffraction beam weakened by contamination of the crystal surface; azimuth curve showing maxima in A-azimuths.

gram was obtained by setting the collector in the axis of the beam at its maximum, and then measuring the collector current as the crystal was rotated. You see that there is a strong maximum in each of the *A*-azimuths, as, of course, there should be.

The corresponding curves for the first beam in the *B*-azimuth are shown in [Fig. 68–12]. Maximum intensity is attained at 65 volts, with the beam at 44 deg.

Now there is an interesting possibility in regard to this discrepancy between the directions taken by the electron beams and those taken by the x-ray beams. It may be that the crystal should be regarded as a refracting medium for electrons—that is, as a medium characterized by an index of refraction different from unity.

I shall take a few minutes to develop this idea. Let us imagine a beam of radiation incident normally on the surface of a crystal of which the index of refraction is μ. The wave-length outside the crystal is λ, and inside is $\lambda' = \lambda/\mu$. There is no change in direction as the beam enters the crystal and the beam of wave-length λ' meets a certain set of atom planes at angle θ [Fig. 68–13]. A regularly reflected beam moves off from these planes provided

$$= \chi \qquad \frac{1}{n}\,(2d\cos\theta).$$

This beam meets the crystal surface at an angle 2θ, but is refracted on passing through the surface and leaves the crystal in the direction θ'. The beam issuing from the crystal appears not to be regularly reflected from any of the principal atom planes.

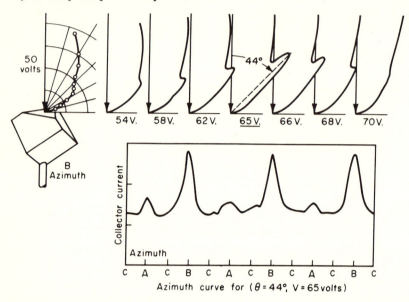

Fig. 68–12. Growth and decay of the "65-volt" beam in the B-azimuth; surface of crystal contaminated by gas. Azimuth curve showing maxima in B-azimuths.

DIFFRACTION BY REFRACTING CRYSTAL

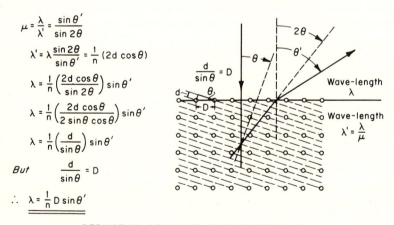

$$\mu = \frac{\lambda}{\lambda'} = \frac{\sin\theta'}{\sin 2\theta}$$

$$\lambda' = \lambda \frac{\sin 2\theta}{\sin\theta'} = \frac{1}{n}(2d\cos\theta)$$

$$\lambda = \frac{1}{n}\left(\frac{2d\cos\theta}{\sin 2\theta}\right)\sin\theta'$$

$$\lambda = \frac{1}{n}\left(\frac{2d\cos\theta}{2\sin\theta\cos\theta}\right)\sin\theta'$$

$$\lambda = \frac{1}{n}\left(\frac{d}{\sin\theta}\right)\sin\theta'$$

But $\qquad \dfrac{d}{\sin\theta} = D$

$$\therefore \quad \lambda = \frac{1}{n}D\sin\theta'$$

DERIVATION OF PLANE GRATING FORMULA

Fig. 68–13. Diffraction by refracting crystal.

And now I am going to ask you to follow through the brief mathematical deduction on the left in [Fig. 68–13] as it leads to an interesting and important relation. We treat electron radiation as if it were light, and write $\mu = \lambda/\lambda' = \sin \theta'/\sin 2\theta$. Solving this for λ', we have $\lambda' = \lambda \sin 2\theta/\sin \theta'$, but by Bragg's law $\lambda' = (2d \cos \theta)/n$. Equating these expressions for λ', and solving for λ, we obtain

$$\lambda = \frac{1}{n} \left(\frac{2d \cos \theta}{\sin 2\theta} \right) \sin \theta'.$$

And writing in $2 \sin \theta \cos \theta$ for $\sin 2\theta$ and eliminating $2 \cos \theta$, this reduces to

$$\lambda = \frac{1}{n} \left(\frac{d}{\sin \theta} \right) \sin \theta'.$$

But from the construction on the left of the diagram in [Fig. 68–13] we see that $d/\sin \theta$ is equal to D, the distance between adjacent lines of atoms in the surface of the crystal.* We have, therefore,

$$\lambda = \frac{1}{n} D \sin \theta'.$$

This is an extremely useful relation, as it enables us to calculate the wave-length of a diffraction beam (provided we know its order n) from the distance between lines of atoms in the surface of the crystal and the angle at which the beam emerges. We do not need to know with what set of atom planes a given beam is associated, and neither do we need to know the index of refraction of the crystal.

The idea of regarding the crystal as a refracting medium for electrons is due to Dr. Eckart of the California Institute of Technology, although we had already assumed that the wave-lengths of diffraction beams could be calculated from this formula.

We therefore apply this formula to the electron diffraction beams for which we have data. The distance between the lines of atoms lying normal to the A- and B-azimuths is 2.15 Å. The beam which is observed in the A-azimuth when the bombarding potential is 54 volts lies at $\theta' = 50$ degrees. The wave-length of "54-volt electrons" should then be given by

$$\lambda = \frac{2.15}{n} \sin 50° = \frac{1.65}{n}.$$

But since this is the first beam that appears in the A-azimuth it is certainly a first order beam, and therefore $\lambda = 1.65$ Å. When we make a

---

* In general $d/\sin \theta = D/m$, where m represents an integer. The conclusion is unaffected, however, by this circumstance.

similar calculation for the 65-volt beam in the B-azimuth, we find $\lambda = 1.50$ A.

That one can calculate the wave-length of a stream of electrons in a straightforward and simple way seems, of course, very surprising, and yet it is much less surprising today than it would have been, say, five years ago. During the last four or five years there has been a rapidly growing conviction that the principles of mechanics, in their various formulations, as we have known them, are really only first approximations to what we may call the true principles of mechanics. They are remarkably close approximations for most purposes—for the purposes of mechanical engineering and astronomy it is unlikely that they can be improved upon either for convenience or reliability—and yet there is the conviction that classical mechanics is in a sense a degenerate form of the true mechanics, and therefore of limited applicability. It is a first approximation to the true mechanics applicable only in those cases in which the products of the momenta and linear dimensions used in describing the system are large compared to the Planck constant of action h—large, that is, compared to 10^{-26} erg sec. We are to feel no hesitation for example in using classical mechanics in dealing with the mechanics of the solar system; the linear dimensions involved are of the order of the major axes of the orbits of the planets, the momenta involved are the momenta of the planets, and the products of these quantities are enormously great compared to the value of h. On the other hand, we are not to suppose that the approximate form of the true mechanics which is applicable to the solar system is applicable also to a system such as the Bohr atom. Here the products of linear dimensions and momenta are not large compared to h. They are in fact of the same order as h, and laws of mechanics as we have known them are therefore of no service. They are of limited applicability, and do not apply in this case.

This conviction has grown out of dissatisfaction with the ever-mounting artificiality of the Bohr atom model as means for describing and correlating the data of spectroscopy. It has led to attempts in various quarters to discover or invent a new system of mechanics which will degenerate to our ordinary mechanics in the case of gross systems, but which will be applicable as well and without forcing to systems involving atoms and electrons. One of these attempts was made by L. de Broglie who put forward the idea, a little more than three years ago, that every mechanical phenomenon is in some sense a wave phenomenon—that every problem in mechanics is in a way a problem in optics—that in the rigorous solution of all such problems one must always concern himself with the propagation and interference of waves. This idea has been taken up with great enthusiasm by theoretical physicists, notably by Schroedinger, and has enjoyed a rapid and remarkable development. This development is known as the undulatory or wave theory of mechanics, and it gives promise of being perhaps the sorely needed true mechanics. It is yet in a state of flux—no one, I think, knows what its final form will be. Ideas regarding its form and interpretation are constantly changing, and yet from its inception in the hands of De Broglie to the present time there has persisted the idea that a freely moving particle of momentum (mv) is equivalent to, or has associated with it, a train of waves of wave-length h/mv. Whether the particle is itself a group of waves—whether the waves are to be thought of as real physical waves such as we have supposed light waves to be, or whether the waves are purely analytical—a mathematical convenience only—no one, I think, knows.

The development of this theory has so far been directed almost entirely toward giving us a new picture of the atom, and a new and less arbitrary set of rules for correlating and interpreting the data of spectroscopy. Not so much attention has been paid to aperiodic phenomena such as we are here concerned with, and yet a few months after we had begun our experiments, but more than a year before we had obtained any of the results I have described, the prediction was made by Elsasser in Germany that evidence for the wave nature of mechanics would be found in the interaction between a stream of electrons and a crystal.

Most of you know already, of course, that the electron wave-lengths obtained by the measurements I have been describing are in good agreement with the values of h/mv of this new theory of mechanics. We have

$$\lambda = h/mv,$$

and for electrons of moderate speeds such as we have used we have also

$$\frac{mv^2}{2} = \frac{Ve}{300},$$

where e represents the charge of the electron in electrostatic units and V the bombarding potential in volts.

Eliminating the velocity v between these equations, we obtain

$$\lambda = \left(\frac{h^2}{me}\right)^{\frac{1}{2}} \left(\frac{150}{V}\right)^{\frac{1}{2}} \text{cm.}$$

The value of $(h^2/me)^{\frac{1}{2}}$ differs from 1×10^{-8} by about 2 parts in a thousand so that to a close approximation

$$\lambda = \left(\frac{150}{V}\right)^{\frac{1}{2}} 10^{-8} \text{cm.}$$

or

$$= \left(\frac{150}{V^{\frac{1}{2}}}\right)^{\frac{1}{2}} \text{Å.}$$

$$= \frac{12.25}{V^{\frac{1}{2}}}.$$

The value of h/mv for electrons that have been accelerated from rest through a potential difference of 54 volts is

$$12.25/(54)^{1/2} = 1.67 \text{ Å.,}$$

which is in good agreement with the value 1.65 Å. which we find by our measurements. For "65-volt" electrons the theoretical wave-length is 1.52 Å. and our observed value is 1.50 Å.

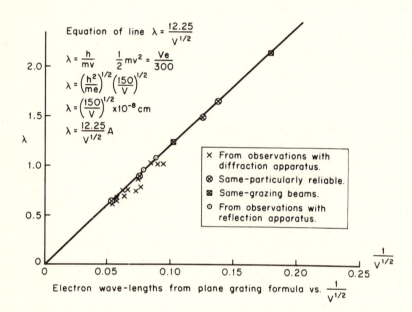

Fig. 68–14. Graphical comparison of all experimentally determined values of electron wavelengths with the relation $\lambda = h/mv$.

We have made in all twenty or more determinations of electron wavelengths. All of these values are plotted in [Fig. 68–14] against the reciprocal of the square-root of the accelerating or bombarding potential. The values which we have reason to believe are the most reliable are enclosed in circles or in squares. The straight line through the origin is the graph of the equation

$$\lambda = 12.25/V^{1/2}.$$

If the experimentally determined wave-lengths agreed exactly with the values of h/mv, all of these points would fall accurately on this line. The departures are none of them greater than can be reasonably accounted for by the uncertainty of the measurements. We may say, I think, that in certain circumstances a stream of electrons of speed *v* behaves as if it were a beam of waves of wave-length *h/mv,* in accordance with the postulates of the wave mechanics.

And now I would like to return for a few minutes to a further consideration of the regularly reflected beam.

You will remember that we plotted the intensity of the electron reflection beam for angle of incidence ten degrees against the square root of the bombarding potential and obtained a curve characterized by a series of maxima at nearly equal intervals.

We can now calculate the positions these maxima would occupy if the index of refraction of nickel for electrons were unity. We have

$$\frac{1}{\lambda} = \frac{mv}{h} = \frac{V^{\frac{1}{2}}}{12.25} = n \frac{1}{2d \cos \theta},$$

that is, we assume the wave-length of the electrons to be $h/mv = 12.25/V^{\frac{1}{2}}$ and apply the Bragg formula to find the values of $V^{\frac{1}{2}}$ at which the reflected beam should exhibit intensity maxima. Substituting for d and θ their values, 2.03 Å. and 10 deg., we find

$$V^{\frac{1}{2}} = n \times 3.06.$$

If the index were unity, the maxima should be found at these values of $V^{\frac{1}{2}}$. These positions are indicated in [Fig. 68–15].

The observed maxima lie to the left of the calculated positions, the displacement decreasing, however, toward the higher orders. This is the type of displacement to be expected if the index of refraction of the nickel for electrons is greater than unity. We can in fact use these displacements to calculate values of the refractive index. The more general form of the Bragg formula applicable to the case in which the index is not unity is

$$V^{\frac{1}{2}} = n \left(\frac{12.25}{2d(\mu^2 - \sin^2 \theta)^{\frac{1}{2}}} \right).$$

Using this formula and the data now available, we have indices of refraction for electrons of various speeds and these are plotted in the lower diagram in [Fig. 68–15]. The values indicated by circles are from the observations at ten degrees incidence, and the others are from observations at other angles.

We see that the index approaches unity as the speed of the electrons is increased; that is, the results indicate that the purely geometrical differences between the reflection and diffraction of x-rays on the one hand and of electrons on the other disappear for electrons of high speed. That this is true is evident from the very interesting experiments recently reported by Prof. G. P. Thomson of the University of Aberdeen who has studied the diffraction of beams of high-speed electrons (15,000 to 60,000 volts) by extremely thin metal foils. What Prof. Thomson observes is that electrons of these speeds are diffracted by the polycrystalline metal in the way familiar to us in the powder method of x-ray diffraction devised independently by Hull, and Debye and Scherrer. The cross-section of the

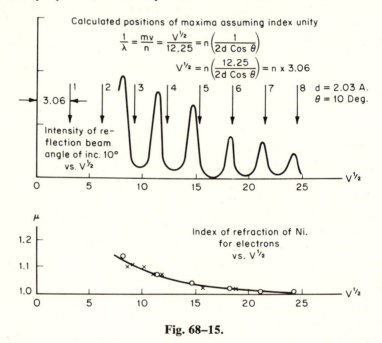

Fig. 68–15.

transmitted beam consists of a central spot surrounded by a number of concentric rings. These rings seem to correspond exactly to the rings that would be observed if the incident beam were a beam of x-ray of wavelength equal to h/mv. For electrons of such high speeds the index of refraction of metals is apparently very nearly unity.

Are electrons waves? The easiest way of answering this question is to ask another. *Are x-rays waves?* If x-rays are waves, then so also are electrons. But we are no longer so certain as we used to be that x-rays are waves. The Compton effect and the photoelectric effect are most simply described by supposing that there is some sense in which x-rays are particles.

It is all rather paradoxical and confusing. We must believe not only that there is a certain sense in which rabbits are cats, but that there is also a certain sense in which cats are rabbits.

I would not have you think, however, that confusion in these matters is universal. There are plenty of theoretical physicists to whom these matters are not at all confusing. I am sure that Professor Swann here would not admit to the least confusion. I may cite also Professor C. G. Darwin of the University of Edinburgh. In a recent article on this subject Prof. Darwin writes:

"The central difficulty of the quantum theory has always been the conflict between waves and particles. On the one hand, we have the theorems of conservation of matter, energy, etc.; these tell us that matter keeps together, and endow a particle or a quantity of energy with individuality, so that we can trace its history. On the other hand, we have the theorems of interference—of light and now of matter as well, which as definitely tell us that the things which we before regarded as particles must spread, and so must lose their individuality. The recent work of Bohr explains, at any rate in outline, how the apparent contradiction is to be reconciled. The two lines of thought are not contradictory, but complementary. They do not come into conflict because they never meet. To verify conservation we must obviously have an enclosed system, and this excludes observation of what happens in the enclosure. If nothing is observable, it is only proper to say that nothing is happening; the system is settled into a spaceless and timeless stationary state outside our intuitions. On the other hand, if we want to observe what happens, we must make a hole in the enclosure and see what leaks out. By the very act conservation is destroyed, but in exchange we get interference phenomena, and these introduce geometry and so a connection with space and time. This very inadequate description shows that we are entitled, when we want to discuss happenings in space and time, to make full u~e of the wave theory and to pay no attention to the conservation difficulties, because in fact these do not arise."

As you see, it is really all very simple.

69

ooooooooooo

THE ELECTRON AND
RELATIVITY

ooooooooooo

Paul Adrian Maurice Dirac
(b. 1902)

The quantum mechanics, as we have already noted, seemingly developed along two divergent lines: one ending with the matrix mechanics of Born, Heisenberg, and Jordan; the other, with the wave mechanics of De Broglie and Schroedinger. For some time it appeared that the two theories, although giving the same results, were unrelated and irreconcilable. For how could the Heisenberg infinite arrays or matrices—representing the positions and momenta of electrons, and identified with all possible electromagnetic radiation that an atom can emit during transitions of the electron—be equivalent to the position and the momentum of a wave packet? Dirac was one of the first to clarify this point and to show that both the Schroedinger wave picture and the Heisenberg matrix structure are two aspects of a much more general theory of operators.

It occurred to Dirac, in a moment of deep insight, that the p and q matrices that Heisenberg had introduced to represent the momentum and the position of an electron are just special cases of a general group of quantities, which are characteristic of quantum mechanics, and have no counterpart in classical physics. Dirac pointed out that when we pass over from classical physics to quantum mechanics, the ordinary algebraic rules do not apply to all the quantities with which we are forced to deal. There are, indeed, two kinds of quantities in nature: one, the ordinary numbers of arithmetic, which Dirac called c-numbers; and the other, the observable quantities that describe the behavior of a physical system. Dirac

1166

called these observables *q*-numbers, and stated that these *q*-numbers are governed by an algebra different from that which governs ordinary *c*-numbers.

Dirac generalized Heisenberg's results in the following way. We know that for the Heisenberg *p*'s and *q*'s (the momenta and positions of a moving particle), the product *pq* is different from *qp*, because these *q*'s and *p*'s are matrices in Heisenberg's scheme. We may, however, look upon this inequality of the two products from a more general and somewhat abstract point of view, and simply say that *pq* is different from *qp* not because they are matrices, but because we are dealing with quantities that are governed by a different kind of algebra, a non-communicative [1] algebra. That Heisenberg represents these quantities as matrices is the result of a very special way of looking at them. But this method of observation does not really capture the essence of the quantities.

This was Dirac's starting point, and he went on to show that the quantities that Heisenberg had represented as matrices, the *p*'s and *q*'s, are but special cases of a general class of *q*-numbers, all of which are governed by a noncommutative algebra. Mathematicians for years had been dealing with noncommutative algebras, an algebra in which the product of two factors depends on their order. Consequently, Dirac had little trouble in applying these mathematical ideas to his *q*-numbers and developing the algebra that governs them. Dirac demonstrated that in dealing with the observable phenomena of quantum mechanics (the *q*-numbers) it is not necessary to represent these quantities as matrices, or in any other formal way, to understand the processes within the atom, or the behavior of electrons and other fundamental particles. All one need know about the observable *q*-numbers in order to understand their physics is the algebra that governs them. Representing them in one way or another is merely a matter of mathematical convenience dictated by the particular problem with which one is dealing.

We may illustrate this point by considering the Schroedinger and the Heisenberg pictures of the momentum of a particle. In the Heisenberg picture the momentum is represented as a particular kind of infinite matrix, whereas one gets the Schroedinger equation for a particle only if

---

[1] Noncommutative means that the product of two factors is different if the order of the two factors is changed. This kind of algebra is quite different from ordinary arithmetic where 3×4 is the same as 4×3. The concept of noncommutativity can be understood in terms of ordinary experiences. Every chemist and cook knows that the final product that one gets depends on the order in which things are done. Beating egg whites first and then adding them to a cake is not the same as first adding them and then beating the mixture. Similarly, pulling the trigger of a gun and then putting the bullet in the gun does not give the same result as first inserting the bullet and then pulling the trigger. Thus these operations are noncommutative.

the momentum is represented as a mathematical operator of a special kind, a so-called differential operator. Both the Heisenberg and the Schroedinger pictures (matrices and waves) are correct; they are, however, dependent upon special representations of q-numbers, which are themselves mere abstract, algebraic representations of the operators whose values are sought in making laboratory measurements of physical systems.

Dirac expanded the idea of an operator to include all physical quantities, such as the energy and the angular momentum of a system, as well as the p's and q's, the linear momentum and the position. In fact, any quantity represented in terms of the p's and q's can be thought of as an operator, for all one need do to obtain the operator corresponding to this quantity (the quantity is called a function of the p's and q's) is to replace each q or p that appears in the quantity by the suitable operator.

As an example, we consider the expression for the energy of a system, for example, the energy of an electron in a hydrogen atom. This mathematical expression can, on the basis of classical physics, be expressed in terms of the position and the momentum of the electron, that is, the p's and q's of the electron. To obtain the operator that represents the energy of the electron in quantum mechanics we must replace each p and q by its own appropriate operator. If the Heisenberg representation for these operators is used, the energy becomes an infinite matrix, but if the Schroedinger representation is used the energy becomes a differential operator and the quantity on which it operates is the Schroedinger wave function.

To complete this theory Dirac had to show how to apply these ideas to any general situation involving a variety of measurable, observed quantities. For example, suppose we are dealing with an electron whose position at some instant we know with infinite accuracy. Now the noncommutative algebra comes into play, for the theory tells us that two quantities that do not commute cannot be measured with infinite accuracy simultaneously. This means that we can have no knowledge of the momentum of the electron at the instant we know its position. But we also can know nothing about the energy of the electron since the energy involves the momentum. Indeed, the precise knowledge of the position of the electron, because of the noncommutative nature of the quantities, precludes the further knowledge of measurable quantities that can be constructed from knowledge of the momentum.

Dirac describes this situation by supposing that the electron is in a particular quantum state into which it has been forced by the measurement of its position. This measurement, which has destroyed our knowledge of any observable quantity whose algebraic expression does not commute with the position operator q, has taken the electron from one state about which we had some precise information (for instance, the energy) into another state about which our measurement has given us some other precise information, but at the same time has destroyed our original information.

By introducing the concept of the state of a system Dirac generalized the uncertainty relationship in the following way. We know from classical physics that whenever we are dealing with a physical system, we require the knowledge of more than one quantity to describe the behavior of the system in its entirety. This arises because the system, in general, has more than one degree of freedom. Thus, in the case of an electron moving freely in space, we have three degrees of freedom (the three independent directions in space along which the electron move) to consider, so that the measurements of three distinct quantities have to be made before the state of the electron is fully known. Since this is the case, Dirac pointed out that these three measurements must be of a sort to give simultaneous, infinitely precise information about these three quantities. It follows, then, because a noncommutative algebra is equivalent to an uncertainty principle, that all operators must commute if they represent observables whose values must be precisely known to define the state of a system completely.

Now the operators that represent the observables of a system have their classical counterparts in certain algebraic expressions involving the p's and q's of the electrons in the system, and it is not always an easy matter to determine whether or not these operators commute. Of course, since these operators are composed of p's and q's, the commutative properties of the p's and q's should enable one to determine the commutation properties of these operators; but, in general, difficulties are associated with this procedure so that it is convenient to introduce a way of determining whether operators commute without having recourse to the p's and q's directly. Dirac discovered how to do this by carrying over into quantum mechanics certain mathematical expressions which had been introduced into classical mechanics by Poisson. Poisson had shown that the equations of motion in classical mechanics can be expressed in terms of certain quantities that are known as Poisson brackets. There are very definite classical rules for calculating these brackets for any two algebraic quantities that depend on the p's and q's which describe the mechanical system we are dealing with. Although these rules have nothing to do with quantum mechanics or noncommutative algebra, Dirac showed that if F and G are any two observables, then the value of the commutator $[FG - GF]$ in quantum mechanics is, except for a numerical constant, equal to the classical Poisson bracket for these two quantities, multiplied by Planck's constant. Thus, if the Poisson bracket vanishes the two quantities commute.

In the excerpt from his book on quantum mechanics, which we have included here, Dirac discusses the important concept of the state of a system in quantum mechanics and stresses the essential difference between this concept and the same concept in classical physics. This difference, as Dirac so aptly points out, lies in the principle of superposition of states, which has no analog in classical physics. It is ". . . one of the most fundamental and most drastic . . ." of a new set of accurate laws required to set up the quantum mechanics. Essentially, this principle of superposition says that a system in quantum mechanics must be looked upon as being simultaneously in a whole set of states rather than in some particular state, as is the case in classical physics.

Dirac illustrates this by considering the polarization of a beam of light consisting of photons and also the interference of photons. The essential point here is that regardless of whether we are dealing with polarization or with interference we are always led to a picture in which we must consider the photon as being simultaneously in two different states. In the case of the interference phenomenon we are forced to picture each photon as being ". . . partly in each of the two components into which the incident beam is split . . ." even though the photon must be regarded as an indivisible particle. Of course, the photon can never actually be found in both beams simultaneously, but this is because in the very process of looking for the photon we force it into one or the other of the partial beams.

We may draw an analogy with classical physics to illustrate this point, and at the same time show how quantum physics differs from classical physics, by considering a person moving in a direction that is 30° north of east. This motion can be represented by an arrow of appropriate length pointing in this direction. We may now say that this person is moving simultaneously in an eastward direction and in a northward direction. Of course, the eastward and northward motion are not equal. In classical physics there is no doubt about the state of motion of the person; saying that he is moving partly in an eastward and partly in a northward direction is a convenient mathematical scheme for representing the fact that the vector describing the actual motion can be pictured as consisting of a vector lying in the eastward direction and another one lying in the northward direction (the two, of course, being of unequal length, in general). It is clear, however, that in classical physics this is merely a way of talking, and if one wants to find the direction in which the man is walking one must look in the direction that is 30° north of east.

The quantum-mechanical way of describing the motion of the person would be to say that the person is really moving partly along the east-west line and partly along the north-south line; the probability of finding him moving entirely along either of these directions is determined by the cosine of the angle which the actual motion of the person makes with each of these directions. Moreover, in the process of looking for the person along one direction or the other we would force him to move entirely in the direction in which we found him to be moving. Of course, it is clear that such considerations cannot apply to a person or any other massive object, but this is merely because we disturb a massive object only very minutely when we look for it. In the case of an electron this is not so, and the disturbance or perturbation we introduce when we make any measurement on it forces it to change suddenly from one state to another.

We must now see how Dirac's idea of states very brilliantly connected the Schroedinger wave function with the probability concept ascribed to the Schroedinger wave function by Born. If we consider an electron about which we wish to obtain some information, it is necessary for us to perform some measurement to get this information. Before we perform this measurement, the electron is in some definite state but it is not a pure state in the sense that we have no definite information about it. We must therefore consider it as a combination of many different pure states, each one entering into the composition of the actual state of the electron with a different weight. When we perform a measurement and obtain definite information about the electron, we force it into one of the pure states, and the probability of our finding it in one of these pure states when we carry out our measurement is given by the weight with which that particular pure state enters into the composition of the original state of the electron. As long as we perform no measurement on the electron, the state of the electron (that is, the wave function that describes it) changes continuously and this continuous change is described by the Schroedinger equation. Any measurement, however, causes a sudden change.

The picture we obtain with Dirac, then, is the following: At any instant of time we can describe the behavior of a system by a mathematical quantity that represents what Dirac has called the state of the system, and if the system is left to itself, this mathematical quantity (function) changes continuously according to a definite mathematical prescription that is called the Schroedinger equation. However, whenever a measurement is made on the system, the state of the system changes suddenly, since in performing our measurement we have disturbed the system and thus forced it into a new state. After the measurement the system continues to change its state continuously according to the Schroedinger wave equation.

The importance of the Schroedinger wave function in this Dirac picture of states is that it enables us to pass from one pure state to another by means of a mathematical transformation in which the Schroedinger function is involved. Thus, suppose that at some instant of time we definitely knew the position of the electron. We would then have no knowledge at that moment of the energy of the electron. Let us now measure the energy of the electron and thus force it into a definite energy state, which means that we have learned about the energy of the electron but we know nothing about where it is. When we have done this, it is equivalent to solving the Schroedinger equation, so that the Schroedinger wave function may thus be considered as the quantity that enables us to pass from a state of the system in which we know the position precisely, at some moment, to one in which we know the energy precisely, at the same moment. The probability interpretation of the Schroedinger wave function given by Born then means that if the electron is in a state in which its energy is precisely known, the value of the Schroedinger wave function, at a particular point of space, when multiplied by the value of its complex conjugate, gives the probability for finding the electron at this point in space.

While matrix mechanics was being developed by the Göttingen group under Born, and wave mechanics was being proposed by Schroedinger in his famous wave equation, the form of quantum mechanics described above, more general than either, was being developed in England by Paul A. M. Dirac, who must be ranked as one of the giants of modern physics. Dirac's success in deriving his form of quantum mechanics, which is now universally used, stemmed from his general philosophy that mathematics is not just the handmaiden of physics, but an integral part of it, and that one should not peer too deeply behind the mathematics to find the physical reality because they are too closely interrelated. This led him to seek the most general and elegant mathematical methods of presenting a physical theory, for he felt that the most refined representation would reveal physical realities that would be otherwise obscured, as is the case in approximate or nongeneral mathematical procedures. Indeed, he has felt that every mathematical theory has its physical counterpart. This philosophy has also led him to follow the physical consequences of the mathematics of any theory to their ultimate conclusion, however strange and contrary to our experience these conclusions might appear. Dirac's great genius lies in his ability to follow unbeaten paths and to use unorthodox mathematical methods whenever necessary to develop his physical theories. It is quite understandable that he should have taken this approach, for his graduate studies were in mathematics; in a sense, he entered physics through the backdoors of mathematics and engineering.

He was born on August 8, 1902, in Bristol, England, of a Swiss father and an English mother. After attending elementary and secondary schools in Bristol, Dirac entered Bristol University where he studied electrical engineering, receiving his Bachelor of Science degree in 1921. At this point, a definite change occurred in his concept of the knowledge required to become a good physicist; as a result, he studied mathematics at Bristol for two years after receiving his undergraduate degree. From there he went on to St. John's College, Cambridge, as a research student in mathematics and received his Ph.D. in mathematics in 1926. He remained at St. John's College as a fellow and finally, in 1932, was named Lucasian professor of mathematics at Cambridge. The emphasis on Dirac's mathematical skills is evident.

Dirac received his degrees in mathematics just when the world of physics was exploding with activity; this period is still considered the golden age of physics. The years from 1926 to 1932 were his most creative and his contributions to physics cover a wide range of subjects.

The year 1926 was particularly fruitful, for not only did Dirac present his own general version of quantum mechanics, but he also wrote his famous papers on quantum electrodynamics (the quantum mechanics of the radiation field) and developed the quantum statistics of particles that obey the Pauli exclusion principle. This quantum statistics is now known as the Fermi-Dirac statistics, since Fermi made the discovery shortly before, an independently of, Dirac.

Dirac's first important contribution to physics was his formulation of quantum mechanics, in which neither the Schroedinger wave equation nor the Born-Heisenberg matrices are introduced. Instead, a general non-commutative algebra for all physical observables is introduced, and the physical properties of a system are then contained in the algebraic rules governing the multiplication of any two physical observables. Dirac showed that the Born-Heisenberg and Schroedinger formulations are special cases of the general theory.

Dirac's next great contribution was the demonstration of the relationship of the various formulations of quantum mechanics to one another and how to make the transition from one to the other. This constitutes what is now called the transformation theory of quantum mechanics.

Almost at the same time Dirac was developing a quantum electrodynamics in which he pictured the radiation field itself as quantized. The absorption of a photon is pictured as a quantum process in which the quantum state of the radiation field changes through the disappearance (or destruction) of a photon, and emission of radiation is shown as a quantum change of the field resulting in the creation of a photon. Dirac pictures all radiation processes as describable in terms of creation and destruction of photons and obtains the general quantum laws of radiation as a consequence of the algebra of his creation and destruction operators. Following closely upon this work, he developed the special quantum statistical mechanics that bears his and Fermi's names.

Each of these developments is a great achievement in itself. For one man to have done all of this while still very young and in a span of a few years is a mark of tremendous genius. Dirac was immediately recognized as one of the giants on an equal footing with Heisenberg, Pauli, Schroedinger, and the other originators of the quantum mechanics.

But his greatest creation was yet to come—his relativistic theory of the electron, in 1928, for which he shared the Nobel Prize in 1933 with Schroedinger. Dirac's approach to this problem shows his great physical intuition and an unusually ingenious utilization of mathematical and physical knowledge. The problem that he faced was to derive a wave equation that satisfied the demands of the theory of relativity and, at the same time, to retain the De Broglie-Schroedinger wave picture of the electron. Dirac achieved this by using a special mathematical technique (his famous spin matrices) in which the spin of the electrons enters automatically, without requiring separate introduction. Thus, Dirac showed that the spin is a consequence of the relativity theory.

At this point he demonstrated that the negative energy solutions of his wave equation must have their physical counterpart, although negative energy has no meaning in classical physics. Dirac's interpretation of negative energy states led to his theory of "holes," namely, that empty negative energy states (holes) are positively charged particles. These are the positrons that were later discovered by Carl Anderson. This theory of holes—stemming from his relativistic wave equation—opened up vast new fields in physics, and, as Dirac himself first suggested, the possibility, now completely verified, that every particle in nature had its antiparticle (hole) counterpart.

After discovering the relativistic wave equation, Dirac spent many years improving the mathematical formulation of quantum mechanics; at the same time, he tried to eliminate certain undesirable intrinsic features of all quantum theories which resulted in infinite answers to certain simple questions regarding the manner of the absorption and emission of radiation by the electron. These investigations were to be the starting point from which Tomonaga, Schwinger, Feynman, and other contemporary physicists were to develop methods that can be used in conjunction with the Dirac theory to give reasonable (noninfinite) answers to reasonable questions.

Dirac's contribution to physics goes beyond quantum mechanics and the theory of the wave electron. He has also done some interesting and provocative work in cosmology. Based on very general principles, he has proposed the theory that the constants of nature, such as Newton's gravitational constant, do not remain the same but change with time because of the expansion of the universe. Recently, Dirac has introduced methods of quantizing Einstein's gravitational field to obtain a quantum theory of gravity. Although he has not been alone in this, his procedure bears the usual Dirac stamp of individuality and ingenuity.

Dirac has lectured extensively and given courses in quantum mechanics and quantum field theory in universities throughout the world, and has been a visiting professor regularly at the Institute of Advanced Studies at Princeton.

Dirac's lectures reflect, as one would expect from a man of his stature, his remarkable grasp of physics. The subject matter is presented with great simplicity and clarity; the emphasis is always on the physical concepts, with formalism relegated to a minor role. His book, *The Principles of Quantum Mechanics,* now in its third edition, is a model of textbook writing and is one of the best introductions to the operator approach to quantum mechanics.

Since 1937, Dirac has been married to Margit Wigner of Budapest, the sister of the Nobel Prize physicist, Eugene Wigner.

ଡ଼ଡ଼ଡ଼ଡ଼ଡ଼ଡ଼ଡ଼ଡ଼

D I R A C

The Principle of Superposition [2]

THE NEED FOR A QUANTUM THEORY

CLASSICAL MECHANICS HAS BEEN DEVELOPED continuously from the time of Newton and applied to an ever-widening range of dynamical systems, including the electromagnetic field in interaction with matter. The underlying ideas and the laws governing their application form a simple and elegant scheme which, one would be inclined to think, could not be seriously modified without having all its attractive features spoilt. Nevertheless it has been found possible to set up a new scheme, called quantum mechanics, which is more suitable for the description of phenomena on the atomic scale and which is in some respects more elegant and satisfying than the classical scheme. This possibility is due to the changes which the new scheme involves being of a very profound character and not clashing with the features of the classical theory that make it so attractive, as a result of which all these features can be incorporated in the new scheme.

The necessity for a departure from classical mechanics is clearly shown by experimental results. In the first place the forces known in classical electrodynamics are inadequate for the explanation of the remarkable stability of atoms and molecules, which is necessary in order that materials

---

[2] Paul A. M. Dirac, *The Principles of Quantum Mechanics* (London: Clarendon Press, 1930), pp. 1–15.

may have any definite physical and chemical properties at all. The introduction of new hypothetical forces will not save the situation, since there exist general principles of classical mechanics, holding for all kinds of forces, leading to results in direct disagreement with observation. For example, if an atomic system has its equilibrium disturbed in any way and is then left alone, it will be set in oscillation and the oscillations will get impressed on the surrounding electromagnetic field, so that their frequencies may be observed with a spectroscope. Now whatever the laws of force governing the equilibrium, one would expect to be able to include the various frequencies in a scheme comprising certain fundamental frequencies and their harmonics. This is not observed to be the case. Instead, there is observed a new and unexpected connexion between the frequencies, called Ritz's Combination Law of Spectroscopy, according to which all the frequencies can be expressed as differences between certain terms, the number of terms being much less than the number of frequencies. This law is quite unintelligible from the classical standpoint.

One might try to get over the difficulty without departing from classical mechanics by assuming each of the spectroscopically observed frequencies to be a fundamental frequency with its own degree of freedom, the laws of force being such that the harmonic vibrations do not occur. Such a theory will not do, however, even apart from the fact that it would give no explanation of the Combination Law, since it would immediately bring one into conflict with the experimental evidence on specific heats. Classical statistical mechanics enables one to establish a general connexion between the total number of degrees of freedom of an assembly of vibrating systems and its specific heat. If one assumes all the spectroscopic frequencies of an atom to correspond to different degrees of freedom, one would get a specific heat for any kind of matter very much greater than the observed value. In fact the observed specific heats at ordinary temperatures are given fairly well by a theory that takes into account merely the motion of each atom as a whole and assigns no internal motion to it at all.

This leads us to a new clash between classical mechanics and the results of experiment. There must certainly be some internal motion in an atom to account for its spectrum, but the internal degrees of freedom, for some classically inexplicable reason, do not contribute to the specific heat. A similar clash is found in connexion with the energy of oscillation of the electromagnetic field in a vacuum. Classical mechanics requires the specific heat corresponding to this energy to be infinite, but it is observed to be quite finite. A general conclusion from experimental results is that oscillations of high frequency do not contribute their classical quota to the specific heat.

As another illustration of the failure of classical mechanics we may consider the behaviour of light. We have, on the one hand, the phenomena of interference and diffraction, which can be explained only on the basis of a wave theory; on the other, phenomena such as photo-electric emission and scattering by free electrons, which show that light is composed of small particles. These particles, which are called photons, have each a definite energy and momentum, depending on the frequency of the light, and appear to have just as real an existence as electrons, or any other particles known in physics. A fraction of a photon is never observed.

Experiments have shown that this anomalous behaviour is not peculiar to light, but is quite general. All material particles have wave properties, which can be exhibited under suitable conditions. We have here a very striking and general example of the breakdown of classical mechanics—not merely an inaccuracy in its laws of motion, but *an inadequacy of its concepts to supply us with a description of atomic events.*

The necessity to depart from classical ideas when one wishes to account for the ultimate structure of matter may be seen, not only from experimentally established facts, but also from general philosophical grounds. In a classical explanation of the constitution of matter, one would assume it to be made up of a large number of small constituent parts and one would postulate laws for the behaviour of these parts, from which the laws of the matter in bulk could be deduced. This would not complete the explanation, however, since the question of the structure and stability of the constituent parts is left untouched. To go into this question, it becomes necessary to postulate that each constituent part is itself made up of smaller parts, in terms of which its behaviour is to be explained. There is clearly no end to this procedure, so that one can never arrive at the ultimate structure of matter on these lines. So long as *big* and *small* are merely relative concepts, it is no help to explain the big in terms of the small. It is therefore necessary to modify classical ideas in such a way as to give an absolute meaning to size.

At this stage it becomes important to remember that science is concerned only with observable things and that we can observe an object only by letting it interact with some outside influence. An act of observation is thus necessarily accompanied by some disturbance of the object observed. We may define an object to be big when the disturbance accompanying our observation of it may be neglected, and small when the disturbance cannot be neglected. This definition is in close agreement with the common meanings of big and small.

It is usually assumed that, by being careful, we may cut down the disturbance accompanying our observation to any desired extent. The concepts of big and small are then purely relative and refer to the gentleness of our means of observation as well as to the object being described. In order to give an absolute meaning to size, such as is required for any theory of the ultimate structure of matter, we have to assume that *there is a limit to the fineness of our powers of observation and the smallness of the accompanying disturbance—a limit which is inherent in the nature of things and can never be surpassed by improved technique or increased skill on the part of the observer.* If the object under observation is such that the unavoidable limiting disturbance is negligible, then the object is big in the absolute sense and we may apply classical mechanics to it. If, on the other hand, the limiting disturbance is not negligible, then the object is small in the absolute sense and we require a new theory for dealing with it.

A consequence of the preceding discussion is that we must revise our ideas of causality. Causality applies only to a system which is left undisturbed. If a system is small, we cannot observe it without producing a serious disturbance and hence we cannot expect to find any causal connexion between the results of our observations. Causality will still be assumed to apply to undisturbed systems and the equations which will be set up to describe an undisturbed system will be differential equations expressing a causal connexion between conditions at one time and conditions at a later time. These equations will be in close correspondence with the equations of classical mechanics, but they will be connected only indirectly with the results of observations. There is an unavoidable indeterminacy in the calculation of observational results, the theory enabling us to calculate in general only the probability of our obtaining a particular result when we make an observation.

THE POLARIZATION OF PHOTONS

The discussion in the preceding section about the limit to the gentlenesss with which observations can be made and the consequent indeterminacy in the results of those observations does not provide any quantitative basis for the building up of quantum mechanics. For this purpose a new set of accurate laws of nature is required. One of the most fundamental and most drastic of these is the *Principle of Superposition of States.* We shall lead up to a general formulation of this principle through a consideration of some special cases, taking first the example provided by the polarization of light.

It is known experimentally that when plane-polarized light is used for ejecting photo-electrons, there is a preferential direction for the electron emission. Thus the polarization properties of light are closely connected with its corpuscular properties and one must ascribe a polarization to the photons. One must consider, for instance, a beam of light plane-polarized in a certain direction as consisting of photons each of which is plane-polarized in that direction and a beam of circularly polarized light as consisting of photons each circularly polarized. Every photon is in a certain *state of polarization,* as we shall say. The problem we must now consider is how to fit in these ideas with the known facts about the resolution of light into polarized components and the recombination of these components.

Let us take a definite case. Suppose we have a beam of light passing through a crystal of tourmaline, which has the property of letting through only light plane-polarized perpendicular to its optic axis. Classical electrodynamics tells us what will happen for any given polarization of the incident beam. If this beam is polarized perpendicular to the optic axis, it will all go through the crystal; if parallel to the axis, none of it will go through; while if polarized at an angle α to the axis, a fraction $\sin^2\alpha$ will go through. How are we to understand these results on a photon basis?

A beam that is plane-polarized in a certain direction is to be pictured as made up of photons each plane-polarized in that direction. This picture leads to no difficulty in the cases when our incident beam is polarized perpendicular or parallel to the optic axis. We merely have to suppose that each photon polarized perpendicular to the axis passes unhindered and unchanged through the crystal, while each photon polarized parallel to the axis is stopped and absorbed. A difficulty arises, however, in the case of the obliquely polarized incident beam. Each of the incident photons is then obliquely polarized and it is not clear what will happen to such a photon when it reaches the tourmaline.

A question about what will happen to a particular photon under certain conditions is not really very precise. To make it precise one must imagine some experiment performed having a bearing on the question and inquire what will be the result of the experiment. Only questions about the results of experiments have a real significance and it is only such questions that theoretical physics has to consider.

In our present example the obvious experiment is to use an incident beam consisting of only a single photon and to observe what appears on the back side of the crystal. According to quantum mechanics the result of this experiment will be that sometimes one will find a whole photon, of energy equal to the energy of the incident photon, on the back side and other times one will find nothing. When one finds a whole photon, it will be polarized perpendicular to the optic axis. One will never find only a part of a photon on the back side. If one repeats the experiment a large number of times, one will find the photon on the back side in a fraction $\sin^2\alpha$ of the total number of times. Thus we may say that the photon has a probability $\sin^2\alpha$ of passing through the tourmaline and appearing on the back side polarized perpendicular to the axis and a probability $\cos^2\alpha$ of being absorbed. These values for the probabilities lead to the correct classical results for an incident beam containing a large number of photons.

In this way we preserve the individuality of the photon in all cases. We are able to do this, however, only because we abandon the determinacy of the classical theory. The result of an experiment is not determined, as it would be according to classical ideas, by the conditions under the control of the experimenter. The most that can be predicted is a set of possible results, with a probability of occurrence for each.

The foregoing discussion about the result of an experiment with a single obliquely polarized photon incident on a crystal of tourmaline answers all that can legitimately be asked about what happens to an obliquely polarized photon when it reaches the tourmaline. Questions about what decides whether the photon is to go through or not and how it changes its direction of polarization when it does go through cannot be investigated by experiment and should be regarded as outside the domain of science. Nevertheless some further description is necessary in order to correlate the results of this experiment with the results of other experiments that might be performed with photons and to fit them all into a general scheme. Such further description should be regarded, not as an attempt to answer questions outside the domain of science, but as an aid to the formulation of rules for expressing concisely the results of large numbers of experiments.

The further description provided by quantum mechanics runs as follows. It is supposed that a photon polarized obliquely to the optic axis may be regarded as being partly in the state of polarization parallel to the axis and partly in the state of polarization perpendicular to the axis. The state of oblique polarization may be considered as the result of some kind of superposition process applied to the two states of parallel and perpendicular polarization. This implies a certain special kind of relationship between the various states of polarization, a relationship similar to that between polarized beams in classical optics, but which is now to be applied, not to beams, but to the states of polarization of one particular photon. This relationship allows any state of polarization to be resolved into, or expressed as a superposition of, any two mutually perpendicular states of polarization.

When we make the photon meet a tourmaline crystal, we are subjecting it to an observation. We are observing whether it is polarized parallel or perpendicular to the optic axis. The effect of making this observation is to force the photon entirely into the state of parallel or entirely into the state of perpendicular polarization. It has to make a sudden jump from being partly in each of these two states to being entirely in one or other of them. Which of the two states it will jump into cannot be predicted, but is governed only by probability laws. If it jumps into the parallel state it gets absorbed and if it jumps into the perpendicular state it passes through the crystal and appears on the other side preserving this state of polarization.

INTERFERENCE OF PHOTONS

In this section we shall deal with another example of superposition. We shall again take photons, but shall be concerned with their position in space and their momentum instead of their polarization. If we are given a beam of roughly monochromatic light, then we know something about the location and momentum of the associated photons. We know that each of them is located somewhere in the region of space through which the beam is passing and has a momentum in the direction of the beam of magnitude given in terms of the frequency of the beam by Einstein's photo-electric law—momentum equals frequency multiplied by a universal constant. When we have such information about the location and momentum of a photon we shall say that it is in a definite *translational state*.

We shall discuss the description which quantum mechanics provides of the interference of photons. Let us take a definite experiment demonstrating interference. Suppose we have a beam of light which is passed through some kind of interferometer, so that it gets split up into two components and the two components are subsequently made to interfere. We may, as in the preceding section, take an incident beam consisting of only a single photon and inquire what will happen to it as it goes through the apparatus. This will present to us the difficulty of the conflict between the wave and corpuscular theories of light in an acute form.

Corresponding to the description that we had in the case of the polarization, we must now describe the photon as going partly into each of the two components into which the incident beam is split. The photon is then, as we may say, in a translational state given by the superposition of the two translational states associated with the two components. We are thus led to a generalization of the term "translational state" applied to a photon. For a photon to be in a definite translational state it need not be associated with one single beam of light, but may be associated with two or more beams of light which are the components into which one original beam has been split.* In the accurate mathematical theory each translational state is associated with one of the wave functions of ordinary wave optics, which wave function may describe either a single beam or two or more beams into which one original beam has been split. Translational states are thus superposable in a similar way to wave functions.

Let us consider now what happens when we determine the energy in one of the components. The result of such a determination must be either

---

* The circumstance that the superposition idea requires us to generalize our original meaning of translational states, but that no corresponding generalization was needed for the states of polarization of the preceding section, is an accidental one with no underlying theoretical significance.

the whole photon or nothing at all. Thus the photon must change suddenly from being partly in one beam and partly in the other to being entirely in one of the beams. This sudden change is due to the disturbance in the translational state of the photon which the observation necessarily makes. It is impossible to predict in which of the two beams the photon will be found. Only the probability of either result can be calculated from the previous distribution of the photon over the two beams.

One could carry out the energy measurement without destroying the component beam by, for example, reflecting the beam from a movable mirror and observing the recoil. Our description of the photon allows us to infer that, *after* such an energy measurement, it would not be possible to bring about any interference effects between the two components. So long as the photon is partly in one beam and partly in the other, interference can occur when the two beams are superposed, but this possibility disappears when the photon is forced entirely into one of the beams by an observation. The other beam then no longer enters into the description of the photon, so that it counts as being entirely in the one beam in the ordinary way for any experiment that may subsequently be performed on it.

On these lines quantum mechanics is able to effect a reconciliation of the wave and corpuscular properties of light. The essential point is the association of each of the translational states of a photon with one of the wave functions of ordinary wave optics. The nature of this association cannot be pictured on a basis of classical mechanics, but is something entirely new. It would be quite wrong to picture the photon and its associated wave as interacting in the way in which particles and waves can interact in classical mechanics. The association can be interpreted only statistically, the wave function giving us information about the probability of our finding the photon in any particular place when we make an observation of where it is.

Some time before the discovery of quantum mechanics people realized that the connexion between light waves and photons must be of a statistical character. What they did not clearly realize, however, was that the wave function gives information about the probability of *one* photon being in a particular place and not the probable number of photons in that place. The importance of the distinction can be made clear in the following way. Suppose we have a beam of light consisting of a large number of photons split up into two components of equal intensity. On the assumption that the intensity of a beam is connected with the probable number of photons in it, we should have half the total number of photons going into each component. If the two components are now made to inferfere, we should require a photon in one component to be able to interfere with one in the other. Sometimes these two photons would have to annihilate one another and other times they would have to produce four photons. This would contradict the conservation of energy. The new theory, which connects the wave function with probabilities for one photon, gets over the difficulty by making each photon go partly into each of the two components. Each photon then interferes only with itself. Interference between two different photons never occurs.

The association of particles with waves discussed above is not restricted to the case of light, but is, according to modern theory, of universal applicability. All kinds of particles are associated with waves in this way and conversely all wave motion is associated with particles. Thus all particles can be made to exhibit interference effects and all wave motion has its energy in the form of quanta. The reason why these general phenomena are not more obvious is on account of a law of proportionality between the mass or energy of the particles and the frequency of the waves, the coefficient being such that for waves of familiar frequencies the associated quanta are extremely small, while for particles even as light as electrons the associated wave frequency is so high that it is not easy to demonstrate interference.

SUPERPOSITION AND INDETERMINACY

The reader may possibly feel dissatisfied with the attempt in the two preceding sections to fit in the existence of photons with the classical theory of light. He may argue that a very strange idea has been introduced —the possibility of a photon being partly in each of two states of polarization, or partly in each of two separate beams—but even with the help of this strange idea no satisfying picture of the fundamental single-photon processes has been given. He may say further that this strange idea did not provide any information about experimental results for the experiments discussed, beyond what could have been obtained from an elementary consideration of photons being guided in some vague way by waves. What, then, is the use of the strange idea?

In answer to the first criticism it may be remarked that the main object of physical science is not the provision of pictures, but is the formulation of laws governing phenomena and the application of these laws to the discovery of new phenomena. If a picture exists, so much the better; but whether a picture exists or not is a matter of only secondary importance. In the case of atomic phenomena no picture can be expected to exist in the usual sense of the word "picture," by which is meant a model functioning essentially on classical lines. One may, however, extend the meaning of the word "picture" to include any *way of looking at the fundamental laws which makes their self-consistency obvious*. With this extension, one may gradually acquire a picture of atomic phenomena by becoming familiar with the laws of the quantum theory.

With regard to the second criticism, it may be remarked that for many simple experiments with light, an elementary theory of waves and photons connected in a vague statistical way would be adequate to account for the results. In the case of such experiments quantum mechanics has no further information to give. In the great majority of experiments, however, the conditions are too complex for an elementary theory of this kind to be applicable and some more elaborate scheme, such as is provided by quantum mechanics, is then needed. The method of description that quantum mechanics gives in the more complex cases is applicable also to the simple cases and although it is then not really necessary for accounting for the experimental results, its study in these simple cases is perhaps a suitable introduction to its study in the general case.

There remains an overall criticism that one may make to the whole scheme, namely, that in departing from the determinacy of the classical theory a great complication is introduced into the description of Nature, which is a highly undesirable feature. This complication is undeniable, but it is offset by a great simplification, provided by the general *principle of superposition of states,* which we shall now go on to consider. But first it is necessary to make precise the important concept of a "state" of a general atomic system.

Let us take any atomic system, composed of particles or bodies with specified properties (mass, moment of inertia, etc.) interacting according to specified laws of force. There will be various possible motions of the particles or bodies consistent with the laws of force. Each such motion is called a *state* of the system. According to classical ideas one could specify a state by giving numerical values to all the coordinates and velocities of the various component parts of the system at some instant of time, the whole motion being then completely determined. Now the argument of [the opening section] shows that we cannot observe a *small* system with that amount of detail which classical theory supposes. The limitation in the power of observation puts a limitation on the number of data that can be assigned to a state. Thus a state of an atomic system must be specified by fewer or more indefinite data than a complete set of numerical values for all the coordinates and velocities at some instant of time. In the case when the system is just a single photon, a state would be completely specified by a given state of motion in the sense of [interference of photons] together with a given state of polarization in the sense of [polarization of photons].

A state of a system may be defined as an undisturbed motion that is restricted by as many conditions or data as are theoretically possible without mutual interference or contradiction. In practice the conditions could be imposed by a suitable preparation of the system, consisting perhaps in passing it through various kinds of sorting apparatus, such as slits and polarimeters, the system being left undisturbed after the preparation. The word "state" may be used to mean either the state at one particular time (after the preparation), or the state throughout the whole of time after the preparation. To distinguish these two meanings, the latter will be called a "state of motion" when there is liable to be ambiguity.

The general principle of superposition of quantum mechanics applies to the states, with either of the above meanings, of any one dynamical system. It requires us to assume that between these states there exist peculiar relationships such that whenever the system is definitely in one state we can consider it as being partly in each of two or more other states. The original state must be regarded as the result of a kind of *superposition* of the two or more new states, in a way that cannot be conceived on classical ideas. Any state may be considered as the result of a superposition of two or more other states, and indeed in an infinite number of ways. Conversely any two or more states may be superposed to give a new state. The procedure of expressing a state as the result of superposition of a number of other states is a mathematical procedure that is always permissible, independent of any reference to physical conditions, like the procedure of resolving a wave into Fourier components. Whether it is useful in any particular case, though, depends on the special physical conditions of the problem under consideration.

In the two preceding sections examples were given of the superposition principle applied to a system consisting of a single photon. [The second section] dealt with states differing only with regard to the polarization and [the third section] with states differing only with regard to the motion of the photon as a whole.

The nature of the relationships which the superposition principle requires to exist between the states of any system is of a kind that cannot be explained in terms of familiar physical concepts. One cannot in the classical sense picture a system being partly in each of two states and see the equivalence of this to the system being completely in some other state. There is an entirely new idea involved, to which one must get accustomed and in terms of which one must proceed to build up an exact mathematical theory, without having any detailed classical picture.

When a state is formed by the superposition of two other states, it will have properties that are in some vague way intermediate between those of the two original states and that approach more or less closely to those of either of them according to the greater or less "weight" attached to this state in the superposition process. The new state is completely defined by the two original states when their relative weights in the superposition process are known, together with a certain phase difference, the exact meaning of weights and phases being provided in the general case by the mathematical theory. In the case of the polarization of a photon their meaning is that provided by classical optics, so that, for example, when two perpendicularly plane polarized states are superposed with equal weights, the new state may be circularly polarized in either direction, or linearly polarized at an angle $\frac{1}{4}\pi$, or else elliptically polarized, according to the phase difference.

The non-classical nature of the superposition process is brought out clearly if we consider the superposition of two states, *A* and *B,* such that there exists an observation which, when made on the system in state *A,* is certain to lead to one particular result, *a* say, and when made on the system in state *B* is certain to lead to some different result, *b* say. What will be the result of the observation when made on the system in the superposed state? The answer is that the result will be sometimes *a* and sometimes *b,* according to a probability law depending on the relative weights of *A* and *B* in the superposition process. It will never be different from both *a* and *b*. *The intermediate character of the state formed by superposition thus expresses itself through the probability of a particular result for an observation being intermediate between the corresponding probabilities for the original states,* not through the result itself being intermediate between the corresponding results for the original states.*

In this way we see that such a drastic departure from ordinary ideas as the assumption of superposition relationships between the states is possible only on account of the recognition of the importance of the disturbance accompanying an observation and of the consequent indeterminacy in the result of the observation. When an observation is made on any atomic system that is in a given state, in general the result will not be determinate, i.e., if the experiment is repeated several times under identical conditions several different results may be obtained. It is a law of nature, though, that if the experiment is repeated a large number of times, each particular result will be obtained in a definite fraction of the total number of times, so that there is a definite *probability* of its being obtained. This probability is what the theory sets out to calculate. Only in special cases when the probability for some result is unity is the result of the experiment determinate.

The assumption of superposition relationships between the states leads to a mathematical theory in which the equations that define a state are linear in the unknowns. In consequence of this, people have tried to establish analogies with systems in classical mechanics, such as vibrating strings or membranes, which are governed by linear equations and for which, therefore, a superposition principle holds. Such analogies have

---

* The probability of a particular result for the state formed by superposition is not always intermediate between those for the original states in the general case when those for the original states are not zero or unity, so there are restrictions on the "intermediateness" of a state formed by superposition.

led to the name "Wave Mechanics" being sometimes given to quantum mechanics. It is important to remember, however, that *the superposition that occurs in quantum mechanics is of an essentially different nature from any occurring in the classical theory,* as is shown by the fact that the quantum superposition principle demands indeterminacy in the results of observations in order to be capable of a sensible physical interpretation. The analogies are thus liable to be misleading.

MATHEMATICAL FORMULATION OF THE PRINCIPLE

A profound change has taken place during the present century in the opinions physicists have held on the mathematical foundations of their subject. Previously they supposed that the principles of Newtonian mechanics would provide the basis for the description of the whole of physical phenomena and that all the theoretical physicist had to do was suitably to develop and apply these principles. With the recognition that there is no logical reason why Newtonian and other classical principles should be valid outside the domains in which they have been experimentally verified has come the realization that departures from these principles are indeed necessary. Such departures find their expression through the introduction of new mathematical formalisms, new schemes of axioms and rules of manipulation, into the methods of theoretical physics.

Quantum mechanics provides a good example of the new ideas. It requires the states of a dynamical system and the dynamical variables to be interconnected in quite strange ways that are unintelligible from the classical standpoint. The states and dynamical variables have to be represented by mathematical quantities of different natures from those ordinarily used in physics. The new scheme becomes a precise physical theory when all the axioms and rules of manipulation governing the mathematical quantities are specified and when in addition certain laws are laid down connecting physical facts with the mathematical formalism, so that from any given physical conditions equations between the mathematical quantities may be inferred and vice versa. In an application of the theory one would be given certain physical information, which one would proceed to express by equations between the mathematical quantities. One would then deduce new equations with the help of the axioms and rules of manipulation and would conclude by interpreting these new equations as physical conditions. The justification for the whole scheme depends, apart from internal consistency, on the agreement of the final results with experiment.

We shall begin to set up the scheme by dealing with the mathematical relations between the states of a dynamical system at one instant of time, which relations will come from the mathematical formulation of the principle of superposition. The superposition process is a kind of additive process and implies that states can in some way be added to give new states. The states must therefore be connected with mathematical quantities of a kind which can be added together to give other quantities of the same kind. The most obvious of such quantities are vectors. Ordinary vectors, existing in a space of a finite number of dimensions, are not sufficiently general for most of the dynamical systems in quantum mechanics. We have to make a generalization to vectors in a space of an infinite number of dimensions, and the mathematical treatment becomes complicated by questions of convergence. For the present, however, we shall deal merely with some general properties of the vectors, properties which can be deduced on the basis of a simple scheme of axioms, and questions of convergence and related topics will not be gone into until the need arises. . . .

ೲೲೲೲೲೲೲ

We shall now take up what is possibly the most interesting of Dirac's numerous and important contributions, namely, a new concept of the vacuum.

Quantum mechanics, introduced in its wave form by Schroedinger, and in the form of a matrix mechanics by Born, Jordan, and Heisenberg, was expressed in its most general form by Dirac in the transformation theory. Dirac's interpretation was remarkably successful in solving problems involving the interactions of fundamental particles. In spite of these successes it became increasingly evident that in its original form the Schroedinger theory was incomplete. This is evident from a consideration of the fine structure of spectral lines, for there is nothing in the Schroedinger wave theory that is the counterpart of the spin of the electron, introduced by Goudsmit and Uhlenbeck to explain this fine structure. It remained for Dirac to remove this last inadequacy of the theory and to derive an improved wave equation, which automatically introduces spin into the theory. This new wave equation of Dirac's also brought with it difficulties of a profound nature that were finally eliminated only by a radical revision of our concept of the vacuum. This particular problem is the subject of the following paper by Dirac. To understand the nature of this new concept of the vacuum, let us first examine the manner in which Dirac had to alter the Schroedinger wave equation in order to introduce the spin of the electron.

That the Schroedinger wave equation is incomplete is disclosed by the Schroedinger wave function for the electron, which contains only the three quantum numbers already introduced in the extended Bohr theory of the atom by Sommerfeld and others. To describe the spin of an electron, however, a fourth quantum number is needed. Moreover, Pauli had already demonstrated this on the basis of relativity theory, which demands that all descriptions of particles be in terms of four coordinates, or four degrees of freedom, not three. For this reason Pauli suggested that a fourth degree of freedom (a fourth quantum number) be assigned to the electron to explain the fine structure of the spectral lines. To explain the doubling of the spectral lines Pauli restricted this fourth quantum number to only two values; this fitted neatly into the spin concept of Goudsmit and Uhlenbeck, who postulated that in a magnetic field the spin of the electron can align itself either in the direction of the field ("parallel alignment") or opposite to the field ("antiparallel alignment").

To describe an electron interacting in the most general way with an electromagnetic field, Pauli therefore replaced the single Schroedinger wave equation with two similar equations, each containing an added term representing the interaction of the magnetic moment of the spinning electron with the magnetic field; one equation represented the parallel arrangement of spin and field, the other the antiparallel arrangement. Although the use of two simultaneous equations to describe the motion of the electron seems at first glance to destroy the idea of a wave associated with the electron, we can see that actually this is not the case, for something of the same sort happens in the electromagnetic picture of light. There, too, one has to introduce a group of equations to describe the propagation of a light wave because one has to deal with vectors, the electric and magnet field strengths, each consisting of three components.

By introducing a matrix with two rows and two columns to represent the spin of the electron, Pauli was able to combine his two equations into a single equation that bears a formal resemblance to the Schroedinger equation, with two exceptions: an additional term appears in the Pauli equation that represents the interaction of the spin with the magnetic field; the wave function consists of two components that represent the two possible spin orientations of the electron.

In his famous paper, "The Relativistic Theory of the Electron," which appeared in 1928 in the *Proceedings of the Royal Society,* Dirac derives the spin properties of the electron by combining the wave mechanics of Schroedinger with the special theory of relativity. From what we have already said it is clear that the Schroedinger equation is deficient, since it is based entirely on nonrelativistic considerations. A number of physicists, including Schroedinger himself, had attempted to obtain a relativistic wave equation before Dirac solved the problem. But previous attempts had failed because in relativity theory it is not the energy that is directly related to the square of the momentum, but rather the square of the energy; therefore, the energy itself has to be expressed as the square root of a quantity involving the momentum. Since the momentum must be taken as an operator, one cannot work with the square root, because the square root of a sum of operators is not defined and there is no way to interpret it physically.

To overcome this difficulty, physicists, such as Klein, Gordon, and Schroedinger, set up a relativistic wave equation in terms of the square of the energy instead of in terms of the energy itself. Thus, their wave equation, which is, indeed, in accord with the requirements of relativity theory, contains the operator that corresponds to the square of the energy, instead of the operator that corresponds to the energy, which is the quantity that appears in the nonrelativistic Schroedinger equation and in the Pauli spin equations. The mathematical operator in quantum mechanics that corresponds to the energy in classical mechanics is the time rate of change, i.e., the derivative with respect to the time. Thus, the square of the energy must correspond to the operator representing the time rate of change of the time rate of change, or the second time rate of change. However, the substitution of the second time rate of change for the time rate of change, itself, leads to a serious difficulty since it is impossible to correlate the wave function with the probability for finding an electron at a given point of space-time, as was done by Born for the nonrelativistic wave function. Indeed, it is clear that this so-called second-order wave equation (the appearance of the second time rate of change operator gives it this name) cannot represent the motion of a single particle, since it leads to probabilities that can be understood only in terms of the motions of many particles having both negative and positive electric charges.

Dirac overcame this difficulty by first discovering a wave equation that is relativistically correct, yet contains only the first time rate of change operator. He did this by taking the expression for the square of the energy in its correct relativistic form and factoring it; he split it into a product of two equivalent terms. Then Dirac used only one of these terms to obtain the wave equation. It turned out, however, that this factorization process automatically introduced matrices into the mathematics, structures similar in nature to those Pauli had introduced in an *ad hoc* fashion. The Dirac matrices thus entered into the theory quite naturally, merely in virtue of the requirement that the final wave equation involve only the first time rate of change operator. This was all to the good, since, as we have noted, the introduction of Pauli-like matrices must lead to particles having spin.

There is, however, one important difference between the matrices that appear in the Dirac equation of an electron and those of Pauli. Whereas the latter are just three matrices, each having two rows and two columns, the former constitute a group of four matrices, each one having four rows and four columns. In fact, three of the Dirac matrices can be obtained by taking each Pauli spin matrix twice and arranging these into a four-rowed structure. The significance of the appearance of four-rowed matrices in the wave equation is that the equation becomes fourfold, with the wave function composed of four components. Dirac showed that his equation gives the same results that Pauli had obtained by arbitrarily introducing spin into the Schroedinger mathematics. But Dirac's work goes further because it introduces a four-component wave function, governed by four simultaneous wave equations. The sudden appearance of this fourfold wave function gave rise to a grave and apparently insurmountable difficulty.

The relativistic Dirac theory shows that the electron is a far more complicated structure than was ever dreamed of before, that it possesses properties even beyond those of spin. This is apparent from the four-component wave function itself, since we know from Pauli's work that to describe the spin alone only a two-component wave function is required. If, then, only two of the components of the Dirac wave function are needed to describe a spinning electron, what is the role of the other two components? When Dirac examined these other two components, he was inclined to dismiss them as nonsensical, for although they also describe a spinning electron there is one important difference. It is an electron that has less than zero energy; that is, it is an electron with negative energy and hence, in terms of our ordinary understanding of things, an impossibility. Dirac suggested that we disregard these other two components of his wave function and use only the two "sensible" components.

But if one tries to describe an electron using only the two positive energy components of the Dirac wave function, the description does not tally with the observations. Thus it turns out that if one uses only the two "sensible" components in describing an electron in a "box," one suddenly discovers that this description allows the electron to leave the box (seemingly without passing through the walls) and to appear outside it. In other words, all four wave components have to be employed to describe an electron properly, and here the full dilemma of the situation is clearly revealed. For if one pictures the negative-energy states of the electron as having physical reality, how can ordinary matter occupying the ordinary positive-energy states exist? Would not all the electrons in the states of positive energy (that is, all matter) jump down into the unoccupied negative-energy states, thus bringing about a cataclysmic annihilation of all matter? This is precisely what the Dirac equations say must happen, and it was to show a way out of this difficulty that Dirac published the paper that follows this discussion.

Dirac solves the problem in a most ingenious fashion—a tribute to his great imaginative powers—endowing the theory with a new dimension hitherto undreamed of. He imparts a new meaning to the vacuum. Since the negative-energy states cannot be eliminated from the theory without destroying it, and since such states, if left empty, would lead to the complete collapse of the physical world, Dirac eliminates the difficulty by supposing that each negative-energy state is already occupied by an electron. This saves the entire theory, for the Pauli exclusion principle now prevents the collapse by stating that only one electron can occupy a particular energy state at any time. Thus, by filling the entire vacuum with an infinitude of electrons in states of negative energy (electrons in negative-energy states cannot be observed), we can use the Dirac theory to describe ordinary electrons in positive-energy states.

There is one error in Dirac's paper, later corrected by J. R. Oppenheimer and by Dirac himself. As Dirac pointed out, a negative-energy state that for some reason or other is lacking an electron behaves like a hole in a sea of negative-energy states, or like a bubble in an ocean of water. Hence it resembles a positive charge with positive mass (the absence of negative charge and of negative energy or mass is equivalent to the presence of positive charge and positive energy). This led Dirac to his idea that the protons are these "holes" in the vacuum. We know now that this was an incorrect interpretation. The "holes" that behave like positive charges are, indeed, particles in their own right, the so-called positrons. They were discovered in 1934 by Carl Anderson in cosmic ray photographs. Since positrons can annihilate electrons, it is customary to consider them as antielectrons; with the recent discovery by Segré and Chamberlain of antiprotons and antineutrons, there is good reason to suppose that our universe is composed of equal quantities of matter and of antimatter.

Dirac's paper is an excellent example of the unorthodoxy in his approach to a physical problem and his boldness in postulating ideas that do such violence to the traditional ideas of space, time, and matter. In this respect, Dirac is closer to Einstein than are any of the other physicists of the modern quantum-mechanical era. We may note further in this connection that Dirac is able to extract from the formalism of a theory everything that is of physical significance. For him a particular mathematical expression or relationship goes beyond the correlation that it may establish between two or more entities. Its very form and the branch of mathematics from which it stems are of deep physical significance.

There is another feature of Dirac's approach to theoretical physics which is of interest. This is his insistence on making the mathematical formulation of a theory as beautiful as possible. He feels that a theory that is expressed in an inelegant and cumbersome mathematical form cannot be correct and must be incomplete in some respect. An example of this is the formulation of the relativistic wave equation as compared to that of the nonrelativistic Schroedinger equation. In one of his articles, Dirac points out that the former is much more beautiful than the latter and that, if Schroedinger had insisted on beauty, he might well have arrived at the correct relativistic equation.

୦୦୦୦୦୦୦

A Theory of Electrons and Protons [3]

NATURE OF THE NEGATIVE ENERGY DIFFICULTY

THE RELATIVITY QUANTUM THEORY OF an electron moving in a given electromagnetic field, although successful in predicting the spin properties of the electron, yet involves one serious difficulty which shows that some fundamental alteration is necessary before we can regard it as an accurate description of nature. This difficulty is connected with the fact that the wave equation, which is of the form

$$\left[\frac{W}{c} + \frac{e}{c} A_0 + \rho_1 \left(\boldsymbol{\sigma}, \mathbf{p} + \frac{e}{c} \mathbf{A} \right) + \rho_3 mc \right] \psi = 0, \tag{1}$$

has, in addition to the wanted solutions for which the kinetic energy of the electron is positive, an equal number of unwanted solutions with negative kinetic energy for the electron, which appear to have no physical meaning. Thus if we take the case of a steady electromagnetic field, equation (1) will admit of periodic solutions of the form

$$\psi = u \, e^{-iEt/\hbar}, \tag{2}$$

where u is independent of t, representing stationary states, E being the total energy of the state, including the relativity term mc^2. There will then exist solutions (2) with negative values for E as well as those with positive values; in fact, if we take a matrix representation of the operators $\rho_1\sigma_1$, $\rho_1\sigma_2$, $\rho_1\sigma_3$, ρ_3 with the matrix elements all real, then the conjugate complex of any solution of (1) will be a solution of the wave equation obtained from (1) by reversal of the sign of the potentials A, and either the original wave function or its conjugate complex must refer to a negative E.

The difficulty is not a special one connected with the quantum theory of the electron, but is a general one appearing in all relativity theories, also in the classical theory. It arises on account of the fundamental fact that in the relativity Hamiltonian equation of the classical theory, namely,

$$\left(\frac{W}{c} + \frac{e}{c} A_0 \right)^2 - \left(\mathbf{p} + \frac{e}{c} \mathbf{A} \right)^2 - m^2 c^2 = 0, \tag{3}$$

---

[3] Dirac, *Proceedings of the Royal Society* (*London*), Series A, 128 (1930), 360–365.

there is an ambiguity in the sign of W, or rather $W + eA_0$. Although the operator on the wave function in (1) is linear in W, yet it is, roughly speaking, equivalent to the left-hand side of (3) and the ambiguity in sign persists. The difficulty is not important in the classical theory, since here dynamical variables must always vary continuously, so that there will be a sharp distinction between those solutions of the equations of motion for which $W + eA_0 \geqq mc^2$ and those for which $W + eA_0 \leqq - mc^2$, and we may simply ignore the latter.

We cannot, however, get over the difficulty so easily in the quantum theory. It is true that in the case of a steady electromagnetic field we can draw a distinction between those solutions of (1) of the form (2) with E positive and those with E negative and may assert that only the former have a physical meaning (as was actually done when the theory was applied to the determination of the energy levels of the hydrogen atom), but if a perturbation is applied to the system it may cause transitions from one kind of state to the other. In the general case of an arbitrarily varying electromagnetic field we can make no hard-and-fast separation of the solutions of the wave equation into those referring to positive and those to negative kinetic energy. Further, in the accurate quantum theory in which the electromagnetic field also is subjected to quantum laws, transitions can take place in which the energy of the electron changes from a positive to a negative value even in the absence of any external field, the surplus energy, at least $2mc^2$ in amount, being spontaneously emitted in the form of radiation. (The laws of conservation of energy and momentum require at least two light-quanta to be formed simultaneously in such a process.) Thus we cannot ignore the negative-energy states without giving rise to ambiguity in the interpretation of the theory.

Let us examine the wave functions representing states of negative energy a little more closely. If we superpose a number of these wave functions in such a way as to get a wave packet, the motion of this packet will be along a classical trajectory given by the Hamiltonian (3) with $W + eA_0$ negative. Such a trajectory, it is easily seen, is a possible trajectory for an ordinary electron (with positive energy) moving in the electromagnetic field with reversed sign, or for an electron of charge $+ e$ (and positive energy) moving in the original electromagnetic field. Thus *an electron with negative energy moves in an external field as though it carries a positive charge.*

This result has led people to suspect a connection between the negative-energy electron and the proton or hydrogen nucleus. One cannot, however, simply assert that a negative-energy electron is a proton, as that would lead to the following paradoxes:

(i) A transition of an electron from a state of positive to one of negative energy would be interpreted as a transition of an electron into a proton, which would violate the law of conservation of electric charge.

(ii) Although a negative-energy electron moves in an external field as though it has a positive charge, yet, as one can easily see from a consideration of conservation of momentum, the field it produces must correspond to its having a negative charge, *e.g.,* the negative-energy electron will repel an ordinary positive-energy electron although it is itself attracted by the positive-energy electron.

(iii) A negative-energy electron will have less energy the faster it moves and will have to absorb energy in order to be brought to rest. No particles of this nature have ever been observed.

A closer consideration of the conditions that we should expect to hold in the actual world suggests that the connection between protons and negative-energy electrons should be on a somewhat different basis and this will be found to remove all the above-mentioned difficulties.

SOLUTION OF THE NEGATIVE ENERGY DIFFICULTY

The most stable states for an electron (*i.e.,* the states of lowest energy) are those with negative energy and very high velocity. All the electrons in the world will tend to fall into these states with emission of radiation. The Pauli exclusion principle, however, will come into play and prevent more than one electron going into any one state. Let us assume there are so many electrons in the world that all the most stable states are occupied, or, more accurately, that *all the states of negative energy are occupied except perhaps a few of small velocity.* Any electrons with positive energy will now have very little chance of jumping into negative-energy states and will therefore behave like electrons are observed to behave in the laboratory. We shall have an infinite number of electrons in negative-energy states, and indeed an infinite number per unit volume all over the world, but if their distribution is exactly uniform we should expect them to be completely unobservable. *Only the small departures from exact uniformity, brought about by some of the negative-energy states being unoccupied, can we hope to observe.*

Let us examine the properties of the vacant states or "holes." The problem is analogous to that of the X-ray levels in an atom with many electrons. According to the usual theory of the X-ray levels, the hole that is formed when one of the inner electrons of the atom is removed is describable as an orbit and is pictured as the orbit of the missing electron before it was removed. This description can be justified by quantum mechanics, provided the orbit is regarded, not in Bohr's sense, but as something representable, apart from spin, by a three-dimensional wave function. Thus the hole or vacancy in a region that is otherwise saturated with electrons is much the same thing as a single electron in a region that is otherwise devoid of them.

In the X-ray case the holes should be counted as things of negative energy since to make one of them disappear (*i.e.*, to fill it up), one must add to it an ordinary electron of positive energy. Just the contrary holds, however, for the holes in our distribution of negative-energy electrons. These holes will be things of positive energy and will therefore be in this respect like ordinary particles. Further, the motion of one of these holes in an external electromagnetic field will be the same as that of the negative-energy electron that would fill it, and will thus correspond to its possessing a charge $+ e$. We are therefore led to the assumption that *the holes in the distribution of negative-energy electrons are the protons.* When an electron of positive energy drops into a hole and fills it up, we have an electron and proton disappearing together with emission of radiation.

A difficulty arises when we consider the field produced by the distribution of negative energy electrons. There is an infinite density of electricity which according to Maxwell's equation

$$\text{div } \mathbf{E} = -4\pi\rho, \tag{4}$$

should produce an electric field of infinite divergence. It seems natural, however, to interpret the ρ in Maxwell's equation (4) as the departure from the normal state of electrification of the world, which normal state of electrification, according to the present theory, is the one where every electronic state of negative energy and none of positive energy is occupied. This ρ will then consist of a charge $- e$ arising from each state of positive energy that is occupied, together with a charge $+ e$ arising from each state of negative energy that is unoccupied. Thus the field produced by a proton will correspond to its having a charge $+ e$.

In this way we can get over the three difficulties mentioned at the end of the preceding section. We require to postulate only one fundamental kind of particle, instead of the two, electron and proton, that were previously necessary. The mere tendency of all the particles to go into their states of lowest energy results in all the *distinctive* things in nature having positive energy.

Can the present theory account for the great dissymmetry between electrons and protons, which manifests itself through their different masses and the power of protons to combine to form heavier atomic nuclei? It is evident that the theory gives, to a large extent, symmetry between electrons and protons. We may interchange their rôles and assert that the protons are the real particles and the electrons are merely holes in the distribution of protons of negative energy. The symmetry is not, however, mathematically perfect when one takes interaction between the electrons into account. If one neglects the interaction, the Hamiltonian describing the whole system will be of the form ΣH_a, where H_a is the Hamiltonian or energy of an electron in state a and the summation is taken over all occupied states. This differs only by a constant (*i.e.*, by something independent of which states are occupied) from the sum $\Sigma(-H_a)$ taken over all unoccupied states. Thus we get formally the same dynamical system if we consider the unoccupied states or protons each to contribute a term $-H_a$ to the Hamiltonian. On the other hand, if we take interaction between the electrons into account we get an extra term of the form ΣV_{ab} in the Hamiltonian, the summation being taken over all pairs of occupied states (a, b), and this is not equivalent to any sum taken over pairs of unoccupied states. The interaction would therefore give an essentially different Hamiltonian if we regard the protons as the real particles that occupy states.

The consequences of this dissymmetry are not very easy to calculate on relativistic lines, but we may hope it will lead eventually to an explanation of the different masses of proton and electron. Possibly some more perfect theory of the interaction, based perhaps on Eddington's calculation of the fine structure constant e^2/hc, is necessary before this result can be obtained.

APPLICATION TO SCATTERING

As an elementary application of the foregoing ideas we may consider the problem of the scattering of radiation by an electron, free or bound. A scattering process ought, according to theory, to be considered as a double transition process, consisting of first an absorption of a photon with the electron simultaneously jumping to any state, and then an emission with the electron jumping into its final state, or else of first the emission and then the absorption. We therefore have to consider altogether three states of the whole system, the *initial state* with an incident photon and the electron in its initial state, an *intermediate state* with either two or no photons in existence and the electron in any state, and the *final state* with the scattered photon and the electron in its final state. The initial and final states of the whole system must have the same total energy, but the intermediate state, which lasts only a very short time, may have a considerably different energy.

The question now arises as to how one is to interpret those scattering processes for which the intermediate state is one of negative energy for the electron. According to previous ideas these intermediate states had no real physical meaning, so it was doubtful whether scattering processes that arise through their agency should be included in the formula for the scattering coefficient. This gave rise to a serious difficulty, since in some important practical cases nearly all the scattering comes from intermediate states with negative energy for the electron. In fact for a free electron and radiation of low frequency, where the classical formula holds, the whole of the scattering comes from such intermediate states.

According to the theory of the present paper it is absolutely forbidden, by the exclusion principle, for the electron to jump into a state of negative energy, so that the double transition processes with intermediate states of negative energy for the electron must be excluded. We now have, however, another kind of double transition process taking place, namely, that in which first one of the distribution of negative-energy electrons jumps up into the required final state for the electron with absorption (or emission) of a photon, and then the original positive-energy electron drops into the hole formed by the first transition with emission (or absorption) of a photon. Such processes result in a final state of the whole system indistinguishable from the final state with the more direct processes, in which the same electron makes two successive jumps. These new processes just make up for those of the more direct processes that are excluded on account of the intermediate state having negative energy for the electron, since the matrix elements that determine the transition probabilities are just the same in the two cases, though they come into play in the reverse order. In this way the old scattering formulas, in which no intermediate states are excluded, can be justified.

70

ooooooooooo

"HOLES" IN THE DIRAC THEORY

ooooooooooo

J. Robert Oppenheimer (b. 1904)

When Dirac proposed his relativistic theory of the electron, it appeared to be overburdened with difficulties as a result of predicting the existence of an infinite continuum of negative energy states. According to this theory, the universe consists of two parts divided by the line of zero energy: Above this line are the states of positive energy, most of which are unoccupied, since the amount of matter in the universe is negligible compared to the amount of empty space; below the line are the states of negative energy, whose very existence poses a dilemma. Quantum mechanics predicts that ordinary electrons have a finite probability of jumping down into these negative-energy states with the emission of radiation. Thus if all of these states were empty, no particles, such as ordinary electrons, could exist; there would be a finite probability for all of them to fall into negative-energy states.

To overcome this difficulty Dirac proposed the idea that all but a few of these negative-energy states are filled with electrons with negative energy. Of course, an electron with negative energy has no real meaning, and certainly has no classical counterpart. But the idea makes it possible to work with the Dirac theory of the electron, which accounts beautifully for all the observed phenomena involving these particles. By placing electrons in most of the negative-energy states, Dirac made it impossible for ordinary electrons to jump down, since the Pauli exclusion principle permits only one electron in each state. Dirac proposed further that negative-energy states that do not have electrons represent protons, since such holes in the sea of negative-energy electrons behave like positive

1199

charges. In this way Dirac hoped to account both for protons and electrons. He suggested that the difference in mass between the electron and the proton might be accounted for by the interaction of the ordinary electrons with the infinite sea of negative-energy electrons.

This proposal to account for the proton proved untenable, as demonstrated by J. R. Oppenheimer in the first paper that follows this commentary. Oppenheimer points out that to assume that the ordinary protons in the universe are gaps in the sea of negative-energy electrons leads to insurmountable difficulties.

To begin with, the assumption that there are no distinct positive charges, in their own right, requires an infinite distribution of positive charge to compensate for the effect of the infinite distribution of the negative-energy electrons on the scattering of light and on other electromagnetic phenomena. Moreover, if the Dirac holes were protons, the scattering of light by protons would have to be explained by a process involving the interaction of the ordinary electrons with the holes. Consequently, the formula which shows how the scattering depends on the mass of the proton would be wrong. The correct scattering formula requires that the scattering vary inversely as the square of the mass of the scattering particle whereas the hole theory gives a different mass dependence.

Finally, as Oppenheimer notes, no protons could exist in nature (nor could electrons) if the gaps or holes in Dirac's sea of negative-energy electrons were protons. The theory shows that if any hole is present, there is a finite probability for an electron in its neighborhood to jump down into the hole and thus to destroy itself as it fills the hole. Under these conditions, Oppenheimer shows that in an ordinary sample of matter there are so many protons around that, if they were holes, all the electrons in this matter would jump down into the holes in less than a billionth of a second. This means that there can be no empty negative-energy states under ordinary conditions.

Oppenheimer therefore proposes to retain the picture of the electron and the proton as two independent particles of opposite sign and dissimilar mass and to picture all of Dirac's negative-energy states as filled. With all the negative-energy states filled there can be no transitions of ordinary electrons from their positive-energy states to the negative continuum and all the difficulties pointed out by Oppenheimer thereby disappear.

At this point Oppenheimer was but one step away from predicting the existence of the positron, which was discovered in cosmic rays a few years later by Carl Anderson. We now know that it is not necessary for all the negative-energy states to be filled. Under certain conditions, if enough energy is available, an electron in a state of negative energy can be lifted into a state of positive energy so that a pair is created—an ordinary electron and a Dirac hole, which behaves like a positively charged particle with exactly the same mass as the ordinary electron. These short-lived "holes" are the positrons.

Following Oppenheimer's refutation of the Dirac proton proposal, we reproduce a lecture by the physicist that deals with the various aspects of electron theory in an unusually penetrating and lucid fashion.

It is a curious fact that despite the technical dominance of the United States in the first two decades of this century and the excellence of its educational system, there was, during this period, no American school of physics comparable in any way to those that sprang up in Europe. There were, of course, excellent experimentalists, such as Michelson, Millikan, Compton, and Davisson, but there were scarcely any first-rate theoreticians, without whose stimulus and constant analysis of existing theories in the light of new experimental data no great progress can occur. With the exception of a few isolated cases, such as Willard Gibbs of Yale, who laid the foundations of statistical mechanics in the early part of this century, most of the great ideas that influenced the experimental physicists in the United States came from Europe.

In the 1920's, when the great quantum-mechanical ferment was stirring European physics and, as the great German mathematician, David Hilbert, put it, Nobel prizes were lying around to be picked up in the streets, American theoretical physics began its spectacular growth, which resulted in its present dominant position. At that time such excellent theoretical physicists as G. Breit (a Russian exile), Van Vleck, Condon, and Slater were beginning to attract more and more brilliant young college students to physics; by the time J. Robert Oppenheimer began to hold sway in California, enough good raw material was around for him to organize what might be called an American school of theoretical physics. An additional impetus was given to American physics in the 1930's by the influx of such European physicists as Wigner, Einstein, Bethe, and Fermi.

Oppenheimer was very well suited for this task by virtue of his innate ability and the excellence of his schooling. He was born in New York City on April 22, 1904, of well-to-do German-Jewish parents, who gave him every encouragement in his intellectual pursuits. From early boyhood he showed a pronounced interest in science and mathematics: while still in high school he mastered calculus. His interest in science extended to all phases that required an orderly analysis of data and a formulation of new concepts. In addition to his abiding interest in science, Oppenheimer was also deeply concerned with the humanities, with the social sciences, and with the arts; indeed, throughout his life he has never allowed his deep dedication to science to rob him of the pleasures that can be found in other pursuits.

After graduating from high school he went to Harvard, where he received his A.B. degree in 1925. During this phase of his education, he so clearly gave evidence of his great skill in mathematical physics that there was no question but that he would become one of the top theoretical physicists of the coming period. From Harvard he went on to the University of Göttingen to study with Born, who was then the leading spirit in the development of the quantum mechanics. At that time the atmosphere in Göttingen was particularly appealing to a young graduate student interested in the new ideas that were rapidly altering the basic concepts of physics, for, in addition to Born himself and outstanding experimentalists such as James Frank, it had attracted many of the young Ph.D.'s who were the source of these new ideas—men like Heisenberg and P. Jordan, who were Born's assistants, and other young physicists like Kramers, Pauli, Fermi, Dirac, Weisskopf, and Wigner. It seemed as though no promising student of theoretical physics could consider his education complete without spending some time at Göttingen.

Göttingen had something else to offer—its school of mathematicians. Starting with the great Gauss and continuing with such men as Riemann, Klein, Minkowski, and Hilbert, Göttingen had become the center of the kind of mathematics that the new physics required. Minkowski had developed the four-dimensional geometry that was needed for a full understanding of the relativity theory and David Hilbert had formulated the mathematics required for the full flowering of the quantum mechanics. He had developed the mathematics of an abstract infinite-dimensional function space—called Hilbert space—that, in a sense, occupies the same position in quantum mechanics that Minkowski's four-dimensional space occupies in relativity theory. Besides the resident professors of mathematics like Hilbert, young mathematicians like John von Neumann, who did much to relate Hilbert's mathematics directly to the quantum mechanics, and Van der Waerden, who formulated the mathematics of spinors—mathematical quantities that play an important role in the Dirac theory of the electron—were constantly visiting Göttingen.

When Oppenheimer came to Göttingen, Heisenberg had just completed his first important paper on the matrix mechanics and Schroedinger had published his first paper on the wave mechanics. Born, himself, then became interested in the interpretation of the Schroedinger wave function and hit upon the idea of analyzing collisions between particles to arrive at the correct interpretation. Thus Oppenheimer was quite naturally brought into this work; in collaboration with Born, he published some basic papers on collision theory. As a result of this work, he received his Ph.D. at Göttingen in 1927 at the age of twenty-three.

From Göttingen he went to Zurich and then to Leyden as a fellow of the Institute of International Education. In 1929 he became assistant professor of Theoretical Physics at both the California Institute of Technology and the University of California, and then in quick succession became associate professor in 1931 and full professor in 1936 at both institutions.

During this period, Oppenheimer contributed many important papers to quantum mechanics and to atomic theory. At the same time, he attracted the best of the young American physicists and even some Europeans, so that the University of California became the American center of theoretical physics and remained so until the Institute of Advanced Study at Princeton began to outstrip it.

Oppenheimer's research activities cut across many branches of physics. In addition to his work on the properties of the Dirac electron, and on the interpretation of the negative-energy states that are a consequence of the Dirac relativistic wave equation, he made important contributions to the theory of cosmic rays, to nuclear physics, to fundamental particles, and to astrophysics. In his work in cosmic rays he was one of the first physicists to study and analyze the origin of cosmic ray showers. These are large bundles of secondary particles originating from a single high-energy cosmic ray particle (proton). As Oppenheimer demonstrated, the primary proton creates many pairs of electrons and positrons along its path as it passes through the earth's atmosphere; these secondary particles form the showers that accompany the primary cosmic ray particles.

When the neutron was discovered in 1932, and nuclear physics began to occupy the minds of physicists more and more, Oppenheimer quite naturally began to work in this field; in addition to many other papers, he wrote an important paper, in collaboration with Volkov, on the application of neutron physics to stars. He showed that, under appropriate conditions, a star can contract gravitationally to such an extent that all the protons inside the star are changed into neutrons and a pure neutron star, with a diameter of about 10 miles, results.

With the beginning of World War II, Oppenheimer, like most other leading physicists, became involved in the problem of nuclear fission. When it became clear that a chain reaction was possible, he was chosen (by almost unanimous agreement among the physicists working on the atomic bomb project) to head the work at Los Alamos where the bomb was finally to be constructed.

Immediately after the war he became director of Los Alamos, which was one of the first of a number of permanent National Scientific Laboratories established in the wake of the vast scientific-military research activity. In 1947 he left Los Alamos to become director of the Institute of Advanced Studies at Princeton, where he remained until his retirement in 1965. During this period, Oppenheimer devoted himself to his own research and to making the institute the outstanding center of theoretical physics in the world. His research dealt with the theory of fundamental particles, and particularly with the nature of mesons—the particles by means of which nucleons (protons and neutrons) attract each other. He was one of the first physicists to postulate the existence of a neutral pi-meson in addition to positively and negatively charged pi-mesons.

Oppenheimer has received many honors for his contributions to physics and the world of science in general. In addition to receiving the Fermi award he is an honorary fellow of Christ's College, Cambridge, a member of the National Academy of Sciences, fellow of the American Philosophical Society, fellow of the American Academy of Arts and Sciences, honorary member of the Japanese Academy of Sciences, of the Royal Danish Academy of Sciences and Letters, of the Brazilian Academy of Sciences.

From 1946 to 1952 Oppenheimer was chairman of the General Advisory Committee of the Atomic Energy Commission, and from 1949 to 1955 he was a member of the Board of Overseers of Harvard. In 1948 American physicists honored him by electing him President of the American Physical Society—the highest honor they can bestow upon a colleague.

୦୦୦୦୦୦୦୦

OPPENHEIMER

On the Theory of Electrons and Protons [1]

IN A RECENT PAPER DIRAC has suggested that the reason why the transitions of an electron to states of negative energy, which are predicted by his theory of the electron, do not in fact occur is that nearly all of the states of negative energy are already occupied. Dirac has further shown that the unoccupied states of negative energy have many of the properties of protons; that, for instance, they may be represented by wave functions which would be taken to correspond to a particle of positive charge and positive mass. He has further shown that the mass associated with these gaps is not necessarily the same as that of the electron, and he has suggested the assumption that the gaps are protons. In order to account for the fact that the divergence of the electric field is not, in spite of the infinite electron density, everywhere infinite, Dirac further assumes that only the departures from the normal state in which all nega-

---

[1] J. Robert Oppenheimer, *Physical Review,* 35 (1930), 562 f.

tive states are filled are to be counted in computing the charge density for Maxwell's fourth equation

$$\text{div } E = -4\pi\rho. \tag{1}$$

Finally, Dirac is able to account for the validity of the Thomson formula for the scattering of soft light by a free electron, in spite of the fact that the derivation of this formula on his theory of the electron—a derivation which makes explicit use of the transitions to states of negative energy which are now forbidden, is invalid. According to Dirac, the scattering takes place by a double electron jump, in which a negative * electron jumps up to some state of positive energy, and the original positive electron falls down into the gap left.

There are several grave difficulties which arise when one tries to maintain the suggestion that the protons are the gaps of negative energy, and that there are no distinctive particles of positive charge. In the first place, we can easily see that Dirac's theory requires an infinite density of positive electricity; and since we should expect the De Broglie waves of this charge to be quantized, we should expect some corpuscular properties for the positive charges. The reason why the theory requires an infinite positive charge is this: If the explanation of the scattering of an electron is to be tenable, a negative electron must interact with the electromagnetic field in the way predicted by Dirac's theory of the electron; for otherwise the scheme proposed would not give the Thomson formula. But this means that there must be a term involving the current and charge vector of the negative electrons in the total energy momentum tensor for matter and radiation. Thus by (1), the divergence of the electric field will be everywhere infinite unless there is an infinite density of positive electricity to compensate the negative electrons.

A further difficulty appears when we try to compute the scattering of soft light by a proton. This difficulty is not unconnected with the difference in mass between the electron and proton, and makes it seem improbable that this difference can be explained on the basis suggested by Dirac. For the scattering process must in this case be regarded as a double jump of a single electron, in which a negative electron jumps to some state of positive energy, and then falls back into the hole that is the original proton. Now it is easy to see that the probability of this scattering is determined by precisely the same matrix components as those which give the electron scattering, and that the present theory gives equal scattering coefficients for electron and proton. Of course, the interaction between electrons is omitted in this computation; but the difficulty is this, that such interaction

---

* By a negative electron we mean an electron of negative energy.

would affect electron scattering and proton scattering in precisely the same way; whereas the Thomson formula requires the latter to be smaller by a factor proportional to the square of the ratio of the masses.

Finally, there is a numerical discrepancy to be noted. According to Dirac's suggestions, the filling of the proton gaps in the distribution of negative electrons should correspond to the annihilation of an electron and a proton, and should thus, under all normal conditions, be a very rare occurrence. Now if we consider for definiteness a free electron in an enclosure in which there are n_p free protons per unit volume, we may readily compute the rate at which the electron should, by the Dirac radiation theory, fall into one of the corresponding gaps. The conservation laws require that at least two quanta be emitted in this process; and it is sufficient to consider jumps in which no more than two quanta are emitted. The details of the calculation will be published elsewhere; if we neglect the interaction of the electron with the negative electrons we obtain for the mean lifetime of the electron:

$$T = Gm^2c^3e^{-4}/n_p \qquad\qquad (2)$$

where G is a numerical constant of the order of unity, e the charge, and m the mass of the electron. Now again it is difficult to see what large errors could be involved in the computation, since the matrix components which give (2) are of precisely the same type as those which give correctly the Thomson formula and the optical transition probabilities of the electron; and (2) gives a mean lifetime for ordinary matter of the order of 10^{-10} seconds.

Thus we should hardly expect any states of negative energy to remain empty. If we return to the assumption of two independent elementary particles, of opposite charge and dissimilar mass, we can resolve all the difficulties raised in this note, and retain the hypothesis that the reason why no transitions to states of negative energy occur, either for electrons or protons, is that all such states are filled. In this way, we may accept Dirac's reconciliation of the absence of these transitions with the validity of the scattering formulae.

Electron Theory [2]

. . . ELECTRON THEORY . . . IS A VERY odd piece of theory indeed. It is an almost perfect theory, in many contexts. It makes

---

[2] Oppenheimer, *Physics Today,* 10 (1957), 12–20.

it possible for us to predict what we observe with an accuracy of one part in a billion or better than that. It is a theory which is almost closed, almost self-consistent and almost perfect. Yet it has one odd feature: if you try to make it quite perfect, then it is nonsense; and this may have a bit of a moral although I am not going to draw the moral in any great detail.

I would like to tell this as a narrative. I cannot teach electron theory; it is a very hard subject; it is a recondite one. I cannot tell you in detail how one is sure when one looks at the results of an experiment—one is never sure, but how one is convinced—that this experiment means what it says: how, when you see a certain black line on a photographic plate, you know that it was made by an electron; how when you hear a count in a counter, or when you see a constellation of crisscrosses in a photographic film under a microscope, you say, yes, that was an electron that did it. This is part of the cumulative character of science: these things have been learned really over the centuries, and you go to school and you find out what has been learned. You find out you can use a sort of shorthand. Instead of saying that curve (the set of drops that seems to be distributed along a curved path whose picture you have taken; it was formed in a gas which was supersaturated, which was exposed to cosmic rays) represents a positive electron, you just say, that is a positive electron, or positron. There is a lot of learning in that and I am going to short-circuit it.

I am also going to have to short-circuit the mathematical apparatus which we use, not always successfully, to decide what are the logical consequences of an assertion, what is the content of the theory, because this also is something which people will go to school for many years to learn. So that my description is going to be the kind of thing that you have to do in this world. You have to say, "I will tell you a story about it. I hope you believe me. If you do not believe me I hope you will be interested enough to spend eight years to find out whether I was telling the truth." . . .

The electron is one of the fundamental particles of physics. By that we mean only that it has not proven possible, profitable, useful, to regard it as made up of something else. It is only one of a rather large number of such particles. My own count at the moment is 24; but physics is one of those subjects in which you have to have a bit of a theory before you can count, because you do not know what you are identifying until you have a bit of a theory. The electron is the oldest (the first to be found), the best studied, in many ways the simplest particle; it is one of the very few particles which is stable, which does not, that is, of itself, come apart and disappear into something else. It was discovered at about the turn of the century by J. J. Thomson. It is, as you know, the ingredient which gives chemical and most physical properties to ordinary atoms and molecules. It is very light compared to a nucleus, being about 2000 times lighter than the nucleus of hydrogen, the lightest one. It is probably the only particle in nature of which we have much understanding; I have to say that though this is a great deal of understanding, it is far from a complete one.

With Rutherford's discovery of the atomic nucleus, and Bohr's invention, one had the familiar picture (which is not right but which has been so useful): of an atom consisting of a heavy nucleus, quite small (about a thousand times smaller than atomic dimensions), with almost all of the mass and a charge equal to the atomic number. Around this nucleus is a constellation of electrons which Bohr rather cautiously said were in a certain set of stationary states and which he pictured even rather more cautiously in terms of elliptical orbits. These orbits being very large compared to the nucleus, their properties determine the chemistry and the ordinary physics of matter.

Things were not, however, quite simple, because at the time of the electron's discovery there were two basic theories into which to fit the electron's behavior. One was Newton's mechanics, which said that a particle moved so that the mass times the acceleration was equal to the force; and the force on the electron was the electric force which acted directly on its charge, and the magnetic force which acted if it were in motion. And the other theory was that of Maxwell; which describes how electric and magnetic fields are produced. They are produced by charges and they propagate with the velocity of light; Maxwell in his famous equations said just how that was. So you had a theory that told you how charge produces an electric field and how an electron should move in that electric field. This was all fine; it had to be most radically modified.

But, even before coming to that modification, I should recall an attempt, associated with Lorentz, to see if one could understand the electron itself in terms of these two theories, Newton's equations of motion and Maxwell's theory about how charges make fields. I will say a word about this, not because we are worried about it today—it is obsolete, it is wrong —but because it illustrates with peculiar and rather elementary vividness something that has happened very recently and that is so hard to explain that I can only say it happened and cannot adequately explain it.

The old idea was this: If you have charge producing field and field acting on charge, is it possible that the electron itself is a structure whose own field explains its existence? That is, the charge is accumulated in this way and the forces that the charge produces keep the electron intact. What else happens, when you have an electron that is moving subject to an external force? It is also charged; it must be producing a field; it will respond to this field. The program then looks like this: You say, "I have an electron and Newton's law tells me that the mass, m, times the acceleration, x'', which is the second time derivative of the coordinate, is equal to the force exerted on it from the outside. $mx'' = F$." Then, you try to ask, what kind of effects will the fact that there is a bit of charge, what kind of effects will that have on the behavior of the electron itself?

Well, you start out and say, "I do not know how big the electron is but let me say it is about that big" [see Fig. 70–1] and then let me calculate. Then we find that there are two kinds of effects the field makes. One is the building up of all the electric fields around here [see Fig. 70–2]. This gives energy and therefore inertia and mass to the electron and you think you may be able to calculate this out.

Fig. 70–1.   Fig. 70–2.

In the second place, we notice also that when the electron is subject to nonuniform motion, then the fields are altered and new forces are introduced which depend on the motion. All of this, in general, depends on the structure, and—as in some respects we shall rediscover later—we find that as we make the electron smaller and smaller, the energy of the field grows larger, and the mass becomes infinite. The effect of the complicated motion of the electron becomes simple and turns out to be independent of the dimensions of the electron; all structure-dependent effects vanish. This equation, $mx'' = F$, becomes complicated by the addition of a term depending on the third derivative of x. The complete equation is

$$-\frac{2}{3}\frac{x'''e^2}{c^3} + mx'' = F$$

where e is the electron's charge, and c the velocity of light.

Well, the physicists of this day (and this is a half century ago) said, "The mass of the electron is known. It is not infinite. I will put in the right mass." This is the term $-\frac{2}{3}x'''e^2/c^3$ which seems to be truly independent of how this charge is distributed, if the distribution is small enough. This has the effect of slowing up an electron which is accelerated. It turns out to have just the effect of taking away from the motion of the electron the energy which the electron must radiate when it is in agitated motion, as an electron in any radio antenna behaves. Now the only point that I want to make about this equation—and believe me, though it may look complicated, it is easy compared to what is coming—the only point that I want to make is the following: If you forget this term, then there are solutions which tell you that if there is a force, the object is accelerated; and, if there is no force, then the only solution is a straight line motion; this is what Newton said. If there is no force acting, the body should move in a straight line, and the electron does that. If you put this term $-\frac{2}{3}x'''e^2/c^3$ in as a correction, there is no correction, because the third derivative of the coordinate is zero for a body moving in a straight line. That is correct. But if you get smart and say, "I can solve this equation," then there are solutions of the form,

$$x = x_0 \exp(t/T).$$

So that means an electron will exponentially accelerate itself; T equals $2e^2/3mc^3$. It is a very short time, about 10^{-23} seconds.

People have coped with this paradox in a variety of ways, but the obvious answer is that that equation was not meant to be treated that way. If you treat this term as a correction, it never does you any harm; it is small for most motions and it agrees with experiment when you try it out. But if you take it completely seriously you get an answer which permits a kind of motion that does not appear in real life. This is a first sign of the fact that the theory of the electron works only when you regard the charge on the electron as it is in fact, as a rather small quantity. I should just point out that the denominator, T, is proportional to e^2, and I will show you another one like that later.

In order to get on at all with the theory of the electron, great reforms had to be made, and were made, in Newtonian-Maxwellian physics. The first of these was the special theory of relativity which, starting with the idea that signals cannot be transmitted faster than light, redefined the notion of simultaneity and the measurements of interval of space and time; showed that a moving object does its stuff more slowly than an object at rest, merely by virtue of being in motion; showed that the mass of a body, the inertia of a body, increased with its energy content and so led to the $E = mc^2$ of Einstein; showed that the definitions of simultaneity, length, and interval all depend on relative uniform motion; and established the fact that the phenomena of nature are the same in (are uninfluenced by) uniform motion, that they will be the same irrespective of whether you see something in uniform motion or not. The theory of relativity took over from Newton most of his laws of motion, but with some modification.

This is the first of those great conservative traits in electron theory which I want to point out. The most important of Newton's laws—the conservation of momentum, the fact that a body not acted on by a force has its velocity and its momentum preserved, the fact that action and reaction are equal and opposite—these were not altered by the special theory of relativity. Only the connection between the acceleration and the velocity, only the relations between mass and velocity, were altered.

That was one great change in the earlier years of the century. The other is harder to describe briefly. It is much deeper; it is very important. This second great change was the discovery of the true nature of atomic mechanics, a discovery which, in some ways, shattered both the Newtonian and Maxwellian framework very much more deeply than relativity. This was the discovery both of the quantum of action and the place of the quantum in the description of atomic systems. The history is a very long one; but we can summarize it by reminding you that it was a resolution of the dual character of light: the character of light as a wave motion, as Maxwell said it was and as we know from everyday experience, with interference on the radio and all the rest of it; and the character of light as always involving a corpuscular discrete exchange of energy and momentum between light and matter in phenomena where they interact.

Einstein discovered the light quanta in the same year that he discovered the special theory of relativity; and twenty years later a way of reconciling this duality was made, not only for light, but for all objects, for all matter, for electrons, for everything else. It is a very practical thing, the wave character of the electron. It is not only necessary for understanding atoms, but it is directly related to the kind of bonding that occurs in organic molecules which seems to us so inescapable a precondition for life itself. The wave character of the proton is what enables it to get into nuclei in the sun and in the other stars and keeps them shining. The wave character of the neutron is what makes it possible to build reactors with materials available on earth and have them react. This pervades all of nature as we know it.

Perhaps the simplest way to summarize what this revolution was, is to say that on the one hand it established a relation between the dynamical description of objects, an electron you may think of, and the waves associated with them. If you have any body—it might be a house, but it should not be because it would not be very interesting, but an electron is a good example—if you have anything and it has an energy content E, then this would be related to the frequency, v, of the wave representing the situation by the relation of $E = hv$, where h is Planck's constant; and, if the momentum is P, that will be related to the wave number, K, of the wave by this simple relation, $P = hK$, where again h is Planck's constant. So you have a code of translation from the description in terms of particles to the description in terms of waves.

This code leads to a very basic point: there are a variety of ways of exploring and objectifying the state of an electron in nature and some of them are exclusive of others. An attempt to make a wave which is very much localized (therefore to know that the electron is in a small region of space) will interfere with the use of limited ranges of wave numbers or momenta. Formally one gets that the lack of definition in the coordinate of an electron Δx, and the lack of definition of momentum ΔP, have a product which cannot be smaller than this constant h.

$$\Delta x \Delta P \geqq h.$$

The equation concerning energy we shall need to use later. We may say that in a time interval, Δt, the energy of a system cannot be defined better than is given by this relation:

$$\Delta t \Delta E \geqq h.$$

If you want a definition of energy better than this ΔE you must take the time longer than this Δt.

This is a very rough way of talking about the wave mechanics, but it must suffice to get us on. I need to remind you that on the basis of a little bit of relativity and a lot of atomic mechanics most of the physical and chemical properties of ordinary matter and a great deal of the properties of nuclei too (composed of neutrons and protons), have found an orderly explanation—not always a complete one, because things can be too complicated to work out, but one which we believe is, in principle, adequate. So that the whole of physics for the last 30 years has been directed towards questions more or less exclusively evoked by doing abnormal things with matter rather than by simply observing its normal behavior.

And how is that? It is many different things. But, for one thing, these relations $\Delta x \Delta P \geqq h$ and $\Delta t \Delta E \geqq h$, and Einstein's relation $E = mc^2$, together give you another code of translation; and that code says that there is a relation between length and time on the one hand and energy and momentum on the other. A time can be connected with an energy by the relation $T = h/E$, and with a mass by the relation $T = h/E = h/mc^2$. A length can be connected with a mass by the relation $L = h/P = h/mc$. And what that means is that if you wish to study the finer structure, in space or in time, of matter, you will be led to use very high energy or very massive particles. But, if you wish to study very massive particles, you will need a lot of energy; if you want to explore smaller and smaller regions of space, you will have high energies to deal with. And this is, of course, the reason for the overwhelming importance of accelerators and cosmic rays in this aspect of the progress of physics.

In all of this development of atomic mechanics, there has been a trait of conservatism and a use of the idea of analogy similar to those that I mentioned in relativity. Things like these—limits on the accuracy with which you can define position or momentum of particles, dualisms between waves and particles and so on—sound very radical. But, throughout, there has been first a principle and then a discovery that in all situations in which it is all right to use a picture of waves, the Maxwellian description of these waves (or whatever one had in classical physics) shall not be monkeyed with. It is right. Wherever it is right to use a Newtonian picture of an orbit, that orbit will be followed. It is only when one has a situation where these ideas do not apply that one cannot use the classical formal laws. And it is true that all the laws of quantum theory, esthetically and in symbols, are very much like the classical laws that they supersede. This trait of conservatism, this use of analogy, is what has made atomic physics so rapidly a success. It is a revolutionary business; I am not playing that down; but it is only revolutionary at one point. It is revolutionary only at this point regarding the duality of waves and particles. It takes everything else more or less as it finds it and preserves it, and it has led to some really astonishing successes.

The question, then, is what happens when you take this new machine, the quantum theory, the wave particle duality on the one hand and relativity on the other, and you put some of the old questions about the electron itself. You think that you would like to understand the motion of electrons in external fields; you would like to understand their behavior; you would like to understand how they emit radiation and all the rest of it. That is the electron theory, which has come to be a great success, and of which I wanted to talk.

There are two basic processes. They do not always occur, but given the right circumstances they will occur. One of them is very familiar and one of them is very unfamiliar. The familiar process is that by which an electron, if it is not moving uniformly, will give out some radiation. This is what happens to electrons in antennae when you get radio waves; it is what happens when electrons are stopped by the electric fields surrounding the nuclei in the target of an x-ray tube, and you get the x-rays from it; it is a very well studied thing. I just have to indicate that there is something (F) to accelerate the electron (e) or change its motion in order to give the γ-ray (γ)

$$F + e \rightarrow \gamma \text{ (Process 1)}.$$

This is different from the electrodynamics of 1900 only in that we know that these γ-rays have their corpuscular property, and some of the detailed rules for the rate at which this process happens correspondingly change.

The other process was really a new one when it was discovered twenty years ago; it is typical of the wave character of electrons that it should occur. In this process, we have a γ-ray plus some kind of electromagnetic field. They do something that was not anticipated. They produce two things, an electron and a positive electron or positron. The two are called a pair.

$$\gamma + F \rightarrow e^- + e^+ \text{ (Process 2)}.$$

These particles (electron and positron) are identical except in the sign of their charge. The fact that the laws of physics should allow a positive electron is not new; that is true of classical physics as it is of the physics of this century. The fact that this will happen, this materialization process, is a pretty direct consequence of rather general things, of relativity, and of the wave particle duality of quantum theory. I know of no description which satisfies the requirements that nothing travels faster than light, which satisfies the rules of the quantum theory, and which has in it light and electrons that does not make this process a necessary thing. It has not been proved that no such theory exists, because that would be a kind of hard thing to prove, but I have never seen one and it has been tried for a long time to devise one. This pair production was a theoretical prediction which the theorists who made it were somewhat reluctant to believe until the positive electron was discovered. It was discovered in the cosmic rays by Anderson and immediately gave an immense stimulus to electron theory.

These two processes, as they occur in nature, give rise to one of the phenomena which Carlson studied with success and great interest. The cosmic rays are many things: they have a mysterious origin, and they are interesting for all sorts of reasons; but a very great part of their interest is that they are a wonderful source of radiation of high energy, energy which may go up to a hundred thousand times, or even a million times, the energies now available in accelerators and may go even higher than that. So that if a phenomenon depends on having a lot of energy available, the cosmic rays are a good place to look for it.

Now let us see what happens if we have an electron and it comes somewhere near the nucleus of an atom where there are strong electric fields. It will be accelerated, and in the course of that it will give off a γ-ray, and then the electron will go on with a little less energy. But now if the γ-ray comes near the nucleus of another atom it will make a pair, an electron and positron pair; and one of these may come near another atom and give off another γ-ray [see Fig. 70–3].

Carlson and I worked on this a little and found that this distance d is not very long. On the average it is about a quarter of an inch of lead, something like that, or only about a foot of water. Not very big distances are involved. These multiplicative processes were found in cosmic rays. In fact they had been there all along. One was shy about saying what they were. They are really impressive. The very high-energy ones spread in the air. There may be at one time a million of these things in one event. They may cover a part of a square mile in distance while building up this enormous multiplicative event which is called a cascade or shower. And this is a kind of vivid demonstration of the elementary action of the radiation of light (γ-rays) by an electron, and the conversion of light into electron pairs, one after the other, in different events.

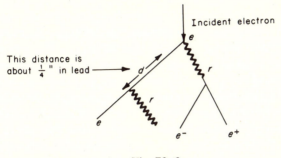

Fig. 70–3.

Part of the importance of this finding of Carlson's was that one saw these cascades in the cosmic rays and was sure that this was largely a correct theory. Carlson had worried a good deal about whether the quantum theory of electrons in radiation was correct at all, because in the cosmic rays there are many particles that do not radiate. They just go straight along and do not multiply at all; they penetrate through lots of lead. There are other particles that do quite different things. So very grave doubt was cast on the correctness of these theoretical ideas. But our doubts were largely resolved (and since have been even more resolved) when we saw that there were things that behaved just this way and really quantitatively just this way.

One of the important points, then, is that because of that certitude and because, in the cosmic rays, there were things which did not behave this way, which did not multiply, which did not give cascades, one knew that there were other particles in the cosmic rays than the familiar ingredients of matter. And that started a search and a period of discovery which has been accelerating and has been of most extraordinary vigor in the last years; so that, at the moment, we have some two dozen elementary particles, most of them radioactive and unstable, all of them transmuting one into the other when they collide, though not without some inhibitions. They all transmute into something, but they do not all transmute into everything. These discoveries appear to be taking us very close indeed to the elements of the subatomic world, to the actual atoms of which matter is made. This development is one of the by-products of the theory of cascade showers. Some of these objects, not electrons, are quite inert and are connected with electrons only by incredibly weak forces so that transitions occur very slowly indeed. Most of them, on the other hand, have very strong interactions with each other, which make the transitions occur rapidly and make their production and their destruction very common events. There are forces in nature enormously weaker than electric forces and there are forces very much stronger than electric forces. Electric forces and electron theory appear to occupy a middle ground.

The success of the theory of the electron, basing itself on these elementary reactions, with a quantitative and relatively straightforward way of describing how often and under what conditions they happen, led to at least two attempts at an analogous theory. One was Fermi's theory to describe the radioactivity of nucleons. The simplest example, though it was not originally an example, is that the neutron is radioactive. It produces a proton, an electron, and another little object which is called a neutrino and is hard to find. Fermi made the theory of this in exact analogy to the transition of an electron from one state to another, electrons being accelerated and in the process a γ-ray appearing. Instead of the process

$$e_{\text{state 1}} \rightarrow e_{\text{state 2}} + \gamma,$$

he said a neutron goes into a proton and in the process an electron plus a neutrino appears:

$$N \rightarrow P + (e + \nu).$$

He initially made the theory formally very similar. It turned out, with rather minor modifications, that this gives a powerful and helpful description of the phenomena of radioactivity; its connection with many other problems in physics has remained an indigestible question.

The Japanese physicist Yukawa made an even more daring and, as we shall see, not so totally successful analogy to electron theory. He said, "There are these strong forces, which hold nuclear matter together, forces from neutrons interacting with protons, neutrons with neutrons and so on. They are very strong; they have very short range and, when momentum goes from one particle to the other, this very often involves an exchange of charge between one particle and the other." He said, "I know that if this were electrodynamics there would be a field of force stretching from one electron to the other. This field would correspond to the wave aspect of light quanta which go from one electron to the other. The quanta that go from one nucleon to another may be charged and that would account for this phenomenon of charge exchange. If they were heavy, that would explain the fact that nuclear forces do not act over a big distance but have a range." Thus, he would point to the formula $\Delta t \Delta E \gtrsim h$, and he would say that an object of mass M has an energy Mc^2 and can last a time certainly not greater than h/Mc^2, because that is the uncertainty relation. It can travel certainly no greater distance than hc/Mc^2. Then

$$R = hc/Mc^2 = h/Mc$$

should be the relation between the range (R) of the forces and the mass of the particles that are associated with the field. He did say this, and he said a few more things, and some very great truths have been in this theory; it has occupied physicists for a long time. In this complex analogy that Yukawa made between the forces between nucleons due to these new particles (which are called mesons) and the forces between electrons due to light quanta, Yukawa was trying to keep the theories formally as similar as possible.

But before one can really get into that, we had better say a few words about some of the things that have happened to electron theory. Because, as of the turn of the century, it was not free of some contradictions and some troubles. If an electron can emit γ-radiation, then, when an electron is just standing around, it will not free that γ-radiation because there is no source for the energy. It is not accelerated or anything. But it will emit γ-radiation and then reabsorb it, and the time will just be about h times the reciprocal of the energy of the γ-ray. If a γ-ray can make pairs, it will not do so when it is just traveling through free space and there is nothing for it to hit. But part of the time it will exist in the form, not of a γ-ray but of a pair of electrons, electron and positron. Those electrons, in turn, will sometimes be accompanied by secondary γ-rays and those γ-rays sometimes in turn by secondary pairs. This sounds terrible; but fortunately each step in the process is less and less probable and by about a factor of 1000, because the number, e^2/hc, which measures the relative probability of these various steps in the sequence, is about one-thousandth. That means that it is only one-thousandth as probable that you find two γ-rays around an electron as that you find one, and it is only a thousandth as probable that you will find one as you find none.

Still, these complications have two kinds of consequences. One is that, if you want to talk about the real world, you ought to talk about the electron with its family, all its γ-rays and pairs and all the rest, and ask what they do. And this turned out to be very important since the family changes the properties of the electrons a little. It changes its magnetic properties and changes the energy levels of the simplest systems; such as hydrogen (an electron in the field of a proton) or positronium (the system made up of one positive and one negative electron, twice the size of the hydrogen atom, behaving very much like the hydrogen atom). These changes were discovered experimentally in the years after the war, and are just a description of the altered character of the electron because of these virtual cascades that go on all the time. So it is also with light. The properties of light itself in the free world, when it is all by itself, are not altered; but the properties of light in its interaction with matter, with charges, the properties of light which make it shake off pairs when two light quanta collide, are altered. This is one reason for wanting to give a description of these interactions. The changes are, of course, small because the charge is small.

The other reason is the following: we had made electron theory for a long time but we had always been rather careful not to make it too well. We had calculated how often something would happen and we had done it roughly, and then we had not made corrections for all these complications that I have just outlined. The reason we did not make corrections is that each correction, though it had a small coefficient (e^2/hc), also had a large coefficient which was multiplied into it and which was, in general, infinite. It was infinite, because, although the effects of γ-rays on electrons and of electrons on γ-rays are small for any given γ-ray, if you go to γ-rays of infinitely high frequency, if you consider more and more small-scale disturbances, these effects add up and accumulate to an infinite amount.

A discovery was made about eight years ago, a very beautiful one. It was this: there are two kinds of phenomena; the kind of phenomena which depend in a sensitive way on the behavior of electrons and γ-rays for arbitrarily high frequency, arbitrarily small space-time phenomena; and those which are relatively insensitive. The only two which depend on the high-frequency behavior, which is the root behavior in the very small spaces, very short times, are the charge of the electron and its mass; and these are the things that are infinitely affected by those phenomena, very much as in the classical theory of Lorentz. And physicists then said, "Good, we will give up this attempt. We cannot calculate the mass of the electron. It would be meaningless anyway in a theory in which there are no other particles, because we could give meaning only to its ratio to the mass of something else. We would like to calculate the charge; we would like to calculate that number one in a thousand; but we will give that up too. These things we will measure; then everything else will be given by the theory in a finite way." So they said; and this is what is called the renormalization program. It has the double purpose of translating from a description of an electron with none of its cloud and company of γ-rays and electrons around it to the description of the electron as it really is, and to do the same for the γ-ray; and, at the same time, of removing from the description those features (namely, the mass and charge) which would come out infinite and which are nonsensical.

A basic idea behind renormalization is that electrodynamics cannot be the whole story. But if you try instead to modify electrodynamics in other ways (and it has been tried many different times and many different ways), to say that for very small regions of space and time things will be different, it is very hard to make such a modification (lacking any real knowledge of the physics of that region) which is even formally consistent with the requirements of good sense, of causality, of the continued existence of matter, of complementarity, and the rest of it.

The renormalized theory has been very successful. It is the theory which has made it possible to predict the levels of hydrogen to a part in ten billion, to do very well with the spectrum of positronium, and to give a very accurate account of phenomena at ordinary energies. The reason for the success is that one can do the corrections for the additional electrons and γ-rays, step by step, expanding always to take more and more complicated situations; and each step is much smaller than the one that came before, maybe some hundred times smaller.

At very very high energies this convergence is not so good any more and that has been known a long time. People have had the curiosity, the morbidity, to ask, "Well, suppose that I do not do this step by step, suppose I try to do the whole thing. I might like to do that because, if I could get rid of this expansion, I might even get some insight into the value of the constant, e^2/hc. I could say how things would behave even if it were a large constant." And there a very odd thing has turned up. It has turned out that for ordinary phenomena one can probably get things accurate to one part in ten to the fiftieth or something like that, and at energies as high as the highest cosmic-ray energies one still is almost certainly making no appreciable mistake in the discussion of electrodynamic things with electron theory. Nevertheless, if one tries to do it just a little bit better and get it exact, and get it so that it holds at all energies, then the theory seems to turn out to have no meaning whatever.

In fact, in all efforts so far, it predicts something like this: that the electron should have another state, another configuration with a mass which is negative and is enormously negative,

$$m' \sim -m \exp(hc/2e^2).$$

The exponent is about five hundred; you might say that sounds pretty bad. But it is not only that the mass is negative and enormous—this alone would be bothersome; but whenever this state occurs, it occurs in such a way that, if something goes into that state, it increases the probability of things going into other states. So we are producing more and more electrons and more and more phenomena whenever we have a collision or whenever anything occurs. This is just another way of saying utter nonsense; it is utter nonsense of rather the same kind that we ran into with the Lorentz theory (and the Dirac modification of the Lorentz theory) of an electron. One has pushed the theory too far. One has pushed it to the point where it is saying to us, "I am not logically consistent.* You have left out something and that has made a hole in me, which I show, although I cannot say what belongs in the hole."

What belongs in the hole, of course, is all the rest of the world. It is those weak interactions which occur in β decay, it is those strong interactions, and those 24 different kinds of particles which may some day be 30 or 40 or even an infinite number, which appear in the great laboratory of the cosmic rays. It is all the rest of physics, which is not very closely tied in, and which leaves electrodynamics and electron theory an almost perfect, but not a perfect subject.

The analogies, especially Yukawa's analogy, have not fared so well. The reason is not because his quanta have a mass and his quanta have a charge. The primary reason is that his analogue of the number e^2/hc is not small at all but very large; and therefore, in this situation, the nucleon is very often accompanied, not by one meson but by several. These things cannot be treated as corrections; and the fact that they cannot be summed, that one cannot treat them in any other way than as corrections, means that one does not have in a strict sense much of a theory at all. However, it has been possible, with a good deal of sophistication, to use this analogy, together with a good deal of experimental information, to coordinate phenomena of scattering, of meson production, and of nuclear interactions— those phenomena which occur for mesons of rather low energy (comparable with the meson rest energy μc^2) and those phenomena which have to do with internuclear forces at rather large distances (comparable with the meson Compton wavelength, $h/\mu c$).

This is a first and very modest step in the beginnings of sorting out the new physics. These 24 particles are there, and, as I said, there are perhaps more. They have very odd properties. They were wholly unexpected. The theory of Yukawa, which was supposed to tie together a few of them— certain mesons and the nucleons—would, if it were true, cover only a very small subsection of the field. It does not cover that except in a more and more limited area. This subsection is not separate from the rest of the field as electron theory is from most things. It is clear that we are in for one of the very difficult, probably very heroic, and at least thoroughly unpredictable revolutions in physical understanding and physical theory. . . .

Through all of this story there has gone a theme of the use of analogy

---

* The question of the consistency of electrodynamics, or perhaps more realistically, the nature of the inconsistency of electrodynamics, has continued to occupy attention during the past two years. It is not definitely or rigorously settled.

in building physical theory: the analogy between Newton's laws and the laws of relativity, the analogy between Newton's laws and the laws of atomic physics, the analogy between Maxwell's waves and the waves of quantum physics, the analogy between Fermi's theory of β decay and the quantum theory of radiation, between Yukawa's theory of mesons and nuclear forces and the quantum theory of the electron.

Over and over again, we have used formal analogies. This is not strange. We are trying always to feel our way into something new and unexperienced. We take into it what we have, which is our own experience, in this case of the physical world, and we seek a relevant pattern of form and order. Number plays a part in the expression of this, but is not essential to it; the notion of analogy is deeper than the notion of formulae, though not deeper perhaps than all parts of mathematics. These analogies are sometimes right and sometimes wrong. Analysis, the confrontation of the full logical consequences of what it is that we have asserted with what we have learned to observe, is the final arbiter of whether the analogy is right and how far it is right. It determines the truth of the conjecture. But, without the analogy, there would be no conjecture, no way to go into a new field.

You have, in entering novelty, to use what you know. You would not be able to make meaningful mistakes without analogy. You would not be able to try things out, the failure of which was interesting. You start thinking by the use of analogy. Analogy is not the criterion of truth; it is an instrument of creation, and the sign of the effort of human minds to cope with something novel, something fresh, something unexpected. Analogies play, in the relation between sciences, a very great part, sometimes a harmful one; and they also play a decisive part in what little there is that natural science can teach of general use in general human experience.

One of the great things of this century is how illuminating and relevant the experience of the quantum theory, of complementarity, has been; how wide the scope of those analogies; I think for our children it will be better understood. What am I speaking of? The uncertainty in the position of an electron can be very small, the uncertainty in its momentum can be very small, but no experiment, no situation, can be devised which makes them both very small at the same time. This means that the physicist, or anybody else, has some choice as to what he is going to look at in a system, what he is going to realize. Is he going to realize a positioned electron or an electron which has a well-defined velocity and wavelength? He can do one or the other but they are complementary in the sense that there is no piece of equipment which will do both for him. He cannot realize them both together; one says that they are complementary situations.

But life is full of that, of course. We all know it in the relations between our acts and our introspection, our thinking about our acts. Hamlet has said it better than Planck's constant. We know it in the difference between, in the inherent inability fully to combine, the ideals of love and the ideals of justice. They are just about two different things; balance between them, yes, but fulfillment of both simultaneously, I think we know that that is not possible. We know it in the difference between a piece of knowledge, a piece of equipment, or a man regarded on the one hand as an instrument and on the other hand as an end or a purpose or an object; the difference between the inevitable and universal transcience of events and their eternal and timeless quality. This is part of life; and it is simply a rich set of analogies to the rather sharply defined, nonambiguous, straightforward complementarity that one found in the heart of the atom.

So it is I think, also, for the electron theory. All of life has both its aspects, being complete in itself and referring outside itself. Closure and openness are with us all the time. Here is this quite beautiful theory, perhaps one of the most perfect, most accurate, and most lovely that man has discovered. We have external proof, but above all internal proof, that it has only a finite range, that it does not describe everything that it pretends to describe. The range is enormous, but internally the theory is telling us, "Do not take me absolutely or seriously. I have some relation to a world that you are not talking about when you are talking about me." This is a kind of rebuke, of course, to anyone who believes that any specialty can wholly exhaust life or its meaning. . . .

71

oooooooooo

COMPLEMENTARITY

ooooooooooo

Niels Bohr (1885-1962)

Quantum mechanics, the modern picture of matter and energy, has evolved from a number of apparently contradictory theories. In 1924, De Broglie, who initiated the new developments, indicated quite clearly that particles such as electrons have wave properties that can be described in terms of wavelengths and frequencies related to their momenta and Planck's constant of action. Schroedinger subsequently developed the wave equation for a particle, the solution of which gives its possible states of energy, and allows one to follow the motion of the particle to within certain limits of accuracy. Born then demonstrated that the waves associated with a particle as obtained from the solution of the Schroedinger equation, must be interpreted as probability amplitudes for finding the particle in a given region of space at any given moment. Thus, a particle appears to behave like a wave in the sense that one has to associate with its motion a probability amplitude that obeys a wave equation. In spite of this probability interpretation, one must still speak of a particle as having an *actual* wave character. This led to apparent paradoxes that persuaded Einstein to question very seriously the entire foundation of quantum mechanics and to doubt that it could give a complete description of nature. We propose to discuss how these paradoxes arose, as well as how they were resolved by Bohr in terms of still another approach to quantum mechanics.

While De Broglie and Schroedinger were developing the wave mechanics, Born, Heisenberg, Dirac, and Jordan were approaching the problem from an entirely different point of view, as we have seen in previous chapters. They showed that the emission and absorption of quanta of energy, or photons, by electrons is comprehensible only if the position of an electron and its momentum are treated as operators instead of ordinary numbers. These quantities obey a different kind of algebra from that of ordinary numbers: an algebra, as we have noted, that is noncommutative, whereby the product of momentum and position differs from that of position and momentum.

Born and his collaborators proved that the difference between these two products is proportional to Planck's constant of action *h,* a discovery that led to matrix mechanics. Matrix mechanics gives correct descriptions of the energy states of an electron inside an atom as does Schroedinger's wave equation. Although first Schroedinger and later Dirac showed that these two descriptions are equivalent, with differences attributable only to the varying points of view of the observers, there still appeared to be an inherent contradiction between the theories, since, on the one hand, the De Broglie-Schroedinger picture describes the electron as a wave, while matrix mechanics treats electrons as particles, describing their dynamic behavior with a new kind of algebra. The following questions then arose: Is a particle really a particle or is it a wave? And if it can be both particle and wave, when is it one and when the other? The same question, of course, arose in connection with the photon picture of radiation; here, too, one can ask whether one is dealing with particles or waves. We shall now see how Bohr approached this problem and resolved the paradox by using Heisenberg's important discovery.

Heisenberg was the first to recognize that the need for noncommutative algebra to treat the momentum and position of a particle implies, in Bohr's words, a "peculiar indeterminacy" associated with these quantities. As Heisenberg pointed out, this indeterminacy arises because of the quantum of action; if we wish to determine the position of an electron by detecting it with a photon, the interaction between the electron and the photon must involve an action interchange that cannot be smaller than Planck's constant *h*; hence, the electron's momentum is uncertain by an amount obtained by dividing *h* by the uncertainty in the position of the electron. This is Heisenberg's uncertainty principle, already discussed in Chapter 66.

It is clear from elementary considerations that an uncertainty principle implies certain wave aspects of a particle. For if we have a wavelength λ, then the uncertainty in the position of the wave packet cannot be smaller than λ. The uncertainty principle then tells us that there must be a momentum associated with the packet that equals Planck's constant *h* divided by λ. This is exactly the relationship between the wavelength and the momentum of a particle that De Broglie discovered. Consequently, the uncertainty principle indicates that we may consider a particle as a wave packet.

The wave picture also tells us that there is an uncertainty relationship associated with the energy of a particle and the time required to measure the energy. If we wish to measure the frequency of a wave, the uncertainty in this measurement cannot be less than the reciprocal of the time allotted for the measurement. Using Planck's simple formula relating energy to frequency, this means that the uncertainty in the energy of a particle multiplied by the time duration of the measurement cannot be smaller than Planck's constant of action.

We come now to the nature of the paradox that bedeviled quantum mechanics in its early years; it was the subject of many penetrating and profound discussions between Einstein and Bohr. At issue was a problem best illustrated by the behavior of a beam of electrons passing through a screen with two holes in it and then striking a second screen. If each electron is treated as a plane wave, then when this wave passes through the two holes, two new spherical waves move away from the screen on the other side (one from each hole), and these two waves then interfere with one another to give the typical wave interference pattern on the second screen where the electrons are recorded. This pattern is present regardless of how weak the electron beam is, and that is, even though the electrons hit the recording screen at widely separated time intervals. Eventually, the pattern is enhanced as more and more electrons hit the screen and the interference pattern becomes more and more clearly defined. The remarkable thing is that the wave interference pattern is present even though each electron strikes a single definite point on the second screen and is recorded there as a particle.

This state of affairs appears to hold the following inherent contradiction: We start out with a set of initial conditions which can be stated quite unambiguously in the usual classical terms: particles (electrons) are emitted by a source (let us say, a cathode) in a given direction, pass through two holes in a screen, and then are recorded as particles on a screen. In principle, we could determine the initial position and momentum of each electron, with an accuracy governed by the Heisenberg uncertainty principle. And we know the position of each electron at the end of the experiment since it strikes a point on the recording screen. In other words, our description of the experiment at its beginning and end is given in classical terms, but no such description can be given concerning the behavior of the particles between the beginning and end of the experiment. Thus, it is impossible to follow the detailed motion of a particle from its beginning to its end, and to say through which hole in the first screen the particle passed, and at the same time to obtain an interference pattern. In other words if we are to obtain an interference pattern, we must give up the possibility of giving a complete description of the motion of the particles.

This seeming paradox led Einstein to reject the ability of quantum mechanics to give a complete description of physical phenomena. Einstein believed that quantum mechanics was a statistical description of nature, that it could refer only to a collection of particles, and could not be the ultimate answer to the motion of a single particle. He felt that physicists would in time find some way to describe completely the behavior of a single particle and that such a description would go beyond the quantum-mechanical or wave description.

Einstein presented a number of idealized experiments to be analyzed, in order to ascertain whether it might be possible to obtain a more complete description than wave mechanics could give. For example, in the case of the electrons passing through the two holes in the screen, Einstein argued that a careful analysis of the momentum transferred to the screen by the electron should tell us through which hole the electron had passed, and that this would enable us to predict where on the recording screen the electron would land. This would provide more information than is derived from quantum mechanics. In the same way Einstein proposed other experiments, such as that of weighing a box containing radiation before and after allowing a small amount of the radiant energy to leave the box. In this way he proposes to determine the moment this energy left the box as well as determining the exact amount of energy that has left. This, too, would be more than quantum mechanics can tell us.

In this same article Bohr discusses another famous paper by Einstein, Podolsky, and Rosen that has had an important influence on the thinking of physicists since its publication in 1935. Here again Einstein and his collaborators question the completeness of the quantum-mechanical description of nature, and they analyze a simple experiment to illustrate their point. They consider two particles that come together, interact, and then separate. According to classical physics one should be able to determine or predict the position and momentum of either particle at any moment by observing the other particle and using the conservation principles. The situation is different, however, in quantum mechanics, because of the uncertainty principle (momentum and position do not commute).

Consider the position and momentum of each particle at any moment after they have collided and separated. Although the uncertainty principle tells us that we cannot measure simultaneously the position and momentum of either particle with infinite accuracy, we can show (using quantum mechanics) that the difference between the positions of the two particles and the sum of their momenta can be measured simultaneously as accurately as we please. If we measure the position of one of the particles, we can calculate the position of the other particle, but this precludes any knowledge about the momentum of the second particle. On the other hand, if we measure the momentum of the first particle we can determine the momentum of the second particle from our quantum-mechanical knowledge of the sum of the two momenta. In other words, even though the two particles have separated, our knowledge of the second particle still is determined by what measurement we make on the first particle.

To Einstein this meant that quantum mechanics does not give a complete description of nature, since it appears to introduce a mysterious connection between two particles that are no longer interacting. It is difficult to see how measuring something on one particle can determine what we can measure accurately on the other particle. Bohr analyzes this difficulty, again on the basis of his principle of complementarity.

The concept of the complementarity of physical quantities has played an important role in the development of the philosophy of modern physics and in the theory of measurement. Essentially, it tells us that there are always two complementary and mutually exclusive ways of looking at a physical phenomenon, depending on how we arrange our apparatus to measure the phenomenon. According to Bohr, when we deal with an electron, we must use both the wave picture and the particle picture; one is complementary to the other in the sense that the more our apparatus is designed to look for the electron as a particle, the less the electron behaves like a wave and vice versa.

Heisenberg himself has given a few examples to illustrate how the very process of measurement forces us to discard the classical deterministic approach to physics. Thus, classically it is entirely correct to speak of the precise orbit of a particle, but such descriptions must be rejected in quantum mechanics where it is meaningless to speak of an orbit, since we can never determine more than one point of an orbit at any time observationally. In the very process of pinpointing a particle by bouncing a γ-ray photon off it we knock the particle out of its orbit. γ-ray photons are required for accurate position measurements because they have very short wavelengths, but they are very energetic because of their high frequencies and thus strongly disturb the particle. Thus the orbit of a particle, which is its deterministic description since an orbit would enable us to predict where the particle is at any time in the future, is complementary to its space-time description (the space-time description means giving the position at a particular time).

Heisenberg also considered the flow of radiation through two holes in a screen. He pointed out that the wave description leading to the well-known interference pattern formed (when the radiation is collected on a photographic plate behind the two holes) is complementary to the photon description which would allow one to determine through which of the two holes each photon passes. Thus a wave picture precludes a detailed description of what happens to each photon between the beginning and the end of the experiment. As long as we wish to obtain an interference pattern, it is meaningless to ask through which of the holes any particular photon passes.

In each of the experiments outlined by Einstein, the challenge was taken up by Bohr, the great champion and spiritual leader of quantum mechanics. To answer Einstein, Bohr developed a remarkable generalization of quantum mechanics, which is referred to as the principle of complementarity, or the Copenhagen interpretation of the quantum theory. Bohr's analysis of Einstein's experiments occurred at a series of international meetings of world physicists; the paper that follows this commentary is a compendium of discussions with Einstein, which Bohr wrote for the volume of *Living Philosophers* that was dedicated to Einstein on his seventieth birthday.

In every case Bohr was able to show that, taking the Heisenberg uncertainty relations into account properly, the very conservation principles themselves (conservation of energy and of momentum) make a detailed space-time description of the particle between the beginning and the end of the experiment impossible, if we try to obtain an accurate picture of the energy-momentum interchange between the particle and the apparatus (the holes in the screen). On the other hand, any attempt to obtain an accurate space-time description destroys the possibility of obtaining, in Bohr's words, a "closer account as regards the balance of momentum and energy." Bohr pointed out that the complete description of an experiment must tell not only what happens to the particle we are studying but also must take into account the interaction of the particle and the apparatus. In the article that follows, Bohr says that the description of an experiment must take into account "the impossibility of any sharp separation between the behavior of atomic objects and the interaction with the measuring instruments which serve to define the conditions, under which the phenomena appear."

This interaction between the observed system and the observer's apparatus leads to Bohr's concept of complimentarity, according to which, to quote a passage from the paper that follows:

> . . . We are presented with the choice of *either* tracing the path of a particle *or* observing interference effects, which allows us to escape from the paradoxical necessity of concluding that the behaviour of an electron or photon should depend on the presence of a slit in the diaphragm through which it could be proved not to pass. We have here to do with a typical example of how the complementary phenomena appear under mutually exclusive experimental arrangements and are just faced with the impossibility, in the analysis of quantum effects, of drawing any sharp separation between an independent behaviour of atomic objects and their interaction with measuring instruments which serve to define the conditions under which the phenomena occur.

ᴑᴑᴑᴑᴑᴑᴑᴑ

B O H R

Discussion with Einstein on Epistemological Problems in Atomic Physics [1]

. . . THE MANY OCCASIONS THROUGH THE years on which I had the privilege to discuss with Einstein epistemological problems raised by the modern development of atomic physics have come back vividly to my mind and I have felt that I could hardly attempt anything better than to give an account of these discussions which, even if no complete concord has so far been obtained, have been of greatest value and stimulus to me. I hope also that the account may convey to wider circles an impression of how essential the open-minded exchange of ideas has been for the progress in a field where new experience has time after time demanded a reconsideration of our views.

From the very beginning the main point under debate has been the attitude to take to the departure from customary principles of natural philosophy characteristic of the novel development of physics which was initiated in the first year of this century by Planck's discovery of the universal quantum of action. This discovery, which revealed a feature of atomicity in the laws of nature going far beyond the old doctrine of the limited divisibility of matter, has indeed taught us that the classical theories of physics are idealizations which can be unambiguously applied only in the limit where all actions involved are large compared with the quantum. The question at issue has been whether the renunciation of a causal mode of description of atomic processes involved in the endeavours to cope with the situation should be regarded as a temporary departure from ideals to be ultimately revived or whether we are faced with an irrevocable step towards obtaining the proper harmony between analysis and synthesis of physical phenomena. To describe the background of our discussions and to bring out as clearly as possible the arguments for the contrasting viewpoints, I have felt it necessary to go to a certain length in recalling some

---

[1] Niels Bohr, in *Library of Living Philosophers,* VII (1949), pp. 201–241.

main features of the development to which Einstein himself has contributed so decisively.

As is well known, it was the intimate relation, elucidated primarily by Boltzmann, between the laws of thermodynamics and the statistical regularities exhibited by mechanical systems with many degrees of freedom, which guided Planck in his ingenious treatment of the problem of thermal radiation, leading him to his fundamental discovery. While, in his work, Planck was principally concerned with considerations of essentially statistical character and with great caution refrained from definite conclusions as to the extent to which the existence of the quantum implied a departure from the foundations of mechanics and electrodynamics, Einstein's great original contribution to quantum theory (1905) was just the recognition of how physical phenomena like the photo-effect may depend directly on individual quantum effects.* In these very same years, when, in developing his theory of relativity, Einstein laid a new foundation for physical science, he explored with a most daring spirit the novel features of atomicity which pointed beyond the whole framework of classical physics.

With unfailing intuition Einstein thus was led step by step to the conclusion that any radiation process involves the emission or absorption of individual light quanta or "photons" with energy and momentum

$$E = h\nu \quad \text{and} \quad P = h\sigma \tag{1}$$

conforming with the basic ideas of the quantum theory of atomic constitution. To this purpose, Einstein formulated general statistical rules regarding the occurrence of radiative transitions between stationary states, assuming not only that, when the atom is exposed to a radiation field, absorption as well as emission processes will occur with a probability per unit time proportional to the intensity of the irradiation, but that even in the absence of external disturbances spontaneous emission processes will take place with a rate corresponding to a certain *a priori* probability. Regarding the latter point, Einstein emphasized the fundamental character of the statistical description in a most suggestive way by drawing attention to the analogy between the assumptions regarding the occurrence of the spontaneous radiative transitions and the well-known laws governing transformations of radioactive substances.

In connection with a thorough examination of the exigencies of thermodynamics as regards radiation problems, Einstein stressed the dilemma still further by pointing out that the argumentation implied that any radiation process was "undirected" in the sense that not only is a momentum

---

* A. Einstein, *Ann. d. Phys.*, 17, 132 (1905).

corresponding to a photon with the direction of propagation transferred to an atom in the absorption process, but that also the emitting atom will receive an equivalent impulse in the opposite direction, although there can on the wave picture be no question of a preference for a single direction in an emission process. Einstein's own attitude to such startling conclusions is expressed in a passage at the end of article, which may be translated as follows:

> These features of the elementary processes would seem to make the development of a proper quantum treatment of radiation almost unavoidable. The weakness of the theory lies in the fact that, on the one hand, no closer connection with the wave concepts is obtainable and that, on the other hand, it leaves to chance (*Zufall*) the time and the direction of the elementary processes; nevertheless, I have full confidence in the reliability of the way entered upon.

When I had the great experience of meeting Einstein for the first time during a visit to Berlin in 1920, these fundamental questions formed the theme of our conversations. The discussions, to which I have often reverted in my thoughts, added to all my admiration for Einstein a deep impression of his detached attitude. Certainly, his favoured use of such picturesque phrases as "ghost waves (*Gespensterfelder*) guiding the photons" implied no tendency to mysticism, but illuminated rather a profound humour behind his piercing remarks. Yet, a certain difference in attitude and outlook remained, since, with his mastery for co-ordinating apparently contrasting experience without abandoning continuity and causality, Einstein was perhaps more reluctant to renounce such ideals than someone for whom renunciation in this respect appeared to be the only way open to proceed with the immediate task of co-ordinating the multifarious evidence regarding atomic phenomena, which accumulated from day to day in the exploration of this new field of knowledge.

In the following years, during which the atomic problems attracted the attention of rapidly increasing circles of physicists, the apparent contradictions inherent in quantum theory were felt ever more acutely. Illustrative of this situation is the discussion raised by the discovery of the Stern-Gerlach effect in 1922. On the one hand, this effect gave striking support to the idea of stationary states and in particular to the quantum theory of the Zeeman effect developed by Sommerfeld; on the other hand, as exposed so clearly by Einstein and Ehrenfest, it presented with unsurmountable difficulties any attempt at forming a picture of the behaviour of atoms in a magnetic field. Similar paradoxes were raised by the discovery by Compton (1924) of the change in wave-length accompanying the scattering of X-rays by electrons. This phenomenon afforded, as is well known, a most direct proof of the adequacy of Einstein's view regarding the transfer of energy and momentum in radiative processes; at the same time, it was equally clear that no simple picture of a corpuscular collision could offer an exhaustive description of the phenomenon. Under the impact of such difficulties, doubts were for a time entertained even regarding the conservation of energy and momentum in the individual radiation processes; a view, however, which very soon had to be abandoned in face of more refined experiments bringing out the correlation between the deflection of the photon and the corresponding electron recoil.

The way to the clarification of the situation was, indeed, first to be paved by the development of a more comprehensive quantum theory. A first step towards this goal was the recognition by de Broglie in 1925 that the wave-corpuscle duality was not confined to the properties of radiation, but was equally unavoidable in accounting for the behaviour of material particles. This idea, which was soon convincingly confirmed by experiments on electron interference phenomena, was at once greeted by Einstein, who had already envisaged the deep-going analogy between the properties of thermal radiation and of gases in the so-called degenerate state. The new line was pursued with the greatest success by Schrödinger (1926) who, in particular, showed how the stationary states of atomic systems could be represented by the proper solutions of a wave-equation to the establishment of which he was led by the formal analogy, originally traced by Hamilton, between mechanical and optical problems. Still, the paradoxical aspects of quantum theory were in no way ameliorated, but even emphasized, by the apparent contradiction between the exigencies of the general superposition principle of the wave description and the feature of individuality of the elementary atomic processes.

At the same time, Heisenberg (1925) had laid the foundation of a rational quantum mechanics, which was rapidly developed through important contributions by Born and Jordan as well as by Dirac. In this theory, a formalism is introduced, in which the kinematical and dynamical variables of classical mechanics are replaced by symbols subjected to a non-commutative algebra. Notwithstanding the renunciation of orbital pictures, Hamilton's canonical equations of mechanics are kept unaltered and Planck's constant enters only in the rules of commutation

$$qp - pq = \sqrt{-1}\ \frac{h}{2\pi} \qquad\qquad (2)$$

holding for any set of conjugate variables q and p. Through a representation of the symbols by matrices with elements referring to transitions between stationary states, a quantitative formulation of the correspondence principle became for the first time possible. It may here be recalled that an important preliminary step towards this goal was reached through the establishment, especially by contributions of Kramers, of a quantum theory of dispersion making basic use of Einstein's general rules for the probability of the occurrence of absorption and emission processes.

This formalism of quantum mechanics was soon proved by Schrödinger to give results identical with those obtainable by the mathematically often more convenient methods of wave theory, and in the following years general methods were gradually established for an essentially statistical description of atomic processes combining the features of individuality and the requirements of the superposition principle, equally characteristic of quantum theory. Among the many advances in this period, it may especially be mentioned that the formalism proved capable of incorporating the exclusion principle which governs the states of systems with several electrons, and which already before the advent of quantum mechanics had been derived by Pauli from an analysis of atomic spectra. The quantitative comprehension of a vast amount of empirical evidence could leave no doubt as to the fertility and adequacy of the quantum-mechanical formalism, but its abstract character gave rise to a widespread feeling of uneasiness. An elucidation of the situation should, indeed, demand a thorough examination of the very observational problem in atomic physics.

This phase of the development was, as is well known, initiated in 1927 by Heisenberg, who pointed out that the knowledge obtainable of the state of an atomic system will always involve a peculiar "indeterminacy." Thus, any measurement of the position of an electron by means of some device, like a microscope, making use of high frequency radiation, will, according to the fundamental relations (1), be connected with a momentum exchange between the electron and the measuring agency, which is the greater the more accurate a position measurement is attempted. In comparing such considerations with the exigencies of the quantum-mechanical formalism, Heisenberg called attention to the fact that the commutation rule (2) imposes a reciprocal limitation on the fixation of two conjugate variables, q and p, expressed by the relation

$$\Delta q \cdot \Delta p \approx h, \tag{3}$$

where Δq and Δp are suitably defined latitudes in the determination of these variables. In pointing to the intimate connection between the statistical description in quantum mechanics and the actual possibilities of measurement, this so-called indeterminacy relation is, as Heisenberg showed, most important for the elucidation of the paradoxes involved in the attempts of analyzing quantum effects with reference to customary physical pictures.

The new progress in atomic physics was commented upon from various sides at the International Physical Congress held in September 1927, at

Como in commemoration of Volta. In a lecture on that occasion, I advocated a point of view conveniently termed "complementarity," suited to embrace the characteristic features of individuality of quantum phenomena, and at the same time to clarify the peculiar aspects of the observational problem in this field of experience. For this purpose, it is decisive to recognize that, *however far the phenomena transcend the scope of classical physical explanation, the account of all evidence must be expressed in classical terms.* The argument is simply that by the word "experiment" we refer to a situation where we can tell others what we have done and what we have learned and that, therefore, the account of the experimental arrangement and of the results of the observations must be expressed in unambiguous language with suitable application of the terminology of classical physics.

This crucial point, which was to become a main theme of the discussions reported in the following, implies the *impossibility of any sharp separation between the behaviour of atomic objects and the interaction with the measuring instruments which serve to define the conditions under which the phenomena appear.* In fact, the individuality of the typical quantum effects finds its proper expression in the circumstance that any attempt of subdividing the phenomena will demand a change in the experimental arrangement introducing new possibilities of interaction between objects and measuring instruments which in principle cannot be controlled. Consequently, evidence obtained under different experimental conditions cannot be comprehended within a single picture, but must be regarded as *complementary* in the sense that only the totality of the phenomena exhausts the possible information about the objects.

Under these circumstances an essential element of ambiguity is involved in ascribing conventional physical attributes to atomic objects, as is at once evident in the dilemma regarding the corpuscular and wave properties of electrons and photons, where we have to do with contrasting pictures, each referring to an essential aspect of empirical evidence. . . . Any arrangement suited to study the exchange of energy and momentum between the electron and the photon must involve a latitude in the space-time description of the interaction sufficient for the definition of wave-number and frequency which enter into the relation (1). Conversely, any attempt [at] locating the collision between the photon and the electron more accurately would, on account of the unavoidable interaction with the fixed scales and clocks defining the space-time reference frame, exclude all closer account as regards the balance of momentum and energy.

As stressed in the lecture, an adequate tool for a complementary way of description is offered precisely by the quantum-mechanical formalism which represents a purely symbolic scheme permitting only predictions, on lines of the correspondence principle, as to results obtainable under conditions specified by means of classical concepts. It must here be remembered that even in the indeterminacy relation (3) we are dealing with an implication of the formalism which defies unambiguous expression in words suited to describe classical physical pictures. Thus, a sentence like "we cannot know both the momentum and the position of an atomic object" raises at once questions as to the physical reality of two such attributes of the object, which can be answered only by referring to the conditions for the unambiguous use of space-time concepts, on the one hand, and dynamical conservation laws, on the other hand. While the combination of these concepts into a single picture of a causal chain of events is the essence of classical mechanics, room for regularities beyond the grasp of such a description is just afforded by the circumstance that the study of the complementary phenomena demands mutually exclusive experimental arrangements.

The necessity, in atomic physics, of a renewed examination of the foundation for the unambiguous use of elementary physical ideas recalls in some way the situation that led Einstein to his original revision on the basis of [the] application of space-time concepts which, by its emphasis on the primordial importance of the observational problem, has lent such unity to our world picture. Notwithstanding [the] novelty of approach, causal description is upheld in relativity theory within any given frame of reference, but in quantum theory the uncontrollable interaction between the objects and the measuring instruments forces us to a renunciation even in such respect. This recognition, however, in no way points to any limitation of the scope of the quantum-mechanical description, and the trend of the whole argumentation presented in the Como lecture was to show that the viewpoint of complementarity may be regarded as a rational generalization of the very ideal of causality.

At the general discussion in Como, we all missed the presence of Einstein, but soon after, in October 1927, I had the opportunity to meet him in Brussels at the Fifth Physical Conference of the Solvay Institute, which was devoted to the theme "Electrons and Photons." At the Solvay meetings, Einstein had from their beginning been a most prominent figure, and several of us came to the conference with great anticipations to learn his reaction to the latest stage of the development which, to our view, went far in clarifying the problems which he had himself from the outset elicited so ingeniously. During the discussions, where the whole subject was reviewed by contributions from many sides and where also the arguments mentioned in the preceding pages were again presented, Einstein expressed, however, a deep concern over the extent to which causal account in space and time was abandoned in quantum mechanics.

To illustrate his attitude, Einstein referred at one of the sessions to the simple example, illustrated by [Fig. 71–1], of a particle (electron or photon) penetrating through a hole or a narrow slit in a diaphragm placed at some distance before a photographic plate. On account of the diffraction of the wave connected with the motion of the particle and indicated in the figure by the thin lines, it is under such conditions not possible to predict with certainty at what point the electron will arrive at the photographic plate, but only to calculate the probability that, in an experiment, the electron will be found within any given region of the plate. The apparent difficulty, in this description, which Einstein felt so acutely, is the fact that, if in the experiment the electron is recorded at one point A of the plate, then it is out of the question of ever observing an effect of this electron at another point (B), although the laws of ordinary wave propagation offer room for a correlation between two such events.

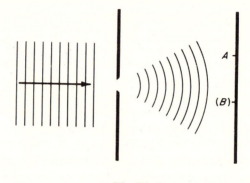

Fig. 71–1.

Einstein's attitude gave rise to ardent discussions within a small circle, in which Ehrenfest, who through the years had been a close friend of us both, took part in a most active and helpful way. Surely, we all recognized that, in the above example, the situation presents no analogue to the application of statistics in dealing with complicated mechanical systems, but rather recalled the background for Einstein's own early conclusions about the unidirection of individual radiation effects which contrasts so strongly with a simple wave picture. The discussions, however, centered on the question of whether the quantum-mechanical description exhausted the possibilities of accounting for observable phenomena or, as Einstein maintained, the analysis could be carried further and, especially, of whether a fuller description of the phenomena could be obtained by bringing into consideration the detailed balance of energy and momentum in individual processes.

To explain the trend of Einstein's arguments, it may be illustrative here to consider some simple features of the momentum and energy balance in connection with the location of a particle in space and time. For this purpose, we shall examine the simple case of a particle penetrating through a hole in a diaphragm without or with a shutter to open and close the hole, as indicated in [figs. 71–2 and 71–3], respectively. The equidistant parallel lines to the left in the figures indicate the train of plane waves corresponding to the state of motion of a particle which, before reaching the diaphragm, has a momentum P related to the wave-number σ by the second of equations (1). In accordance with the diffraction of the waves when passing through the hole, the state of motion of the particle to the right of the diaphragm is represented by a spherical wave train with a suitably defined angular aperture θ and, in case of [Fig. 71–3], also with a limited radial extension. Consequently, the description of this state involves a certain latitude Δp in the momentum component of the particle parallel to the diaphragm and, in the case of a diaphragm with a shutter, an additional latitude ΔE of the kinetic energy.

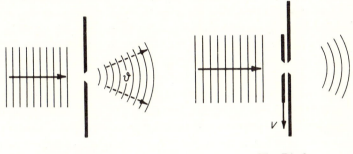

Fig. 71–2.   Fig. 71–3.

Since a measure for the latitude Δq in location of the particle in the plane of the diaphragm is given by the radius a of the hole, and since $\theta \approx (1/\sigma a)$, we get, using (1), just $\Delta p \approx \theta P \approx (h/\Delta q)$, in accordance with the indeterminacy relation (3). This result could, of course, also be obtained directly by noticing that, due to the limited extension of the wave-field at the place of the slit, the component of the wave-number parallel to the plane of the diaphragm will involve a latitude $\Delta \sigma \approx (1/a) \approx (1/\Delta q)$. Similarly, the spread of frequencies of the harmonic components in the limited wave-train in [Fig. 71–3] is evidently $\Delta \nu \approx (1/\Delta t)$, where Δt is the time interval during which the shutter leaves the hole open and, thus, represents the latitude in time of the passage of the particle through the diaphragm. From (1), we therefore get

$$\Delta E \cdot \Delta t \approx h, \tag{4}$$

again in accordance with the relation (3) for the two conjugated variables E and t.

From the point of view of the laws of conservation, the origin of such latitudes entering into the description of the state of the particle after passing through the hole may be traced to the possibilities of momentum and energy exchange with the diaphragm or the shutter. In the reference system considered in [figs. 71–2 and 71–3], the velocity of the diaphragm may be disregarded and only a change of momentum Δp between the particle and the diaphragm needs to be taken into consideration. The shutter, however, which leaves the hole opened during the time Δt, moves with a considerable velocity $v \approx (a/\Delta t)$, and a momentum transfer Δp involves therefore an energy exchange with the particle, amounting to $v\Delta p \approx (1/\Delta t)\, \Delta q\, \Delta p \approx (h/\Delta t)$, being just of the same order of magnitude as the latitude ΔE given by (4) and, thus, allowing for momentum and energy balance.

The problem raised by Einstein was now to what extent a control of the momentum and energy transfer, involved in a location of the particle in space and time, can be used for a further specification of the state of the particle after passing through the hole. Here, it must be taken into consideration that the position and the motion of the diaphragm and the shutter have so far been assumed to be accurately co-ordinated with the space-time reference frame. This assumption implies, in the description of the state of these bodies, an essential latitude as to their momentum and energy, which need not, of course, noticeably affect the velocities, if the diaphragm and the shutter are sufficiently heavy. However, as soon as we want to know the momentum and energy of these parts of the measuring arrangement with an accuracy sufficient to control the momentum and energy exchange with the particle under investigation, we shall, in accordance with the general indeterminacy relations, lose the possibility of their accurate location in space and time. We have, therefore, to examine how far this circumstance will affect the intended use of the whole arrangement and, as we shall see, this crucial point clearly brings out the complementary character of the phenomena.

Returning for a moment to the case of the simple arrangement indicated in [Fig. 71–1], it has so far not been specified to what use it is intended. In fact, it is only on the assumption that the diaphragm and the plate have well-defined positions in space that it is impossible, within the frame of the quantum-mechanical formalism, to make more detailed predictions as to the point of the photographic plate where the particle will be recorded. If, however, we admit a sufficiently large latitude in the knowledge of the position of the diaphragm it should, in principle, be possible to control the momentum transfer to the diaphragm and, thus, to make more detailed predictions as to the direction of the electron path from the hole to the recording point. As regards the quantum-mechanical description, we have to deal here with a two-body system consisting of the diaphragm as well as of the particle, and it is just with an explicit application of conservation laws to such a system that we are concerned in the Compton effect where, for instance, the observation of the recoil of the electron by means of a cloud chamber allows us to predict in what direction the scattered photon will eventually be observed.

The importance of considerations of this kind was, in the course of the discussions, most interestingly illuminated by the examination of an arrangement where between the diaphragm with the slit and the photographic plate is inserted another diaphragm with two parallel slits, as is shown in [Fig. 71–4]. If a parallel beam of electrons (or photons) falls from the left on the first diaphragm, we shall, under usual conditions, observe on the plate an interference pattern indicated by the shading of the photographic plate shown in front view to the right of the figure. With intense beams, this pattern is built up by the accumulation of a large num-

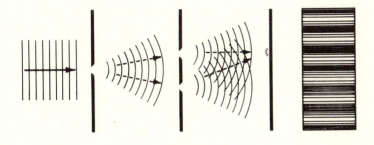

Fig. 71–4.

ber of individual processes, each giving rise to a small spot on the photographic plate, and the distribution of these spots follows a simple law derivable from the wave analysis. The same distribution should also be found in the statistical account of many experiments performed with beams so faint that in a single exposure only one electron (or photon) will arrive at the photographic plate at some spot shown in the figure as a small star. Since, now, as indicated by the broken arrows, the momentum transferred to the first diaphragm ought to be different if the electron was assumed to pass through the upper or the lower slit in the second diaphragm, Einstein suggested that a control of the momentum transfer would permit a closer analysis of the phenomenon and, in particular, to decide through which of the two slits the electron had passed before arriving at the plate.

A closer examination showed, however, that the suggested control of the momentum transfer would involve a latitude in the knowledge of the position of the diaphragm which would exclude the appearance of the interference phenomena in question. In fact, if ω is the small angle between the conjectured paths of a particle passing through the upper or the lower slit, the difference of momentum transfer in these two cases will, according to (1), be equal to $h\sigma\omega$ and any control of the momentum of the diaphragm with an accuracy sufficient to measure this difference will, due to the indeterminacy relation, involve a minimum latitude of the position of the diaphragm, comparable with $1/\sigma\omega$. If, as in the figure, the diaphragm with the two slits is placed in the middle between the first diaphragm and the photographic plate, it will be seen that the number of fringes per unit length will be just equal to $\sigma\omega$ and, since an uncertainty in the position of the first diaphragm of the amount of $1/\omega\sigma$ will cause an equal uncertainty in the positions of the fringes, it follows that no interference effect can appear. The same result is easily shown to hold for any other placing of the second diaphragm between the first diaphragm and the plate, and would also be obtained if, instead of the first diaphragm, another of these three bodies were used for the control, for the purpose suggested, of the momentum transfer.

This point is of great logical consequence, since it is only the circumstance that we are presented with a choice of *either* tracing the path of a particle *or* observing interference effects, which allows us to escape from the paradoxical necessity of concluding that the behaviour of an electron or a photon should depend on the presence of a slit in the diaphragm through which it could be proved not to pass. We have here to do with a typical example of how the complementary phenomena appear under mutually exclusive experimental arrangements and are just faced with the impossibility, in the analysis of quantum effects, of drawing any sharp separation between an independent behaviour of atomic objects and their interaction with the measuring instruments which serve to define the conditions under which the phenomena occur.

Our talks about the attitude to be taken in face of a novel situation as regards analysis and synthesis of experience touched naturally on many aspects of philosophical thinking, but, in spite of all divergencies of approach and opinion, a most humorous spirit animated the discussions. On his side, Einstein mockingly asked us whether we could really believe that the providential authorities took recourse to dice-playing (". . . *ob der liebe Gott würfelt*"), to which I replied by pointing at the great caution, already called for by ancient thinkers, in ascribing attributes to Providence in every-day language. I remember also how at the peak of the discussion Ehrenfest, in his affectionate manner of teasing his friends, jokingly hinted at the apparent similarity between Einstein's attitude and that of the opponents of relativity theory; but instantly Ehrenfest added that he would not be able to find relief in his own mind before concord with Einstein was reached.

Einstein's concern and criticism provided a most valuable incentive for us all to reexamine the various aspects of the situation as regards the description of atomic phenomena. To me it was a welcome stimulus to clarify still further the rôle played by the measuring instruments and, in order to bring into strong relief the mutually exclusive character of the experimental conditions under which the complementary phenomena appear, I tried in those days to sketch various apparatus in a pseudo-realistic style of which the following figures are examples. Thus, for the study of an interference phenomenon of the type indicated in [Fig. 71–4], it suggests itself to use an experimental arrangement like that shown in [Fig. 71–5], where the solid parts of the apparatus, serving as diaphragms and plate-holder, are firmly bolted to a common support. In such an arrangement, where the knowledge of the relative positions of the diaphragms and the photographic plate is secured by a rigid connection, it is

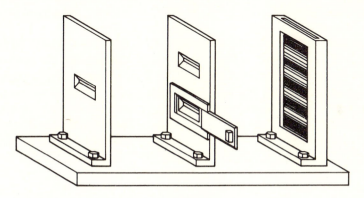

Fig 71–5.

obviously impossible to control the momentum exchanged between the particle and the separate parts of the apparatus. The only way in which, in such an arrangement, we could insure that the particle passed through one of the slits in the second diaphragm is to cover the other slit by a lid, as indicated in the figure; but if the slit is covered, there is of course no question of any interference phenomenon, and on the plate we shall simply observe a continuous distribution as in the case of the single fixed diaphragm in [Fig. 71–1].

In the study of phenomena in the account of which we were dealing with detailed momentum balance, certain parts of the whole device must naturally be given the freedom to move independently of others. Such an apparatus is sketched in [Fig. 71–6], where a diaphragm with a slit is suspended by weak springs from a solid yoke bolted to the support on which also other immobile parts of the arrangement are to be fastened. The scale on the diaphragm together with the pointer on the bearings of the yoke refer to such study of the motion of the diaphragm, as may be required for an estimate of the momentum transferred to it, permitting one

to draw conclusions as to the deflection suffered by the particle in passing
through the slit. Since, however, any reading of the scale, in whatever
way performed, will involve an uncontrollable change in the momentum
of the diaphragm, there will always be, in conformity with the indeterminacy principle, a reciprocal relationship between our knowledge of
the position of the slit and the accuracy of the momentum control.

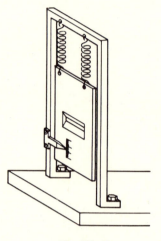

Fig. 71–6.

In the same semi-serious style, [Fig. 71–7] represents a part of an arrangement suited for the study of phenomena which, in contrast to those
just discussed, involve time co-ordination explicitly. It consists of a shutter rigidly connected with a robust clock resting on the support which
carries a diaphragm and on which further parts of similar character, regulated by the same clock-work or by other clocks standardized relatively to
it, are also to be fixed. The special aim of the figure is to underline that a
clock is a piece of machinery, the working of which can completely be
accounted for by ordinary mechanics and will be affected neither by reading of the position of its hands nor by the interaction between its acces-
sories and an atomic particle. In securing the opening of the hole at a definite moment, an apparatus of this type might, for instance, be used for an
accurate measurement of the time an electron or a photon takes to come
from the diaphragm to some other place, but evidently, it would leave no
possibility of controlling the energy transfer to the shutter with the aim of
drawing conclusions as to the energy of the particle which has passed
through the diaphragm. If we are interested in such conclusions we must,
of course, use an arrangement where the shutter devices can no longer serve
as accurate clocks, but where the knowledge of the moment when the hole

in the diaphragm is open involves a latitude connected with the accuracy of the energy measurement by the general relation (4).

The contemplation of such more or less practical arrangements and their more or less fictitious use proved most instructive in directing attention to essential features of the problems. The main point here is the distinction between the *objects* under investigation and the *measuring instruments* which serve to define, in classical terms, the conditions under

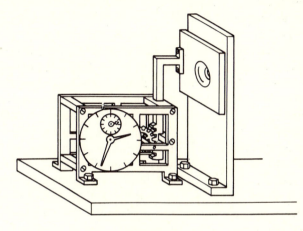

Fig. 71–7.

which the phenomena appear. Incidentally, we may remark that, for the illustration of the preceding considerations, it is not relevant that experiments involving an accurate control of the momentum or energy transfer from atomic particles to heavy bodies like diaphragms and shutters would be very difficult to perform, if practicable at all. It is only decisive that, in contrast to the proper measuring instruments, these bodies together with the particles would in such a case constitute the system to which the quantum-mechanical formalism has to be applied. As regards the specification of the conditions for any well-defined application of the formalism, it is moreover essential that the *whole experimental arrangement* be taken into account. In fact, the introduction of any further piece of apparatus, like a mirror, in the way of a particle might imply new interference effects essentially influencing the predictions as regards the results to be eventually recorded.

The extent to which renunciation of the visualization of atomic phenomena is imposed upon us by the impossibility of their subdivision is strikingly illustrated by the following example to which Einstein very early called attention and often has reverted. If a semi-reflecting mirror is placed in the way of a photon, leaving two possibilities for its direction of propagation, the photon may either be recorded on one, and only one, of two photographic plates situated at great distances in the two directions in question, or else we may, by replacing the plates by mirrors, observe effects exhibiting an interference between the two reflected wavetrains. In any attempt of a pictorial representation of the behaviour of the photon we would, thus, meet with the difficulty: to be obliged to say, on the one hand, that the photon always chooses *one* of the two ways and, on the other hand, that it behaves as if it had passed *both* ways.

It is just arguments of this kind which recall the impossibility of subdividing quantum phenomena and reveal the ambiguity in ascribing customary physical attributes to atomic objects. In particular, it must be realized that—besides in the account of the placing and timing of the instruments forming the experimental arrangement—all unambiguous use of space-time concepts in the description of atomic phenomena is confined to the recording of observations which refer to marks on a photographic plate or to similar practically irreversible amplification effects like the building of a water drop around an ion in a cloud-chamber. Although, of course, the existence of the quantum of action is ultimately responsible for the properties of the materials of which the measuring instruments are built and on which the functioning of the recording devices depends, this circumstance is not relevant for the problems of the adequacy and completeness of the quantum-mechanical description in its aspects here discussed.

These problems were instructively commented upon from different sides at the Solvay meeting, in the same session where Einstein raised his general objections. On that occasion an interesting discussion arose also about how to speak of the appearance of phenomena for which only predictions of statistical character can be made. The question was whether, as to the occurrence of individual effects, we should adopt a terminology proposed by Dirac, that we were concerned with a choice on the part of "nature" or, as suggested by Heisenberg, we should say that we have to do with a choice on the part of the "observer" constructing the measuring instruments and reading their recording. Any such terminology would, however, appear dubious since, on the one hand, it is hardly reasonable to endow nature with volition in the ordinary sense, while, on the other hand, it is certainly not possible for the observer to influence the events which may appear under the conditions he has arranged. To my mind, there is no other alternative than to admit that, in this field of experience, we are dealing with individual phenomena and that our possibilities of handling the measuring instruments allow us only to make a choice between the different complementary types of phenomena we want to study.

. . . In relativity theory, the emphasis on the dependence of all phenomena on the reference frame opened quite new ways of tracing general physical laws of unparalleled scope. In quantum theory, it was argued, the logical comprehension of hitherto unsuspected fundamental regularities governing atomic phenomena has demanded the recognition that no sharp separation can be made between an independent behaviour of the objects and their interaction with the measuring instruments which define the reference frame.

In this respect, quantum theory presents us with a novel situation in physical science, but attention was called to the very close analogy with the situation as regards analysis and synthesis of experience, which we meet in many other fields of human knowledge and interest. As is well known, many of the difficulties in psychology originate in the different placing of the separation lines between object and subject in the analysis of various aspects of psychical experience. Actually, words like "thoughts" and "sentiments," equally indispensable to illustrate the variety and scope of conscious life, are used in a similar complementary way as are space-time co-ordination and dynamical conservation laws in atomic physics. A precise formulation of such analogies involves, of course, intricacies of terminology, and the writer's position is perhaps best indicated in a passage in the article, hinting at the mutually exclusive relationship which will always exist between the practical use of any word and attempts at its strict definition. The principal aim, however, of these considerations, which were not least inspired by the hope of influencing Einstein's attitude, was to point to perspectives of bringing general epistemological problems into relief by means of a lesson derived from the study of new but fundamentally simple physical experience.

At the next meeting with Einstein at the Solvay Conference in 1930, our discussions took quite a dramatic turn. As an objection to the view that a control of the interchange of momentum and energy between the objects and the measuring instruments was excluded if these instruments should serve their purpose of defining the space-time frame of the phenomena, Einstein brought forward the argument that such control should be possible when the exigencies of relativity theory were taken into consideration. In particular, the general relationship between energy and mass, expressed in Einstein's famous formula

$$E = mc^2 \qquad\qquad (5)$$

should allow, by means of simple weighing, to measure the total energy of any system and, thus, in principle to control the energy transferred to it when it interacts with an atomic object.

As an arrangement suited for such purpose, Einstein proposed the device indicated in [Fig. 71–8], consisting of a box with a hole in its side, which could be opened or closed by a shutter moved by means of a clock-work within the box. If, in the beginning, the box contained a certain amount of radiation and the clock was set to open the shutter for a very short interval at a chosen time, it could be achieved that a single photon was released through the hole at a moment known with as great accuracy as desired. Moreover, it would apparently also be possible, by weighing the whole box before and after this event, to measure the energy of the photon with any accuracy wanted, in definite contradiction to the reciprocal indeterminacy of time and energy quantities in quantum mechanics.

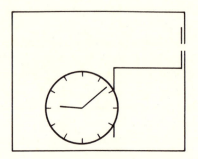

Fig. 71–8.

This argument amounted to a serious challenge and gave rise to a thorough examination of the whole problem. At the outcome of the discussion, to which Einstein himself contributed effectively, it became clear, however, that this argument could not be upheld. In fact, in the consideration of the problem, it was found necessary to look closer into the consequences of the identification of inertial and gravitational mass implied in the application of relation (5). Especially, it was essential to take into account the relationship between the rate of a clock and its position in a gravitational field—well known from the red-shift of the lines in the sun's spectrum—following from Einstein's principle of equivalence between gravity effects and the phenomena observed in accelerated reference frames.

Our discussion concentrated on the possible application of an apparatus incorporating Einstein's device and drawn in [Fig. 71–9] in the same pseudo-realistic style as some of the preceding figures. The box, of which a section is shown in order to exhibit its interior, is suspended in a spring-balance and is furnished with a pointer to read its position on a scale fixed to the balance support. The weighing of the box may thus be performed with any given accuracy Δm by adjusting the balance to its zero position by means of suitable loads. The essential point is now that any determination of this position with a given accuracy Δq will involve a minimum latitude Δp in the control of the momentum of the box con-

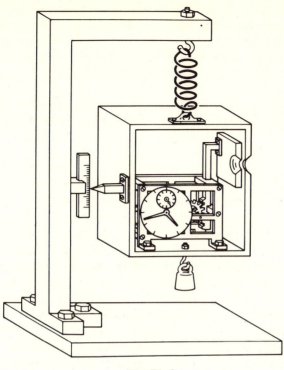

Fig. 71–9.

nected with Δq by the relation (3). This latitude must obviously again be smaller than the total impulse which, during the whole interval T of the balancing procedure, can be given by the gravitational field to a body with a mass Δm, or

$$\Delta p \approx \frac{h}{\Delta q} < T \cdot g \cdot \Delta m, \tag{6}$$

where g is the gravity constant. The greater the accuracy of the reading q of the pointer, the longer must, consequently, be the balancing interval T, if a given accuracy Δm of the weighing of the box with its content shall be obtained.

Now according to general relativity theory, a clock, when displaced in the direction of the gravitational force by an amount of Δq, will change its rate in such a way that its reading in the course of a time interval T will differ by an amount ΔT given by the relation

$$\frac{\Delta T}{T} = \frac{1}{c^2} g \Delta q. \tag{7}$$

By comparing (6) and (7) we see, therefore, that after the weighing procedure there will in our knowledge of the adjustment of the clock be a latitude

$$\Delta T > \frac{h}{c^2 \Delta m}.$$

Together with the formula (5), this relation again leads to

$$\Delta T \cdot \Delta E > h,$$

in accordance with the indeterminacy principle. Consequently, a use of the apparatus as a means of accurately measuring the energy of the photon will prevent us from controlling the moment of its escape.

The discussion, so illustrative of the power and consistency of relativistic arguments, thus emphasized once more the necessity of distinguishing, in the study of atomic phenomena, between the proper measuring instruments which serve to define the reference frame and those parts which are to be regarded as objects under investigation and in the account of which quantum effects cannot be disregarded. Notwithstanding the most suggestive confirmation of the soundness and wide scope of the quantum-mechanical way of description, Einstein nevertheless, in a following conversation with me, expressed a feeling of disquietude as regards the apparent lack of firmly laid down principles for the explanation of nature, in which all could agree. From my viewpoint, however, I could only answer that, in dealing with the task of bringing order into an entirely new field of experience, we could hardly trust in any accustomed principles, however broad, apart from the demand of avoiding logical inconsistencies and, in this respect, the mathematical formalism of quantum mechanics should surely meet all requirements.

The Solvay meeting in 1930 was the last occasion where, in common discussions with Einstein, we could benefit from the stimulating and mediating influence of Ehrenfest, but shortly before his deeply deplored death in 1933 he told me that Einstein was far from satisfied and with his usual acuteness had discerned new aspects of the situation which strengthened his critical attitude. In fact, by further examining the possibilities for the application of a balance arrangement, Einstein had perceived alternative procedures which, even if they did not allow the use he originally intended, might seem to enhance the paradoxes beyond the possibilities of logical solution. Thus, Einstein had pointed out that, after a preliminary weighing of the box with the clock and the subsequent escape of the photon, one was still left with the choice of either repeating the weighing or opening the box and comparing the reading of the clock with the standard time scale. Consequently, we are at this stage still free to choose whether we want to draw conclusions either about the energy of the photon or about the moment when it left the box. Without in any way interfering with the photon between its escape and its later interaction with other suitable measuring instruments, we are, thus, able to make accurate predictions pertaining *either* to the moment of its arrival *or* to the amount of energy liberated by its absorption. Since, however, according to the quantum-mechanical formalism, the specification of the state of an isolated particle cannot involve both a well-defined connection with the time scale and an accurate fixation of the energy, it might thus appear as if this formalism did not offer the means of an adequate description.

Once more Einstein's searching spirit had elicited a peculiar aspect of the situation in quantum theory, which in a most striking manner illustrated how far we have here transcended customary explanations of natural phenomena. Still, I could not agree with the trend of his remarks as reported by Ehrenfest. In my opinion, there could be no other way to deem a logically consistent mathematical formalism as inadequate than by demonstrating the departure of its consequences from experience or by proving that its predictions did not exhaust the possibilities of observation, and Einstein's argumentation could be directed to neither of these ends. In fact, we must realize that in the problem in question we are not dealing with a *single* specified experimental arrangement, but are referring to *two* different, mutually exclusive arrangements. In the one, the balance together with another piece of apparatus like a spectrometer is used for the study of the energy transfer by a photon; in the other, a shutter regulated by a standardized clock together with another apparatus of similar kind, accurately timed relatively to the clock, is used for the study of the time of propagation of a photon over a given distance. In both these cases, as also assumed by Einstein, the observable effects are expected to be in complete conformity with the predictions of the theory.

The problem again emphasizes the necessity of considering the *whole* experimental arrangement, the specification of which is imperative for any well-defined application of the quantum-mechanical formalism. Incidentally, it may be added that paradoxes of the kind contemplated by Einstein are encountered also in such simple arrangements as sketched in [Fig. 71–6]. In fact, after a preliminary measurement of the momentum of the diaphragm, we are in principle offered the choice, when an electron or photon has passed through the slit, either to repeat the momentum measurement or to control the position of the diaphragm and, thus, to make predictions pertaining to alternative subsequent observations. It may also be added that it obviously can make no difference as regards observable effects obtainable by a definite experimental arrangement, whether our plans of constructing or handling the instruments are fixed beforehand or whether we prefer to postpone the completion of our planning until a later moment when the particle is already on its way from one instrument to another.

In the quantum-mechanical description our freedom of constructing and handling the experimental arrangement finds its proper expression in the possibility of choosing the classically defined parameters entering in any proper application of the formalism. Indeed, in all such respects quantum mechanics exhibits a correspondence with the state of affairs familiar from classical physics, which is as close as possible when considering the individuality inherent in the quantum phenomena. Just in helping to bring out this point so clearly, Einstein's concern had therefore again been a most welcome incitement to explore the essential aspects of the situation.

The next Solvay meeting in 1933 was devoted to the problems of the structure and properties of atomic nuclei, in which field such great advances were made just in that period due to the experimental discoveries as well as to new fruitful applications of quantum mechanics. It need in this connection hardly be recalled that just the evidence obtained by the study of artificial nuclear transformations gave a most direct test of Einstein's fundamental law regarding the equivalence of mass and energy, which was to prove an evermore important guide for researches in nuclear physics. It may also be mentioned how Einstein's intuitive recognition of the intimate relationship between the law of radioactive transformations and the probability rules governing individual radiation effects was confirmed by the quantum-mechanical explanation of spontaneous nuclear disintegrations. In fact, we are here dealing with a typical example of the statistical mode of description, and the complementary relationship between energy-momentum conservation and time-space coordination is most strikingly exhibited in the well-known paradox of particle penetration through potential barriers.

Einstein himself did not attend this meeting, which took place at a time darkened by the tragic developments in the political world which were to influence his fate so deeply and add so greatly to his burdens in the service of humanity. A few months earlier, on a visit to Princeton where Einstein was then guest of the newly founded Institute for Advanced Study to which he soon after became permanently attached, I had, however, opportunity to talk with him again about the epistemological aspects of atomic physics, but the difference between our ways of approach and expression still presented obstacles to mutual understanding. While, so far, relatively few persons had taken part in the discussions reported in this article, Einstein's critical attitude towards the views on quantum theory adhered to by many physicists was soon after brought to public attention through a paper with the title "Can Quantum-Mechanical Descriptions of Physical

Reality Be Considered Complete?," published in 1935 by Einstein, Podolsky and Rosen.

The argumentation of this paper is based on a criterion which the authors express in the following sentence: "If, without in any way disturbing a system, we can predict with certainty (i.e., with probability equal to unity) the value of a physical quantity, then there exists an element of physical reality corresponding to this physical quantity." By an elegant exposition of the consequences of the quantum-mechanical formalism as regards the representation of a state of a system, consisting of two parts which have been in interaction for a limited time interval, it is next shown that different quantities, the fixation of which cannot be combined in the representation of one of the partial systems, can nevertheless be predicted by measurements pertaining to the other partial system. According to their criterion, the authors therefore conclude that quantum mechanics does not "provide a complete description of the physical reality," and they express their belief that it should be possible to develop a more adequate account of the phenomena.

Due to the lucidity and apparently incontestable character of the argument, the paper of Einstein, Podolsky and Rosen created a stir among physicists and has played a large rôle in general philosophical discussion. Certainly the issue is of a very subtle character and suited to emphasize how far, in quantum theory, we are beyond the reach of pictorial visualization. It will be seen, however, that we are here dealing with problems of just the same kind as those raised by Einstein in previous discussions, and, in an article which appeared a few months later, I tried to show that from the point of view of complementarity the apparent inconsistencies were completely removed. The trend of the argumentation was in substance the same as that exposed in the foregoing pages, but the aim of recalling the way in which the situation was discussed at that time may be an apology for citing certain passages from my article.

Thus, after referring to the conclusions derived by Einstein, Podolsky and Rosen on the basis of their criterion, I wrote:

Such an argumentation, however, would hardly seem suited to affect the soundness of quantum-mechanical description, which is based on a coherent mathematical formalism covering automatically any procedure of measurement like that indicated. The apparent contradiction in fact discloses only an essential inadequacy of the customary viewpoint of natural philosophy for a rational account of physical phenomena of the type with which we are concerned in quantum mechanics. Indeed the *finite interaction between object and measuring agencies* conditioned by the very existence of the quantum of action entails—because of the impossibility of controlling the reaction of the object on the measuring instruments, if these are to serve their purpose—the necessity of a final renunciation of the classical ideal of causality and a radical revision of our attitude towards the problem of physical reality. In fact, as we shall see, a criterion of reality like that proposed by the named authors contains—however cautious its formulation may appear—an essential ambiguity when it is applied to the actual problems with which we are here concerned.

As regards the special problem treated by Einstein, Podolsky and Rosen, it was next shown that the consequences of the formalism as regards the representation of the state of a system consisting of two interacting atomic objects correspond to the simple arguments mentioned in the preceding in connection with the discussion of the experimental arrangements suited for the study of complementary phenomena. In fact, although any pair q and p, of conjugate space and momentum variables obeys the rule of non-commutative multiplication expressed by (2), and can thus only be fixed · with reciprocal latitudes given by (3), the difference $q_1 - q_2$ between two space co-ordinates referring to the constituents of the system will commute with the sum $p_1 + p_2$ of the corresponding momentum components, as follows directly from the commutability of q_1 with p_2 and q_2 with p_1. Both $q_1 - q_2$ and $p_1 + p_2$ can, therefore, be accurately fixed in a state of the complex system and, consequently, we can predict the values of either q_1 or p_1 if either q_2 or p_2, respectively, are determined by direct measurements. If, for the two parts of the system, we take a particle and a diaphragm, like that sketched in [Fig. 71–6], we see that the possibilities of specifying the state of the particle by measurements on the diaphragm just correspond to the situation described [earlier], where it was mentioned that, after the particle has passed through the diaphragm, we have in principle the choice of measuring either the position of the diaphragm or its momentum and, in each case, to make predictions as to subsequent observations pertaining to the particle. As repeatedly stressed, the principal point is here that such measurements demand mutually exclusive experimental arrangements.

The argumentation of the article was summarized in the following passage:

From our point of view we now see that the wording of the above-mentioned criterion of physical reality proposed by Einstein, Podolsky, and Rosen contains an ambiguity as regards the meaning of the expression "without in any way disturbing a system." Of course there is in a case like that just considered no question of a mechanical disturbance of the system under investigation during the last critical stage of the measuring procedure. But even at this stage there is essentially the question of *an influence on the very conditions which define the possible types of predictions regarding the future behaviour of the system.* Since these conditions constitute an inherent element of the description of any phenomenon to which the term "physical reality" can be properly attached, we see that the argumentation of the mentioned authors does not justify their conclusion that quantum-mechanical description is essentially incomplete. On the contrary, this description, as appears from the preceding discussion, may be characterized as a rational utilization of all possibilities of unambiguous interpretation of measurements, compatible with the finite and uncontrollable interaction between the objects and the measuring instruments in the field of quantum theory. In fact, it is only the mutual exclusion of any two experimental procedures, permitting the unambiguous definition of complementary physical quantities, which provides room for new physical laws, the coexistence of which might at first sight appear irreconcilable with the basic principles of science. It is just this entirely new situation as regards the description of physical phenomena that the notion of *complementarity* aims at characterizing.

Rereading these passages, I am deeply aware of the inefficiency of expression which must have made it very difficult to appreciate the trend of the argumentation aiming to bring out the essential ambiguity involved in a reference to physical attributes of objects when dealing with phenomena where no sharp distinction can be made between the behaviour of the objects themselves and their interaction with the measuring instruments. I hope, however, that the present account of the discussions with Einstein in the foregoing years, which contributed so greatly to make us familiar with the situation in quantum physics, may give a clearer impression of the necessity of a radical revision of basic principles for physical explanation in order to restore logical order in this field of experience.

Einstein's own views at that time are presented in an article "Physics and Reality," published in 1936 in the *Journal of the Franklin Institute*. Starting from a most illuminating exposition of the gradual development of the fundamental principles in the theories of classical physics and their relation to the problem of physical reality, Einstein here argues that the quantum-mechanical description is to be considered merely as a means of accounting for the average behaviour of a large number of atomic systems and his attitude to the belief that it should offer an exhaustive description of the individual phenomena is expressed in the following words: "To believe this is logically possible without contradiction; but it is so very contrary to my scientific instinct that I cannot forego the search for a more complete conception."

Even if such an attitude might seem well-balanced in itself, it nevertheless implies a rejection of the whole argumentation . . . that, in quantum mechanics, we are not dealing with an arbitrary renunciation of a more detailed analysis of atomic phenomena, but with a recognition that such an analysis is *in principle* excluded. The peculiar individuality of the quantum effects presents us, as regards the comprehension of well-defined evidence, with a novel situation unforeseen in classical physics and irreconcilable with conventional ideas suited for our orientation and adjustment to ordinary experience. It is in this respect that quantum theory has called for a renewed revision of the foundation for the unambiguous use of elementary concepts, as a further step in the development which, since the advent of relativity theory, has been so characteristic of modern science.

In the following years, the more philosophical aspects of the situation in atomic physics aroused the interest of ever larger circles and were, in particular, discussed at the Second International Congress for the Unity of Science in Copenhagen in July 1936. In a lecture on this occasion, I tried especially to stress the analogy in epistemological respects between the limitation imposed on the causal description in atomic physics and situations met with in other fields of knowledge. A principal purpose of such parallels was to call attention to the necessity in many domains of general human interest to face problems of a similar kind as those which had arisen in quantum theory and thereby to give a more familiar background for the apparently extravagant way of expression which physicists have developed to cope with their acute difficulties.

Besides the complementary features conspicuous in psychology and already touched upon, examples of such relationships can also be traced in biology, especially as regards the comparison between mechanistic and vitalistic viewpoints. Just with respect to the observational problem, this last question had previously been the subject of an address to the International Congress on Light Therapy held in Copenhagen in 1932, where it was incidentally pointed out that even the psycho-physical parallelism as envisaged by Leibniz and Spinoza has obtained a wider scope through the development of atomic physics, which forces us to an attitude towards the problem of explanation recalling ancient wisdom, that when searching for harmony in life one must never forget that in the drama of existence we are ourselves both actors and spectators.

Utterances of this kind would naturally in many minds evoke the impression of an underlying mysticism foreign to the spirit of science; at the above mentioned Congress in 1936 I therefore tried to clear up such misunderstandings and to explain that the only question was an endeavour to clarify the conditions, in each field of knowledge, for the analysis and synthesis of experience. Yet, I am afraid that I had in this respect only little success in convincing my listeners, for whom the dissent among the physicists themselves was naturally a cause of scepticism as to the necessity of going so far in renouncing customary demands as regards the explanation of natural phenomena. Not least through a new discussion with Einstein in Princeton in 1937, where we did not get beyond a humorous contest concerning which side Spinoza would have taken if he had lived to see the development of our days, I was strongly reminded of the importance of utmost caution in all questions of terminology and dialectics.

These aspects of the situation were especially discussed at a meeting in Warsaw in 1938, arranged by the International Institute of Intellectual Co-operation of the League of Nations. The preceding years had seen great progress in quantum physics due to a number of fundamental discoveries regarding the constitution and properties of atomic nuclei as well as due to important developments of the mathematical formalism taking the requirements of relativity theory into account. In the last respect, Dirac's ingenious quantum theory of the electron offered a most striking illustration of the power and fertility of the general quantum-mechanical way of description. In the phenomena of creation and annihilation of electron pairs we have in fact to do with new fundamental features of atomicity, which are intimately connected with the non-classical aspects of quantum statistics expressed in the exclusion principle, and which have demanded a still more far-reaching renunciation of explanation in terms of a pictorial representation.

Meanwhile, the discussion of the epistemological problems in atomic physics attracted as much attention as ever and, in commenting on Einstein's views as regards the incompleteness of the quantum-mechanical mode of description, I entered more directly on questions of terminology. In this connection I warned especially against phrases, often found in the physical literature, such as "disturbing of phenomena by observation" or "creating physical attributes to atomic objects by measurements." Such phrases, which may serve to remind of the apparent paradoxes in quantum theory, are at the same time apt to cause confusion, since words like "phenomena" and "observations," just as "attributes" and "measurements," are used in a way hardly compatible with common language and practical definition.

As a more appropriate way of expression I advocated the application of the word *phenomenon* exclusively to refer to the observations obtained under specified circumstances, including an account of the whole experimental arrangement. In such terminology, the observational problem is free of any special intricacy since, in actual experiments, all observations are expressed by unambiguous statements referring, for instance, to the registration of the point at which an electron arrives at a photographic plate. Moreover, speaking in such a way is just suited to emphasize that the appropriate physical interpretation of the symbolic quantum-mechanical formalism amounts only to predictions, of determinate or statistical character, pertaining to individual phenomena appearing under conditions defined by classical physical concepts.

Notwithstanding all differences between the physical problems which have given rise to the development of relativity theory and quantum theory, respectively, a comparison of purely logical aspects of relativistic and complementary argumentation reveals striking similarities as regards the renunciation of the absolute significance of conventional physical attributes of objects. Also, the neglect of the atomic constitution of the measuring instruments themselves, in the account of actual experience, is equally characteristic of the applications of relativity and quantum theory. Thus, the smallness of the quantum of action compared with the actions involved in usual experience, including the arranging and handling of physical apparatus, is as essential in atomic physics as is the enormous number of atoms composing the world in the general theory of relativity which, as often pointed out, demands that dimensions of apparatus for measuring angles can be made small compared with the radius of curvature of space.

In the Warsaw lecture, I commented upon the use of not directly visualizable symbolism in relativity and quantum theory in the following way:

> Even the formalisms, which in both theories within their scope offer adequate means of comprehending all conceivable experience, exhibit deep-going analogies. In fact, the astounding simplicity of the generalization of classical physical theories, which are obtained by the use of multidimensional geometry and non-commutative algebra, respectively, rests in both cases essentially on the introduction of the conventional symbol $\sqrt{-1}$. The abstract character of the formalisms concerned is indeed, on closer examination, as typical of relativity theory as it is of quantum mechanics, and it is in this respect purely a matter of tradition if the former theory is considered as a completion of classical physics rather than as a first fundamental step in the thoroughgoing revision of our conceptual means of comparing observations, which the modern development of physics has forced upon us.

It is, of course, true that in atomic physics we are confronted with a number of unsolved fundamental problems, especially as regards the intimate relationship between the elementary unit of electric charge and the universal quantum of action; but these problems are no more connected with the epistemological points here discussed than is the adequacy of relativistic argumentation with the issue of thus far unsolved problems of cosmology. Both in relativity and in quantum theory we are concerned with new aspects of scientific analysis and synthesis and, in this connection, it is interesting to note that, even in the great epoch of critical philosophy in the former century, there was only question to what extent *a priori* arguments could be given for the adequacy of space-time coordination and causal connection of experience, but never question of rational generalizations or inherent limitations of such categories of human thinking.

Although in more recent years I have had several occasions of meeting Einstein, the continued discussions, from which I always have received new impulses, have so far not led to a common view about the epistemological problems in atomic physics, and our opposing views are perhaps most clearly stated in a recent issue of *Dialectica,* bringing a general discussion of these problems. Realizing, however, the many obstacles for mutual understanding as regards a matter where approach and background must influence everyone's attitude, I have welcomed this opportunity of a broader exposition of the development by which, to my mind, a veritable crisis in physical science has been overcome. The lesson we have hereby received would seem to have brought us a decisive step further in the never-ending struggle for harmony between content and form, and taught us once again that no content can be grasped without a formal frame and that any form, however useful it has hitherto proved, may be found to be too narrow to comprehend new experience.

Surely, in a situation like this, where it has been difficult to reach mutual understanding not only between philosophers and physicists but even between physicists of different schools, the difficulties have their root not seldom in the preference for a certain use of language suggesting itself from the different lines of approach. In the Institute in Copenhagen, where through those years a number of young physicists from various countries came together for discussion, we used, when in trouble, often to comfort ourselves with jokes, among them the old saying of the two kinds of truth. To the one kind belong statements so simple and clear that the opposite assertion obviously could not be defended. The other kind, the so-called "deep truths," are statements in which the opposite also contains deep truth. Now, the development in a new field will usually pass through stages in which chaos becomes gradually replaced by order; but it is not least in the intermediate stage where deep truth prevails that the work is really exciting and inspires the imagination to search for a firmer hold. For such endeavours of seeking the proper balance between seriousness and humour, Einstein's own personality stands as a great example and, when expressing my belief that through a singularly fruitful co-operation of a whole generation of physicists we are nearing the goal where logical order to a large extent allows us to avoid deep truth, I hope that it will be taken in his spirit and may serve as an apology for several utterances in the preceding pages.

The discussions with Einstein which have formed the theme of this article have extended over many years which have witnessed great progress in the field of atomic physics. Whether our actual meetings have been of short or long duration, they have always left a deep and lasting impression on my mind, and when writing this report I have, so-to-say, been arguing with Einstein all the time even when entering on topics apparently far removed from the special problems under debate at our meetings. As regards the account of the conversations I am, of course, aware that I am relying only on my own memory, just as I am prepared for the possibility that many features of the development of quantum theory, in which Einstein has played so large a part, may appear to himself in a different light. I trust, however, that I have not failed in conveying a proper impression of how much it has meant to me to be able to benefit from the inspiration which we all derive from every contact with Einstein.

PART

XIII

NEW PARTICLES AND
ATOMIC ACCELERATORS

72

○○○○○○○○○○

THE POSITIVE ELECTRON–
THE FIRST PARTICLE OF
ANTIMATTER

○○○○○○○○○○

Carl D. Anderson (b. 1905)

As noted in Chapter 71, one of the most remarkable implications of Dirac's theory of the electron is the existence of an infinite sea of negative energy electrons at all points of the vacuum. Although this follows directly from the mathematics of the theory, it was very difficult to accept this result when the theory was first announced, since the very idea of a negative energy particle is "unphysical"—contrary to our feeling that the laws of physics must describe a real observable world.

Because of this, Dirac himself at first proposed that the negative-energy electron states inherent in his theory be regarded as mathematical fictions and that they be disregarded in the application of his theory to physical phenomena. However, the theory gives a correct description of the behavior of an electron only if the negative-energy states are actually taken into account. To do so is to impart a physical reality to the negative-energy states; one must then assign to each of them one electron (thus introducing an infinite number of negative-energy electrons in the vacuum), for otherwise all the positive-energy electrons in the universe would jump down to the negative-energy states and the material universe would disappear instantaneously in a vast burst of energy. The presence of negative-energy electrons in all the negative-energy states prevents such a catastrophe, owing to the Pauli exclusion principle.

When Dirac proposed this picture of an infinite sea of negative-energy

1261

electrons, he indicated that it would lead to no conflict with observation, since such a sea of negative-energy electrons can never be observed. All that is observable is some departure from this uniform distribution of negative-energy electrons in the vacuum. Dirac showed that such a departure can occur if one of the negative-energy electrons absorbs enough energy (in the form of a photon or by means of some sort of collision) to lift it into a state of positive energy.

If this were to happen, the negative state occupied by the negative-energy electron would be empty and the negative-energy electron itself would appear as a real electron with positive energy. The hole in the sea of negative-energy electrons thus created would now be observable as a positively charged particle with positive energy. In this way a pair of particles would be created, one an ordinary electron, and the other a positively charged particle with the same mass as the electron. Dirac suggested that the chance of creating such a pair in some laboratory on the earth would be small because it would require energy equivalent to at least twice the mass of the electron. However, enough energy is present in cosmic radiation to create such a pair as it passes through a sheet of matter. Therefore, one should look at the photographs of cosmic ray tracks to detect such a pair; this, indeed, is how the positrons were first discerned.

On August 2, 1932, Carl Anderson found tracks of positively charged particles in his cosmic ray photographs. He knew they were not tracks of protons, the only positively charged particles recognized at that time. To study the energy and the charge on cosmic ray particles one introduces a magnetic field in the cloud chamber through which the particles pass. The magnetic field turns the negatively charged particles in one direction and the positively charged particles in the other. If one knows the mass of the particle, one can then calculate its energy from the curvature of its path in the magnetic field. If the path is only slightly curved, the energy is large; if the path is highly curved, the energy is small. For a particle of given charge and mass, the radius of curvature of the path varies as the square root of the kinetic energy of the particle.

From the large curvatures of the paths of the particles described in the paper that follows this commentary, Anderson knew that if these particles were protons, they would have had rather low energies. In fact they would have had hardly enough kinetic energy to go more than a few millimeters in air, whereas the lengths of the actual paths in air were found to be ten or more times greater than would be expected for a proton of such energy. The particles were also discovered to have enough energy to penetrate 6 mm of lead. From this type of analysis Anderson concluded that these positive particles must have masses of the order of magnitude of that of the electron and must have a unit positive charge.

At first, Anderson did not identify these positive electrons or positrons with the Dirac holes in the sea of negative-energy states because the early photographs did not show a pair being created, as demanded by the Dirac theory. However, this was due to faulty observation. Soon afterwards it was found that whenever the track of a positron appeared on a photographic plate, it was accompanied by the track of an electron of opposite curvature. Moreover, the positron tracks were always found to end abruptly, whereas the electron tracks were always observed to twist around and die out gradually.

It is easy to see the reason for this on the basis of the Dirac theory. Since a positron is a hole in a sea of negative-energy states, any electron it meets will be annihilated with the emission of energy. Thus, the positron disappears abruptly at the end of a short path because there are always many free electrons about in the cloud chamber. The electron that is created in the pair, on the other hand, is an ordinary particle that loses its kinetic energy slowly through collisions with other ordinary particles in the cloud chamber. Its track is therefore an intricate one. As the electron loses kinetic energy and slows down, the magnetic field in the cloud chamber curves the electron more and more sharply so that the path may end in a series of small loops.

Anderson's discovery, for which he won the Nobel Prize, established the Dirac theory as one of the most reliable in physics, and for the first time showed that the complexities of elementary-particle physics were far greater than had been imagined. It also opened up a vast new domain of research and indicated the possibility of negative-energy protons and neutrons. These particles were discovered many years later. We now know that for every type of fundamental particle in the universe there is an antiparticle; the members of any pair are related to one another in the same way as the electron is related to the positron. This has led to the concept of antimatter and to the speculation that there are parts of our universe (perhaps half of it) that consist of antimatter. When matter and antimatter meet, they destroy one another and give rise to pure energy.

Carl David Anderson was born in New York of Swedish parents on September 3, 1905. After the usual American boyhood, with its grammar and high-school education, Anderson entered the California Institute of Technology, and in 1927 received his B.Sc. degree in physics and engineering. After that he devoted all his time to physics and in 1930 received his Ph.D. degree in physics from the same institution, where he remained as research fellow until 1933. He was then appointed assistant professor of physics and, in 1939, full professor, a position which he currently holds. The early period in Anderson's career was his most productive, for in 1932 he discovered the positron, for which he received the Nobel Prize in

1936; two years later, working with Neddermeyer, he discovered the mu-meson.

Although Anderson began his research career in the field of X-rays, and wrote his Ph.D. thesis on the emission of electrons from gases by X-rays, under the direction of Robert Millikan, he soon turned to cosmic rays. Once Millikan and Anderson decided to investigate cosmic rays by means of the Wilson cloud chamber, as had been done for the first time in 1927 by the Russian physicist Skobelzyn, it was only a matter of time for the positron to be discovered.

By designing his instrument properly and working with powerful magnetic fields, Anderson was able to measure cosmic ray events of much higher energy than had previously been done. After finding tracks of positively charged particles, which Anderson proved could not be those of protons, he suggested that they were the Dirac positrons. This was later confirmed in independent experiments by Blackett and Occhialini. After completing this basic work, Anderson studied various other cosmic ray phenomena, particularly the characteristics of cosmic ray showers. This led to his discovery of the mu-meson.

During World War II Anderson was active on various military research problems.

In addition to the Nobel Prize, Anderson received the gold medal of the City of New York, an honorary Doctor of Science degree from Colgate University, and the Elliot Cresson medal of the Franklin Institute.

ooooooo

ANDERSON

The Positive Electron [1]

ON AUGUST 2, 1932, DURING the course of photographing cosmic-ray tracks produced in a vertical Wilson chamber (magnetic field of 15,000 gauss) designed in the summer of 1930 by Professor R. A. Millikan and the writer, the tracks shown in Fig. 72–1 were obtained, which seemed to be interpretable only on the basis of the existence in this case of a particle carrying a positive charge but having a mass of

---

[1] Carl D. Anderson, *Physical Review*, 43 (1933), 491–494.

the same order of magnitude as that normally possessed by a free negative electron. Later study of the photograph by a whole group of men of the Norman Bridge Laboratory only tended to strengthen this view. The reason that this interpretation seemed so inevitable is that the track appearing on the upper half of the figure cannot possibly have a mass as large as that of a proton for as soon as the mass is fixed the energy is at once fixed by the curvature. The energy of a proton of that curvature comes out 300,000 volts, but a proton of that energy according to well established and universally accepted determinations has a total range of about 5 mm in air while that portion of the range actually visible in this case exceeds 5 cm without a noticeable change in curvature. The only escape from this conclusion would be to assume that at exactly the same instant (and the sharpness of the tracks determines that instant to within about a fiftieth of a second) two independent electrons happened to produce two tracks so placed as to give the impression of a single particle shooting through the lead plate. This assumption was dismissed on a probability basis, since a sharp track of this order of curvature under the experimental conditions prevailing occurred in the chamber only once in some 500 exposures, and since there was practically no chance at all that two such tracks should line up in this way. We also discarded as completely untenable the assumption of an electron of 20 million volts entering the lead on one side and coming out with an energy of 60 million volts on the other side. A fourth possibility is that a photon, entering the lead from above, knocked out of the nucleus of a lead atom two particles, one of which shot upward and the other downward. But in this case the upward moving one would be a positive of small mass so that either of the two possibilities leads to the existence of the positive electron.

In the course of the next few weeks other photographs were obtained which could be interpreted logically only on the positive-electron basis, and a brief report was then published with due reserve in interpretation in view of the importance and striking nature of the announcement.

MAGNITUDE OF CHARGE AND MASS

It is possible with the present experimental data only to assign rather wide limits to the magnitude of the charge and mass of the particle. The specific ionization was not in these cases measured, but it appears very probable, from a knowledge of the experimental conditions and by comparison with many other photographs of high- and low-speed electrons taken under the same conditions, that the charge cannot differ in magnitude from that of an electron by an amount as great as a factor of two. Furthermore, if the photograph is taken to represent a positive particle penetrating the 6 mm lead plate, then the energy lost, calculated for unit charge, is approximately 38 million electron-volts, this value being practically independent of the proper mass of the particle as long as it is not too many times larger than that of a free negative electron. This value of 63 million volts per cm energy-loss for the positive particle it was considered legitimate to compare with the measured mean of approximately 35 million volts for negative electrons of 200–300 million volts energy since the rate of energy-loss for particles of small mass is expected to change only very slowly over an energy range extending from several million to several hundred million volts. Allowance being made for experimental uncertainties, an upper limit to the rate of loss of energy for the positive particle can then be set at less than four times that for an electron, thus fixing, by the usual relation between rate of ionization and charge, an upper limit to the charge less than twice that of the negative electron. It is concluded, therefore, that the magnitude of the charge of the positive electron which we shall henceforth contract to positron is very probably equal to that of a free negative electron which from symmetry considerations would naturally then be called a negatron.

It is pointed out that the effective depth of the chamber in the line of sight which is the same as the direction of the magnetic lines of force was 1 cm and its effective diameter at right angles to that line 14 cm, thus insuring that the particle crossed the chamber practically normal to the lines of force. The change in direction due to scattering in the lead, in this case about 8° measured in the plane of the chamber, is a probable value for a particle of this energy though less than the most probable value.

The magnitude of the proper mass cannot as yet be given further than to fix an upper limit to it about twenty times that of the electron mass. If [Fig. 72–1] represents a particle of unit charge passing through the lead plate then the curvatures, on the basis of the information at hand on ionization, give too low a value for the energy-loss unless the mass is taken less than twenty times that of the negative electron mass. Further determinations of $\underline{H}\rho$ for relatively low energy particles before and after they cross a known amount of matter, together with a study of ballistic effects such as close encounters with electrons, involving large energy transfers, will enable closer limits to be assigned to the mass.

To date, out of a group of 1300 photographs of cosmic-ray tracks 15 of these show positive particles penetrating the lead, none of which can be ascribed to particles with a mass as large as that of a proton, thus establishing the existence of positive particles of unit charge and of mass small compared to that of a proton. In many other cases due either to the short section of track available for measurement or to the high energy of the particle it is not possible to differentiate with certainty between protons and positrons. A comparison of the six or seven hundred positive-ray tracks which we have taken is, however, still consistent with the view that the positive particle which is knocked out of the nucleus by the incoming primary cosmic ray is in many cases a proton.

From the fact that positrons occur in groups associated with other tracks it is concluded that they must be secondary particles ejected from an atomic nucleus. If we retain the view that a nucleus consists of protons and neutrons (and α-particles) and that a neutron represents a close com-

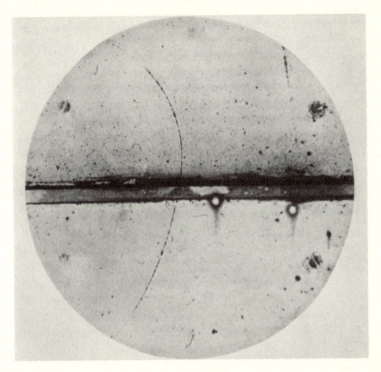

Fig. 72–1. A 63 million volt positron ($H\rho = 2.1 \times 10^5$ gauss-cm) passing through a 6 mm lead plate and emerging as a 23 million volt positron ($H\rho = 7.5 \times 10^4$ gauss-cm). The length of this latter path is at least ten times greater than the possible length of a proton path of this curvature.

bination of a proton and electron, then from the electromagnetic theory as to the origin of mass the simplest assumption would seem to be that an encounter between the incoming primary ray and a proton may take place in such a way as to expand the diameter of the proton to the same value as that possessed by the negatron. This process would release an energy of a billion electron-volts appearing as a secondary photon. As a second possibility the primary ray may disintegrate a neutron (or more than one) in the nucleus by the ejection either of a negatron or a positron with the result that a positive or a negative proton, as the case may be, remains in the nucleus in place of the neutron, the event occurring in this instance without the emission of a photon. This alternative, however, postulates the existence in the nucleus of a proton of negative charge, no evidence for which exists. The greater symmetry, however, between the positive and negative charges revealed by the discovery of the positron should prove a stimulus to search for evidence of the existence of negative protons. If the neutron should prove to be a fundamental particle of a new kind rather than a proton and negatron in close combination, the above hypotheses will have to be abandoned for the proton will then in all probability be represented as a complex particle consisting of a neutron and positron.

While this paper was in preparation press reports have announced that P. M. S. Blackett and G. Occhialini in an extensive study of cosmic-ray tracks have also obtained evidence for the existence of light positive particles confirming our earlier report.

I wish to express my great indebtedness to Professor R. A. Millikan for suggesting this research and for many helpful discussions during its progress. The able assistance of Mr. Seth H. Neddermeyer is also appreciated.

73

ooooooooooo

THE DISCOVERY OF THE
DEUTERON

ooooooooooo

Harold Clayton Urey (b. 1893)

With the discovery of the neutron, discussed in Chapter 74, it immediately became clear to physicists that all the difficulties formerly associated with trying to construct nuclei with protons and electrons would disappear. The nucleus could be pictured as consisting only of neutrons and protons, and no conflicts with the Heisenberg uncertainty principle, or the known spin-and-statistical properties of nuclei would arise. For an electron to reside in a nucleus, its De Broglie wavelength would have to be about as small as the nucleus, which would require it to move so fast (the wavelength varies inversely with the speed) that it could not be contained by known nuclear forces. Electrons would also give nuclei of even atomic weight and odd atomic number the wrong spins.

The discovery of the existence of the neutron eliminated these difficulties and revolutionized the theory of the atomic nucleus. Instead of considering the electrostatic interaction between electrons and a nucleus, as in atomic structure, one treats the nuclear interactions between neutrons and protons. In general, however, this is a much more difficult problem than the electron-nucleus problem in atomic structure, because protons and neutrons are of about the same mass; therefore, one faces the "many-body" problem, whereas in the study of electrons moving about a nucleus, the motion of an individual electron can be treated quite accurately, without considering the presence of any of the other electrons.

However, the nuclear "two-body" problem (a nucleus consisting of a single proton and a single neutron) is comparatively easy. Such a nucleus exists in the deuteron, or heavy hydrogen, which is the simplest compound nucleus known. It has been investigated more extensively than any other nuclear structure. Theoreticians quickly realized the usefulness of a thorough analysis of this system for an understanding of nuclear forces, which could not be obtained easily from a study of more complex nuclei.

There are two phases to the study of the two-body, or the two-nucleon, nuclear system. On the one hand, we may investigate how two nucleons (two protons or a proton and a neutron) collide without combining to form a stable, compound system. This is called the two-body scattering problem, on which a great deal of experimental and theoretical work has been done. The other phase of the two-body system deals with the stable, compound system, the deuteron or the hydrogen 2 nucleus. The problem associated with this system is, in principle, the same as that with the hydrogen atom—to find the stationary states or, what is the same thing, the energy levels. One applies the same technique as for the hydrogen atom. Just as Schroedinger set up a wave equation to describe the motion of the electron in the electrostatic field of the proton, one sets up a wave equation to describe the motions of the proton and the neutron in their mutual nuclear field of force. There is, however, one important difference between the hydrogen problem and the deuteron problem. Whereas the mathematical form of the force between the electron and the proton (the Coulomb force) is known, the mathematical formula for the nuclear force is not.

Consequently, various types of forces were used with the hope that the experimental evidence would decide which one was correct. The idea was to calculate the energy levels (and other nuclear features) with various mathematical expressions for the force, and then to check the results with observations made on the two-body system itself. Hence, the existence of a stable two-body nucleus was of great significance.

Fortunately, this particle was discovered by Harold C. Urey in 1932 almost coincidentally with the neutron, so that theory could be tested directly by comparing the theoretical models with the observed properties of the deuteron. In the paper from the *Physical Review* by Urey, F. G. Brickwedde, and G. M. Murphy that follows this commentary, the techniques employed to isolate the heavy isotope of hydrogen are outlined and analyzed. After presenting various chemical and physical arguments in support of the existence of such an isotope, the authors consider various methods for separating the isotopes, and conclude that fractional distillation offers the best chance for success. Although this procedure had not been very successful in other cases, they argue that it has a much better chance to succeed in hydrogen, since the mass ratios of the different hydrogen isotopes are much larger than for the heavier elements. To see how effective fractional distillation might be for hydrogen, the authors first make an approximate calculation of the vapor pressure of the three molecular isotopes H^1H^1 (ordinary hydrogen), H^1H^2 (hydrogen-deuteron) and H^1H^3 (hydrogen-tritium) in equilibrium with their solid phases. The greater the difference in vapor pressure is for these various isotopes, the more easily they can be separated by fractional distillation.

To calculate the vapor pressure of each isotopic gas in equilibrium with its solid phase, the authors write down an expression for the free energy of the solid phase and the free energy of the gaseous phase (which contains the vapor pressure as one of its terms) and then equate the two. Since the free energy of a system is a measure of the amount of work that the system can do, it is clear that if two phases (solid and gaseous phases, for example) are to be in equilibrium, the free energy of one phase must equal that of the other; if this were not so, one phase would do work on the other, until both free energies were equal.

By this procedure, the authors found that the calculated vapor pressure for the H^1H^2 molecule should be about a third that of the ordinary hydrogen molecule (H^1H^1) when the gas is in equilibrium with the solid phase at the triple point temperature of ordinary hydrogen. However, this does not give an accurate description of the experimental situation, since one must really know the vapor pressure of the gaseous phase in equilibrium with the liquid phase and not the solid phase, because fractionation is carried out from the liquid phase. However, since the theory of liquids was quite unsatisfactory when this experiment was performed, the authors simply argue that the ratio of the vapor pressures for the gas in equilibrium with the liquid phase close to the solidification temperature should be about the same as for the solid phase. From this they conclude that fractional distillation can produce an appreciable concentration, since the lightest isotope (ordinary hydrogen) will evaporate more rapidly than the heavier ones.

Three different lots of liquid hydrogen were prepared by Dr. F. G. Brickwedde for the experiment; one was six liters, and each of the other two were four liters. The six liter lot was allowed to evaporate at the usual boiling point of liquid hydrogen, 20.4°K, and the gas evaporating from the last few cc's of liquid was collected for analysis. The procedure used with the two four liter lots was to carry out the evaporation close to the triple point temperature of ordinary hydrogen, 13.95°K and to collect in the same way the gas evaporated from the last few cc's of liquid. Each of the gas samples was then introduced into a discharge tube and the light from the discharge analyzed with the aid of a 21 foot grating spectrograph. Simple Bohr theory shows that for atoms of given atomic number, the line spectrum should be slightly different for atoms having nuclei of different mass, i.e., for different isotopes. Hence the heavy hydrogen atoms should produce a line spectrum with slightly different wavelengths than those characteristic of light hydrogen atoms. When the spectroscopic measurements were made, the gas sampled evaporated at 20°K showed nothing but lines (disregarding the molecular rotation spectrum) appropriate to light hydrogen, but each of the two samples evaporated close to 13.95°K gave faint lines in the positions expected for hydrogen of mass 2. It would be expected that greater fractionation would occur at the lower temperature, so the appearance of H^2 lines for this condition gave added confidence in the result.

When this experiment was performed in late 1931 and early 1932, the neutron had not yet been discovered and the authors still discussed the structure of the nucleus in terms of electrons and protons as its constituents.

The son of a country clergyman, Harold Clayton Urey was born in Walkerton, Indiana, on April 25, 1893. His father died when he was six years old and his mother remarried, again to a clergyman. His early schooling was obtained in the Indiana public schools and he graduated from high school in 1911. Being unable to go directly to college, Urey taught for several years in rural schools before entering the University of Montana in 1914. Three years later he obtained his Bachelor of Science degree in chemistry; because the country was then engaged in World War I, he took a position in Philadelphia in a chemical plant engaged in war production. Later, writing about this experience, he described it as most fortunate, for it convinced him that industrial chemistry was not his major interest and definitely directed him toward academic work. The direction of this academic work was to the University of Montana where he became instructor in chemistry. Five years later, in 1921, he went to the University of California at Berkeley to study for a doctorate in chemistry under Professor Gilbert N. Lewis. Lewis was an inspiring teacher and leader in chemistry and undoubtedly greatly influenced Urey's career.

Following the award of his Ph.D. degree, Urey received a fellowship from the American-Scandinavian Foundation which he used for a year's postdoctoral study at Bohr's Institute for Theoretical Physics in Copenhagen. Returning to the United States in 1924, he served for five years as associate in chemistry at the Johns Hopkins University in Baltimore. It was during this time that he prepared with Arthur E. Ruark his widely used book *Atoms, Molecules and Quanta*, published in 1930.

In 1929 Urey accepted a position as associate professor of chemistry at Columbia University and very shortly thereafter began the investigation for which he received the Nobel Prize in 1934—the isolation of the hydrogen isotope of mass two, "heavy hydrogen" or deuterium. This research was carried out with the assistance of Dr. Ferdinand G. Brickwedde, then head of the cryogenic section of the U.S. National Bureau of Standards and Dr. George M. Murphy at Columbia University.

Research with heavy hydrogen and methods of concentrating stable isotopes occupied Urey during the following years until the United States' entry in World War II. As a consequence of his experience in isotope separation he was appointed to head the group designated as the SAM (Substitute Alloy Materials) Laboratory established at Columbia University to investigate the separation of the uranium isotopes 235 and 238 for the purposes of making an atomic bomb. This laboratory was part of the Army's Manhattan District Project and subsequently became the research laboratory that provided the fundamental data necessary for the construction of the large-scale diffusion separation plant built by the Kellex Corporation at Oak Ridge, Tennessee.

In 1945, at the end of the war, Urey joined the Institute for Nuclear Studies at the University of Chicago and became distinguished service professor of chemistry. His scientific interests now took a new direction and he began research on the origin of the earth and the planetary system, the evolution of life on the earth and the temperatures of the oceans in past geologic ages. His book, *The Planets, Their Origin and Development,* was published by the Yale University Press in 1952. In 1958 he left the University of Chicago to assume the chair of professor of chemistry-at-large in the University of California, La Jolla. He is now living in La Jolla.

ооооооо

U R E Y ,   B R I C K W E D D E ,   and   M U R P H Y

A Hydrogen Isotope of Mass 2 and Its Concentration [1]

THE POSSIBILITY OF THE EXISTENCE of isotopes of hydrogen has been discussed for a number of years. Older discussions involved Prout's hypothesis and dealt with the question as to whether hydrogen consisted of a mixture of isotopes, one having an atomic weight exactly one, and another or others with integral values, in such proportions as to give an average atomic weight of 1.008. The result of an exact determination in 1927 with the mass spectrograph by

---

[1] Harold C. Urey, F. G. Brickwedde, and G. M. Murphy, *Physical Review,* 40 (1932), 1–15.

Aston of the atomic weight of the hydrogen isotope of mass-number one not only proved that it is not integrally equal to unity but the agreement with the chemically determined value was so close that it was considered unlikely that hydrogen had more than the single isotope of mass-number one. The discovery of the oxygen isotopes by Giauque and Johnston in 1929 showed that the chemical standard of atomic weights was not the same as that used by Aston and that agreement between the chemical determinations and Aston's values should not be expected. When the atomic weights of hydrogen as determined chemically and by the mass spectrograph are reduced to a common standard, the previous apparent agreement is destroyed and they differ. Birge and Menzel showed that this discrepancy could be explained by the presence of an isotope of hydrogen of mass-number two, present to the extent of one part in 4500.

Quite independently of such a quantitative basis of prediction as is furnished by the agreement or disagreement of the atomic weights determined chemically and with the mass spectrograph, one may be led by other lines of reasoning to expect heavier isotopes of hydrogen and helium, as well, even though the atomic weights reduced to a common standard do agree, for it is only necessary to assume that they are so rare that they can not be detected by atomic weight determinations within the limits of the experimental accuracy. The recent discoveries of rare isotopes emphasize that it may be impossible ever to disprove the existence of any nuclear species. Recent systematic arrangements of nuclear species lead one to expect isotopes of hydrogen of masses 2 and 3 and an isotope of helium of mass 5. Beck leaves a place in his tables for H^3 and He^5. Johnston has question marks in his table for H^2, H^3, He^5 and Li^5. Urey makes no definite predictions but presents a proton-electron plot which shows the regularities very well, the three isotopes, H^2, H^3, and He^5 being required to give this plot a completed appearance.

METHODS OF CONCENTRATION

Birge and Menzel remark that the discovery of a hydrogen isotope of higher mass-number by the methods of molecular spectra would be difficult though not impossible. The maximum abundance of an isotope of mass-number 2 which can be expected is that given by Birge and Menzel for if any isotope of higher mass number were present the abundance of the isotopes would all necessarily be less. It seemed essential to find some way of concentrating the heavier isotopes if they were to be detected by spectroscopic methods. Any of the various methods used for concentrating isotopes should be more effective in the case of these isotopes of hydrogen because of the large ratio of masses. Of these methods, that of fractional distillation should give the largest supply with the least effort. This method has been tried in a number of cases but with little success except in the case of neon.

The vapor pressures of the molecules H^1H^1, H^1H^2, H^1H^3 in equilibrium with their pure solids can be calculated if the following postulates are made: (1) the rotational and vibrational energies of the molecules are the same in the solid and gaseous states and thus need not be considered in the calculations of vapor pressures; (2) the free energy of the solids can be calculated from the Debye theory of the solid state, assuming that the Θ's of the three solids are inversely proportional to the square roots of the molecular weights; (3) the free energy of the gas is given by the free energy equation of an ideal monatomic gas.

At equilibrium, the free energy of the gas is equal to the free energy of the solid, and since all the quantities may be evaluated, we may calculate the vapor pressures of the isotopic molecules. The free energy and entropy of hydrogen gas are given by the following expressions:

$$F_g = E_g + RT - TS_g \tag{1}$$

$$S_g = \frac{3}{2} R \ln M + \frac{5}{2} R \ln T - R \ln P + C + R \ln R \tag{2}$$

where M is the molecular weight, P is the pressure in atmospheres, R is the gas constant in cal. per mole per degree and C is the Sackur-Tetrode constant and equals -11.053 cal. per degree and

$$E_g = \frac{3}{2} RT + \chi. \tag{3}$$

χ is the heat of vaporization at absolute zero from a hypothetical solid hydrogen without zero point energy, which for convenience is chosen as the standard reference energy state to which the internal energies of the solid and gaseous phases are referred. χ is assumed to be the same for the isotopic molecules. The differences between the values of the internal energy of the gas at the triple point of hydrogen (13.95° K) as calculated by Eq. (3) and by the more exact equations for a degenerate gas are negligibly small.

The free energy of solid hydrogen is given by:

$$F_s = E' + T\Phi(M, T) + PV. \tag{4}$$

Because of the small volume of solid hydrogen the PV term may be neglected without serious error. The quantity E' is the zero point energy (Nullpunktsenergie) and must be included. The function $\Phi(M, T)$ may be obtained from the Debye theory of specific heats.

Solving these equations for $\ln P$ after equating (1) and (4) and dividing through by RT, we have:

$$\ln P = \frac{E'}{RT} + \frac{\Phi}{R} + \frac{3}{2}\ln M + \frac{5}{2}\ln T + \frac{C}{R} + \ln R - \frac{5}{2} - \frac{\chi}{RT}. \quad (5)$$

The only terms on the right of (5) which depend on the mass are the 1st, 2nd, and 3rd, since χ has been assumed to be the same for isotopic molecules. If we indicate the two molecules H^1H^1 and H^1H^2 by subscripts we have the ratio of their vapor pressures given by:

$$\ln P_{11}/P_{12} = \frac{1}{RT}(E'_{11} - E_{12}') + \frac{1}{R}(\Phi_{11} - \Phi_{12})$$
$$+ \frac{3}{2}\ln M_{11}/M_{12}. \quad (6)$$

The quantity $\Phi(M, T)$ is a function of $h\nu/kT$, where ν is the characteristic frequency for the solid state; $h\nu/k$ for ordinary hydrogen as determined by Simon and Lange is 91. Since the characteristic frequency ν is inversely proportional to the square root of the molecular weight, the argument of Φ may be determined for the isotopic molecules and the value of Φ taken from the tables. The calculation of the ratio P_{11}/P_{12} is made for the temperature $13.95°$ K, the triple point for ordinary hydrogen. The ratio P_{11}/P_{13} is calculated in a similar way.

The numerical values for $h\nu/k$ and Φ are [shown in Table 73-1].

TABLE 73-1

Molecule	M	$h\nu/k$	Φ
H^1H^1	2	91	-0.1339
H^1H^2	3	74.29	-0.2251
H^1H^3	4	64.36	-0.3364

The value of the zero point energy is $9/8 h\nu$ per molecule and may be easily calculated for the isotopic molecules. The values of E' thus become $(9/8)R(h\nu)/k;$ or $(9/8)R\Theta$. Substituting the numerical values in (6), we get:

$$P_{11}/P_{12} = 2.688, \quad P_{11}/P_{13} = 3.354.$$

If the calculation is carried through assuming that the zero point energy is zero, it is found that on this basis the *heavier* isotopic molecules should have the higher vapor pressures which is contrary to experience not only with the hydrogen isotopes but with all other isotopes.

This calculation of the ratios of the vapor pressures has been made for the solid state. A similar calculation cannot be made for the liquid state since the theory is inadequate. It seems reasonable to expect that differences between the vapor pressures of the isotopes should persist beyond the melting point and that a fractionation of the liquid solution should be possible.

The Rayleigh distillation formula integrated for ideal solutions is:

$$\left(\frac{1 - N_0}{1 - N}\right)^{\alpha/(1-\alpha)} \left(\frac{N}{N_0}\right)^{1/(1-\alpha)} = \frac{W_0}{W} \tag{7}$$

where N and N_0 are the mole fractions of the less volatile constituent left in the still and in the original sample respectively and W and W_0 are the moles of both constituents left in the still and in the original sample respectively, and α is the distribution coefficient equal to the ratio of the vapor pressure of the less volatile constituent to that of the more volatile constituents. If N_0 and N are small as compared to 1 as is the case for the distillation of these isotopes of hydrogen, this formula reduces to:

$$\left(\frac{N}{N_0}\right)^{1/(1-\alpha)} = \frac{W_0}{W}. \tag{8}$$

This formula has been used in estimating the increased concentrations expected.

If we assume that the mole fraction of H^2 is $\frac{1}{4500}$ in the original hydrogen, that $\alpha = \frac{1}{2.688}$ and that $W_0/W = 4000$, we secure about 4 mole percent as the value of N. Since we have not secured such high concentrations, we conclude that either the ratio of vapor pressures of the solids is quite different from those of the liquids at the same temperature, or that some of the assumptions made in regard to the solids are not sufficiently exact. We have made this calculation in order to see whether the separation by fractionation was likely to be effective.

PREPARATION OF THE CONCENTRATED HYDROGEN SAMPLES

Each of the different samples of hydrogen, which were later examined spectroscopically, was prepared from liquid hydrogen made by circulating about 400 cubic feet of free gas through a liquefier of the ordinary Hampson type in which, after precooling with liquid air boiling at reduced pressure, it was expanded from a pressure of about 2500 pounds per square inch to atmospheric pressure. As the liquid hydrogen was obtained it was collected in storage containers from which it was transferred to an unsilvered triple walled flask of about 1600 cm³ capacity in which the concentration of the isotope was effected. After filling the flask, the liquid hydrogen was allowed to evaporate until only about ⅓ or ¼ remained, when the flask was refilled and the procedure was repeated until all the liquid had been transferred. The flask was connected by vacuum tight joints to the glass bulbs in which the hydrogen gas evaporating from the last two or three cubic centimeters of liquid was collected. These bulbs were connected to a Hyvac pump for exhaustion and flushing out previous to the collection of the final concentrate. Proper precautions were taken to prevent the entry of air into the system while the samples were being collected. This method of evaporation is somewhat less efficient than the method assumed in the calculation above and accounts, at least in part, for the lower efficiency observed.

Sample I was collected from the end portion of six liters of liquid hydrogen evaporated at atmospheric pressure, and samples II and III, each, from four liters evaporated at a pressure only a few millimeters above the triple point. The process of liquefaction could have had only a small effect in changing the relative concentrations of the isotopes since no appreciable increase in the concentration of the isotopic molecule H^1H^2 over that in ordinary hydrogen was detected for sample I obtained from six liters of liquid hydrogen evaporated at atmospheric pressure.

SPECTRUM ANALYSIS

It is possible to detect the hydrogen isotopes from the positions of the atomic lines, since the Balmer lines of any heavier isotopes will be displaced to the violet side of the H^1 Balmer lines. Assuming that the masses of the isotopic hydrogen nuclei of mass-numbers 2 and 3 are exactly twice and three times the mass of the proton, the calculated wave-lengths of the isotopic lines and the observed wave-lengths of the H^1 lines are [shown in Table 73–2].

TABLE 73–2

	α	β	γ	δ
H^1	6562.793	4861.326	4340.467	4101.738
H^2	6561.000	4860.000	4339.282	4100.619
H^3	6560.400	4859.56₆	4338.882	4100.239

The second order of a 21 foot grating with a dispersion of 1.3A per mm was used to analyze the spectrum from a Wood hydrogen discharge tube run in his so-called black stage. This tube was 1 cm in diameter and was excited by a current of about 1 ampere at 3000 to 4000 volts; the radiation was sufficiently intense to record the $H^1\beta$ and $H^1\gamma$ lines in about 1 sec., though the lines were broad and unresolved under these conditions. By greatly decreasing the current and increasing the exposure time to about 16 sec., it was possible to resolve the $H^1\beta$ line into a doublet, but a simple calculation showed that the time of exposure necessary to record the isotope lines under conditions necessary to resolve them would be prohibitively long. We therefore worked with the high current density in order to decrease the exposure time.

The usual method of securing clean atomic hydrogen spectra by flowing moist hydrogen through the tube was not used, as the samples were limited in amount. They were not moistened by saturation with ordinary water since we did not wish to contaminate them with ordinary hydrogen from the water. The sample of hydrogen was contained in a glass bulb with two stop-cocks attached in series so that a small sample of hydrogen (about 2 cc) could be admitted to the discharge tube at one time. The stop-cock grease was a disadvantage since it was probably the source of the cyanogen bands in our tube which was troublesome when working with $H\delta$. The hydrogen gas was either not moistened at all, in which case the molecular spectrum was rather strong, or, it was moistened by attaching near the electrodes small side tubes containing copper oxide or, by admitting oxygen gas in small amounts. The copper oxide in the side tubes was reduced by atomic hydrogen diffusing in from the discharge tube and water was formed. When oxygen was used, some of the oxygen bands and lines appeared which, however, caused no trouble. None of these methods of suppressing the molecular spectrum was as effective as the flowing stream of moist hydrogen gas and at times the molecular spectrum became intense in spite of all our efforts to keep the tube in a good black stage.

Before working on the evaporated samples of hydrogen, ordinary hydrogen was tried first in order to overcome any difficulties in the method of excitation. The sample of hydrogen evaporated at the boiling point (Sample I) was next investigated, but no isotopes present in the estimated concentrations could be found, though faint lines appeared at the calculated positions for H^2 lines. Returning then to ordinary hydrogen, these same lines were found with about the same intensity as in sample I. It was difficult to be certain that these lines were not irregular ghosts. All other lines near the Balmer lines could be accounted for as known molecular lines. Turning then to sample II, evaporated near the triple point, the H^2 lines were found greatly enhanced relative to the H^1 lines thus showing that an appreciable increased concentration of the H^2 isotope had been secured and that the lines could not be ghosts since their intensity varied relative to the known symmetrical ghosts. Sample III was investigated subsequently and found to have a higher concentration of H^2 than sample II.

The measurements on ordinary hydrogen will be discussed first. A great many plates were taken with ordinary hydrogen with the tube in the black stage and one with the tube in the white stage. (Copper oxide was blown into the discharge tube to produce an intense molecular spectrum.) In [Table 73–3] we give the measurements made on plates (34t, 35t) showing the $H\beta$ and $H\gamma$ regions with the tube in the white stage, and measurements made on plates (36t, 37t) with the tube in the black stage. The times of exposure and currents through the tube were the same for all these plates. For comparison we give the wave-lengths given by Gale, Monk and Lee, and by Finkelnburg for the molecular spectrum in these regions and the calculated wave-lengths of the Balmer lines of H^2 and H^3. The positions of the H^1 lines were secured by taking the means of the positions of the symmetrical ghosts and all the lines were measured relative to the standard iron lines.

TABLE 73–3

		35t	37t	Gale, Monk and Lee	Finkelnburg
$H^1\beta$	4861.326	4861.322	4861.320	4861.328	
		4860.892	—	4860.806	
		4860.636	4860.633	—	4860.620
		4860.104	—	4860.108	4860.134
$H^2\beta$	4860.000	—	4859.975	—	—
$H^3\beta$	4859.566	—	—	—	—
		34t	36t		
$H^1\gamma$	4340.467	4340.465	4340.486	4340.470	4340.466
		4340.084	—	—	4340.154
		4339.847	4339.879	4339.817	4339.845
		4339.568	4339.599	4339.534	4339.538
$H^2\gamma$	4339.282	—	4339.318	—	—
$H^3\gamma$	4338.8_{82}	—	—	—	—

The discrepancies between our values and those of the other authors are rather large. In view of the fact that the molecular lines on our plates were so weak that the measurements of their positions were very difficult, the agreement obtained was considered satisfactory. The $H^2\gamma$ line appeared as a slight irregularity on a microphotometer curve of the plate 34t but could not be measured with the comparator. The measurements on other plates taken of the atomic spectrum of ordinary hydrogen run very much the same, sometimes with other observed molecular lines on them. The average displacements of the H^2 lines from all plates taken with ordinary hydrogen are given in [Table 73–4].

TABLE 73–4

	Hα	Hβ	Hγ	Hδ
Calcd. displacement	1.793	1.326	1.185	1.119
Obs.				
Ordinary hydrogen	—	1.346	1.206	1.145
Sample I	—	1.330	1.199	1.103
Samples II and III	1.791	1.313	1.176	1.088

The measurements of plates taken with the hydrogen of sample I under the same conditions as with ordinary hydrogen run very much the same as those for ordinary hydrogen. It was impossible by visual observation to be certain of any difference between the intensity of the H^2 lines on the plates for ordinary hydrogen and for sample I, although there were fewer molecular lines on sample I plates than on ordinary hydrogen plates. From this it was concluded that there was no appreciable increase in the concentration of the isotope H^2 in sample I evaporated from six liters of liquid hydrogen at atmospheric pressure over that in ordinary hydrogen and that at 20° K, the vapor pressures of the H^1H^1 and H^1H^2 isotopic molecules must be nearly, if not actually, equal. The mean wave-length displacements of the H^2 lines from the H^1 lines on these plates are given in [Table 73–4]. The agreement with the calculated displacements is better than in the case of ordinary hydrogen. This may indicate a greater ease of measurement due to an increased photographic density of the H^2 lines on sample I plates from which it might be concluded that there was a slight increase in the concentration of the heavier isotope.

When observations were made on samples II and III evaporated just above the triple point, the H^2 lines stood out so clearly from the background that there was no longer any possibility of confusing them with the molecular lines and no further measurements of the molecular lines were made. The measurement of the positions of the H^2 lines on these plates relative to the ghosts of the H^1 lines could be made with ease. The mean displacements listed in [Table 73–4] for samples II and III are the most reliable ones obtained.

A mercury line falls at 4339.23, while the calculated wave-length of $H^2\gamma$ is 4339.282. Mercury got into our discharge tube due to various efforts we made to depress the molecular spectrum in the stationary gas.

This occurred while we were working with samples II and III. On some plates this mercury line appears as a very faint black edge on the broad atomic line. In other cases, it was more intense and appeared as a very sharp line.

[Fig. 73–1] shows enlarged prints of plates taken with sample II of the $H^1\alpha$, $H^1\beta$, and $H^1\gamma$ lines with the isotope lines appearing as faint companions on the high frequency side of the H^1 lines. The pair of sym-

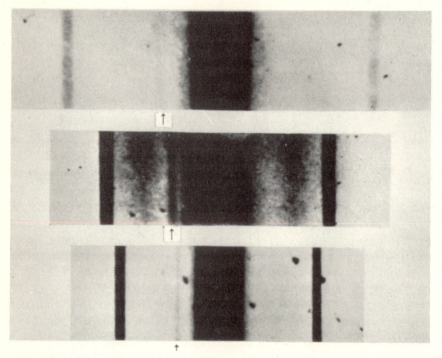

Fig. 73–1. Enlargement of the $H\alpha$, $H\beta$ and $H\gamma$ lines. The faint lines appearing on the high-frequency side of the heavily over-exposed H^1 lines are the lines due to H^2. The symmetrical pair of lines in each case are ghosts.

metrical lines in each case are the ghosts. [Fig. 73–2] shows the $H\beta$ lines for ordinary tank hydrogen and for the evaporated hydrogen, sample II, the condition of the discharge and the time of exposure being approximately the same. The isotope H^2 line for sample II is considerably more intense than for ordinary hydrogen, showing that a considerable increase in the concentration of this isotope was affected by evaporation near the triple point. Similar plates have been obtained for $H\gamma$. The $H^2\alpha$ line was obtained only with samples II and III.

The lines of H^2 are broad as is to be expected if they consist of close unresolved doubtlets, but they are not so broad and diffuse as the lines

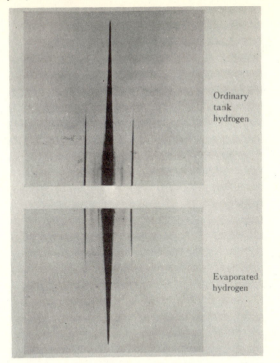

Ordinary
tank
hydrogen

Evaporated
hydrogen

Fig. 73–2. The H lines for ordinary tank hydrogen and sample II of the evaporated hydrogen. Although the intensity of the main line is about the same for both exposures, the H$^2\beta$ line is considerably more intense in the second case showing the increased concentration.

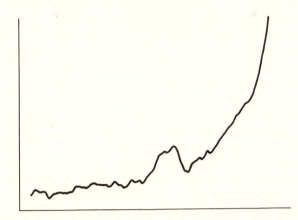

Fig. 73–3. Microphotometer curve of H$^2\alpha$ showing the doublet separation which is from 0.10 to 0.12A.

of H^1 probably due to less Doppler broadening. The H$^2\alpha$ line is just resolved into a close doublet on two plates. Visual settings on these lines with the comparator were difficult. One plate measured in this way gave a doublet separation of 0.16A. Microphotometer curves also show the doublet separation and the separation secured in this way is from 0.10 to 0.12A. These latter figures are the more reliable and agree with the observed separation of the H$^1\alpha$ line of 0.135A, being somewhat lower than the value for the well resolved line as is to be expected for partially resolved lines. [Fig. 73–3] shows a microphotometer curve of this line. By itself it is not entirely convincing because of the irregularities due to grain size of the plate. That the resolution is real is proven by visual observation of the plate.

RELATIVE ABUNDANCE

When using ordinary hydrogen, the H$^2\beta$ line appears as a rather sharp line lying in a clear part of the plate between the region of halation from the main line and the main line itself. As the time of exposure is increased, the irradiated region and the region of halation build up the diffuse background of the plate so rapidly that the H^2 line does not become more distinct. However, in the case of sample II and sample III, the H^2 lines come out with a very much greater distinctness so that it is possible to secure these lines without bad halation from the main line. Thus there is no doubt that there has been a very distinct increase in concentration of the H^2 isotope relative to the H^1 isotope in the process of evaporation. It is difficult, however, to give an exact estimate of the relative abundance from the intensity of spectral lines which lie so close together with one so much more intense than the other. Moreover, a comparison of exposure times is not entirely satisfactory because we note that the H^2 lines are distinctly sharper than the H^1 lines so that if the same amounts of energy were emitted by the two varieties of atoms, the H^2 lines should appear to be the more intense, since this energy would fall in a narrower region on the plate. Comparison of the relative intensities of the ghosts of the H^1 lines and the H^2 lines meets with this same difficulty for the ghosts are distinctly more diffuse than the H^2 lines. The best that can be done, therefore, is to give rather rough estimates of the relative abundance judging from times of exposure.

In the case of ordinary hydrogen, it was found that when the discharge tube was running with such an intensity that the H^1 lines could be recorded within one second, that it required somewhat more than an hour to just detect the H^2 lines. It is, therefore, estimated that the relative abundance of the isotopes in ordinary hydrogen is about 1 in 4000 or less. We believe that the estimate of Birge and Menzel based on the atomic weights is consistent with our observations and that their estimate is probably the more reliable.

In the case of sample II, the $H^2\beta$ and $H^2\gamma$ lines could be photographed in ten minutes and the corresponding H^1 lines in one second. From this it is estimated that the relative abundance of H^2 in sample II was 1 in 600, but this, it is believed, is too high because in this case the discharge tube was running better than before and it should have been possible to photograph the H^1 lines in less than a second. Again, the intensities of the ghost lines produced by the grating used are about $\frac{1}{200}$th of the intensities of the main lines and the H^2 lines have an intensity equal to about $\frac{1}{4}$th of that of the ghost lines as determined by relative exposure times of 1 to 4. This gives a ratio of about 1 in 800. This is about the best estimate that we were able to make of the relative intensities in this sample. Sample III contains H^2 in larger amounts than sample II, perhaps as much as 1 part in 500 to 600.

[Fig. 73–4] shows microphotometer curves of the $H\beta$ lines from three samples of hydrogen. The plates were selected so that the densities of the

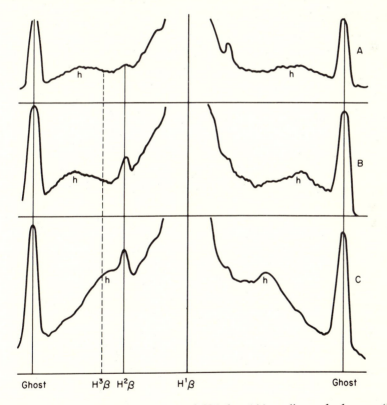

Ghost $H^3\beta$ $H^2\beta$ $H^1\beta$ Ghost

Fig. 73–4. Microphotometer curves of $H\beta$ for (A) ordinary hydrogen (B) sample II (C) sample III. The calculated position of $H^3\beta$ is indicated although there is no evidence for its existence from these curves. The h's indicate regions of halation.

ghost lines were as nearly alike as possible. Visual comparison of the plates shows that the variations in the densities of the ghost lines are such that the intensities are in the order $A > B > C$. The heights of the micro-photometric curves of the ghosts in [Fig. 73–4] would not seem to sub-stantiate this statement. The ghost curves of B and C are higher than that of A because of a more continuous background in A due partly to the dif-ferent distribution of the halation. The fourth order ghosts on the plates are not complicated in this way and visually have the intensity order $A > B > C$. The line to the right of the main H^1 line with an intensity in A greater than in either B or C is a molecular line. The increase in the intensity of the $H^2\beta$ line for samples II and III as recorded by curves B and C over that for ordinary hydrogen, Curve A, can easily be seen. This shows that the concentration of the H^2 isotope was markedly in-creased by evaporation at the triple point. The heights of the curves above the estimated continuous backgrounds are in the ratio $A : B : C = 4 : 16 : 17$, thus substantiating the estimates of increased concentration from exposure times.

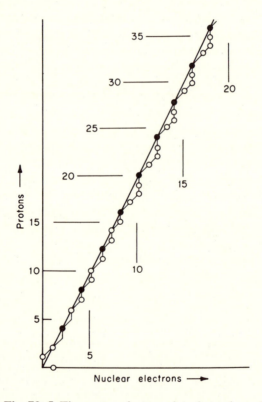

Fig. 73–5. The proton-electron plot of atomic nuclei.

A SYSTEM OF ATOMIC NUCLEI

It is of interest to see how the H^2 nucleus fits into a system of atomic nuclei. Periodic systems have been proposed by several authors and are largely equivalent. The simple proton-electron plot shows regularities in a very good way and the accompanying figure [Fig. 73–5] shows the regularities up to A^{36}. The figure suggests that H^3 and He^5 should exist. No evidence for H^3 has as yet been found, but further concentration (see below) may yet show that this nuclear species exists. It should be possible to concentrate He^5 by the distillation of liquid helium, and this method may show that this nucleus also exists.

OTHER METHODS FOR CONCENTRATING THE HEAVIER ISOTOPES OF HYDROGEN

It seems entirely feasible to construct a fractionating column that will greatly increase the efficiency of the distillation method for separating these isotopes. This method has the distinct advantage that it is capable of producing large samples. On the other hand, it requires rather large volumes of gas, so that after the isotope has been concentrated in small volumes by the fractional distillation and rectification of liquid hydrogen, further concentration may be better carried out using diffusion methods. Stern and Vollmer used such a method in an attempt to find isotopes of hydrogen and oxygen, working on the hypothesis that the non-integral atomic weight of hydrogen might be due to a higher isotope. They report that a heavier hydrogen isotope is not present to the extent of 1 part in 100,000. Their negative result emphasizes the difficulties of diffusion methods which for success require carefully controlled conditions. Such an apparatus as has been described by Hertz should be very effective for the separation of the hydrogen isotopes. Work is in progress on the construction of such an apparatus for further concentration beyond the state that we can reach with distillation methods. . . .

74

ooooooooooo

DISCOVERY OF THE
NEUTRON

ooooooooooo

James Chadwick (b. 1891)

In the second decade of the twentieth century physicists were concerned primarily with the outer regions of the atom and with the development of the theoretical procedures necessary to understand the behavior of the electrons as they move around the nucleus; the third decade marked the exploration of the nucleus itself. Of course, well before the 1930's Rutherford had used α particles ejected from radioactive nuclei to study the nuclei of other atoms, and in 1929 Gamow had applied quantum mechanics to an analysis and explanation of the emission of α-particles from radioactive nuclei. But many difficulties had stood in the way of carrying out detailed experimental investigations of the structure of the nucleus and no theoretical model had yet been introduced that could account for even the most elementary observed properties of atomic nuclei.

Since the electric charge on the atomic nucleus increases by one unit as we move from one element to the next in the periodic table, we must have very energetic protons or α particles to penetrate the repulsive Coulomb barrier of the heavier nuclei. With only these particles (electrons are not massive enough to do much damage to a nucleus) available before 1932, the amount of nuclear investigation was necessarily meager. Rutherford succeeded in bringing about nuclear transformations, but on a very small scale, since he had at his disposal only minute quantities of radioactive material. With the development of the cyclotron by E. O. Laurence, and linear types of accelerators, beams of high-energy protons became available, but, again, in rather small quantities and at energies that were suitable only for working with light nuclei.

1288

More serious than the practical difficulties that hampered nuclear research were the theoretical contradictions. The essential difficulty lay in trying to account for the mass of a nucleus and its charge in terms of the fundamental particles that were known at the time—the electron and the proton. It was quite natural to suppose that the nucleus of an atom consisted of electrons and protons, since protons were positively charged and electrons were known to be emitted by radioactive nuclei. To illustrate the nature of the difficulty let us consider the nucleus of the helium atom, the α particle. We know that its mass is very nearly four times that of a single proton; and hence, our first inclination is to assume that it contains four protons to account for this mass. However, this would give us a nucleus with twice the observed charge. To overcome this all we need do, it appears, is add two electrons to the four protons inside the nucleus; we then have a structure that seems to mirror reality. This was, indeed, the earliest model proposed, and it seemed satisfactory until the advent of quantum mechanics and the uncertainty principle. It then became obvious that an electron cannot exist inside a nucleus. There is just no room inside a nucleus for a wave packet as large as that of an electron. Trying to put it there is like trying to force an elephant into a dog house.

Now let us consider the application of the uncertainty principle to an electron in a nucleus. Since we can calculate the size of any nucleus, we can also know the position of an electron assumed to lie inside it—with enormously high accuracy, of the order of a ten-trillionth of a centimeter, since this is the size of a nucleus. But applying the uncertainty principle, it follows that there is a correspondingly high uncertainty in the momentum and therefore in the kinetic energy of the electron. In fact a simple calculation, on the basis of the formula for the De Broglie wavelength, shows that the electron would have to be moving with such high speed inside a nucleus that it could not possibly be held imprisoned by forces of the order we know are present in the nucleus. In short, the wave pattern that describes the electron is so distended that it cannot be contained within a nucleus.

There is still another objection to having electrons inside nuclei, and this relates to the spin properties of electrons, protons, and nuclei. Electrons and protons both have the same spin, which we may take as half a unit (actually it is one half the fundamental unit of angular momentum, which is Planck's constant divided by 2π). If a nucleus consisted of electrons and protons, its spin would be the sum of the spins of the constituent particles. In general these spins arrange themselves so that they cancel out in pairs. This means that the spin of a nucleus should either be zero or $\frac{1}{2}$, depending upon whether the total number of electrons plus protons is even or odd. As an example we consider the nucleus of nitrogen, which must contain at least seven protons to account for its seven-fold positive charge. To justify a mass of 14, the proton-electron model of the nitrogen nucleus would have to assign seven more protons to the nucleus—as well as seven electrons in order to achieve a positive charge equal to seven. But this would leave us with 21 spinning particles altogether inside the nucleus; hence the spin of the nitrogen nucleus would have to be $\frac{1}{2}$ or some odd integral multiple of $\frac{1}{2}$. Experiments, however, show that the spin is zero so that this proton-electron model is untenable.

This contradiction was removed from nuclear theory when Chadwick proved the existence of a new type of particle, the neutron, in 1932. In his paper, reproduced at the end of this chapter, Chadwick carefully examines the experiments of Bothe and Becker as well as those of Mme. Curie-Joliot and of Webster involving the bombardment of light elements by α particles. Up to the time that Chadwick carried out his analysis of these experiments it was thought that the radiation emitted as a result of these bombardments (particularly in the case of beryllium) was electromagnetic in nature (that is, photons), but extremely energetic, as indicated by the penetrating power of this radiation. Chadwick very ingeniously showed, however, that the protons ejected from hydrogen-containing material (paraffin wax, for example) by this radiation do not follow the accepted pattern as predicted by well established theory. Moreover, he pointed out that there is no nuclear mechanism that can give rise to such energetic electromagnetic radiation from nuclei bombarded by α particles. As a result of these considerations, Chadwick decided to carry out further experiments on the radiation emitted when beryllium is bombarded by α particles.

After carefully studying the effects of the beryllium radiation on atoms of various kinds, Chadwick concluded that the only way to account for the effects of this radiation on these atoms was either to "relinquish the application of the conservation of energy and momentum in these collisions or to adopt another hypothesis about the nature of the radiation." As he points out, all the difficulties disappear if the beryllium radiation is pictured as being *not* electromagnetic but rather as consisting of neutral particles with masses equal to the mass of the proton. Because of the large mass of such a particle it can easily eject atoms from various targets with the velocities that Chadwick and the other investigators had observed when the beryllium "radiation" impinged upon matter. Furthermore, because these neutral particles of Chadwick's have no charge, and are thus not repelled by the electric fields surrounding nuclei, they are highly penetrating.

In bombarding various substances with these "neutrons," as Chadwick called them, he undoubtedly had created artificially radioactive isotopes without realizing it. It was not until a few years later that a systematic investigation of this artificial radioactivity was carried out by Joliot and his wife, and independently by Fermi. A point of interest in connection with the introduction of the neutron is that, as Chadwick notes, the need for such a particle had already been recognized by Rutherford as early as 1920. How vastly different the world might now be in its political, scientific, and geographical division, had Rutherford pursued his idea experimentally and discovered the neutron then! For in the 1920's and early 1930's the center of scientific investigation was in Germany. In the United States, fundamental scientific work on a much smaller scale was then being done. Very likely the atomic bomb would have been developed first in Europe, undoubtedly by the Germans.

To see how the neutron swept away all the difficulties that plagued nuclear physicists let us consider the nitrogen nucleus again. Now with only neutrons and protons, we account for the charge and the mass of the nitrogen nucleus by introducing just seven protons and seven neutrons; since each of these has a half unit of spin (the neutron has the same spin properties as the electron and the proton), the spin of the nucleus must either be zero or some integer value. The value turns out to be zero as determined by actual measurement.

As far as there being sufficient room inside a nucleus to accommodate a neutron, the situation is quite different from that for an electron. Of course, the uncertainty principle still applies and the uncertainty in the momentum of the neutron in a nucleus is as large as it would be for an electron. But because the mass of the neutron is about 2000 times larger than that of the electron, its kinetic energy (for the same amount of momentum) is some 2000 times smaller. Therefore, the neutron is not too energetic to remain bound in the nucleus.

In the second half of his paper Chadwick speculated about the nature of the neutron and concluded that it was a proton and an electron in very close combination, since it has no charge and has a mass slightly less than the hydrogen atom but larger than that of the proton. According to this point of view, which was held by many physicists in the period immediately following the discovery of the neutron, this particle was assumed to be a compound structure. However, principally as the result of the ideas of Heisenberg, the compound picture was soon discarded and the neutron was admitted into the gallery of fundamental particles already occupied by the electron, the proton, the positron, and the photon. We now consider the neutron and the proton as two different energy states of the same fundamental particle, the nucleon. Since the neutron is more massive than the proton, it represents the nucleon in a higher energy state. If left to itself, the neutron must decay into a proton with the emission of an electron and a neutrino.

The most recent experiments show that the neutron has a half-life of about 12 minutes. Under ordinary conditions inside a nucleus the nuclear forces between the proton and the neutron prevent the neutron from decaying into a proton. But in nuclei in which the number of neutrons is much larger than the number of protons, this does happen and electrons are then emitted. Such nuclei are called β-radioactive and the electrons are called β rays.

One of the consequences of the decay of a neutron into a proton is the need to introduce still another fundamental particle, the neutrino (the little neutral one), a name that was suggested first by Fermi. Such a particle was proposed by Pauli to explain certain discrepancies in the spin and energy balance of nuclei involved in β-radioactivity. When a neutron changes into a proton with the emission of an electron, the total spin of the nucleus no longer balances. We start with one half unit of spin, the neutron, and end with two half units, the electron and the proton. The only way total spin balance can be maintained is by the introduction of another half unit of spin, which is the exact function of the neutrino.

It also leads to a correct energy balance, for without the neutrino the principle of the conservation of energy would be violated.

In 1920 Rutherford had proposed a neutral particle, formed by the combination of an electron and proton, as the first step in the formation of a nucleus. On the basis of Rutherford's suggestion, Glasson and Roberts attempted to observe the formation of such a particle by passing electrons through hydrogen, but without success. The first successful attempt to detect this neutral particle, now called the neutron, was made in 1932 by Chadwick as a consequence of experiments performed by Mme. and M. Joliot-Curie.

James Chadwick was well equipped intellectually and educationally to carry out the precise and ingenious experiments that led to the discovery of the neutron. He was born in Cheshire, England, on October 20, 1891, the son of John Joseph Chadwick and Ann Mary Knowles. After attending Manchester High School, he enrolled in the University of Manchester in 1908 and graduated from the Honors School of Physics in 1911. He then went to work with Professor Rutherford at the Manchester Physical Laboratory and received his Master of Science degree there in 1913. Simultaneously he received the 1851 Exhibition scholarship, and went to work with Professor H. Geiger in Berlin. He was in Germany in 1914 when World War I broke out and was interned for the duration.

In 1919 Chadwick returned to England and worked with Rutherford at the Cavendish Laboratory on the artificial transformation of light nuclei by bombarding them with α particles, proving his ability as a physicist of top quality. He was elected fellow of Ganville and Caius College in 1921, became assistant director of research of the Cavendish Laboratory in 1923, and was elected fellow of the Royal Society in 1927.

During this period, Chadwick was very actively at work with Rutherford in all kinds of disintegration experiments involving various types of atoms. By 1924, they had demonstrated that the nuclei of all elements ranging up to potassium—except lithium, carbon, and oxygen—could be disintegrated by alpha particles from radium C which have energies of about 7,000,000 volts. The idea of a neutral particle inside the nucleus, as suggested by Rutherford, was very much in Chadwick's mind, even at that time, for he was thinking of various ways to detect such a particle. As early as September 1924, in a letter to Rutherford, he wrote: "I think we shall have to make a real search for the neutron. I believe I have a scheme which may just work, but I must consult Aston first."

Chadwick began his famous neutron experiments in 1931 after Frédéric and Irène Joliot-Curie reported that radiation from beryllium excited by α particles could eject protons from paraffin wax or "any other matter containing hydrogen" placed in its way. H. C. Webster of the Cavendish Laboratory had already detected and examined this strange beryllium radiation and had found that it had peculiar features that could not be explained by the usual theories. In particular, the behavior of the beryllium radiation could not be explained if one assumed that it consisted of high-energy photons. Chadwick therefore started from the hypothesis that this radiation consisted of neutral particles and set out to prove this. As he said, "I therefore began immediately the study of this new effect using different methods—the counter, the expansion chamber, and the high-pressure ionization chamber." With these instruments, which were designed to detect material particles instead of photons, Chadwick discovered the neutron in 1932. This, of course, was the beginning of the vast growth of nuclear physics that culminated in the fission of uranium and the development of the chain-reacting atomic pile. For this research Chadwick received the Hughes medal of the Royal Society in 1932 and the Nobel Prize in 1935.

Chadwick left Cambridge in 1935 to accept the Lyon Jones chair of physics at the University of Liverpool. During World War II Chadwick worked in the United States as head of the British Mission attached to the Manhattan Project for the development of the atomic bomb. After the war, in 1948, he returned to England and retired from his Liverpool chair and from active physics research in general to become Master of Gonville and Caius College, Cambridge. From 1957 to 1962 he was a member of the United Kingdom Atomic Energy Authority.

In 1945 he was knighted. In addition to his Nobel Prize, Sir James has received such awards and honors as the Copley medal in 1950 and the Franklin Medal in 1951, as well as honorary doctorates from the University of Reading, Dublin, Leeds, Oxford, and McGill, among others; he is a member of several foreign academies.

Chadwick lives at Denbigh, North Wales, with his wife, the former Aileen Stewart-Brown of Liverpool; they have twin daughters.

ooooooo

CHADWICK

The Existence of a Neutron [1]

IT WAS SHOWN BY BOTHE and Becker that some light elements when bombarded by α-particles of polonium emit radiations which appear to be of the γ-ray type. The element beryllium gave a particularly marked effect of this kind, and later observations by Bothe, by Mme. Curie-Joliot and by Webster showed that the radiation excited in beryllium possessed a penetrating power distinctly greater than that of any γ-radiation yet found from the radioactive elements. In Webster's experiments the intensity of the radiation was measured both by means of the Geiger-Müller tube counter and in a high pressure ionization chamber. He found that the beryllium radiation had an absorption coefficient in lead of about $0 \cdot 22$ cm.$^{-1}$ as measured under his experimental conditions. Making the necessary corrections for these conditions, and using the results of Gray and Tarrant to estimate the relative contributions of scattering, photoelectric absorption, and nuclear absorption in the absorption of such penetrating radiation, Webster concluded that the radiation had a quantum energy of about 7×10^6 electron volts. Similarly he found that the radiation from boron bombarded by α-particles of polonium consisted in part of a radiation rather more penetrating than that from beryllium, and he estimated the quantum energy of this component as about 10×10^6 electron volts. These conclusions agree quite well with the supposition that the radiations arise by the capture of the α-particle into the beryllium (or boron) nucleus and the emission of the surplus energy as a quantum of radiation.

The radiations showed, however, certain peculiarities, and at my request the beryllium radiation was passed into an expansion chamber and several photographs were taken. No unexpected phenomena were observed though, as will be seen later, similar experiments have now revealed some rather striking events. The failure of these early experiments was partly due to the weakness of the available source of polonium, and partly

---

[1] J. Chadwick, *Proceedings of the Royal Society* (London, *Series A*, 136 (1932), 692–707.

to the experimental arrangement, which, as it now appears, was not very suitable.

Quite recently, Mme. Curie-Joliot and M. Joliot made the very striking observation that these radiations from beryllium and from boron were able to eject protons with considerable velocities from matter containing hydrogen. In their experiments the radiation from beryllium was passed through a thin window into an ionisation vessel containing air at room pressure. When paraffin wax, or other matter containing hydrogen, was placed in front of the window, the ionisation in the vessel was increased, in some cases as much as doubled. The effect appeared to be due to the ejection of protons, and from further experiment they showed that the protons had ranges in air up to about 26 cm., corresponding to a velocity of nearly 3×10^9 cm. per second. They suggested that energy was transferred from the beryllium radiation to the proton by a process similar to the Compton effect with electrons, and they estimated that the beryllium radiation had a quantum energy of about 50×10^6 electron volts. The range of the protons ejected by the boron radiation was estimated to be about 8 cm. in air, giving on a Compton process an energy of about 35×10^6 electron volts for the effective quantum.*

There are two grave difficulties in such an explanation of this phenomenon. Firstly, it is now well established that the frequency of scattering of high energy quanta by electrons is given with fair accuracy by the Klein-Nishina formula, and this formula should also apply to the scattering of quanta by a proton. The observed frequency of the proton scattering is, however, many thousand times greater than that predicted by this formula. Secondly, it is difficult to account for the production of a quantum of 50×10^6 electron volts from the interaction of a beryllium nucleus and an α-particle of kinetic energy of 5×10^6 electron volts. The process which will give the greatest amount of energy available for radiation is the capture of the α-particle by the beryllium nucleus, Be^9, and its incorporation in the nuclear structure to form a carbon nucleus C^{13}. The mass defect of the C^{13} nucleus is known both from data supplied by measurements of the artificial disintegration of boron B^{10} and from observations of the band spectrum of carbon; it is about 10×10^6 electron volts. The mass defect of Be^9 is not known, but the assumption that it is zero will give a maximum value for the possible change of energy in the reaction $Be^9 + \alpha \rightarrow C^{13} +$ quantum. On this assumption it follows that the energy of the quantum emitted in such a reaction cannot be greater than about 14×10^6 electron volts. It must, of course, be admitted that this argument from mass defects is based on the hypothesis that the nuclei are made as

---

* Many of the arguments of the subsequent discussion apply equally to both radiations, and the term "beryllium radiation" may often be taken to include the boron radiation.

far as possible of α-particles; that the Be⁹ nucleus consists of 2 α-particles + 1 proton + 1 electron and the C¹³ nucleus of 3 α-particles + 1 proton + 1 electron. So far as the lighter nuclei are concerned, this assumption is supported by the evidence from experiments on artificial disintegration, but there is no general proof.

Accordingly, I made further experiments to examine the properties of the radiation excited in beryllium. It was found that the radiation ejects particles not only from hydrogen but from all other light elements which were examined. The experimental results were very difficult to explain on the hypothesis that the beryllium radiation was a quantum radiation, but followed immediately if it were supposed that the radiation consisted of particles of mass nearly equal to that of a proton and with no net charge, or neutrons. . . .

OBSERVATIONS OF RECOIL ATOMS

The properties of the beryllium radiation were first examined by means of the valve counter used in the work on the artificial disintegration by α-particles and described fully there. Briefly, it consists of a small ionisation chamber connected to a valve amplifier. The sudden production of ions in the chamber by the entry of an ionising particle is detected by means of an oscillograph connected in the output circuit of the amplifier. The deflections of the oscillograph were recorded photographically on a film of bromide paper.

The source of polonium was prepared from a solution of radium (D + E + F) by deposition on a disc of silver. The disc had a diameter of 1 cm. and was placed close to a disc of pure beryllium of 2 cm. diameter, and both were enclosed in a small vessel which could be evacuated

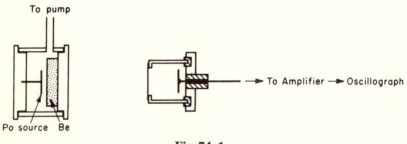

Fig. 74–1.

[Fig. 74–1]. The first ionisation chamber used had an opening of 13 mm. covered with aluminium foil of 4·5 cm. air equivalent, and a depth of 15 mm. This chamber had a very low natural effect, giving on the average only about 7 deflections per hour.

When the source vessel was placed in front of the ionisation chamber, the number of deflections immediately increased. For a distance of 3 cm. between the beryllium and the counter the number of deflections was nearly 4 per minute. Since the number of deflections remained sensibly the same when thick metal sheets, even as much as 2 cm. of lead, were interposed between the source vessel and the counter, it was clear that these deflections were due to a penetrating radiation emitted from the beryllium. It will be shown later that the deflections were due to atoms of nitrogen set in motion by the impact of the beryllium radiation.

When a sheet of paraffin wax about 2 mm. thick was interposed in the path of the radiation just in front of the counter, the number of deflections recorded by the oscillograph increased markedly. This increase was due to particles ejected from the paraffin wax so as to pass into the counter. By placing absorbing screens of aluminium between the wax and the counter the absorption curve shown in [Fig. 74–2], curve A, was obtained.

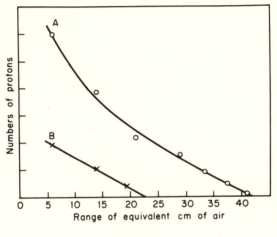

Fig. 74–2.

From this curve it appears that the particles have a maximum range of just over 40 cm. of air, assuming that an Al foil of $1 \cdot 64$ mg. per square centimetre is equivalent to 1 cm. of air. By comparing the sizes of the deflections (proportional to the number of ions produced in the chamber) due to these particles with those due to protons of about the same range it was obvious that the particles were protons. From the range-velocity curve for protons we deduce therefore that the maximum velocity imparted to a proton by the beryllium radiation is about $3 \cdot 3 \times 10^9$ cm. per second, corresponding to an energy of about $5 \cdot 7 \times 10^6$ electron volts.

The effect of exposing other elements to the beryllium radiation was then investigated. An ionisation chamber was used with an opening covered with a gold foil of 0·5 mm. air equivalent. The element to be examined was fixed on a clean brass plate and placed very close to the counter opening. In this way, lithium, beryllium, boron, carbon and nitrogen, as paracyanogen, were tested. In each case the number of deflections observed in the counter increased when the element was bombarded by the beryllium radiation. The ranges of the particles ejected from these elements were quite short, of the order of some millimetres in air. The deflections produced by them were of different sizes, but many of them were large compared with the deflection produced even by a slow proton. The particles therefore have a large ionising power and are probably in each case recoil atoms of the elements. Gases were investigated by filling the ionisation chamber with the required gas by circulation for several minutes. Hydrogen, helium, nitrogen, oxygen, and argon were examined in this way. Again, in each case deflections were observed which were attributed to the production of recoil atoms in the different gases. For a given position of the beryllium source relative to the counter, the number of recoil atoms was roughly the same for each gas. This point will be referred to later. It appears then that the beryllium radiation can impart energy to the atoms of matter through which it passes and that the chance of an energy transfer does not vary widely from one element to another.

It has been shown that protons are ejected from paraffin wax with energies up to a maximum of about $5·7 \times 10^6$ electron volts. If the ejection be ascribed to a Compton recoil from a quantum of radiation, then the energy of the quantum must be about 55×10^6 electron volts, for the maximum energy which can be given to a mass m by a quantum $h\nu$ is $\dfrac{2}{2 + mc^2/h\nu} \cdot h\nu$. The energies of the recoil atoms produced by this radiation by the same process in other elements can be readily calculated. For example, the nitrogen recoil atoms should have energies up to a maximum of 450,000 electron volts. Taking the energy necessary to form a pair of ions in air as 35 electron volts, the recoil atoms of nitrogen should produce not more than about 13,000 pairs of ions. Many of the deflections observed with nitrogen, however, corresponded to far more ions than this; some of the recoil atoms produced from 30,000 to 40,000 ion pairs. In the case of the other elements a similar discrepancy was noted between the observed energies and ranges of the recoil atoms and the values calculated on the assumption that the atoms were set in motion by recoil from a quantum of 55×10^6 electron volts. The energies of the recoil atoms were estimated from the number of ions produced in the counter, as given by the size of the oscillograph deflections. A sufficiently good measurement of the ranges could be made either by varying the distance between the element and the counter or by interposing thin screens of gold between the element and the counter.

The nitrogen recoil atoms were also examined, in collaboration with Dr. N. Feather, by means of the expansion chamber. The source vessel was placed immediately above an expansion chamber of the Shimizu type, so that a large proportion of the beryllium radiation traversed the chamber. A large number of recoil tracks was observed in the course of a few hours. Their range, estimated by eye, was sometimes as much as 5 or 6 mm. in the chamber, or, correcting for the expansion, about 3 mm. in standard air. These visual estimates were confirmed by a preliminary series of experiments by Dr. Feather with a large automatic expansion chamber, in which photographs of the recoil tracks in nitrogen were obtained. Now the ranges of recoil atoms of nitrogen of different velocities have been measured by Blackett and Lees. Using their results we find that the nitrogen recoil atoms produced by the beryllium radiation may have a velocity of at least 4×10^8 cm. per second, corresponding to an energy of about $1 \cdot 2 \times 10^6$ electron volts. In order that the nitrogen nucleus should acquire such an energy in a collision with a quantum of radiation, it is necessary to assume that the energy of the quantum should be about 90×10^6 electron volts, if energy and momentum are conserved in the collision. It has been shown that a quantum of 55×10^6 electron volts is sufficient to explain the hydrogen collisions. In general, the experimental results show that if the recoil atoms are to be explained by collision with a quantum, we must assume a larger and larger energy for the quantum as the mass of the struck atom increases.

THE NEUTRON HYPOTHESIS

It is evident that we must either relinquish the application of the conservation of energy and momentum in these collisions or adopt another hypothesis about the nature of the radiation. If we suppose that the radiation is not a quantum radiation, but consists of particles of mass very nearly equal to that of the proton, all the difficulties connected with the collisions disappear, both with regard to their frequency and to the energy transfer to different masses. In order to explain the great penetrating power of the radiation we must further assume that the particle has no net charge. We may suppose it to consist of a proton and an electron in close combination, the "neutron" discussed by Rutherford in his Bakerian Lecture of 1920.

When such neutrons pass through matter they suffer occasionally close collisions with the atomic nuclei and so give rise to the recoil atoms which are observed. Since the mass of the neutron is equal to that of the proton, the recoil atoms produced when the neutrons pass through matter containing hydrogen will have all velocities up to a maximum which is the same as the maximum velocity of the neutrons. The experiments showed that the maximum velocity of the protons ejected from paraffin wax was about $3 \cdot 3 \times 10^9$ cm. per second. This is therefore the maximum velocity of the neutrons emitted from beryllium bombarded by α-particles of polonium. From this we can now calculate the maximum energy which can be given by a colliding neutron to other atoms, and we find that the results are in fair agreement with the energies observed in the experiments. For example, a nitrogen atom will acquire in a head-on collision with the neutron of mass 1 and velocity $3 \cdot 3 \times 10^9$ cm. per second a velocity of $4 \cdot 4 \times 10^8$ cm. per second, corresponding to an energy of $1 \cdot 4 \times 10^6$ electron volts, a range of about $3 \cdot 3$ mm. in air, and a production of ions of about 40,000 pairs. Similarly, an argon atom may acquire an energy of $0 \cdot 54 \times 10^6$ electron volts, and produce about 15,000 ion pairs. Both these values are in good accord with experiment.

It is possible to prove that the mass of the neutron is roughly equal to that of the proton, by combining the evidence from the hydrogen collisions with that from the nitrogen collisions. In the succeeding paper, Feather records experiments in which about 100 tracks of nitrogen recoil atoms have been photographed in the expansion chamber. The measurement of the tracks shows that the maximum range of the recoil atoms is $3 \cdot 5$ mm. in air at $15°$ C. and 760 mm. pressure, corresponding to a velocity of $4 \cdot 7 \times 10^8$ cm. per second according to Blackett and Lees. If M, V be the mass and velocity of the neutron then the maximum velocity given to a hydrogen atom is

$$u_p = \frac{2M}{M+1} \cdot V,$$

and the maximum velocity given to a nitrogen atom is

$$u_n = \frac{2M}{M+14} \cdot V,$$

whence

$$\frac{M+14}{M+1} = \frac{u_p}{u_n} = \frac{3 \cdot 3 \times 10^9}{4 \cdot 7 \times 10^8},$$

and

$$M = 1 \cdot 15.$$

The total error in the estimation of the velocity of the nitrogen recoil atom may easily be about 10 per cent., and it is legitimate to conclude that the mass of the neutron is very nearly the same as the mass of the proton.

We have now to consider the production of the neutrons from beryllium by the bombardment of the α-particles. We must suppose that an α-particle is captured by a Be^9 nucleus with the formation of a carbon C^{12} nucleus and the emission of a neutron. The process is analogous to the well-known artificial disintegrations, but a neutron is emitted instead of a proton. The energy relations of this process cannot be exactly deduced, for the masses of the Be^9 nucleus and the neutron are not known accurately. It is, however, easy to show that such a process fits the experimental facts. We have

$Be^9 + He^4 +$ kinetic energy of α
$\qquad = C^{12} + n^1 +$ kinetic energy of $C^{12} +$ kinetic energy of n^1.

If we assume that the beryllium nucleus consists of two α-particles and a neutron, then its mass cannot be greater than the sum of the masses of these particles, for the binding energy corresponds to a defect of mass. The energy equation becomes

$(8 \cdot 00212 + n^1) + 4 \cdot 00106 +$ K.E. of $\alpha > 12 \cdot 0003 + n^1$
$\qquad\qquad\qquad\qquad\qquad\qquad\qquad + $ K.E. of $C^{12} +$ K.E. of n^1

or

K.E. of $n^1 <$ K.E. of $\alpha + 0 \cdot 003 -$ K.E. of C^{12}.

Since the kinetic energy of the α-particle of polonium is $5 \cdot 25 \times 10^6$ electron volts, it follows that the energy of emission of the neutron cannot be greater than about 8×10^6 electron volts. The velocity of the neutron must therefore be less than $3 \cdot 9 \times 10^9$ cm. per second. We have seen that the actual maximum velocity of the neutron is about $3 \cdot 3 \times 10^9$ cm. per second, so that the proposed disintegration process is compatible with observation.

A further test of the neutron hypothesis was obtained by examining the radiation emitted from beryllium in the opposite direction to the bombarding α-particles. The source vessel [Fig. 74–1] was reversed so that a sheet of paraffin wax in front of the counter was exposed to the "backward" radiation from the beryllium. The maximum range of the protons ejected from the wax was determined as before, by counting the numbers of protons observed through different thicknesses of aluminium interposed between the wax and the counter. The absorption curve obtained is shown in curve B, [Fig. 74–2]. The maximum range of the protons was about 22 cm. in air, corresponding to a velocity of about $2 \cdot 74 \times 10^9$ cm. per second. Since the polonium source was only about 2 mm. away from the beryllium, this velocity should be compared with that of the neutrons emitted not at 180° but at an angle not much greater than 90° to the direction of the incident α-particles. A simple calculation shows that the velocity of the neutron emitted at 90° when an α-particle of full range is captured by a beryllium nucleus should be $2 \cdot 77 \times 10^9$ cm. per second, taking the velocity of the neutron emitted at $0°$ in the same process as $3 \cdot 3 \times 10^9$ cm. per second. The velocity found in the above experiment should be less than this, for the angle of emission is slightly greater than $90°$. The agreement with calculation is as good as can be expected from such measurements.

THE NATURE OF THE NEUTRON

It has been shown that the origin of the radiation from beryllium bombarded by α-particles and the behaviour of the radiation, so far as its interaction with atomic nuclei is concerned, receive a simple explanation on the assumption that the radiation consists of particles of mass nearly equal to that of the proton which have no charge. The simplest hypothesis one can make about the nature of the particle is to suppose that it consists of a proton and an electron in close combination, giving a net charge 0 and a mass which should be slightly less than the mass of the hydrogen atom. This hypothesis is supported by an examination of the evidence which can be obtained about the mass of the neutron.

As we have seen, a rough estimate of the mass of the neutron was obtained from measurements of its collisions with hydrogen and nitrogen atoms, but such measurements cannot be made with sufficient accuracy for the present purpose. We must turn to a consideration of the energy relations in a process in which a neutron is liberated from an atomic nucleus; if the masses of the atomic nuclei concerned in the process are accurately known, a good estimate of the mass of the neutron can be deduced. The mass of the beryllium nucleus has, however, not yet been measured, and, as was shown [earlier], only general conclusions can be drawn from this reaction. Fortunately, there remains the case of boron. It was stated in [the first section] that boron bombarded by α-particles of polonium also emits a radiation which ejects protons from materials containing hydrogen. Further examination showed that this radiation behaves in all respects like that from beryllium, and it must therefore be assumed to consist of neutrons. It is probable that the neutrons are emitted from the isotope B^{11}, for we know that the isotope B^{10} disintegrates with the emission of a proton. The process of disintegration will then be

$$B^{11} + He^4 \rightarrow N^{14} + n^1.$$

The masses of B^{11} and N^{14} are known from Aston's measurements, and the further data required for the deduction of the mass of the neutron can be obtained by experiment.

In the source vessel of [Fig. 74–1] the beryllium was replaced by a target of powdered boron, deposited on a graphite plate. The range of the protons ejected by the boron radiation was measured in the same way as with the beryllium radiation. The effects observed were much smaller than with beryllium, and it was difficult to measure the range of the protons accurately. The maximum range was about 16 cm. in air, corresponding to a velocity of $2 \cdot 5 \times 10^9$ cm. per second. This then is the maximum velocity of the neutron liberated from boron by an α-particle of polonium of velocity $1 \cdot 59 \times 10^9$ cm. per second. Assuming that momentum is conserved in the collision, the velocity of the recoiling N^{14} nucleus can be calculated, and we then know the kinetic energies of all the particles concerned in the disintegration process. The energy equation of the process is

Mass of B^{11} + mass of He^4 + K.E. of He^4
$$= \text{mass of } N^{14} + \text{mass of } n^1 + \text{K.E. of } N^{14} + \text{K.E. of } n^1.$$

The masses are $B^{11} = 11 \cdot 00825 \pm 0 \cdot 0016$; $He^4 = 4 \cdot 00106 \pm 0 \cdot 0006$; $N^{14} = 14 \cdot 0042 \pm 0 \cdot 0028$. The kinetic energies in mass units are α-particle $= 0 \cdot 00565$; neutron $= 0 \cdot 0035$; and nitrogen nucleus $= 0 \cdot 00061$. We find therefore that the mass of the neutron is $1 \cdot 0067$. The errors quoted for the mass measurements are those given by Aston. They are the maximum errors which can be allowed in his measurements, and the probable error may be taken as about one-quarter of these. Allowing for the errors in the mass measurements it appears that the mass of the neutron cannot be less than $1 \cdot 003$, and that it probably lies between $1 \cdot 005$ and $1 \cdot 008$.

Such a value for the mass of the neutron is to be expected if the neutron consists of a proton and an electron, and it lends strong support to this view. Since the sum of the masses of the proton and electron is $1 \cdot 0078$, the binding energy, or mass defect, of the neutron is about 1 to 2 million electron volts. This is quite a reasonable value. We may suppose that the proton and electron form a small dipole, or we may take the more attractive picture of a proton embedded in an electron. On either view, we may expect the "radius" of the neutron to be a few times 10^{-13} cm.

THE PASSAGE OF THE NEUTRON THROUGH MATTER

The electrical field of a neutron of this kind will clearly be extremely small except at very small distances of the order of 10^{-12} cm. In its passage through matter the neutron will not be deflected unless it suffers an intimate collision with a nucleus. The potential of a neutron in the field of a nucleus may be represented roughly by [Fig. 74–3]. The radius of the collision area for sensible deflection of the neutron will be little greater than the radius of the nucleus. Further, the neutron should be able to penetrate the nucleus easily, and it may be that the scattering of the neutrons will be largely due to the internal field of the nucleus, or, in other words, that the scattered neutrons are mainly those which have penetrated the potential barrier. On these views we should expect the collisions of a neutron with a nucleus to occur very seldom, and that the scattering will be roughly equal in all directions, at least as compared with the Coulomb scattering of a charged particle.

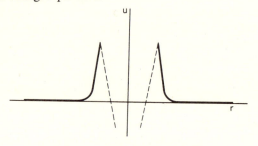

Fig. 74–3.

These conclusions were confirmed in the following way. The source vessel, with Be target, was placed rather more than 1 inch from the face of a closed counter filled with air [Fig. 74–1]. The number of deflections, or the number of nitrogen recoil atoms produced in the chamber, was observed for a certain time. The number observed was 190 per hour, after allowing for the natural effect. A block of lead 1 inch thick was then introduced between the source vessel and the counter. The number of deflections fell to 166 per hour. Since the number of recoil atoms produced must be proportional to the number of neutrons passing through the counter, these observations show that 13 per cent. of the neutrons had been absorbed or scattered in passing through 1 inch of lead.

Suppose that a neutron which passes within a distance p from the centre of the lead nucleus is scattered and removed from the beam. Then the fraction removed from the beam in passing through a thickness t of lead will be $\pi p^2 nt$, where n is the number of lead atoms per unit volume. Hence $\pi p^2 nt = 0 \cdot 13$, and $p = 7 \times 10^{-13}$ cm. This value for the collision radius with lead seems perhaps rather small, but it is not unreasonable. We may compare it with the radii of the radioactive nuclei calculated from the disintegration constants by Gamow and Houtermans, viz., about 7×10^{-13} cm.

Similar experiments were made in which the neutron radiation was passed through blocks of brass and carbon. The values of p deduced in the same way were 6×10^{-13} cm. and $3 \cdot 5 \times 10^{-13}$ cm. respectively.

The target areas for collision for some light elements were compared by another method. The second ionisation chamber was used, which could be filled with different gases by circulation. The position of the source vessel was kept fixed relative to the counter, and the number of deflections was observed when the counter was filled in turn with hydrogen, nitrogen, oxygen, and argon. Since the number of neutrons passing through the counter was the same in each case, the number of deflections should be proportional to the target area for collision, neglecting the effect of the material of the counter, and allowing for the fact that argon is monatomic. It was found that nitrogen, oxygen, and argon gave about the same number of deflections; the target areas of nitrogen and oxygen are thus roughly equal, and the target area of argon is nearly twice that of these. With hydrogen the measurements were very difficult, for many of the deflections were very small owing to the low ionising power of the proton and the low density of the gas. It seems probable from the results that the target area of hydrogen is about two-thirds that of nitrogen or oxygen, but it may be rather greater than this.

There is as yet little information about the angular distribution of the scattered neutrons. In some experiments kindly made for me by Dr. Gray and Mr. Lea, the scattering by lead was compared in the backward and forward directions, using the ionisation in a high pressure chamber to measure the neutrons. They found that the amount of scattering was about that to be expected from the measurements quoted above, and that the intensity per unit solid angle was about the same between 30° to 90° in the forward direction as between 90° to 150° in the backward direction. The scattering by lead is therefore not markedly anisotropic.

Two types of collision may prove to be of peculiar interest, the collision of a neutron with a proton and the collision with an electron. A detailed study of these collisions with an elementary particle is of special interest, for it should provide information about the structure and field of the neutron, whereas the other collisions will depend mainly on the structure of the atomic nuclei. Some preliminary experiments by Mr. Lea, using the pressure chamber to measure the scattering of neutrons by paraffin wax and by liquid hydrogen, suggest that the collision with a proton is more frequent than with other light atoms. This is not in accord with the experiments described above, but the results are at present indecisive. These collisions can be more directly investigated by means of the expansion chamber or by counting methods, and it is hoped to do so shortly.

The collision of a neutron with an electron has been examined in two ways, by the expansion chamber and by the counter. An account of the expansion chamber experiments is given by Mr. Dee in the third paper of this series. Mr. Dee has looked for the general ionisation produced by a large number of neutrons in passing through the expansion chamber, and also for the short electron tracks which should be the result of a very close collision between a neutron and an electron. His results show that collisions with electrons are extremely rare compared even with those with nitrogen nuclei, and he estimates that a neutron can produce on the average not more than 1 ion pair in passing through 3 metres of air.

In the counter experiments a beam of neutrons was passed through a block of brass, 1 inch thick, and the maximum range of the protons ejected from paraffin wax by the emergent beam was measured. From this range the maximum velocity of the neutrons after travelling through the brass is obtained and it can be compared with the maximum velocity in the incident beam. No change in the velocity of the neutrons due to their passage through the brass could be detected. The accuracy of the experiment is not high, for the estimation of the end of the range of the protons was rather difficult. The results show that the loss of energy of a neutron in passing through 1 inch of brass is not more than about $0 \cdot 4 \times 10^6$ electron volts. A path of 1 inch in brass corresponds as regards electron collisions to a path of nearly 2×10^4 cm. of air, so that this result would suggest that a neutron loses less than 20 volts per centimetre path in air in electron collisions. This experiment thus lends general support to those with the expansion chamber, though it is of far inferior accuracy. We conclude that the transfer of energy from the neutron to electrons is of very rare occurrence. This is not unexpected. Bohr has shown on quite general ideas that collisions of a neutron with an electron should be very few compared with nuclear collisions. Massey, on plausible assumptions about the field of the neutron, has made a detailed calculation of the loss of energy to electrons, and finds also that it should be small, not more than 1 ion pair per metre in air.

GENERAL REMARKS

It is of interest to examine whether other elements, besides beryllium and boron, emit neutrons when bombarded by α-particles. So far as experiments have been made, no case comparable with these two has been found. Some evidence was obtained of the emission of neutrons from fluorine and magnesium, but the effects were very small, rather less than 1 per cent. of the effect obtained from beryllium under the same conditions. There is also the possibility that some elements may emit neutrons spontaneously, e.g., potassium, which is known to emit a nuclear β-radiation accompanied by a more penetrating radiation. Again no evidence was found of the presence of neutrons, and it seems fairly certain that the penetrating type is, as has been assumed, a γ-radiation.

Although there is certain evidence for the emission of neutrons only in two cases of nuclear transformations, we must nevertheless suppose that the neutron is a common constituent of atomic nuclei. We may then proceed to build up nuclei out of α-particles, neutrons, and protons. and we are able to avoid the presence of uncombined electrons in a nucleus. This has certain advantages for, as is well known, the electrons in a nucleus have lost some of the properties which they have outside, *e.g.,* their spin and magnetic moment. If the α-particle, the neutron, and the proton are the only units of nuclear structure, we can proceed to calculate the mass defect or binding energy of a nucleus as the difference between the mass of the nucleus and the sum of the masses of the constituent particles. It is, however, by no means certain that the α-particle and the neutron are the only complex particles in the nuclear structure, and therefore the mass defects calculated in this way may not be the true binding energies of the nuclei. In this connection it may be noted that the examples of disintegration discussed by Dr. Feather in the next paper are not all of one type, and he suggests that in some cases a particle of mass 2 and charge 1, the hydrogen isotope recently reported by Urey, Brickwedde and Murphy, may be emitted. It is indeed possible that this particle also occurs as a unit of nuclear structure.

It has so far been assumed that the neutron is a complex particle consisting of a proton and an electron. This is the simplest assumption and it is supported by the evidence that the mass of the neutron is about $1 \cdot 006$, just a little less than the sum of the masses of a proton and an electron. Such a neutron would appear to be the first step in the combination of the elementary particles towards the formation of a nucleus. It is obvious that this neutron may help us to visualise the building up of more complex structures, but the discussion of these matters will not be pursued further for such speculations, though not idle, are not at the moment very fruitful. It is, of course, possible to suppose that the neutron may be an elementary particle. This view has little to recommend it at present, except the possibility of explaining the statistics of such nuclei as N^{14}.

There remains to discuss the transformations which take place when an α-particle is captured by a beryllium nucleus, Be^9. The evidence given here indicates that the main type of transformation is the formation of a C^{12} nucleus and the emission of a neutron. The experiments of Curie-Joliot and Joliot, of Auger, and of Dee show quite definitely that there is some radiation emitted by beryllium which is able to eject fast electrons in passing through matter. I have made experiments using the Geiger point counter to investigate this radiation and the results suggest that the electrons are produced by a γ-radiation. There are two distinct processes which may give rise to such a radiation. In the first place, we may suppose that the transformation of Be^9 to C^{12} takes place sometimes with the formation of an excited C^{12} nucleus which goes to the ground state with the emission of γ-radiation. This is similar to the transformations which are supposed to occur in some cases of disintegration with proton emission, *e.g.*, B^{10}, F^{19}, Al^{27}; the majority of transformations occur with the formation of an excited nucleus, only in about one-quarter is the final state of the residual nucleus reached in one step. We should then have two groups of neutrons of different energies and a γ-radiation of quantum energy equal to the difference in energy of the neutron groups. The quantum energy of this radiation must be less than the maximum energy of the neutrons emitted, about $5 \cdot 7 \times 10^6$ electron volts. In the second place, we may suppose that occasionally the beryllium nucleus changes to a C^{13} nucleus and that all the surplus energy is emitted as radiation. In this case the quantum energy of the radiation may be about 10×10^6 electron volts.

It is of interest to note that Webster has observed a soft radiation from beryllium bombarded by polonium α-particles, of energy about 5×10^5 electron volts. This radiation may well be ascribed to the first of the two processes just discussed, and its intensity is of the right order. On the other hand, some of the electrons observed by Curie-Joliot and Joliot had energies of the order of 2 to 10×10^6 volts, and Auger recorded one example of an electron of energy about $6 \cdot 5 \times 10^6$ volts. These electrons may be due to a hard γ-radiation produced by the second type of transformation.*

It may be remarked that no electrons of greater energy than the above appear to be present. This is confirmed by an experiment made in this laboratory by Dr. Occhialini. Two tube counters were placed in a horizontal plane and the number of coincidences recorded by them was observed by means of the method devised by Rossi. The beryllium source was then brought up in the plane of the counters so that the radiation passed through both counters in turn. No increase in the number of coincidences could be detected. It follows that there are few, if any, β-rays produced with energies sufficient to pass through the walls of both counters, a total of 4 mm. brass; that is, with energies greater than about 6×10^6 volts. This experiment further shows that the neutrons very rarely produce coincidences in tube counters under the usual conditions of experiment.

---

* Although the presence of fast electrons can be easily explained in this way, the possibility that some may be due to secondary effects of the neutrons must not be lost sight of.

FERMI'S CONTRIBUTIONS

ooooooooooo

Enrico Fermi (1901-1954)

The science of physics was born in Italy at the close of the sixteenth century with the investigations of Galileo. By the beginning of the twentieth century, the center of scientific activity had shifted to the great German universities, which drew researchers from England and the Continent. Physics developed slowly in Italy, and during the first two decades of the present century there was no Italian physicist with the international stature of men like Kelvin, Poincaré, Lorentz, or Planck. But just as modern physics entered a golden age in the 1920's with the exciting developments in quantum physics and atomic structure, Enrico Fermi appeared; singlehanded, without the benefit of training at the European scientific schools, he raised Italian physics to a summit of achievement.

Endowed with creativity, great mathematical gifts, and a veritable genius for implementing theory and experiment, Fermi attracted the best of the young Italian physicists to Rome, where he organized what came to be known as the Roman school of physics. By the time Fermi left Italy in 1938, the year he won the Nobel Prize, his school was sought after by young physicists of many lands, as well as the leading international scientists of the day. From 1934 on, through the efforts of Fermi and his group of nuclear experts, Rome had become an important center of nuclear research.

In his first papers, Fermi, at the age of twenty, dealt with relativistic electrodynamics, in particular with the electromagnetic mass of charged particles, such as electrons, and with the general problem of the equivalence of gravitational and inertial mass. In the course of this work he proved an important theorem in the absolute differential calculus, which is the mathematics used in the general relativity theory. In addition, he cleared up a certain difficulty that had cropped up in the assumption of the equivalence of mass and energy.

Shortly after his initial work, Fermi began an investigation of certain theoretical problems in classical mechanics governing groups of bodies, and became especially interested in statistical mechanics. This interest, which never left him, soon led him to an analysis of the statistical mechanics of a gas consisting of particles that obey the Pauli exclusion principle—particles such as electrons with a spin of $1/2$. In this analysis Fermi derived his famous quantum-mechanical statistics of degenerate matter, which was introduced independently but somewhat later by Dirac, and is now known as the Fermi-Dirac statistics. That Fermi quickly realized the significance of his work for the understanding of very dense matter and the behavior of solids is indicated by his subsequent series of papers dealing with the quantum mechanics of metals, in which electrons are treated as a degenerate gas. This work became the foundation of modern solid-state physics, and is today the basis for the analysis of white dwarfs and the evolution of stars in their super-dense phase.

Fermi developed his statistical mechanics by applying quantization to the molecules of a gas. He reasoned correctly that since at very low temperatures both the specific heat and the equation of state of a gas differ from the classical expressions, some type of degeneracy must set in that can be accounted for only by the quantum theory. Einstein had already shown that the correct specific heats of solids at low temperature cannot be obtained without quantizing the vibrations of the molecules. Moreover, Bose and Einstein, separately, had developed a new kind of statistical mechanics for gases. This statistics, based on the quantum theory, leads to an equation of state for a gas different from the classical equation of state. Indeed, Bose introduced the new statistics in order to obtain the Planck radiation formula for a photon gas.

The Bose-Einstein statistics and the Fermi statistics are similar in the sense that they both take into account the quantum properties of matter (in fact, it can be shown that each of these two types of statistics is equivalent to taking into account the wave properties of particles). But they differ in the way that quantization is applied to the gas. The region of agreement between these two statistics, as well as the area in which they part company with the classical Boltzmann statistics, is related to the identity of the molecules composing the gas. Classical statistics is set up on the assumption that a certain state of a gas (its pressure, and its temperature for a given volume) is defined by the way the molecules in the gas are distributed in the volume and by their motions. It was noted in Chapter 61, on the Bose statistics, that each classical state is defined by a particular partition of the molecules in a given volume element according to the possible states of energy and momentum. In the classical analysis, each molecule is assigned its own identity, and it is assumed that one molecule can be distinguished from any other. This leads to the classical or Boltzmann statistics.

Both the Bose statistics and the Fermi statistics are similar to classical statistics in that they too define the state of a system in terms of the way the molecules in a given element of volume are distributed among the possible states of energy and momentum. However, in counting the number of different distributions of molecules that can lead to a given state of the gas (a given temperature and pressure), both Bose and Fermi state that all molecules are exactly the same. Consequently, two different distributions involving merely the interchange of any two molecules cannot be distinguished from one another and must be counted as identical. This identity of all the molecules (assuming, of course, that our gas consists of just one kind of molecule, for example, hydrogen) and the inability to distinguish one from another arise from the wave properties of particles, since there is no way to differentiate between two similar waves.

This method of treating molecules distinguishes quantum statistics from classical statistics and is common to both the Fermi and Bose treatments. They differ from each other, however, in the manner in which molecules in a given small volume element are assigned to different states of energy and momentum. In the Bose statistics there is no restriction on the number of molecules in the small volume element that can be assigned to the same state of energy and momentum. But in the Fermi statistics the situation is quite different. Fermi was guided by Pauli's discovery that the electrons inside an atom arrange themselves in such a way that no two electrons have the same set of four quantum numbers; that is, no two are in the same state of motion. In other words, the electrons influence one another in such a way as to pre-empt or exclude identical motion in the same volume element. This is the famous exclusion principle which we discuss elsewhere in this book.

Fermi was prompted to use the exclusion principle to set up the statistics of an ideal gas. He reasoned that if the molecules of a gas had no influence on one another (as one assumes in the case of a classical ideal gas), then the gas would never exhibit "degeneracy" at low temperatures. He therefore proposed to introduce the concept of the influence of one molecule on another. He did not intend this to be the usual type of classical influence that is expressed in terms of forces between the molecules. Insofar as forces between molecules go, the situation here is the same as in the classical case; the new kind of influence between any two molecules is of a quantum-mechanical nature and stems from the fact that no two molecules can be distinguished from each other. Fermi therefore introduces the Pauli exclusion principle and limits the way in which molecules in a gas can move by supposing that in any small element of volume of a gas no two molecules can be in the same state of motion (the same energy and direction of motion) or, as expressed by the Pauli exclusion principle, may not have the same set of quantum numbers.

The Fermi statistics was first elucidated in a paper entitled "On Quantizing an Ideal Monatomic Gas." This principle later became known as the Fermi-Dirac statistics because of Dirac's independent research, which was made known in a paper published about six months after Fermi's. Fermi's paper, one of the masterpieces of reasoning in the history of theoretical physics, is an excellent example of his approach to a problem. It is presented with such simplicity that anyone with a knowledge of elementary calculus can follow the mathematics. Throughout, the emphasis is on the physical content of the theory; the mathematical formalism is used merely to elucidate the physics. It is the first of the Fermi selections that follow this commentary.

Fermi opens with the statement that classical thermodynamics leads to a constant molecular heat for a gas, whereas the experimental data demand that the molecular heat vanish at absolute zero; therefore, it is necessary to quantize the motions of the molecules of a gas. He then proposes to carry out a new type of quantization by introducing the Pauli exclusion principle. He pictures each molecule as being in an external force field so that its motion is periodic and therefore can be characterized by a set of quantum numbers. He pictures each molecule oscillating about the origin as though it were connected to the origin by a perfect spring (simple harmonic motion, the quantum harmonic oscillator); but he points out that this is only an artifice and can be replaced by any number of other types of force fields with the same result.

Fermi then writes down the set of quantum numbers that define the motion of each molecule (these are the well-known quantum numbers of the harmonic oscillator: an integer for each degree of freedom of motion). The motion of each molecule is then described by three integers, one for each of the three mutually perpendicular directions in space. With these quantum numbers he then applies the Pauli exclusion principle by imposing the condition that no two molecules in the gas can have the same set of integers describing their motion; in counting configurations all molecules must be treated as identical so that two configurations differing only by the permutations of molecules are the same. This imposes a definite condition on the way a given amount of energy in the gas can be distributed among the molecules because the energy of a harmonic oscillator (a molecule in this case) is determined by its quantum numbers. Thus, only one molecule can be at rest (energy zero), only three moving with one quantum of energy each, no more than six moving with two quanta of energy, and so on. This use of the exclusion principle thus enables Fermi to obtain a general formula for the way the total kinetic energy in a gas can be distributed among the *N* molecules. From this he is then able to write down the formula for the number of molecules having a given energy in a gas at a given absolute temperature as a function of the temperature, and this leads to the new equation of state of the gas.

The statistics for a degenerate gas thus obtained was used shortly after by Sommerfeld to explain the properties of metals by treating the electrons in the metal as a degenerate gas. In their now famous work, H. Bethe and A. Sommerfeld developed the physics of degenerate systems to a point where it could be used in the analysis of all types of solid-state problems.

Dirac later showed that the Bose-Einstein statistics, which does not limit the number of molecules that can be assigned to the same state of motion, and the Fermi-Dirac statistics, which limits to one the number of molecules in each energy state, are both derivable from quantum mechanics and are special cases of a very general principle of symmetry. Dirac demonstrated that two types of particles occur in nature that have to be described by wave functions with different symmetry. Particles such as electrons, protons, neutrons, and neutrinos, which have a half unit of spin (or an odd multiple of a half unit), are described by wave functions whose signs change when the coordinates of the positions and spin of the particles are replaced by their negative values in the wave functions. These particles obey the Fermi-Dirac statistics. Particles that have an integral multiple of the unit of spin (such as photons) are described by symmetrical wave functions (they do not change sign when the coordinates change sign) and these obey the Bose-Einstein statistics.

Another outgrowth of Fermi's work in statistical mechanics is his famous model of the atom. Fermi reasoned that one may treat the cloud of electrons surrounding the nucleus inside a heavy atom like a degenerate gas obeying the Pauli exclusion principle (the electrons arrange themselves one per atomic energy level), and that one may therefore apply to such an atom the Fermi-Dirac statistics. In this way he showed how various atomic problems can be treated statistically, to give results that are fairly accurate. Although Fermi was unaware of it, a similar theory had been developed a year earlier by L. H. Thomas, so that today this work is referred to as the Thomas-Fermi model of the atom. This model is of basic importance in the study of crystal structure and other solid-state problems.

During this same period, which extended from about 1924 to 1928, Fermi became involved in a wide range of problems in optics, spectroscopy, and molecular structure. He published papers on the quantum mechanics of the interference of light, on the spectroscopy of alkali atoms, on the hyperfine structure of spectral lines and the magnetic moments of nuclei, and on molecular spectra. His work on the quantum mechanics of the interference of light was prompted by his reading of Dirac's papers on the quantum mechanics of the emission and absorption of radiation. After he had mastered Dirac's treatment, he reformulated the theory and recast it into a much simpler and more amenable mathematical form. This work (not included in these volumes) became one of the most popular and famous articles in the *Reviews of Modern Physics* (1932), and for years served all newcomers as the gateway to the quantum electrodynamics. It is a model of beauty and clarity and indicates what a magnificent teacher Fermi was. The content of this paper is contained in a series of courses that he gave at the Henri Poincaré Institute in Paris in 1929 and at the 1930 Summer School of Theoretical Physics in Ann Arbor, Michigan. Fermi became a fixture at the Ann Arbor school and was there almost every summer until he finally left Italy. During this period he influenced the trend in American physics and made a summer's stay at the University of Michigan one of the most exciting intellectual adventures in science.

This extremely productive period was followed by Fermi's investigations into nuclear theory, which was to occupy him for most of his remaining years and was to lead to his discovery of the self-sustaining chain reaction of uranium and to the theory of the atomic pile. Fermi had spent most of his formative years in Italy; except for a rather profitless year at Göttingen (part of which was spent at Leyden) he came into very little direct contact with physicists of international reputation. However, as his papers became known to increasing numbers of physicists throughout the world, he was invited to attend international conferences and to present papers. By the end of the 1920's his reputation was well established and he was recognized as the outstanding representative of Italian physics. Near the end of the 1920's, many of the international conferences devoted increasing time and publication space to problems of nuclear physics. Although the neutron had not yet been discovered, sufficient experimental data had been collected to present important questions in nuclear physics to scientists attending conferences. Two of the puzzling features about the nucleus at that time concerned the β-decay of nuclei (the radioactivity of heavy nuclei with the emission of electrons) and the composition of nuclei. Since electrons are emitted from nuclei during β-decay, it was thought that nuclei consisted of both protons and electrons in the proper number to give the correct charge and mass. But this picture was in conflict with the principles of wave mechanics—in particular, with the Heisenberg uncertainty principle. Because of the wave structure of the electron, it can be shown that an electron inside a nucleus would have to move about with so much kinetic energy that it could not be held there by the known forces. Using the Heisenberg uncertainty principle we can see this at once. Since the nucleus is very tiny, the position of the electron inside a nucleus would be so accurately known that its momentum would according to the uncertainty principle be extremely large and hence its kinetic energy would be very large.

The other puzzle in connection with the β-decay of nuclei involved the energy of the emitted electron. Since all the nuclei of the same radioactive element decay into identical, less massive nuclei with the emission of an electron, the energy given up by each nucleus must always be the same: it is measured by the difference between the mass of the initial nucleus and the mass of the final nucleus. Hence, it was argued, each electron emitted should emerge with the same kinetic energy. But this does not agree with observation. We find, in β-decay, that there is a spectrum of energy values for the emitted electrons, ranging from zero to a maximum value. Yet the actual energy lost is always equal to the difference in mass between the initial and final nuclei multiplied by the square of the speed of light, regardless of how energetic is the emitted electron. This was a surprising result, because at that time there was no direct experimental evidence that any particle other than the electron was emitted during β-decay. Some of the outstanding physicists, particularly Bohr, argued that if electrons were inside a nucleus they would have to be treated outside the framework of quantum mechanics; moreover, that energy would not be conserved during the β-decay process. Bohr was further prompted to take this position, by the difficulty in accounting for the spin and the statistics of nuclei after they have undergone β-decay. Since the electron has a half unit of spin and obeys the Fermi statistics, all nuclei suffering β-decay should change their spins by one-half unit and also change their statistics. This is not the case. The spin changes either by one unit or not at all and the statistics of the nuclei remain unchanged.

Pauli, however, did not go along with Bohr and felt that the principle of the conservation of energy should not be abandoned. He pointed out that one can retain the energy principle and at the same time account for the energy spectrum of the electrons emitted in β-decay, as well as for the spin and statistics of the decaying nuclei, by assuming that another particle, in addition to the electron, is emitted during β-decay. Pauli described this hypothetical particle as one with no charge, with practically no rest mass, with a half unit of spin (Fermi statistics), but capable of carrying energy. Later, during the conference at which Pauli proposed the new particle, Fermi referred to it as the "neutrino" and the name has stuck to it ever since. We now know that the neutrino is an actual, fundamental particle; recently, two different kinds of neutrinos have been discovered.

Shortly after this, in 1932, the neutron was discovered and its properties correctly analyzed in England by Chadwick and in France by Curie and Joliot. In Italy the brilliant theoretical physicist E. Majorana, whose gifts exceeded Fermi's in some phases of mathematical physics, immediately saw the importance of the neutron as a constituent of the nucleus and developed a nuclear model based on protons and neutrons. Majorana's ideas about nuclear forces are still valid and of great importance, but he never followed up this work because of the severe melancholy and depression that frequently incapacitated him. Fermi took over the neutron as his own special pet and in his hands it became the dominant tool of nuclear research. Fermi realized that the properties of the neutron (chiefly its charge neutrality) made it especially suitable for penetrating the positively charged nucleus. In 1938, he received the Nobel Prize for "his demonstration of the existence of new radioactive elements produced by neutron irradiation, and for his related discovery of nuclear reactions brought about by slow neutrons." In his Nobel address, he stated that the most natural choice of bombarding particle to effect nuclear transformations and artificial radioactivity was the neutron, rather than the α particle. Fermi reasoned that α particles could be successful in such efforts only with the very light elements because the nuclear charge beyond atomic number 15 is so great as to inhibit α particle capture by the nucleus. This, however, does not apply to neutrons so that these particles can be used for all atomic numbers. He stated his point of view as follows:

> Compared with α-particles, the neutrons have the obvious drawback that the available neutron sources emit only a comparatively small number of neutrons. Indeed neutrons are emitted as products of nuclear reactions, whose yield is only seldom larger than 10^{-4}. This drawback, however, is compensated by the fact that neutrons, having no electric charge, can reach the nuclei of all atoms, without having to overcome the potential barrier, due to the Coulomb field that surrounds the nucleus. Furthermore, since neutrons practically do not interact with electrons, their range is very long, and the probability of a nuclear collision is correspondingly larger than in the case of α-particle or proton bombardment.[1]

Fermi, using the neutron, investigated all the elements of the atomic table. He conceived the experiments, designed the apparatus, and predicted his results theoretically. Fortunately, his recruitment in earlier years of young Italian physicists now stood him in good stead. He led a group of devoted, brilliant men who collaborated beautifully in the Herculean task he set for them. His idea was to bombard each element with neutrons in turn, and to determine the nature of the end products.

In the second paper of the group following this commentary, Fermi describes how his team began with hydrogen and systematically bombarded all the elements up to uranium. He began the experiments himself with rather crude homemade Geiger counters, using very weak neutron sources. He obtained no results with the elements from hydrogen through oxygen, but this did not deter him; finally, he met success with fluorine, which showed a strong radioactivity as the result of the bombardment.

During these continuing investigations many problems both of an ex-

---

[1] Enrico Fermi, "Nobel Prize Address, 1938," *Collected Papers.* . . . (Chicago: University of Chicago Press, 1962).

perimental and theoretical nature arose and in each case Fermi found the correct solution. One of the most interesting developments was the great increase in artificial radioactivity resulting from the use of slow neutrons. This was an accidental discovery, made when elements irradiated on wooden tables proved much more active than those irradiated on marble tables. Fermi quickly understood the significance of this. The difference was due to the effect of the intervening wood, which slowed down the neutrons much more effectively than did the marble. To demonstrate this Fermi placed paraffin filters between the neutron beam and the irradiated target and thus increased enormously the resulting artificial radioactivity of the target. Fermi correctly pointed out that the light elements in paraffin similar to those in wood, particularly hydrogen, slow down the neutrons through collisions with their own atomic nuclei. The slow neutrons, spending more time in the neighborhood of an irradiated target nucleus, can then do more damage.

One of the most puzzling historical features of Fermi's bombardment of nuclei with neutrons concerns the production of elements with atomic number higher than 92, i.e., uranium. In the note Fermi sent to *Nature* in 1934 concerning this research, which we include among our selections, he analyzes the possible reactions that can be obtained and concludes that the evidence strongly favors the "transuranic" (across the boundary of uranium) elements 93 and 94. At this point in their investigations, in 1934, the Rome group was on the threshold of discovering the fission of uranium. Some five years later Hahn and Strassman made this discovery in Germany and communicated their data to Lise Meitner, then in exile in Sweden, ushering in the Atomic Age. It is now clear that the fission fragments were present in the earlier Rome uranium-irradiation experiments. Emilio Segrè, one of Fermi's outstanding collaborators and disciples, who received the Nobel Prize for discovering the antiproton, believes that the failure to detect fission was due to the use of an aluminum sheet covering the uranium and the thorium, which filtered out all the fission fragments. Although the possibility of fission had been called to Fermi's attention by I. Noddack, who wrote an article predicting it, Fermi dismissed this possibility because the data on the mass defects of nuclei seemed to preclude it. It later turned out that these data were wrong.

Although Fermi was then still engaged in theoretical physics, most of it was in connection with the nuclear experimental work. In a letter written in April 1934, Rutherford welcomed Fermi into the experimental fraternity. He congratulated Fermi on his "successful escape from theoretical physics." Rutherford also remarks in this letter that even Dirac was doing some experimental work which all "seems to be a good augury for the future of theoretical physics." This semideparture from the provinces of theory was marked by another great paper by Fermi that appeared in the *Zeitschrift für Physik* in 1934. This paper presents a complete theory of β-decay and β-emission; with some minor modifications and extensions, the theory is still the accepted one. Starting from the idea that the nucleus contains no electrons, Fermi argues that the electron and the neutrino that are emitted in β-decay are created at the moment of their emission as is the photon at the moment of its emission from an electron. Just as the emission of the photon by an electron is due to the transition of the electron from one state of energy to another state, so, too, is β-emission the result of the transition of the nucleus from one energy state to another. In this case, however, Fermi pictures the electron and the neutrino as being emitted by a neutron in the nucleus. Like Heisenberg, he looks upon the proton and the neutron as two different energy states of the same fundamental particle. Transitions from one state to the other occur because of the emission or absorption of electrons and neutrinos. With this as a basis, Fermi sets up the mathematical machinery for describing β-decay.

He does this by carrying out the analogy between β-emission and the emission and absorption of photons. He employs a formula to describe the interaction of a nucleon (neutron or proton) with an electron and neutrino that is similar to the equation used to explain photon emission. Fermi uses the same quantum-mechanical technique that Dirac and others utilized to set up a quantum electrodynamics of radiation. This is the so-called technique of second quantization in which one introduces annihilation and creation operators to describe the processes under consideration. Thus, since electrons and neutrinos appear suddenly in β-decay processes, Fermi describes the phenomena in terms of electrons and neutrino creation operators, which he treats in the usual quantum mechanical fashion.

This theory successfully explains the spectral shape of β-ray emission, the lifetimes of β-emitters, positron decay, orbital electron capture, and so on. What is more interesting is that the type of interaction that Fermi used at the time is now recognized as a special case of a more general "universal Fermi interaction," which is now used to describe the decay of the muon and its interaction with protons.

Shortly after Fermi came to New York in 1939 to accept a professorship at Columbia University, the fission of the uranium atom was discovered and Fermi devoted his full time to uranium research. Together with Leo Szilard, he was instrumental in interesting the government in nuclear fission. Since Fermi at that time was the greatest authority on neutrons, it was quite natural that he should have become a moving spirit and dominant force in the Manhattan Project. This neutron research finally culminated in the first self-sustaining nuclear-chain reaction under the stadium at the University of Chicago, when the nuclear reactor there became critical on December 2, 1942.

Following the war, Fermi returned to his forsaken theoretical work. He began to devote more and more time to high-energy research and to fundamental-particle physics. The properties of such particles as the pi- and mu-mesons interested him greatly, and he also began some investigations into the nature and origin of cosmic rays. One of the mechanisms now accepted for the creation of cosmic rays was discovered by Fermi and presented in one of his last great theoretical papers. In the final years of his life he became interested in the problems of galactic structure, and with S. Chandrasekhar wrote a basic paper on the importance of galactic magnetic fields in the equilibrium of the spiral arms of galaxies.

A few years before his death in 1954, Fermi was invited to give the Silliman Foundation lectures at Yale University; he chose as his topic "Elementary Particles." These lectures have been collected in book form and are excellent examples of the simplicity of Fermi's lecture technique. Some pages from the opening chapter of those lectures are included as our final Fermi selection. To listen to Fermi was a most inspiring experience, not only for the student but also for the hardened worker in physics. He had the knack of all great teachers: he made you wonder why there had ever been any difficulty in understanding the topic he was presenting.

Enrico Fermi, born in Rome on September 29, 1901, was the third child of Alberto Fermi and Ida DeGattis, both of whom originally came from the north Italian town of Piacenza. Like all great geniuses, and especially those in physics (with the possible exception of Einstein), Enrico demonstrated his ability and his interest in physics at a very early age. He told Emilio Segrè that when he was about ten years old he tried to understand why a circle is represented by the equation $x^2 + y^2 = r^2$.

He spent his early school years in Rome and while still a high-school student he began to educate himself in physics by reading, in the Latin, a book on mathematical physics written in 1840 by a Jesuit. That he mastered its nine hundred pages is indicated by the numerous notations he made in its margins. He must certainly have been an amazing phenomenon to those who knew him in his early years, for he questioned everybody he met about mathematics and physics. Thus when, at the age of thirteen, he met one of his father's colleagues, A. Amidei, an engineer, he asked him whether it was true that there is a branch of mathematics in which important geometric properties are derived without using the "notion of measure." He was referring to projective geometry which was just then becoming very popular among mathematicians. Amidei told Fermi that this was so and lent him a book on the subject. Amidei then went on to say, in a letter to Segrè, that after a few days Fermi had read the introduction and the first three lessons, and after two months he had mastered the text, demonstrated all the theorems, and quickly solved the more than two hundred problems at the end of the book.

At the age of seventeen Fermi finished his secondary school studies and took the entrance examination for admission to the Scuola Normale Superiore at Pisa. His examination paper must certainly have amazed the examiners, for instead of giving the usual high-school level solutions to the problems, he applied the most advanced mathematical techniques, such as partial differential equations and Fourier analysis, to problems in sound.

Fermi was one of those remarkable people who excel in everything they attempt, and so he was an outstanding, if not the number one, student in all his subjects at Pisa. He was particularly good in languages and had no trouble in learning them by just working with a dictionary, and he spoke and wrote German perfectly. After beginning his university career as a mathematician, Fermi changed to physics and began studying the most advanced treatises available. Whatever he read he quickly assimilated and made part of his own technique.

Fermi's quality of mind and his deep physical insight at this time (between the ages of eighteen and twenty) are clearly indicated by the books he read and his own notebooks. He devoted himself only to the most important material and authors; the pertinent points of each subject were carefully developed in neatly written pages.

After obtaining his doctorate in 1922 from the Scuola Normale, Fermi returned to Rome, where he lived with his parents until he received a scholarship in 1923 to study with Born at Göttingen, which was then one of the major centers of quantum-mechanical activity. He spent another year at Leyden with P. Ehrenfest and then took a temporary post at the University of Florence; while there he discovered the Fermi statistics and published the paper which we have translated and included in this chapter.

In 1926 the first chair in theoretical physics was established at the University of Rome; Fermi became its first occupant. Here he began one of the most fruitful periods in all scientific history. He accomplished much research, and also trained physicists of great ability.

When Fermi was awarded the Nobel Prize in 1938, he did not return to Italy, since the collaboration between Mussolini and Hitler made the expression of free thought impossible; indeed, it threatened the very safety of his family. He came to Columbia University as professor of physics in 1930 and remained there until 1942, when he went to the University of Chicago to direct the experiments that led to the first chain-reacting pile and to the atomic bomb.

After the war he accepted a professorship at the Institute of Nuclear Studies at the University of Chicago and remained there until his death from cancer on November 29, 1954. During these later years of his life he applied himself to the physics of high-energy particles and cosmic rays, and, as in all his other ventures into physics, he sought to emphasize the physical content of a theory rather than the formalism.

Fermi was a rare human being who illuminated the lives of all who worked or came into contact with him. He had the remarkable quality of making everyone he spoke to or worked with feel that there was no real intellectual difference between them, and what Fermi could accomplish could be done by anyone else with a little effort. From this stemmed Fermi's entire philosophy of teaching, writing, and lecturing. He was convinced that many of the difficulties of the student arose because of a formalistic instead of a physical presentation of the material by the teacher. Fermi's books, articles, and papers are models of excellence and a delight to the reader.

Just as he had a zest for physics and took great joy in its pursuit, he approached all of life in that spirit. He had a great amount of physical stamina and was fond of sports, excelling in tennis, swimming, mountain climbing, and skiing. His wife Laura, a son Giulio, and a daughter Nella survive him.

Numerous honors and prizes were awarded to him for his work. He was the first recipient of the $50,000 prize that bears his name and is awarded by the United States Government for achievement in atomic research.

○○○○○○○

F E R M I

On Quantizing an Ideal Monatomic Gas [2]

IN CLASSICAL THERMODYNAMICS THE MOLECU-lar heat (at constant volume) is

$$c = (\tfrac{3}{2})k. \tag{1}$$

If, however, we are to apply Nernst's heat theorem to a gas we must consider (1) merely as an approximation for high temperatures since c must vanish in the limit as $T = 0$. We are therefore forced to assume that the motion of a molecule in an ideal gas is quantized; this quantization manifests itself for low temperatures by certain degeneracy phenomena so that

---

[2] Enrico Fermi, trans. Editors, *Zeitschrift für Physik,* 36 (1926), 902–912.

the specific heat and the equation of state depart from their classical counterparts.

The aim of the present paper is to present a method of quantization of an ideal gas which, according to our opinion, is as independent of arbitrary assumptions about the statistical behavior of the gas molecules as is possible.

In recent times, numerous attempts have been made to determine the equation of state of a perfect gas. The equations of state of the various authors and ours differ from each other and from the classical equation of state

$$PV = NkT$$

by the terms, which become appreciable only at very low temperatures and high pressures; unfortunately, real gases depart most strongly from ideal gases under these conditions so that the significant degeneracy phenomena have not been observable up until now. In any case, it may well be that a deeper knowledge of the equation of state may enable us to separate the degeneracy from the remaining deviations from the equation $PV = NkT$ so that it may be possible to decide experimentally which of the degeneracy theories is correct.

To apply the quantum rules to the motions of the molecules, we can proceed in various ways; the result, however, is always the same. For example, we may picture the molecules as being enclosed in a parallelopiped container with elastically reflecting walls; then the motion of the molecules flying back and forth between the walls is conditionally periodic and can therefore be quantized; more generally, we may picture the molecules as moving in an external force field, such that their motion is conditionally periodic; the assumption that the gas is ideal permits us to neglect the interactions of the molecules, so that their mechanical motions occur only under the influence of the external field. It is clear, however, that the quantization of the molecular motion made under the assumption of the complete independence of the molecules from one another is not sufficient to account for the expected degeneracy. We can see this best in the example of molecules in a container if we note that as the linear dimensions of the container increase, the energy levels of the quantum states of each molecule become denser and denser, so that for vessels of macroscopic dimensions all influences of the discontinuity of the energy values practically disappear. This influence, moreover, depends on the volume of the container, even if the number of molecules in it are so chosen that the density remains constant.

By analyzing this state of affairs quantitatively, we can convince ourselves that we only then obtain a degeneracy of the expected magnitude when we choose the vessel so small that it contains, on the average, just one molecule.

We therefore surmise that the quantization of ideal gases requires an addition to the Sommerfeld quantum condition.

Now recently Pauli, following upon an investigation by E. C. Stoner, proposed the rule that if an electron inside an atom has quantum numbers (including the magnetic quantum number) with definite values, then no other electron can exist in the atom in an orbit which is characterized by the same quantum numbers. In other words, a quantum state (in an external magnetic field) is already completely filled by a single electron.

Since this Pauli rule has proved extremely fruitful in the interpretation of spectroscopic phenomena, we want to see whether it may not also be useful in the problem of the quantization of ideal gases.

We shall show that this is, indeed, the case, and that the application of Pauli's rule allows us to present a completely consistent theory of the degeneracy of an ideal gas.

We therefore assume in the following that, at most, one molecule with given quantum numbers can exist in our gas: as quantum numbers we must take into account not only those that determine the internal motions of the molecule but also the numbers that determine its translational motion.

We must first place our molecules in a suitable external force field so that their motion is conditionally periodic. This can be done in an infinitude of ways; since, however, the result does not depend on the choice of the force field, we shall impose on the molecules a central elastic force directed toward a fixed point O (the coordinate origin) so that each molecule becomes a harmonic oscillator. This central force will keep our gas mass in the neighborhood of O; the gas density will decrease with increasing distance from O and vanish at infinity. If v is the proper frequency of the oscillators, then the force exerted on the molecules is

$$4\pi^2 v^2 mr$$

where m is the mass of the molecule and r its distance from O. The potential energy of the attractive force is then

$$u = 2\pi^2 v^2 mr^2$$

Let s_1, s_2, s_3 be the quantum numbers of a molecule oscillator. These quantum numbers are essentially not sufficient to characterize the molecule, for we must add to these the quantum numbers of the internal motions. We limit ourselves, however, to monatomic molecules and assume, in addition, that all the molecules in our gas are in the ground state and that this state is single (does not split in a magnetic field). We need not worry about the internal motion then, and we may then consider our molecules simply as mass points. The Pauli rule, therefore, states in our case that in the entire mass of gas at most only one molecule can have the given quantum numbers s_1, s_2, s_3.

The total energy of this molecule is given by

$$w = h\nu(s_1 + s_2 + s_3) = h\nu s. \tag{2}$$

The total energy can thus be an arbitrary integral multiple of $h\nu$; the value $sh\nu$, however, can be realized in many ways. Each realization implies a solution of the equation

$$s = s_1 + s_2 + s_3 \tag{3}$$

where s_1, s_2, s_3 can assume the values 1, 2, 3 . . . . We know that (3) has

$$Q_s = \frac{(s+1)(s+2)}{2} \tag{4}$$

solutions. The energy 0 can thus be realized in one way, the energy $h\nu$ in three ways, the energy $2h\nu$ in six ways, and so on. We shall simply call a molecule with energy $sh\nu$ an $((s))$-molecule.

According to our assumption, there can be in our entire gas mass only $Q_s((s))$-molecules; thus, at most, one molecule with energy zero, at most, three with energy $h\nu$ at most, six with energy $2h\nu$, and so on.

To see clearly the results of this state of affairs, we consider the extreme case in which the absolute temperature of our gas is zero. Let N be the number of molecules. At absolute zero our gas must be in its lowest energy state. If there were no restrictions on the number of molecules of a given energy, then every molecule would be in a state of zero energy ($s_1 = s_2 = s_3 = 0$). According to the foregoing, however, at most, only one molecule can have zero energy; hence, if N were 1, then this single molecule would have energy zero; if N were 4, one molecule would have energy zero and the three others would occupy the three available places with energy $h\nu$; if N were 10, one molecule would be in the zero energy position, three others in the three places with energy $h\nu$, and the six remaining ones in the six places with energy $2h\nu$ and so on.

At the absolute zero point, our gas molecules arrange themselves in a kind of shell-like structure which has a certain analogy to the shell-like arrangement of electrons in an atom with many electrons.

We now want to investigate how a certain amount of energy

$$W = Eh\nu \tag{5}$$

(E = integer) is distributed among our molecules.

Let N_s be the number of molecules in a state with energy shv. According to our assumption

$$N_s \leq Q_s. \tag{6}$$

We have, further, the equations

$$\sum N_s = N \tag{7}$$

$$\sum sN_s = E \tag{8}$$

which state that the total number and total energy of the molecules are N and Ehv, respectively.

We now want to calculate the number P of arrangements of our N molecules for which N_0 are at places with energy 0, N_1 at places with energy hv, N_2 at places with energy $2hv$, etc. Two such arrangements are to be considered identical if the places occupied by the molecules are the same: thus two arrangements which differ only in a permutation among the molecules in their places are to be considered as one. If we considered two such arrangements as different, we would have to multiply P by the constant N!; we can easily see, however, that this can have no influence on what follows. In the above-defined sense, the number of arrangements of N_s molecules among the Q_s places of energy, shv is given by

$$\binom{Q_s}{N_s}.$$

We therefore find for P the expression

$$P = \binom{Q_0}{N_0}\binom{Q_1}{N_1}\binom{Q_2}{N_2}\ldots\ldots = \Pi\binom{Q_s}{N_s}. \tag{9}$$

We obtain the most probable values of the N_s by seeking the maximum of P under the constraints (7) and (8). By applying Stirling's theorem we may write, with sufficient approximation for our case

$$\log P = \sum \log \binom{Q_s}{N_s}$$
$$= -\sum \left(N_s \log \frac{N_s}{Q_s - N_s} + Q_s \log \frac{Q_s - N_s}{Q_s} \right) \tag{10}$$

We thus seek the values of N_s that satisfy (7) and (8) and for which $\log P$ becomes a maximum. We find

$$\alpha e^{-\beta s} = \frac{N_s}{Q_s - N_s}$$

where α and β are constants. This equation gives us

$$N_s = Q_s \frac{\alpha e^{-\beta s}}{1 + \alpha e^{-\beta s}} \qquad (11)$$

The values of α and β can be found from equations (7) and (8) or, conversely, we may consider α and β as given; then (7) and (8) determine the total number and total energy of our configuration. We find, namely,

$$N = \sum_0^\infty Q_s \frac{\alpha e^{-\beta s}}{1 + \alpha e^{-\beta s}}$$

$$\frac{W}{h\nu} = E = \sum_s s Q_s \frac{\alpha e^{-\beta s}}{1 + \alpha e^{-\beta s}} \qquad (12)$$

The absolute temperature T of the gas is a function of N and E or also of α and β. This function can be determined by two methods, which, however, lead to the same result. We could, for example, according to the Boltzmann entropy principle set

$$S = k \log P$$

and then calculate the temperature from the formula

$$T = \frac{dW}{dS}$$

This method, however, has the disadvantage common to all methods based on the Boltzmann principle, that for its application we must make a more or less arbitrary assumption about the probability of a state. Therefore, we proceed as follows: we note that the density of our gas is a function of the distance which vanishes for infinite distances. For infinitely large r, therefore, the degeneracy phenomena also vanish and the statistics of our gas go over to classical statistics. In particular, for $r = \infty$ the mean kinetic energy of a molecule must become $(\frac{3}{2})kT$ and the velocity distribution must go over to the Maxwellian. We can thus obtain the temperature from the distribution of velocities in the region of infinitesimal densities; and since the entire gas is at the same constant temperature, we then at the same time obtain the temperature of the high density region also. For this determination we use, so to speak, a gas thermometer with an infinitely attenuated ideal gas.

To begin with, we calculate the density of molecules with kinetic energy between L and $L + dL$ at the distance r. The total energy of these molecules lies, according to (1), between

$$L + 2\pi^2 v^2 m r^2 \quad \text{and} \quad L + 2\pi^2 v^2 m r^2 + dL.$$

Now the total energy of a molecule is shv. For our molecules s must therefore lie between s and $s + ds$, where

$$s = \frac{L}{hv} + \frac{2\pi^2 v m r^2}{h} \qquad ds = \frac{dL}{hv} \qquad (13)$$

We now consider a molecule whose motion is characterized by the quantum numbers s_1, s_2, s_3. Its coordinates x, y, z are given by

$$x = \sqrt{Hs_1} \cos (2\pi vt - \alpha_1), \, y = \sqrt{Hs_2} \cos (2\pi vt - \alpha_2) \qquad (14)$$
$$z = \sqrt{Hs_3} \cos (2\pi vt - \alpha_3)$$

as functions of the time. Here

$$H = \frac{h}{2\pi^2 v m}: \qquad (15)$$

α_1, α_2, α_3 are phase constants which may take on all sets of values with equal probability. From this and from equation (14) it follows that

$$|x| \leq \sqrt{Hs_1}, \, |y| \leq \sqrt{Hs_2}, \, |z| \leq \sqrt{Hs_3},$$

and that the probability that x, y, z lie between the limits x and $x + dx$, y and $y + dy$, z and $z + dz$, has the value

$$\frac{dxdydz}{\pi^3 \sqrt{(Hs_1 - x^2)(Hs_2 - y^2)(Hs_3 - z^2)}}$$

If we do not know the individual values of s_1, s_2, s_3 but only their sum, then our probability is given by

$$\frac{1}{Q_s} \frac{dxdydz}{\pi^3} \sum \frac{1}{\sqrt{(Hs_1 - x^2)(Hs_2 - y^2)(Hs_3 - z^2)}} \qquad (16)$$

The sum is to be extended over all integer solutions of equation (3) which satisfy the inequalities

$$Hs_1 \geq x^2, \, Hs_2 \geq y^2, \, Hs_3 \geq z^2$$

If we multiply the probability (16) with the number N_s of $((s))$-molecules, we obtain the number of $((s))$-molecules in the volume element $dxdydz$. Taking account of (11) we thus find that the density of $((s))$-molecules at the position x, y, z is given by

$$N_s = \frac{ae^{-\beta s}}{1 + ae^{-\beta s}} \frac{1}{\pi^3} \sum \frac{1}{\sqrt{(Hs_1 - x^2)(Hs_2 - y^2)(Hs_3 - z^2)}}$$

For sufficiently large s we can replace the sum by a double integral; after carrying out the integration we find

$$N_s = \frac{2}{\pi^2 H^2} \frac{\alpha e^{-\beta s}}{1 + \alpha e^{-\beta s}} \sqrt{Hs - r^2}$$

Using (13) and (15) we now find that the density of molecules with kinetic energy between L and $L + dL$ at the position x, y, z is given by the following expression

$$N(L)dL = N_s ds = \frac{2\pi(2m)^{3/2}}{h^3} \sqrt{L}\ dL\ \frac{\alpha e^{-\frac{2\pi^2 \nu m \beta r^2}{h}} e^{-\frac{\beta L}{h\nu}}}{1 + \alpha e^{-\frac{2\pi^2 \nu m \beta r^2}{h}} e^{\frac{-\beta L}{h\nu}}} \quad (17)$$

This formula must be compared with the classical expression for the Maxwellian distribution:

$$N^*(L)dL = K\sqrt{L}\ dLe^{-L/kt} \quad (17')$$

We see then that in the limit for $\nu = \infty$ (17) goes over into (17') if we just set

$$\beta = \frac{h\nu}{kT}. \quad (18)$$

Now (17) can be written as follows:

$$N(L)dL = \frac{(2\pi)(2m)^{3/2}}{h^3} \sqrt{L}\ dL\ \frac{Ae^{-L/kT}}{1 + Ae^{-L/kT}} \quad (19)$$

where

$$A = \alpha e^{-\frac{2\pi^2 \nu^2 m r^2}{kT}} \quad (20)$$

The total density of molecules at the distance r now becomes

$$N = \int_0^\infty N(L)dL = \frac{(2\pi mkT)^{3/2}}{h^3} F(A), \quad (21)$$

where we have placed

$$F(A) = \frac{2}{\sqrt{\pi}} \int_0^\infty \frac{A\sqrt{x}\ e^{-x}dx}{1 + Ae^{-x}} \quad (22)$$

The mean kinetic energy of the molecules at the distance r is

$$\bar{L} = \frac{1}{N} \int_0^\infty L\,N(L)\,dL = (\tfrac{3}{2})kT\,\frac{G(A)}{F(A)} \qquad (23)$$

where

$$G(A) = \frac{4}{3\sqrt{\pi}} \int_0^\infty \frac{A x^{3/2} e^{-x}\,dx}{1 + A e^{-x}} \qquad (24)$$

Through (21) we can determine A as a function of density and temperature; when we put this into (19) and (20) we obtain the velocity distribution and the mean kinetic energy as a function of density and temperature.

To obtain the equation of state we use the virial theorem. According to this the pressure is given by

$$p = \frac{2}{3} N\bar{L} = NkT\,\frac{G(A)}{F(A)}; \qquad (25)$$

again A is to be found from (12) as a function of density and temperature.

Before we go further we give some of the mathematical properties of $F(A)$ and $G(A)$.

For $A \leqq 1$ we can express both functions by convergent series

$$\begin{cases} F(A) = A - \dfrac{A^2}{2^{3/2}} + \dfrac{A^3}{3^{3/2}} - \cdots \\[3mm] G(A) = A - \dfrac{A^2}{2^{5/2}} + \dfrac{A^3}{3^{5/2}} - \cdots \end{cases} \qquad (26)$$

For large A we have the asymptotic expressions

$$\begin{cases} F(A) = \dfrac{4}{3\sqrt{\pi}}(\log A)^{3/2}\left[1 + \dfrac{\pi^2}{8(\log A)^2} + \cdots\right] \\[4mm] G(A) = \dfrac{8}{15\sqrt{\pi}}(\log A)^{5/2}\left[1 + \dfrac{5\pi^2}{8(\log A)^2} + \cdots\right] \end{cases} \qquad (27)$$

Further, the relationship

$$\frac{dG(A)}{F(A)} = d\log A \qquad (28)$$

holds.

We must still introduce another function $P(\Theta)$ defined by

$$P(\Theta) = \Theta\,\frac{G(A)}{F(A)}, \quad F(A) = \frac{1}{\Theta^{3/2}} \tag{29}$$

For very large and very small Θ respectively, $P(\Theta)$ can be calculated from the approximations

$$\begin{cases} P(\Theta) = \Theta\left\{1 + \frac{1}{2^{5/2}\Theta^{3/2}} + \ldots \ldots\right\} \\[2mm] P(\Theta) = \frac{3^{2/3}\pi^{1/3}}{5.2^{1/3}}\left\{1 + \frac{5.2^{2/3}\pi^{1/3}}{3^{7/3}}\,\Theta^2 + \ldots\right\} \end{cases} \tag{30}$$

Using (29), (28), (27), we see further that

$$\int_0^\Theta \frac{dP(\Theta)}{\Theta} = \tfrac{5}{3}\,\frac{G(A)}{F(A)} - \tfrac{2}{3}\log A \tag{31}$$

We can now eliminate A from the equation of state (25) and (23) and we obtain the pressure and the mean kinetic energy as explicit functions of density and temperature:

$$p = \frac{h^2 N^{5/3}}{2\pi m}\,P\left(\frac{2\pi mkT}{h^2 N^{2/3}}\right) \tag{32}$$

$$\bar{L} = \tfrac{3}{2}\,\frac{h^2 N^{2/3}}{2\pi m}\,P\left(\frac{2\pi mkT}{h^2 N^{2/3}}\right) \tag{33}$$

In the limit of weak degeneracy (T large and N small) the equation of state has the following form:

$$p = NkT\left\{1 + (\tfrac{1}{16})\,\frac{h^3 N}{(\pi mkT)^{3/2}} + \ldots\right\} \tag{34}$$

The pressure is thus larger than the classical pressure ($p = NkT$). For an ideal gas with the atomic weight of helium at $T = 5°$ and a pressure of 10 atm, the difference is about 15%.

In the limit of large degeneracy, (32) and (33) become

$$\begin{aligned} p &= (\tfrac{1}{20})\left(\frac{6}{\pi}\right)^{2/3}\frac{h^2 N^{5/3}}{m} + \frac{2^{1/3}}{3^{5/2}}\,\pi^{8/3}\,\frac{mN^{1/3}k^2T^2}{h^2} + \ldots \\[2mm] \bar{L} &= (\tfrac{3}{40})\left(\frac{6}{\pi}\right)^{2/3}\frac{h^2 N^{2/3}}{m} + \frac{2^{1/3}\pi^{8/3}}{3^{2/3}}\,\frac{mk^2T^2}{h^2 N^{2/3}} + \ldots \end{aligned} \tag{35}$$

From this we see that the degeneracy leads to a zero point pressure and a zero point energy.

From (35) we can also obtain the specific heat at low temperatures. We find

$$C_v = \frac{d\overline{L}}{dT} = \frac{2^{1/3}\pi^{5/3}}{3^{2/3}} \frac{mk^2T}{h^2N^{2/3}} + \ \cdots \qquad (36)$$

The specific heat vanishes at absolute zero and is proportional to the absolute temperature at low temperatures. . . .

ooooooo

FERMI, AMALDI, D'AGOSTINO, RASETTI, and SEGRÈ

Artificial Radioactivity Produced by Neutron Bombardment [3]

INTRODUCTION

THIS PAPER AIMS AT GIVING a fuller account of experiments made in the Physical Laboratory of the University of Rome, on new radio-elements produced by neutron bombardment. Preliminary results have already been announced in short communications.

Curie and Joliot first discovered that the product atom of an artificial disintegration need not always correspond to a stable isotope, but could also disintegrate with a relatively long mean life with emission of light particles. As bombarding particles they used α-particles from polonium, and found that the light particle emitted was generally a positron. Similar results were obtained on several elements by other experimenters using α-particles, and artificially accelerated protons and deutons.

The use of charged particles for the bombardment limits the possibility of an activation only to light elements. Indeed, only about ten elements up to the atomic number 15 could be activated by these methods.

It seemed therefore convenient to try the effect of a neutron bombardment, as these particles can reach the nucleus even of the heaviest ele-

[3] Fermi *et al.*, *Proceedings of the Royal Society* (London), Series A, 146 (1934), 483–499.

ments. Available neutron sources are, of course, much less intense than α-particles or proton or deuton sources. But it was reasonable to assume that this factor would be partly compensated by the higher efficiency of neutrons in producing disintegrations. Indeed, experiment showed that more than forty elements out of about sixty investigated could be activated by this method.

THE EXPERIMENTAL METHOD

The neutron source consisted of a sealed glass tube about 6 mm in diameter and 15 mm in length, containing beryllium powder and radon in amounts up to 800 millicuries. According to the ordinarily assumed yield of neutrons from beryllium, the number of neutrons emitted by this source ought to be of the order of 1000 neutrons per second per millicurie. These neutrons are distributed over a very wide range of energies from zero up to 7 or 8 million volts, besides a very small percentage having energies about twice as high as this limit.

The neutrons are mixed with a very intensive γ-radiation. This does not, however, produce any inconvenience, as the induced activity is tested after irradiation, and it was shown that radon without beryllium produced no effect. The neutrons from beryllium are accompanied by a γ-radiation harder than any emitted by the radon products (5 to 6 million volts—about one γ-quantum per neutron). It seems, however, most unlikely that the observed effects are in any way connected with this γ-radiation, as a γ-radiation of enormously greater intensity and only slightly lower energy produces no effect.

The emission of electrons from the activated substances was tested with Geiger-Müller counters about 5 cm in length and 1·4 cm diameter. The walls of the counter were of thin aluminium foil, 0·1 to 0·2 mm in thickness. The applied voltage ranged between 1000 and 1500 volts. The amplified impulses were counted on a mechanical meter worked by a thyratron.

The substances to be investigated were generally put into form of cylinders, which could be fitted round the counter in order to minimize the loss in intensity through geometrical factors. During irradiation the material was located as close as possible round the source. Substances which had to be treated chemically after irradiation were often irradiated as concentrated water solutions in a test tube.

The decay curves of the induced activity were for many elements simple exponentials. Sometimes they could be analysed into two or more exponentials; it was then convenient to irradiate the substance for different lengths of time in order to activate the various components with different intensity. The existence of several mean lives is, sometimes, certainly due to different isotopic constituents of the element; when a single isotope is present it may be attributed to alternative processes of disintegration, and sometimes (uranium) to a chain of disintegrations. The intensity of activation varies within a wide range among the different elements. In some the effect is hardly measurable, the number of impulses produced by the irradiated substance being of the order of magnitude of the number of spontaneous impulses in the counter. In others the activation is so strong that when the substance is placed too near the counter the number of impulses is of the order of some thousands per minute, so that they cannot be counted because of lack of resolving power.

No accurate measurement of the intensity of activation of the different elements was carried out, as it would require experimenting in well-defined geometrical condition, and a knowledge of the efficiency of our counters in counting electrons, and of the absorption in the substance and in the aluminium foil. However, a very rough evaluation of these factors was made, and for some elements a number expressing the intensity of activation (i) is given. This intensity is defined as the number of disintegrations per second which take place in 1 gm of the element, placed at the distance of 1 cm from a neutron source consisting of one millicurie of radon (in equilibrium with its decay products) and beryllium powder. The substance was always irradiated until saturation of the active product was reached. The efficiency of our counters (including absorption in the aluminium foil and geometrical factors) was about $\frac{1}{20}$, as determined by the measurement of the impulses from known quantities of potassium and uranium.

From this number expressing the intensity it is easy to obtain the cross-section for the activating neutron impact, if the number of neutrons emitted per second by a one millicurie source is known. Assuming this number to be 1000, one finds immediately the cross-section

$$\sigma = 2 \cdot 10^{-26} \, i \cdot A,$$

A being the atomic weight of the element.

In order to be able to discuss the nuclear reaction giving rise to the active element, it is essential to identify it chemically. It is reasonable to assume that the atomic number of the active element should be close to the atomic number Z of the bombarded element. As the amount of the active substance is exceedingly small (in the most favourable cases about 10^9 atoms), there is no hope of separating it by ordinary methods. The irradiated substance was therefore dissolved, and small amounts of the inactive elements, which are suspected of being isotopic with the active product, were added. These added elements and the irradiated element were then chemically separated from each other, and separately tested for activity. It is generally found that the activity follows definitely one element. The active product can then be considered as identified with this element.

A preliminary investigation of the penetrating power of the β-rays of the new radio-elements has been carried out. For this purpose counters of the standard type were used, and the substance, instead of being put quite close to the counter, was shaped in the form of a cylinder of inner diameter somewhat larger than the diameter of the counter in order to allow cylindrical aluminum screens of different thicknesses to be interposed. In this way absorption curves of a more or less exponential type were obtained. As the geometrical conditions of this absorption measure are different from the standard ones, and moreover, the number of impulses instead of the total ionization is computed, we checked the method by measuring the absorption coefficients for known radioactive substances; as expected, we found a difference (about 20%). The data are corrected for this factor.

In several cases the absorption by 2 mm of lead was not complete; this was assumed as a proof of the existence of a γ-radiation.

It was very important to determine whether the emitted particles were positive or negative electrons. Owing to the weakness of the radiation it seemed convenient to use for this purpose Thibaud's method of the inhomogeneous magnetic field. Even by this intensive arrangement this investigation had to be limited to elements which could be strongly activated (Al, Si, P, S, Cr, As, Br, Rh, Ag, I, Ir, U). In every case only negative electrons were observed. This, however, does not exclude that a small percentage (up to about 15%) of the emitted particles might be positrons.

For a few very strongly activated elements the emitted electrons could be also photographed in a Wilson chamber.

EXPERIMENTAL RESULTS

The elements investigated are here arranged in order of atomic number; a summary of the results is to be found in a table at the end of the paper.

1—*Hydrogen.* Shows no effect when water is irradiated 14 hours with a 670-millicuries source.

3—*Lithium.* The hydroxide irradiated 14 hours with 750 millicuries is inactive.

4—*Beryllium.* Shows an extremely weak activity which might well be due to impurities.

5—*Boron.* Same as beryllium.

6—*Carbon.* Paraffin irradiated 15 hours with 220 millicuries is inactive.

7—*Nitrogen.* Guanidine carbonate (about 35% N) irradiated 14 hours with 500 millicuries is inactive.

8—*Oxygen.* No activity: see hydrogen.

9—*Fluorine.* This element irradiated as calcium fluoride can be strongly activated ($i = .0 \cdot 7$). As calcium proves to be inactive, the effect is due to fluorine. The activity decreases with a very short half period, about 9 seconds. No chemical separation was possible in this case. However, as it is known that fluorine disintegrates under neutron bombardment with emission of an α-particle, the active nucleus is probably N^{16}. This unstable isotope goes over to stable O^{16} with emission of an electron. The remarkable stability of the latter nucleus agrees with the observed very high energy of the β-rays; the intensity reduces to half value in $0 \cdot 24$ gm/cm² Al. This and all the following absorption data are given for aluminium.

11—*Sodium.* This element has been irradiated as carbonate. Sodium shows a fairly strong activation, decreasing with a period of about 40 seconds.

12—*Magnesium.* This element can be fairly strongly activated, and the decay curves show the existence of two periods, of about 40 seconds and 15 hours. Half-value thickness for the long period $0 \cdot 06$ gm/cm².

The active element decaying with the 15 hours' period could be chemically separated. The irradiated magnesium was dissolved, and a sodium salt was added. The magnesium was then precipitated as phosphate and found to be inactive, while the sodium which remains in the solution carries the activity. The active atom is thus proved not to be an isotope of magnesium, and as neon also can be excluded, we assume it to be an isotope of sodium, formed according to the reaction:

$$Mg_{12}^{24} + n_0^{1} = Na_{11}^{24} + H_1^{1}.$$

[The reports on the elements between 13 and 92 have been omitted—Editors.]

92—*Uranium.* We give here only the main results on this element, as its behaviour has been discussed recently elsewhere.

Besides the half-periods of 10 seconds, 40 seconds and 13 minutes, we have identified later one more of about $1 \cdot 5$ hours. The intensity of the activation is of the order of $0 \cdot 5$ for each of these lives. We have already discussed experiments which appear to prove that the 13 minutes' active product is not isotopic with any of the elements with atomic number from 86 to 92 (emanation, ekacæsium, radium, actinium, thorium, protactinium, uranium). These experiments have been repeated under different conditions, chiefly in order to obtain a negative proof of the identity of the 13-minute product with protactinium, this proof being the most difficult to establish on account of the short period of the available Pa isotope, UX$_2$. The manganese reaction which has already been described gives a yield of about 15% for the 13-minute product. Its yield for UX$_2$ depends widely upon the conditions of the reaction and may be varied between 2% and 10%, account being taken of the natural decay of this substance. A more effective reaction for obtaining the 13-minute active product is the following: irradiated uranium nitrate is dissolved in diluted hydrochloric acid; some rhenium nitrate is added, and then rhenium is precipitated as sulphide by addition of sodium thiosulphate. This precipitate carries about 50% of the activity; and sometimes more. The percentage of UX$_1$ and of UX$_2$ found in the rhenium precipitate varies also with the conditions of the reaction (particularly with the acidity), but can be made very low, probably less than 1%. It was actually possible to separate the 13-minute active product and to measure its period using uranium which had not been purified at all from UX. The 90-minute active product has apparently chemical properties very analogous to those of the 13-minute active product, as in every type of reaction they are always obtained in about the same percentage. These activities seem, therefore, both to be due to products with atomic number higher than 92, and possibly to isotopes of a same element.

THEORETICAL DISCUSSION

We want here to discuss, from the theoretical point of view, the processes that may take place under neutron bombardment. At the present state of the nuclear theory these considerations can have only a provisional character. We can resume the empirical results of the preceding sections in the following points.

(*a*) A large percentage of elements of any atomic weight can be activated [, and] from this point of view no special difference can be noticed between light and heavy elements.

(*b*) The cross-sections for neutron impact for the elements which can be most intensely activated are of the order of the geometrical cross-section of the nucleus. This means that a large percentage of the neutrons which hit the nucleus produce an active atom.

(*c*) The active product is sometimes an isotope of the original atom (atomic number Z); in other cases its atomic number is lower by one or two units. In this respect there appears to be a difference between light and heavy elements. For light elements the atomic number of the active product is usually lower than Z, while in the five cases investigated for heavy, non-spontaneously radioactive elements, the active product is always an isotope of the bombarded element.

(*d*) The emitted electrons always have a negative charge, or at least no positrons could ever be detected.

There seems to be no special difficulty in explaining the general mechanism of the activation for light elements. This seems to consist usually in the capture of the impinging neutron, followed immediately by the expulsion of an α-particle or a proton. If the energy of the emitted α-particle or proton is of some million volts, it results from Gamow's theory that the time which is necessary to emit the particle is extremely short, and there is therefore a fairly high probability for the process to happen before the neutron has left the nucleus. After this process, which may last a time of the order of 10^{-20} seconds, the nucleus has been transformed into a new one having, on the average, an atomic weight higher than would belong to its nuclear charge, as the processes of absorbing a neutron and emitting an α-particle or a proton increase the neutron/proton ratio in the nucleus. This is probably the reason why an emission of negative electrons is always observed. The process of the electron emission re-establishes the correct value for neutron/proton ratio, and corresponds to the formation of a stable isotope.

As the atomic weight of the bombarded element increases, the potential barrier around the nucleus becomes an increasingly strong obstacle to the emission of heavy, positively-charged particles; it is therefore easy to understand why processes with emission of protons and α-particles become very improbable.

The reactions whose theoretical interpretation seems to meet with difficulties are those, normally occurring among heavy elements, in which the activated atom is isotopic with the original atom. The simplest hypothesis would be to assume a capture of the impinging neutron, giving rise to an unstable isotope of the bombarded element with an atomic weight higher by one unit than before the process. This hypothesis, which would be in agreement with the observed fact of the emission of negative electrons, gives rise, however, to serious theoretical difficulties when one tries to explain how a neutron can be captured by the nucleus in a stable or quasi-stable state. It is generally admitted that a neutron is attracted by a nucleus only when its distance from the centre of the nucleus is of the order of 10^{-12} cm. It follows that a neutron of a few million volts' energy can remain in the nucleus (*i.e.*, have a strong interaction with the constituent particles of the nucleus) only for a time of the order of 10^{-21} seconds; that is, of the classical time needed to cross the nucleus. The neutron is captured if, during this time, it is able to lose its excess energy (*e.g.*, by emission of a γ-quantum). If one evaluates the probability of this emission process by the ordinary methods one finds a value much too small to account for the observed cross-sections. In order to maintain the capture hypothesis, one must then either admit that the probability of emission of a γ-quantum (or of an equivalent process, as, for example, the formation of an electron-positron pair) should be much larger than is generally assumed; or that, for reasons that cannot be understood in the present theory, a nucleus

TABLE 75 – 1

Atomic number.	Isotopes.	Half-period.	Intensity.	Mean energy of β-rays in 10^6 volts.	γ-rays.	Active isotope.
1 H	**1, 2**	—	—			
3 Li	6, 7	?	?			
4 Be	9	?	?			
5 B	**10, 11**	—	—			
6 C	**12**, 13	—	—			
7 N	**14**, 15	—	—			
8 O	16, 17, 18	9 s.	s	2	yes	N^{16} (?)
9 F	**19**	40 s.	m			
11 Na	**23**	40 s.; 15 h.	$m; m$	—; ·5	?; yes	—; Na^{24}
12 Mg	**24**, 25, 26	12 m.; 15 h.	$s; s$	·6; ·5	yes; yes	—; Na^{24}
13 Al	**27**	3 m.	s	1·3	yes	Al^{28}
14 Si	**28**, 29, 30	3 m.; 3 h.	$m; s$	—; ·7	?	Si^{31}
15 P	**31**	13 d.	m	·8		P^{32}
16 S	32, 33, 34	13 d.	m	·8	—	P^{32}
17 Cl	**35**, 37					
20 Ca	40, 42, 43, 44					
22 Ti	46, 47, **48**, 49, 50	3 m.	w			

23 V	**51**	4 m.	*m*	1·3		V^{52} (?)
24 Cr	50, **52**, 53, 54	4 m.	*m*	1·3	yes	V^{52}
25 Mn	**55**	4 m.; 150 m.	*m; m*	—; 1·3		V^{52}, Mn^{56}
26 Fe	54, **56**	150 m.	*m*	1·3	yes	Mn^{56}
27 Co	**59**	150 m.	*w*			Mn^{56}
28 Ni	**58**, **60**, 61, 62		—			
29 Cu	**63**, **65**	6 m.	*m*			
30 Zn	**64**, **66**, 67, 68, 70	6 m.; ?	*w; w*			Cu; —
31 Ga	**69**, **71**	30 m.	*m*			
33 As	**75**	1 d.	*s*	1·3	yes	As^{76}
34 Se	74, 76, 77, **78**, **80**, 82	35 m.	*w*			
35 Br	**79**, **81**	30 m.; 6 h.	*s; s*	—; ·7 (?)	—	Br^{80}, Br^{82}
37 Rb	**85**, **87**	20 m.	*w*			
38 Sr	86, 87, **88**		—			
39 Y	**89**	—	—			
40 Zr	90, 91, **92**, 94, 96	?	*w*			
42 Mo	92, 94, 95, 96, 97, **98**, 100	15 m.; (?)	*w; w*			
44 Ru	96, 98, 99, 100, **101**, **102**, 104		—			
45 Rh	**103**	50 s.; 5 m.	*s; m*	·8	—	
46 Pd		6 h. (?)	*w*	·3	—	
47 Ag	**107**, **109**	20 s.; 2 m.	*s; s*	—; ·7	—	
48 Cd	110, 111, **112**, 113, **114**, 116	70 m.	*w*			
50 Sn	112, 114, 115, 116, 117, **118**, 119, **120**, 121, 122, 124	—	—			

could remain for at least 10^{-16} seconds in an energy state high enough to permit the emission of a neutron.

An alternative hypothesis is to admit that the impinging neutron is not captured, but causes the expulsion of another neutron from the nucleus. This process could be described as follows: the primary neutron loses part of its energy, bringing the nucleus into an excited state by a sort of in-elastic impact. One can easily understand theoretically that these processes may take place in a large percentage of the collisions between nuclei and neutrons. If the excitation energy is large enough, a neutron can be emitted before the nucleus loses its energy by emission of a γ-quantum. The atom formed by such a process is an isotope of the original one, with atomic weight lower by one unit.

An objection which may be raised against this hypothesis is that if the number of neutrons decreases instead of increasing, it is, *a priori,* more likely that the atom, in the following disintegration, should emit a positron than a negative electron as observed. However, in the few cases investi-gated of heavy elements which are activated by neutron bombardment and are transformed into their isotopes, when the isotopic constitution of the neighbouring elements is known, there always exists a stable isotope of the element $Z + 1$, having atomic weight one unit less than the original element, as a possible end-product of the transformation.

One has, moreover, to bear in mind that if an unstable nucleus has energetically the possibility of emitting both an electron and a positron, the theory of the β-rays gives *ceteris paribus* the emission of an electron as the most probable.

In conclusion, the choice between these two alternatives seems at pres-ent rather uncertain, and further experiments must be performed to test this point.

TABULAR SUMMARY

The main results of this investigation are summarized in [Table 75–1]. Column 1 contains the atomic number and symbol of the elements investi-gated. Column 2 gives the isotopic constitution; numbers in bold type refer to isotopes which represent more than 20% of the element. Column 3 gives the observed half-periods; a heavy —— means that the activity was sought for and not found. Column 4 gives a rough evaluation of the in-tensity s (strong), m (medium), w (weak). Column 5 gives the average energy of the electrons in million volts; this was obtained from the ab-sorption measurement by a rather rough extrapolation based on the ab-sorption coefficients of ordinary β-active substances without strong γ-rays (Ra E and UX_2). Column 6 shows whether γ-rays were observed or not; a line means that γ-rays have been sought for and not observed. Column 7 gives a probable active product; for simplicity we have always assumed that the neutron is captured; if, instead, a neutron was emitted, the corresponding atomic weights should be decreased by two units. When two or more periods are present, the data of columns 4, 5, 6 and 7 refer to the different periods in their order.

 oooooooo

F E R M I

Possible Production of Elements of Atomic Number Higher than 92 [4]

UNTIL RECENTLY IT WAS GENERALLY admitted that an atom resulting from artificial disintegration should normally correspond to a stable isotope. M. and Mme. Joliot first found evidence that it is not necessarily so; in some cases the product atom may be radioactive with a measurable mean life, and go over to a stable form only after emission of a positron.

The number of elements which can be activated either by the impact of an α-particle or a proton or a deuton is necessarily limited by the fact that only light elements can be disintegrated, owing to the Coulomb repulsion.

This limitation is not effective in the case of neutron bombardment. The high efficiency of these particles in producing disintegrations compensates fairly for the weakness of available neutron sources as compared with α-particle or proton sources. As a matter of fact, it has been shown that a large number of elements (47 out of 68 examined until now) of any atomic weight could be activated, using neutron sources consisting of a small glass tube filled with beryllium powder and radon up to 800 millicuries. This source gives a yield of about one million neutrons per second.

All the elements activated by this method with intensity large enough for a magnetic analysis of the sign of the charge of the emitted particles were found to give out only negative electrons. This is theoretically understandable, as the absorption of the bombarding neutron produces an excess in the number of neutrons present inside the nucleus; a stable state is

[4] Fermi, *Nature,* 133 (1934), 898 f.

therefore reached generally through transformation of a neutron into a proton, which is connected to the emission of a β-particle.

In several cases it was possible to carry out a chemical separation of the β-active element, following the usual technique of adding to the irradiated substance small amounts of the neighbouring elements. These elements are then separated by chemical analysis and separately checked for the β-activity with a Geiger-Müller counter. The activity always followed completely a certain element, with which the active element could thus be identified.

In three cases (aluminium, chlorine, cobalt) the active element formed by bombarding the element of atomic number Z has atomic number $Z - 2$. In four cases (phosphorus, sulphur, iron, zinc) the atomic number of the active product is $Z - 1$. In two cases (bromine, iodine) the active element is an isotope of the bombarded element.

This evidence seems to show that three main processes are possible: (a) capture of a neutron with instantaneous emission of an α-particle; (b) capture of the neutron with emission of a proton; (c) capture of the neutron with emission of a γ-quantum, to get rid of the surplus energy. From a theoretical point of view, the probability of processes (a) and (b) depends very largely on the energy of the emitted α- or H-particle; the more so the higher the atomic weight of the element. The probability of process (c) can be evaluated only very roughly in the present state of nuclear theory; nevertheless, it would appear to be smaller than the observed value by a factor 100 or 1,000.

It seemed worth while to direct particular attention to the heavy radioactive elements thorium and uranium, as the general instability of nuclei in this range of atomic weight might give rise to successive transformations. For this reason an investigation of these elements was undertaken by the writer in collaboration with F. Rasetti and O. D'Agostino.

Experiment showed that both elements, previously freed of ordinary active impurities, can be strongly activated by neutron bombardment. The initial induced activity corresponded in our experiments to about 1,000 impulses per minute in a Geiger counter made of aluminium foil of 0·2 mm. thickness. The curves of decay of these activities show that the phenomenon is rather complex. A rough survey of thorium activity showed in this element at least two periods.

Better investigated is the case of uranium; the existence of periods of about 10 sec., 40 sec., 13 min., plus at least two more periods from 40 minutes to one day is well established. The large uncertainty in the decay curves due to the statistical fluctuations makes it very difficult to establish whether these periods represent successive or alternative processes of disintegration.

Attempts have been made to identify chemically the β-active element with the period of 13 min. The general scheme of this research consisted in adding to the irradiated substance (uranium nitrate in concentrated solution, purified of its decay products) such an amount of an ordinary β-active element as to give some hundred impulses per minute on the counter. Should it be possible to prove that the induced activity, recognisable by its characteristic period, can be chemically separated from the added activity, it is reasonable to assume that the two activities are not due to isotopes.

The following reaction enables one to separate the 13 min.-product from most of the heaviest elements. The irradiated uranium solution is diluted in 50 per cent nitric acid; a small amount of a manganese salt is added and then the manganese is precipitated as dioxide (MnO_2) from the boiling solution by addition of sodium chlorate. The manganese dioxide precipitate carries a large percentage of the activity.

This reaction proves at once that the 13 min.-activity is not isotopic with uranium. For testing the possibility that it might be due to an element 90 (thorium) or 91 (palladium), we repeated the reaction at least ten times, adding an amount of uranium $X_1 + X_2$ corresponding to about 2,000 impulses per minute; also some cerium and lanthanum were added in order to sustain uranium X. In these conditions the manganese reaction carried only the 13 min.-activity; no trace of the 2,000 impulses of uranium X_1 (period 24 days) was found in the precipitate; and none of uranium X_2, although the operation had been performed in less than two minutes from the precipitation of the manganese dioxide, so that several hundreds of impulses of uranium X_2 (period 75 sec.) would have been easily recognisable.

Similar evidence was obtained for excluding atomic numbers 88 (radium) and 89 (actinium). For this, mesothorium-1 and -2 were used, adding barium and lanthanum; the evidence was completely negative, as in the former case. The eventual precipitation of uranium-X, and mesothorium-1, which do not emit β-rays penetrating enough to be detectable in our counters, would have been revealed by the subsequent formation respectively of uranium-X_2 and mesothorium-2.

Lastly, we added to the irradiated uranium solution some inactive lead and bismuth, and proved that the conditions of the manganese dioxide reaction could be regulated in such a way as to obtain the precipitation of manganese dioxide with the 13 min.-activity, without carrying down lead and bismuth.

In this way it appears that we have excluded the possibility that the 13 min.-activity is due to isotopes of uranium (92), palladium (91), thorium (90), actinium (89), radium (88), bismuth (83), lead (82). Its behaviour excludes also ekacæsium (87) and emanation (86).

This negative evidence about the identity of the 13 min.-activity from a large number of heavy elements suggests the possibility that the atomic number of the element may be greater than 92. If it were an element 93, it would be chemically homologous with manganese and rhenium. This hypothesis is supported to some extent also by the observed fact that the 13 min.-activity is carried down by a precipitate of rhenium sulphide insoluble in hydrochloric acid. However, as several elements are easily precipitated in this form, this evidence cannot be considered as very strong.

The possibility of an atomic number 94 or 95 is not easy to distinguish from the former, as the chemical properties are probably rather similar. Valuable information on the processes involved could be gathered by an investigation of the possible emission of heavy particles. A careful search for such heavy particles has not yet been carried out, as they require for their observation that the active product should be in the form of a very thin layer. It seems therefore at present premature to form any definite hypothesis on the chain of disintegrations involved.

Quanta of a Field as Particles [5]

INTRODUCTION

PERHAPS THE MOST CENTRAL PROBLEM in theoretical physics during the last twenty years has been the search for a description of the elementary particles and of their interactions. The radiation theory of Dirac and the subsequent development of quantum electrodynamics form the present basis for our understanding of the electromagnetic field and its associated particles, the photons. In particular, this theory is capable of explaining the processes of creation of photons when light is emitted and of destruction of photons when light is absorbed. The field theories of other elementary particles are patterned on that of the photon. The assumption is made that for each type of elementary particle there exists an associated field of which the particles are the quanta. In addition to the electromagnetic field an electron-positron field, a nucleon field, several meson fields, etc., are also introduced.

The Maxwell equations that describe the macroscopic behavior of the electromagnetic field have been known for a long time. It is therefore natural to assume that these are the basic equations one should attempt to quantize in constructing a quantum electrodynamics. This has been done with a considerable measure of success. In the past two or three

[5] Fermi, *Elementary Particles* (New Haven: Yale University Press, 1951), pp. 1–7.

years the last remaining difficulties associated with the infinite value of the electromagnetic mass and the so-called vacuum polarization have been largely resolved through the work of Bethe, Schwinger, Tomonaga, Feynman, and others. They have been able to interpret satisfactorily the Lamb shift in the fine structure of hydrogen and the anomaly of the intrinsic magnetic moment of the electron as due to the interaction with the radiation field.

Next to the photons the particles which are best known experimentally and best understood theoretically are the electrons and positrons. In the field theory of electrons and positrons the relativistic equations of Dirac are taken as the field equations of the electron-positron field. The procedure of quantization in this case must, however, be of a type such as to yield the Pauli principle for electrons and positrons instead of the Bose-Einstein statistics that applies to the photons. This can be done with the second quantization procedure of Jordan and Wigner.

Less convincing are the attempts at a similar description of fields about which we have much scantier experimental knowledge.

Protons and neutrons which, like the electrons, obey the Pauli principle and have spin ½ are usually also described by a Dirac equation. This goes of course beyond our present experimental knowledge because until now no negative protons (the analogue of the positrons) have been discovered. Neither have anti-neutrons been discovered. These hypothetical particles are the counterpart of the neutron in the same sense that the positron is the counterpart of the electron. The anti-neutron differs from the neutron in that its intrinsic magnetic moment is directed parallel to the spin angular momentum, instead of anti-parallel, as it is for the ordinary neutron. Also, additional complications are encountered because according to the simple form of the Dirac theory one would expect the magnetic moment of the proton to be 1 nuclear magneton and that of the neutron to be 0. The fact that the proton has instead a moment of 2.7896 and the neutron of -1.9103 nuclear magnetons is currently attributed to the action of the meson field surrounding the nucleons. If this view is accepted we are led to the conclusion that the physical proton and neutron are in fact much more complicated objects than they seem when described in terms of the Dirac theory.

So far we have discussed particles whose basic properties are known in great detail. But there are other particles whose existence is known or suspected and whose properties are in several cases only conjectured.

The existence of the neutrino has been suggested by Pauli as an alternative to the apparent lack of conservation of energy in beta disintegrations. It is neutral. Its mass appears to be either zero or extremely small (less than a few kev energy equivalent). Its spin is believed to be ½; its magnetic moment either zero or very small. In the theory of the beta decay the neutrino is usually described in terms of a Dirac equation that gives two types of neutrino, neutrino proper and anti-neutrino, related to each other like the electron and the positron. This is not the only mathematical possibility. Another one has been suggested by Majorana in which there is no anti-neutrino. In the application to the beta theory worked out by Furry the Majorana theory usually gives the same results as the Dirac theory except in the case of the very improbable double-beta processes recently investigated by Fireman. The beta-ray theory based on the neutrino hypothesis has had some success in explaining the general features of the beta disintegrations and in particular the energy distribution of the emitted electrons. On the other hand, until now no really convincing form of this theory has been discovered. Instead of one satisfactory beta theory there are several of them, none quite acceptable.

A great deal of work has been devoted to the field theory of mesons first proposed by Yukawa in his attempt to explain nuclear forces. The meson of Yukawa should be identified with the π-meson of Powell (briefly called here pion). The μ-meson of Powell (called here muon) is instead a disintegration product of the pion, only weakly linked to the nucleons and therefore of little importance in the explanation of nuclear forces. The Yukawa theory has proved a very valuable guide in experimental research and probably contains many correct leads to a future theory. In particular, it is partly responsible for the discovery of the production of mesons in the collision of fast nucleons. On the other hand, the attempts to put this theory in a quantitative form have had very mediocre success. Often a ponderous mathematical apparatus is used in deriving results that are no better than could be obtained by a sketchy computation of orders of magnitude. This unsatisfactory situation will perhaps improve only when more experimental information becomes available to point the way to a correct understanding.

The purpose of this discussion is not to attempt a mathematical treatment of the field theories but rather to exemplify semiquantitative procedures that are simple and may be helpful in the interpretation of experiments. There are several cases in which not much would be gained by a more elaborate mathematical treatment since a convincing treatment has not yet been discovered. In other cases the qualitative discussion presented here may serve as an introduction to more complete elaborations of the subject.

THE ELECTROMAGNETIC FIELD

As a first example of the quantization of a field the case of the electromagnetic field and of its photons will be discussed. Unfortunately the electromagnetic field has a rather complicated structure since it is specified at each point by the electric and the magnetic vectors. On the other hand, it is the most familiar field and its quantum properties are most clearly understood.

In quantum mechanics observable physical quantities are described by operators obeying a non-commutative law of multiplication. This is true, for example, of the coordinates and the components of the momentum of a mass point. It is true also of other types of observables like, for example, any component of the electric field at a given point of space. In quantum electrodynamics the components of the field or the potentials at a position in space are considered as operators which in general do not commute with each other. A field, however, is a system with an infinite number of degrees of freedom and from this fact many complications arise.

No attempt will be made here to give a complete description of the quantization procedure adopted; it is described in detail in more specialized publications. Only the simplest ideas of the radiation theory will be outlined. . . .

Since the early attempts at setting up the statistics of radiation it has been customary to talk of radiation oscillators. The electromagnetic field enclosed in a cavity with perfectly reflecting walls is capable of oscillating according to a number of different modes with different characteristic frequencies. Each mode can be excited independently of the others and has properties quite similar to those of an oscillator. In particular, one of the modes can take up an amount of energy:

$$\hbar\omega_s(n_s + \tfrac{1}{2}) \tag{1}$$

where ω_s is the angular frequency of the mode and $n_s = 0, 1, 2 \cdots$. The additional term $\hbar\omega_s/2$, the so-called zero-point energy, can be neglected as a non-essential additive constant to the energy.* With this renormalization the total energy content of the radiation field may be written

$$W = \sum_s \hbar\omega_s n_s \tag{2}$$

each term of the sum represents the contribution to the total energy of one vibrational mode.

---

* Actually, this constant is infinitely large. The number of oscillators of frequency between ω and $\omega + d\omega$ is given by (7). Consequently the total amount of zero-point energy is

$$\int_0^\infty \frac{\hbar\omega}{2} \frac{\Omega\omega^2}{c^2\pi^2} d\omega$$

This integral is obviously divergent at large frequencies. This is the first but not the worst example of infinities that one encounters in field theories.

In the language of the photons (2) indicates that there are n_s photons of energy $\hbar\omega_s$. Each one of them is thought of as a corpuscle with a momentum p_s related to the wave length λ_s by the de Broglie relationship:

$$p_s = \frac{2\pi\hbar}{\lambda_s} = \frac{\hbar}{\lambda_s} = \frac{\hbar\omega_s}{c}. \tag{3}$$

The representation of the electromagnetic field in terms of oscillators is incomplete. It is suitable to represent radiation phenomena but does not include, for example, an electrostatic field. One can show, however, that the radiation phenomena can be treated separately from the electrostatic phenomena. A complete description of electrodynamics is obtained by considering on one hand the radiation field due to the superposition of transversal waves of all frequencies and on the other hand the Coulomb forces between electric charges. In the present discussion we shall be primarily interested in the behavior of the radiation field and therefore we shall limit ourselves to the transversal waves.

As long as no perturbation disturbs the electromagnetic field the quantum numbers n_s of the radiation oscillators will be constants and there will be no change in the number of photons. A perturbation will induce transitions whereby the number n_s may either increase (emission or creation of quanta) or decrease (absorption or destruction of quanta). In order to understand this fundamental point we shall discuss first an ordinary linear oscillator. This can be excited to the nth quantum state. The excitation energy of this state excluding the rest energy is $\hbar\omega n$. We say that the excitation amounts to n quanta of energy $\hbar\omega$ each. The number n of quanta will be a constant as long as the oscillator is left alone. Perturbations, however, may either increase or decrease the quantum number n. According to the general principles of quantum mechanics transitions will occur from an initial to a final value of the quantum number n when the matrix element of the perturbation corresponding to these values of the quantum number is different from zero. For example, if the perturbation is proportional to the abscissa x of the oscillator, the possible transitions will be those between values of n for which the matrix element of x does not vanish. These matrix elements are calculated in all elementary textbooks on quantum mechanics. They are different from zero only for transition of the quantum number from n to either $n+1$ or $n-1$. For a linear oscillator of mass m and frequency ω the only non-vanishing matrix elements of the coordinate x are

$$x(n \to n-1) = \sqrt{\frac{\hbar}{2m\omega}}\sqrt{n};$$

$$x(n \to n+1) = \sqrt{\frac{\hbar}{2m\omega}}\sqrt{n+1}. \tag{4}$$

The processes of creation and destruction of photons in the radiation theory are closely tied to this property of the oscillator. Indeed, the radiation field is equivalent to an assembly of linear oscillators. Transitions in which the excitation number n_s of one of the radiation oscillators increases are processes in which photons are created (emission of radiation). Transitions in which n_s decreases describe the destruction of photons (absorption of radiation).

In working out a quantitative radiation theory one finds it simpler to describe the field in terms of the vector potential A rather than of the electric and magnetic fields. As long as the discussion is limited to the radiation theory the scalar potential can always be assumed to be zero since an electromagnetic wave can be described by the vector potential only. The vector potential $A(r)$ at a point r is the sum $\Sigma\ A_s(r)$ of the vector potentials A_s contributed by the various modes.

A_s represents the field of the sth mode. Its magnitude is proportional to the coordinate of the radiation oscillator number s. Like this coordinate A_s has matrix elements inducing transitions from n_s to $n_s \pm 1$. The vector potential $A(r)$ at a given position in space is the sum of the quantities $A_s(r)$. $A(r)$ will therefore also be an operator having nonvanishing matrix elements for transitions in which the quantum number n_s of one of the oscillators changes to $n_s \pm 1$.*

Note that while $A(r)$ is an operator, the vector r that defines the position in space at which the vector potential is observed is an ordinary classical vector.

The actual values of the matrix elements can be obtained . . . by expressing A in terms of the oscillator coordinates and using (4). One finds the following result for the matrix elements of the observable $A(r)$ corresponding to transitions in which one photon $\hbar\omega_s$ is either created or destroyed:

$$A(r)(n_s \to n_s + 1) = \epsilon_s \frac{\sqrt{2\pi\hbar c}}{\sqrt{\Omega\hbar\omega_s}} e^{(i/\hbar)p_s \cdot r} \sqrt{n_s + 1}$$

$$A(r)(n_s \to n_s - 1) = \epsilon_s \frac{\sqrt{2\pi\hbar c}}{\sqrt{\Omega\hbar\omega_s}} e^{(i/\hbar)p_s \cdot r} \sqrt{n_s}$$

(5)

Here p_s is the momentum of the photon. Its magnitude is

$$|p_s| = \hbar\omega_s/c \qquad (6)$$

while ϵ_s is a unit vector perpendicular to p_s and pointing in the direction of the polarization.

---

* In the photon language a change from n_s to $n_s + 1$ means that a photon of the corresponding frequency has been created, and a change from n_s to $n_s - 1$ means that a photon has been destroyed.

The formula giving the number of oscillation modes of frequency between ω and $\omega + d\omega$ will also be given:

$$dN = \frac{\Omega}{\pi^3 c^3}\, \omega^2\, d\omega = 2\Omega\, \frac{4\pi p^2\, dp}{8\pi^3 \hbar^3}. \tag{7}$$

In the last form of dN the factor $\Omega \times 4\pi p^2\, dp$ is the volume element of phase space. This, divided by the cube of Planck's constant $\hbar = 2\pi h$, gives the number of modes except for the factor 2, due to the two possible polarization directions.

The second of the two expressions (5) contains the factor

$$u_s = \frac{1}{\sqrt{\Omega}}\, e^{(i/\hbar)p_s \cdot r}$$

which can be regarded as the eigenfunction of a photon of momentum p_s (normalized plane wave). This is a particular case of a general rule. The matrix element for the destruction of a particle is proportional to the eigenfunction [wavelength] of the state of the particle that is destroyed.

A similar rule is:

The matrix element for the creation of a particle is proportional to the complex conjugate of the eigenfunction of the state of the particle that is created.

This second rule is exemplified by the first formula (5) which gives the matrix element for the creation of a photon and is proportional to

$$u_s^* = \frac{1}{\sqrt{\Omega}}\, e^{-(i/\hbar)p_s \cdot r}.$$

76

ooooooooooo

ARTIFICIAL NUCLEAR
DISINTEGRATION

ooooooooooo

John Douglas Cockcroft (b. 1897)
Ernest Thomas Sinton Walton
(b. 1903)

The fact that atoms are not immutable and that change may occur in them was shown in 1902 by Rutherford and Soddy, as discussed in Chapter 32. But their results, while founded on incontrovertible chemical evidence, gave no clue as to how such changes came about. At that time the structure of the atom was unknown. As we have seen in Chapter 44, Rutherford solved the puzzle of atomic structure in 1911 by proposing an arrangement consisting of a nucleus and planetary electrons, a structure amply confirmed by the experiments of Geiger and Marsden. The subsequent investigations of Moseley, discussed in Chapter 54, showed that the system of increasingly heavier natural elements was based on the successive addition of units of positive charge to the nucleus, balanced electrically by the addition of extra-nuclear electrons. These developments made it clear, as Soddy pointed out in 1913, that radioactivity was a nuclear phenomenon.

As a next step along this path of reasoning it would appear logical to ask, if nuclear changes took place naturally in radioactivity, whether it was practical to produce similar changes artificially, and thus transmute elements at will. If such thoughts arose they do not seem to have been voiced; the attention of physicists was elsewhere, deeply engrossed in the multitude of problems posed by the Bohr theory of the extra-nuclear electrons. But the next great problem was surely the understanding of the nucleus. And, again, the first step, as described in Chapter 49, was taken by Rutherford. In 1919, he effected the first artificial transmutation by bombarding the nitrogen nucleus with high energy α particles.

But another decade was necessary to permit the developments that would lead to an effective technology: the accurate determination of nuclear masses, the development of wave mechanics, and, finally, the development of machines to produce highly energetic charged particles. By the end of the third decade of the twentieth century, Gamow, and independently Gurney and Condon, had shown that the wave properties of particles could account for the radioactivity of such atoms as uranium. But if nuclear theory is to be compared with actual nuclear structure, a nuclear spectrum is required; only from such a spectrum can energy levels be determined and compared with predictions of the theory. But while atomic spectra can be obtained by applying excitation energies of the order of a few volts, the production of nuclear spectra requires excitation energies of the order of a million volts or larger. Actually a two-fold problem was posed by nuclear research: how to build machines to produce charged particles (or photons) of the required energies; how to determine the kinds of particles best suited to be effective nucleus-penetrating projectiles.

In principle, we can use the same kinds of particles to excite nuclei as to excite the outer electrons of an atom. But in practice things are not so simple. Although the atomic electrons are easily disturbed by radiation, the excitation of nuclei with energetic photons (γ-rays) is a very tricky matter. Atomic energy levels lie very close together and are excited by a large frequency range of photons (from the X-ray end of the spectrum to the infrared). But the energy levels in a nucleus are spaced at fairly large intervals, so that for each nucleus only a few γ-ray frequencies will work. About 1930 the only γ-rays available were those emitted by radioactive nuclei like uranium. These were generally not of the correct frequencies to excite the nuclei that were being studied; in any case, the intensities of the γ-rays then available, and the range of their frequencies, were too small to be of much use. Nevertheless, various attempts were being made to obtain artificial radioactivity with the means at hand.

Since γ-rays were relatively ineffectual, physicists began intensive work with particle collisions (in line with the researches and suggestions of Rutherford, Chadwick, Ellis and others). These investigators, particularly Rutherford, had used α particles from radioactive sources to bombard nuclei of various kinds and some nuclear transformations had been produced. In the earliest experiments, as recounted in Chapter 49, Rutherford, in 1919, had bombarded light atoms, such as nitrogen and oxygen, with α particles, and had disrupted the nitrogen nucleus. However, natural radioactive sources of particles were much too limited to be very useful for a systematic study of nuclei.

Since the neutron had not yet been discovered when particle accelerators were first produced, charged particles still had to be used to probe nuclei. It was therefore necessary to devise various schemes to accelerate such particles to energies that would penetrate the nucleus. In considering transformations induced by particle bombardment of the nucleus, two facts must be taken into account: (1) that the nucleus and the bombarding projectile (α particle, proton, and so on) are electrically charged; (2) that the colliding particles have a wave character. Consequently one must apply quantum mechanics (that is, the Schroedinger wave equation) to the interaction of charged particles. Since the nucleus and the α particles are both positively charged and repel each other, the problem is essentially that of the penetration of potential barriers by particles. This is how Gamow, and Condon and Gurney, analyzed the problem of radioactive emission in α-particle decay (discussed in Chapter 67) which is the inverse of the penetration problem.

The quantum-mechanical theory of the penetration of potential barriers shows that for a given nucleus the depth of penetration of the bombarding particle increases with increasing energy but decreases with increasing mass and charge of the projectile. In other words, for a given energy it is advantageous to use as "bullets" the lightest particles with the smallest charge, all other things being equal. This immediately points to electrons or protons. However, the electron cannot serve in this capacity because electrons cannot form even quasi-stable systems within nuclei and hence cannot excite nuclei. In a sense, trying to excite nuclei with electrons (unless the electrons have enormously high energies and hence very short De Broglie wavelengths) is like trying to excite atomic electrons with radio waves. This, then, left the choice between protons and α particles. Since one can show, from the theory of the penetration of potential barriers, that a one-million volt proton has as much penetrating power as a sixteen-million volt α particle, the proton was finally chosen as the projectile to use in probing the nucleus.

The only question that could not be answered in that pre-neutron period was whether the proton or α particle is more effective in exciting the nucleus once the potential barrier is penetrated. Two phases are involved in nuclear excitation: one is the penetration of the barrier, the other the capture of the particle by the nucleus. Only if there is a good chance that a particle will combine, at least briefly, with the nucleus after penetration of the barrier will the nucleus be excited or possibly disrupted. But this question can be answered only on the basis of a theory from which the energy levels of nuclei can be determined. Since such a theory did not exist, it was felt that, all other things being equal, the proton was to be preferred.

The problem of producing particles of sufficient energy to excite nuclear reactions was attempted almost simultaneously by Cockcroft and Walton in England, and by Van de Graaff and Lawrence and Livingston in the United States. The method adopted by these investigators for attaining the necessary accelerating voltages differed. Cockcroft and Walton decided that the most promising method was to rectify high voltage low frequency alternating current; Van de Graaff believed that the development of a high voltage electrostatic generator offered the most advantages; Lawrence and Livingston favored the application of a series of incremental pulsed voltages applied to ions confined in a spiral path by a magnetic field. This device, the cyclotron, has proved to be the most useful for producing the highest energy particles. Each of these methods will be reviewed.

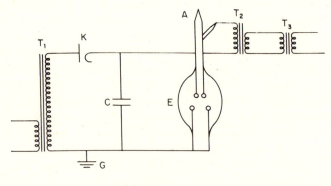

Fig. 76–1.

The first system that successfully produced artificial nuclear reactions was that of Cockcroft and Walton and we shall therefore review it first. Of the three accelerators it is the least novel. The necessary high voltage is obtained by means of a conventional a.c. transformer. One of its secondary terminals is connected to the plate of a kenetron and the other to one plate of a suitable capacitor. The kenetron is a two element (filament and plate) electron tube capable of rectifying alternating current at high potential. In the simplest arrangement the circuit was then completed by connecting the filament of the kenetron to the other plate of the capacitor. The two electrodes of the accelerating tube were then connected in parallel with the capacitor. A sketch of the arrangement is shown in Fig. 76–1. Here T_1 is the transformer which supplies the high voltage a.c. rectified by the kenetron K; T_2 and T_3 are transformers used in connection with the hydrogen discharge tube A.

The current required for the operation of the accelerator is only a few microamperes so that the potential supplied to the accelerating tube E is kept sensibly constant by a small capacitor C. The hydrogen discharge tube A, supplying protons to the accelerator tube, is shown in more detail in Fig. 76–2. The protons from the discharge are used as projectiles to induce nuclear reactions. These protons, as may be envisioned by reference to Fig. 76–2, enter the target chamber F where they are incident on the material whose nucleus is to be studied. The details of this target arrangement are sketched in the first figure of Cockcroft and Walton's paper which follows.

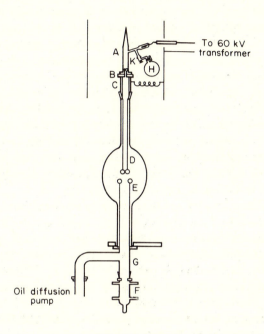

Fig. 76–2.

With the apparatus described above, the first substance studied was lithium. A round target of the element, 5 cm in diameter, was placed at an angle of 45° to the beam of accelerated protons. An opening in the tube opposite the target and at right angles to the proton beam was closed by a zinc sulphide screen, suitable to give scintillations on the impact of α particles. Mica absorbers placed in front of the screen prevented scattered protons from striking it. When 125 kilovolt protons were incident on the target, scintillations began to appear. Several tests, described in the paper, proved that the scintillations were produced by α particles. Cockcroft and Walton therefore concluded that the bombardment had resulted in the formation of unstable beryllium 8 which then split into two parts. The reaction may be written as follows:

$$_1H^1 + {}_3Li^7 \rightarrow {}_4Be^8 \rightarrow {}_2He^4 + {}_2He^4$$

The evidence for the pair production of α particles was next investigated with results supporting the above conclusions. A series of heavier elements up to uranium was then subjected to proton bombardment, in some instances up to 600kv. The preliminary results obtained with these elements suggested that in most instances the ejected particles were α-particles.

It is interesting that the experiment of Cockcroft and Walton on the artificial disintegration of lithium was the first of its kind to excite the imagination of the public and to give the layman a feeling that physicists might have got hold of something of world-shaking importance. There were numerous interviews, articles in the papers, pictures of the apparatus, and inquiries from newspapers all over the world. One telegram from Rutherford from the Associated Press of America requested assistance in preparing an article for the American public stating that the 1400 newspapers they served in North and South America "would be deeply grateful if you would grant us an explanatory interview on your recent experiments in splitting the atom. We have in mind nothing sensational." No answer to this telegram has ever been found.

The significance of this experiment deserves to be pointed out. Cockcroft and Walton were the first to construct an ion accelerator of sufficient energy to produce nuclear disintegrations. The way was thus opened to study one of the previously almost inaccessible, but most important, fields of physics. The results showed that nuclei could be disrupted by particles of lower energy than previously supposed. From the balancing of the disintegration equation for Li^7, Einstein's mass-energy equivalence was proved without doubt. For this pioneering work Cockcroft and Walton received the Nobel Prize in physics for 1951. Their paper describing the research follows their biographical sketches.

Sir John Douglas Cockcroft was born in Todmorden, England, on May 27, 1897. His father was a cotton manufacturer, but Cockcroft showed no interest in the family business; instead, he was strongly attracted to science and mathematics. After a traditional British education, he matriculated at Manchester University and studied mathematics under Horace Lamb. With the advent of World War I, Cockcroft joined the British Armed Forces in 1915 and served in the Royal Field Artillery. At the end of the war he returned to Manchester to study electrical engineering at the College of Technology, after which he worked as an engineer for the Metropolitan-Vickers Electrical Company. Soon his deep interest in mathematics and the physical sciences drew him back to the university.

Like Dirac, he left engineering to study mathematics at St. John's College, Cambridge. There he took the mathematical tripos in 1924 and embarked upon physics as a career. Like many brilliant young experimentalists of the period, he went to the Cavendish Laboratory and worked under Lord Rutherford.

Cockcroft did not go at once into experimental nuclear physics. At that time it appeared that the only way of penetrating the nucleus was with the α particles emitted by such radioactive nuclei as uranium and radium; this procedure was not too promising for large-scale investigations. Only a few nuclei could be transmuted; moreover, Rutherford himself had already done the basic work in this field, so that little more could be done along these lines. Cockcroft therefore chose another research field and began working with the great Russian physicist P. Kapitza on the production of intense magnetic fields and the generation of low temperatures.

In 1928 he turned to nuclear physics with an entirely new idea of penetrating nuclei with artificially accelerated protons, instead of with natural α particles. Experimental studies had shown that the energies of α particles emitted by radioactive nuclei are, in general, much smaller than one would expect if these particles were propelled from the nucleus by the full Coulomb repulsion. This was extremely puzzling and was not understood until the theoretical investigations of Gamow, and of Condon and Gurney, showed that α particles, because of their wave nature, do indeed *penetrate* the Coulomb potential barrier at relatively low energies.

Cockcroft, on reading these papers, had the brilliant idea of reversing this phenomenon experimentally. If low-energy charged particles can leave nuclei in this way, why can they not enter nuclei in the same fashion? Everything known about the laws of physics pointed to the correctness of this idea, for if a particle's motion is exactly reversed in a field of force at any point in its orbit, the particle must retrace its orbit exactly. Cockcroft was therefore convinced that the wave properties of protons would allow these particles to enter light nuclei at low energies.

In 1928, when Cockcroft was still formulating his ideas, Gamow visited the Cavendish Laboratory and Cockcroft outlined his plan to him. Supported by Gamow, he sent a memorandum to Rutherford proposing that boron and lithium be bombarded by accelerated protons. In this memorandum he showed that boron can be penetrated by a proton of only 300 kilovolts of energy and that the conditions for lithium are even more favorable. Rutherford agreed to the proposal, and Cockcroft was joined in his project by Dr. Ernest T. Walton, who was then developing one of the first linear accelerators, as well as one of the earliest betatrons. Their collaboration in 1932 resulted in the first proton-induced artificial nuclear disintegrations.

Cockcroft continued his experimental work on the artificial transmutation of elements and in 1933 produced a wide variety of such phenomena, using both protons and deuterons as his projectiles. At the same time he produced artificial radioactivity of various nuclei by proton bombardment. His experimental abilities were quickly recognized and he was appointed director of the Royal Society Mond Laboratory in Cambridge. At that time he was already a fellow of St. John's College, having been elected in 1929; he then became, in turn, university demonstrator and lecturer. In 1939 he was appointed Jacksonian professor of natural philosophy.

When World War II broke out in 1939, Cockcroft accepted the wartime post of assistant director of scientific research in the Ministry of Supply and devoted his skills to the development of a coast-to-coast radar defense system. In the autumn of 1940 he came to the United States as a member of the Tizard Mission and then returned to England to become head of the Air Defense Research and Development Establishment. In 1944 Cockcroft went to Canada as head of the Canadian Atomic Energy Project and became director of the Montreal and Chalk River Laboratories. He remained in Canada for two years, and then, in 1946, returned to England as director of the Atomic Energy Research Establishment at Harwell. In 1954 Cockcroft was appointed a research member of the United Kingdom Atomic Energy Authority, and remained with this agency as a full-time member until 1959, when he was elected master of Churchill College, Cambridge. He then continued with the Atomic Energy Authority on a part-time basis. Following this he was appointed chancellor of the Australian National University at Canberra.

He has received many honors for his scientific work. He has been president of the Institute of Physics, of the Physical Society (British), and of the British Association for the Advancement of Science. He is a fellow of the Royal Society and has received honorary doctorates from many universities.

In 1925 he married Eunice Elizabeth Crabtree; they have four daughters and a son.

Ernest Thomas Sinton Walton's unusual capabilities as an experimentalist were put to good use when he entered the field of physics, for he completed his studies just when physicists were seeking ways of penetrating the nucleus with high-speed charged particles.

Walton's path from his early schooling to a career in science was quite direct. He was born on October 6, 1903, in Dungarvan, Waterford County, on the south coast of Ireland, the son of a Methodist minister from County Tipperary, who, because of his calling, had to move every few years. As a consequence Ernest Walton attended various schools. His aptitude in mathematics and science was evident at a very early age and he was encouraged to continue these studies. He was therefore sent as a boarder to the Methodist College in Belfast in 1915, and there he did brilliant work in mathematics and physics. In 1922 he was awarded a scholarship and entered Trinity College, Dublin, where he read honors courses in mathematics and experimental physics. He graduated with highest honors in these subjects in 1926 and received his Master of Science degree in 1927.

On receiving a research scholarship in 1927 from the Royal Commissioner for the Exhibition of 1851, he went to Cambridge University to work at the Cavendish Laboratory under Lord Rutherford. Although Walton's first research papers dealt with hydrodynamics, he shifted to particle accelerators when he began working with Rutherford. A senior research award from the Department of Scientific and Industrial Research in 1930 permitted him to continue with his graduate studies and research, and in 1931 he received his Ph.D. degree.

During this period Walton met Cockcroft, who was already working on the problem of using relatively low-energy protons to penetrate nuclei by taking advantage of the wave character of the proton, which permits it to pass through the Coulomb barrier. Realizing that protons of only a few hundred kilovolts, instead of millions of volts, would do the job, and that this was well within the technological capabilities of that time, Walton worked on improving the high-voltage X-ray and cathode-ray tubes that were then available. Finally, in collaboration with Cockcroft, he constructed a linear accelerator that produced protons of the right energy, which were then used to disintegrate lithium and to transmute boron. Walton shared the Nobel Prize with Cockcroft in 1951 for this pioneer work.

From 1932 to 1934 he was Clerk Maxwell scholar at Cambridge. He then returned to Trinity College, Dublin, as fellow. In 1946 he was appointed the Erasmus Smith professor of natural and experimental philosophy and in 1960 he was elected senior fellow.

In addition to his academic work, Walton has participated in other educational, civic, and religious activities. He has been connected with the Dublin Institute for Advanced Studies, the Institute for Industrial Research and Standards, the Royal City of Dublin Hospital, the Royal Irish Academy, the Royal Dublin Society, and other institutions.

In addition to the Nobel Prize, he received the Hughes medal in 1938—again jointly with Sir John Cockcroft—and in 1959 the Queen's University in Belfast awarded him an honorary Doctor of Science degree. Walton has published numerous papers in the journals of various scientific societies on hydrodynamics, nuclear physics, and microwaves.

In 1934 Walton married Freda Wilson, the daughter of a Methodist minister, and a former student of Methodist College in Belfast. They have two sons and two daughters.

ooooooo

COCKCROFT and *WALTON*

Experiments with High Velocity Positive Ions. II. The Disintegration of Elements by High Velocity Protons [1]

INTRODUCTION

IN A PREVIOUS PAPER WE have described a method of producing high velocity positive ions having energies up to 700,000 electron volts. We first used this method to determine the range of high-speed protons in air and hydrogen and the results obtained will be described in a subsequent paper. In the present communication we describe experiments which show that protons having energies above 150,000 volts are capable of distintegrating a considerable number of elements.

Experiments in artificial disintegration have in the past been carried out with streams of α-particles as the bombarding particles; the resulting transmutations have in general been accompanied by the emission of a proton and in some cases γ-radiation. The present experiments show that under the bombardment of protons, α-particles are emitted from many elements; the disintegration process is thus in a sense the reverse process to the α-particle transformation.

THE EXPERIMENTAL METHOD

Positive ions of hydrogen obtained from a hydrogen canal ray tube are accelerated by voltages up to 600 kilovolts in the experimental tube described in [a previous paper] and emerge through a 3-inch diameter brass tube into a chamber well shielded by lead and screened from electrostatic fields. To this brass tube is attached by a flat joint and plasticene seal the apparatus shown in [Fig. 76–3]. A target, A, of the metal to be investigated is placed at an angle of 45 degrees to the direction of the proton stream. Opposite the centre of the target is a side tube across which is sealed at B either a zinc sulphide screen or a mica window.

---

[1] J. D. Cockcroft and E. T. S. Walton, *Proceedings of the Royal Society, Series A,* 137 (1932), 229–243.

In our first experiments we used a round target of lithium 5 cm. in diameter and sealed the side tube with a zinc sulphide screen, the sensitive surface being towards the target. The distance from the centre of the target to the screen was 5 cm. A sheet of mica, C, of stopping power 1·4 cm. was placed between the screen and target and was more than adequate to prevent any scattered protons reaching the screen, since our range determinations and the experiments of Blackett have shown that the maximum range of protons accelerated by 600 kilovolts is of the order of 10 mm. in air. The screen is observed with a microscope having a numerical aperture of 0·6, the area of screen covered being 12 sq. mm. This arrangement with the fluorescent surface inside the vacuum is generally used in the preliminary investigations of elements and when it is necessary to detect the presence of particles of short range.

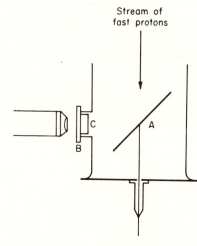

Fig. 76–3.

The current to the target is measured by a galvanometer and controlled by varying the speed of the motor used for driving the alternator exciting the discharge tube. Currents of up to 5 microamperes can be obtained. Since metals bombarded by high-speed positive ions emit large numbers of secondary electrons for each incident ion, it is necessary to prevent the emission of these electrons if an accurate determination of the number of incident ions is required. This has been effected by applying a magnetic field of the order of 700 gauss to the target. Since it is well known that the majority of the secondary electrons have energies below 20 volts, such a field should be adequate to prevent secondary electron emission being a serious source of error.

An accurate determination of the exact composition of the beam of ions has not yet been made, but deflection experiments with a magnetic field in a subsidiary apparatus have shown that approximately half the current is carried by protons and half by H_2^+ ions. The number of neutral atoms appears to be small.

The accelerating voltage used in the experiments is controlled by varying the field of the alternator exciting the main high tension transformer. The secondary voltage of this transformer is measured by the method described in an earlier paper, which rectifies the current passing through a condenser. A microammeter on the control table allows a continuous reading of this voltage to be obtained. The value of the steady potential produced by the rectifier system varies between 3 and 3·5 times the maximum of the transformer voltage according to the brightness of the rectifier filaments. The actual value of the voltage is determined by using a sphere gap consisting of two 75-cm. diameter aluminium spheres, one of which is earthed. In each experiment the multiplication factor of the rectifier system is determined for several voltages and intermediate points obtained by interpolation. The accuracy of the determination of the voltage by the sphere gaps has been checked by measuring the deflection of the protons in a magnetic field. It has been found that corrections of the order of 15 per cent. may be required as a result of the proximity of neighbouring objects or unfavourable arrangements of the connecting leads. The voltages given in this paper have all been corrected by reference to the magnetic deflection experiments.

THE DISINTEGRATION OF LITHIUM

When the current passing to the target was of the order of 1 microampere and the accelerating potential was increased to 125 kilovolts, a number of bright scintillations were observed on the screen, the numbers being proportional to the current collected and of the order of 5 per minute per microampere at 125 kilovolts.

No scintillations were observed when the proton current was cut off by shutting off the discharge tube excitation or by interposing a brass flap between the beam and the target. Since the scintillations were very similar in appearance and brightness to α-particle scintillations, the apparatus was now changed to allow a determination of their range to be made. For this purpose a mica window having a stopping power of 2 cm. was sealed to the side tube in place of the fluorescent screen, which was now placed outside the window. It was then possible to insert mica screens of known stopping power between the window and the screen. In this way it became apparent that the scintillations were produced by particles having a well-defined range of about 8 cm. Variations of voltage between 250 and 500 kilovolts did not appear to alter the range appreciably.

In order to check this conclusion, the particles were now passed into a

Shimizu expansion chamber, through a mica window in the side of the chamber having a stopping power of 3·6 cm. When the accelerating voltage was applied to the tube a number of discrete tracks were at once observed in the chamber whose lengths agreed closely with the first range determinations. From the appearance of the tracks and the brightness of the scintillations it seemed now fairly clear that we were observing α-particles ejected from the lithium nuclei under the proton bombardment, and that the lithium isotope of mass 7 was breaking up into two α-particles.

In order to obtain a further proof of the nature of the particles the experiments were repeated with an ionisation chamber amplifier and oscillograph of the type described by Wynn Williams and Ward. The mica window on the side tube was reduced to a thickness corresponding to a stopping power of 1·2 mm. with an area of about 1 sq. cm., the mica being supported on a grid structure. The lithium target was at the same time reduced in size to a circle of 1 cm. diameter in order to reduce the angular spread of the particles entering the counter. The ionisation chamber was of the parallel plane type having a total depth of 3 mm. and was sealed by an aluminium window having a stopping power of 5 mm. The degree of resolution of the amplifier and oscillograph was such that it was possible to record accurately up to 2000 particles per minute. With the full potential applied to the apparatus but with no proton current, the number of spurious deflections in the oscillograph was of the order of 2 per minute, whilst with an accelerating potential of 500 kilovolts and a current of 0·3 microamperes the number of particles entering the ionisation chamber per minute was of the order of 700.

The oscillograph records obtained as additional mica absorbers are inserted . . . [show] that the size of the deflections increases as additional mica is inserted, whilst the numbers fall off rapidly when the total absorber thickness is increased beyond 7 cm. In [Fig. 76–4] is plotted the number of particles entering the chamber per minute per microampere for increasing absorber thickness and for accelerating potentials of 270 kilovolts and 450 kilovolts. The stopping power of the mica screens of windows has been checked and the final range determination made by a comparison with the α-particles from thorium C. We find that the range is 8·4 cm. Preliminary observations showed that between the lowest and highest voltages used, the range remained approximately constant. It is, however, of great interest to test whether the whole of the energy of the proton is communicated to the α-particles, and it is intended at a later date to examine this point more carefully. The general shape of the range curve, together with the evidence from the size of the oscillograph deflections, suggests that the great majority of the particles have initially a uniform velocity, but further investigation will be required with lower total absorption to exclude the possibility of the existence of particles of short range.

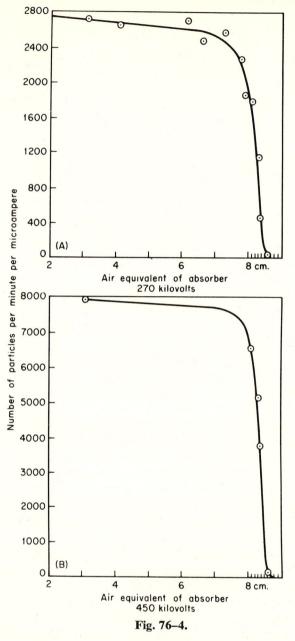

Fig. 76–4.

As is well known, the size of the oscillograph kicks are a measure of the ionisation produced by the particles. At the beginning of the range the size of the kicks observed was very uniform, whilst the average size varied with the range of the particle corresponding to the ionisation given by the Bragg curve. [Fig. 76–5] shows the variation of the ionisation of the most numerous particles with range.

The sizes of the deflections were now compared with the deflections produced in the same ionisation chamber by α-particles from a polonium source. It has been shown in this way that the maximum deflection for the two types of particle is the same. This result, together with the uniformity of the ionisation produced by the particles, is sufficient to exclude the possibility of some of the particles being protons, since the maximum ionisation produced by a proton is less than 40 per cent. of the maximum ionisation produced by an α-particle.

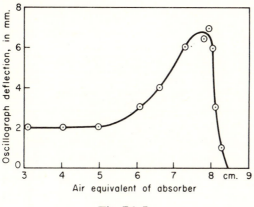

Fig. 76–5.

The variation of the numbers of particles with accelerating voltage was determined from the oscillograph records between 200 kilovolts and 500 kilovolts. For voltages between 70 kilovolts and 250 kilovolts, the numbers of particles entering the ionisation chamber were counted by a single stage thyratron counter of the type described by Wynn Williams and Ward. The results are plotted in [Fig. 76–6]. The number increase roughly exponentially with the voltage at the lower voltages and linearly with voltage above 300 kilovolts.*

It is of great interest to estimate the number of particles produced by the bombardment of a thick layer of lithium by a fixed number of protons. In making this estimate we have assumed that the particles are emitted uniformly in all directions and that the molecular ions produce no effect. With these assumptions the number of disintegrations for a voltage of 250

---

* All the measurements in a single run, in which more than 2000 particles were counted are included in the figure. The spread of the points in the centre part of the curve is probably due to variations in the vacuum and therefore in the voltage applied during the experiment. In other runs no evidence was obtained for such a variation.

kilovolts is 1 per 10^9 protons, and for a voltage of 500 kilovolts is 10 per 10^9 protons.

In considering the variation in numbers of particles with voltage it has, of course, to be borne in mind that with a thick target the effects are due to protons of all energies from the maximum to zero energy. It will be

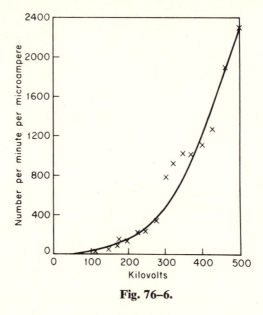

Fig. 76–6.

very important to determine the probability of disintegration for protons of one definite energy, and for this purpose it will be necessary to use thin targets. Preliminary experiments using evaporated films of lithium show that the probability or "excitation" function does not increase so rapidly with voltage as for the thick target, but owing to the small numbers of particles obtainable these experiments have not yet been completed.

THE INTERPRETATION OF RESULTS

We have already stated that the obvious interpretation of our results is to assume that the lithium isotope of mass 7 captures a proton and that the resulting nucleus of mass 8 breaks up into two α-particles. If momentum is conserved in the process, then each of the α-particles must take up equal amounts of energy, and from the observed range of the α-particles we conclude that an energy of 17·2 million volts would be liberated in this disintegration process. The mass of the Li_7 nucleus from Costa's determination is 7·0104 with a probable error of 0·003. The decrease of mass in the disintegration process is therefore $7·0104 + 1·0072 - 8·0022 =$

0·0154 ±0·003. This is equivalent to an energy liberation of (14·3 ± 2·7) × 10⁶ volts. We conclude, therefore, that the observed energies of the α-particles are consistent with our hypothesis. An additional test can, however, be applied. If momentum is conserved in the disintegration, the two α-particles must be ejected in practically opposite directions and, therefore, if we arrange two zinc sulphide screens opposite to a small target of lithium as shown in the arrangement of [Fig. 76–7], we should observe a large proportion of coincidences in the time of appearance of the scintillations on the two screens. The lithium used in the experiments was evaporated on to a thin film of mica having an area of 1 sq. mm. and a stopping power of 1·1 cm., so that α-particles ejected from the lithium would pass easily through the mica and reach the screen on the opposite side of the lithium layer.

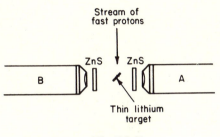

Fig. 76–7.

The two screens were observed through microscopes each covering an area of 7 sq. mm. and a tape recording machine was used to record the scintillations, a buzzer being installed in the observation chamber to prevent the noise of the recording keys being audible to the observers. Five hundred and sixty-five scintillations were observed in microscope A and 288 scintillations in microscope B, the former being nearer the target. Analysis of the records showed that the results are consistent with the assumption that about 25 per cent. of the scintillations recorded in B have a corresponding scintillation in A. If we calculate the chance of a scintillation being recorded by B within x seconds of the record of a scintillation in A, assuming a perfectly random distribution of scintillations, and compare this with the observed record, the curve shown in [Fig. 76–8] is obtained. It will be seen that as the interval x is made less, the ratio of the observed to the random coincidences increases. We also plot for comparison the theoretical curve (shown by broken line) which would be obtained if there were 25 per cent. of coincidences. It will be seen that the two curves are in good accord. The number of coincidences observed is about that to be expected on our theory of the disintegration process, when we take into account the geometry of the experimental arrangement and the efficiency of the zinc sulphide screens. It is clear that there is strong evidence supporting the hypothesis that the α-particles are emitted in pairs. A more complete investigation will be made later, using larger areas for the counting device, when it is to be expected that the fraction of coincidences should increase.

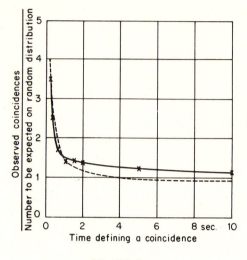

Fig. 76–8.

COMPARISON WITH THE GAMOW THEORY

In a paper which was largely responsible for stimulating the present investigation, Gamow has calculated the probability W_1^* of a particle of charge Ze, mass m and energy E entering a nucleus of charge $Z'e$. Gamow's formula is

$$W_1^* = e^{\frac{-4\pi\sqrt{2m}}{h} \cdot \frac{ZZ'e^2}{\sqrt{E}}} \cdot J_k$$

where J_k is a function varying slowly with E and Z. Using this formula, we have calculated W_1^*, the probability of a proton entering a lithium nucleus, for 600, 300 and 100 kilovolts and find the values $0 \cdot 187$, $2 \cdot 75 \times 10^{-2}$ and $1 \cdot 78 \times 10^{-4}$. Using these figures, our observed variation of proton range with velocity for a thick target and assuming a target area of 10^{-25} cm.^{2}, the number of protons N required to produce one disintegration may be calculated. For 600 kilovolts we find N to be of the order of 10^6, and for 300 kilovolts of the order of 2×10^7.

The order of magnitude of the numbers observed is thus smaller than the number predicted by the Gamow theory, but a closer comparison must be deferred until the results for a thin target are available.

THE DISINTEGRATION OF OTHER ELEMENTS

Preliminary investigations have been made to determine whether any evidence of disintegration under proton bombardment could be obtained for the following elements: Be, B, C, O, F, Na, Al, K, Ca, Fe, Co, Ni, Cu, Ag, Pb, U. Using the fluorescent screen as a detector we have observed some bright scintillations from all these elements, the numbers varying markedly from element to element, the relative orders of magnitude being indicated by [Fig. 76–9] for 300 kilovolts. The results of the scintillation

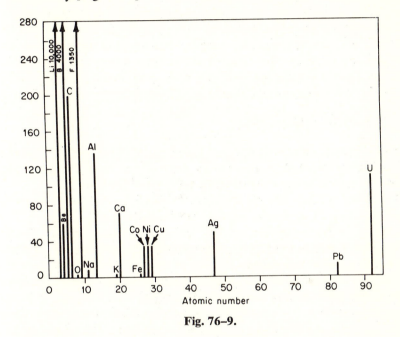

Fig. 76–9.

method have been confirmed by the electrical counter for Ca, K, Ni, Fe and Co, and the size of the oscillograph kicks suggests that the majority of the particles ejected are α-particles.

The numbers of particles counted have up to the present not been sufficient to enable these figures to be taken as anything other than an order of magnitude. In particular, the possibility must be borne in mind that some of the particles observed may be due to impurities. It may, however, be of some interest to describe briefly the general character of the effects observed in some of the more interesting cases.

Beryllium. Two types of scintillation were observed with beryllium, a few bright scintillations having the appearance of α-particle scintillations together with a much greater number of faint scintillations appearing at about 500 kilovolts, the numbers increasing rapidly with voltage. We were not able to observe the faint scintillations outside the vacuum chamber, so that they are presumably due to particles of short range.

Boron. Next to lithium, boron gave the greatest number of scintillations, most of the particles having a range of about $3 \cdot 5$ cm. Scintillations were first observed at voltages of the order of 115 kilovolts, the numbers increasing by more than 100 between this voltage and 375 kilovolts. The interesting problem as to whether the boron splits up into three α-particles or into Be_8 plus an α-particle must await an answer until more detailed investigation is made.

Fluorine. Fluorine was investigated in the form of a layer of powdered calcium fluoride. A few scintillations were first observed at a voltage of 200 kilovolts, the numbers increasing by a factor of about 100 between this and 450 kilovolts. The range of the particles was found to be about $2 \cdot 8$ cm. On the assumption that they are α-particles, the energy would be $4 \cdot 15 \times 10^6$ electron volts. If now we assume that the reaction is

$$F_{19} + H_1 = O_{16} + He_4$$

it is of particular interest to compare the observed energy with the energy to be expected from the mass changes, since all the masses involved are known, from the work of Aston, with fairly good precision.

Using Aston's data, the energy liberated should be $5 \cdot 2 \times 10^6$ electron volts. Allowing for the energy taken by the recoil of the oxygen nucleus and the energy of the bombarding proton, the energy of the α-particle should be about $4 \cdot 3$ million volts, giving a range of $2 \cdot 95$ cm. in air, in good accord with the observed ranges.

Sodium. A small number of bright scintillations were observed beginning at 300 kilovolts, the particles having ranges between 2 and $3 \cdot 5$ cm. In addition to the bright scintillations, a number of faint scintillations were observed similar to those seen in the case of beryllium. The faint scintillations are again presumably due to particles of short range since they could not be observed outside the tube. The probable α-particle transition would be

$$Na_{23} + H_1 = Ne_{20} + He_4.$$

Potassium. Potassium is of special interest on account of its radioactivity. The very small effects observed may easily be due to an impurity. The most likely reaction to occur

$$K_{39} + H_1 = A_{36} + He_4,$$

would probably have a negative energy balance.

Iron, Nickel, Cobalt, Copper. These elements follow each other in the periodic table, so that the small result obtained for iron compared with that for the following three elements is of special interest. The effect for iron is of the same order as that for potassium, and again may be due to impurity. For these elements most of the particles had a range of about 2·5 cm., but a few particles were present having a slightly longer range.

Uranium. Using potentials of up to 600 kilovolts and strong proton currents, the number of scintillations observed was about four times the natural radioactive effect, and the artificially produced particles appeared to have a longer range than the natural ones. The numbers obtained did not appear to vary markedly with voltage.

We hope in the near future to investigate the above and other elements in much greater detail and in particular to determine whether any of the effects described are due to impurities. There seems to be little doubt, however, that most of the effects are due to transformations giving rise to an α-particle emission. In view of the very small probability of a proton of 500 kilovolts energy penetrating the potential barrier of the heavier nuclei by any process other than a resonance process, it would appear most likely that such processes are responsible for the effects observed with the heavier elements.

We have seen that the three elements, lithium, boron and fluorine, give the largest emission of particles, the emission varying similarly with rise of voltage. These elements are all of the $4n + 3$ type, and presumably the nuclei are made up of α-particles with the addition of three protons and two electrons. It is natural to suppose that the addition of a captured proton leads to the formation of a new α-particle inside the nucleus. In the case of lithium, it seems probable that the capture of the proton, the formation of the α-particle and the disintegration of the resulting nucleus into two α-particles must at this stage be regarded as a single process, the excess energy appearing in the form of kinetic energy of the expelled α-particles.* . . .

---

* Such a view does not preclude the possibility that sometimes part of the energy may appear in another form, for example, as γ-radiation.

77

ooooooooooo

THE ELECTROSTATIC
GENERATOR

ooooooooooo

Robert Jemison Van de Graaf
(b. 1901)

In the commentary of Chapter 76, which introduced this group of papers on particle accelerators, emphasis was placed on the need to develop machines that could produce a wide range of particle energies in order to match the widely spaced energy levels of the nucleus. A successful start on this problem was made by Cockcroft and Walton, who used an extension of conventional alternating current-rectifier techniques to produce a steady, high voltage. But to produce, by this method, the extremely high steady voltage over the range demanded raises inherent difficulties not easily overcome. The limitations of the high voltage-rectifier method were realized by Robert Van de Graaff who had set about solving this problem of high voltage by a path that differed from that of Cockcroft and Walton. Realizing the advantages of a *steady* high potential for ion acceleration, Van de Graaff tried to find a simple means of achieving it.

Logically the simplest solution seemed to demand a return to the earliest methods for generating high potentials, an electrostatic method in which charges are continuously carried to a hollow sphere to raise its potential. The sphere can be charged to voltages limited only by the corona breakdown at the surface of the sphere. To carry the charge, Van de Graaff hit on the idea of using a continuous belt on which charge could be sprayed by the brush discharge between a metal surface and a group of charged points. A belt moving over a pulley near the ground and another inside the sphere carry the charge from the charging position into the interior of the sphere where it is drawn off by a second series of sharp points and conveyed to the surface of the sphere. Diagrams of this action in which two spheres are employed, one of which is charged positively and the other negatively, are shown in figs. 77–1, 77–2, 77–3 of Van de Graaff's paper, which follows. Various details of the method are discussed including the efficiency and some of the disturbing factors.

Robert Jemison Van de Graaff was born in Tuscaloosa, Alabama, on Dec. 20, 1901. He obtained a B.S. degree in 1922 from the University of Alabama and an M.S. degree in 1923. In 1924–25, he was a student at the Sorbonne. In 1925, he won a Rhodes Scholarship and, for the next three years, continued his study of physics at Oxford, where he was awarded the Doctor of Philosophy degree in 1928. It was during his period at Oxford that he conceived the idea of developing high voltages by means of the continuous charging of a high potential spherical electrode. In 1929, a small model of what we now call the Van de Graaff Generator was built "to demonstrate the soundness of the principles involved." It performed as expected, generating a maximum potential of 80,000 volts.

From 1929 to 1931, Van de Graaff held a National Research Council Fellowship at Princeton University. This period was devoted to the further development of his electrostatic method for generating high voltages; a larger generator was constructed, and its operation tested in vacuum in order to determine the value of vacuum insulation. To determine the usefulness of the generator for scientific research and as a particle accelerator, a 1.5 million volt generator was completed in 1931. Thereafter larger, higher-voltage generators were made at the Massachusetts Institute of Technology where Dr. Van de Graaff was appointed research associate during the years 1931–34. In 1934, he was appointed Associate Professor of Physics, an appointment that he held until 1960. During World War II, he served as director of a project sponsored by the government's office of Scientific Research and Development to develop radiographic equipment for surveying the internal mechanical structure of metals and welded seams. In 1926, he became a director of the High Voltage Engineering Co. of Cambridge, Mass., and the following year, a member of its executive committee, positions which he still holds.

The Van de Graaff generator is now in wide use throughout the world not only as an ion accelerator for studies in low-energy nuclear physics, but for such purposes as X-ray radiography, radiation therapy, food sterilization, and on a limited scale as an ion injector for the very high energy particle accelerators.

For his scientific work Dr. Van de Graaff has been honored by the award of the Elliott Cresson medal of the Franklin Institute and the Duddell medal of the Physical Society of Great Britain. In 1936, he married Catherine Boyden. They have two sons and live in Lexington, Mass.

ooooooo

VAN DE GRAAFF, COMPTON,
and VAN ATTA

The Electrostatic Production of High Voltage for Nuclear Investigations [1]

INTRODUCTION

ANY BASIC DEVELOPMENT IN SCIENCE calls for a new technique fundamentally adapted to the new purpose. Such a basic development has been in progress for the last thirty-six years and it has now reached such a stage as to be recognized as a major field of physics— nuclear physics. To justify this statement it is only necessary to point out that in the atomic nuclei reside all the positive electricity, much of the negative electricity and by far the greater part of the mass and energy in the universe. As yet we know relatively little about this world of electricity, mass and energy, and our attempts to produce an impression on it have been still less successful. Nevertheless, recent years have demonstrated the possibility of successful attack upon the nucleus by one weapon, the high-speed particle. The new technique which is therefore demanded is a powerful, controllable source of high-speed particles. In this paper is described a high-voltage generator which, with accessory discharge tubes and sources of ions, appears adapted to this technique.

Since progress in this new field of nuclear physics will require a great investment in apparatus, time and effort, it is important to consider carefully the possible techniques and whether this investment may be justified by the importance of the results to be expected. This leads to a consideration of the effects on the progress of physical theory of basic experimental developments initiated at the close of the last century.

About 1895 the discovery of x-rays and other experimental developments made possible an effective entry into the outer structure of the atom and the investigation of this aspect of atomic structure has been the main business of physics since that time. The distinguishing feature of those experimental innovations which led to the present knowledge of the outer atom is that they made possible physical observations on a scale of di-

---

[1] R. J. Van de Graaff, K. T. Compton, and L. C. Van Atta, *Physical Review*, 43 (1933), 149–157.

mensions thousands of times smaller, with resultant energy concentrations thousands of times larger than were previously possible. Thus it became possible to deal individually with the basic physical entities, thereby removing the limitations of the statistical approach formerly necessary. Such observations showed clearly the insufficiency of classical laws and paved the way for quantum theory and for relativity.

Just as x-rays and other radiation phenomena of extranuclear electrons unfolded for us the extranuclear structure of atoms, so the discovery of radioactivity in 1896 opened the way to the first knowledge of the inner structure of the atomic nucleus. Furthermore, the high-speed particles from radioactive substances have themselves been the agencies through which was obtained the first evidence of the possibility of atomic transformation. Simultaneously with these experimental developments, the theory of relativity, through Einstein's principle of interconvertibility of mass and energy, has given a partial basis for guidance in interpretation and investigation of nuclear changes. These developments in nuclear physics have suggested with increasing emphasis the tremendous possibilities which should accrue from further development in the technique of nuclear investigation, through the use of swift particles of controllable nature and speed produced and applied through the agency of high voltage. In fact, the recent brilliant experiments of Cockcroft and Walton have given concrete evidence that these expectations were justifiable.

It may be hoped that experimental entry into the nucleus will extend the technique of physical exploration in a manner analogous to the extension which opened up the outer structure of the atom. It will again be possible to study a system thousands of times smaller, with energy concentrations correspondingly greater, further facilitating the study of individual rather than statistical processes. This may result in a system of nuclear mechanics accompanied by the same sort of broadening of basic scientific and philosophical ideas as accompanied the creation of quantum mechanics.

Within the almost unknown nuclear world of electricity and energy may also lie the explanation of certain extranuclear phenomena, which, modern quantum theory notwithstanding, still remain obscure. Just as the discovery of nuclear charge led immediately to the interpretation and simplification of that complicated group of chemical phenomena partially classified by the periodic table, so similarly it is possible that further discoveries regarding the atomic nucleus may lead to a similar interpretation and simplification of some extranuclear problems still outstanding.

PRODUCTION OF HIGH VOLTAGE

In approaching the problem of a high-voltage technique fundamentally adapted to meet the new demands in the most perfect and ultimate manner, it is well to review the development of the high-voltage art to its present state. Before the time of Faraday electrostatic generators were employed. However, industrial developments of the past hundred years have found their most suitable embodiment in applications of Faraday's principles of electromagnetism. Thus modern high-voltage technique has evolved almost completely under this influence. Step-up transformers have been used, with the addition of rectifiers and condensers when an approximately steady direct current was desired. These electromagnetic devices are admirably suited for the production of large currents within the general range of voltages corresponding to extranuclear phenomena. There are, however, inherent difficulties in the extension of such devices into the range of extremely high voltages which are demanded by nuclear physics. Such difficulties include the tremendous expense and size of such generators, necessitated by insulation requirements. There is also the limitation that the efficiency of high-voltage a.c. devices decreases rapidly as higher voltages are sought, because of the parasitic charging currents which are required to bring the apparatus to high potential at every cycle, even though no power is being drawn by it. The importance of this feature is not generally realized, but may be illustrated by the statement that the most favorable arrangement of the two terminals alone, neglecting the circuits, would require about 10,000 kva to impress 10,000,000 volts at 60 cycles, exclusive of useful output or corona leakage.

There are, in addition, numerous other important advantages of steady direct current over any current of a surging, alternating or rippling character. These include:

(1) Possibility of obtaining strictly homogeneous beams of electrified particles.

(2) Possibility of accurate focussing which becomes relatively more important as the voltage and therefore the length of discharge tubes is increased.

(3) Elimination of stray radiation which arises in a variety of ways from a discharge tube and generating apparatus operating at unsteady voltages, and which renders difficult the careful shielding necessary to permit the use of the delicate instruments and sensitive amplifiers required in so many applications of these voltages.

(4) Ability to use the ion source to full capacity since the useful voltage is applied all of the time. (The order of advantage in this respect runs from the impulse generator and Tesla coil, which utilize the source only during roughly a millionth of the time, through the induction coil, the a.c. transformer, the transformer with rectifier, to, finally, the electrostatic d.c. generator.)

(5) Ability to measure the high potentials accurately as, for instance, by the use of null or compensation methods.

(6) Elimination of breakdown in vacuum tubes due to reversal of the voltage—a phenomenon inherently associated with the walls of vacuum tubes even under the best available conditions of evacuation.

(7) Ability to utilize the advantages of geometrical dissymmetry between positive and negative electrodes in vacuum in such a way that the field is minimum at the surface of the negative electrode, where difficulties from field currents are most serious—an advantage which finds its maximum embodiment when the cathode is a hollow sphere surrounding a central spherical anode.

(8) In a variety of other ways through the elimination of time variations in the electrical conditions of the apparatus.

In view of these considerations it seemed desirable to develop an electrostatic high-voltage generator, since electrostatic methods yield directly a steady unidirectional voltage such as is desired. Maximum simplicity was sought in the design. The simplest terminal assembly appeared to be a sphere mounted on an insulating column. Since the sphere must be charged and since the process should be continuous the charge carrier should approach the sphere, enter it, and, after depositing its charge inside, should return parallel to its path of approach. This immediately suggested the action of a belt, a device long used for the transmission of mechanical power.

The logic of the situation therefore pointed directly to a generator consisting of a hollow spherical conducting terminal supported on an insulating column, a moving belt to carry electric charge to the sphere, a device for depositing the charge onto the belt in a region of low potential remote from the sphere, and a device for removing this charge from the belt inside the sphere and transferring it to the sphere. A refinement of these essentials was the addition of an induction device whereby charge of the opposite sign was carried by the belt on its return journey, thus doubling the current output. A second refinement consisted of a self-exciting charging device whereby the entire generator could be made to operate independently of any external source of electricity. Not only does this device attain the desired result in what appears to be the simplest possible manner, but it is also interesting to note that the energy transformations in its operations are exceedingly simple, consisting only in the transformation of the energy required to drive the belt into work done in separating and transferring electric charge from earth potential to sphere potential.

Historical Note

The basic idea of a belt type of generator probably dates from Kelvin's famous water dropper, and in fact, Kelvin suggested such a generator, in which charges would be carried to the electrode on a belt conveyer consisting of alternately insulated metal segments. Righi made such a generator with the segmented belt carried through the sphere. Later Burboa designed a generator with a belt functioning somewhat as an elongated disk of a Wimshurst machine, with a complicated set of inductors and brushes. Mention also should be made of a generator designed by Swann, in which charge was conveyed by a succession of falling metal spheres, thus coming closer to Kelvin's original water dropper but with the added suggestion that this apparatus could be made to operate in vacua theoretically up to such voltages as would prevent the falling of the spheres by electrostatic forces. Still more recently Vollrath constructed a similar generator in which the current is carried by an air blast of electrified dust in an insulating tube.

PRINCIPLES OF OPERATION

The simplest embodiment of these principles is illustrated schematically in [Fig. 77–1], which is appropriate to a generator, where P and N are the positive and negative spherical terminals and the belts of silk, or any other flexible insulating material, are shown transporting positive and

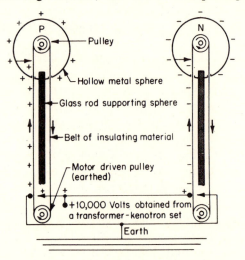

Fig. 77–1.

negative electricity, respectively, from the charging outfit connected with ground to the two spheres. The charge is "sprayed" onto each belt as it passes between a metallic surface and one or more sharp points so adjusted as to maintain a brush discharge from the points toward the surface. When connected as shown, one point sprays positive and the other sprays negative electricity onto its adjacent belt. Within each sphere the charge is drawn off the belt by adjacent sharp points and transferred to the spheres.

Since the interior of the sphere is similar to the interior of a Faraday "ice pail" the charge passes readily between the charged belt and the sphere, irrespective of the potential of the sphere.

The voltage which is attainable in this device is limited only by the corona breakdown at the surface of the spheres, which depends in a known manner upon their size and varies somewhat with the degree of smoothness of their surfaces. The current output is equal to the rate at which charge is carried into the spheres and is therefore equal to the product of the surface density of charge on the belts multiplied by the areal velocity with which the belts enter the spheres. The upper limit for the surface density of charge on the belts is that which gives rise to an electric field equal to the "breakdown" strength of the surrounding air.

It is evident that other insulating media than air at atmospheric pressure might be used to advantage in the operation of such a generator. We believe that its most useful embodiments will prove to be with operation in a high vacuum tank. In any case, the voltage is limited by the electrical breakdown of the surrounding medium whatever it may be, and the current output is determined by the width and velocity of the belt together with the charge density which can be placed on it.

In view of these considerations it is evident that the maximum voltage and also the current of such a generator each vary directly as the breakdown strength of the surrounding medium, so that the power output varies as the square of this breakdown strength. Since generally it will be desirable to provide as large a current output as possible, the belts will be designed to operate at the greatest practicable speed, and multiple belts will be placed as closely together as convenient. It is therefore evident that in any given insulating medium the voltage will vary as the first power, the current as the second power, and the power output as the third power of the linear dimensions. The variation of current with the square of linear dimensions is evident when it is considered that any increase in dimensions permits a corresponding increase in belt width and also a corresponding increase in the number of belts which can be introduced to operate in parallel.

In adapting the design of [Fig. 77–1] to operate in some other medium, such as in a vacuum or in a liquid, it is only necessary to replace the brush discharge method of introducing charge to and from the belt, by some other charging and discharging device appropriate to the medium. Under such conditions it may also be advantageous to construct the belt of alternate conducting and insulating segments.

It is obvious that the current output of this device can be doubled if the belt on its passage out of the sphere can carry away a charge equal and opposite to that brought in by the incoming belt. This can be realized very simply through the separation of induced charges by the arrangement which is shown schematically in [Fig. 77–2]. This exemplifies the first re-finement referred to in the preceding section.

The second refinement there mentioned is illustrated in [Fig. 77–3], in which the transformer-kenetron set which charges the belts is omitted and

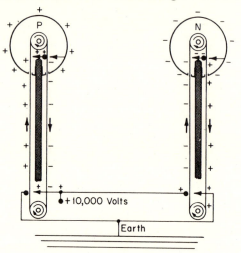

Fig. 77–2.

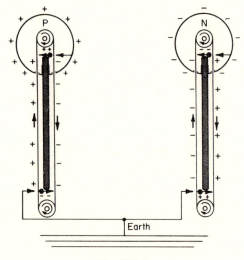

Fig. 77–3.

the connections are made in such a way that a small charge on the moving belt, such as is present due to friction of the belts and pulleys, results in the cumulative separation of positive and negative electricity by induction, thus priming the machine, which immediately begins to operate self-exciting and at full power, in this way dispensing with the necessity of any external electrical connection.

PRELIMINARY MODELS OF THE GENERATOR

(1) In 1929 a small model was constructed and used to demonstrate the soundness of the principles involved. This model was hastily improvised but performed as expected. The highest voltage obtained was about 80,000 volts, being limited by the electrical breakdown of the surrounding air.

(2) Following this there was constructed a larger generator contained in a dismountable tank which could be highly evacuated by a suitably designed combination of high-speed mercury condensation pump and liquid air trap. This type of generator is still in the stage of development but has operated in vacuum at 50,000 volts. Progress has been slow due to the necessity of developing certain necessary points of vacuum technique, and also due to the fact that this work had to be temporarily discontinued for the past eighteen months. However, no unexpected difficulties have been encountered and it is hoped that this generator will be in successful operation in a few months. Thus far experience has confirmed our confidence that vacuum insulation is the ultimate insulation for electrostatic devices and will open up tremendous possibilities in this field.

(3) When it became evident that considerable work would still be required to perfect the vacuum generator, construction was begun in June 1931 of a generator operating in air, powerful enough to be of scientific use and to give a demonstration of the possibilities of generators of this type. This generator was designed for and developed about 1,500,000 volts and delivered a current of about 25 microamperes. It was constructed with 24-inch spherical electrodes mounted on 7-foot upright Pyrex rods and charged by 2.2-inch silk ribbon belts moving with a linear speed of 3500-foot per minute, and it operated either by self-excitation or by the spraying on of charge from a small 10,000-volt transformer kenetron set. It is interesting to note that although it was constructed at a total cost for materials of only about $100 it developed approximately twice the voltage of any previous direct-current source of which we have knowledge. . . .

Current Output

If a charge is uniformly distributed on the surface of a linear strip in a region otherwise free from electrical forces, there is set up a field perpendicular to the strip and proportional to the surface density of charge as given by Coulomb's law. The maximum charge which can be held by the strip is that which gives rise to a field equal to the breakdown strength of the surrounding insulating medium. In the case of air this limiting field is about 30,000 volts per centimeter, from which we calculate that the maximum charge on a belt in air amounts to 2.65×10^{-9} coulombs per sq. cm on each side of the belt. This figure when multiplied by the number of sq. cm of belt surface which enter the sphere per second gives the maximum possible current output in amperes. Of course, this current output will be doubled if the belt leaves the sphere also fully charged, but with electricity of opposite sign. In the generator described above as preliminary model 3, the actual current output amounted to about one-fourth of this theoretical maximum. The reasons for this discrepancy were known at the time, but were neglected in the construction of this demonstration model. By more careful design, the output may be brought closer to the theoretical limit, as more recent tests have shown.

There are several factors which account for this inability to attain ideally maximum current output. (1) Only one side of the belt is "sprayed" with charge. This may be overcome by using, for example, a double layer belt split by an earthed metal separator between two sets of converging spraying points and traversing the rest of its path simply as a 2-ply belt charged on both outside surfaces. (2) There are inevitable irregularities in the surface, and the breakdown of insulation in those regions which are electrically overstressed, results in a diminution of the charge carried in those localities. (3) There is an additional component to the electric field arising from the difference in potential between the sphere and the earth, so that the electric intensity at any point is the vector sum of this field and that arising from the charge of the belt. A nonlinear potential distribution along the belt may result in overstressing of the insulating medium in the region just outside the sphere, resulting in failure of the belt to retain its maximum charge while traversing that region. This difficulty is obviated by the use of a supplementary device for insuring uniform potential distribution, as described below. (4) Of course the charging device must be adequate to supply the charge. With a wide belt, a multiplicity of spraying points may be necessary to insure complete and adequate coverage. (5) If the belt is charged by a brush discharge, as in this model, the surrounding air is of course partially ionized, and this condition tends also to reduce the charge which can be placed on the belt by reducing the breakdown strength of the air in the charging locality to some value less than 30,000 volts per cm. This limitation could be removed by use of a non-ionizing device for charging the belts. The brush discharge method of charging, however, has the great advantage of simplicity.

It is impossible to increase the charge carrying capacity of the belt by any change in distribution of charge within the belt, such as by the substitution of volume charges in a moving element for surface charges. This is due to the fact that the limit to the net charge is set by the field just outside the surface of the moving element and is thus independent of the distribution of charges within it.

A consideration of the nature of the limiting electric field around the belts shows that the ascending and descending belts may be placed as close together as desired without reducing their current carrying capacity, the limitation being set only by mechanical considerations such as friction. For this reason it is possible to introduce multiple belts, alternately ascending and descending and packed very closely together and so to increase the current output to quite large values.

Efficiency

The work involved in operating this generator is consumed in overcoming the friction of the pulleys and the resistance to the motion of the belt in the surrounding medium, and in the transference of electric charge from earth potential to the potential of the spherical terminals. As is well known, a belt is one of the most efficient means of transferring power, and the two inherent types of electrical losses may be reduced to very small amounts. The first of these arises from electrical leakage, which may be controlled and reduced by methods described in the next section. The second is loss in the process of charging and discharging the belts, which may be reduced to that corresponding to the voltage required to maintain corona discharge from the spraying and discharging points, a voltage which is insignificant in comparison with the voltage generated. There are of course no magnetic losses. Thus this type of generator should be capable of operation with high efficiency.

Disturbing Factors

The only disturbing factor which has been found to affect the satisfactory operation of the generator is electrical leakage which is closely identified with two factors, humidity and geometrical design of insulating support. The difficulty is not so much from direct electrical loss by leakage over the surface of the support, as from distortion of the electric field about the spheres by the charges which leak down the supporting insulator and in this way promote insulation breakdown of the air surrounding the insulator near where it enters the sphere. This disturbing factor is completely eliminated by proper design of the insulating support, consisting in the substitution of a hollow insulating cylinder for the insulating rod of model 3. The interior of this cylinder can be maintained at low relative humidity by warming the air within it, so that its interior and exterior surfaces, as well as the belts which run within it, are maintained in the most favorable conditions for elimination of leakage. In addition to improving insulation, the cylindrical support introduces increased mechanical strength, quietness of operation and safety, and certain other advantages.

A number of important advantages are secured by introducing on the surface of the supporting cylinder an artificial leak from the sphere to the ground, so constructed as to give the most favorable distribution of field between the sphere and the earth. This artificial leak may be constructed, for example, by rotating the cylinder in a lathe and drawing on its surface a continuous, closely spaced, helical, India ink line, extending from one end to the other. By means of this artificial leak the vertical field between the earth and the sphere may be made uniform, thus minimizing leakage to earth through the support or the surrounding air, and permitting the maximum charge to be carried by the belt throughout its entire path.

THE LARGE GENERATOR UNDER CONSTRUCTION AT ROUND HILL

The favorable experience with the preliminary models described above appeared to justify the construction of a generator capable of yielding the maximum performance which can reasonably be expected in a generator operating in air, subject to limitations in voltage set by the size of the building in which it is placed. The generator was therefore designed to take full advantage of the largest laboratory space available, which was the airship dock on the estate of Colonel E. H. R. Green, kindly put at our disposal for this purpose. This dock is a building of structural steel covered by corrugated sheet metal and has dimensions approximately $140 \times 75 \times 75$ ft. In the back end of this building a row of low rooms has been erected to serve as shop and office headquarters, while running lengthwise down the middle of the floor space there has been installed a railroad track of 14-ft. gauge, extending through the huge doors at the front of the building out into the open air for a distance of 160 ft. On this track each of the two generating units is mounted on a truck of structural steel, so that their distance may be varied and they may be run out-of-doors for experiments in the open air. In this connection it is interesting to note that Round Hill is extremely exposed to fogs from the ocean, so that the experience with this generator will afford a severe test of the utility of an electrostatic device under adverse conditions.

A detailed description of the large generator [shown in Fig. 77–4] will be postponed to include its performance tests, but the following information may be of interest.

The spheres are of aluminum alloy 15 ft. in diameter with walls $\frac{1}{4}$-inch thick. They were pressed and shipped in "orange peel" sections which were then welded together, and the outer surface ground and polished. Each sphere has four circular holes; a six foot hole on the bottom admits the multiple belts; a trap door on the lower side permits entrance via a ladder from the ground; a trap door on top permits access to the top of the sphere; a trap door on the equator will admit the end of a large discharge tube, spanning the gap between the spheres, to project within the sphere for attachment of subsidiary apparatus and connections and for operation. Preliminary tests on such a discharge tube have been made. The inside of each sphere is itself a laboratory room, provided with a floor and containing accessory apparatus.

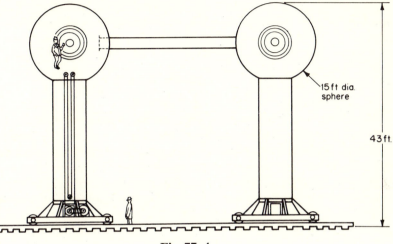

15 ft dia. sphere

43 ft.

Fig. 77–4.

The insulating supports are cylinders of Textolite about 24 ft. high, 6 ft. in diameter and of ⅝-inch wall thickness. Each cylinder consists of three 8-foot sections, joined by internal Textolite bands fastened with Textolite dowel pins. Thus the external surface is smooth for easy application of the artificial surface leak and there is an absence of intermediate metal parts, as their presence would distort the field.

The trucks are made of structural steel and are so designed as to permit easy access to or change of the assembly of motors, pulleys and belts.

These three elements, sphere, insulating support and truck, are fundamental elements of any high-voltage assembly, and permit complete freedom for future experimentation and further development of the devices for generation. At the time of writing the spheres are built and polished, the trucks are completed and the main structure is now being assembled. . . .

On the basis both of theory and of past experience, we expect this generator to develop about 10,000,000 volts. The power output will depend on the number, size and speed of the belts. Present plans are for an output of about 20 kw. This could be greatly increased by the installation of additional belts, but for the initial adjustments only a portion of this power will be required. . . .

78

oooooooooo

THE CYCLOTRON

oooooooooo

Ernest Orlando Lawrence (1901-1958)
Milton Stanley Livingston (b. 1905)

Before Lawrence and Livingston developed their method of accelerating ions, both Cockcroft and Walton and Van de Graaff had reported methods for obtaining high-speed ions. Both of these methods require the generation of high voltages, and, as Lawrence and Livingston point out in the paper that follows, high voltages lead to serious technical difficulties that had not yet been overcome. Lawrence therefore introduced a new procedure: to accelerate ions to very high speeds in a series of steps, each of which would involve only a relatively small voltage. If this were to be done by having the ion move in a straight line, with its speed increased at regular intervals by a stepped accelerating voltage, the length of the device would be unmanageable. Lawrence therefore proposed a spiral path for the ion, which would cause it to move back and forth across a voltage increment in the plane of the spiral path. To arrange this so that the electric field always accelerates the ion, one must first have a magnetic field at right angles to the plane of the path of the ion and then an alternating electric field that changes its direction periodically in phase with the motion of the ion. Such a device is called a "cyclotron."

To understand the nature of the design problem, let us consider an ion that starts moving at right angles to a region across which there is a voltage, as shown in Fig. 78–1 in the Lawrence and Livingston paper. The motion of the ion is thus initially parallel to the electric field. If a constant mag-

1386

netic field is now introduced at right angles to the electric field, the ion will move in a circular orbit of fixed radius. The radius of this orbit increases with the increased speed of the ion. If the speed of the ion were always the same, the radius of the circular orbit of the ion would also always be the same. But suppose the speed of the ion were increased. It would then move in a larger orbit since the magnetic field would still be the same. We now come to a crucial question. Can we change the electric field periodically in such a way that every time an ion passes through the region where the voltage jumps, the field accelerates the ion?

If the ion were always moving with the same speed, the radius of its orbit would always be the same, and it is obvious that the ion would always cross the voltage region at equal time intervals. But the speed of the ion is constantly increasing, so that its orbit gets larger and larger. It is therefore not at once apparent that the time intervals between passages across this region remain the same. But this is, indeed, the case, because the circumference of the orbit and the speed of the ion increase proportionately so that the ion traverses the larger orbit in the same time. This means that, if the direction of the electric field is reversed in time intervals equal to the time it takes the ion to go halfway around, all the ions will be acted upon by the field in exactly the same way at all times. In other words, the electric field can be regularly alternated in such a way as always to give the ion an additional push when it crosses the voltage region. This is the basic principle of the cyclotron as it was developed by Lawrence.

It is easy to see that, with a device of this sort, protons or other light ions can be accelerated to high speeds by having them cross the electric field often enough. The important thing is that this could now be done in a relatively small space. Thus, as Lawrence and Livingston point out, one need only have a potential of 4,000 volts across the accelerating gap to obtain speeds corresponding to 1,200,000 volts for protons, if each proton is sent across the gap 150 times. By then, the proton will be moving in so large an orbit that it will be near the edge of the apparatus.

The analysis of the cyclotron action given by the authors shows that the energy finally acquired by an ion in its maximum orbit (that is, when it reaches the periphery of the apparatus and is ready to be expelled) depends on the square of the magnetic field strength and on the square of the radius of this final orbit (equation (4) in the paper). The stronger the magnetic field, the more the orbit is curved, and the more frequently the ion is forced to cross the electric field to be accelerated before it circles out to the periphery. The larger the radius of the orbit, the faster the ion must be moving, hence possessing more energy.

Although the principle of the cyclotron is fairly simple as outlined by Lawrence and Livingston, the actual construction and operation presented many problems. Factors such as the arrangement of the ion source, the constancy and uniformity of the magnetic field, and the focusing action of the magnetic and electric fields require care if optimum results are to be achieved. Although in their initial experiments Lawrence and Livingston obtained proton beams of 1,200,000 volts, they were already thinking in terms of 25,000,000 (and higher) volt protons. With their work we see the first indications of what the future could hold in the field of high-energy accelerators.

In 1928, three years after Ernest Orlando Lawrence had received his Ph.D. in physics from Yale University, and just after he had joined the faculty of the University of California, he carefully took an inventory of what research work he had already done and laid out a plan of action for the future. At that time, although atomic physics seemed to offer the most exciting opportunities for a young physicist, Lawrence was strongly attracted by nuclear physics, which he correctly evaluated as "the next great frontier of the experimental physicist." He was particularly stimulated by the pioneer experiments of Rutherford and saw that experiments of this sort could be carried out extensively only if it were possible to devise some means "of accelerating charged particles to high velocities—to energies measured in millions of electron volts, a task which appeared formidable, indeed!"

It must be remembered that the neutron had not yet been discovered so that only charged particles (protons or α particles) could be used to probe the nucleus; to overcome the repulsion of the nucleus, these would have to be speeded up to very high energies. Keeping this in mind Lawrence decided that the greatest promise lay in constructing ion accelerators, and he began to investigate the machines that were then available. Discarding the idea of making improved models of such devices, since he felt that they were already in the hands of very competent people, he searched for new methods of producing high voltages; by chance, in 1929, he ran across an article by a German engineer, Wideröe, that contained the germ of the idea for the cyclotron. Although Lawrence could not read German, the diagrams in the article were enough to start him off in the right direction, and so the era of large, nuclear-smashing machines was born. Although the first cyclotron was a small device, about one foot across, there appeared to be no limit, in principle, to the ultimate size of such an instrument. Since then, accelerators have steadily been increasing in size.

Lawrence, himself, was well equipped intellectually, and by training, to do the kind of imaginative experimental work that this project required. He was born August 8, 1901, at Canton, South Dakota, of Norwegian immigrants, but his parents had good educational backgrounds and his father became superintendent of schools. Lawrence attended elementary and high school in Canton and then went on to St. Olaf College. In 1919 he entered the University of South Dakota and received his B.A. degree in chemistry in 1922. From there he went in succession to the University of Minnesota, receiving his M.A. in chemistry, to the University of Chicago, where he studied physics, and then to Yale University, where he received his Ph.D. in physics in 1925. This was a rather remarkable achievement in those days since few students were able to complete their doctorate in less than six years after graduating from college.

Receiving a National Research Fellowship, he spent the next two years at Yale, and was then appointed an assistant professor—again achieving something of a record since he was only twenty-six years old. He remained on the Yale faculty for only a year, accepting an appointment as associate professor of physics at the University of California, Berkeley. Two years later he was promoted to a full professorship, the youngest at Berkeley, and in 1936, at the age of thirty-five, he was named director of the university's radiation laboratory. He had already invented a cyclotron in 1929 so that his reputation as a top physicist was well established.

Lawrence was deeply involved in nuclear physics when World War II began, so that it was quite natural for him to be assigned one of the major roles in the development of the atomic bomb, to which he made important contributions. Like most of those working on this project, he was firmly convinced of the need to bring about international control of the bomb or, at least, international agreement on the suspension of testing. He worked hard at this and was a member of the 1958 Geneva Conference.

Lawrence's interests in and contributions to physics were extremely broad, as indicated by his published papers, which averaged 3½ a year from 1924 to 1940—an almost unbelievable productivity. During this time he made better and larger models of the cyclotron, discovered many radioactive isotopes of known elements, applied the cyclotron to medical and biological problems, became consultant to the Institute of Cancer Research at Columbia University, invented a method of obtaining time intervals as short as three billionths of a second, and devised very precise methods for measuring the values of atomic constants.

He received numerous awards and honors such as the Elliott Cresson medal of the Franklin Institute, the Comstock prize of the National Academy, the Hughes medal of the Royal Society, the 1939 Nobel Prize, the Duddell medal of the Physical Society of Great Britain, the Faraday medal, the Enrico Fermi Award, and the Medal for Merit. He was an officer of the Legion of Honor and held honorary doctorates from one British and thirteen American universities.

Lawrence was a very vigorous man, interested in many intellectual and physical activities including literature, music, boating, tennis, and ice-skating. He was devoted to his wife, the former Mary Kimerly Blumer, whom he married in 1923, and their six children. He died on August 27, 1958, at Palo Alto, California.

ooooooo

LAWRENCE and LIVINGSTON

Production of High Speed Ions [1]

INTRODUCTION

THE CLASSICAL EXPERIMENTS OF RUTHERFORD and his associates and Pose on artificial disintegration, and of Bothe and Becker on excitation of nuclear radiation, substantiate the view that the nucleus is susceptible to the same general methods of investigation that have been so successful in revealing the extra-nuclear properties of the atom. Especially do the results of their work point to the great fruitfulness of studies of nuclear transitions excited artificially in the laboratory. The development of methods of nuclear excitation on an extensive scale is thus a problem of great interest; its solution is probably the key to a new world of phenomena, the world of the nucleus.

But it is as difficult as it is interesting, for the nucleus resists such experimental attacks with a formidable wall of high binding energies. Nuclear energy levels are widely separated and, in consequence, processes of nuclear excitation involve enormous amounts of energy—millions of volt-electrons.

It is therefore of interest to inquire as to the most promising modes of nuclear excitation. Two general methods present themselves: excitation by absorption of radiation (gamma radiation), and excitation by intimate nuclear collisions of high speed particles.

Of the first it may be said that recent experimental studies of the absorption of gamma radiation in matter show, for the heavier elements, variations with atomic number that indicate a quite appreciable nuclear effect. This suggests that nuclear excitation by absorption of radiation is perhaps a not infrequent process, and therefore that the development of an intense artificial source of gamma radiation of various wave-lengths would be of considerable value for nuclear studies. In our laboratory, as elsewhere, this is being attempted.

But the collision method appears to be even more promising, in consequence of the researches of Rutherford and others cited above. Their pioneer investigations must always be regarded as really great experi-

---

[1] E. O. Lawrence and M. S. Livingston, *Physical Review,* 42 (1932), 20–35.

mental achievements, for they established definite and important information about nuclear processes of great rarity excited by exceedingly weak beams of bombarding particles—alpha-particles from radioactive sources. Moreover, and this is the point to be emphasized here, their work has shown strikingly the great fruitfulness of the kinetic collision method and the importance of the development of intense artificial sources of alpha-particles. Of course it cannot be inferred from their experiments that alpha-particles are the most effective nuclear projectiles: the question naturally arises whether lighter or heavier particles of given kinetic energy would be more effective in bringing about nuclear transitions.

A beginning has been made on the theoretical study of the nucleus and a partial answer to this question has been obtained. Gurney and Condon and Gamow have independently applied the ideas of the wave mechanics to radioactivity with considerable success. Gamow has further considered along the same lines the penetration into the nucleus of swiftly moving charged particles (with excitation of nuclear transitions in mind) and has concluded that, for a given kinetic energy, the lighter the particle the greater is the probability that it will penetrate the nuclear potential wall. This result is not unconnected with the smaller momentum and consequent longer wave-length of the lighter particles; for it is well-known that transmission of matter waves through potential barriers becomes greater with increasing wave-lengths.

If the probability of nuclear excitation by a charged particle were mainly dependent on its ability to penetrate the nuclear potential wall, electrons would be the most effective. However, there is considerable evidence that nuclear excitation by electrons is negligible. It suffices to mention here the current view that the average density of the extra-nuclear electrons is quite great in the region of the nucleus, i.e., that the nucleus is quite transparent to electrons; in other words, there are no available stable energy levels for them.

On the other hand, there is evidence that there are definite nuclear levels for protons as well as alpha particles; indeed, there is some justification for the view that the general principles of the quantum mechanics are applicable in the nucleus to protons and alpha particles. It is not possible at the present time to estimate the relative excitation probabilities of the protons and alpha-particles that succeed in penetrating the nucleus. However, it does seem likely that the greater penetrability of the proton * is an advantage outweighing any differences in their excitation characteristics. Protons thus appear to be most suited to the task of nuclear excitation.

---

* According to Gamow's theory a one million volt-proton has as great a penetrating power as a sixteen million volt alpha-particle.

Though at present the relative efficacy of protons and alpha-particles cannot be established with much certainty, it does seem safe to conclude at least that the most efficacious nuclear projectiles will prove to be swiftly moving ions, probably of low atomic number. In consequence it is important to develop methods of accelerating ions to speeds much greater than have heretofore been produced in the laboratory.

The importance of this is generally recognized and several laboratories are developing techniques of the production and the application to vacuum tubes of high voltages for the generation of high speed electrons and ions. Highly significant progress in this direction has been made by Coolidge, Lauritsen, Tuve, Breit, Hafstad, Dahl, Brasch and Lange, Cockcroft and Walton, Van de Graaff and others, who have developed several distinct techniques which have been applied to voltages of the order of magnitude of one million.

These methods involving the direct utilization of high voltages are subject to certain practical limitations. The experimental difficulties go up rapidly with increasing voltage; there are the difficulties of corona and insulation and also there is the problem of design of suitable high voltage vacuum tubes.

Because of these difficulties we have thought it desirable to develop methods for the acceleration of charged particles that do not require the use of high voltages. Our objective is two fold: first, to make the production of particles having kinetic energies of the order of magnitude of one million volt-electrons a matter that can be carried through with quite modest laboratory equipment and with an experimental convenience that, it is hoped, will lead to a widespread attack on this highly important domain of physical phenomena; and second, to make practicable the production of particles having kinetic energies in excess of those producible by direct high voltage methods—perhaps in the range of 10,000,000 volt-electrons and above.

A method for the multiple acceleration of ions to high speeds, primarily designed for heavy ions, has recently been described in this journal. The present paper is a report of the development of a method for the multiple acceleration of light ions. Particular attention has been given to the acceleration of protons because of their apparent unique utility in nuclear studies. In the present work relatively large currents of 1,220,000 volt-protons have been generated and there is foreshadowed in the not distant future the production of 10,000,000 volt-protons.

THE EXPERIMENTAL METHOD

In the method for the multiple acceleration of ions to high speeds, recently described, the ions travel through a series of metal tubes in synchronism with an applied oscillating electric potential. It is so arranged that as an ion travels from the interior of one tube to the interior of the next there is always an accelerating field, and the final velocity of the ion on emergence from the system corresponds approximately to a voltage as many times greater than the applied voltage between adjacent tubes as there are tubes. The method is most conveniently used for the acceleration of heavy ions; for light ions travel faster and hence require longer systems of tubes for any given frequency of applied oscillations.

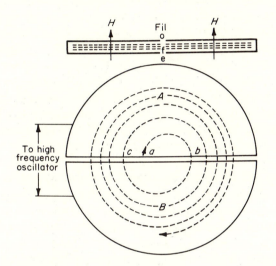

Fig. 78–1. Experimental method for multiple acceleration of ions.

The present experimental method makes use of the same principle of repeated acceleration of the ions by a similar sort of resonance with an oscillating electric field, but has overcome the difficulty of the cumbersomely long accelerating system by causing, with the aid of a magnetic field, the ions to circulate back and forth from the interior of one electrode to the interior of another.

This may be seen most readily by an outline of the experimental arrangement [Fig. 78–1]. Two electrodes A, B in the form of semi-circular hollow plates are mounted in a vacuum tube in coplanar fashion with their diametral edges adjacent. By placing the system between the poles of a magnet, a magnetic field is introduced that is normal to the plane of the plates. High frequency electric oscillations are applied to the plates so that there results an oscillating electric field in the diametral region between them.

With this arrangement it is evident that, if at one moment there is an ion in the region between the electrodes, and electrode A is negative with respect to electrode B, then the ion will be accelerated to the interior of the former. Within the electrode the ion traverses a circular path because of the magnetic field, and ultimately emerges again between the electrodes; this is indicated in the diagram by the arc *a .. b*. If the time consumed by the ion in making the semi-circular path is equal to the half period of the electric oscillations, the electric field will have reversed and the ion will receive a second acceleration, passing into the interior of electrode B with a higher velocity. Again it travels on a semi-circular path (*b .. c*), but this time the radius of curvature is greater because of the greater velocity. For all velocities (neglecting variation of mass with velocity) the radius of the path is proportional to the velocity, so that the time required for traversal of a semi-circular path is independent of the ion's velocity. Therefore, if the ion travels its first half circle in a half cycle of the oscillations, it will do likewise on all succeeding paths. Hence it will circulate around on ever widening semi-circles from the interior of one electrode to the interior of the other, gaining an increment of energy on each crossing of the diametral region that corresponds to the momentary potential difference between the electrodes. Thus, if, as was done in the present experiments, high frequency oscillations having peak values of 4000 volts are applied to the electrodes, and protons are caused to spiral around in this way 150 times, they will receive 300 increments of energy, acquiring thereby a speed corresponding to 1,200,000 volts.

It is well to recapitulate these remarks in quantitative fashion. Along the circular paths within the electrodes the centrifugal force of an ion is balanced by the magnetic force on it, i.e., in customary notation,

$$\frac{mv^2}{r} = \frac{Hev}{c}. \tag{1}$$

It follows that the time for traversal of a semi-circular path is

$$t = \frac{\pi r}{v} = \frac{\pi mc}{He} \tag{2}$$

which is independent of the radius r of the path and the velocity v of the ion. The particle of mass m and charge e thus may be caused to travel in phase with the oscillating electric field by suitable adjustment of the magnetic field H: the relation between the wave-length λ of the oscillations and the corresponding synchronizing magnetic field H is in consequence

$$\lambda = \frac{2\pi mc^2}{He}. \tag{3}$$

Thus for protons and a magnetic field of 10,000 gauss the corresponding wave-length is 19.4 meters; for heavier particles the proper wave-length is proportionately longer.*

It is easily shown also that the energy V in volt-electrons of the charged particles arriving at the periphery of the apparatus on a circle of radius r is

$$V = 150 \frac{H^2 r^2}{c^2} \frac{e}{m}. \tag{4}$$

Thus, the theoretical maximum producible energy varies as the square of the radius and the square of the magnetic field.

EXPERIMENTAL ARRANGEMENT

The experimental arrangement is shown diagrammatically in some detail in [Fig. 78–2]. . . . The description of the apparatus follows.

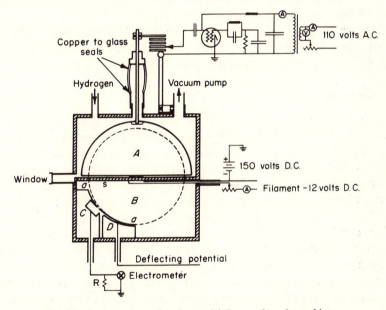

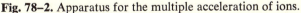

Fig. 78–2. Apparatus for the multiple acceleration of ions.

---

* It should be mentioned that, for a given wave-length, the ions resonate with the oscillations when magnetic fields of ⅓, ⅕, etc., of that given by Eq. (3) are used. Such types of resonance were observed in the earlier experimental studies. In the present experiments, however, the high speed ions resulting from the primary type of resonance only were able to pass through the slit system to the collector, because of the high deflecting voltages used.

The Accelerating System

Though there are obvious advantages in applying the high frequency potentials with respect to ground to both accelerating electrodes, in the present experiments it was found convenient to apply the high frequency voltage to only one of the electrodes, as indicated in [Fig. 78–2]. This electrode was a semi-circular hollow brass plate 24 cm in diameter and 1 cm thick. The sides of the hollow plate were of thin brass so that the interior of the plate had approximately these dimensions. It was mounted on a water-cooled copper re-entrant tube which in turn passed through a copper to glass seal. The electrode insulated in this way was mounted in an evacuated brass box having internal dimensions 2.6 cm by 28.6 cm by 28.6 cm, there being thus a lateral clearance between the electrode and walls of the brass chamber of 8 mm.

The brass box itself constituted the other electrode of the accelerating system. Across the mid-section of the brass chamber parallel to the diametral edge of the electrode A was placed a brass dividing wall S with slits of the same dimensions as the opening of the nearby electrode. This arrangement gave rise to the same type of oscillating electric fields as would have been produced had there been used two insulated semi-circular electrodes with their diametral edges adjacent and parallel.

The Source of Ions

An ideal source of ions is one that delivers to the diametral region between the electrodes large quantities of ions with low components of velocity normal to the plane of the accelerators. This requirement has most conveniently been met in the present experiments merely by having a filament placed above the diametral region from which a stream of electrons pass down along the magnetic lines of force, generating ions of gases in the tube. The ions so formed are pulled out sideways by the oscillating electric field. The electrons are not drawn out because of their very small radii of curvature in the magnetic field. Thus, the beam of electrons is collimated and the ions are formed with negligible initial velocities right in the region where they are wanted. The oscillating electric field immediately draws them out and takes them on their spiral paths to the periphery. This arrangement is diagrammatically shown in the upper part of [Fig. 78–1].

The Magnetic Field

This experimental method requires a highly uniform magnetic field normal to the plane of the accelerating system. For example, if the ions are to circulate around 100 times, thereby gaining energy corresponding to 200 times the applied voltage, it is necessary that the magnetic field be uniform to a fraction of one percent. A general consideration of the matter leads one to the conclusion that, if possible, the magnetic field should be constant to about 0.1 percent from the center outward. Though this presumably difficult requirement has been met easily by an empirical method of field correction, the magnet used in the present experiments has pole faces machined as accurately as could be done conveniently. . . . The pole faces were 11 inches in diameter and the gap separation was $1\frac{1}{2}$ inches. Armco iron was used throughout the magnetic circuit. The magnetomotive force was provided by two coils of number 14 double cotton-covered wire of 2,000 turns each. No water cooling was incorporated, for the magnet was not intended for high fields. In practice the magnet would give a field of 14,000 gauss for considerable periods without overheating. The pole faces were made parallel to about 0.2 percent and so it was to be expected that the magnetic field produced would be uniform. Exploration with a bismuth spiral confirmed this expectation, since it failed to show an appreciable variation of the magnetic field in the region between the poles, excepting within an inch of the periphery.

The Collector System

In planning a suitable arrangement for collecting the high speed ions at the periphery of the apparatus, it was clearly desirable to devise something that would collect the high speed ions only and which would also measure their speeds. One might regard it as legitimate to suppose that the magnetic field itself and the distance of the collector from the center of the system would determine the speeds of the ions collected. This would be true provided there were no scattering and reflection of ions. To eliminate these extraneous effects a set of 1 mm slits was arranged on a circle *a .. a,* as shown in [Fig. 78–2], of radius about 12 percent greater than the circle, indicated by the dotted line in the figure, having its center at the center of the tube and a radius of 11.5 cm. The two circles were tangent at the first slit as shown. The ions on arrival at the first slit would be traveling presumably on circles approximately like the dotted line, and hence would not be able to pass through the second and third slits to the Faraday collector *C*. Electrostatic deflecting plates *D*, separated by 2 mm, were placed between the first two slits, making possible the application of electrostatic fields to increase the radius of curvature of the paths of the high speed ions sufficiently to allow them to enter the collector. By applying suitable high potentials to the deflecting system in this way, only correspondingly high speed ions were registered.

The collector currents were measured by an electrometer shunted with a suitable high resistance leak.

The Oscillator

The high frequency oscillations applied to the electrode were supplied by a 20 kilowatt Federal Telegraph water-cooled power tube in a "tuned plate tuned grid" circuit, for which the diagram of [Fig. 78–2] is self-explanatory.

THE FOCUSSING ACTIONS

When one considers the circulation of the ions around many times as they are accelerated to high speeds in this way, one wonders whether in practice an appreciable fraction of those starting out can ever be made to arrive at the periphery and to pass through a set of slits perhaps 1 mm wide and 1 cm long. The paths of the ions in the course of their acceleration would be several meters, and, because of the unavoidable spreading effects of space charge, thermal velocities and contact electromotive forces, as well as inhomogeneities of the applied fields, it would appear that the effective solid angle of the peripheral slit for the ions starting out would be exceedingly small.

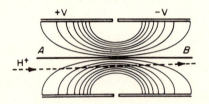

Fig. 78–3. The focusing action of the electric field between the accelerating electrodes.

Fortunately, however, this does not turn out to be the case. The electric and magnetic fields have been so arranged that they provide extremely strong focussing actions on the spiraling ions, which keep them circulating close to the median plane of the accelerating system.

[Fig. 78–3] shows the focussing action of the electric fields. There is depicted a cross-section of the diametral region between the accelerating electrodes with the nature of the field indicated by lines of force. There is shown also a dotted line which represents qualitatively the path of an ion as it passes from the interior of one electrode to the interior of the other. It is seen that, since it is off the median plane in electrode A, on crossing to B it receives an inward displacement towards the median plane. This is because of the existence of the curvature of the field, which over certain regions has an appreciable component normal to the plane, as indicated. If the velocity of the ion is very high in comparison to the increment of velocity gained in going from plate A to plate B, its displacement towards the center will be relatively small and, to the first approximation, it may be described as due to the ion having been accelerated inward on the first half of its path across and accelerated outward by an equal amount during the remainder of its journey, the net result being a displacement of the ion towards the center without acquiring a net transverse component of velocity. In general, however, the outward acceleration during the second half will not quite compensate the inward acceleration of the first, resulting in a gain of an inward component of velocity as well as an inward displacement. In any event, as the ion spirals around it will migrate back and forth across the median plane and will not be lost to the walls of the tube.

The magnetic field also has a focussing action. [Fig. 78–4] shows diagrammatically the form of the field produced by the magnet. In the central region of the pole faces the magnetic field is quite uniform and normal to the plane of the faces; but out near the periphery the field has a curvature. Ions traveling on circles near the periphery experience thereby mag-

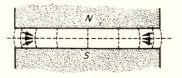

Fig. 78–4. Focusing action of magnetic field.

netic forces, indicated by the arrows. If the circular path is on the median plane then the magnetic force is towards the center in that plane. If the ion is traveling in a circle off the median plane, then there is a component of magnetic force that accelerates it towards the median plane, thereby giving effectively a focussing action.

We have experimentally examined these two focussing actions, using a probe in front of the first slit of the collector system that could be moved up and down across the beam by means of a ground joint. It was found that the focussing actions were so powerful that *the beam of high speed ions had a width of less than one millimeter.* Such a narrow beam of ions of course is ideal for many experimental studies.

As a further test of the focussing action of the two fields, the median plane of the accelerating system was lowered 3 mm with respect to the plane of symmetry of the magnetic field. It was found that the high speed ion beam at the periphery traveled in a plane that was between the planes of symmetry of the two fields showing that both focussing actions were operative and at the periphery were of the same order of magnitude.

EXPERIMENTAL RESULTS

. . . It is of course evident that the upper limit to the number of times the ions will circulate is determined by the degree of uniformity of the average value of the magnetic field along the spiral paths. Indeed, it would seem difficult to construct a magnet with pole faces giving fields of sufficient uniformity to allow more than 100 accelerations of the ions. But happily there is a very simple empirical way of correcting for the lack of uniformity of the field, that makes possible a surprisingly large voltage amplification. This is accomplished by insertion of thin sheets of iron between the tube and the magnet; either in the central region or out towards the periphery, as may be needed. If the magnetic field is, on the average, slightly less out towards the periphery so that the ions lag in phase more and more with respect to the oscillations as they spiral around, they may be brought back into step again by the insertion near the periphery of a strip of iron of suitable width, thickness and extension. If, on the other hand, the ions tend to get ahead in phase in this region, an effective correction can be made by inserting a suitable iron sheet in the central region.

It should be emphasized in this connection that the requirement is not that the magnetic field has to be uniform everywhere to the extent indicated above; small deviations from uniformity are allowable provided that the average value of the magnetic field over the paths of the ions is such that they traverse successive revolutions in equal intervals of time. Thus, small magnetic field adjustments can be accomplished by increasing or decreasing the field over small portions of successive circular paths of the ions. In the present experiments the most satisfactory adjustment was made by the insertion of a sheet of iron 0.025 cm thick having a shape much like an exclamation point extending radially with the thick end 8 cm wide in the central region and the narrow end 3 cms wide at the periphery. Insertion of this correcting "shim" *increased the amplification factor* (that is, the ratio of the equivalent voltage of the ions arriving at the collector to the maximum high frequency voltage applied to the tube) *from about 75 to about 300*. These figures are of necessity somewhat rough estimates, because no means were conveniently at hand to measure the high frequency voltages applied to the tube. Our estimates are based solely on sparking distances in air, and hence it is not unlikely that the voltage amplifications were even greater.

The greatest voltage amplification was obtained when generating the highest speed ions, 1,220,000 volt-protons. In all our work we have found the experimental method to be increasingly effective in this regard, as in others, as we go to higher voltages.

For example, the optimum pressure of hydrogen in the tube has been found to increase from less than 10^{-4} mm of Hg when generating 200,000 volt-protons to more than 10^{-3} mm when producing 1,000,000 volt-protons. By the optimum pressure is meant the pressure that gives the largest current to the collector for a given electron emission from the filament. The reason for this is, of course, connected with the fact that the effective mean free path of the spiralling particles increases with voltage. . . .

DISCUSSION

The present experiments have accomplished one of the objectives set forth in the introduction, namely, the development of a convenient method for the production of protons having kinetic energies of the order of magnitude of 1,000,000 volt-electrons. It is well to emphasize two particular features that have contributed more than anything else to the effectiveness of the method: the *focussing actions of the electric and magnetic fields,* and the *simple means of empirically correcting the magnetic field* by the introduction of suitable iron strips. The former has solved the practical problem of generation of intense high speed ion beams of restricted cross-section so much desired in studies of collision processes. The latter has eliminated the problem of uniformity of magnetic field, making possible voltage amplifications of more than 300. This in turn has practically eliminated any difficulties associated with generation and application to the accelerating electrodes of required high frequency voltages. In consequence, we have here a source of high speed light ions that is readily constructed and assembled in a relatively small laboratory space out of quite modest laboratory equipment. The beam of ions so produced has valuable characteristics of convenience and flexibility for many experimental investigations; there are obvious advantages of a steady beam of high speed ions of but one millimeter diameter generated in an apparatus on an ordinary laboratory table. Moreover, the apparatus evolved in the present work is in no respects capricious, but functions always in a satisfactorily predictable fashion. This is illustrated by the fact that the accelerating tube can be taken apart and reassembled, and then within a few hours after re-evacuation steady beams of 1,200,000 volt-protons can always be obtained.

But it is perhaps of even more interest to inquire as to the practical limitations of the method; to see what extensions and developments are foreshadowed by the present experiments.

Of primary importance is the probable experimental limitation on the producible proton energies. The practical limit is set by the size of the electromagnet available; for the final equivalent voltage of the ions at the periphery is proportional to the square of the magnetic field strength and to the square of the radius of the path. For protons, it is not feasible to use magnetic fields much greater than employed in the present work (about 14,000 gauss) because of the difficulties of application of suitably higher frequency oscillations—that is to say, it is not desirable to go much below 14 meters wave-length. However, it is entirely practicable to use a much larger magnet than that employed in the present experiments. At the present time a magnet having pole faces 114 cm in diameter is being installed in our laboratory. As will be seen from Eq. (4), a magnetic field of 14,000 gauss over such a large region *makes possible the production of* 25,000,000 *volt-protons*.

Of course, it may be argued that there are other difficulties which preclude ever reaching such a range of energies. For example, there is the question of whether it is possible to obtain such a great amplification factor that the high frequency voltages necessarily applied to the accelerating electrodes are low enough to be realizable in practice. In the present experiments an amplification of 300 was obtained with no great effort, and it would seem that with more careful correction of the field this amplification could be considerably increased at higher voltages. In the higher range of speeds the variation of mass with velocity begins to be appreciable, but presents no difficulty as it can be allowed for by suitable alteration of the magnetic field in the same empirical manner as is done to correct its otherwise lack of uniformity.

Assuming then a voltage amplification of 500, the production of 25,000,000 volt-protons would require 50,000 volts at a wave-length of 14 meters applied across the accelerators; thus, 25,000 volts on each accelerator with respect to ground. *It does appear entirely feasible to do this,* although to be sure a considerable amount of power would have to be supplied because of the capacity of the system.

Of similar interest is the matter of maximum obtainable beam intensities. In the present experiments no efforts have been made to obtain high intensities and the collector currents have usually been of the order of magnitude of 10^{-9} amp. Using the present method of generation of the ions, there are two factors that can be drawn upon to increase the yield of high speed ions—the electron emission and the pressure of hydrogen in the tube. The electron emission can easily be increased from 10 to 100 times over that used in the present experiments. The effective free paths of the protons increase with voltage so that, as was found to be the case, the maximum usable pressure of hydrogen is governed by the setting in of a high frequency discharge in the tubes due to the voltage on the accelerators. This appears to occur at a pressure greater than 10^{-3} mm of Hg; the reason the critical pressure is so high is probably to be associated with the quenching action of the magnetic field. These considerations make it seem reasonable to expect that, using the present ion source, *high speed ion currents of as much as 0.1 microampere can readily be obtained.*

At all events, it seems that the focussing of the spiralling ions is so effective that a quite considerable portion of those starting out arrive at the collector and that the beam intensity is determined largely by the source.

This method of multiple acceleration is capable of yields of the same order of magnitude as would conceivably result from the direct application of high voltages.

For a given experimental arrangement the energy of the ions arriving at the collector varies inversely as their masses and directly as their charges. Thus, the large magnet mentioned above makes possible the production of 12,500,000 volt hydrogen molecule ions and doubly charged helium ions (alpha-particles) as well as 25,000,000 volt-protons. Moreover, generating the theoretically maximum value of ion energies becomes much easier with increasing atomic weight because the wave-length of the applied high frequency oscillations increases in a like ratio. For example, using a magnetic field of 14,000 gauss over a region 114 cm in diameter, 2,800,000 volt nitrogen ions could be generated by applying 123 meter oscillations. Broadly speaking, then, the apparatus is well adapted to the production of ions of all the elements up to atomic weight 25 having kinetic energies in excess of 1,000,000 volt-electrons.

79

∘∘∘∘∘∘∘∘∘∘

THE DISCOVERY OF
INDUCED RADIOACTIVITY

∘∘∘∘∘∘∘∘∘∘∘

Jean Frédéric Joliot (1900-1958)
Irène Curie Joliot (1897-1956)

Irène Curie, the elder of the two daughters of Pierre and Marie Curie, was born in Paris in 1897. She received her early education in a cooperative school arranged by Marie Curie for the children of her intimate friends. This unusual school, which existed for only a few years, had remarkable teachers: Paul Langevin, Jean Perrin, Mme. Perrin, and Mme. Curie. For her secondary education Irène was sent to a private school, the Collège Sévigné. During World War I, she assisted her mother with the operation of mobile X-ray units for the French army and at the Radium Institute with the training of X-ray technicians. With such a background it is not surprising that after the war Irène became an assistant in the Institute and began independent research in radioactivity. It was at the Institute in 1925 that she met Frédéric Joliot who, through the influence of Langevin, had been appointed as assistant to Mme. Curie.

Frédéric Joliot was also a Parisian, the youngest of four girls and two boys in a middle-class family. His father, the owner of a hardware store, was fifty-seven when Frédéric was born and his mother, the daughter of one of the chief chefs of Napoleon III, was forty-five. Frédéric was given an education designed to prepare him for a favored position in society. He attended the Lycée Lakanal where his high spirits and amiable manners made him popular with his schoolmates and his outstanding prowess in football made him, as he once remarked, "a semiprofessional."

1404

At the conclusion of his course at the Lycée, Joliot decided to be an engineer. To prepare for engineering instruction he attended the École Lavoisier for two years before entering the School of Physics and Chemistry of the City of Paris, the same school where Pierre and Marie Curie had made their discovery of radium. Here he was a student in the physics courses given by Paul Langevin. The acuteness of Langevin's mind, his grasp of physics and his radical social ideas all made a deep and lasting impression on his young and able pupil.

In 1923 Joliot, then twenty-three years old, having majored in physics and chemistry, graduated with high honors from the École. Although anxious to devote his future to scientific research, he felt himself ill prepared and for the next year he worked as an engineer in the Arbed steel mills in Luxembourg. This position was terminated by a call for military service in which he was reunited with an engineering school friend, R. Biquard, at the artillery school at Poitiers. Biquard also shared Joliot's scientific ambitions and at the end of a year's service, Biquard asked Langevin about the possibility of both young men engaging in laboratory work at the École. The upshot of this request was that Langevin engaged Biquard and obtained an appointment for Joliot as assistant to Madame Curie at the Radium Institute.

In 1926, after a year at the Institute, Joliot married Irène Curie. In order not to lose the magic of the Curie name, the couple combined both surnames into the family name Joliot-Curie. This hyphenation led, perhaps because of Frédéric's lively personality and some alliteration, to the nickname of the "Jolly-Curios." Following their marriage the couple engaged in joint research. Some of their early notable accomplishments were the demonstration of the materialization of γ radiation into positron-electron pairs and the opposite phenomenon of annihilation radiation, and the development of a very intense source of α particles from polonium, which they used to induce nuclear reactions in atoms of the light elements. Bothe and Becker in Germany carrying out the latter research noticed that the incidence of these α particles on beryllium produced a very penetrating radiation which they assumed to be hard γ rays. The Joliots, following up this experiment, which was reported in January 1932, found that if a block of paraffin were placed in the path of these supposed γ rays protons were ejected from the paraffin with velocities up to a tenth that of light and energies up to 5.3 Mev. To explain this result it was assumed that a Compton type head-on collision had occurred between the γ-ray photon and the recoiling proton. But this explanation required that the γ-ray photons needed energies up to 52 Mev, considerably in excess of known γ-ray energies from radioactive substances.

In thinking over these difficulties James Chadwick at the Cavendish Laboratory, Cambridge, realized that the energy difficulties could be resolved if one supposed that instead of the γ rays from beryllium, neutral particles were emitted. The idea of a neutral particle was not new, in fact Rutherford had suggested the existence of such a particle some years earlier. Adopting this hypothesis, Chadwick was able to confirm it within a month, and it was in this way that the neutron was discovered.

In continuing their program of investigation of nuclear reactions induced by α particles incident on the atoms of the light elements, they found that, in the cases of aluminum and boron, the emitted particles consisted of neutrons and positrons, the latter particle having been discovered by C. D. Anderson at the California Institute of Technology in September of 1932. In common with other physicists, the Joliots believed at first that both particles were emitted simultaneously from the struck nucleus. However, in checking this assumption by removing the aluminum target from the path of the α rays, they found that while the neutron emission stopped at once, the positron emission continued but at a decreasing rate. It was thus clear that a new phenomenon of unusual importance had been discovered, induced radioactivity. But it was also clear that the induced radioactivity appeared because an unstable nucleus had been created. The supposed reactions

$$_2He^4 + {}_{13}Al^{27} \rightarrow {}_{15}P^{30} + {}_0n^1$$
$$_{15}P^{30} \rightarrow {}_{14}Si^{30} + {}_1e^0 + \nu$$

involving the formation of unstable phosphorus 30, which decays to stable Si^{30} by positron emission, were soon verified by chemical methods. Thus if the aluminum sample after exposure to the polonium α radiation is dissolved in HCl and the solution rapidly evaporated, the dry residue shows no positron activity. As the reaction equations indicate, the activity should accompany the phosphorus that is produced. This passes off as the gas PH_3 and if this gas is collected and tested, the positron activity is immediately found.

A short paper announcing their discovery of induced radioactivity was published by the Joliots in the *Comptes Rendus* on January 15, 1934. A translation of their paper follows this commentary. This discovery set off similar researches in physics laboratories around the world, and it was soon found that neutrons were very effective in producing radioactive isotopes of many elements. The application of such isotopes as tracers in many processes has given added importance to this effect. For their discovery the Joliots were awarded the 1935 Nobel Prize in chemistry. Following the receipt of the Nobel Prize, increasing demands were made on both the Joliots for administration and the research team of man and wife was no longer able to continue. In 1936 Irène was appointed to fill the post that her mother had held as Professor and Director of the Curie Radium Laboratory in the Sorbonne. Joliot was appointed as Professor at the Collège de France in 1937. He began at once to develop a laboratory there for nuclear research, and he was involved also in the development of the National Center for Scientific Research (CNRS).

In September of 1938, Irène and a co-worker, P. Savitch, following up some researches of Hahn and Strassman on the beta activity resulting from the irradiation of uranium by slow neutrons, showed that one of the four resulting activities was apparently due to lanthanum, an element of much smaller atomic number than uranium. This led Hahn and Strassman, who ascribed the activity to isotopes of radium, to repeat their work. After a very careful investigation they concluded, in December 1938, that the active product was an isotope of barium and that its decay product was chemically identical with lanthanum. The presence of these elements remained a puzzle until the following month, January 1939, when Meitner and Frisch proposed as the explanation the fission of the uranium nucleus. At this point, Joliot immediately began investigation of the fission process; almost simultaneously with Frisch he showed that the fission energy was about 200 Mev and that the process gave rise to elements between bromine (atomic number 35) and cerium (atomic number 58). With Halban and Kovarski he showed that about three neutrons are produced per fission and saw the possibility of a chain reaction with the release of enormous energy.

The conquest of France by the Nazi armies in June 1940 ended any further work on uranium fission. Elsewhere such investigations went on with increasing vigor on account of their possible military significance, but the results no longer appeared in the professional journals. The 200 liter supply of heavy water, which Joliot wished to use as a neutron moderator for uranium experiments, he sent to England just one step ahead of the Germans. It was carried by his colleagues Halban and Kovarski. Joliot remained at the Collège de France and became active in organizing and directing units in the Resistance movement. Throughout the war he continued to direct anti-German activities often at great personal peril, and he was twice arrested by the Nazis.

Following the liberation, Joliot assumed, as Director, the heavy administrative duties necessary to revitalize and extend the activities of the National Center for Scientific Research and he began efforts to establish in the government a French Atomic Energy Commission. When this body was established by de Gaulle in 1946, Joliot was appointed High Commissioner. In this capacity he was responsible for the construction of the first French nuclear reactor that commenced operation in the Fort de Chatillon in December 1948. In 1946 he was elected a foreign member of the Royal Society and a year later awarded the Society's Hughes medal. Despite these signal achievements and awards, his commitment to political activity brought about his dismissal as High Commissioner in 1950 on the grounds of membership in the French Communist party. Irène, also a member of the Commission, terminated her connection with that body the following year.

Joliot returned to his posts in the CNRS and the Collège de France, but his health began to fail and he had to restrict his activity. In 1955 he fell seriously ill, and, while he was recuperating in March 1956, Irène died of leukemia induced by long exposure to radiation. Shortly thereafter Joliot succeeded to her chair in the Faculté des Sciences in the Sorbonne and the directorship of the Curie laboratory. But Joliot himself never completely recovered, and while on vacation in Brittany in August 1958 he suffered an accident from which he died several days later. A daughter, Hélène, and a son, Pierre, carry on the scientific tradition of the family.

The original paper of the Joliot-Curies, announcing the discovery of induced radioactivity, follows.

ooooooo

I. JOLIOT-CURIE and
J. F. JOLIOT-CURIE

A New Type of Radioactivity [1]

WE HAVE RECENTLY SHOWN BY Wilson's method that certain light elements (beryllium, boron, aluminum) emit positive electrons when they are bombarded with α rays from polonium. According to our interpretation, the emission of positive electrons from Be is due to the *internal materialization* of γ rays, while the positive electrons emitted by B and Al are *electrons of transmutation* accompanying the emission of neutrons.

In seeking to determine the mechanism of these emissions we have discovered the following phenomena:

The emission of positive electrons by certain light elements irradiated by α rays from polonium continues for a time more or less long after removal of the source of α rays, amounting to more than a half hour in the case of boron.

---

[1] Irène Joliot-Curie and J. F. Joliot-Curie, *Comptes Rendus,* 198 (1934), 254 f—trans. by Editors.

We placed a sheet of aluminum 1 mm from a polonium source. The Al, having been irridiated for about 10 minutes, was placed under a Geiger-Müller counter whose aperture was covered by an aluminum screen 0.07 mm thick. We observed that the sheet emits a radiation whose intensity decreases exponentially as a function of the time with a period of 3 min 15 sec. An analogous result is obtained with boron and magnesium but the decay periods are different, 14 min for boron and 2 min 30 sec for magnesium.

The intensity of the radiation immediately after exposure to the rays increases with the time of irradiation up to a limiting value. One has then initial intensities of the same order for B, Mg, Al; about 150 counts per minute using a 60-millicurie source of polonium.

With elements H, Li, Be, C, N, O, F, Na, Ca, Ni, and Au, no effect has been observed. (Thus this phenomenon cannot be ascribed to a contamination from the polonium source.) For certain of these elements, the phenomenon is probably not produced; but for others, the decay period is probably too short.

The experiments made by the Wilson method, or by the trochoid method introduced by Thibaud, have shown that the radiation emitted by boron and by aluminum consists of positive electrons. It is probable that the radiation is the same from magnesium.

On introducing copper screens between the counter and the irradiated foils, one finds that the major part of the radiation from Al is absorbed in 0.88 gm/cm^2 and for B and Mg, in 0.26 gm/cm^2. These correspond, by assuming the same law of absorption as for negative electrons, to an energy of 2.2×10^6 eV for Al, and 0.7×10^6 eV for B and Mg.

When the energy of the α rays irradiating the Al was reduced, the number of positive electrons diminished but the decay period does not appear modified. When the energy of the α rays is reduced below 10^6 eV one observes scarcely any of these electrons.

These experiments show the existence of a new type of radioactivity with emission of positive electrons. We think that the emission process for aluminum is:

$$_{13}^{27}\mathrm{Al} + {_2^4}\mathrm{He} \rightarrow {_{15}^{30}}\mathrm{P} + {_0^1}n$$

The isotope $_{15}^{30}\mathrm{P}$ of phosphorus is radioactive with a period of 3 min 15 sec and emits positive electrons according to the reaction

$$_{15}^{30}\mathrm{P} = {_{14}^{30}}\mathrm{Si} + {_1}\epsilon^0$$

An analogous reaction may be envisioned for boron and magnesium, the unstable nuclei being $_7^{13}\mathrm{N}$ and $_{14}^{27}\mathrm{Si}$; the isotopes $_7^{13}\mathrm{N}$, $_{14}^{27}\mathrm{Si}$, $_{15}^{30}\mathrm{P}$ are able to exist only for a very short time; that is why they are not observed in nature.

We consider as unlikely the following explanation

$$^{27}_{13}\text{Al} + ^{4}_{2}\text{He} \rightarrow ^{30}_{14}\text{Si} + ^{1}_{1}\text{H} \qquad ^{30}_{14}\text{Si} \rightarrow ^{30}_{14}\text{Si} + \epsilon^{+} + \epsilon^{-},$$

the isotope $^{30}_{14}\text{Si}$ being excited and able to deactivate itself in the course of time, the energy being materialized and giving a pair of electrons. One does not observe the emission of negative electrons and it is theoretically very improbable that the energy difference between the electrons is such that the negatives are not observed. Besides, this process supposes an extraordinarily long duration of the excited state with a coefficient of internal materialization of unity.

Finally, it has been possible for the first time to create, with the aid of an external agent, radioactivity of certain atomic nuclei which exist for a measurable time in the absence of the exciting cause.

[Such] lasting radioactivities, similar to those which we have observed, ought without doubt to exist in the case of bombardment by other particles. The same radioactive atom could without doubt be created by several nuclear reactions. For example, the nucleus $^{13}_{7}\text{N}$, which is radioactive according to our hypothesis, ought to be obtained by the action of a deuton on carbon after the emission of a neutron.

80

ooooooooooo

PREDICTION OF THE MESON

ooooooooooo

Hideki Yukawa (b. 1907)

We have already noted that until the discovery of the neutron in 1933 only two fundamental particles of matter were recognized by physicists: the proton and the electron. Strictly speaking, the photon also had some claim to being a fundamental particle at that time, but since the photon is a corpuscle of radiation, it was felt that it should not be counted among fundamental particles of matter. The neutrino had been postulated as a necessary consequence of β-decay (emission of electrons) of radioactive nuclei, and although Fermi had constructed a beautiful β-decay theory using neutrinos, these elusive particles were still not fully accepted since they had not yet been detected experimentally. The neutron was thus the first of a series of new particles that were soon to flood the detecting devices of physicists and to demand their rightful places in whatever model of nature (that is, of the structure of matter) physicists were constructing.

The very discovery of the neutron pointed clearly to the need for additional "fundamental" particles for the following reason. Neutrons and protons, the fundamental constituents of the nucleus, exert enormous short-range forces on each other to keep the nucleus a tightly bound particle. But how are these short-range forces between neutrons and protons exerted? One way of discussing such forces is to introduce the concept of action at a distance, but such an approach cannot be treated by standard quantum-mechanical methods. Instead of action at a distance one therefore introduces a force field, which is then quantized. Let us consider briefly how the field concept helps us understand how electrically charged particles interact with one another.

Although in classical physics it is customary to speak of the force between two electrons or between an electron and a proton in terms of action at a distance, which is given mathematically by Coulomb's law of

1411

force, the modern description of electromagnetic forces between charged particles is expressed in terms of the electromagnetic field. This automatically leads to a quantum-mechanical formulation of the interaction between charged particles because the electromagnetic radiation field can be quantized. Indeed, as we know, quantum mechanics had its origin in the quantum theory of radiation, which began with Planck's radiation formula for black-body radiation and was then more fully developed with the introduction of Einstein's concept of the photon. To picture radiation as consisting of photons is, of course, a quantization procedure, and one can then introduce a quantum theory of interaction of a charged particle with a surrounding electromagnetic field by picturing the charged particle as absorbing and emitting the photons of this radiation field. Such a quantum-mechanical theory of the interaction of a charged particle with a radiation field was first developed in a series of elegant papers by Dirac, and later, from a slightly different and somewhat simpler point of view, by Fermi. The photons are thus the quanta of the radiation field.

In terms of these quanta one describes the interaction between two charged particles (e.g., two electrons or an electron and a proton) as arising from the mutual emission and absorption of photons. Thus, one electron emits a photon, which is then absorbed by the other electron (or proton), and vice versa.

This tossing back and forth of photons between two charged particles gives rise to the electromagnetic forces between them. This was first demonstrated mathematically in a famous paper by Bethe and Fermi, who showed that if two charged particles are at rest, their mutual absorption and emission of photons (treated quantum mechanically) leads directly to Coulomb's law of electrostatic force. Later it was also shown by other physicists, such as Møller and Breit, that by the same procedure one can obtain the electromagnetic force between two particles when they are in motion.

Another interesting physical phenomenon can be discussed in terms of the quantized electromagnetic field. A single charged particle such as an isolated electron is surrounded by its own electromagnetic field and can therefore interact with this field. This idea was first introduced into physics from a classical point of view by H. A. Lorentz, who described this interaction of the electron with its own electromagnetic field by picturing the electron as exerting a force on itself. He calculated this force by a straightforward application of classical electromagnetic theory to a spherical electron. He considered each little piece of the sphere as exerting an electromagnetic force on every other little piece, and obtained the total force of the electron on itself by adding up all of these constituent forces.

The quantum-mechanical description of the interaction of the electron with itself, that is, with its own electromagnetic field, proceeds differently.

We picture the electron as emitting a photon momentarily (called a virtual photon) and then immediately reabsorbing this photon. Actually, the electron need not absorb this same photon. As long as it immediately absorbs another photon of its own radiation field, the electron interacts with its own radiation field and hence with itself.

This virtual emission and absorption of photons (giving, as it does, a picture of the charged particle) gives rise to its so-called self-energy—the total energy concentrated in the particle, which would be released if the particle were completely destroyed.

This, of course, should exactly equal mc^2 according to the theory of relativity, where m is the mass of the particle and c is the speed of light. It is also the work required to assemble the particle against the repulsion of its own total electric charge; in other words, it is the work that must be done to assemble the particle against the force of the particle on itself. Hence, one should be able to calculate the self-energy of an electron solely by analyzing its interaction with its own surrounding electromagnetic field.

This is done quantum mechanically by computing the contribution to the interaction energy of the electron with its own field when the electron emits and immediately reabsorbs a virtual photon. If one then sums over all such virtual emissions and absorptions, one should get the total self-energy of the electron. Unfortunately, when this is done one obtains an infinite value for this self-energy. The reason is that the electron can emit virtual photons of any frequency and hence very energetic photons (that is, high-frequency photons). These contribute very heavily to the self-energy of the electron and ultimately, since there is an infinitude of very high-frequency photons, give an infinite result. This, of course, is a severe deficiency of the theory, which, in a sense, has been swept under the scientific rug by special mathematical schemes that enable us to overlook, or at least to work with, these infinities.

We come now to the important contribution of Hideki Yukawa, who developed a quantized field theory of the forces between nucleons by quantizing the nuclear force field in complete analogy with the electromagnetic radiation field.

As soon as nuclear forces were discovered, physicists realized that these forces would have to be described in terms of a quantized force field. A serious difficulty arose in carrying out such a plan when the neutron was first discovered. Unlike the electromagnetic field that revealed its quanta (photons) very early in the game, the nature of the nuclear force field and the properties of its quanta remained a mystery.

One attempt to pierce the mystery and develop a quantum theory of nuclear forces was made by Fermi in his famous 1934 paper, in which he presented a theory of β radioactivity (the emission of electrons and neutrinos by radioactive nuclei). His idea at that time was that a neutron and a proton interact with each other by their mutual emission and absorption of electrons and neutrinos. According to this picture, the electrons and neutrinos together constitute the quanta of the nuclear force field just the way the photons are the quanta of the electromagnetic radiation field.

This initially seemed reasonable, but it soon became clear that it could not be the true picture, since nuclear forces are extremely strong, whereas the interaction between nucleons and electrons and neutrinos is extremely weak. In other words, if a gas of nucleons is bombarded by streams of electrons and neutrinos hardly any interaction takes place. Consequently, Fermi gave up the idea of introducing electrons and neutrinos as the quanta of the nuclear force field even though his theory gives an excellent description of beta radioactivity. Nevertheless, physicists everywhere were convinced that some kind of quanta would have to be introduced to describe the nuclear forces between nucleons, but that they would not be electrons and neutrinos.

The first step in establishing a quantum field theory of nuclear interactions was taken by the Japanese physicist Hideki Yukawa in a famous paper that appeared in 1934, and that we reproduce following this commentary. Yukawa assumed that the Fermi process (the emission of an electron and a neutrino when a neutron changes into a proton) does not always occur; in fact, it is rather rare as compared to another process. Yukawa describes this second process as one in which a much heavier particle than an electron-neutrino pair is emitted by the neutron and then absorbed by the proton. If such a process does occur and is much more probable than the Fermi process, it must generate strong interactions between the neutron and the proton and thus account for nuclear forces. Such a process would have no effect on the Fermi β-decay process, so that no conflict would arise between the Yukawa theory and the experimentally verified Fermi theory.

With this idea as a starting point, Yukawa set out to develop a quantum field theory of nuclear forces and to derive some of the properties of the quanta of this field. He proceeded by analogy with the electromagnetic field that is also described by quanta (the Einstein photons).

The photons of the electromagnetic field are described by Maxwell's equations, from which one can deduce that the motion of the photons is described by a wave equation. This wave equation, of course, is valid only for particles like photons that have no rest mass; since the Coulomb force is much smaller than the nuclear forces between nucleons, and of a much longer range, the same kind of wave equation that describes photons cannot describe the quanta that are required for the strong nuclear interactions. Yukawa at once saw where the difficulty lay and how the correct answer could be obtained. He points out in his paper that the wave equation for photons leads to an interaction between two charged particles that varies inversely as the distance between the two particles (the Coulomb potential), and thus gives rise to an inadequately small force at short distances. To obtain nuclear forces one needs a law of interaction that increases much faster as the distance gets smaller than the Coulomb law. Yukawa noted that this type of law can be obtained from the Coulomb law by multiplying the latter by an exponential function of the distance. Such a law cannot be obtained from the kind of wave equation that describes photons; in fact, as Yukawa indicates in this paper, the wave equation for the quanta of the nuclear force field must differ from that of photons by an additional term. The rationale for the introduction of this term is that the quanta of the nuclear force field must be massive particles—their rest mass must be considerably larger than that of the electron—if they are to account for nuclear forces, whereas the electromagnetic photons have no rest mass. The added term in the wave equation for the heavy quanta signifies the mass of these particles.

Yukawa showed that the solution of this wave equation for heavy quanta gives nuclear interactions of the right size and of the type demanded by the experimental evidence; that is, they are exchange forces of the sort that Heisenberg first suggested to describe the interactions of neutrons and protons. According to the Yukawa picture, a neutron emits a heavy quantum, which is then absorbed by the proton. In the process, the neutron changes to a proton and the proton becomes a neutron. Immediately following this, the proton (which is now a neutron) emits its own heavy quantum that is absorbed by the original neutron (now a proton), and so on. Thus the neutron and proton behave as though they were changing places by tossing a heavy quantum between them.

In this analysis Yukawa introduced a new kind of charge (nuclear charge) between nucleons that plays the same role in the nuclear force field as the electrostatic charge on electrons and protons plays in the electromagnetic field. However, the nuclear and electric charges are in no way connected, and the former is numerically much larger than the latter. To obtain the physical properties of the heavy quanta Yukawa applies his theory to certain experimentally-observed phenomena (e.g., scattering of nucleons, β decay, and so on). He shows that the rest mass of the heavy quanta must be about 200 times that of the electron. In addition, it is clear from the analysis that heavy quanta must be particles with zero spin (or perhaps spin one) instead of spin one half as in the case of electrons, neutrinos, protons, and neutrons. To see this we note first that these heavy quanta obey the same kind (except for the mass term) of wave equation as do photons; they must therefore have the same statistical properties as the latter and hence an integer spin value. (Photons have a spin one and all particles with integer spin, e.g., 0, 1, 2, and so on, must obey the same statistics, the so-called Einstein-Bose statistics, as do photons.) Second, since a neutron becomes a proton when it emits a heavy quantum, and the proton spin is the same as the neutron spin (that is, one half), the spin of heavy quantum must be zero (or one).

When Yukawa first presented his theory, there was no evidence for the existence of the heavy quanta he proposed because, as he pointed out, heavy quanta pass back and forth between two nucleons, but they remain undetectable unless the nucleons have kinetic energies with respect to each other that are at least equal to the mass of a heavy quantum times the square of the speed of light. In other words, there must be enough kinetic energy present to create those heavy quanta.

Although the physics laboratories at that time did not have accelerators large enough to accelerate nucleons to the required energy, cosmic ray nucleons do have such large energies. Shortly after Yukawa had published his paper, a number of physicists, in particular C. D. Anderson and S. H. Neddermayer, working with cosmic rays discovered heavy particles with masses more than 200 times the mass of the electron in cosmic ray showers. At first it was thought that these particles (now called mu-mesons or muons) were the Yukawa heavy quanta, but experimental evidence soon showed that this was not the case. The mu-mesons interact much too weakly with nuclei to be the Yukawa quanta. We also know now that the mu-mesons, which have a mass about 208 times that of the electron, have the wrong spin (their spin is one half) and hence obey the same statistics as do electrons (the Fermi-Dirac statistics). Today we believe that the mu-meson is an excited state of the electron. In fact, a mu-meson has a very short life (about one one-millionth of a second) and decays into an electron by emitting two neutrinos. Electrons, neutrinos, and mu-mesons are called leptons and form a single family of particles.

A few years after the mu-mesons were discovered, other mesons, slightly more massive than mu-mesons, were discovered by C. F. Powell and G. P. Occhialini in cosmic rays. These particles, the famous pi-mesons, have all the properties required by the Yukawa theory. We now know that they are indeed the heavy quanta of the nuclear force field. Nucleons interact with each other by tossing pi-mesons (also called pions) back and forth. Each pion has a rest mass about 273 times that of the electron and it has a spin zero. There are three kinds of pi-mesons with different electrical properties; one is electrically neutral, one has a unit positive electric charge (like the proton), and the other has a unit negative electric charge like the electron.

Since nucleons can interact by tossing any of the three kinds of pi-mesons back and forth between them, it follows that the nuclear force between nucleons is charge-independent. In other words, the nuclear force between two protons (disregarding the Coulomb electric force of repulsion) is equal to that between two neutrons and equal to that between a neutron and a proton. This fact plays a very important role in the structure of nuclei. The proton interacts with another proton by tossing neutral pions between themselves and this is also true for the interaction between two neutrons. But a neutron and a proton interact by tossing either positive or negative pions back and forth.

A pion is not a stable particle and decays into a muon in about three one-hundred millionths of a second by emitting a neutrino.

The essential difference between modern physics and classical physics in their treatments of forces between particles is in the concept of the field as a carrier of these forces. The idea of the classical field of force began with Newton, was then greatly expanded by Maxwell, and reached its highest and most fruitful development in the hands of Einstein. This development was classical in the sense that the field was pictured as continuous and not quantized. Planck's discovery of the quantum of energy and Einstein's photon concept showed that the electromagnetic radiation field must be quantized. Later, Bethe and Fermi showed that the Coulomb force between two charges can be derived as a consequence of the absorption and the emission of photons by the two charges. However, until 1935, when Yukawa published his famous paper on the forces between nucleons (that is, nuclear forces) it was thought that only particles with zero rest mass, such as photons, could be the quanta of a force field. Yukawa showed that this is not so and that particles (now called heavy quanta or mesons) can also be the quanta of a force field.

That Yukawa should have arrived at this important discovery before any of the European or American physicists did is all the more remarkable, when one realizes that Fermi had almost arrived at a similar solution with his theory of β decay and that Yukawa had very little contact with European physicists. In a sense, he is a self-taught physicist who created his own school of physics and was responsible for the rapid rise of theoretical physics in Japan.

Yukawa was born in Toyko, January 23, 1907, the third son of Takiyi Ogawa, who later become professor of geology at Kyoto University. The young Yukawa was raised and received his early education in Kyoto and then went on to Kyoto University, from which he graduated in 1929. After graduation, he continued with his studies in theoretical physics and became interested in problems related to nuclear physics and the structure of elementary particles. From his very first concern with these problems, Yukawa's approach to their solution showed a high degree of originality and clear evidence of a brilliant mind. His ability was quickly recognized and he was appointed lecturer at Kyoto University and lecturer and assistant professor at Osaka University. In 1938 he was awarded the D.Sc. degree and in the following year became professor of theoretical physics at Kyoto University. He remained at these academic posts until 1939. This was a very fruitful period for Yukawa; he published many papers on nuclear physics, including his famous paper, in 1935, "On the Interaction of Elementary Particles. I," which he had completed at the age of twenty-seven. In this paper he developed his heavy quantum field theory of nuclear forces and postulated the existence of the meson.

When mesons were subsequently discovered by Anderson and Neddermeyer and proved to be mu-mesons and not the pi-mesons (discovered later by Powell) required by the Yukawa theory, Yukawa was greatly encouraged and continued to develop the theory of the meson field.

In 1948, after World War II, he was invited to the Institute of Advanced Study at Princeton as visiting professor and then, in 1949, became visiting professor of physics at Columbia University. While he was at Columbia he was awarded the Nobel Prize in physics for 1949.

When Yukawa returned to Japan he devoted himself to the development of a new type of field theory called the nonlocal field, from which he hoped to derive the various elementary particles.

For a few years during the 1950's Yukawa was professor of physics at Columbia University, where he lectured on his nonlocal field theory. He then returned to Japan, where he still resides; he is currently professor of theoretical physics at Kyoto University, as well as director of the Research Institute for Fundamental Physics at Kyoto.

He is a member of the Japan Academy, the Physical Society, and the Science Council of Japan, and is professor emeritus of Osaka University. He is also a foreign associate of the National Academy of Sciencies of the United States. He has been honored by learned societies and universities of many lands. He was awarded an honorary degree by the University of Paris and is an honorary member of the Royal Society of Edinburgh and the Indian Academy of Sciences, among others.

Yukawa has done much to bring Japanese physics to its present state of eminence, not only by his research work and his work with graduate students, but also by his interest in undergraduate education in the physical sciences. He has stimulated interest in physics by his books, among which are *Introduction to Quantum Mechanics* and *The Theory of Elementary Particles*. Since 1946, he has also been editor of the *Progress of Theoretical Physics* (Kyoto).

Many of the outstanding theoretical physicists in Japan owe their present positions in part to the training they received under Yukawa and to the inspiration they found in his research work. One of his outstanding students was Tomonaga, who independently of Schwinger and Feynman introduced the basic ideas that finally led to the present improved formulation of quantum electrodynamics; this enables physicists to answer questions relating to the interaction of electrons and the electromagnetic field without running into infinities.

He lives in Kyoto with his wife, whom he married in 1932, and two sons.

ooooooo

Y U K A W A

On the Interaction of Elementary Particles [1]

INTRODUCTION

AT THE PRESENT STAGE OF the quantum theory little is known about the nature of interaction of elementary particles. Heisenberg considered the interaction of "Platzwechsel" between the neutron and the proton to be of importance to the nuclear structure.

Recently Fermi treated the problem of β-disintegration on the hypothesis of "neutrino". According to this theory, the neutron and the proton can interact by emitting and absorbing a pair of neutrino and electron. Unfortunately the interaction energy calculated on such assumption is much too small to account for the binding energies of neutrons and protons in the nucleus.

To remove this defect, it seems natural to modify the theory of Heisenberg and Fermi in the following way. The transition of a heavy particle from neutron state to proton state is not always accompanied by the emission of light particles, i.e., a neutrino and an electron, but the energy liberated by the transition is taken up sometimes by another heavy particle, which in turn will be transformed from proton state into neutron state. If the probability of occurrence of the latter process is much larger than that of the former, the interaction between the neutron and the proton will be much larger than in the case of Fermi, whereas the probability of emission of light particles is not affected essentially.

Now such interaction between the elementary particles can be described by means of a field of force, just as the interaction between the charged particles is described by the electromagnetic field. The above considerations show that the interaction of heavy particles with this field is much larger than that of light particles with it.

In the quantum theory this field should be accompanied by a new sort of quantum, just as the electromagnetic field is accompanied by the photon.

---

[1] Hideki Yukawa, *Progress of Theoretical Physics* (Kyoto), 17 (1935), 48–57.

In this paper the possible natures of this field and the quantum accompanying it will be discussed briefly and also their bearing on the nuclear structure will be considered.

Besides such an exchange force and the ordinary electric and magnetic forces there may be other forces between the elementary particles, but we disregard the latter for the moment.

Fuller account will be made in the next paper.

FIELD DESCRIBING THE INTERACTION

In analogy with the scalar potential of the electromagnetic field, a function $U(x, y\, z, t)$ is introduced to describe the field between the neutron and the proton. This function will satisfy an equation similar to the wave equation for the electromagnetic potential.

Now the equation

$$\left\{ \Delta - \frac{1}{c^2} \frac{\partial^2}{\partial t^2} \right\} U = 0 \tag{1}$$

has only static solution with central symmetry $\frac{1}{r}$, except the additive and the multiplicative constants. The potential of force between the neutron and proton should, however, not be of Coulomb type, but decrease more rapidly with distance. It can be expressed, for example by

$$+ \text{ or } -g^2 \frac{e^{-\lambda r}}{r}, \tag{2}$$

where g is a constant with the dimension of electric charge, i.e., cm.$^{3/2}$ sec.$^{-1}$ gr.$^{1/2}$ and λ with the dimension cm.$^{-1}$

Since this function is a static solution with central symmetry of the wave equation

$$\left\{ \Delta - \frac{1}{c^2} \frac{\partial^2}{\partial t^2} - \lambda^2 \right\} U = 0, \tag{3}$$

let this equation be assumed to be the correct equation for U in vacuum. In the presence of the heavy particles, the U-field interacts with them and causes the transition from neutron state to proton state.

Now, if we introduce the matrices

$$\tau_1 = \begin{pmatrix} 0 & 1 \\ 1 & 0 \end{pmatrix}, \tau_2 = \begin{pmatrix} 0 & -i \\ i & 0 \end{pmatrix}, \tau_3 = \begin{pmatrix} 1 & 0 \\ 0 & -1 \end{pmatrix}$$

and denote the neutron state and the proton state by $\tau_3 = 1$ and $\tau_3 = -1$ respectively, the wave equation is given by

$$\left\{\Delta - \frac{1}{c^2}\frac{\partial^2}{\partial t^2} - \lambda^2\right\} U = -4\pi g\tilde{\Psi}\,\frac{\tau_1 - i\tau_2}{2}\,\Psi, \tag{4}$$

where Ψ denotes the wave function of the heavy particles, being a function of time, position, spin as well as τ_3', which takes the value either 1 or -1.

Next, the conjugate complex function $\tilde{U}(x, y, z, t)$, satisfying the equation

$$\left\{\Delta - \frac{1}{c^2}\frac{\partial^2}{\partial t^2} - \lambda^2\right\} \tilde{U} = -4\pi g\tilde{\Psi}\,\frac{\tau_1 + i\tau_2}{2}\,\Psi, \tag{5}$$

is introduced, corresponding to the inverse transition from proton to neutron state.

Similar equation will hold for the vector function, which is the analogue of the vector potential of the electromagnetic field. However, we disregard it for the moment, as there's no correct relativistic theory for the heavy particles. Hence simple non-relativistic wave equation neglecting spin will be used for the heavy particle, in the following way

$$\left\{\frac{h^2}{4}\left(\frac{1+\tau_3}{M_N} + \frac{1-\tau_3}{M_P}\right)\Delta + ih\frac{\partial}{\partial t} - \frac{1+\tau_3}{2}M_Nc^2 - \frac{1-\tau_3}{2}M_Pc^2\right.$$
$$\left. - g\left(\tilde{U}\frac{\tau_1 - i\tau_2}{2} + U\frac{\tau_1 + i\tau_2}{2}\right)\right\}\Psi = 0, \tag{6}$$

where h is Planck's constant divided by 2π and M_N, M_P are the masses of the neutron and the proton respectively. The reason for taking the negative sign in front of g will be mentioned later.

The equation (6) corresponds to the Hamiltonian

$$H = \left(\frac{1+\tau_3}{4M_N} + \frac{1-\tau_3}{4M_P}\right)p^2 + \frac{1+\tau_3}{2}M_Nc^2 + \frac{1-\tau_3}{2}M_Pc^2$$
$$+ g\left(\tilde{U}\frac{\tau_1 - i\tau_2}{2} + U\frac{\tau_1 + i\tau_2}{2}\right) \tag{7}$$

where p is the momentum of the particle. If we put $M_Nc^2 - M_Pc^2 = D$ and $M_N + M_P = 2M$, the equation (7) becomes approximately

$$H = \frac{p^2}{2M} + \frac{g}{2}\{\tilde{U}(\tau_1 - i\tau_2) + U(\tau_1 + i\tau_2)\} + \frac{D}{2}\tau_3, \tag{8}$$

where the constant term Mc^2 is omitted.

NEW PARTICLES AND ATOMIC ACCELERATORS

Now consider two heavy particles at points (x_1, y_1, z_1) and (x_2, y_2, z_2) respectively and assume their relative velocity to be small. The fields at (x_1, y_1, z_1) due to the particle at (x_2, y_2, z_2) are, from (4) and (5),

$$U(x_1, y_1, z_1) = g \frac{e^{-\lambda r_{12}}}{r_{12}} \frac{(\tau_1^{(2)} - i\tau_2^{(2)})}{2}$$

and

$$\tilde{U}(x_1, y_1, z_1) = g \frac{e^{-\lambda r_{12}}}{r_{12}} \frac{(\tau_1^{(2)} + i\tau_2^{(2)})}{2},$$

$$(9)$$

where $(\tau_1^{(1)}, \tau_2^{(1)}, \tau_3^{(1)})$ and $(\tau_1^{(2)}, \tau_2^{(2)}, \tau_3^{(2)})$ are the matrices relating to the first and the second particles respectively, and r_{12} is the distance between them.

Hence the Hamiltonian for the system is given, in the absence of the external fields, by

$$H = \frac{p_1^2}{2M} + \frac{p_2^2}{2M} + \frac{g^2}{4} \{ (\tau_1^{(1)} - i\tau_2^{(1)})(\tau_1^{(2)} + i\tau_2^{(2)}).$$

$$+ (\tau_1^{(1)} + i\tau_2^{(1)})(\tau_1^{(2)} - i\tau_2^{(2)}) \} \frac{e^{-\lambda r_{12}}}{r_{12}} + (\tau_3^{(1)} + \tau_3^{(2)})D = \frac{p_1^2}{2M}$$

$$+ \frac{p_2^2}{2M} + \frac{g^2}{2} (\tau_1^{(1)}\tau_1^{(2)} + \tau_2^{(1)}\tau_2^{(2)}) \frac{e^{-\lambda r_{12}}}{r_{12}} + (\tau_3^{(1)} + \tau_3^{(2)})D, \quad (10)$$

where p_1, p_2 are the momenta of the particles.

This Hamiltonian is equivalent to Heisenberg's Hamiltonian, if we take for "Platzwechselintegral"

$$J(r) = -g^2 \frac{e^{-\lambda r}}{r}, \quad (11)$$

except that the interaction between the neutrons and the electrostatic repulsion between the protons are not taken into account. Heisenberg took the positive sign for $J(r)$, so that the spin of the lowest energy state of H^2 was O, whereas in our case, owing to the negative sign in front of g^2, the lowest energy state has the spin 1, which is required from the experiment.

Two constants g and λ appearing in the above equations should be determined by comparison with experiment. For example, using the Hamiltonian (10) for heavy particles, we can calculate the mass defect of H^2 and the probability of scattering of a neutron by a proton provided that the relative velocity is small compared with the light velocity.

Rough estimation shows that the calculated values agree with the experimental results, if we take for λ the value between 10^{12}cm^{-1}. and 10^{13}cm^{-1}. and for g a few times of the elementary charge e, although no direct relation between g and e was suggested in the above considerations.

NATURE OF THE QUANTA ACCOMPANYING THE FIELD

The U-field above considered should be quantized according to the general method of the quantum theory. Since the neutron and the proton both obey Fermi's statistics, the quanta accompanying the U-field should obey Bose's statistics and the quantization can be carried out on the line similar to that of the electromagnetic field.

The law of conservation of the electric charge demands that the quantum should have the charge either $+e$ or $-e$. The field quantity U corresponds to the operator which increases the number of negatively charged quanta and decreases the number of positively charged quanta by one respectively. $\tilde{U}$, which is the complex conjugate of U, corresponds to the inverse operator.

Next, denoting

$$p_x = -ih\frac{\partial}{\partial x}, \text{ etc., } W = ih\frac{\partial}{\partial t},$$

$$m_U c = \lambda h,$$

the wave equation for U in free space can be written in the form

$$\left\{ p_x^2 + p_y^2 + p_z^2 - \frac{W^2}{c^2} + m_U c^2 \right\} U = 0, \tag{12}$$

so that the quantum accompanying the field has the proper mass $m_U = \dfrac{\lambda h}{c}$.

Assuming $\lambda = 5 \times 10^{12}\text{cm}^{-1}$., we obtain for m_U a value 2×10^2 times as large as the electron mass. As such a quantum with large mass and positive or negative charge has never been found by the experiment, the above theory seems to be on a wrong line. We can show, however, that, in the ordinary nuclear transformation, such a quantum can not be emitted into outer space.

Let us consider, for example, the transition from a neutron state of energy W_N to a proton state of energy W_P, both of which include the proper energies. These states can be expressed by the wave function

$$\Psi_N(x, y, z, t, 1) = u(x, y, z)e^{-iW_N t/h}, \ \Psi_N(x, y, z, t, -1) = 0$$

and

$$\Psi_P(x, y, z, t, 1) = 0, \ \Psi_P(x, y, z, t, -1) = v(x, y, z)e^{-iW_P t/h},$$

so that, on the right hand side of the equation (4), the term

$$-4\pi g\tilde{v}u e^{-it(W_N - W_P)/\hbar}$$

appears.

Putting $U = U'(x, y, z)e^{i\omega t}$, we have from (4)

$$\left\{\Delta - \left(\lambda^2 - \frac{\omega^2}{c^2}\right)\right\} U' = -4\pi g\tilde{v}u, \tag{13}$$

where $\omega = \dfrac{W_N - W_P}{h}$. Integrating this, we obtain a solution

$$U'(r) = g \int\int\int \frac{e^{-\mu|r-r'|}}{|r-r'|} \tilde{v}(r')u(r')dv', \tag{14}$$

where $\mu = \sqrt{\lambda^2 - \dfrac{\omega^2}{c^2}}$.

If $\lambda > \dfrac{|\omega|}{c}$ or $m_U c^2 > |W_N - W_P|$, μ is real and the function $J(r)$ of Heisenberg has the form $-g^2 \dfrac{e^{-\mu r}}{r}$, in which μ, however, depends on $|W_N - W_P|$, becoming smaller and smaller as the latter approaches $m_U c^2$. This means that the range of interaction between a neutron and a proton increases as $|W_N - W_P|$ increases.

Now the scattering (elastic or inelastic) of a neutron by a nucleus can be considered as the result of the following double process: the neutron falls into a proton level in the nucleus and a proton in the latter jumps to a neutron state of positive kinetic energy, the total energy being conserved throughout the process. The above argument, then, shows that the probability of scattering may in some cases increase with the velocity of the neutron.

According to the experiment of Bonner, the collision cross section of the neutron increases, in fact, with the velocity in the case of lead whereas it decreases in the case of carbon and hydrogen, the rate of decrease being slower in the former than in the latter. The origin of this effect is not clear, but the above considerations do not, at least, contradict it. For, if the binding energy of the proton in the nucleus becomes comparable with $m_U c^2$, the range of interaction of the neutron with the former will increase considerably with the velocity of the neutron, so that the cross section will decrease slower in such case than in the case of hydrogen, i.e., free proton. Now the binding energy of the proton in C^{12}, which is estimated from the difference of masses of C^{12} and B^{11}, is

$$12,0036 - 11,0110 = 0,9926.$$

This corresponds to a binding energy 0,0152 in mass unit, being thirty times the electron mass. Thus in the case of carbon we can expect the effect observed by Bonner. The arguments are only tentative, other explanations being, of course, not excluded.

Next if $\lambda < \dfrac{|\omega|}{c}$ or $m_U c^2 < |W_N - W_P|$, μ becomes pure imaginary and U expresses a spherical undamped wave, implying that a quantum with energy greater than $m_U c^2$ can be emitted in outer space by the transition of the heavy particle from neutron state to proton state, provided that $|W_N - W_P| > m_U c^2$.

The velocity of U-wave is greater but the group velocity is smaller than the light velocity c, as in the case of the electron wave.

The reason why such massive quanta, if they ever exist, are not yet discovered may be ascribed to the fact that the mass m_U is so large that condition $|W_N - W_P| > m_U c^2$ is not fulfilled in ordinary nuclear transformation.

§4. THEORY OF β-DISINTEGRATION

Hitherto we have considered only the interaction of U-quanta with heavy particles. Now, according to our theory, the quantum emitted when a heavy particle jumps from a neutron state to a proton state can be absorbed by a light particle which will then in consequence of energy absorption rise from a neutrino state of negative energy to an electron state of positive energy. Thus an anti-neutrino and an electron are emitted simultaneously from the nucleus. Such intervention of a massive quantum does not alter essentially the probability of β-disintegration, which has been calculated on the hypothesis of direct coupling of a heavy particle and a light particle, just as, in the theory of internal conversion of γ-ray, the intervention of the proton does not affect the final result. Our theory, therefore, does not differ essentially from Fermi's theory.

Fermi considered that an electron and a neutrino are emitted simultaneously from the radioactive nucleus, but this is formally equivalent to the assumption that a light particle jumps from a neutrino state of negative energy to an electron state of positive energy.

For, if the eigenfunctions of the electron and the neutrino be ψ_k, ϕ_k respectively, where $k = 1, 2, 3, 4$, a term of the form

$$-4\pi g' \sum_{k=1}^{4} \tilde{\psi}_k \phi_k \qquad (15)$$

should be added to the right hand side of the equation (5) for $\tilde{U}$, where g' is a new constant with the same dimension as g.

Now the eigenfunctions of the neutrino state with energy and momentum just opposite to those of the state ϕ_k is given by $\phi_{k'} = -\delta_{kl}\tilde{\phi}_l$ and conversely $\phi_k = \delta_{kl}\tilde{\phi}_{l'}$, where

$$\delta = \begin{pmatrix} 0 & -1 & 0 & 0 \\ 1 & 0 & 0 & 0 \\ 0 & 0 & 0 & 1 \\ 0 & 0 & -1 & 0 \end{pmatrix},$$

so that (15) becomes

$$-4\pi g' \sum_{k,\,l=1}^{4} \tilde{\psi}_k \delta_{kl} \tilde{\phi}_{l'}. \tag{16}$$

From equations (13) and (15), we obtain for the matrix element of the interaction energy of the heavy particle and the light particle an expression

$$gg' \int \dots \int \tilde{v}(r_1) u(r_1) \sum_{k=1}^{4} \tilde{\psi}_k(r_2) \phi_k(r_2) \frac{e^{-\lambda r_{12}}}{r_{12}} dv_1 dv_2, \tag{17}$$

corresponding to the following double process: a heavy particle falls from the neutron state with the eigenfunction $u(r)$ into the proton state with the eigenfunction $v(r)$ and simultaneously a light particle jumps from the neutrino state $\phi_k(r)$ of negative energy to the electron state $\psi_k(r)$ of positive energy. In (17) λ is taken instead of μ, since the difference of energies of the neutron state and the proton state, which is equal to the sum of the upper limit of the energy spectrum of β-rays and the proper energies of the electron and the neutrino, is always small compared with $m_U c^2$.

As λ is much larger than the wave numbers of the electron state and the neutrino state, the function $\dfrac{e^{-\lambda r_{12}}}{r_{12}}$ can be regarded approximately as a δ-function multiplied by $\dfrac{4\pi}{\lambda^2}$ for the integrations with respect to x_2, y_2, z_2. The factor $\dfrac{4\pi}{\lambda^2}$ comes from

$$\iiint \frac{e^{-\lambda r_{12}}}{r_{12}} dv_2 = \frac{4\pi}{\lambda^2}.$$

Hence (17) becomes

$$\frac{4\pi gg'}{\lambda^2} \iiint \tilde{v}(r) u(r) \sum_{k} \tilde{\psi}_k(r) \phi_k(r) dv \tag{18}$$

or by (16)

$$\frac{4\pi gg'}{\lambda^2} \int \int \int \tilde{v}(r)u(r) \sum_{k,\,l} \tilde{\psi}(r)\delta_{kl}'\tilde{\phi}_l'(r)dv, \qquad (19)$$

which is the same as the expression (21) of Fermi, corresponding to the emission of a neutrino and an electron of positive energy states $\phi_k'(r)$ and $\psi_k(r)$, except that the factor $\dfrac{4\pi gg'}{\lambda^2}$ is substituted for Fermi's g.

Thus the result is the same as that of Fermi's theory, in this approximation, if we take

$$\frac{4\pi gg'}{\lambda^2} = 4 \times 10^{-50} \text{ cm}^3 \cdot \text{erg},$$

from which the constant g' can be determined. Taking, for example, $\lambda = 5 \times 10^{12}$ and $g = 2 \times 10^{-9}$, we obtain $g' \cong 4 \times 10^{-17}$, which is about 10^{-8} times as small as g.

This means that the interaction between the neutrino and the electron is much smaller than that between the neutron and the proton so that the neutrino will be far more penetrating than the neutron and consequently more difficult to observe. The difference of g and g' may be due to the difference of masses of heavy and light particles.

SUMMARY

The interactions of elementary particles are described by considering a hypothetical quantum which has the elementary charge and the proper mass and which obeys Bose's statistics. The interaction of such a quantum with the heavy particle should be far greater than that with the light particle in order to account for the large interaction of the neutron and the proton as well as the small probability of β-disintegration.

Such quanta, if they ever exist and approach the matter close enough to be absorbed, will deliver their charge and energy to the latter. If, then, the quanta with negative charge come out in excess, the matter will be charged to a negative potential.

These arguments, of course, of merely speculative character, agree with the view that the high speed positive particles in the cosmic rays are generated by the electrostatic field of the earth, which is charged to a negative potential.

The massive quanta may also have some bearing on the shower produced by cosmic rays.

NEWER DEVELOPMENTS IN ATOMIC AND NUCLEAR THEORY

81

ooooooooooo

MESONS

ooooooooooo

Cecil Frank Powell (b. 1903)

The problem of determining the nature of nuclear forces, that is, the forces acting between two protons or neutrons, was extremely important for understanding the structure of nuclei and of high-energy processes. Certain elementary facts were already known about these forces before the discovery of the way in which nucleons actually interact. Nuclear forces operate only at extremely short ranges: they are practically zero when the distance between the two interacting nucleons exceeds one trillionth of a centimeter, and they are very strong. Because of these properties, physicists reasoned that the nuclear force field (the medium through which the force is transmitted from one nucleon to the other) must consist of massive particles that are tossed back and forth between the two nucleons.

We have already seen that this idea was the basis of Yukawa's theory of nuclear forces. In analogy with the emission and absorption of photons by electrons and protons, Yukawa pictured nucleons as emitting and absorbing massive particles (the quanta of the nuclear force field). From his theory he calculated a mass of about 150 times that of the electron for these massive quanta, and showed that two nucleons tossing such particles back and forth would exert just the kind of forces on one another that are demanded by the stability and other observed properties of nuclei.

After Yukawa had published his paper, physicists began to look around for these heavy quanta, or mesons, as they were called. Since these massive intermediate particles can come into being only if energy equivalent to their own mass is available (according to Einstein's formula $E = mc^2$), physicists naturally looked to cosmic rays for such particles. Cosmic rays enter the earth's atmosphere with vast amounts of energy and should therefore, on occasion, create mesons from their own store of energy.

1431

Intermediate particles, which seemed to have the desired Yukawa properties, were discovered between 1936 and 1938 by Anderson, Neddermeyer, and others. These particles, which exhibit all the properties of electrons except that they are about 200 times more massive, were called mu-mesons (they are now called muons).

At first physicists thought that these were just the heavy quanta which would account for the strong, short-range nuclear forces, because it had been observed that the mu-mesons decay into electrons and neutrinos, as demanded by the Yukawa theory. However, the lifetimes of these particles were found to be about twenty times longer than the theory predicted. This was the first indication that the mu-mesons might not be the heavy nuclear force quanta. Moreover, only positive and negative mu-mesons (both of the same mass) were found, the former decaying into positrons and the latter into electrons. This was another drawback, since one would also require neutral mu-mesons (of the same mass as the charged mesons) to account for the nuclear forces between protons and between neutrons, which are the same as the nuclear forces between a neutron and a proton.

Finally (and this was the telling argument against the mu-meson), experimental physicists found that these particles interact only very weakly with nuclei. If they were the quanta required by the Yukawa theory, they should have been absorbed very strongly by nuclei. Instead, they tended to move in orbits around nuclei for their entire lifetimes (about two millionths of a second) before decaying. During this time, even though they were close to the nucleus, they scarcely interacted with it (except for the Coulomb electrostatic interaction). If the mu-mesons were the Yukawa quanta, they should have been captured by nuclei, which would have disintegrated in the process. Since this does not occur, physicists rejected the Yukawa-quantum role for the mu-mesons and began to seek other heavy particles in cosmic rays.

It soon became clear from further analyses of cosmic-ray events that other mesons are present in cosmic rays, and that these do, indeed, cause the disintegration of nuclei when they are brought to rest in various substances. Such disintegration can be observed because in the process slow protons, neutrons, α particles, and other nuclear remnants are emitted. Furthermore, it was found that these very mesons at times decay spontaneously, in about three one-hundred millionths of a second, with the emission of slower secondary particles; these secondaries were observed to have all the properties of mu-mesons. From all of this, it is clear that there are two mesons in cosmic rays, one of which we may call the primary, or pi-meson, and the other the mu-meson. Today we refer only to the pi-meson (or pion) as a meson, and classify the mu-meson with the electron and the neutrino to form the group that is called the leptons.

The pion has the very properties required by a Yukawa heavy quantum: its mass is about 273 times that of the electron (the mass of the muon is about 207 electron-masses); the pion has a very short lifetime; it causes the disintegration of a nucleus when close enough to it. Moreover, direct cosmic-ray evidence shows that pions are ejected from nuclei when the latter disintegrate after collisions with very energetic protons (the primary particles in cosmic rays). Then the negatively charged pions (the secondary particles in cosmic rays) disrupt other nuclei in their paths as they come to rest, showing that they interact very strongly with nuclei. Neutral pi-mesons, as well as negatively and positively charged pi-mesons, have been discovered. Thus, the pions are, indeed, the carriers of the force field between nucleons postulated and described by Yukawa.

Powell's account of the discovery of the mu- and pi-mesons is included in this chapter. In 1947 he and Occhialini discovered pion tracks on special photographic plates exposed to cosmic rays. Powell received the Nobel Prize in 1950 for developing special photographic techniques for the study of cosmic rays and applying the techniques to the analysis of mesons found in such rays.

Cecil Frank Powell was born on December 5, 1903, at Tonbridge in Kent, England, where his father's family had long been gunsmiths. Powell showed his intellectual aptitude quite early by winning a scholarship at the age of eleven to the Judd School in Tonbridge, where he excelled in mathematics and the sciences.

On leaving the Judd School Powell won an open scholarship to the Sidney Sussex College, Cambridge, where he continued his scientific studies, and from which he graduated in 1924 at the head of his class, with highest honors in science. By this time he had decided to become a physicist; he went on to do graduate work at the Cavendish Laboratory under C. T. R. Wilson and Lord Rutherford, receiving his Ph.D. in 1927. During this period Powell developed the interests that ultimately led to his discovery of the pi-meson and the Nobel Prize in physics. Stimulated by his work with Wilson, he developed an interest in improved techniques for tracking particles that might be used in cosmic-ray studies during balloon flights. Upon receiving his doctorate, Powell moved to the University of Bristol as research assistant to A. M. Tyndall, in the H. H. Wills Physical Laboratory, and was subsequently appointed lecturer and then reader in physics. For a time he became engrossed in the physics of earthquakes and spent the year 1936 as a seismologist with an expedition that was studying quakes in the West Indies.

When he returned to Bristol, Powell began work on a Cockcroft generator for accelerating protons and deuterons to very high speeds in order to study the scattering of neutrons by protons. Although he used the

Wilson cloud chamber to detect the scattered particles, he was not satisfied with it and sought better techniques for discerning the charged particles and measuring the lengths of their tracks. Photographic emulsions had been used early in the twentieth century to detect emanations from radioactive elements. Yet few nuclear physicists resorted to photographic techniques because they appeared to be less reliable than the cloud-chamber method and more difficult to interpret. Moreover, the photographic plates required special sensitizing in order to react to swift particles, and plates of varying sensitivity had to be used for different particles. In 1935, Zhadanov, in Leningrad, and the Ilford Laboratories in England, independently produced emulsions that could detect fast protons without previous sensitization.

One advantage of a photographic emulsion over the cloud chamber is that the emulsion detects and tracks charged particles continuously; the cloud chamber does so only momentarily, while it is expanding. Therefore, a particle like a meson, which has a very short life, can be overlooked in the cloud chamber. Moreover, the length of the track in the cloud chamber is not related in any simple way to the energy of the incident particle, whereas the length of the track in the emulsion gives an accurate measure of its energy. With these things in mind, Powell applied photographic techniques more and more extensively to nuclear research. Between 1939 and 1945 he had perfected photographic emulsions to such an extent that their superiority over the cloud chamber was undisputable.

During this same period, Powell decided to use his photographic techniques in conjunction with balloon flights to study cosmic rays. In 1947, plates with a new emulsion that Powell had developed the year before were exposed to cosmic radiation on Pic du Midi, 2,800 meters above sea level. A study of the tracks on these plates led Powell and G. P. S. Occhialini to announce the discovery of the pi-meson—the particle needed to explain nuclear forces as predicted by the theory of Yukawa. The chance of detecting such a particle by a cloud chamber is extremely slight because its rate of decay in flight is most rapid. However, in an emulsion, such a particle can be brought to rest before decay takes place, thus enabling the interactions with atomic nuclei to be observed.

In 1948, following his discovery of the pi-meson, Powell was appointed Melville Wills professor of physics at Bristol, where he still carries on his research and teaching activities. From 1952 to 1957 he was director of various European expeditions for making high-altitude balloon flights in Sardinia and in the Po Valley. Powell has done research in many fields and has written extensively on the discharge of electricity through gases, as well as on nuclear physics, cosmic rays, and photographic techniques. He is a fellow of the Royal Society and a foreign member of the Academy of Sciences of the USSR. In 1961 he was awarded the Hughes and the Royal medals. The universities of Dublin, Bordeaux, and Warsaw have awarded him honorary Doctor of Science degrees. Since 1932, Powell has been married to Isobel Therese Artner, who has assisted him in his research.

ଦଠଠଠଠଠ

P O W E L L

Mesons [1]

INTRODUCTION

THE PREVIOUS REPORTS IN THIS series which bear on the subject of mesons were written by Heitler (1939) and Peierls (1940), and contained an account of the main features of our knowledge of these particles up to the end of 1939. Since that date, and especially in the past four years, there has been a rapid development of the subject; and to-day, although many points of detail remain to be elucidated, it seems reasonable to suppose that the most important facts—at least about the most common of the different types of mesons—have been established, and that the relationship of the particles to the cosmic radiation is well understood.

In giving an account of the discoveries of the last ten years I propose to begin with a brief historical survey of the main line of development, then to discuss in more detail the properties of the π- and μ-mesons, together with the evidence for the existence of other types, and finally, to give an account of our present picture of the principal processes associated with the creation of mesons which take place as a result of the passage of cosmic radiation through the atmosphere.

A part of decisive importance in the extension of our knowledge of mesons has been played by the development of new technical resources: the method of recording the tracks of charged particles as a result of their passage through photographic emulsions. Apart from the well-known features of the method—its simplicity and flexibility, the "integrating" property of the emulsion due to its continuous sensitivity, and the direct and detailed insight into nuclear processes which it allows—it has the advantage of providing a remarkably extended time-scale for the study of

---

[1] C. F. Powell, *Reports on Progress in Physics*, 13 (1950), 350–384. Reprinted by permission of The Institute of Physics and The Physical Society.

certain types of transient phenomena. In particular, particles of very short life-time, such as the π-mesons, which commonly decay "in flight" when moving in the atmosphere, are arrested in a solid material in a time interval more than a thousand times shorter than when moving in a gas. It is thus possible to study the spontaneous decay of the particles when stopped in an emulsion, or their interaction with nuclei, and thus to observe phenomena which it has proved very difficult, or impossible, to record by other methods.

Because of the important rôle which it has played, an account of the results obtained with the new method necessarily forms an important part of the present report. It is an interesting feature of the historical development of the subject that the π-mesons were discovered very shortly after the development of those technical resources necessary for their observation.

HISTORICAL SURVEY

The "Heavy Quanta" of Yukawa

The idea that there should exist in nature particles with a mass intermediate between that of the proton and that of the electron first appeared, in 1935, as a result of theoretical speculations by Yukawa. It had been known for some years that the forces between the nucleons of a nucleus—the protons and the neutrons of which it is composed—cannot be electromagnetic in origin. The observed degree of stability of the nuclei can only be accounted for if it is assumed that special forces of a new type—the nuclear forces—come into play between the nucleons, forces which we do not meet in other fields.

Further, it had been shown, as a result of accurate determinations of the masses of the nuclei, that the energy which has to be supplied in order to remove a nucleon from a nucleus—the "binding-energy" per nucleon—does not change widely in passing from the light to the heavy elements of the Periodic Table. It follows that the nuclear forces are of "short range," that they vary with the distance between two nucleons more rapidly than in the case of forces governed by an inverse-square law.

Proceeding from these facts, and on the basis of a formal analogy described in detail in the previous Reports, Yukawa concluded that free "quanta" should exist corresponding to the nuclear field analogous to the photons of the electromagnetic field, that they should have a finite rest-mass of about 150 m_e, where m_e is the mass of the electron, and that they should be unstable and decay with the emission of an electron, the lifetime of the particles being about 10^{-7} sec. Just as the electromagnetic field of an electron can be regarded, in the quantum theory of radiation, as equivalent to the emission of photons, and the force between two electrons as due to a mutual emission and absorption of photons, so the forces of nuclear cohesion between nucleons was attributed by Yukawa to the "virtual" exchange of charged quanta between the neutrons and protons in a nucleus.

The hypothetical "heavy quanta" of the nuclear field were thus visualized as differing in important respects from photons. In the first place, the finite rest-mass of the particles was a necessary consequence of the short-range character of the nuclear forces. Secondly, since the continuous exchange of "quanta" between the neutrons and protons in a nucleus was assumed to be accompanied by an exchange of charge, the neutrons becoming protons and vice versa, it was assumed that, at least in some cases, the "quanta" carry a positive or negative electric charge. And thirdly, the assumption of the instability of the particles was introduced in order to account for the β-activity of radioactive substances; the process of nuclear decay being attributed to the spontaneous disintegration of the charged "quanta" into electrons and neutrinos.

In addition to the charged quanta, it appeared necessary to postulate the existence of neutral particles of a similar type in order to account for the forces between like nucleons: between neutrons and neutrons, protons and protons. These forces are known to be of the same order of magnitude as those between protons and neutrons; and, if they have a similar origin, the particles involved in the exchange must be electrically neutral. In what follows it will be convenient to refer to these hypothetical "quanta," both charged and neutral, as Yukawa particles.

The actual emission of the particles from stable nuclei was not to be expected because such processes are energetically impossible, but in the nuclear collisions involving particles of great energy which occur in the cosmic radiation it was anticipated that such a limitation would not be present.

Discovery of the μ-Mesons

What appeared to be a remarkable verification of the correctness of Yukawa's speculations was provided by observations of Anderson and Neddermeyer and of other workers, including Street and Stevenson, in experiments on the nature of particles in the cosmic radiation in the years 1936–8. This radiation can be divided, phenomenologically, into two components with different absorption coefficients in matter. The "soft" component, which is rapidly absorbed in lead, is responsible for the well-known phenomena of the "cascade showers" commonly studied with Wilson expansion-chambers and counters, and was known to be due to photons and electrons. Anderson showed that among the particles of the "hard" or penetrating component there were present particles of mass about 200 m_e, which were able, unlike the electrons, to penetrate many centimeters of lead without losing a large fraction of their energy by the well-known process of "bremsstrahlung." These particlular particles are now commonly referred to as μ-mesons, and the latest measurements of their mass give the value of $(215 \pm 5)m_e$.

The view that the μ-mesons were to be identified with the particles of Yukawa was strengthened by observations which suggested that they are unstable and that they decay with a life-time of about $1 \cdot 5 \times 10^{-6}$ sec., a value only about ten times greater than that anticipated by Yukawa. Further, it was found possible to modify some of the original features of the theory, and thus to account for the magnetic moments of the proton and the neutron and for certain features of the states of energy of the light nuclei, notably the ground and first excited states of the deuteron.

These remarkable successes encouraged the hope that the fundamental features of Yukawa's views were substantially correct, that the μ-mesons were to be identified with the Yukawa particles, and that it would be possible to elaborate the theory to provide a firm basis for the description of the main features of the atomic nuclei and of nuclear collision processes. These hopes were reflected in the previous Reports, but already certain serious theoretical difficulties were beginning to emerge.

The Fate of the μ-Mesons

The original estimates of the life-time of the μ-mesons were based on the observation that the reduction in the intensity of a stream of these particles in the atmosphere depends not only on the mass (gm/cm^2) of material traversed, but on the length of the path in which the matter is distributed. The penetration of a given mass of air produces a greater diminution of intensity the lower the density. This effect could only be interpreted by assuming that the removal of mesons by interaction with atoms is accompanied by a spontaneous decay of the particles, the latter process becoming increasingly probable the greater the time of flight.

Decisive support for the view that the μ-mesons do indeed suffer spontaneous decay with the emission of a charged particle of small rest-mass, tentatively assumed to be an electron, was provided by experiments of Williams and Roberts. These workers obtained two photographs, by means of a Wilson chamber operated in a magnetic field, of penetrating particles which, after passing through a lead plate, reached the end of their range in the gas of the chamber. From the end of the resultant track a fast particle originated which had a specific ionization near the minimum value for a particle with the elementary electronic charge, and of which the momentum, as determined by the observed curvature of the trajectory in the magnetic field, was equal to 70 ± 35 Mev/c.

The observed specific ionization of the decay particle showed that it was ejected with a velocity closely approaching that of light, c. It therefore followed that its kinetic energy E was approximately equal to pc, where p is the momentum of the particle, and that the energy of the particle was of the order of 50 MeV. This result suggested that in the spontaneous decay of the μ-meson the momentum of the emitted charged particle is balanced by that of a single neutral particle of small rest-mass, a neutrino; for in such a case the total energy corresponding to the disappearance of the rest-mass of the present meson, ~ 100 MeV., will be shared equally between the two products into which it decays, and the energy of emission of the electron will be unique and equal to approximately 50 MeV. We shall see in a later paragraph that this conclusion was incorrect.

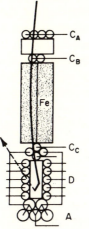

Fig. 81–1. A characteristic modern design of apparatus for the determination of the life time of +ve or −ve μ-mesons. The two halves of the block of iron are magnetized so that in each case the magnetic intensity is normal to the plane of the paper; but in one half the intensity is directed outward from the paper, and the other half, into it. This arrangement serves to concentrate particles of one sign. Those particles are selected which discharge a counter in C_A, C_B, and C_C and which do not discharge counters A. Such particles have been arrested in the absorber, and the time interval is measured between their instant of arrival and the subsequent discharge of a counter of the set D. The distribution in the values of this time interval gives a measure of the half-value period of the particles. By reversing the magnetic fields, particles of opposite sign can be collected.

A more direct and precise determination of the life-time of the μ-mesons was carried out by Rasetti, and later, with great accuracy, by Rossi and Nereson and Chaminade *et al.,* by the method of "delayed coincidences." In principle, the method consisted in detecting, by suitable arrays of counters, the instants of arrival of μ-mesons of the cosmic radiation [Fig. 81–1]. The apparatus selects those particles which, having penetrated a thick layer of lead, are brought to rest in a second block of material; and the time interval is measured between the instant of arrest of a μ-meson and the subsequent discharge of another set of counters by the action of the charged particle which is emitted in the process of decay. The distribution in the observed values of the time delay was found to be similar to that expected from the exponential law of decay characteristic of radioactive substances. The mean life-time of the particles, according to the latest determinations by this method, is $2 \cdot 15 \times 10^{-6}$ sec.

Hitherto, the results of most of the new experiments had given support for Yukawa's speculations. It was, however, difficult to understand why experiments with Wilson chambers indicated that μ-mesons interact very rarely with nuclei in passing through matter. Further difficulties began to appear when observations to distinguish the properties of positive and negative μ-mesons were undertaken.

It had been suggested by Tomonaga and Araki that when a positive μ-meson is brought to rest in a material we must assume that it will be prevented from approaching a nucleus as a result of the Coulomb repulsion between like charges, and will remain free until the instant of its decay. On the other hand, the electrostatic forces will tend to make the negative particles approach nuclei. It was anticipated that if the spin of the particles is equal to that of an electron, they will fall to states of lower energy round the nucleus, the transitions being accompanied by the emission of radiation or of Auger electrons. As a result of the much greater mass of the particles as compared with that of the electron, they will, in their state of lowest energy, be two hundred times nearer to the nucleus than an electron in its "K-orbit"; and when in this state they will spend an appreciable fraction of their time in the nucleus itself. In accordance with these anticipations, both Rasetti and Rossi found that only about half the mesons arrested in their apparatus gave evidence of decay.

In order to confirm the view that the μ^--particles do indeed interact with nuclei when arrested in solid substances before they have had time to decay, experiments were therefore undertaken by Conversi, Pancini and Piccioni. Delayed coincidence experiments were made with positive and negative μ-particles, the two types being separated from one another by magnetic deflection before being allowed to enter the recording apparatus. When the particles were brought to rest in iron, it was found, in accordance with anticipation, that the positive mesons decayed with a life-time equal to that found for the undifferentiated particles, whilst the negative particles disappeared wihout giving rise to a decay electron.

The above result was at variance with observations by Auger, Maze and Chaminade which indicated that nearly all the negative mesons arrested in aluminium suffer decay. Although this result was subsequently found to be incorrect, the experiments described above were extended to the case in which the μ-particles were arrested in a block of material of low atomic number, and for this purpose graphite was chosen. The remarkable result was obtained that in carbon at least a large proportion of the μ^--particles decay with the emission of an electron.

The time occupied by a meson after being reduced to a velocity in the "thermal" region in falling to the state of lowest energy round a nucleus has been subject to some discussion and will, it appears, depend on the nature of the material in which it is moving; but it was generally considered to be less than about 10^{-12} sec. It was therefore anticipated that such a particle, when brought to rest in solid materials, would approach a nucleus in a time short compared with its life-time. If, further, the μ-mesons are to be identified as the "heavy quanta" of the nuclear field, such a particle should interact with the nucleus, and the probability of its suffering spontaneous decay should be very small. There was no firm basis for estimating the consequences of this nuclear interaction; whether the disappearance of the particle and the resultant liberation of the energy corresponding to its rest-mass would lead to the emission of γ-radiation, to the disintegration of the nucleus, or to other processes, remained uncertain.

In view of these considerations, the experiments of Conversi *et al.* were of decisive importance, for they appeared irreconcilable with the view that the μ-mesons are to be identified with the Yukawa particles. They indicated that in the process of interaction with carbon, a μ^--particle can reside in its k-orbit for a period of the order of 2×10^{-6} sec. without interacting with the nucleus. The conclusion was drawn that the strength of the interaction between μ-particles and nucleons is less, by many orders of magnitude, than that to be expected if the μ-mesons are identified with the heavy quanta of the nuclear field. Some attempts were made to explain the difficulty by assuming that the time occupied by the particle in being brought to rest, and in falling to its state of lowest energy, is much greater than the first estimates had suggested; but whilst some doubt was thrown upon the precise values of this interval, it was made clear that it must be shorter, by some order of magnitude, than the life-times of the particles. A fundamental difficulty therefore remained to be resolved.

Even before the very serious nature of these difficulties had been widely understood, Sakata and Inoue had suggested that the cosmic-ray evidence appeared to indicate the existence of mesons of two types; and Möller, on the basis of very general theoretical considerations, had been led to postulate, tentatively, the existence of several kinds of particles of intermediate mass with genetical relationships between them. A little later, Marshak and Bethe, as a result of the contradiction between the large cross-section for the creation of mesons in nucleon-nucleon collisions, and the subsequent very weak interaction of the penetrating particles with nuclei, suggested that the primary products of the nuclear interactions taking place in the atmosphere are heavy mesons, and that these particles decay spontaneously, with a life-time of the order of 10^{-8} sec., to form the mesons commonly observed among the particles of the penetrating component.

Discovery of the π-Mesons

It was at this stage in the development of the subject that results were obtained in investigations of the cosmic radiation by means of the more sensitive photographic plates—the "Nuclear Research" emulsions produced by Ilford Ltd. It was shown by Perkins and by Occhialini and Powell that if such plates are exposed at mountain altitudes, the tracks of charged mesons brought to rest in the emulsion can be detected. The masses of the particles were estimated by "grain-counts" and by studying the deviations in the trajectories due to multiple Coulomb scattering, and were shown to be of the order of 200–300 m_e. It therefore appeared to be certain that some at least of these particles were identical with the μ-mesons of the penetrating component of the cosmic radiation.

The new plates, whilst greatly superior to the "half-tone" emulsions which they displaced, were not sufficiently sensitive to record the tracks of electrons moving at relativistic velocities, and it was therefore impossible to observe any fast decay particles emitted by the mesons at the end of their range. On the other hand, it was found that about 10% of the mesons, when stopped in the emulsion, led to a nuclear disintegration with the emission of slow protons, α-particles, etc. At the time that this observation was made, it was assumed that this process corresponded to the capture of a μ^--particle by a silver or bromine nucleus in the emulsion: that it was of the same type as that which, in heavier elements, leads to the disappearance of negative μ-mesons before they have had time to decay with the emission of an electron. It was shown later, however, that the mesons which produce nuclear disintegrations are not μ-particles.

Shortly after the observation of the nuclear disintegrations produced by charged mesons, it was discovered in Bristol that about 10% of the mesons, when brought to rest, lead to the emission of a second meson. Further, it was established that the range of the secondary particle is always constant within narrow limits. It was therefore reasonable to assume that it is always ejected with constant velocity, the departures of the individual values of the range from the mean being due to "straggling." This strongly suggested that the process corresponds to the spontaneous decay of the parent particle: that two types of mesons exist of different mass, the kinetic energy of the secondary mesons being provided by the disappearance of part of the rest-mass of the heavier, primary mesons. This was subsequently shown to be the case, and it was proved that the secondary mesons are identical with the μ-mesons of the penetrating component of the cosmic radiation. The heavier primary particles were therefore referred to as π-mesons, and their spontaneous transformation, by analogy with the β-decay, was named the μ-decay.

In addition to the isolated tracks of mesons, plates exposed to cosmic radiation were also found to record nuclear disintegrations from which mesons of low kinetic energy were emitted. A large proportion of these "ejected" mesons, at the end of their range, produce nuclear disintegrations. It was therefore suggested that they are the negative counterparts of the π-mesons, the latter being positively charged and thus unable to interact with nuclei when reduced to low velocities. It was suggested further that the positive and negative π-particles are the primary products of nuclear interactions of great energy occurring in the atmosphere; that being short-lived, however, they decay "in flight" and thus produce the positive and negative μ-mesons of the penetrating component of the cosmic radiation. Further experiments have shown that this view of the origin of the particles, and of their relationship to the cosmic radiation—closely similar to that put forward at the same time by Marshak and Bethe on the basis of other evidence—is substantially correct.

In the three years which have followed the discovery of the π-meson, great progress has been made in the detailed study of the properties of the particles: this development forms the subject of the second section of the report. The observations have been facilitated by the discovery, in Berkeley, of the artificial generation of the π-particles in the bombardment of matter by fast α-particles and protons, and the possibility of making experiments in controlled conditions in the laboratory.

Recent evidence appears to confirm earlier reports from a number of laboratories of the existence of particles of mass about 1,000 m_e which it is convenient to refer to as τ-mesons. The question of the existence of these particles may be of decisive importance for the development of a satisfactory theory of the mesons and of the nuclear forces, and to-day the elucidation of their nature and properties is one of the central problems of nuclear physics.

Nomenclature

Following the first observations of the tracks of mesons in photographic emulsions, and because of the difficulty of determining the mass and the sign of the charge of the particles, they were classified, phenomenologically, according to the secondary processes observed at the end of their range in the emulsion. A π-meson was defined as one which, when at rest, emits a second meson, μ, with a range of about 600 microns. Later experiments have now confirmed the original view that these particles are positively charged, and they will be referred to as π^+- and μ^+-particles, respectively.

Secondly, these mesons which produced an observable nuclear disintegration when stopped in the emulsion were referred to as σ-mesons. It is now known that they are exclusively, or almost exclusively, π^--particles which are captured by nuclei. The resulting nuclear disintegrations which produce tracks of charged particles radiating from a centre are commonly referred to as "stars." The individual tracks making up a "star" are sometimes called the "prongs."

Most of the mesons produced no secondary particles which could be observed in the most sensitive emulsions available in the early experiments, and were classed as ρ-mesons. It is now known that in "electron-sensitive" emulsions—which record the tracks of particles with the elementary electronic charge even when they are moving at relativistic velocities—about 65% of the ρ-mesons give evidence of decay with the emission of a fast electron. This fraction of the ρ-mesons is due mainly to μ^+-particles formed by the decay of π^+-particles outside the emulsion, and to μ^--particles—formed by the decay in flight of π^--particles—which have been captured by the light elements in the gelatine of the emulsion, carbon, oxygen and nitrogen. In addition, however, a small proportion of these ρ-mesons may be due to π^+-particles which have undergone direct β-decay.

Of the 35% of the ρ-mesons without associated electron tracks, the majority are due to μ^--particles which have been captured by the silver and bromine atoms of the emulsion. The particles interact with these nuclei before they have had time to decay, but no charged particles giving visible tracks are produced in the resulting transmutations. In addition, a small fraction of the ρ-mesons is due to π^--particles which have been captured by nuclei without leading to the production of a recognizable disintegration. Such events will occur if neutral particles alone are emitted in the nuclear transmutation resulting from the capture of the meson, as in the case, for example, when the π^--particle interacts with hydrogen.

In describing the properties of the different types of particles, the terms π^+- and π^-- particles or mesons, μ^+- and μ^--particles or mesons will be employed whenever possible, ρ-mesons or σ-mesons being referred to only when the precise nature of the particles under discussion is ambiguous.

Reference has already been made to the distinction between the "hard" and "soft" components of the cosmic radiation, and to the fact that the experiments of Blackett and Occhialini with the counter-controlled Wilson chamber showed that many particles of the "soft" component often arrive together in the form of the well-known "cascade showers," which are produced by the multiplication of an original energetic electron or γ-ray. On the other hand, the experiments of Wataghin, Jánossy and others have shown that the penetrating particles of the "hard" component, most of which we now know to be μ-mesons, can be produced in groups—the so-called "penetrating showers." It will be important, in certain sections of this report, to remember the distinction between the "showers" of the two types.

§3. MASS AND MODE OF DECAY OF THE π-MESONS

The Decay of π^+-Particles

When a positive π-meson is arrested in a solid material it decays spontaneously with the emission of a meson of smaller mass, a μ^+-particle [see Fig. 81–2]. The distribution in range of 90 μ-particles formed by the

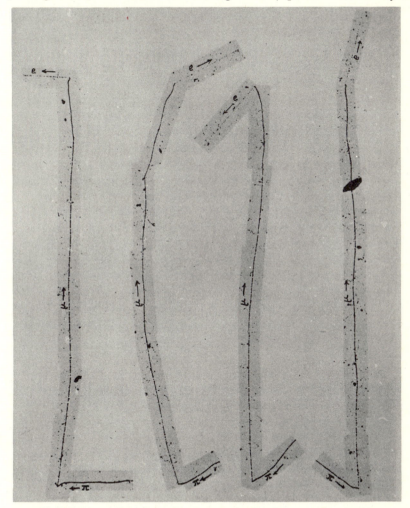

Fig. 81–2. Four examples of the successive decay $\pi \to \mu \to e$. The photomicrographs display the increase in the grain-density of the tracks of the μ-mesons as the particles approach the end of their range. The sparseness of the grains in the tracks of the electrons may be clearly seen.

decay of π^--particles stopped in Ilford C2 photographic emulsions is shown in [Fig. 81–3], the mean value being 612 microns. As mentioned above, the observed distribution is consistent with the assumption that the velocity of ejection of the μ-meson is constant within narrow limits. It follows that during the emission of the μ-meson the momentum balance is provided by the ejection of a single neutral particle. The question of the nature of this particle immediately arises: whether it is a photon, a neutrino, or a neutral particle of considerable rest-mass, i.e. a "neutretto." . . .

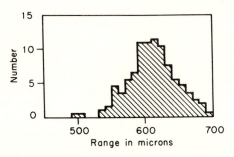

Fig. 81–3. Distribution in the values of the range in Ilford C2 emulsion of $90\mu^+$-particles produced by the decay of π^+-particles arrested in the emulsion. The observed spread is consistent with that expected from "straggling" if the particles are emitted with constant velocity and proves that a π^+-particle must commonly be moving with very low velocity at the instant of its decay. The mean value of the range is 612 μ, and the corresponding value of the kinetic energy $E\mu = 4.15$ Mev.

The Nature of the Neutral Particle Emitted during μ-Decay

Since an application of the conservation laws leads to the conclusion that the neutral particle providing the momentum and energy balance during the decay of a π-meson is of small or zero rest-mass, it may be assumed to be either a γ-ray or a neutrino. Recent observations by O'Ceallaigh (1950) provide strong evidence that the first of these possibilities can be excluded, and it is reasonable to regard the neutral particle as a "neutrino"; i.e. some form of neutral radiation of small or zero rest-mass.

Suppose the process of decay to be accompanied by the emission of a photon which recoils in the opposite direction of the μ-meson. The line of motion of the photon, and its energy $\sim$30 Mev., is defined. If, therefore, a search is made of "electron-sensitive" photographic plates in which the decay of π-mesons is recorded, it should be possible to observe pairs of electrons created by any photons recoiling from the μ-mesons. Photons of energy 30 Mev. produce pairs in photographic emulsions with a divergence of about 3°, and the bisector of the line of motion of the two electrons defines that of the parent photon within narrow limits. Further, in favourable cases, the Coulomb scattering of the electrons enables their energies to be determined, and thence the quantum energy of the photon. Because of these features it is possible to establish whether or not an observed pair has characteristics consistent with its having arisen during the decay of a neighbouring π-meson arrested in the emulsion, or whether it is due to a γ-ray not associated with the decay.

O'Ceallaigh has scrutinized the emulsion in the neighbourhood of π-mesons stopped in plates exposed to cosmic radiation and has found no pairs in a total length of path of the recoiling neutral particles of 38 cm. The conversion length of γ-radiation in the emulsion, for photons of energy equal to 30 Mev., is $6 \cdot 5$ cm. If the process of decay leads to the ejection of a photon, six pairs of electrons should have been observed in the conditions of the experiments, and the probability of observing none is $<0 \cdot 005$. It may therefore be concluded that the momentum balance is provided by a neutral radiation of a different type, by some form of neutrino.

It is well known that during the β-decay of radioactive nuclei there is a disappearance of energy which has been attributed by Fermi and by Pauli to the emission of a neutral particle of low rest-mass—a "neutrino." Further, experiments on the masses and the β-decay of certain of the light nuclei prove that if such particles exist their rest-mass must be less than $0 \cdot 1$ m_e. For some years it has been recognized that important evidence for the existence of the neutrino would be provided if it could be proved that the conservation of momentum, as well as that of mass-energy, required the assumption of the emission of such a neutral particle. A number of experimenters have therefore measured the recoil of the nucleus during β-decay, and have concluded that the results demonstrate the existence of a neutrino.

In the case of the decay of the π-mesons, the secondary charged particle, the μ-meson, is of small rest-mass compared with the atomic nuclei, and the energy of the recoiling neutral particle is large. The momentum and energy of the μ-meson can therefore be determined with precision. Since the possibility can now be excluded that the neutral particle providing the momentum balance is a photon, the observed values of the masses of the π- and μ-mesons and the characteristics of the μ-decay provide important additional evidence for some other form of neutral radiation—for the existence of some form of neutrino.

PROPERTIES OF THE π-MESONS

Charge of the π-Particles

Photomicrographs of examples of the successive decay of π-particles according to the scheme $\pi \rightarrow \mu \rightarrow e$ are shown in [Fig. 81–2]. If charge is to be conserved in these transmutations—and if no particles with a charge much smaller than that of the electron are emitted which escape observation—the charge on the three types of particles must be equal. If the final particle formed in the process of decay is indeed an electron, . . . the charge on the π- and μ-particles must be equal to the elementary electronic charge.

It has been pointed out by Bradner that the consistency between the values of the mass deduced by different methods provides a powerful demonstration that the charge on the π-mesons is very close to the electronic charge. In particular, he has shown that the observed degree of consistency of the measurements indicates that the charge on the π-particles is equal to that of the electron to within 3%.

Life-Time of the π-Particles

The most accurate determinations of the life-time of the π-mesons have been made at Berkeley by the method represented schematically in [Fig. 81–4]. Under the impact of fast α-particles, positive and negative π-mesons are created. Those of the negative π-mesons which emerge from the target in a suitable direction and with momenta in a narrow range of values spiral in the magnetic field in the channel cut in a solid block of metal and are recorded by one or other of two photographic plates [Fig. 81–4]. Because of the well-known "focusing effects" associated with the spiral trajectories of particles in a magnetic field—and in the absence of any spontaneous decay of the particles—the relative numbers recorded in these two plates, per unit area, will be inversely proportional to the lengths of path in the magnetic field, i.e. as 3 to 1 for the particular experimental arrangement shown in [Fig. 81–4]. If, however, the particles suffer decay in flight, the number reaching the plates will be reduced and the effect will be more marked the greater the length of path. There will therefore be departures from the simple ratio to be observed in the case of stable particles.

The method outlined above is practicable only if the life-time is of the same order of magnitude as the period of the motion, T, of the particles in the magnetic field. For particles of mass 275 m_e moving at right angles to a field of 15,000 gauss, $T \sim 10^{-8}$ sec., a value known to be close to that of the π-particles. The latest measurements by this method show that the life-time, τ_π, lies between the values $1 \cdot 4$ and $0 \cdot 9 \times 10^{-8}$ sec.

A determination of the life-time of the π-mesons of the cosmic radiation has also been made by Camerini et al., using a method based on the following considerations: at mountain altitudes (c. 11,000 ft.) the bombardment of matter by fast nucleons of the cosmic radiation stream leads to the creation of π-mesons of great energy. Some of these particles are emitted in the upward direction so that, in addition to the prominent downward flux of μ-mesons constituting the penetrating component, there is a weak upward-moving stream of mesons arising from the surface of the earth.

At their point of creation in the surface layers of the earth the mesons are made up, at least predominantly, of π-particles. As their time of flight increases, the initial stream of π-particles transforms spontaneously into a stream of μ-particles. Photographic plates were therefore exposed at 2 metres above the surface of the earth. Particles of the upward moving stream which stop in the emulsion are identified by the directions of the trajectories at their points of entry into the emulsion in which they are

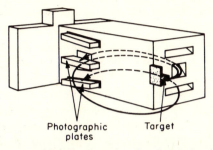

Photographic   Target
plates

Fig. 81–4. Apparatus of Richardson for the determination of the life time of the μ^+-particles generation artificially in the synchrocyclotron. In the absence of decay the numbers of particles per unit of either photographic plate should be inversely as the length of path to the corresponding plate, owing to the effects of semicircular focusing in one plane. The trajectory of the α-particle beam bombarding the target is not shown.

brought to rest. Further, mesons of different types can be distinguished by the secondary processes produced at the end of their range. A study could thus be made of the rate of transformation of the π-particles into μ-particles by determining the proportion of the two types at different heights above the ground. The value thus obtained for the life-time τ_π is $0 \cdot 6 \times 10^{-8}$ sec., a result consistent with that given by the more accurate methods available with artificially produced particles. . . .

Spin of the π^--Particles

It has been suggested by Wentzel that the π^--mesons created in the interaction with matter of a directed beam of fast nucleons might be "polarized": that there might be some degree of orientation of an axis of spin of the particles, with respect to the line of motion of the "primary" nucleons which produced them. Further, it is possible that if the particles are arrested in solid materials, the Coulomb forces brought into play in the atomic encounters which cause the particles to lose kinetic energy would not completely destroy the initial polarization. Such a polarization, if it exists, might be made manifest by privileged directions of emission of the μ^+-particles, created in the spontaneous decay of π^+-particles when at rest, with respect to the line of motion of the "primary" nucleons.

At mountain altitudes (11,000 ft.) the cosmic-ray stream contains a large proportion of protons and neutrons, most of which move down-wards in directions inclined at less than 40° to the vertical. In traversing photographic plates these particles produce nuclear explosions some of which are accompanied by the emission of π^+-mesons, and some of these particles stop in the emulsion. An examination of the directions of motion of the μ^+-particles emitted in the decay of π^+-particles can thus be made. It is found that the particles are emitted at all directions to the vertical and any departures from an isotropic distribution are small.

In the above experiment we are observing the decay of π-mesons which are emitted from nuclear explosions with a wide range of values of the kinetic energy. Further, in many cases the particles may have been pro-duced as one of a number of mesons created in a single nuclear event—as one of a penetrating shower. In these circumstances the absence of an observed anistropy is indecisive and no conclusions regarding the nature of the spin of the π-particles can be drawn from the experiments.

Similar conclusions have been drawn from preliminary experiments made with artificially produced π^+-particles by Richman et al.

Decisive evidence in support of the view commonly held that the π-mesons have spin zero or unity is provided by the experimental evidence of Panofsky et al. (1950) on the capture of π^--particles by protons and of the mode of disintegration of the resulting neutral mesons.

β-Decay of the π-Particles

The properties of the π-particles set out in the preceding sections are closely similar to those attributed to Yukawa particles, except that the for-mer commonly suffer μ-decay instead of β-decay. Observations have been made at Berkeley to determine whether the spontaneous transformation of a π-meson invariably leads to the emission of a μ-meson, or whether it sometimes undergoes β-decay. The proportion of the π^+-particles, identi-fied by their mass, which stop in the emulsion and emit a μ-meson, has been determined. . . .

The experimental results indicate that at least 95% of the π^+-particles undergo μ-decay, and not more than 5% direct β-decay. If therefore we assume that the π-meson can decay in either of two modes, we can set up an upper limit to the decay constant for the process, which leads to the emission of an electron, and an equivalent upper limit to the effective life-time. The result thus obtained is as follows:

$$\tau_\pi(\beta) > 20 \times 10^{-8} = 2 \times 10^{-7} \text{ sec.}$$

This value is very close to that postulated by Yukawa for the life-time, against β-decay, of his heavy quanta. . . .

82

oooooooooooo

THE ANTIPROTON

oooooooooooo

Emilio G. Segrè (. 1905)
Owen Chamberlain (b. 1920)

Dirac had predicted not only the antielectron (the positron) but also an antiproton. But to produce an antiproton would take vastly more energy than was available from the comparatively simple accelerators of the 1930's discussed in chapters 77 and 78. Indeed, the leading physics laboratories of the larger nations, such as the United States and the USSR, are testimony to the increasingly successful technology of atomism, which has produced more and more powerful particle accelerators—in 1946 the synchrocyclotron, built by the University of California, accelerated particles to energies of 200 to 400 million electron-volts (Mev). Later, larger synchrocyclotrons in the United States and in the USSR raised obtainable energies to 700 to 800 million electron-volts. Earlier versions of the Lawrence cyclotron had been unable to push particles beyond about 20 Mev, because at that energy the particles travel so fast that the mass increase with velocity became appreciable, as predicted by Einstein's special theory of relativity. This made the particles lag and fall out of phase with the electrical stimulus they received. To compensate, the synchrocyclotron synchronizes the alternations of the electric field with the increase in mass of the particles.

In 1955, with an accelerator that is called a Bevatron because it has been modified to elevate protons to energies measured in billions of electron volts, two California physicists, Emilio Segrè and Owen Chamberlain, succeeded in creating and identifying the antiproton. After bombarding copper with protons of 6.2 Bev hour after hour, they were able to identify some 250 antiprotons. It was not a simple matter to recognize them. For

1451

every antiproton they produced, some 40,000 particles of other types also came into existence. But an elaborate system of detectors, catalogued in the following paper, were so arranged and designed that only the antiproton could touch all the bases.

The antiproton is as unenduring as the positron. It is quickly snatched up by a normal, positively charged nucleus, where the antiproton and one of the resident protons annihilate one another. In those cases where proton and antiproton pass close by, but do not collide, an antineutron is produced from the antiproton through the neutralization of its charge, the proton itself becoming a neutron.

For their work, Segrè and Chamberlain received the Nobel Prize in physics in 1959.

In 1926 the new Italian school of physics at the University of Rome, of which Senator O. M. Corbino, professor of experimental physics and director of the Physics Institute at the university had dreamed for many years, consisted of one man, Enrico Fermi. Corbino had succeeded in having a chair of theoretical physics established at Rome and had staunchly and successfully supported Fermi's candidacy, but one man, even a Fermi, does not make a school. Consequently, Corbino, when he became acquainted with Rasetti, who had become a friend of Fermi's when they were high-school students together in Pisa, induced Rasetti to transfer from Florence to Rome. With two such members in his school Corbino was greatly encouraged; one morning in June 1927 he announced to his undergraduate class in electricity for engineers that he was looking for one or two outstanding students who were interested in transferring from engineering to physics. He recruited no engineering students, but his glowing account of the great excitement to be found in the pursuit of modern physics induced a student of mathematics, Edoardo Amaldi, the son of a professor of mathematics, to switch to physics. Corbino's class in electricity was designed not only for engineers, but for all other science students not studying physics, so that mathematicians and chemists also attended the course. On the day of Corbino's appeal one of the chemistry students who was in attendance was Laura Capon, who already knew Fermi quite well and was to become his wife a year later.

A fourth member of Corbino's "boys," as his recruits were soon to become known, was Emilio Segrè, who had started out as an engineering student at the University of Rome in 1922, but had not heard of Corbino's appeal and came into the group through his friendship with Rasetti. Segrè was born in Tivoli, Rome, on February 1, 1905, the son of the industrialist Giuseppe Segrè and Amelia Treves. While studying engineering at Rome, he became acquainted with G. Enriques, the son of an outstanding Italian mathematician, and through Enriques he met Rasetti, who aroused his interest in physics. Even before this meeting, Segrè had heard some lectures by Fermi in 1925 and was greatly impressed by the beauty of the new physics as revealed by Fermi. However, it was only after many mountain-climbing discussions with Rasetti that Segrè learned enough about the new physical theories to begin to think of physics as a career.

During the summer of 1927 he came to know Fermi personally and through conversations with him saw that physics was more to his liking than engineering. However, he was not yet entirely convinced. Segrè began reading physics books in earnest during this period; in September 1927 he accompanied Fermi and Rasetti to the international conference at Como where he had the unforgettable experience of meeting great physicists he had read about, such as Lorentz, Rutherford, Planck, Bohr, as well as a group of much younger men, including Heisenberg, Pauli, and Fermi.

In November of that year Segrè began studying physics under Fermi as a fourth-year student and in 1928 received his doctorate, the first to be awarded under Fermi's sponsorship. Segrè interrupted his academic career to serve in the Italian army for one year, but returned to the University of Rome in 1929 to become an assistant to Professor Corbino. Although the theoretical part of the physics program under Fermi was progressing nicely, the experimental work was still weak. To strengthen this part of the program and to import more advanced experimental techniques, Rasetti and Segrè each spent a period abroad. Rasetti went to Millikan's laboratory in Pasadena, California, where he worked on the Raman effect, and Segrè went to Hamburg as a Rockefeller Foundation fellow to study with Otto Stern. He also worked for a short period with Professor Pieter Zeeman in Amsterdam.

In 1932 Segrè returned to Italy to become assistant professor of physics at the University of Rome, where he remained until 1936, working in nuclear physics with Fermi, Rasetti, Amaldi, and D'Agostino, who was the fifth of Corbino's "boys."

In 1936 Segrè was appointed director of the Physics Laboratory at the University of Palermo, where he remained until 1938. The collaboration between Hitler and Mussolini and the racial laws adopted by the Fascist regime made it impossible for him to remain in Italy. In 1938 he left to become a research associate at the University of California Radiation Laboratory in Berkeley and then a lecturer in the physics department there. From 1943 to 1946 he was a group leader at the Los Alamos division of the Manhattan Project. He returned to the University of California in 1946 as professor of physics and has remained in this post since that time.

During his career, Segrè has contributed to various fields of physics, including atomic spectroscopy, the Zeeman effect, molecular beams, neutron physics, nuclear fission, and elementary particle physics. He has also done important work in radio chemistry and collaborated in the discovery of the elements technetium, astatine, and plutonium-239.

At various times in his academic career he has taught at Columbia University, the University of Illinois, and at Rio de Janeiro. For his important contributions to physics, Segrè has been awarded numerous honors in addition to the Nobel Prize. He is a member of the National Academy of Sciences and of various foreign academies.

He is married and has a son and two daughters.

Owen Chamberlain was born on July 10, 1920, in San Francisco, California, and grew up in a physics-oriented atmosphere. His father, a prominent radiologist who was greatly interested in physics, stimulated his son's natural talents in this field, so that when Owen entered Dartmouth College in 1937 he was firmly committed to becoming a research physicist. After receiving his bachelor's degree in 1941, he entered the University of California to do graduate work in physics; but his studies were interrupted by World War II, and he joined the Manhattan Project to work on the atomic bomb.

He began this work at Berkeley, California, under Professor Emilio Segrè and then went on to Los Alamos where he investigated the nuclear capture and scattering cross-sections of intermediate energy neutrons. He also studied the spontaneous fission of heavy nuclei.

After the war Chamberlain continued his graduate studies under Enrico Fermi at the University of Chicago and was awarded his Ph.D. degree in 1949 for experimental work on the diffraction of slow neutrons by liquids. In 1948, after he had completed his experimental work under Fermi, he accepted a teaching post at the University of California in Berkeley and began a series of experiments in collaboration with Professor Segrè. Although these experiments dealt primarily with the scattering of protons by protons, they prepared the way for the discovery of the antiproton in 1955 for which he and Segrè won the Nobel Prize in 1959. Since that time Chamberlain has investigated the interaction of antiprotons with hydrogen and deuterium. He has also studied the production of antineutrons from antiprotons and the scattering of pions.

Chamberlain is a fellow of the American Physical Society and a member of the National Academy of Sciences. In 1957 he was a Guggenheim fellow at the University of Rome and in 1959 he was Loeb lecturer at Harvard University. In 1958 he was appointed professor of physics at the University of California in Berkeley and has retained this post since then.

He married Beatrice Babette Copper in 1943. They have three daughters and one son.

In our discussion of Dirac's relativistic theory of the electron, we pointed out that his equations have two sets of solutions: one gives the motion of an ordinary positive-energy electron and the other describes electrons in states of negative energy. These two sets arise because the theory of relativity leads to an equation which relates the square of the energy, and *not* the energy itself, to the momentum and mass of a particle. To obtain the energy one has to take the square root of this relativistic expression and, as we know, a square root can be either positive or negative. In nonquantum, relativistic mechanics the negative square root is neglected because electrons with negative energy are not observed and have no meaning, but we cannot neglect the negative-energy states of an electron in quantum mechanics because electrons in states of positive energy must jump down into these negative-energy states with the emission of radiation. Thus, according to the Dirac theory, all the observable (that is, positive-energy) electrons would jump down into the states of negative energy if these were empty. To prevent this, Dirac proposed the idea that all the negative-energy states–an infinite number in each volume element of space–are filled with negative-energy electrons. The Pauli exclusion principle prevents the ordinary electrons from jumping down to states of negative energy and thus destroying the universe.

This very imaginative theory was not taken seriously until C. D. Anderson discovered the positron, which has all the properties of a *hole* in Dirac's infinite sea of negative-energy electrons. We know today that if enough energy—about one million volts—is supplied to a Dirac negative-energy electron under the proper conditions, it can be lifted to a state of positive energy, leaving a hole so that a pair is thus created. The electron itself—being in a state of positive energy—now behaves like an ordinary negatively charged particle with positive energy, and the hole, being the absence of negative charge and negative energy, behaves like a particle of positive charge and positive energy.

With Anderson's experimental verification of Dirac's theory of holes, physicists surmised that protons should also exist in states of negative energy and that a hole in this infinite sea of negative-energy protons should be detectable as a negatively charged particle with a mass of the proton. This particle, which was discovered in 1955 by E. Segrè and O. Chamberlain, and for which they received the Nobel Prize in 1959, is now known as the antiproton. Physicists believed in the existence of an antiproton before its discovery because an ordinary proton is governed by the same relativistic equations as an electron. Hence, a proton is described by the same multiplicity of wave functions as an electron, so that negative-energy states of protons must also exist. From this, the existence of antiprotons follows immediately.

Although the theory of the antiproton is quite straightforward, and quite similar to that of the positron, the discovery or the creation of an antiproton is a much more difficult matter than that of the positron. Whereas positrons can be created in the laboratory by bombardment of matter into charged particles or γ-rays of a few million electron volts energy, at least two billion volts of energy are necessary to create a proton-antiproton pair, because the mass of the proton is about 2,000 times that of the electron. In actual practice, a six billion-volt proton as the bombarding particle is necessary to produce a proton-antiproton pair because not all the energy of the bombarding particle, as calculated in the laboratory frame of reference, goes into the creation of the pair. The reason is that the energy that is available for creating a pair must be computed in a frame of reference in which the center of mass of the bombarding particle and the target is at rest, whereas the six billion volts refers to the energy of the bombarding particle in the frame of reference in which the target is at rest (the laboratory itself). The pair creating energy must be computed in this way because the energy associated with the motion of the center of mass of the system does not contribute to pair creation.

Since six billion-volt particle accelerators were not available immediately after the positron was discovered, physicists first looked for antiprotons in cosmic rays where such energies do occur, but the observations were so meager, since, at best, such pair creations are very rare, that no definite conclusions about the existence of antiprotons could be drawn.

Things thus remained in abeyance until the Bevatron at Berkeley, California, was constructed. This accelerator had been designed at the suggestion of Professor Ernest O. Lawrence, specifically with enough energy to create proton-antiproton pairs.

In principle, the experiment to create and detect antiprotons is very simple. One subjects a target to bombardment by six billion-volt (as measured in the laboratory) protons and then looks for negatively charged particles, having the mass of the proton, emanating from the target. The analysis of the particles coming from the target is carried out by means of a magnetic field, which deviates the negatively and positively charged particles in opposite directions to one another. One now chooses a magnetic field of such strength that it causes all the antiprotons (negatively charged particles) having a definite momentum to move along a definite circular path into a detector placed somewhere along its path. At the same time another detector is placed at a different point along the path of the particle to obtain its velocity. Thus, both the momentum of the negatively charged particle, as given by the radius of its path in the magnetic field and the strength of this field, and the speed of the particle, as given by the time it takes this particle to cover the known distance between the two detectors, can be measured. From the measured momentum and the speed, one can then calculate the mass of the particle using the well-known relativistic formula that relates the mass to the speed and momentum of the particle.

Although the theory of the experiment is very simple, it is quite complicated in practice because, to begin with, the arrangement of the apparatus and the alignment of the detectors must be very precise in order to detect a negative particle having just the mass of the proton. In fact, in the first stages of their work, Chamberlain and Segrè failed to detect antiprotons because of an error in their alignment. Furthermore, other negatively charged particles, such as mesons and electrons, having the same momentum as the antiprotons could move along the path of the antiproton, and two of these might trigger the two detectors, giving the impression of a single antiproton. Fortunately, mesons have to move about ten times faster than antiprotons to have the same momentum as the latter and they then are moving fast enough to emit a characteristic type of radiation, first detected by the Russian physicist P. A. Čerenkov. Since the much more slowly moving antiprotons do not emit Čerenkov radiation, a Čerenkov counter can be placed in the path of the deflected particles to differentiate between antiprotons and the less massive particles.

With such an experimental arrangement, and with great care taken in the alignment, Chamberlain and Segrè detected antiprotons even though only one of the 30,000 particles in the magnetically analyzed beam was an antiproton. To prove beyond doubt that they had really detected antiprotons, they then showed that these particles annihilate protons and neutrons. When this happens, about five pi-mesons (pions) are emitted.

After discovering the antiproton, Chamberlain and Segrè began looking for the antineutron, but such a particle is very difficult to detect in the primary beam of particles coming from the target because it is electrically neutral and therefore cannot be separated out of the beam by means of a magnetic field. However, the antineutron can be detected by what is called a charge exchange reaction: an antiproton meets a proton and instead of annihilating one another, the proton gives up its positive electric charge to the antiproton. The proton thus becomes a neutron and the antiproton becomes an antineutron. The antineutron is then annihilated after it has moved a short distance and the products of this annihilation can be detected in a bubble chamber. There the following series of events is observed: (1) the curved track of the incoming antiproton; (2) a sudden end of this track at a point where the charge exchange occurs and the antineutron is created; (3) a point further along where a star is formed by the tracks of secondary particles created when the antineutron is annihilated at this point. Between the point where the antiproton is destroyed and the point of the star, nothing is visible in the bubble chamber because the antineutron is an electrically neutral particle.

The final proof of the existence of the antinucleon came with the analysis of the energy released in its annihilation. Here the situation is not as straightforward as in the annihilation of an electron-positron pair which occurs with the emission of two photons. To prove that the electron and the positron have annihilated each other one simply measures the energy of these two photons (γ-rays) and notes that it equals twice the mass of the electron times the square of the speed of light (Einstein's mass–energy relationship). But when a proton and an antiproton annihilate each other, photons are not emitted directly; instead, different kinds of mesons are released and these decay at different stages so that measuring the total energy of all these decay products and showing that it equals twice the mass of the proton times the square of the speed of light becomes rather complicated. It has been done, however, and the evidence for the antinucleon is conclusive.

When an antinucleon and a nucleon annihilate each other, one observes an annihilation star, with many different particles moving off in various directions. Most of these particles are pi-mesons which decay into mu mesons (muons) and neutrinos in about 10^{-8} seconds. The muons in turn decay into electrons or positrons and neutrinos in a few microseconds and the positrons and electrons annihilate each other to become photons. Thus, in a very small fraction of a second, the nucleon-antinucleon pair decays into photons and neutrinos—particles with zero rest mass—which move off with the speed of light.

The existence of the antinucleon greatly strengthens the belief of physicists that antimatter exists as the normal state of things in a different part of our universe. This opinion was already expressed by Dirac in his Nobel lecture in 1933 when he said,

> If we accept the view of complete symmetry between positive and negative electric charge so far as concerns the fundamental laws of nature, we must regard it rather as an accident that the earth (and presumably the whole solar system) contains a preponderance of negative electrons and positive protons. It is quite possible that for some of the stars it is the other way about, these stars being built up mainly of positrons and negative protons. In fact, there may be half the stars of each kind. The two kinds of stars would both show exactly the same spectra, and there would be no way of distinguishing them by the present astronomical methods.

More recently L. Lederman and his collaborators at Columbia University have created the antideuteron in the laboratory, so that antimatter is now more than a mere hypothesis. In principle, one should be able to detect the presence of antimatter stars in our universe by using the non-conservation of parity discovered by Lee and Yang. Under ordinary conditions, when a nuclear process occurs involving the emission of β-rays, either neutrinos or antineutrinos are emitted. Thus, in the carbon cycle inside ordinary stars antineutrinos are emitted when carbon or nitrogen captures a proton. If the star consisted of antimatter, a neutrino would be emitted instead of an antineutrino. According to the discovery of Lee and Yang, the neutrino and the antineutrino have different spiralities: one advances like a left-handed screw and the other like a right-handed screw. Thus, if the neutrinos coming from a star like the sun did not have the same spirality as those coming from the sun, we would know that that star consists of antimatter.

ɔɔɔɔɔɔɔ

CHAMBERLAIN, SEGRÈ, WIEGAND, and YPSILANTIS

Antiprotons [1]

SINCE THE DEVELOPMENT OF DIRAC'S theory of the electron and the brilliant confirmation of one of its most startling predictions by the discovery of the positron by Anderson, it has been assumed most likely that the proton would also have its charge conjugate, the antiproton. The properties that define the antiproton are: (1) charge equal to the electron charge (also in sign); (2) mass equal to the proton mass; (3) stability against spontaneous decay; (4) ability to become annihilated by interaction with a proton or neutron, probably generating pions and releasing in some manner the energy 2 mc^2; (5) generation in pairs with ordinary nucleons; (6) magnetic moment equal but opposite to that of the proton; (7) fermion of spin ½. Not all these properties are independent, but all might ultimately be subjected to experiment.

In cosmic rays, where such antiprotons could appear, some events have been observed which could be due to antiprotons; but their interpretation is uncertain.

In order to generate antiprotons in the laboratory, an absolute lower limit of the necessary energy is 2 mc^2 — 1·88 BeV.; but the mechanism of the collision and the conservation of momentum influence this lower limit, which becomes 5·6 BeV. if the process is a nucleon-nucleon collision, or 4·4 BeV. if the process is a two-step one with the formation of a pion in a nucleon-nucleon collision followed by a pion-nucleon collision

---

[1] Chamberlain *et al., Nature.* 177 (1956), 11 f.

in which the nucleon-antinucleon pair is generated. These thresholds can be lowered appreciably by internal motions of nucleons in the nucleus. (Energies are quoted in the laboratory system.)

When the Berkeley bevatron was planned, the goal of 6 BeV. was set, in the hope that this energy would be sufficient to creat antiprotons.

The methods of detection of the antiproton can make use of any of the seven properties listed above. It seemed that (1), (2) and (3) might be the easiest to ascertain; (4) would also be highly desirable; whereas (5)– (7) are at present very difficult to observe.

There are classical methods of measuring charge and mass of a particle that go back in their origin to J. J. Thomson. They entail the simultaneous measurement on the same particle of any two of the quantities momentum, velocity or energy, which in turn can be obtained from the observation of electric or magnetic deflexions, time of flight, range, scattering in photographic emulsions, etc. As for the charge, it is sufficient to measure its sign and its absolute value in a rough way only, because it is assumed that it is an integral multiple of the electronic charge.

After a detailed discussion, it was decided that momentum p and velocity v constituted the most promising combination for ascertaining the mass. The first successful experiment was performed at the end of September 1955, as follows. The momentum was measured by passing the particles generated by bombardment of a copper target with $6 \cdot 2$ BeV. protons through two deflecting magnetic fields and two magnetic lenses. This ensemble let through only particles for which $p = 1 \cdot 19$ BeV./c, if their charge is equal to that of the electron, including sign. The velocity was measured by a time-of-flight measurement between two scintillation counters 40 ft. apart. The pulse-size in the scintillators showed that the particles were singly charged.

The chief difficulty of the experiment rests with the fact that the antiprotons are accompanied by many pions—44,000 pions per antiproton in the most favourable conditions. For this reason provision must be made for eliminating spurious background effects. One of the most important steps is the insertion in the beam of two Čerenkov counters: one that is activated by particles with $v/c = \beta > 0 \cdot 79$, and one of a special type that is activated by particles with $0 \cdot 75 < \beta < 0 \cdot 78$. Pions with $p = 1 \cdot 19$ BeV./c have $\beta = 0 \cdot 99$, while antiprotons of the same value of p have $\beta = 0 \cdot 78$, and their respective times of flight for an interval of 40 ft. are 40×10^{-9} sec. and 51×10^{-9} sec. Particles with β in the interval between $0 \cdot 75$ and $0 \cdot 78$ trigger the sweep of an oscilloscope in which the time of flight between two scintillation counters 40 ft. apart is displayed. This time of flight appears as the distance between the two "pips" due to the traversal of the counters. From this time of flight the mass is determined with an accuracy of 10 per cent for each particle. Up to now, about 250 particles have been observed and the average mass is known to about 5 per cent. It is 7,840 $\pm$ 90 electron masses.

The functioning of the whole apparatus is checked by sending through it positive protons in a separate run. These are obtained from a subsidiary target, and their orbits are selected in such a way that they have the same momentum as the antiproton.

The particles are observable after a time of flight of 10^{-7} sec., which rules out particles with a mean life much shorter than 10^{-8} sec., in particular the known hyperons. These measurements are thus in agreement with points (1), (2) and (3) mentioned above, and the identification of the new particle with the antiproton is a natural one, although not absolutely established.

There are also some indications on the fourth point mentioned above, namely, the terminal process of the particle. Particles selected as antiprotons by the apparatus [described above] were sent into a block of heavy glass and the Čerenkov radiation generated in it was measured. This radiation does not correspond, of course, to the entirety of the energy released; actually it is only a small part of it. However, a calibration was performed, and from the pulse size the visible energy was estimated. Values up to 800 MeV. were found. This is consistent with the expected modes of annihilation for an antiproton, and with the energy it would throw into Čerenkov radiation in a detectable form; but it is not sufficient yet for positive identification on that score only.

Another type of observation on the terminal phenomenon accompanying the absorption of the antiproton was also performed with the photographic plate technique. Particles of selected momentum obtained with an arrangement similar to that described [earlier] were slowed down by a copper absorber and finally stopped in a stack of photographic emulsions. Among a background of many pions one particle was found which has protonic mass, comes to rest and produces a star containing six black tracks, one grey proton, one pion of 58 MeV. and one minimum ionization track. The visible energy released is larger than 830 MeV. The total energy released cannot be known, because there are neutral particles emitted; but this amount of visible energy is also consistent with the annihilation of an antiproton.

Clearly many questions are raised by the new particle. Its identification should be further corroborated; it is important to study in detail its annihilation properties for complex nuclei and, possibly even more interesting, the annihilation with hydrogen and deuterium. In addition, the cross-section for nuclear interaction and the mechanism of production are clearly to be investigated.

The existence of the antiproton entails with virtual certainty the existence of the antineutron. Its experimental demonstration is a most interesting problem. Probably the neutron beam of the Berkeley bevatron contains an appreciable number of them, but their disentanglement from the ordinary neutrons appears a formidable task. It is likely that the best approach will be either: (1) to transform an antiproton into an antineutron by a collision with a proton; or (2) to convert an antineutron into an antiproton by collision with an ordinary neutron and detect either the final antineutron in (1) or the final antiproton in (2).

83

ooooooooooo

NUCLEAR MAGNETIC
MOMENT

ooooooooooo

I. I. Rabi (b. 1898)

As the experimental and theoretical aspects of nuclear physics developed, the need for greater accuracy in the measurement of nuclear parameters became ever more imperative. The construction of nuclear models and the introduction of a reasonable picture of nuclear forces depend on a knowledge of these quantities. The nuclear magnetic moment is of particular interest, since the magnetic moment must be carefully taken into account in any model of the nucleus, and in any theory of nuclear forces. The most precise and elegant method for measuring the size of the magnetic moment of a nucleus as well as its sign (that is, if the magnetic moment is parallel to the angular momentum its sign is positive; if antiparallel to the angular momentum of the nucleus, the sign is negative) was developed by I. I. Rabi in his molecular-beam laboratory at Columbia University.

Rabi's molecular-beam method grew out of the experiments of Stern and Gerlach for measuring the magnetic moments of atoms by passing the atoms through inhomogeneous magnetic fields. The Stern-Gerlach experiments were developed to test the theory of space quantization, according to which a spinning atom, whose total angular moment is a certain multiple of the fundamental unit of angular momentum $h/2\pi$, can orient itself only in a discrete number of directions relative to a magnetic field. In the classical picture a spinning atom behaves like a small magnet and therefore precesses about the magnetic field at a frequency (the Larmor frequency) that depends on the strength of the magnetic field multiplied by the ratio of the magnetic moment of the atom to its angular momentum (the so-called gyromagnetic ratio). In this respect, the classical and the quantum-mechanical pictures are the same. But the two pictures differ in that the classical picture includes no restriction on the angle at which the atomic magnet can precess about the magnetic field; according to quantum mechanics, the atomic magnet can precess about the magnetic field only at a discrete number of angular positions related in a simple way to the total angular momentum. Thus, if the total angular momentum of the atom is J, in units of $h/2\pi$, there are just $2J + 1$ angular orientations that the atomic magnet can assume with respect to the external magnetic field. The atom precesses about the magnetic field in any one of these orientations but in no other.

To test this picture of space quantization (discrete orientations with respect to the direction of a magnetic field), Stern and Gerlach proposed the following simple experiment, which will be remembered from Chapter 57:

Allow a parallel beam of similar atoms—all with the same total angular momentum, but of random spatial orientation—to pass through an inhomogeneous magnetic field and analyze the transmitted beam to see whether its structure is unaffected or split into a number of beams. If the composition of the beam is the same as it was prior to its passage through the magnetic field, then there is no such thing as space quantization. If, on the other hand, the transmitted atoms are separated into a discrete number of beams, space quantization is a reality.

To understand this experiment in terms of the quantum-mechanical picture we again note that the atomic beam consists of atoms with their angular momentum vectors, and hence their magnetic moments, oriented randomly in space. The beam of atoms is directed at right angles to the direction of a magnetic field whose strength is inhomogeneous. Since the inclinations of the angular-momentum vectors of the atoms in the beam are initially randomly distributed, those atoms, behaving like little magnets, precess about the magnetic field at all possible angles. But in an inhomogeneous magnetic field, a force is exerted on a magnet in the direction of the inhomogeneity—this force is proportional to the product of the inhomogeneity and the magnitude of the projection of the magnetic moment of the magnet in the direction of the inhomogeneity. This force changes the direction of motion of an atom passing through the magnetic field. Hence if there were no space quantization, the directions of motion of the atoms in the initial beam would be displaced by random amounts perpendicular to the direction of motion of the initial beam of atoms, and the transmitted beam would merely spread out like a fan. But if space quantization is present, then there are only $2J + 1$ orientations along which the atoms in the initial beam become oriented in the region of the magnetic field. As the beam passes through the field, the atoms in each of these orientations suffer a different force arising from the inhomogeneity of the field. Hence the transmitted beam must consist of $2J + 1$ component beams, each one displaced by a different amount relative to the original beam. This is precisely what Stern and Gerlach discovered; it is the starting point of Rabi's investigation of the spins and magnetic moments of nuclei.

Rabi began his work by first improving the experimental techniques that ultimately led to the molecular-beam method. In the original work of Stern and Gerlach the magnetic field was confined to a rather small volume of space (the region between the poles of two magnets), and the beam of atoms interacted with the field for only a short time. Hence these fields had to be quite strong to bring about an appreciable displacement of the component beams. Rabi improved upon this method by producing the necessary magnetic field with electric currents in long wires parallel to the direction of motion of the atoms in the beam. Even though the magnetic fields themselves were weak, sufficient effect was obtained because the beam was in contact with the magnetic field over a longer path than in the Stern-Gerlach experiments. Rabi introduced another important feature in his molecular-beam setup: auxiliary magnetic fields that can be altered at will and can be directed in any desired way relative to the inhomogeneous splitting field or the analyzing magnetic field. These additional fields are particularly interesting when they are changed periodically, either by making them rotate or by making them oscillate at a predetermined frequency. The use of these varying magnetic fields finally led to the molecular-beam resonance method, which yielded the magnitudes of the magnetic moments of nuclei with greater precision as well as the signs of these moments.

The theoretical basis of Rabi's resonance-method of measuring magnetic moments is presented in the first of his papers that follow this commentary. In this paper, Rabi deals with the behavior of a particle with a magnetic moment, such as a nucleus, when it is placed in an inhomogeneous magnetic field to which has been added a weak oscillating or rotating magnetic field. The particle with the magnetic moment is thus in a strong inhomogeneous field plus a weak varying electromagnetic field of a definite frequency. If only the inhomogeneous field were present, the spin axis of the particle would precess about this field at a definite angle in accordance with the requirements of space quantization. But only a finite, discrete number of precessional states would be available to the particle. The imposition of the weak varying electromagnetic field causes the particle to change from one precessional state—that is, from one state of space quantization—to another, either by absorbing or emitting a photon of a frequency equal to the frequency of the varying electromagnetic field. This can happen only if the energy of such a photon is just equal to the difference in energy between the state in which the particle is precessing and one of the other possible precessional states. Since these energy differences are very small, the varying electromagnetic field is a microwave field or even a radiofrequency field. Thus, if the frequency of this field is equal to or very close to the Larmor precession of the particle around the inhomogeneous field direction, it causes transitions to other permissible states of space quantization. The addition of this microwave field was Rabi's major contribution to this type of investigation.

If we are dealing with an electron in a rotating magnetic field and assume that the electron's spin is at first lined up parallel with this magnetic field, we find that after a certain time the spin of the electron has turned over and is antiparallel to the magnetic field. This problem has been approached by E. Majorana and P. Güttinger before Rabi considered it, but they analyzed only a rather special case, whereas Rabi investigated the probability of such transitions of spin in a magnetic field rotating with any orientation in space. The analysis shows that if the frequency of rotation of the magnetic field is close to or equal to the Larmor precession frequency of the particle, the chance for a transition is much greater than in other cases. Rabi's analysis also showed that the probability for a transition is different for positive and negative magnetic moments. This means that a careful analysis of the behavior of the magnetic moment of a particle in a varying magnetic field (the flipping over of the spin) must yield information about the magnitude and the sign of the magnetic moment.

In collaboration with his associates and students, Rabi applied precisely this type of analysis to the magnetic moments of three different nuclei in a famous series of experiments that were first reported in a paper reproduced following this commentary. In this type of experiment a beam of atoms or molecules is subjected to an inhomogeneous field, displacing the atoms from their original path. After the atoms pass through a slit, they are subjected to a second field whose inhomogeneity is opposite to that of the first field but equal in strength. Thus, the atoms are deflected back to their original path and arrive at the detector. If only these two fields were acting on the beam of atoms, the number of atoms detected would be the same as if there were no fields present because the second field would exactly compensate the action of the first field. The third field, either rotating or oscillating, is now introduced in the neighborhood of the slit at right angles to the constant magnetic field. This field induces transitions (that is, flipping over) of the magnetic moments of the atoms just before they enter the second constant inhomogeneous field. Because of these transitions, the second inhomogeneous field cannot compensate the first one completely and the number of atoms arriving at the detector is not the same as before. This effect is most pronounced if the frequency of oscillation of the oscillating field is close to the frequency of the Larmor precession of the atoms in the beam. Since this frequency is proportional to the gyromagnetic ratio of the atom, this ratio (the so-called Landé *g* factor) can be measured, and thus the magnetic moment can be found if the spin or the angular momentum is known. Therefore, if the frequency of the oscillating field is slowly varied, a sharp decrease (the resonance phenomenon) occurs in the number of atoms arriving at the detector when the frequency of the field equals the Larmor frequency. Each such resonance then gives a *g* value, and hence a magnetic moment.

In 1930, a small research room was set aside at the newly constructed Pupin physics laboratories of Columbia University to study the spins and magnetic moments of atomic nuclei, and the physicist placed in charge of this project was the newly appointed assistant professor in theoretical physics, Isidor I. Rabi. This choice was singularly appropriate, for Rabi had worked on the magnetic properties of crystals while a graduate student at Columbia and had spent two years at European laboratories working with Bohr, Pauli, Heisenberg, and, particularly, with Stern, who greatly influenced the direction of Rabi's future research.

Unlike most of the other outstanding physicists, Rabi did not go directly into physics upon completing his undergraduate education, but came to it after an interruption of three years, during which he pursued a business career. Rabi was brought to this country when he was one year old from Raymanov, Austria, where he was born on July 29, 1898. After completing his grammar school and high-school education in Manhattan and Brooklyn he went to Cornell University to study chemistry; from the economic point of view chemistry was considered more lucrative than physics. In any case, chemistry touched the day-to-day lives of people more intimately than did physics, which probably seemed rather esoteric and unrelated to any direct way of earning a livelihood. On receiving his bachelor's degree in chemistry from Cornell in 1919, Rabi left academic pursuits, as noted above, but three years later he returned to Cornell— this time as a graduate student in physics.

When economic reasons prevented him from continuing at Cornell, he matriculated as a graduate student at Columbia University with the idea of supporting himself with part-time work in New York City. Fortunately, he was given a part-time teaching program in physics at the College of the City of New York and thus was able to complete his doctoral work at Columbia, receiving his Ph.D. degree in 1927. With the aid of fellowships, Rabi spent two years at various European universities and then returned to Columbia as lecturer in theoretical physics in 1929.

When he started his remarkable research career at Columbia he was interested in both theoretical and experimental work, for although he is primarily an experimentalist, he also has an excellent grasp of theory. He had, in fact, published some theoretical papers on the quantum mechanics of rotating systems before he began to experiment on the spins and magnetic moments of nuclei. Once he began his experimental work, he devoted all his time to it, except for his hours of teaching.

His first experiment was the measurement of the spin of the sodium nucleus, and the apparatus he used was essentially the same as that used by Stern. He began to improve the Stern molecular-beam technique, and a few years after the completion of this first experiment, he applied the resonance principle to nuclei that were moving through a magnetic field, and thus obtained fantastic precision in his measurements. The principle of this technique is explained in our commentary on Rabi's work. After discovering the resonance method of measuring spins, he applied it to a series of nuclei. These experiments won him the Nobel Prize in physics in 1944.

When Rabi came to Columbia in 1929, he organized a seminar in theoretical physics, which he conducted jointly with Professor Breit of New York University. This attracted outstanding students of physics in the New York metropolitan area and Columbia became a recruiting ground for future theoretical physicists. At the same time, his molecular beam laboratory became more and more successful and began to attract outstanding students of experimental physics, one of whom, P. Kusch, won the Nobel Prize in physics in 1955.

Rabi's method of work at that time was quite different from what one ordinarily would expect of an experimentalist. Although he spent whatever time was necessary in his laboratory to ensure the success of an experiment, he spent most of his time on theory, leaving the technical details of the experiments to his assistants.

In those years, Rabi's office door, as it is now, was always open, and any student or colleague who wished to talk with him was free to do so. Often one would find one or more of his graduate students talking to him while he whittled away at a piece of wood. Although the discussions were generally about physics, it was not unusual to find other subjects, such as literature, politics, and economics, the topics of vehement arguments, for Rabi never allowed his intense pursuit of physics to blind him to the excitement to be found in other intellectual activities.

Much of his success in his work is due to his intellectual tenacity, which never allowed him to lay aside an idea until he had worked out its fullest implications.

In 1940 he took a leave from Columbia to become associate director of the Radiation Laboratory at the Massachusetts Institute of Technology and worked on both radar and the atomic bomb. In 1945, at the end of the war, he returned to Columbia as executive officer of the physics department. After retiring from this post, he continued in the department as Higgins professor of physics. In 1964 a special academic appointment as university professor was created for him, allowing him complete freedom in teaching. He has given a series of lectures on science and history at Columbia—an outgrowth of similar lectures given at Princeton as visiting professor of history, while on leave from Columbia.

In addition to the Nobel Prize, Rabi has received many other honors. In 1939 he was awarded the prize of the American Association for the Advancement of Science, and, in 1942, the Eliott Cresson medal of the Franklin Institute. In 1948 he received both the medal for merit and the King's medal for service in the cause of freedom. He is also an Officer of the Legion of Honor and has been awarded the honorary Doctor of Science degree by Princeton, Harvard, and Birmingham Universities. He was an associate editor of the *Physical Review* for two periods and, in 1950, was elected president of the American Physical Society. He is a member of the National Academy of Sciences, the American Philosophical Society, and the American Academy of the Arts and Sciences.

In 1959 he was appointed a member of the Board of Governors of the Weizmann Institute of Science in Israel and is a foreign member of the Japanese and Brazilian Academies. He is a member of the General Advisory Committee to the Arms Control and Disarmament Agency, the United States National Committee for UNESCO, and the Science Advisory Committee of the International Atomic Energy Agency.

Rabi lives in New York City, with his wife, the former Helen Newmark, whom he married in 1926. They have two married daughters.

ɷɷɷɷɷɷɷ

R A B I

Space Quantization in a Gyrating Magnetic Field [1]

IN A PREVIOUS PAPER THE effect of a rapidly varying magnetic field on an oriented atom possessing nuclear spin and extranuclear angular momentum [was discussed]. It appeared that it was possible to deduce the sign of the magnetic moment of the nucleus from the nature of the nonadiabatic transitions which occur if the field rotates an appreciable amount in the time of a Larmor rotation. This effect was applied experimentally with the method of atomic beams to measure

---

[1] I. I. Rabi, *Physical Review*, 51 (1937), 652–654.

the sign of the [magnetic moment of the] proton, deuteron, K^{39}, etc. The evaluation of the sign was possible because the experiment decided whether the h.f.s. level was normal or inverted. Since the sign of the electronic moment is known to be negative a normal level meant positive nuclear moment and an inverted level negative moment.

Clearly it is desirable to find another effect which will make it possible to find the sign of the nuclear moment in cases where the normal state of the atom is one in which there is no electronic angular momentum as in the alkaline earths. Spectroscopic methods where applicable will yield this information, but there are numerous important instances in which molecular and atomic beam methods are the only ones available. For example, it would be very desirable to measure the sign of the moment of the neutron directly. Although it would be very difficult to apply atomic beam methods to the neutron, the polarization effect of magnetized iron suggested by Bloch may possibly be useful in this connection as a device for measuring the degree of depolarization caused by the nonadiabatic transitions to be described below. Another example is the sign of the moment arising from molecular rotation which results in a positive contribution from the motion of the nuclei about the centroid and a negative contribution from the electrons.

The following considerations should make it possible to make the same sort of observations with simple systems as are made in the Einstein-de Haas and Barnett experiments: namely, the magnitude and sign of the gyromagnetic ratio.

Consider a simple system such as a neutron with magnetic moment $\mu = -g\mu_0 J$, where g is the Landé g factor, J is the total angular moment due to all causes. If g is positive the total moment is negative as in the spinning electron. If g is negative the moment is positive. In a magnetic field H the system precesses with the Larmor frequency $\nu = g\mu_0 H/h$. If g is positive the precession is in the positive direction and if negative in the negative direction. We shall now consider our system initially quantized with magnetic quantum number m in a field H which is constant in magnitude but rotates with a frequency $\omega/2\pi$ about some direction which is at an angle θ with respect to the direction of the field.

This problem was solved by Güttinger for the particular case when the angle is $\pi/2$. He found that transitions will occur to other magnetic levels with quantum number m' when $\omega/2\pi$ is of the order of magnitude of ν. The transition probabilities in this case do not depend on the direction of the field. It will be shown that in the more general case the direction of rotation introduces an asymmetry into the problem and as a consequence with the same $|\nu|$ and $|\omega|$ the transition probabilities will be different depending on whether g is positive or negative. The Majorana and Güttinger arrangements do not possess this property.

It will suffice to consider only the case where $J = \frac{1}{2}$ since the solution of more general problems depends only on the solution of this simple case. The Schrödinger equation for this case is

$$i\hbar\dot\psi = \mathcal{H}\,\psi,$$
$$\mathcal{H} = g(\mu_0/2)(\sigma_1 H_1 + \sigma_2 H_2 + \sigma_3 H_3). \tag{1}$$

If we set

$$\psi = C_{\frac{1}{2}}\psi_{\frac{1}{2}} + C_{-\frac{1}{2}}\psi_{-\frac{1}{2}}$$

we obtain from (1)

$$dC_{\frac{1}{2}}/dt = (-ig\mu_0/2\hbar)[H_3 C_{\frac{1}{2}} + (H_1 - iH_2)C_{-\frac{1}{2}}],$$
$$dC_{-\frac{1}{2}}/dt = (-ig\mu_0/2\hbar)[-H_3 C_{-\frac{1}{2}} + (H_1 + iH_2)C_{\frac{1}{2}}]. \tag{3}$$

With the substitutions

$$H_1 = H \sin\phi \cos\phi,\; H_2 = H \sin\theta \sin\phi,\; H_3 = H \cos\theta,$$
$$g\frac{u_0}{2}\frac{H}{\hbar}\cos\theta = a,\; g\frac{u_0}{2\hbar}H\sin\theta = b,\; \phi = \omega t, \tag{4}$$

which represents a field H constant in magnitude and precessing about the z direction with angular velocity ω, we have

$$dC_{\frac{1}{2}}/dt = -iaC_{\frac{1}{2}} - ibe^{-i\omega t}C_{-\frac{1}{2}},$$
$$dC_{-\frac{1}{2}}/dt = iaC_{-\frac{1}{2}} - ibe^{i\omega t}C_{\frac{1}{2}}. \tag{5}$$

Therefore

$$d^2 C_{\frac{1}{2}}/dt^2 + i\omega\,\frac{d}{dt}C_{\frac{1}{2}} + (a^2 + b^2 - \omega a)C_{\frac{1}{2}} = 0. \tag{6}$$

The solution of this familiar equation is

$$C_{\frac{1}{2}} = Ae^{ip_1 t} + Be^{ip_2 t},$$
$$C_{-\frac{1}{2}} = -e^{i\omega t}\left[\frac{a+p_1}{b}Ae^{ip_1 t} + \frac{a+p_2}{b}e^{ip_2 t}\right],$$
$$p_1 = -(\omega/2) + \frac{1}{2}(\omega^2 + 4a^2 + 4b^2 - 4\omega a)^{\frac{1}{2}},$$
$$p_2 = -(\omega/2) - \frac{1}{2}(\omega^2 + 4a^2 + 4b^2 - 4\omega a)^{\frac{1}{2}}. \tag{7}$$

The quantities A and B are determined from the initial conditions and the normalization condition $|C_{\frac{1}{2}}|^2 + |C_{-\frac{1}{2}}|^2 = 1$. If ψ_α and ψ_β are the vectors which correspond to $m = +\frac{1}{2}, -\frac{1}{2}$, respectively, in the direction of H we obtain

$$
\begin{aligned}
\psi_\alpha &= (2\alpha)^{-\frac{1}{2}}(\beta e^{-i\omega t}\psi_{\frac{1}{2}} + \alpha\psi_{-\frac{1}{2}}), \\
\psi_\beta &= (2\gamma)^{-\frac{1}{2}}(-\beta e^{-i\omega t}\psi_{\frac{1}{2}} + \gamma\psi_{-\frac{1}{2}}), \\
\beta &= \sin\theta,\ \alpha = 1 - \cos\theta,\ \gamma = 1 + \cos\theta, \\
\alpha^2 &+ \beta^2 = 2\alpha,\ \gamma^2 + \beta^2 = 2\gamma.
\end{aligned} \tag{8}
$$

If $\psi(0) = \psi_\alpha(0)$ at $t = 0$ we start with the system quantized in the direction of H with $m = \frac{1}{2}$, and

$$
\begin{aligned}
A + B &= \beta/(2\alpha)^{\frac{1}{2}}, \\
-\left(\frac{a + p_1}{b}\right) A &- \left(\frac{a + p_2}{b}\right) B = \frac{\alpha}{(2\alpha)^{\frac{1}{2}}}.
\end{aligned} \tag{9}
$$

Utilizing these values of A and B and setting $n = (\omega^2 + 4a^2 + 4b^2 - 4\omega h)^{\frac{1}{2}}$ we obtain for the probability amplitudes

$$
C_{\frac{1}{2}} = \frac{1}{(2\alpha)^{\frac{1}{2}}} e^{-(i\omega t/2)} \left[\beta \cos\frac{n}{2}t - i\frac{(2\alpha b + 2\beta a - \beta\omega)}{n} \sin\frac{n}{2}t \right],
$$

$$
\tag{10}
$$

$$
C_{-\frac{1}{2}} = \frac{1}{(2\alpha)^{\frac{1}{2}}} e^{i\omega t/2} \left[\alpha \cos\frac{n}{2}t - i\frac{(2\beta b - 2\alpha a + \alpha\omega)}{n} \sin\frac{n}{2}t \right].
$$

The probability of finding the system in a state with $m = -\frac{1}{2}$ with respect to H is therefore

$$
P_{(\frac{1}{2}, -\frac{1}{2})} = |\psi_\beta^* \psi|^2 = \frac{1}{(4\alpha\gamma)^{\frac{1}{2}}} |-\beta e^{i\omega t}C_{\frac{1}{2}} + \gamma C_{-\frac{1}{2}}|^2 \tag{11}
$$

with the values given in Eq. (12)

$$
P_{(\frac{1}{2}, -\frac{1}{2})} = \frac{\beta^2 \omega^2}{n^2} \sin^2\frac{n}{2}t. \tag{12}
$$

In terms of the Larmor frequency $\nu = g\mu_0 H/h$, the angle θ and the frequency of rotation $r = \omega/2\pi$

$$
P_{(\frac{1}{2}, -\frac{1}{2})} = \frac{\sin^2\theta r^2}{\nu^2 + \nu^2 - 2\nu r \cos\theta} \sin^2\pi t
$$
$$
\times (\nu^2 + r^2 - 2\nu r \cos\theta)^{\frac{1}{2}}. \tag{13}
$$

This result reduces to Güttinger's formula when $\theta = \pi/2$. For other values of θ it is apparent that the transition probability for given θ, H and ω will be quite different depending on whether g is positive or negative since ν appears linearly in the result. Expressed in another way we may say that $P_{(\frac{1}{2}, -\frac{1}{2})}$ depends on the direction of rotation of the field for a given sign and magnitude of g.

Since rotating fields are usually realized by allowing the system to pass through a field which changes in direction from point to point, the total change in direction is fixed. If we set $\phi = 2\pi r t$ we obtain from (15) setting $\nu/r = q$

$$P_{(\frac{1}{2}, -\frac{1}{2})} = \frac{\sin^2 \theta}{1 + q^2 - 2q \cos \theta} \sin^2 \frac{\phi}{2}$$
$$\times (1 + q^2 - 2q \cos \theta)^{\frac{1}{2}}. \quad (14)$$

If we set $q = \cos \theta$ which can be arranged by suitably varying the magnitude and direction of the field,

$$P_{(\frac{1}{2}, -\frac{1}{2})} = \sin^2(\tfrac{1}{2}\phi \sin \theta), \quad (15)$$

which can be made as close to unity as one pleases by arranging experimental conditions so that $2\pi > \phi > \pi$. If one were then to leave everything unchanged but reversed the direction of rotation we would get

$$P_{(\frac{1}{2}, -\frac{1}{2})} = \frac{\sin^2 \theta}{1 + 3 \cos^2 \theta} \sin^2 \left[\frac{\phi}{2} (1 + 3 \cos^2 \theta)^{\frac{1}{2}} \right], \quad (16)$$

a very much smaller quantity.

It is clear therefore that from this qualitative difference and a knowledge of the sense of rotation one can infer the sign of the moment. The magnitude may be inferred from the absolute value of the fields and their direction and the angular velocity of its rotation.

It is unnecessary to consider the details of the realization of these rotating fields and the detection of these transitions since similar conditions have already been obtained in the experiments cited above.

To generalize these results we apply the general result of Majorana for any value of J

$$P_{(\alpha, m, m')} = (\cos \tfrac{1}{2}\alpha)^{4J} (J + m)\,! (J + m')\,!$$
$$\times (J - m)\,! (J - m')\,! \quad (17)$$
$$\times \left[\sum_{\nu = 0}^{2J} \frac{(-1)^\nu (\tan \tfrac{1}{2}\alpha)^{2\nu - m + m'}}{\nu\,! (\nu - m + m')\,! (J - m - \nu)\,! (J - m' - \nu)\,!} \right]^2,$$

where the value of the parameter α is given by

$$\sin^2 \tfrac{1}{2}\alpha = P_{(\frac{1}{2}, -\frac{1}{2})} \tag{18}$$

and depends only on g and not on m or J.

It may be of interest to note that in cases where we have a coupled system such as a nuclear spin coupled to molecular rotation, in which the coupling is weak and g small, the field required for these transitions can be such that the component systems are completely decoupled. As was shown by Motz and Rose, each system would then make these transitions independently. In particular, if the moments of the two systems are opposite in sign it should be possible to arrange conditions so that only one of these two systems makes these transitions. In this case it should be possible by means of the focusing methods developed in this laboratory to measure directly one moment in the presence of another (rotational and nuclear) with only slight interference.

๑๑๑๑๑๑๑๑

RABI, ZACHARIAS,
MILLMAN, and KUSCH

A New Method of Measuring Nuclear Magnetic Moment [2]

IT IS THE PURPOSE OF this note to describe an experiment in which the nuclear magnetic moment is measured very directly. The method is capable of very high precision and extension to a large number and variety of nuclei.

Consider a beam of molecules, such as LiCl, traversing a magnetic field which is sufficiently strong to decouple completely the nuclear spins from one another and from the molecular rotation. If a small oscillating magnetic field is applied at right angles to a much larger constant field, a reorientation of the nuclear spin and magnetic moment with respect to the constant field will occur when the frequency of the oscillating field is close

---

[2] I. I. Rabi, J. R. Zacharias, S. Millman, and P. Kusch, *Physical Review, 53* (1938), 318.

to the Larmor frequency of precession of the particular angular momentum vector in question. This precession frequency is given by

$$v = \mu H/hi = g(i)\mu_0 H/h. \tag{1}$$

To apply these ideas a beam of molecules in a $^1\Sigma$ state (no electronic moment) is spread by an inhomogeneous magnetic field and refocused onto a detector by a subsequent field, somewhat as in the experiment of Kellogg, Rabi and Zacharias. As in that experiment the re-orienting field is placed in the region between the two magnets. The homogeneous field is produced by an electromagnet capable of supplying uniform fields up to 6000 gauss in a gap 6 mm wide and 5 cm long. In the gap is placed a loop of wire in the form of a hairpin (with its axis parallel to the direction of the beam) which is connected to a source of current at radiofrequency to produce the oscillating field at right angles to the steady field. If a re-orientation of a spin occurs in this field, the subsequent conditions in the second deflecting field are no longer correct for refocusing, and the intensity at the detector goes down. The experimental procedure is to vary the homogeneous field for some given value of the frequency of the oscillating field until the resonance is observed by a drop in intensity at the detector and a subsequent recovery when the resonance value is passed.

The re-orientation process is more accurately described as one in which transitions occur between the various magnetic levels given by the quantum number m_i of the particular angular momentum vector in question. An exact solution for the transition probability was given by Rabi for the case where the variable field rotates rather than oscillates. However, it is more convenient experimentally to use an oscillating field, in which case the transition probability is approximately the same for *weak* oscillating fields *near* the resonance frequency, except that θ is replaced by $\theta/2$ in Eq. (13).[3] With this replacement and with passage to the limit of weak oscillating fields, the formula becomes for the case of $i = \frac{1}{2}$

$$P_{(\frac{1}{2}, -\frac{1}{2})} = \frac{\theta^2}{(1-q)^2 + q\theta^2} \sin^2 \{\pi tr[(1-q)^2 + q\theta^2]^{\frac{1}{2}}\}, \tag{2}$$

where θ is $\frac{1}{2}$ the ratio of the oscillating field to the steady field, q is the ratio of the Larmor frequency of Eq. (1) to the frequency r of the oscillating field. The denominator of the expression is the familiar resonance denominator. The formula is generalized to any spin i by formula (17).[4]

In the theory of this experiment, t, in Eq. (2), is replaced by L/v,

---

[3] See preceding paper.
[4] See preceding paper.

where L is the length of the oscillating region of the field, and v is the molecular velocity. $P_{(\frac{1}{2}, -\frac{1}{2})}$ must then be averaged over the Maxwellian distribution of velocities. However, the first term is not affected by the velocity distribution if t is long enough for many oscillations to take place. The average value of the $\sin^2$ term over the velocity distribution is approximately $\frac{1}{2}$.

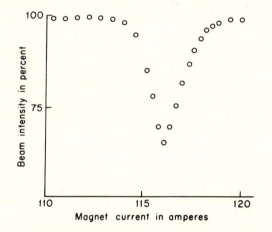

Fig. 83–1. Curve showing refocused beam intensity at various values of the homogeneous field. One ampere corresponds to about 18.4 gauss. The frequency of the oscillating field was held constant at 3.518×10^6 cycles per second.

To produce deflections of the weakly magnetic molecules sufficient to make the apparatus sensitive to this effect, the beam is made 245 cm long; the first deflecting field is 52 cm in length and the second 100 cm.

We have tried this experiment with LiCl and observed the resonance peaks of Li and Cl. The effects are very striking and the resonances sharp [Fig. 83–1]. A full account of this experiment, together with the values of the nuclear moments, will be published when the homogeneous field is recalibrated.

ᴑᴑᴑᴑᴑᴑᴑᴑ

R A B I , M I L L M A N ,
K U S C H , and Z A C H A R I A S

The Molecular Beam Resonance Method for Measuring Nuclear Magnetic Moments [5]

THE MAGNETIC MOMENT OF THE atomic nucleus is one of the few of its important properties which concern both phases of the nuclear problem, the nature of the nuclear forces and the appropriate nuclear model. According to current theories the anomalous moment of the proton is directly connected with the processes from which nuclear forces arise. The question whether the intrinsic moments of the proton and neutron are maintained within the nucleus is part of the problem of two and multiparticle forces between nuclear constituents. With regard to the atomic model it is clear that the nuclear angular momentum does not alone suffice to fix the nature of the wave functions which specify the state of the nucleus. The magnetic moment, on the other hand, is sensitive to the relative contributions of spin and orbital moment and, with the advance of mathematical technique, suffices to decide between the different proposed configurations.

In the light of these considerations it is particularly desirable that nuclear moments be known to high precision because small effects may be of great importance. A case in point is that of $_3Li^7$; according to the calculations of Rose and Bethe the contribution of the orbital motions to the moment of this nucleus is about 10 percent of the total moment. The rest is contributed by the intrinsic proton moment. If the nuclear moment were known to only 10 percent, the importance of this datum would be greatly diminished.

In two letters to this journal, we reported briefly on a new precision method of measuring nuclear moment, and on some results. In this paper we shall give a more detailed account of the method, apparatus and results.

---

[5] Rabi, Millman, Kusch, and Zacharias, *Physical Review*, 55 (1939), 526–535.

METHOD

The principle on which the method is based applies not only to nuclear magnetic moments but rather to any system which possesses angular momentum and a magnetic moment. We consider a system with angular momentum, J, in units of $h/2\pi$, and magnetic moment μ. In an external magnetic field H_0 the angular momentum will precess with the Larmor frequency, ν, (in revolutions per sec.) given by,

$$\nu = \mu H_0/Jh. \qquad (1)$$

Our method consists in the measurement of ν in a known field H_0. The measurement of ν is the essential step in this method, since H_0 may be measured by conventional procedures. Using Eq. (1) we obtain the gyromagnetic ratio. If, in addition, the angular momentum, J, of the system is known, we can evaluate the magnetic moment μ. In its present state of development our method is not suitable for the measurement of J.

The process by which the precession frequency ν is measured has a rather close analog in classical mechanics. To the system described in the previous paragraph, we apply an additional magnetic field H_1, which is much smaller than H_0 and perpendicular to it in direction. If we consider the initial condition such that H_1 is perpendicular to both the angular momentum and H_0, the additional precession caused by H_1 will be such as to increase or decrease the angle between the angular momentum, J, and H_0, depending on the relative directions. If H_1 rotates with the frequency ν this effect is cumulative and the change in angle between H_0 and J can be made large. It is apparent that if the frequency of revolution, f, of H_1 about H_0 is markedly different from ν, the net effect will be small. Furthermore, if the sense of rotation of H_1 is opposite to that of the precession, the effect will also be small. The smaller the ratio H_1/H_0 the sharper this effect will be in its dependence on the exact agreement between the frequency of precession, ν, and the frequency f.

Any method which enables one to detect this change in orientation of the angular momentum with respect to H_0 can therefore utilize this process to measure the precession frequency and therefore the magnetic moment. The general method here outlined includes not only the magnitude but also the sign of the magnetic moment since the direction of precession depends on whether the magnetic moment vector is parallel or antiparallel to J.

The precise form of the initial conditions previously described is not important and we may consider H_1 initially at any angle ϕ with the plane determined by H_0 and J but still perpendicular to H_0. In fact, according to quantum mechanics, we must consider the initial conditions of an ensemble of systems with a definite projection of J and H_0 as uniformly distributed over ϕ. This only means that some systems will increase and other systems will decrease their projections in the direction of H_0.

In practice it is frequently more convenient to use an oscillating field H_1 rather than a rotating field. Although the situation is not quite as clear as for the rotating field, it is reasonable to expect that the effects will be similar if the oscillating field is sufficiently small. A simple calculation shows that no change in the magnitude of the projection of J on H_0 will

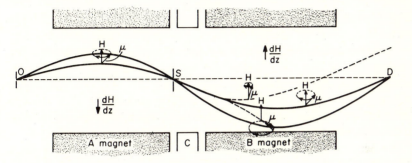

Fig. 83–2. Paths of molecules. The two solid curves indicate the paths of two molecules having different moments and velocities and whose moments are not changed during passage through the apparatus. This is indicated by the small gyroscopes drawn on one of these paths, in which the projection of the magnetic moment along the field remains fixed. The two dotted curves in the region of the B magnet indicate the paths of two molecules the projection of whose nuclear magnetic moments along the field has been changed in the region of the C magnet. This is indicated by means of the two gyroscopes drawn on the dotted curves, for one of which the projection of magnetic moment along the field has been increased and for the other of which the projection has been decreased.

occur unless the frequency of oscillation is close to the frequency of precession. The sign of the moment does not affect any processes when a pure oscillating field is used, since it may be considered as the superposition of two oppositely rotating fields. Hence no information as to the sign of the moment can be obtained when this type of field is substituted for a rotating field.

Although the reorientations of the system under the combined influence of H_0 and H_1 may be detected in a number of ways, the most delicate and precise is that of molecular beams.

The arrangement used in our experiment is shown schematically in [Fig. 83–2]. A stream of molecules coming from the source, O, in a high vacuum apparatus is defined by a collimating slit, S, and detected by some suitable device at D. The magnets, A and B, produce inhomogeneous magnetic fields, the gradients of which, $d|H|/dz$, are indicated by arrows. When these magnets are turned on, molecules having magnetic moments will be deflected in the direction of the gradient if the projection of the moment, μ_z, along the field is positive, and in the opposite direction if μ_z is negative. A molecule starting from O along the direction OS will be deflected in the z direction by the inhomogeneous A field and will not pass through the collimating slit unless its projected moment is very small or it is moving with very high speed. In general, for a molecule having any moment, μ_z, and any energy, $\frac{1}{2}mv^2$, it is possible to find an initial direction for the velocity of the molecule at the source such that the molecule will pass through the collimating slit. This is indicated by the solid lines in the diagram. If d_A denotes the deflection at the detector from the line OSD suffered by the molecule due to the A field alone, it may be expressed by:

$$d_A = (\mu_z/2mv^2)(d|H|/dz)_A G_A.$$

The deflection in the B field will be in a direction opposite to that in the A field and is given by:

$$d_B = (\mu_z/2mv^2)(d|H|/dz)_B G_B.$$

The factors, $(d|H|/dz)_A G_A$ and $(d|H|/dz)_B G_B$, depend only on the geometry of the apparatus and can be adjusted to have the same value. Thus if a molecule of any velocity has the same μ_z in both deflecting fields it will be brought back to the detector by the B field. A simple consideration shows that when the fields A and B are properly adjusted the number of molecules which reaches the detector is the same whether the magnets A and B are on or off. The molecular velocity distribution is also the same.

Magnet C produces the homogeneous field H_0. In addition, there is a device, not pictured in [Fig. 83–2], which produces an oscillating field perpendicular to H_0. If the reorientation which we have described takes place in this region the conditions for deflecting the molecules back to D by means of the B magnet no longer obtain. The molecule will follow one dotted line or the other depending on whether μ_z has become more positive or has changed sign. In fact, if any change in orientation occurs, the molecule will miss the detector and cause a diminution in its reading. We thus have a means of knowing when the reorientation effect occurs.

Since most of the systems in which one is interested have small angular momenta ($<10h/2\pi$) the classical considerations given above have to be reconsidered from the point of view of quantum mechanics. The reorientation process is more accurately described as one in which the system, originally in some state with magnetic quantum number, m, makes a transition to another magnetic level, m'. An exact solution for the transition probability for the case where H_1 rotates and is arbitrary in magnitude was given by Rabi. For the particular case of $J = \frac{1}{2}$ we have,

$$P_{(\frac{1}{2}, -\frac{1}{2})} = \frac{\sin^2 \theta}{1 + q^2 - 2q \cos \theta} \sin^2 \pi t f (1 + q^2 - 2q \cos \theta)^{\frac{1}{2}},$$

where $P_{(\frac{1}{2}, -\frac{1}{2})}$ is the probability that the system, originally in the state $m = \frac{1}{2}$ is found in the state $m = -\frac{1}{2}$ after a time t, q the ratio of the frequency of revolution f to the frequency of precession v $[v = \mu(H_0^2 + H_1^2)^{\frac{1}{2}}/Jh]$, and $\tan \theta = H_1/H_0$.

For an oscillating field, in the limit where $H_1/H_0 \ll 1$, and in the neighborhood of $f = v$ this formula becomes:

$$P_{(\frac{1}{2} - \frac{1}{2})} = \frac{\Delta^2}{(1 - q)^2 + \Delta^2} \sin^2 \pi t f [(1 - q)^2 + \Delta^2]^{\frac{1}{2}}, \qquad (2)$$

where $\Delta = H_1/2H_0$, one-half the ratio of the amplitude of the oscillating field to the static field, and the other symbols retain their meaning. For spins higher than $\frac{1}{2}$ the general formula given by Majorana applies, and

$$P_{(\alpha, m, m')} = (\cos \frac{1}{2}\alpha)^{4J} (J + m)\,! $$
$$\times (J + m')\,! (J - m)\,! (J - m')\,!$$
$$\times \left[\sum_{v=0}^{2J} \frac{(-1)^v (\tan \frac{1}{2}\alpha)^{2v - m + m'}}{v!(v - m + m')(J + m - v)!(J - m' - v)!} \right]^2, \qquad (3)$$

where α is defined through $P_{(\frac{1}{2}, -\frac{1}{2})} = \sin^2 (\alpha/2)$. That is, we calculate α for a system which has the same μ/i but with a spin of $\frac{1}{2}$ and subject to the same field, and use it in Eq. (3).

The orders of magnitude involved can be seen from a simple example: consider a system with spin $\frac{1}{2}$ and a moment of 1 nuclear magneton in a field of 1000 gauss and an oscillating field of 10 gauss amplitude. We assume that the system is moving at a speed of 10^5 cm per second which is of the order of thermal velocities, and set $t = l/v = 10^{-5}l$. The resonance frequency is

$$\frac{\mu H}{hi} = \frac{(0.5 \times 10^{-23})(10^3)}{(6.55 \times 10^{-27})(\frac{1}{2})} \sim 1.5 \times 10^6 \text{ cycles per sec.},$$

which fortunately is in a very convenient range of radiofrequencies. To make the $\sin^2$ terms a maximum at $q = 1$ we set

$$\pi \times 10^{-5}l \times 1.5 \times 10^6 \times 0.5 \times 10^{-2} = \pi/2.$$

Solving for l, we obtain $l = 6.6$ cm, which is a very convenient length for the oscillating field.

The theoretically simplest systems to which these ideas may be applied in the study of nuclear moments are atoms which are normally in a state with electronic angular momentum equal to zero. If the electronic J is not zero, the interaction of the nuclear spin with the electronic angular momentum is of the order of magnitude of its interaction with the applied field H_0. Moreover, the electronic magnetic moment is so much larger than the nuclear moment that the deflections in the A and B fields will be almost entirely due to this electronic moment and the apparatus will accordingly be insensitive to changes in nuclear orientation. Resort must therefore be had to atoms in a state $J = 0$ or to molecules in a $^1\Sigma$ state in which all electronic angular momentum is neutralized to the first order. These considerations do not preclude the study, with these methods, of atoms with electronic angular momentum, as such, but rather point out that they are not the most suitable systems for the investigation of nuclear magnetic moment.

As elementary calculations show, the interactions between the nuclear moments of the nuclei in a molecule in a $^1\Sigma$ state and the other angular momentum vectors, such as molecular rotation, are of the order of magnitude of 100 gauss or less. External fields of a few thousand gauss will therefore decouple all the nuclear spins from each other and from the molecular rotation to such a degree that they may be regarded as free. The other interactions will result in a fine structure of constant or decreasing width as H_0 is increased. These effects on the precision can, therefore, be reduced to any assigned value merely by working at suitably high field.

APPARATUS

The apparatus [Fig. 83–3] is contained in a long brass-walled tube divided into three distinct chambers, each with its own high vacuum pumping system. The source chamber contains the oven which is mounted on tungsten pegs. By means of a screw the mount may be moved, under vacuum, in a direction perpendicular to the beam axis. Stopcock grease and Apiezon Q on the screw preserve vacuum even when the screw is turned. The interchamber contains no essential parts of the apparatus, but provides adequate vacuum isolation of the receiving chamber from the gassing of the heated oven, by means of a narrow slit on each end of the chamber. These slits may be moved under vacuum in a manner similar to the oven mount. The receiving chamber contains most of the essential parts of the apparatus: the two deflecting magnets, A and B, the magnet, C, which produces the constant field, the radio-frequency oscillating field, R, the collimating slit, S, and the 1-mil tungsten filament detector, D.

The A and B fields are electromagnets of the type described by Millman, Rabi and Zacharias and are 52 cm and 58 cm long, respectively. The gap is bounded by two cylindrical surfaces, one convex of radius 1.25 mm, and the other concave of radius 1.47 mm. The gap width in the plane of symmetry, defined by the axes of the two cylindrical surfaces, is 1.0 mm. The nature of the field obtained is approximately the same as that produced by two parallel wires with centers 2.5 mm apart and carrying current in opposite directions. Each magnet has four turns of copper windings; current is supplied by a 3000-ampere-hour, 2-volt storage cell. A current of 300 amperes in the windings yields a field of over 12,000 gauss and a gradient of about 100,000 gauss/cm in the gap.

The C magnet, which produces the homogeneous field, is made of annealed Armco iron and is of conventional design. It is wound with 12 turns of $\frac{3}{16}''$ square copper rod to which $\frac{3}{16}''$ copper tubing has been soldered for cooling purposes. Insulation between turns, and between the windings and the magnet, is provided by mica. The pole faces, separated by a gap of $\frac{1}{4}''$, are 10 cm long and 4 cm high. A field of about 23 gauss is realized in the gap per ampere of current in the exciting coils.

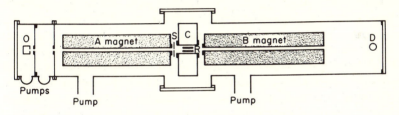

Fig. 83–3. Schematic diagram of apparatus.

In mounting the magnets in the apparatus, care must be taken to avoid regions of weak, rapidly changing fields between magnets. Such regions cause transitions between quantum states of the various magnetic moments associated with the molecule and prevent good refocusing of the beam by the B field. Although the gradient in the B field is necessarily in a direction opposite to that in the A field, the magnetic fields in the planes of symmetry of the two magnets are in the same direction and parallel to that in the C magnet. The magnets are placed as close to each other as the windings will permit. Moreover these windings are completely hidden from the "view" of the molecular beam by mounting slabs of iron as extensions on both ends of the C magnet and on the ends of the A and B magnets facing the C magnet. This arrangement insures a fairly strong field along the entire path of the molecular beam where changes in the over-all magnetic moment of the molecule affects its position at D, i.e., from the beginning of the A field to the end of the B field, and thus limits transitions between the quantum states to the region of the R field, where they may be controlled and studied.

The oscillating field, R, consists of two $\frac{1}{8}''$ copper tubes, 4 cm long, carrying current in opposite directions. These tubes are flattened to permit their insertion between the pole faces of the C magnet when a space of about 1 mm between the tubes is left for the passage of the beam. The plane defined by the centers of these tubes is horizontal and is adjusted to be closely the same as the planes of symmetry of the A and B magnets. These tubes are supported by heavy copper tubing through which electrical and water connections may be made outside the apparatus.

The magnetic field, H_1, produced by a current in the tubes is about 2 gauss/amp. and is approximately vertical and therefore at right angles to the field H_0 produced by the C magnet. The high frequency currents in the tubes are obtained by coupling a loop in series with them to the tank coil of a conventional Hartley oscillator in which an Eimac 250 TL tube is used. The frequencies used for these experiments range from 0.6 to 8 megacycles. The currents producing the oscillating field may be varied from 0 to 40 amperes; the higher currents are more easily obtained at low frequencies.

PROCEDURE

A preliminary line-up of magnets, slits and detector is made by optical means while the apparatus is assembled. If this line-up is sufficiently good, a beam may be sent through the apparatus and a more precise line-up made by means of a triangulation process utilizing the property of rectilinear motion of the molecules in the beam.

The A and B magnets have knife edges at both ends which overlap the gap on the side of the convex pole face by known amounts and extend above the gap into the region above the magnet by a known amount. Since it is impossible to sight through the gaps with a telescope, the preliminary optical line-up is made by sighting on the extensions of the edges in the region above the magnets. In this way it is possible to adjust the plane of symmetry of magnet A to coincide with that of magnet B. The optical line-up is sufficient for this purpose, since no very great precision is needed for this adjustment. It is also possible to adjust optically the lateral position of the magnets as well as the slits and detector to permit a beam to pass through the magnet gaps. The C magnet is lined up so that the median plane of its gap coincides with the centers of the gaps of the A and B magnets. The two wires which produce the radiofrequency field, R, are suspended from a brass plate which is mounted on top of the vacuum chamber, and are so constructed that the width of the assemblage is only very slightly less than the width of the gap in the C magnet. The field R is then arranged in the gap so that it does not short to the poles of the C magnet. Since the width of the gap between the two wires is greater than that of the available working gap in the A and B magnets, this line-up is sufficient for the field R.

A sample of the molecular compound, the magnetic moments of whose constituent nuclei are to be determined, is placed in an oven. The oven is completely closed except for a slit about 0.03 mm wide. It is heated by means of spiral tungsten heaters passed through the oven block and electrically insulated from it by means of quartz tubing. When the temperature of the oven is sufficiently high so that the sample has a vapor pressure of the order of 1 mm of Hg a beam may be observed at the detector and a more precise line-up may be initiated.

In the present apparatus the B magnet is permanently fixed inside the vacuum chamber and all other line-up operations are made with respect to it. By suitable movements of the oven, the collimating slit, and the detector, the beam is shifted until it is cut by each of the two fiduciary knife edges on the B magnet in turn. From a knowledge of the distances separating the various elements involved in a cutoff, it is possible to set the beam parallel to the plane defined by the two edges and to ascertain the distance of the beam from that plane. The only measurements that must be made during this line-up process are the readings of detector positions by means of a calibrated tele-microscope. By successive movements of the oven, collimating slit and detector the beam can be translated parallel to itself by any desired amount. It is thus brought into a position at which one would like to have the plane of the edges of the A field. This field is then moved, in a manner similar to that described for the motion of the oven mount, until its fiduciary edges cut the beam. This operation sets the plane defined by the edges on the A field parallel to the corresponding plane of the B field and at a predetermined distance from it. The beam is then translated to a position approximately midway between these planes.

The experimental criterion which determines the exact position of the beam is that the weakening of a molecular beam at the detector by the A and B fields taken separately must be equal. This may easily be accomplished by a lateral displacement of the beam, since for any such displacement the gradient increases in one of the fields and decreases in the other. When this criterion is satisfied the intensity of the refocused beam with a current of about 300 amp. in the windings of each of the two inhomogeneous fields is about 90 percent of the beam observed in the absence of fields.

As has been pointed out, the refocusing condition obtains only when there is no change in the space quantization of any of the moment vectors associated with the molecule. If weak fields occur in the region between A and B fields, transitions may occur. The refocusing becomes good only when the C field itself is fairly large, and the intensity of the refocused beam is an increasing function of the C field up to a value of about 500 gauss. The resonance minima to be described subsequently are usually observed at fields larger than 1000 gauss.

Because the amplifier is not completely shielded from the oscillator and because the steady deflection of the galvanometer associated with the amplifier due to the oscillator is a function of the frequency, observations are made of the beam intensity as a function of the magnetic field, H_0, when the frequency is held fixed. Curves relating the beam intensity to the field H_0, taken for $_3Li^7$ and $_3Li^6$, $_9F^{19}$ are shown in [figs. 83–4 to 6].

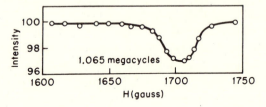

Fig. 83–4. Resonance curve of the Li^6 nucleus observed in LiCl.

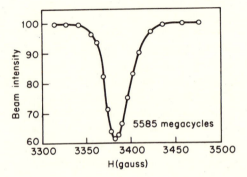

Fig. 83–5. Resonance curve of the Li^7 nucleus observed in LiCl.

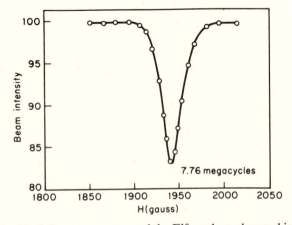

Fig. 83–6. Resonance curve of the F^{19} nucleus observed in NaF.

MAGNETIC AND FREQUENCY MEASUREMENTS

Since the value of the magnetic moment of any nucleus is calculated from an observed magnetic field and an observed frequency it is essential that these quantities be known to a high degree of precision. The frequency of the oscillating magnetic field is determined to better than 0.03 percent by measuring the frequency of the oscillator with a General Radio Type 620A heterodyne frequency meter. It was found that the frequency of the oscillator varied by no more than 0.01 percent during the time required to obtain data on one resonance curve (~ 15 minutes).

A calibration of the magnetic field of the homogeneous C magnet in terms of the current through the exciting coils was made in the usual way by measuring the ballistic deflection of a galvanometer when a flip coil was pulled from the magnetic field. The galvanometer was calibrated by the use of a 50-millihenry mutual inductance, good to $\frac{1}{2}$ percent. Several flip coils were constructed in this laboratory by winding various types and sizes of insulated wire on carefully measured brass spools. Errors in the magnetic field due to uncertainties in flip coil areas are probably not greater than 0.2 percent. A type K potentiometer was used to measure the potential drop across a shunt in series with the C magnet windings. The same shunt was used both in the calibration and in subsequent work, thereby eliminating the necessity of knowing its resistance accurately.

It is important that the magnetic field always returned to the same value for a given magnetizing current. It was found that when a definite, reproducible procedure was used for demagnetizing the homogeneous field and for bringing it up to any state of magnetization, this condition was fulfilled to better than 0.1 percent.

A considerable variation in the value of the mutual inductance was observed, apparently depending on the humidity. The absolute value of the magnetic field is indeterminate to about 0.5 percent due to the uncertainty in the value of the mutual inductance and uncertainty in the areas of the flip coils. This, of course, introduces a corresponding uncertainty in the absolute values of the magnetic moments.

RESULTS

The first nuclei to be studied by this method were $_3Li^6$, $_3Li^7$ and $_9F^{19}$ in the LiCl, LiF, NaF and Li_2 molecules. The resonance minima which are obtained are shown in [figs. 83–4, 5 and 6]. For each nucleus the f/H values corresponding to the resonance minima are constant to a very high degree for wide variations of frequency. This shows that we are dealing

TABLE 83 – 1. *Representing Values of f/H for* Li[6], Li[7] *and* F[19]

Nucleus	Molecule	f Megacycles per Second	H Gauss	$\frac{f}{H}$
Li[6]	LiCl	2.127	3405	624.6
		2.127	3400	625.6
		2.155	3455	623.8
		2.155	3446	625.3
	Li$_2$	1.714	2742	625.0
		1.714	2744	624.7
	LiF	2.193	3506	625.5
		2.193	3501	626.5
Li[7]	LiCl	5.611	3399	1651
		5.610	3400	1650
		6.587	3992	1650
		2.113	1278	1654
		5.552	3383	1651
	LiF	5.621	3401	1653
		6.580	3981	1653
		3.517	2133	1649
	Li$_2$	3.056	1862	1651
		3.084	1879	1652
		3.129	1907	1651
F[19]	NaF	5.634	1407	4001
		5.634	1409	3998
		7.799	1949	4001
		7.799	1953	3992
		7.799	1952	3995
	LiF	4.204	1053	3994
		4.204	1055	3986

with a change of nuclear orientation and not with some molecular transition, since such a transition would not possess a frequency proportional to H. A representative sample of the results is shown in [Table 83–1]. The constancy of f/H also shows that our method of calibration of the C magnet yields accurate results, at least for relative values of the homogeneous field.

The nuclear g is obtained from the observed f/H values by use of the formula

$$g = \frac{4\pi}{e/Mc} \cdot \frac{f}{H} = 1.3122 \times 10^{-3} \frac{f}{H},$$

which follows immediately from Eq. (1) if the magnetic moment μ is measured in units of $eh/4\pi Mc$, the nuclear magneton, and $f = \nu$. The specific charge of the proton in electromagnetic units, e/Mc, is obtained directly from the value of the Faraday (9648.9 e.m.u.) and the atomic weight of hydrogen (1.0081). Expressed in this form our experimental results do not depend upon any inaccuracies in e, h or m/M, the ratio of the electronic mass to the mass of the proton. The nuclear spins of Li^6 and Li^7 are known from atomic beam measurements, and that of F^{19} from band spectra. The nuclear moments are obtained directly by multiplying g by i. The nuclear g's, the spins and the magnetic moments are listed in [Table 83–2]. The values here given are about 0.5 percent lower than, and

T A B L E   8 3 – 2 .   *Nuclear g's and Magnetic Moments*

Nucleus	g	Spin	Moment
$_3Li^6$	0.820	1	0.820
$_3Li^7$	2.167	$\frac{3}{2}$	3.250
$_9F^{19}$	5.243	$\frac{1}{2}$	2.622

are to supersede, those published in the preliminary report. The differences are due to the use of a more trustworthy mutual inductance in the calibration of the magnetic field and to an error in the value of the constant $4\pi/(e/Mc)$ previously used. The identification of the resonance minimum with a particular nucleus is made by using the same element in more than one molecule. For example, two of the resonance minima, observed for each of the molecules, LiCl, LiF and Li_2 have f/H values which are the same in all three cases. These must be attributed to the nuclei of the two isotopes of lithium. Since Li^7 is about 12 times as abundant as Li^6 and since the intensity drop at resonance for one of these minimi is as much as 60 percent of the refocused beam, this minimum can only be assigned to Li^7. No minimum is definitely assigned to a nucleus unless it has been observed in at least two different molecules.

The accuracy of the nuclear moment values depends solely on a knowledge of the magnetic field, H, at which the Larmor frequency associated with the nuclear magnetic moment is equal to the frequency of the oscillating field. The absolute moment values depend upon the absolute calibration of magnetic standards and cannot at present be taken to be better than 0.5 percent. The relative moment values, on the other hand, do not depend on such standards but merely on the accuracy of the shape of the magnetization curve for the homogeneous field, on the reproducibility of a definite field with the same current in the exciting coils of the homogenous field, on the location of a minimum in the resonance curve and on the assumption that any form of interaction tending to broaden the resonance curve and not considered in the simple theory will introduce no asymmetry into the curve. The criterion for the first three points mentioned is the internal consistency of the f/H values obtained under varied conditions. This leads to a precision of about 0.1 percent for the relative moment values of Li^6, Li^7 and F^{19}. From a consideration of the small half-widths observed for the resonance curves (~ 1 percent) and their symmetrical character it seems unlikely that any interactions are present which will tend to shift the minimum by more than 0.2 or 0.3 percent, if at all.

The simple model which we have used to discuss the principles of the method is, no doubt, insufficient to describe the finer details of the results, such as the width and shape of the resonance curves. For this purpose one must consider the various interactions between the nuclear spins of the different nuclei and their interactions with the rest of the molecular structure. The nature of other perturbations and the physical information which can be obtained from detailed observation of resonance minima will be discussed in another paper.

DISCUSSION

One of the important objects of nuclear moment investigations is to ascertain whether the hyperfine structure of atomic energy levels can be accounted for entirely by the assumption that the nucleus interacts with the external electrons as a small magnet. The effects arising from the finite size of the nucleus and its charge distribution (isotope effect and electric quadrupole moment effect) modify slightly the h.f.s. predicted from this simple assumption but are still within the range of electromagnetic interactions. There may possibly be some other interactions with the electron which are not electromagnetic in nature but more like spin dependent nuclear forces. To this end a comparison of the ratio of the magnetic moments of two isotopes measured by our direct methods with that obtained from the results of h.f.s. measurements on the same isotopes is of interest. Since the electronic wave functions are the same for two isotopes, the ratio of the h.f.s. separations $(\Delta\nu)_1/(\Delta\nu)_2$ of a given atomic energy state should yield the ratio of the moments, μ_1/μ_2, very accurately if no other effect enters. It is to be expected that a discrepancy between these two moment ratios will be very small because of the short time which an electron spends in the region very close to the nucleus.

The ratio of the moments of the lithium isotopes, μ_7/μ_6, found by Manley and Millman by the atomic beam zero moment method of measuring h.f.s. separations is 3.89. Our value is 3.963, which is about two percent higher. It is difficult to be certain, at the present time, that this difference represents a real physical effect rather than an experimental error. Although our value can hardly be off by as much as 0.3 percent, the value given by Manley and Millman may possibly be in error because the Li^6 zero moment peak was not completely resolved from the Li^7 background. Further work along this line is clearly desirable. Another method of studying this question is through very accurate calculations of atomic wave functions (particularly in the case of Li) from which the nuclear moment can be calculated from h.f.s. data to a precision comparable with that of our direct measurements. The present status of this side of the problem is that our value of 3.250 for Li^7 is to be compared with 3.29 obtained from the measurements of Granath on the h.f.s. of Li II, and the calculations of Breit and Doerman. Fox and Rabi find 3.14 from atomic beam experiments on Li I and the theory of Goudsmit and that of Fermi and Segrè, while Bartlett, Gibbons and Watson calculate 3.33 from the same data. These differences, though small, may be significant; however, they are, as yet, within the range of accuracy claimed by the calculations.

For $_9F^{19}$, Brown and Bartlett calculate values ranging from 1.9 to 3.8 from the h.f.s. data of Campbell which are to be compared with our value of 2.622. For a discussion of the accuracy and reliability of these calculations see the conclusions of the papers by Bartlett and his co-workers.

From the standpoint of current nuclear theory our results for the ratio of the moments μ_{Li^7}/μ_{Li^6} diverge even more widely from the calculations of Rose and Bethe, than did the previous results of Manley and Millman. In a recent paper, Bethe has sought to improve the previous calculation by the use of an α-particle model. The agreement with experiment is more satisfactory than for the previous theory of Rose and Bethe. Whether this result is accidental remains to be seen from future calculations of other moments with a similar model.

84

ooooooooooo

HYDROGEN AND THE

ELEMENTARY

PARTICLES

ooooooooooo

Willis E. Lamb Jr. (b. 1913)

When Bohr first introduced his theory of the atom, he explained the origin of the spectral lines (the Balmer lines) of hydrogen by means of a single quantum number, n (the principal quantum number) which takes on all integral values 1,2,3... and corresponds to the various permitted orbits. The principal quantum number determines the size of the permitted orbit and is a measure of the total energy of the electron in this orbit, just as in classical physics the semimajor axis of the orbit of a planet determines the total mechanical energy of the planet in this orbit. The original Bohr theory was, however, inadequate in two respects. On the one hand, it gave only circular orbits for the electron in a hydrogen atom; on the other, it did not account for certain fine details of the structure of the hydrogen spectral lines. Moreover, it could not account for the presence of certain lines and the absence of others (that is, the selection rules). Indeed, on the basis of circular orbits alone, the only lines that should be present are those associated with transitions in which the principal quantum number changes by one unit only.

As noted in chapters 57, 58, and 59, Sommerfeld was the first to point out that the introduction of elliptical orbits would automatically introduce a fine structure into the spectral lines of hydrogen if one took into account the relativistic variation of the mass of a particle with its speed. As long as the electron moves in a circular orbit, its speed is constant and there is no variation of its mass. But if the electron moves in an elliptical orbit, its speed becomes greater as it moves closer to the proton, and slower when it is far away, so that the mass of the electron varies continuously. This continuous variation causes the whole orbit to precess so that the electron acquires additional energy. To define the ellipticity of the orbit of the electron, Sommerfeld introduced a second quantum number, *l*, the azimuthal quantum number, which corresponds to the eccentricity of the elliptical orbit of a planet. The azimuthal quantum number is a measure of (is proportional to) the angular momentum of the electron in its orbit. Sommerfeld pointed out that for an orbit of principal quantum number *n* there are just *n* integral values of the azimuthal quantum number, namely, $0,1,2,3 \ldots (n-1)$.

These various azimuthal quantum numbers correspond to the values of the angular momentum of an electron that can be associated with its motion. The smallest value of the azimuthal quantum number (the most highly eccentric ellipse) corresponds to the smallest angular momentum (actually zero); the largest value of the azimuthal quantum number (the roundest ellipse) gives the largest angular momentum of the electron. These *n* different energy sublevels (different because of the relativistic variation of mass with speed) are labeled *S, P, D, F, G,* and so on. Thus 2*S* represents the energy sublevel of an electron with principal quantum number 2 (the second Bohr energy level of the atom) and zero angular momentum; whereas, 2*P* represents an electron in the second energy level of principal quantum number 2, with one unit of angular momentum and so on.

With the introduction of the azimuthal quantum number, it was thought that all the fine details of the spectral lines of hydrogen and other atoms would be accounted for. But a closer examination of the spectral lines, particularly for the alkali atoms, such as sodium, where there is only one outer electron (the outer electrons are responsible for the spectral lines), reveals that each of the orbital angular momentum sublevels, associated with a given principal quantum number, except the level *S* is split into two levels. This was accounted for by assigning a half unit of spin angular momentum to the electron. Since this half unit of spin can only add to the orbital angular momentum, or subtract from it, there are two sublevels (doublets) associated with each value of the orbital angular momentum except the zero value. Thus, for example, one must replace the single level 2*P* by the two levels $2P_{1/2}$ and $2P_{3/2}$, where the subscripts refer to the total angular momentum of the electron, owing to the effects of the particle's spin. To see how we obtain the two possible values $\frac{1}{2}$ and $\frac{3}{2}$ for the total angular momentum of the electron when it is in the 2*P* sublevel, we note that it has just one unit of orbital angular momentum. If its spin axis is parallel to its orbital angular momentum, we must add its one half unit of spin angular momentum to its orbital angular momentum, and we get $1 + \frac{1}{2} = \frac{3}{2}$. If the spin axis is antiparallel (opposite) to the orbital angular momentum, we must subtract the two, and we get $1 - \frac{1}{2} = \frac{1}{2}$. These are the only possibilities; hence, we obtain doublets. In general the level with the higher total angular momentum, in this case the $2P_{3/2}$ level, is a state of higher energy than that with the smaller total angular momentum.

Since these refinements in the Bohr theory had been introduced within the framework of the Bohr postulates, before quantum mechanics and the Schroedinger wave equation had been applied to the atom, there was some reason for believing that the Schroedinger wave equation would give the azimuthal sublevels and the spin doublet structure automatically. This, however, proved not to be the case. Although the solution of the Schroedinger equation for the hydrogen atom does give the azimuthal quantum numbers, in addition to the principal quantum numbers in the proper relationships with one another, it assigns the same energy to each azimuthal sublevel associated with a given principal quantum number. Consequently, the total number of distinct levels in the Schroedinger theory is still given by the principal quantum numbers. The azimuthal quantum number energy sublevels are degenerate, in the sense that to each principal quantum number n the Schroedinger equation assigns n wave or vibrational modes (that is, n wave functions), each with the same energy. Besides this deficiency, the Schroedinger equation gives no spin effects whatsoever.

This is not surprising if one gives it some thought. The different energy values that must be assigned to the azimuthal quantum number sublevels arise because of the variation of the electron's mass with velocity, and this is a relativity effect. The electron spin is also a relativity effect. Hence, it follows that these effects cannot be deduced from the Schroedinger equation since this equation is not in accord with the relativity theory. But since the Dirac equation of the electron was designed specifically to accommodate the special theory of relativity, it corrects the flaws of the Schroedinger equation. When applied to the hydrogen atom, Dirac's equation gives not only the fine structure of the spectral lines associated with the azimuthal quantum numbers of the electron, but also the spin of the electron and the spin doublet structure of the spectral lines.

Some of the most interesting features of the Dirac theory are related to the azimuthal energy levels associated with the principal quantum number $n = 2$. For $n = 2$, there are two azimuthal quantum numbers, 0 and 1, so that there are two azimuthal sublevels, the $2S$ level and the $2P$ level. If we now take the spin of the electron into account, we obtain three levels, one from the S level, the so-called singlet $2^2S_{1/2}$ level and the doublet P state consisting of the two levels $2^2P_{1/2}$ and $2^2P_{3/2}$. The solution of the

Dirac equation gives these terms and in addition the energy values that must be assigned to each of these levels. In terms of energy the $2^2P_{3/2}$ level lies slightly above the $2^2P_{1/2}$ level; an electron jumping from the upper of these levels to the lower would emit a photon of wavelength 2.74 cm, which is in the microwave region of the spectrum. But the $2^2S_{1/2}$ level and the $2^2P_{1/2}$ level coincide exactly according to the Dirac theory.

This theoretical prediction of an exact coincidence was a challenge to experimental spectroscopists. Even before World War II, when microwave techniques were still in their infancy, spectroscopic workers obtained observation data that disagreed with the theory. Houston, Williams, Paternack, and others had found discrepancies; Paternack, in particular, had argued that the $2^2S_{1/2}$ level must lie above the $2^2P_{1/2}$ level. However, the experimental techniques were not sufficiently accurate then to give a definitive answer.

At the end of World War II, however, microwave technology in the neighborhood of the 3-cm wavelength had advanced to such a stage that Willis E. Lamb, then professor of physics at Columbia University, could design a very ingenious and beautiful experiment, based on microwave techniques, to analyze the fine structure of the hydrogen lines for the principal quantum number $n = 2$. This experiment uses the metastable character of the $2^2S_{1/2}$ level, which should be long-lived against a radiative transition to the ground state. The reason that this state is metastable (that is, that it has a much longer life than normal) is that there is a selection rule which forbids the spontaneous transition of an electron from one S level to another S level. This means that the electron cannot jump down from the $2S_{1/2}$ level to the ground state because the ground state is also an S level. Hence once the electron has been forced into the $2^2S_{1/2}$ level by some excitation process, it will stay there for a long time—about one seventh of a second—as compared to the normal life time of about one hundred millionth of a second.

Lamb and Retherford used this metastable state of the hydrogen atom in the following way. They pointed out that if the hydrogen atom is first excited to the $2^2S_{1/2}$ metastable state, it will stay in this state long enough to be recorded by some mechanism that can detect the excitation energy, which is released when the excited atom strikes it. One should therefore be able to detect a beam of such metastable atoms, which are prepared by bombarding unexcited hydrogen atoms with a stream of electrons having the proper kinetic energy. If the beam of excited metastable atoms is perturbed by an external electric field or by radiation of the proper frequency, the metastable atoms can be induced to go from the the metastable S state to one of the P states, from which they can jump down to the ground state in a very short time. If this happens, fewer metastable atoms reach the detector and the current in the detector drops. Lamb and Retherford used this technique and showed that transitions of the metastable atom to the $2^2P_{1/2}$ state can be induced by microwaves of the proper frequency. In this way, they analyzed the fine structure of the $2S$ and $2P$ levels and showed that there is a 1,000 megacycle-per-second separation between the $2^2S_{1/2}$ and the $2^2P_{1/2}$ levels, in disagreement with the prediction of the Dirac theory.

This remarkable experimental result opened up an entirely new field of inquiry for physicists, for the question that arose immediately was whether or not the Dirac theory of the electron is correct. If it is not, wherein does it falter and how is it to be improved? The answers to these questions were given by a group of theoretical and experimental physicists working along different lines, in some cases independently, in other cases, in teams. We shall consider the various theoretical contributions to the solution of this problem and their effects on our knowledge of the properties of the electron in subsequent chapters.

Willis Eugene Lamb, Jr., by education, experience, and intellectual equipment, was one of the very few physicists who could have performed the very delicate microwave experiment, in 1947, which proved that the observed fine structure of the energy levels of the L shell (the levels of principal quantum number $n = 2$) of the hydrogen atom does not agree with the predictions of the Dirac theory. To do this experiment successfully, one had to have a thorough understanding of the Dirac theory of the electron, an excellent working command of the quantum mechanics, a practical understanding of the Rabi molecular-beam technique, and a thorough working knowledge of microwave technology. Lamb, a theoretical physicist by training, had all of these prerequisites in 1945 when he first began to consider this problem.

He was born on July 12, 1913, in Los Angeles, California, and spent his very early years in Oakland. His family then moved back to Los Angeles, and Lamb continued his education there. After graduating from high school in 1930, he entered the University of California at Berkeley, where he majored in chemistry, and received his B.S. degree in 1934. By the time he had completed his undergraduate studies, his interest had shifted from chemistry to theoretical physics, and he decided to do graduate work in physics under J. Robert Oppenheimer.

In 1930 Oppenheimer had shown that if one calculates the interaction of an electron with the quantized electromagnetic field, using the Dirac theory of the electron (in which the electron is treated as a point charge), one obtains infinite and therefore meaningless results. According to this calculation, the interaction of the electron with its own radiation field should cause all the hydrogen energy levels to be shifted by an infinite amount, which of course, physically speaking, is nonsense. In 1934, a calculation by V. Weisskopf showed that this difficulty in the theory arose from the peculiar interaction that exists between the electron and the vacuum in the Dirac theory.

Lamb himself came into contact with this puzzling result during his graduate studies, when Oppenheimer assigned to him a thesis dealing with the field theories of nucleons. His analysis of the problem led to a very small discrepancy from Coulomb's law for the electrostatic field about a proton. Such a discrepancy would, of course, present departures from the Dirac theory of the fine structure of the hydrogen spectral lines, which was then being investigated by spectroscopists. On completing his thesis and receiving his Ph.D. in 1938, Lamb went to Columbia University as an instructor in physics, with the unresolved question of the Dirac theory's validity in its prediction of the fine structure of hydrogen lines still in his mind. Spectroscopists had indicated a discrepancy between theory and observations, at that time, but the results of their experiments were inconclusive. Lamb therefore sought other methods of investigation. The very elegant and highly precise molecular-beam technique, developed by Rabi at Columbia, provided him wth the basis for his own experiment.

At that time, before World War II, the experiment that Lamb was to devise later could not have been carried out because the special microwave techniques it required were not yet known. During the war, however, he worked in the Columbia Radiation Laboratory where he became acquainted with the theory of microwaves and vacuum tube construction techniques. Since his own project in the laboratory dealt with the absorption of centimeter-wavelength microwaves, he acquired the skills that he was able to apply to his Nobel Prize experiment, which involved the absorption of such waves by excited hydrogen atoms.

Lamb's interest in checking the Dirac theory by microwave absorption was aroused in the summer of 1946 when he was teaching a summer session course on atomic physics at Columbia University. In the textbook by Herzberg that he was using, he ran across a reference to some unsuccessful experiments conducted in 1932–1935 that were intended to detect the absorption of short-wavelength radio waves by the excited hydrogen atoms in a discharge tube. At first he contemplated repeating these same experiments using the greatly improved microwave detection techniques, but a careful theoretical analysis of the experiment revealed that the statistical distribution of the excited hydrogen atoms under the stated conditions was such as to defeat the purpose of the experiment. He realized that he could do the same thing by using the Rabi molecular-beam technique in which individual atoms can be excited to the particular state desired, then irradiated by microwaves of the proper wavelength, and finally detected. In this way the absorption can be measured directly by studying the excited beam of atoms after they have passed through the microwave field.

A great deal of preliminary theoretical work had to be done on every phase of this problem before the experiment could actually be performed; the preparation took Lamb a full year. In 1947 he persuaded one of his students, R. C. Retherford, to perform the experiment. It was completely successful, and proved that the fine structure of the hydrogen lines, as predicted by the Dirac theory, does not agree with the observational data. This remarkable experiment led to the mass renormalization theories of Bethe, Schwinger, Feynman, and Tomonaga, and indicated how the Dirac theory must be corrected to conform to the observed results. The discrepancy between the uncorrected Dirac theory predictions and the observed results is now called the "Lamb shift."

During World War II, Lamb was promoted from instructor to associate at Columbia; in 1945 he became assistant professor and in 1947, associate professor. In 1948, after the publication of his experimental results, he was appointed full professor. He remained at the Columbia Radiation Laboratory until 1951, giving graduate physics courses and stimulating theoretical and experimental work in connection with his discovery of the Lamb shift.

In 1951 Lamb left Columbia to become professor of physics at Stanford University in California, where he remained until 1956; during this period he spent one year (1953–1954) as Morris Loeb lecturer at Harvard University. In 1956 he went to Oxford University, England, as fellow of New College and Wykeham professor of physics. He remained at Oxford until 1962, when he left to become the first Henry Ford II professor of physics at Yale University, where he is still actively engaged in teaching and research.

The experimental discovery of the Lamb shift and the new problems arising from it are but one small aspect of his over-all research work. Lamb is a theoretical physicist who has published important papers in almost every field of physics. In nuclear physics he has contributed to an understanding of the interaction of neutrons and matter, the field theories of nuclear forces and nuclear structure, the β-decay process, and the range of fission fragments in nuclear fission. In particle physics, he has investigated cosmic ray showers and pair production. He has also contributed to solid state physics and the physics of crystals; his 1939 paper on the resonance capture of slow neutrons by crystals played an important role in the development of the Mössbauer effect.

He has also done significant work in molecular physics, magnetron oscillators, diamagnetism, nuclear resonance, the theory of the deuteron and the helium nucleus, and in microwave spectroscopy.

In addition to the Nobel Prize, Lamb has received the Rumford Award of the American Academy of Arts and Sciences and the Research Corporation Award. In 1954, the University of Pennsylvania awarded him an honorary Doctor of Science degree. He is a member of the National Academy of Sciences and a fellow of the American Physical Society.

His wife, the former Ursula Schaefer, was a student from Germany when they married in 1939.

ooooooo

L A M B

Fine Structure of the Hydrogen Atom [1]

WHEN THE NOBEL PRIZES WERE first awarded in 1901, physicists knew something of just two objects that are now called "elementary particles," the electron and the proton. A deluge of other "elementary" particles appeared after 1930—the neutron, neutrino, mu meson, pi meson, heavier mesons, and various hyperons. I have heard it said that "the finder of a new elementary particle used to be rewarded by a Nobel prize, but such a discovery now ought to be punished by a $10,000 fine."

In order to determine the properties of elementary particles experimentally, it is necessary to subject them to external forces or to allow them to interact with each other. The hydrogen atom—which is the union of the first known elementary particles, the electron and the proton—has been studied for many years and its spectrum has taught us much about the electron.

HISTORICAL DEVELOPMENTS

In 1885, Balmer found that the wavelengths of 14 lines of the hydrogen spectrum were given by a simple equation. In 1887, Michelson and Morley discovered a fine structure of some of these lines. The quantum theory was founded by Planck in 1900, and in 1913 Bohr gave rules of quantization that permitted a derivation of Balmer's formula. Sommerfeld showed in 1916 that the fine structure of Bohr's energy levels was caused by relativis-

---

[1] Lamb, *Science,* 123 (1956), 439–442. 1955 Nobel Prize address.

tic corrections. In 1924, de Broglie attributed wave properties to the electron, and soon a quantum mechanics of the hydrogen atom emerged from the hands of Heisenberg, Born, and Schroedinger. Spin and magnetic moment of the electron were suggested by Uhlenbeck and Goudsmit in 1925, and their dynamical equations were worked out by Thomas a year later. In 1928, Dirac discovered an equation that described an electron with wave properties, charge, spin, magnetic moment, and a mass depending on velocity as required by relativity theory. The energy levels of hydrogen were given by Dirac's theory with high precision.

Of special interest to us are his predictions, as shown in [Fig. 84–3], of the $n = 2$ group of energy levels, which are 10.2 electron volts above the $n = 1$ ground state. The fine structure splitting $2^2P_{3/2}$–$2^2P_{1/2}$, which according to Dirac's theory arises from spin-orbit interaction, agrees exactly with the separation of the two levels of Sommerfeld's 1916 theory. The exact coincidence in energy of the $2^2S_{1/2}$ and $2^2P_{1/2}$ states is a consequence of the assumed Coulomb law of attraction between electron and proton. Any departure from this law would cause a separation of these levels.

Many spectroscopic studies of the hydrogen fine structure were made to test the Dirac theory, but by 1940 they had failed to establish clearly a decision, although there was evidence strongly supporting the theory. . . .

For the subsequent developments, some chapters from my own peculiar history may be of interest. After undergraduate training as a chemist, I studied theoretical physics under J. R. Oppenheimer at the University of California from 1934 to 1938. My thesis dealt with field theories of nucleons, which predicted a very small discrepancy from Coulomb's law about a proton. At Columbia University after 1938, I came into a close relationship with I. I. Rabi and members of the molecular beam laboratory. My attention was drawn briefly to metastable atoms in connection with a proposed atomic beam experiment. During the war, I received at the Columbia Radiation Laboratory some first-hand acquaintance with microwave radar and vacuum-tube construction techniques. One of the wartime projects in the laboratory was the determination of the absorption coefficient of centimeter waves in atmospheric water vapor, and my interest was started in what was to become the very active postwar field of microwave spectroscopy.

A   W O R K A B L E   S C H E M E

In teaching a summer-session class in atomic physics in 1945 with a textbook by Herzberg I found references to some attempts made in the period 1932–35 to detect absorption of short-wavelength radio waves in a gas discharge of atomic hydrogen. At first it seemed to me that these experiments had failed because of inadequate microwave techniques. I thought of repeating them with the greatly improved facilities that had been developed during the war. On further study, however, I realized that atoms in a gas discharge are strongly perturbed and that all the $n = 2$ states would have nearly equal populations. Under these conditions, there would be no appreciable absorption of radio waves caused by transitions between the three states of interest.

It took almost a full year before a workable scheme was clear in my mind. I considered making use of the possible metastability of the $2^2S_{1/2}$ state of hydrogen. In the simplest terms, this state should be long lived against radiative transition to the ground state because a spherically symmetrical charge and current distribution cannot radiate according to

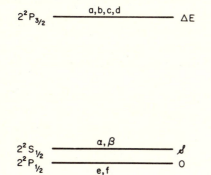

Fig. 84–1. Fine structure of *n*-2 levels of hydrogen according to the Dirac theory.

classical electromagnetic theory. Nevertheless, quite a few papers between 1924 and 1933 were devoted to discussion and experiment to determine whether or not the $2^2S_{1/2}$ state was actually metastable. In 1933, Bethe showed it to be metastable only for the atom in a region sufficiently free of electric fields. However, it was by no means clear that the excitation of the $2^2S_{1/2}$ state could be carried out without destroying the metastability of the state. It was still necessary to detect any interaction of microwaves with the excited atoms, and, as already mentioned, a direct-absorption method applied to a discharge seemed to be out of the question. I decided to try to form a beam of metastable hydrogen atoms. If a radio-induced transition to $2^2P_{1/2}$ or $2^2P_{3/2}$ did take place, the atom would lose its metastability and go in about 10^{-9} second to the ground state with emission of radiation. The beam of metastable atoms would thereby be diminished.

It had been shown in 1924 by Webb at Columbia University that metastable mercury atoms could liberate electrons from metals, but no one had either produced or detected the strange metastable form of hydrogen, and it was not certain that a beam of it could be detected through its ejection of electrons.

On the basis of these rather doubtful prospects, I persuaded Retherford to attempt the experiment represented schematically in [Fig. 84–2].

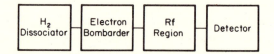

Fig. 84–2. Modified schematic block diagram of apparatus.

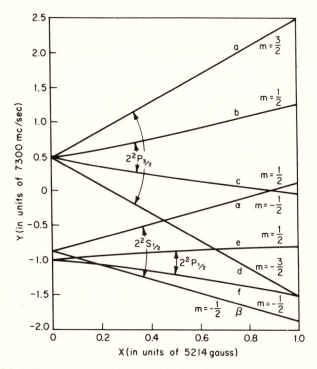

Fig. 84–3. Zeeman energy levels with the $2^2S_{1/2}$ pattern raised by 1000 megacycles per second.

Molecular hydrogen is dissociated in a tungsten oven, and a stream of hydrogen atoms emerges from a slit to be bombarded by electrons, which bring about one atom in 100 million to the metastable state. After a small recoil deflection, the excited atoms move on to a metal surface from which they can eject electrons and thus be detected. Between bombarder and detector, the atoms are exposed to radio waves.

For several good reasons, the whole process is carried out in a magnetic field. The fine structure energy levels are subject to Zeeman splitting, as shown in [Fig. 84–3], and the frequencies of the possible transitions depend on the magnetic field, as shown in [Fig. 84–4]. As the magnetic field is varied with radiofrequency and amplitude held fixed, $2s \rightarrow 2p \rightarrow 1s$ transitions occur, and a certain fraction of the metastable atoms in the beam are quenched and lose their excitation energy. Since atoms in the ground

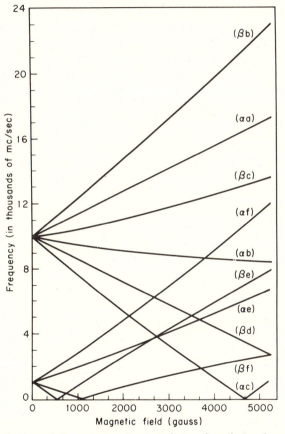

Fig. 84–4. Expected resonance frequencies as functions of magnetic field with the $2^2 S_{\frac{1}{2}}$ state raised by 1000 megacycles per second.

state are unable to eject electrons from the detector, the electrometer current decreases. A typical resonance curve for deuterium is shown in [Fig. 84–5]; a curve for hydrogen is shown in [Fig. 84–6]. The widths of the resonance peaks are partly due to natural radiative decay of the $2p$ state and partly to hyperfine structure, which is just resolved for one of the hydrogen resonances.

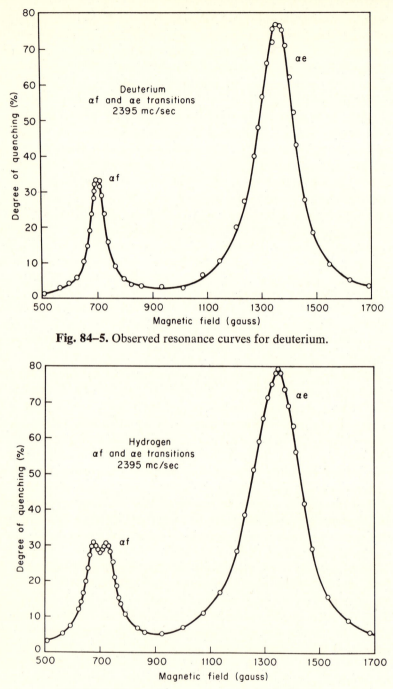

Fig. 84–5. Observed resonance curves for deuterium.

Fig. 84–6. Observed resonance curves for hydrogen.

By careful experimental study and theoretical analysis of such resonance curves, it is possible to determine the energy separations $2^2S_{1/2}–2^2P_{1/2}$ and $2^2P_{3/2}–2^2S_{1/2}$ in zero magnetic field. The accurate measurements by Dayhoff, Triebwasser and Lamb gave 1059.0 and 9912.6 megacycles per second for these separations in deuterium with an accuracy of about ± 0.1 megacycle per second.

Studies of other fine structure states have been made by microwave methods. For the $n = 2$ state of singly ionized helium, the separations are 13 to 16 times larger than they are for hydrogen. In the work of Lamb and Skinner, no beam of metastable ions was formed, but rather the ultraviolet radiation emitted in the decay of $2p$ to $1s$ was used to detect the transitions $2p$ to $2s$ that were induced by microwaves. A similar method was used in the later experiments of Deutsch on positronium, in which a transition from the triplet to singlet state changes the rate of emission of annihilation radiation. Recently the fine structure of the $n = 3$ state of hydrogen was studied by Lamb and Sanders using analogous microwave methods, and the fine structure of the 3^3P state of helium has been determined by Lamb, Maiman, and Wieder.

DEPARTURES FROM THE EXPECTED PATTERN

Let me now tell briefly about the explanation that has been given of the departures from the expected fine structure pattern for hydrogen. The heart of the matter is that the electron does not behave like a point charge as implied in Dirac's equation. If space permitted, I would trace the long history of attempts to make a theory of the internal structure of electrons. This was begun by J. J. Thomson with his calculation of electromagnetic mass and developed by Lorentz using classical electromagnetic theory.

According to relativity theory, energy and mass are proportional to one another. In order to obtain a finite mass of the electron on a purely electromagnetic basis, it was necessary to assign an extended structure to the electron. Attempts to form a satisfactory relativistic theory of an extended charged particle failed.

After quantum mechanics had been applied to matter, it was used by Dirac and by Heisenberg and Pauli to attack the problem of the electromagnetic field and its interaction with charged particles. This theory had many successes. A good account was given of the phenomena of emission, absorption, and scattering of radiation by matter, including the spontaneous radiation postulated by Einstein in 1917. From the quantum electrodynamical point of view, spontaneous emission could be regarded as emission stimulated by the quantum zero-point fluctuations in the electromagnetic fields in the vacuum or lowest energy state.

When, however, the energy of interaction of an electron with the quantized electromagnetic field was calculated by Oppenheimer in 1930, a meaningless result was obtained. According to this theory, not only was the energy infinite, but the frequencies of all spectral lines were displaced by an infinite amount from the values predicted without consideration of radiative interactions. It was pointed out by Weisskopf in 1934 that this ultraviolet catastrophe could be ascribed to the afore-mentioned zero-point fluctuations in the vacuum electromagnetic field. These fluctuations were needed if the correct spontaneous emission was to occur, and yet they led to violent disagreement with observations in other respects. The theory of electromagnetic energy remained in this highly unsatisfactory state until May 1947, when the fine structure deviations were definitely established experimentally.

A month later, Bethe found that quantum electrodynamics had really hidden behind its divergences a physical content that was in very close agreement with the microwave observations. The crucial step due to Bethe was a successful application of the very old idea of renormalization of mass. The quantum theory of radiation predicted that a free electron should have an infinite mass. Some explanation therefore had to be found for the observed fact that the mass was finite. Bethe recognized that this was outside the scope of the theory at that time and simply ignored the electromagnetic mass difficulty. For an electron bound in a hydrogen atom, an infinite energy also occurs, but this was merely a manifestation of the infinite electromagnetic mass that should be eliminated in some future theory. With the mass terms properly subtracted, a finite remainder is obtained that would be zero for a free electron. In the case of a bound electron, the force field modifies the effect of the electromagnetic field, and a finite displacement of energy levels results that is in quite good accord with observation.

A qualitative picture of the level shift was given by Welton in 1948. The fluctuating zero-point electric field of the quantized vacuum acts on an electron bound in a hydrogen atom. As a result, the electron is caused to move about its unperturbed position in a rapid and highly erratic manner. The point electron effectively becomes a sphere of a radius almost 10^{-12} centimeter. Such an electron in a hydrogen atom is not so strongly attracted to the nucleus at short distances as a point electron would be. States of zero orbital angular momentum such as $2^2S_{1/2}$ are therefore raised in energy relative to other states such as 2^2P in which the electron has a smaller probability of being found near the nucleus.

In 1949, a relativistic generalization of Bethe's calculation was given by Kroll and Lamb, which made his results definite. They confirmed additional small contributions of 27 megacycles per second arising from polarization of the vacuum as calculated in 1935 by Uehling on the basis of Dirac's theory of the positron, and of 68 megacycles per second from the anomalous magnetic moment of the electron as suggested by Breit in 1947. Other small corrections have been calculated by various authors, of which the largest was about 7 megacycles per second made by Baranger who took the binding of the electron more exactly into account. At the present time, there is an unexplained residual discrepancy of 0.5 megacycle per second.

CONCLUSIONS

It is very important that this problem should receive further experimental and theoretical attention. When an accuracy of comparison of 0.1 megacycle per second has been reached, it will mean that the energy separations of the 2S and 2P states of hydrogen agree with theory to a precision of a few parts in 10^9 of their binding energy or that the exponent in Coulomb's law of force is 2 with a comparable accuracy. Another way of putting it is to say that the anomalous magnetic moment of the electron would be determined with an accuracy of 1 part in 680, which would provide a useful check on Kusch's more directly measured result. Finally, I might mention that the fine structure doublet separation now provides the most accurate and direct determination of the famous dimensionless number called the fine structure constant, whose numerical value of about 1/137 it will be the task of some future theory to explain.

85

ooooooooooo

MAGNETIC MOMENT OF
THE ELECTRON

ooooooooooo

Polykarp Kusch (b. 1911)

The remarkable experimental result obtained by Lamb and Retherford for the fine structure of the sublevels of the second hydrogen quantum
state led many physicists to suspect that the Dirac theory did not properly
take into account the interaction of the electron with its own radiation
field.

Another discrepancy detected experimentally was the value of the magnetic moment of the electron. The Dirac theory predicts that the electron
must have a half unit of angular momentum arising from its spin. The
negative ratio of the electron's magnetic moment to its own angular momentum, called the g factor, is generally the quantity that is determined
experimentally. The g factor of the free Dirac electron is 2, since when
the Dirac electron is moving freely in space its only angular momentum
is that of its spin, $\frac{1}{2}$. However, for an electron bound inside the atom we
have to consider both spin and orbital effects in determining angular momentum. We therefore have two g values: g_s, associated with spin, and
g_L, associated with orbital angular momentum. (There is, of course, a
g value for total angular momentum of the bound electron, combining
the effects of spin and orbit; this is labeled g_J.) Since the Dirac description
does not give the proper fine structure of the hydrogen levels, physicists
also expected to find that the experimentally determined g_s of a free electron differed from 2, which is the Dirac value. Polykarp Kusch, using the
molecular-beam techniques developed by Rabi, was able to demonstrate
this discrepancy in experiments that measured the magnetic moment of
the electron.

1508

The problem of measuring the magnetic moment of the electron is complicated because it can be done only while the electron is bound inside an atom. This introduces additional effects because the electron has an orbital magnetic moment (arising from its motion around the nucleus) in addition to its intrinsic spin magnetic moment. The external magnetic fields used in Rabi's molecular-beam methods interact with both of these magnetic moments simultaneously, as we have already noted. In the early investigations this difficulty was eliminated by utilizing atoms that have a zero value for the electronic orbital angular momentum; hence the orbital magnetic moment of the electron is zero. This is true for alkali atoms, such as sodium and potassium. However, in very precise measurements another complication arises from the nuclear magnetic moment, which is responsible for the hyperfine structure of the spectral lines of an atom. The nuclear magnetic moment combines with the intrinsic and the orbital magnetic moments of the electron to give a total magnetic moment that interacts with the field.

We have seen in our discussion of Rabi's molecular-beam resonance methods that it is possible to measure the nuclear magnetic moment by a resonance procedure that uses an oscillating magnetic field applied at right angles to a beam of atoms passing through an inhomogeneous magnetic field; measurable disturbances in the beam are then induced if the frequency of the oscillating magnetic field is equal or close to the frequency of the Larmor precession of the nuclear magnetic moment of the atom. From the value of the Larmor precession, which can be deduced from the frequency of the oscillating field, the nuclear g factor and, hence, the nuclear magnetic moment can be calculated. This procedure was first applied to atoms or molecules with zero total spin and zero orbital angular momentum, so that only the nuclear magnetic moment interacted with the magnetic field. Techniques were improved, however; it became possible to use molecular-beam methods to study the interaction of the nuclear magnetic moment with the total electronic magnetic moment, in other words, to analyze the magnetic hyperfine structure of the atom.

Kusch and Millman applied these resonance techniques to the measurement of the magnetic moment of the proton, expressed in units of the electronic magnetic moment, by comparing the resonance effects for hydrogen atoms and molecules with those for alkali atoms. In this way one could simultaneously obtain information about the g factor for the spin magnetic moment of the electron and the g factor for the spin magnetic moment of the proton. A comparison of these values, on the assumption that the g value for the electron spin is 2 (that is, that the magnetic moment of the electron is just 1 Bohr magneton), led to a discrepancy between the value for the magnetic moment of the proton measured in this way and that measured by direct resonance methods. Rabi and his co-workers found such a discrepancy in analyzing the hyperfine structure of hydrogen; it became clear that the intrinsic magnetic moment of the electron must differ from 1 Bohr magneton by about 1 per cent. This discrepancy suggested the need of a very precise determination of the g factor for the spin magnetic moment of the electron; this was undertaken by Kusch and Foley.

The experiments consisted in determining the ratio of the g value for the spin of the electron to the g value for the orbital angular momentum of the electron. This was done by considering two of the same atoms in two different magnetic states and determining the g value for the total angular momentum in each of these states. The ratio of these g values gives the ratio of the spin g value to the orbital angular momentum value. Since the orbital g value is 1, this procedure immediately provides the g value for the spin. The experimental data show that the magnetic moment of the electron is somewhat larger than 1 Bohr magneton. The value thus found is equal to that first calculated by Julian Schwinger by taking into account the mass renormalization of the electron. This corrected value of the magnetic moment of the electron is referred to as the "anomalous magnetic moment" of the electron.

It is a remarkable coincidence that Polykarp Kusch and Willis Lamb, working independently of each other in the Columbia University molecular beam laboratories on two apparently unrelated physical phenomena, should have almost simultaneously discovered two different discrepancies with the Dirac theory of the electron, which were soon to be resolved by a single theoretical correction. That Kusch should have discovered the anomalous magnetic moment of the electron is quite understandable in the light of his extensive background in the field of molecular and atomic beam spectroscopy, dating back to 1937. He first began experimental work with molecular beams at that time at Columbia University, shortly after he received his Ph.D. in physics.

He was born on January 26, 1911, in Blankenburg, Germany, but has lived in the United States (of which he is a citizen) since the age of one year. His father, a clergyman, brought the family to the Midwest in 1912, where young Kusch received his elementary and high-school education. While in high school, his interests turned to chemistry; like Rabi and Lamb, he decided on chemistry as a career when he entered college, but soon after starting his undergraduate work at the Case Institute of Technology in Cleveland, Ohio, he shifted to experimental physics. After receiving his B.S. degree in physics in 1931, he entered the University of Illinois to pursue his graduate studies. He was awarded the M.S. degree in 1933 and the Ph.D. degree in 1936. The research for which he was granted his doctorate dealt with optical molecular spectroscopy and was performed under the guidance of Professor F. Wheeler Loomis.

After spending the year 1936 at the University of Minnesota working with Professor John T. Tate in the field of mass spectroscopy, he came to Columbia University as an instructor in physics and began his association with Professor I. I. Rabi at the latter's molecular-beam laboratory. There Kusch participated with other collaborators of Rabi in the series of experiments that won Rabi the Nobel Prize and prepared Kusch for his own important work. The general principles of radio frequency spectroscopy by Rabi's molecular-beam resonance methods were first described in a paper published in the *Physical Review* in 1939 by Rabi, S. Millman, Kusch, and G. Zacharias. In another group of experiments in which Kusch participated, the Rabi method was applied to study the magnetic hyperfine structure of the spectral lines of various isotopes of the alkali atoms. A paper describing these experiments was published in 1940 by Rabi and his group, with Kusch collaborating.

In 1940, working with Millman, Kusch performed the first of a series of experiments that were to lead him step by step to the measurement of the anomalous magnetic moment of the electron and to the Nobel Prize in 1955. After this work (described in a 1941 paper in the *Physical Review*) was completed, Kusch, like most other physicists, worked for the war effort on military projects: first at the Westinghouse Electric Corporation, then at the Bell Telephone Laboratories, and finally at the Columbia University Radiation Laboratory. This experience gained for him a good working knowledge of microwave techniques and vacuum-tube technology and its application to problems in experimental physics.

Immediately after the war, Kusch returned to the Columbia University physics department and quickly advanced through the various professorial ranks to become a full professor in 1949. During this period, he completed the research projects that the war had interrupted. In a series of papers, published jointly with his colleague H. Foley, he investigated the question of the anomalous magnetic moment of the electron. He showed experimentally that the intrinsic magnetic moment of the electron is about 0.1 per cent larger than that predicted by the Dirac theory. This is in complete agreement with the theoretical calculations of Schwinger, based on new procedures introduced by Schwinger in quantum electrodynamics.

Kusch and his collaborators subsequently increased the accuracy of their experiments and showed that the observed magnetic moment of the electron agrees with the improved theory to about one part in a billion. This result is extremely important since it demonstrates the high degree of accuracy of the improved quantum electrodynamics in analyzing the interaction of an electron and an electromagnetic field.

After completing this work on the magnetic moment of the electron, Kusch became interested in problems in chemical physics, to which he applied the molecular-beam techniques that had proved so fruitful in the study of the atom and the nucleus.

Although he is still actively engaged in research, Kusch is devoting much of his time to educational problems and to the problems arising from the impact of science on society.

Kusch has been awarded the honorary Sc.D. degree by the Case Institute of Technology, Ohio State University, the University of Illinois, and Colby College. In 1956 he was elected to the National Academy of Sciences.

His first wife, the former Edith Starr McRoberts, with whom he had three daughters, died in 1959. In 1960 he married Betty Pezzoni, with whom he has another daughter.

ᴏᴏᴏᴏᴏᴏᴏ

K U S C H

Magnetic Moment of the Electron [1]

I MUST SAY, AND WITH considerable regret, that I am not a theoretical physicist. A penetrating analysis of the part that the discovery and measurement of the anomalous magnetic moment of the electron has played in the development of certain aspects of contemporary theoretical physics must be left to the group of men who have in recent years devised the theoretical structure of quantum electrodynamics. My role has been that of an experimental physicist who, by observation and measurement of the properties and operation of the physical world, supplies the data that may lead to the formulation of conceptual structures. The consistency of the consequences of a conceptual structure with the data of physical experiment determines the validity of that structure as a description of the physical universe.

Our early predecessors observed nature as it was displayed to them. As knowledge of the world increased, however, it was not sufficient to observe only the most apparent aspects of nature to discover its more subtle properties; rather, it was necessary to interrogate nature and often to compel nature, by various devices, to yield an answer concerning its functioning. It is precisely the role of the experimental physicist to arrange devices and procedures that will provide information that will enable us to make

---

[1] P. Kusch, *Science*, 123 (1956), 207–211. 1955 Nobel address.

quantitative statements concerning the properties and behavior of nature. It is in this spirit that I will discuss here my participation in a sequence of earlier experiments that made possible the precision determination of the magnetic moment of the electron. I will then discuss the experiments themselves—the experiments that have yielded our present knowledge of the magnetic properties of the electron.

ATOMIC AND MOLECULAR BEAMS

Research with atomic and molecular beams has had a long and fruitful record in the history of the growth of our present knowledge of the matter. The experiments that I shall discuss are some in which the method of atomic and molecular beams is used essentially as a spectroscopic device for the observation of spectral lines in the range of frequencies within which power may be generated by electronic means. The general principles of radio-frequency spectroscopy by the method of molecular beams were first described by Rabi and a group of his co-workers of which I was fortunate to be a member. It is here sufficient to say that a transition between energy levels may be observed through the circumstance that the magnetic moment of an atom or molecule may be changed in a transition. The method is characterized by a very high-potential resolution; in many observations of the frequency of a line, an accuracy of better than 1 part in 1 million has been achieved. It is of particular value as a tool in the investigation of the details of interactions within atoms and molecules because small interactions appear as first-order effects rather than as small superpositions on the relatively enormous energies that characterize optical spectra.

ELECTRON PROPERTIES

The fact that the electron has a spin of $\frac{1}{2}$ and a magnetic moment at least approximately equal to 1 Bohr magneton has long been recognized. Uhlenbeck and Goudsmit first postulated these properties of the electron to explain the fine structure in atomic spectra and what has been called the anomalous Zeeman effect. An enormous body of evidence has given ever-increasing support to these postulates. The relativistic Dirac theory of the electron assumed a particle that was endowed with the properties of mass and charge. The spin and magnetic moment postulated by Uhlenbeck and Goudsmit were then found to be a consequence of the relativistic invariance of the Dirac equation. Indeed, one of the great triumphs of the Dirac electron theory was the prediction of these postulated electron properties. The spin and moment of the electron were thus removed from the realm of *ad hoc* assumptions, justified by experimental evidence, to the realm of an integral part of quantum theory. The Dirac electron theory did not, however, consider the interaction of the quantized electromagnetic field with the electron.

I shall talk of the measurement of the g value rather than the magnetic moment of the electron. The g value is, as usual, the negative ratio of the magnetic moment in terms of the Bohr magneton μ_0 and the angular momentum in units of $h/2\pi$. Since, in all cases here under discussion, the angular momentum of the system is known, the moment can immediately be obtained from the g value. The most elementary of the g values, g_L, is that associated with the orbital motion of the electron. Its value is 1 within small and calculable corrections. The electron also has a magnetic moment by virtue of its angular momentum about a spin axis. The g value associated with the spin, g_S, is the quantity here under investigation; a value of 2 was obtained for it in the Dirac electron theory. Now the electrons in an atom have both spin and orbital angular momentum. To the total electronic angular momentum J, we assign the g value g_J. The atom contains a nucleus that may have a nuclear angular momentum and hence a nuclear magnetic moment. The nuclear g value, g_N, is designated as g_P in the special case when the nucleus is a proton. To the total angular momentum of the atom we assign the g value g_F.

EARLY MEASUREMENTS

The earliest measurements by the molecular-beams magnetic resonance method were undertaken by a group, of which I was a member, that worked in Rabi's laboratory and under his direction. The measurements consisted of the determination of nuclear g values by the observation in a molecule of the nuclear resonance frequency in a classically determined magnetic field. Even in the great national laboratories dedicated to the maintenance of physical standards, a precision of only about 1 part in 40,000 has been achieved in the measurement of a field. In a well-equipped laboratory that lacks the equipment and tradition of meticulous intercomparison of electric standards, a precision of perhaps $\frac{1}{4}$ percent may be achieved in the determination of the magnitude of a field. While ratios of nuclear g values may be found without an explicit knowledge of the field, the accuracy of the determination of a nuclear moment in terms of the Bohr or nuclear magneton is limited by the uncertainty in the measurement of a field as well as by the uncertainties in a prior measurement of the Bohr or nuclear magneton. Thus, the desirability of a direct measurement of a nuclear g value in terms of the Bohr magneton is apparent.

The molecular-beam magnetic resonance method was originally applied to the determination of the nuclear g values in molecules that did not have a net electronic orbital or spin angular momentum. It is, however, possible to apply the same experimental techniques to an investigation of the hyperfine structure of atoms. If we observe transitions between the various F levels at zero or very low magnetic field, the hyperfine structure separation may readily be found. At a higher magnetic field, the observation of the frequency of transition between magnetic sublevels yields again the zero-field hyperfine structure splitting, the quantity $g_J\mu_0H/h$, and the quantity g_N/g_J, although the latter quantity can be found with only limited precision. The group of which I was a member at Columbia made the first such studies on the commonly occurring isotopes of the alkali atoms and determined the magnetic hyperfine structure interaction constants of the alkali atoms. Extensive subsequent work in the observation of atomic hyperfine structure has, of course, been done in many laboratories with results of great interest in the study of higher order moments in nuclei and of the properties of radioactive nuclei. The alkali atoms were particularly adaptable to the original experimental work first because the beams of the atoms may readily be produced and detected and second because they occur in $^2S_{1/2}$ states, almost wholly free of perturbation by other states.

The possibility of measuring the moment of a nucleus in terms of the Bohr magneton is a consequence of the possibility of observing both nuclear resonance in molecules with a frequency $g_N\mu_0H/h$ and transitions among the magnetic components of hyperfine structure levels for which the dependence of frequency on field is of the order of $g_J\mu_0H/h$. Millman and I then addressed ourselves to the problem of measuring the moment of the proton in terms of the electron spin moment. The experimental problems were considerable and arose from three factors.

The first of these was related to the fact that the effective moment of a molecule of zero electronic angular momentum is of the order of a nuclear magneton while that of an atom is of the order of a Bohr magneton. Deflecting fields that allow the observation of a change in trajectory of a molecule in which a hydrogen nucleus has undergone a transition will deflect an atom through unmanageably large excursions if the field is arbitrary. However, all atoms in which magnetic hyperfine structure occurs and in which the spin of the nucleus is greater than $\frac{1}{2}$ have, in certain states, zero magnetic moments at definite values of the magnetic field, which may be very high. Atoms in such states may thus traverse a carefully adjusted inhomogeneous field without catastrophic deflections; and a transition from such a state may at once be detected because the terminal state is generally characterized by a large magnetic moment. Thus, it is possible to choose the deflecting field in such a way that a change in the spin orientation of a nucleus in a molecule and a transition among the magnetic levels of the hyperfine structure may both be detected.

The second of our experimental problems was related to the production of a beam of molecules that contained hydrogen and, simultaneously, an alkali atom, which was requisite for the detection of beams by the techniques then available to us. Since atomic lines were to be observed at the same field as nuclear resonance lines, the simultaneous production of a beam of alkali atoms was necessary. We used beams of sodium and potassium hydroxides evaporated from silver ovens and noted that, at the temperatures required to generate a beam of the hydroxide, the reaction between an alkali halide and metallic calcium proceeded at such a rate that a convenient beam of atoms appeared.

The third experimental problem was associated with the need of applying to the same circuit, in succession, two frequencies that differed by as much as a factor of 70 and with the prewar difficulty of generating sufficient power at high radio frequencies.

Extensive intercomparison of the frequencies of the resonance line of the proton and of lines in the hyperfine structure spectra of sodium, rubidium, and cesium—for each of which a prior determination of the interaction constants had been made—led to a determination of the ratio of the proton moment and the spin magnetic moment of the electron in the calibrating atoms, which we, of course, assumed to be the Bohr magneton. The magnetic moment of the proton in terms of the nuclear magneton that was found on the basis of the assumption that the spin moment of the electron was indeed the Bohr magneton differed from the moment as determined from the measurement of a frequency in a classically determined field by about 0.1 percent. When, at a much later date, it was found that the spin magnetic moment of the electron deviates from the Bohr magneton by the order of 0.1 percent, the direction of the deviation in the older experiment was examined. It is perhaps a good commentary on the hazards of experimental physics that no significant effect had escaped us but that the error in the mutual inductance which we had used in the calibration of the magnetic field was of the order of 0.2 percent rather than 0.1 percent.

After World War II, Nafe and Nelson, working with Rabi, made the first of the measurements of the hyperfine structure splitting of hydrogen in the ground state. Now the hyperfine structure of hydrogen may be calculated explicitly in terms of the magnetic moment of the proton, the spin magnetic moment of the electron, and the electronic wave function at the nucleus. However, a discrepancy of about $\frac{1}{4}$ percent was noted between the observed and predicted magnitude of the hyperfine structure splitting when the value of the proton moment found by Millman and me was used. The assumption that the spin moment of the electron is 1 Bohr magneton enters into the calculation twice—first as an intrinsic property of the electron and second in the calculation of the proton moment from the observed ratio of the proton moment and the spin moment of the electron. The discrepancy led Breit to suggest that the electron may possess an intrinsic magnetic moment greater than μ_0 by the order of $\alpha\mu_0$, where α is the usual fine structure constant.

ANOMALOUS MAGNETIC MOMENT

The question of the existence of an anomalous magnetic moment was then investigated in detail by Foley and me. In this inquiry, as in all others conducted in the atomic and molecular beams laboratory at Columbia University, we profited by Rabi's advice. The procedure that we employed made use of the fact that the g_J value associated with a state is a linear combination of the electronic orbital and spin g values, g_L and g_S and that this combination is different for different states. That is, there is a contribution to the total electronic magnetic moment of an atom both from the orbital motion of the electrons and from the spin of the electrons; the contribution from each of these factors is dependent on the state of the atom. Since we considered only atoms with single electrons outside closed shells, Russell-Saunders coupling is a good approximation and the coefficients that relate the various g values are known. The ratio of the g_J values of two atoms that occur in different spectroscopic states yields g_S/g_L to an accuracy limited by the precision of observation and the precision with which the coefficients relating the various g values are known.

The intercomparison of g values to obtain a value of g_S can only be made if atoms in several different spectroscopic states are available for observation. After our first investigation of the hyperfine structures of the alkali atoms, all in the $^2S_{1/2}$ state, Hardy and Millman studied the hyperfine structure of indium in the $^2P_{1/2}$ state. Just after the war, Becker and I determined the interaction constants that characterize the hyperfine structure of both the isotopes of gallium in the $^2P_{1/2}$ state. Gallium atoms in the excited and metastable $^2P_{3/2}$ state also occur in an atomic beam, and it was possible to determine the interaction constants for both isotopes in this state as well. We thus had available for study atoms in three different spectroscopic states.

In principle, the determination of the ratio of two g_J values is simple. Suppose we observe transitions for which F is constant and m_F changes by ± 1 for two different atoms or for the same atom in two different states. To the extent to which strictly low field conditions prevail, all lines in a given F state have the same frequency, and the ratio of the frequencies of such lines in two different states at a fixed field is simply the ratio of the g_F values. From this ratio, the ratio g_S/g_L for the electron may readily be derived with some additional knowledge of the properties of the nucleus in each atom. However, the hyperfine structure splitting of atomic states is generally small (from 200 to 20,000 megacycles per second) and the energies of the levels are far from linearly dependent on magnetic field at usefully high fields. Nevertheless, it is possible to obtain expressions for the energies of all levels in the hyperfine structure in terms of the zero field hyperfine structure splitting, the ratio g_N/g_J, and the quantity $g_J\mu_0 H/h$, or, where such expressions cannot be explicitly found, to determine the energies from the appropriate secular determinants. From the observed frequencies of appropriate lines and with a prior knowledge of the interaction constants which characterize an atom in the state in question, it is then possible to determine $g_J\mu_0 H/h$. Measurement of this quantity at the same field for atoms in two different states yields, at once, the important ratio g_S/g_L. The determination is independent of a knowledge of the magnetic field and of any fundamental constants.

EXPERIMENTAL DETAILS

It is, perhaps, worthwhile to remark on some experimental details. The field in which the transition frequency was measured was so chosen that all the observed lines had a frequency of the order of 1 megacycle per second, per gauss. To avoid excessive distortion of the lines due to inhomogeneity of the field, a great deal of adjustment of the field was required before the lines approximated in width their theoretical value.

Special arrangements were made to allow the rapid interchange of ovens so that lines of different atoms could be measured in rapid succession. A considerable number of oscillators was required so that several frequencies which differed by large factors could be applied to the radiofrequency circuits that induced the transitions. Although the lines should, in principle, be measured at a fixed if unknown field, the actual measurements were made in a field that varied monotonically throughout a series of observations. The variation of field has the annoying effect of requiring a large body of data to establish the frequencies of two or more lines at a fixed field, but it also aids in avoiding repetitive errors that may occur when a reading of a fixed quantity is repeated.

Three intercomparisons of g_J values were made in these experiments. The results are given in [Table 85–1].

TABLE 85–1. *Observed ratios of atomic g values and the corresponding values of* g_S/g_L.

Comparison	Nominal	Observed	g_S/g_L
$g_J(^2P_{3/2}\mathrm{Ga})/g_J(^2P_{1/2}\mathrm{Ga})$	2	$2(1.00172 \pm 0.00006)$	$2(1.00114 \pm 0.00004)$
$g_J(^2S_{1/2}\mathrm{Na})/g_J(^2P_{1/2}\mathrm{Ga})$	3	$3(1.00242 \pm 0.00006)$	$2(1.00121 \pm 0.00003)$
$g_J(^2S_{1/2}\mathrm{Na})/g_J(^2P_{1/2}\mathrm{In})$	3	$3(1.00243 \pm 0.00010)$	$2(1.00121 \pm 0.00005)$

It is to be noted that the ratio g_S/g_L which has been determined has been found from the ratio of the g_J values on the basis of the assumption that the coupling is Russell-Saunders coupling. Hence the deviation of the ratio g_S/g_L from its nominal value of 2 as determined from any pair of atoms or any pair of states does not constitute clear evidence that the spin moment of the electron is other than 1 Bohr magneton because of the possibility of occurrence of significant perturbations of the states. Theoretical arguments, however, indicate that such perturbations must be small. On experimental grounds, the agreement of the ratio obtained in three different ways from different atoms in different spectroscopic states offers overwhelming evidence that the spin moment of the electron does indeed differ from its nominal value by the indicated amount. The discrepancies between the three values of the ratio may, however, arise from perturbations of the indicated energy levels.

A later intercomparison of the g_J values of the alkali atoms and a comparison of the g_J value of potassium and hydrogen has demonstrated that the g_J values of the three alkali atoms of lowest atomic number are indeed equal to the spin g value of the electron to within 1 part in 40,000. A further intercomparison by Mann and me of the g_J values of indium in the $^2P_{1/2}$ and $^2P_{3/2}$ states has given further confirmation to the interpretation of the discrepancy between a measured ratio of g_J values and the nominal value.

The experiments that have been described were performed at a field of about 400 gauss. In a wholly independent series of experiments, Taub and I determined the ratio of the g_J value of indium in the $^2P_{1/2}$ state and that of sodium in the $^2S_{1/2}$ state by observations of lines in the hyperfine structure spectrum at fields that ranged from 3300 to 12,000 gauss. The method was to determine the nuclear g value of the proton in an alkali hydroxide in terms of the g_J values of indium and sodium. The result, insofar as it concerns the proton, is of no further interest here in view of the highly refined experiments which have been made in later years that allow the precise and direct determination of the nuclear g value of the proton in terms of both the nuclear and the Bohr magneton. The result, however, is of interest because it yields again the ratio of the g_J values in two different states on the basis of measurements at fields which differed from those in the earlier experiments by an order of magnitude. We found that

$$g_S/g_L = 2(1 + 0.00119)$$

We may therefore conclude on the basis of all evidence that the electron does indeed possess an "intrinsic" or "anomalous" magnetic moment over and above that deduced from the Dirac theory and whose magnitude is very close to 0.119 percent of the Bohr magneton.

THEORETICAL INTERPRETATION

Perhaps it is well, at this point, to make a brief statement of the theoretical status of the spin magnetic moment of the electron. Soon after the publication of our first results, which gave substance to the assertion that the electron does have an anomalous moment, Schwinger gave a result, based on new procedures in quantum electrodynamics, that

$$g_S/g_L = 2(1 + \alpha/2\pi) = 2(1.00116)$$

The result is in excellent agreement with experimental measurements of the same quantity. The effect of the increased electron moment arises essentially as a consequence of the quantization of the electromagnetic field which always has a residual zero-point amplitude. Although the existence of this field had previously been recognized, it had not been possible to deal with the interaction prior to the formulation of contemporary quantum electrodynamics. The importance of the observation of the anomalous magnetic moment of the electron is in part in the demonstration that the procedures of quantum electrodynamics are, in fact, satisfactory in formulating a description of nature.

HIGH-PRECISION MEASUREMENTS

It is obvious that a more detailed study of the magnetic moment of the electron than that described thus far was desirable. The objective of a more extended investigation lies in the avoidance of theoretical difficulties in the interpretation, to a high precision, of the electronic g values of complex atoms. In the absence of substantial difficulties of interpretation, the very great precision of which spectroscopy by the method of atomic beams is capable may be used to obtain results of sufficient precision to test the validity of the calculations of quantum electrodynamics when they are made to a higher order than those originally made by Schwinger.

Barring only a measurement of the spin moment of the free electron itself, the best measurement that one may hope to make is on the electron in the hydrogen atom. In this atom in the ground state, the electron has no orbital angular momentum and hence there is no contribution to the electronic magnetic moment from the orbital motion. The entire electronic magnetic moment arises from the spin moment of the electron. Koenig, Prodell, and I have determined the ratio of the electronic g value g_J of the hydrogen atom and the nuclear g value of the proton by experimental procedures to be described. To a very high order of accuracy, g_J is equal to g_S', the spin g value of the electron bound in the hydrogen atom. The value of g'_S differs from g_S of the free electron through a small relativistic effect of about 18 parts per million. Corrections due to a mixing of states and relativistic effects are well known and do not limit the accuracy with which the ratio g_S/g_P may be determined at the present time. Gardner and Purcell have measured the ratio $2g_L/g_P$ of the cyclotron frequency of the electron and the precession frequency of the proton in a magnetic field to an accuracy of about 1 part in 80,000. Our result, when combined with that of Gardner and Purcell, yields g_S/g_L.

As a preliminary procedure, Prodell and I determined the hyperfine structure separation of hydrogen with high precision. A subsequent investigation by both Wittke and Dicke and by us indicated an excessively optimistic estimate of the uncertainty. However, the value of the zero field hyperfine structure splitting of hydrogen that we used was sufficiently good to contribute no error to the value of g_J/g_P that was comparable to other uncertainties.

The apparatus designed for the purpose of these experiments had for the magnet that determined the transition frequencies one with a much better field homogeneity than that which usually characterizes the magnets used in atomic beams experiments. Ordinarily in an atomic beams apparatus, the magnet that determines the splitting of the levels is internal to the vacuum system. This arrangement permits small magnet gaps to be used and hence the production of large fields with electromagnets of moderate dimensions and power consumption. The use of a small gap, however, leads to a considerable hazard of field inhomogeneity. In the present case, the magnet was external to the vacuum envelope, the pole faces were of large diameter to reduce edge effects, and the magnet could be carefully shimmed after each change of externally imposed experimental parameters and from day to day to give good homogeneity in the volume within which transitions were observed. The deflecting magnets consisted of current-carrying conductors rather than the iron magnets that have become conventional in atomic beams experiments. This choice was made because of the smaller distortion of the transition field by current-carrying conductors than by massive blocks of iron.

RESULTS

The experiment involved the measurement of the frequency of transition between the levels $m = 0$ and $m = -1$ in the state for which $F = 1$ alternately with the proton resonance frequency in the same magnetic field. The frequency of the first of these lines is of the order of 3600 megacycles per second at a field of 1500 gauss. The frequency of the proton resonance line is about 6.5 megacycles per second at the same field and is found by the methods of nuclear resonance in the same region of space as that traversed by the beam. An important component of the equipment is a device that can insert a cylindrical sample of water or mineral oil into a region as closely coincident as inherent limitations permit to that in which the atomic line has been observed. Various small corrections relating to the residual inhomogeneity of the field, bulk diamagnetism of the matter in the cylindrical sample that we employed, the presence of paramagnetic ions when we observed the resonance in water, and the differential internal diamagnetic shielding between oil and water must be applied.

We found that

$$g_J/g_P = -658.2171 \pm 0.0006$$

where g_P is the nuclear g value observed in a spherical sample of mineral oil. It is to be noted that this is only an apparent value of g_P because the externally applied field is modified by the internal diamagnetic shielding of the proton by the electrons in the molecules containing the proton. It is, nevertheless, of value to give the result in this form since the ratio $2g_L/g_P$ measured by Gardner and Purcell also refers to a spherical sample of mineral oil.

Application of a small relativistic term yields g_S, the spin g value of the electron in terms of g_P:

$$g_S/g_P = -658.2288 \pm 0.0006$$

The combination of this result with that of Gardner and Purcell

$$2g_L/g_P = -657.475 \pm 0.008$$

yields

$$g_S/g_L = 2(1.001146 \pm 0.000012)$$

where the principle uncertainty arises from the result of Gardner and Purcell. Since g_L equals 1, we can write

$$g_S = 2\mu_s = 2(1.001146 \pm 0.000012)$$

where μ_s is the spin magnetic moment of the electron in terms of μ_0.

The same result has subsequently been obtained by Beringer and Heald who used a different experimental method involving, for atomic hydrogen, a microwave absorption technique and, for the observation of the proton resonance frequency, the usual nuclear resonance technique. The primary result obtained by them was

$$g_J/g_P = -658.2181 \pm 0.0003$$

In view of the stated uncertainties and the possibility of differences in the internal diamagnetic shielding in different samples of mineral oil, the agreement is good. Because of the limited accuracy for the result $2g_L/g_P$, the value of g_S/g_L is not affected, within the range of its uncertainty, by the discrepancy in the two results.

CONCLUSION

It is interesting to examine the ratio of g_S/g_L obtained by the sequence of experiments just described in light of the theoretical calculations of the electron moment. The result gives unambiguous evidence that the electron moment is anomalous and that the deviation of the moment from its nominal value is about $\alpha\mu_0/2\pi$. Karplus and Kroll have calculated to a higher order the radiative correction to the spin moment of the electron and have found for the spin g value

$$g_S = 2(1 + \alpha/2\pi - 2.973\,\alpha^2/\pi^2) = 2(1.0011454)$$

The result of the experiment is in remarkable agreement with the calculation, especially since the uncertainty in the experiment is much greater than the discrepancy between the experimental and calculated values. The agreement offers conclusive evidence of the validity of the calculation to the order α and very strong support to the validity of the calculations to the order α^2. Thus the new procedures of quantum electrodynamics—which have, perhaps, a questionable a priori validity—are demonstrated to be, in practice, valid for the interpretation of certain observed phenomena and, therefore, useful in the exploration of other aspects of the behavior of matter.

86

ooooooooooo

HIGH-ENERGY PHYSICS

ooooooooooo

Hans A. Bethe (b. 1906)

Julian Schwinger (b. 1918)

Richard P. Feynman (b. 1918)

The subject of modern physics is unquestionably linked with men like Einstein, Planck, and Bohr, whose names are associated with the basic theories of the subject. But an examination of the literature shows important contributions by others who did not discover a new theory but who clarified, expanded, and analyzed the basic theories. Hans A. Bethe is one of these great physicists whose work is of such importance that one can think of hardly any phase of the subject without referring to him. From the time quantum mechanics was discovered, while he was still a student, he has been publishing original papers that have contributed much to our understanding of modern physics.

He was born on July 2, 1906, in Strasbourg, Germany, and studied physics at the University of Frankfurt from 1924 to 1926, and at the University of Munich, where he received his Ph.D. under Arnold Sommerfeld in 1928. The papers he began to publish at this stage of his career, young as he was, clearly indicated that he was to become one of the dominant figures of modern physics.

After receiving his doctorate, Bethe returned to Frankfurt in 1928, where he taught physics for a year. From there he went to the University of Stuttgart, where he spent another year teaching, and then was invited to the University of Munich as lecturer (*Privatdozent*). He remained at

Munich until 1933 when the Nazis came to power; he then left Germany, ultimately to become a citizen of the United States.

During this three-year period Bethe published numerous papers on the quantum theory of the atom. One of the most important, written jointly with Enrico Fermi while Bethe was a fellow at Rome, deals with quantum electrodynamics and is one of the earliest applications of this important subject to the study of the interaction of charged particles. This period in Bethe's career was also marked by his emergence as a great expositor of modern physical theories. His book-length article on the quantum mechanics of the atom in the original edition of the *Handbuch der Physik* is a model of clarity and an example of this kind of writing at its best. For years this treatise was the constant companion of the graduate student of theoretical physics. More recently, Bethe, in collaboration with E. Salpeter, revised and enlarged the original article for the new edition. Bethe wrote another famous article during his Munich period in collaboration with Arnold Sommerfeld. It deals with the electron theory of metals and is the first systematic treatment of the application of Fermi-Dirac statistics to the study of metals. These two articles established Bethe as an important physicist.

On leaving Germany, Bethe first went to England and spent a year at the University of Manchester. From there he went to the University of Bristol and remained there for a year as a fellow. These two years (1933–1935) in England were very fruitful. He published papers in numerous fields of physics with special emphasis on atomic collision processes, the radiation from accelerated electrons, nuclear physics, and solid state physics. In collaboration with Peierls he gave the first theoretical analysis of the two-body nuclear system (the deuteron) showing that quantum mechanics can be applied to the study of the nucleus with the same success as to the study of the atom.

In 1935 Bethe came to the United States to accept an assistant professorship of physics at Cornell University. In 1937 he was promoted to a full professorship and has held this post since then. From 1935 until the beginning of World War II, Bethe devoted himself to research (primarily in nuclear physics and its applications to astrophysics), teaching, and writing. His three famous articles on nuclear physics—one written in collaboration with R. F. Bacher, one by himself, and one in collaboration with Livingston—which first appeared in the *Reviews of Modern Physics,* quickly became standard treatises, essential to a comprehension of nuclear physics. Like his articles on the atom, these nuclear physics treatises show Bethe's remarkable qualities as a teacher.

During this period Bethe contributed important papers to solid state physics, meson physics, and astrophysics. His work in astrophsyics was of a trail-blazing quality. He laid down the general principles of energy production in stars and developed the first models of the solar interior, using thermonuclear energy sources. This work served as a guide to future research in this field which has grown so vastly since the war.

During World War II, Bethe became a staff member of the Radiation Laboratory at MIT and did research there during the year 1942–1943. He then went to the atomic bomb project at the Los Alamos Scientific Laboratory as chief of the Theoretical Division and remained there from 1943 to 1946, when he returned to Cornell to resume his research, teaching, writing, and lecturing. Since the war his research has dealt with quantum electrodynamics, meson theory, and shock wave theory. His 1947 paper on the Lamb shift was a crucial step in the subsequent development of the new formulation of quantum electrodynamics since it showed—though only by approximate methods—that the physical content of quantum electrodynamics agrees with the observations and that its apparent infinities are a result of the incorrect treatment of the mass of the electron.

Shortly after Bethe came to Cornell he acquired a nationwide reputation as a great teacher and lecturer, and he has been in constant demand by other universities. In 1941 he came to Columbia University as visiting professor and gave a course of lectures on nuclear physics. In 1948 he returned to Columbia, again as a visiting professor, and lectured on the new methods in quantum electrodynamics developed by Schwinger, Feynman, and Dyson. In the year 1955–1956 he was visiting professor at Cambridge University, England.

Since 1947 he has been a consultant for the Los Alamos Scientific Laboratory; since 1953 for the Atomic Power Development Association; since 1955 for the Avco Research Laboratory and the Atomic Power Division of General Dynamics. Since 1956 he has been a member of the President's Science Advisory Committee.

Bethe has received many honors and awards for his scientific work. In 1938 and in 1940 he received the A. Cressy-Morrison award of the New York Academy of Sciences for his work in astrophysics. In 1946 he was awarded the U.S. medal of merit, and in 1948 the Draper medal of the National Academy of Sciences. He received the much coveted Planck medal of Germany in 1955, and more recently the $50,000 Enrico Fermi prize for his contributions to nuclear physics in the field of atomic energy. He has been awarded honorary Doctor of Science degrees by the Polytechnic Institute of Brooklyn, the University of Chicago, the University of Birmingham, England, and Harvard University.

He is a member of the National Academy of Sciences, a fellow of the American Physical Society, of which he was elected President in 1954, and a fellow of the Royal Society of London. He is also a member of the American Astronomical Society and of the Philosophical Society.

In recent years, Bethe has concerned himself with the application of atomic energy to peaceful uses. He has been a dedicated advocate of the international control of atomic energy and has argued vigorously for the abolition of the bomb and, as a minimum, for the discontinuance of the testing of nuclear weapons. As a member of the United States Delegation to Discussions on Discontinuance of Nuclear Weapons he was instrumental in bridging the gap between the Russian and American positions, and thus helped materially in bringing about the present cessation of above-ground tests.

He is a physically vigorous man who lives his life as zestfully as he pursues physics. Although devoted to many intellectual pursuits, he finds time to ski, to hike, and to carry on other activities. In 1939 he married Rose Ewald, the daughter of the physicist and crystallographer, Prof. P. P. Ewald. They have two children.

Although American theoretical physics began its remarkable growth in the late 1920's, its full flowering did not come until a decade later. This rapid development was, of course, greatly spurred on by the scientific needs of the military during World War II.

The period just preceding the war is particularly noteworthy because it marked the debut of two outstanding theoretical physicists, Julian Schwinger and Richard P. Feynman, both of whom were born in the same year, in the same city; they were educated in the same school system and made their most important contributions in the same field of physics.

Julian Schwinger was born in New York City on February 12, 1918; he received all of his education, including his Ph.D., in New York City. He demonstrated his remarkable mathematical ability while still in elementary school; by the time he was ready for high school he had taught himself calculus and was able to solve differential equations. Even at that time his interests tended to theoretical physics; he began to read advanced treatises in various branches of physics, with special emphasis on electromagnetic theory and relativity. Like most of the intellectually gifted New York City youngsters of that period, Schwinger thought of a college education in terms of the College of the City of New York (CCNY), which offered a free higher education to all New York City residents who could qualify. At that time, CCNY had under its jurisdiction a preparatory high school, Townsend Harris High School, which was available to the outstanding elementary-school graduates. Schwinger, quite naturally, entered this school, which stressed the classics, languages, and mathematics.

The close association between the Townsend Harris faculty and the CCNY faculty soon brought Schwinger to the attention of some of the members of the physics department of the college; by the time he matriculated as a freshman, his reputation as a prodigy was well established.

He entered CCNY at the age of fifteen and, although he attended the usual freshman and sophomore courses, he could usually be found spending his spare time in the physics library immersed in some advanced book in physics or working out problems in relativity theory or quantum mechanics in his notebook.

In 1935, his sophomore year, Schwinger began attending the theoretical seminar in physics at Columbia University, conducted by I. Rabi and G. Breit. Schwinger soon attracted Rabi's attention by clarifying a very subtle and puzzling point in the famous paper by Einstein, Podolsky and Rosen that had just been published. Rabi was so impressed that he suggested that Schwinger leave CCNY and come to Columbia on a scholarship. Consequently, in September 1935, Schwinger entered Columbia College as a junior. Even before coming to Columbia, he had already attracted the attention of Pauli, who referred to him as "the physicist in knee pants"; Bethe, in a letter to Rabi, expressed the opinion that Schwinger knew 90 per cent of all the physics that was then known and that he could pick up the other 10 per cent whenever he wanted to.

During the spring and summer of 1935 Schwinger submitted his first original papers for publication; since then he has not stopped publishing. After entering Columbia, Schwinger continued with his own theoretical research. By the time he received his baccalaureate degree in the fall of 1936, he had already written his Ph.D. thesis on the scattering of neutrons.

After spending two more years at Columbia to complete his graduate residence requirement for his doctorate, he received a National Research Fellowship and spent some time at the University of Wisconsin and at the University of California, where he worked with Oppenheimer. During this period he published a series of important papers on nuclear forces.

In 1941 Schwinger went to Purdue University as instructor in physics and soon after was promoted to assistant professor. He left Purdue in 1943 to become a staff member of the Radiation Laboratory at MIT and remained there until 1945. During this period he developed powerful mathematical methods for treating problems in electromagnetic theory. These methods, called variational methods, proved to be very useful later in the handling of nuclear scattering problems and in field theory.

In 1945, at the end of World War II, Schwinger accepted an associate professorship in physics at Harvard; in 1947, at the age of twenty-nine, he was promoted to a full professorship—the youngest full professor in Harvard's history.

All the theoretical work that Schwinger had done up to this point was, in a sense, preparatory to his discovery of the mass and charge renormalization in quantum electrodynamics. His amazing grasp of the physics of quantum field theory and the ease with which he handled the complex mathematical formalism of this branch of physics led him quite naturally to an understanding of the difficulties that beset the theory and how these could be eliminated by recasting the theory in a completely covariant form, that is, in agreement with relativity at all stages. With this revised and relativistically correct version of quantum electrodynamics, Schwinger derived the Lamb shift from the theory and showed that the calculated magnetic moment of the electron is not one Bohr magneton, as predicted by the Dirac theory, but somewhat larger and in complete agreement with Kusch's measurements.

Schwinger continued working in quantum electrodynamics and field theory in the years following his first investigations, and published a series of important papers covering all phases of the subject. These papers are distinguished by their mathematical elegance and the use of powerful analytical techniques. During the last few years he has devoted himself to the construction of a field theory of fundamental particles in analogy with the electrodynamic field theory of photons.

For his contributions to quantum electrodynamics, Schwinger received the prize of the National Academy of Sciences in 1949 and the Einstein award in 1951. He is a member of the National Academy of Sciences, a fellow of the American Physical Society and of the American Academy. In 1961 he was appointed visiting professor of physics, at the University of California. He was awarded the 1965 Nobel Prize in physics together with R. P. Feynman and Shinichiro Tomonaga.

Richard P. Feynman, a few months younger than Julian Schwinger, was born in New York City on May 11, 1918. Like Schwinger he received his early education in the New York City public schools. While still in high school, Feynman demonstrated his precocity by doing advanced mathematics while his classmates were busy with the usual class work. His high-school physics teacher recalls that he always allowed Feynman to sit in the back of the room solving problems in advanced calculus while the other students were busy with high-school physics.

On graduating from high school, Feynman entered MIT to begin his studies in mathematics and physics. He received his B.S. degree from MIT in 1939 and went on to Princeton University as a Proctor fellow to do graduate work with Professor John A. Wheeler. While at Princeton he became interested in electrodynamics and, particularly, in the problems of the emission and absorption of radiation by charged particles. This led him to the fundamental problem of the interaction between charged particles and whether such an interaction is best treated as "action at a distance" or the action of a field. His concern with problems of this sort later led him to his graphic procedures in quantum electrodynamics.

After receiving his Ph.D. degree in 1942 from Princeton, he worked on the atomic bomb project at Los Alamos and remained there until 1945. From Los Alamos Feynman went to Cornell University, first as associate professor and then as full professor of physics. This period was marked by his work in quantum electrodynamics and his discovery of what are now called the "Feynman graphs," a very elegant and simple graphic procedure for analyzing the different processes that occur when a charged particle interacts with another charged particle or with the electromagnetic field.

Feynman arrived at his graphic representation of quantum electrodynamical processes after he had undertaken a critical analysis of quantum mechanics and had reformulated it in terms of a least action principle—the Lagrangian formulation. This approach to quantum mechanics is described in a famous paper that appeared in 1948 in the *Reviews of Modern Physics*. In this formulation the emphasis is not on the detailed behavior of a system from moment to moment, but rather on its over-all behavior, as though its entire past and future were exposed to one's view. This naturally led to a diagrammatic formulation of the problem. It is a remarkable coincidence that Feynman and Schwinger, working from such different points of view, should have arrived at the same solutions to the problems of quantum electrodynamics and should have published their results at about the same time.

Feynman left Cornell University in 1951 to become Richard Chase Tolman professor of theoretical physics at the California Institute of Technology; he has remained in this position since then. For a number of years after his first historic papers on quantum electrodynamics, Feynman continued publishing papers in this field, clarifying many subtle points and improving the mathematical techniques. After it became clear that the new quantum electrodynamics had attained the desired plateau of excellence, Feynman turned his attention to the application of his field of theoretical methods to nuclear forces and to high-energy particle physics. Working with Gell-Mann he reformulated the interaction between fundamental particles in terms of a general type of interaction that can be applied universally. In recent years Feynman has also done extensive work in low-temperaure physics, with particular emphasis on the properties of liquid helium and superconductivity.

In 1954 he received the Einstein award for his contributions to quantum electrodynamics and was a co-recipient in 1965 of the Nobel Prize in physics. He is a member of the National Academy of Sciences and fellow of the American Physical Society.

In all of his work, whether research, teaching, or writing, Feynman has always been concerned with emphasizizing the physical aspects of a problem and freeing it as much as possible from complex mathematical formalism. This is evident, not only in his original papers, but also in such of his advanced treatises as his "Quantum Electrodynamics," and his "Fundamental Processes."

The following Bethe paper concerns the so-called Lamb shift. Since the shift in the $2s$ energy level of the hydrogen atom found by Lamb and Retherford does not agree with the Dirac theory of the electron, theoretical physicists, immediately after the Lamb-Retherford experiment, began to probe existing theories to discover the difficulty, and to determine just how the Dirac theory had to be corrected to account for the observed energy levels. Such outstanding contemporary theoretical physicists as Tomonaga, Schwinger, and Feynman tackled the problem and eventually solved it. In particular, Schwinger and Feynman ultimately improved quantum electrodynamics to such a degree that it was able to reconcile many of the differences that had arisen. Thus with their improved quantum electrodynamics we can account for the Lamb-Retherford energy-level shift as well as the anomalous magnetic moment of the electron measured experimentally by Kusch. But it was Bethe, who, in the paper that follows, brought into sharp focus the inability of the Dirac theory to adequately treat the interaction of the electron with its own radiation field.

According to the Dirac theory, the electron must be treated like a point charge. But such a finite charge concentrated in a point and therefore having an infinite charge density, would have an infinite interaction energy with its own radiation field. Consequently, if one uses the Dirac theory to calculate the effect that the interaction of the electron with its own field has on the energy levels of the electron in the hydrogen atom, one obtains an infinite answer. This is, indeed, the result that Oppenheimer obtained in 1930 when he applied the standard perturbation techniques to the Dirac equations. This infinite result arises because the Dirac equations describe only a bare electron, without a surrounding electromagnetic field. The actual radiation field surrounding the true electron behaves like an additional mass (the electromagnetic mass) so that the mass that appears in a Dirac equation is not the quantity that applies in the true description of the electron.

To see why the radiation field of the electron influences the hydrogen energy levels, or, for that matter, the energy levels of any atom, we consider a very energetic photon in the radiation field of the electron. It is transiently absorbed by a negative-energy electron (one of an infinitude, according to the Dirac theory) in the neighborhood of our electron. Momentarily, then, a positron-electron pair is created (the negative-energy electron enters a state of positive energy and leaves a hole). This pair is equivalent to an electric dipole (the polarization of the vacuum, as it is called). By means of its electric field, the dipole disturbs the electron in the hydrogen atom and therefore alters the energy levels. If one applies the standard perturbation techniques of the Dirac electron to calculate the value of this disturbance, one obtains an infinite result, as already noted. The Dirac theory thus says that all the energy levels of the atom are shifted by an infinite amount, as a result of the interaction of the electron with its own radiation field. This, of course, is nonsense. The error in the theory arises because the electron is regarded as a point; there is therefore no limit as to how energetic the photons may be with which the electron can interact. According to Dirac, pairs can be created by photons ranging in frequency all the way from those corresponding to mc^2 to infinity. This is essentially equivalent to saying that the interaction of the electron with the radiation field leads to an infinite correction to the mass of the electron.

Although, as Schwinger pointed out, and as he and Feynman successfully demonstrated later, it is necessary to treat the interaction of the electron and the radiation field by a precise relativistic procedure if one is to see how these infinite corrections are to be side-stepped and how the correct electromagnetic shift of the energy levels is to be obtained, Bethe was the first to obtain a fairly accurate value by an approximate nonrelativistic method. His reasoning was as follows: The Dirac and Schroedinger equations of the electron describe a mechanical electron, that is, one without a surrounding electromagnetic field. Any calculations performed with either of these equations (such as determining the energy levels of the hydrogen atom) therefore omit the interaction of the electron with this electromagnetic field. However, when the results obtained with the theory are compared with the observations, the numerical value for the mass of the electron that is put into the equations is the one obtained observationally. But this observed value is not the bare mechanical mass. What we detect in any experiment is the total mass of the electron, and this total mass is a combination of the bare mechanical mass and the electromagnetic mass arising from the interaction of the electron with its electromagnetic field. If we try to calculate this electromagnetic contribution to the mass, we get an infinite answer. This infinite answer, however, should not prevent us from calculating the effect that the interaction of the electron with its own electromagnetic field has on the energy levels of the electron when it is bound to a proton. For this purpose we should note that the infinite contribution to the energy-level shift that we get from the theory (by perturbation calculations) is due entirely to the infinite contribution to the mass. In other words, when we try to calculate the energy level shift, we cannot avoid getting infinite terms that come from the contribution of the radiation field to the mass of the electron, since the mass of the electron is present in the expression for the energy levels. We may put it another way. Since the wave equation of the electron takes account only of the bare electron without its radiation field a perturbation calculation must be performed to find out how the interaction of the electron with its field affects the energy levels. But this perturbation calculation gives not only the effect on the energy levels, but also a correction to the mass of the electron (the electromagnetic mass), which unfortunately turns out to be infinite. Hence the shift in the energy levels obtained in this way is infinite because the corrected mass of the electron is involved in this energy-level shift.

How can this be avoided? We note first that we need not calculate the contribution of the radiation field to the mass of the electron to obtain the correct energy levels because we obtain this automatically by inserting the observed mass of the electron into our equations. If we work with the observed electronic mass, the contribution of the radiation field to the total mass of the electron is automatically taken into account. Any calculation containing this mass contribution is redundant and should be corrected by subtracting from it the electromagnetic mass contribution. But how is this to be done without at the same time subtracting what we are seeking, namely, the contribution of the radiation field to the energy levels? Here Bethe used a very ingenious procedure. The contribution of the radiation field (that is, the interaction of the electron with its own electromagnetic field) to the total mass of the electron is the same whether the electron is moving freely in space or whether it is bound to the proton to form the hydrogen atom. However, in the latter case the perturbation calculation also contains the terms we seek, that is, the radiation corrections of the energy levels of the bound electron. Hence, if from the expression for the shift in the energy levels, we subtract the expression for the interaction of the free electron with its electromagnetic field, we should be left with the radiation-field corrections to the hydrogen-energy levels.

This is the nature of the analysis that Bethe carried out in the subsequent paper, but he had to take into account one more point because his calculation is nonrelativistic. Part of the calculation involved summing over all the frequencies of the photons that can occur in the radiation field of the electron. Since the nonrelativistic theory places no limit on these frequencies, the sum (after the subtraction procedure described above is carried out) again gives an infinite result. Bethe argued, however, that the correct relativistic theory using the same subtraction technique would give a natural upper limit to the frequencies of the photons that must be summed over. He further argued that this natural limit is energetically equal to the total mass (in energy units, mc^2) of the electron. With this assumption Bethe obtained an expression for the correction to the shift in the 2s-energy level of the electron in the hydrogen atom that is in very good agreement with the experimental results of Lamb and Retherford.

Bethe's paper was important because it showed clearly that the difficulty in the theory lay in the infinite correction to the self-energy of the electron and that a proper mathematical procedure can cope with this difficulty by subtracting the infinite terms from the physically meaningful results. Later a complete and relativistically correct procedure was developed by Schwinger and independently by Feynman in a self-consistent way. This led not only to the proper correction to the mass of the electron but also to a correction to the charge on the electron. In both cases these corrections are infinite, but these infinities cause no trouble because they are introduced as renormalizations of the mass and the charge of the electron and these quantities in the equations are then replaced by their experimental values.

ӨӨӨӨӨӨӨ

BETHE

The Electromagnetic Shift of Energy Levels [1]

BY VERY BEAUTIFUL EXPERIMENTS, LAMB and Retherford have shown that the fine structure of the second quantum state of hydrogen does not agree with the prediction of the Dirac theory. The $2s$ level, which according to Dirac's theory should coincide with the $2p_{1/2}$ level, is actually higher than the latter by an amount of about 0.033 cm^{-1} or 1000 megacycles. This discrepancy had long been suspected from spectroscopic measurements. However, so far no satisfactory theoretical explanation has been given. Kemble and Present, and Pasternack have shown that the shift of the $2s$ level cannot be explained by a nuclear interaction of reasonable magnitude, and Uehling has investigated the effect of the "polarization of the vacuum" in the Dirac hole theory, and has found that this effect also is much too small and has, in addition, the wrong sign.

Schwinger and Weisskopf, and Oppenheimer have suggested that a possible explanation might be the shift of energy levels by the interaction of the electron with the radiation field. This shift comes out infinite in all existing theories, and has therefore always been ignored. However, it is possible to identify the most strongly (linearly) divergent term in the level shift with an electromagnetic *mass* effect which must exist for a bound as

[1] Bethe, *Physical Review,* 72 (1947), 339–341.

well as for a free electron. This effect should properly be regarded as already included in the observed mass of the electron, and we must therefore subtract from the theoretical expression, the corresponding expression for a free electron of the same average kinetic energy. The result then diverges only logarithmically (instead of linearly) in non-relativistic theory: Accordingly, it may be expected that in the hole theory, in which the *main* term (self-energy of the electron) diverges only logarithmically, the result will be *convergent* after subtraction of the free electron expression. This would set an effective upper limit of the order of mc^2 to the frequencies of light which effectively contribute to the shift of the level of a bound electron. I have not carried out the relativistic calculations, but I shall assume that such an effective relativistic limit exists.

The ordinary radiation theory gives the following result for the self-energy of an electron in a quantum state m, due to its interaction with transverse electromagnetic waves:

$$W = -(2e^2/3\pi\hbar c^3) \int_0^K kdk \sum_n |\mathrm{v}_{mn}|^2/(E_n - E_m + k), \qquad (1)$$

where $k = \hbar\omega$ is the energy of the quantum and v is the velocity of the electron which, in non-relativistic theory, is given by

$$\mathrm{v} = \mathrm{p}/m = (\hbar/im)\nabla. \qquad (2)$$

Relativistically, v should be replaced by $c\alpha$ where α is the Dirac operator. Retardation has been neglected and can actually be shown to make no substantial difference. The sum in (1) goes over all atomic states n, the integral over all quantum energies k up to some maximum K to be discussed later.

For a free electron, v has only diagonal elements and (1) is replaced by

$$W_0 = -(2e^2/3\pi\hbar c^3) \int kdk\mathrm{v}^2/k. \qquad (3)$$

This expression represents the change of the kinetic energy of the electron for fixed momentum, due to the fact that electromagnetic mass is added to the mass of the electron. This electromagnetic mass is already contained in the experimental electron mass; the contribution (3) to the energy should therefore be disregarded. For a bound electron, v^2 should be replaced by its expectation value, $(\mathrm{v}^2)_{mm}$. But the matrix elements of v satisfy the sum rule

$$\sum_n |\mathrm{v}_{mn}|^2 = (\mathrm{v}^2)_{mm}. \qquad (4)$$

Therefore the relevant part of the self-energy becomes

$$W' = W - W_0 = \frac{2e^2}{3\pi\hbar c^3} \int_0^K dk \sum_n \frac{|\,v_{mn}\,|^2 (E_n - E_m)}{E_n - E_m + k}. \tag{5}$$

This we shall consider as a true shift of the levels due to radiation inter-action.

It is convenient to integrate (5) first over k. Assuming K to be large compared with all energy differences $E_n - E_m$ in the atom,

$$W' = \frac{2e^2}{3\pi\hbar c^3} \sum_n |\,v_{mn}\,|^2 (E_n - E_m) \ln \frac{K}{|\,E_n - E_m\,|}. \tag{6}$$

(If $E_n - E_m$ is negative, it is easily seen that the principal value of the integral must be taken, as was done in (6).) Since we expect that relativity theory will provide a natural cut-off for the frequency k, we shall assume that in (6)

$$K \approx mc^2. \tag{7}$$

(This does not imply the same limit in Eqs. (2) and (3).) The argument in the logarithm in (6) is therefore very large; accordingly, it seems permissible to consider the logarithm as constant (independent of n) in first approximation.

We therefore should calculate

$$A = \sum_n A_{nm} = \sum_n |\,p_{nm}\,|^2 (E_n - E_m). \tag{8}$$

This sum is well known; it is

$$A = \sum |\,p_{nm}\,|^2 (E_n - E_m) = -\hbar^2 \int \psi_m{}^* \nabla V \cdot \nabla \psi_m d\tau$$
$$= \tfrac{1}{2}\hbar^2 \int \nabla^2 V \psi_m{}^2 d\tau = 2\pi\hbar^2 e^2 Z \psi_m{}^2(0), \tag{9}$$

for a nuclear charge Z. For any electron with angular momentum $l \neq 0$, the wave function vanishes at the nucleus; therefore, the sum $A = 0$. For example, for the $2p$ level the negative contribution $A_{1S,\,2P}$ balances the positive contributions from all other transitions. For a state with $l = 0$, however,

$$\psi_m{}^2(0) = (Z/na)^3/\pi, \tag{10}$$

where n is the principal quantum number and a is the Bohr radius.

Inserting (10) and (9) into (6) and using relations between atomic constants, we get for an S state

$$W_{ns}' = \frac{8}{3\pi} \left(\frac{e^2}{\hbar c}\right)^3 \mathrm{Ry} \frac{Z^4}{n^3} \ln \frac{K}{\langle E_n - E_m \rangle_{\mathrm{Av}}}, \qquad (11)$$

where Ry is the ionization energy of the ground state of hydrogen. The shift for the $2p$ state is negligible; the logarithm in (11) is replaced by a value of about -0.04. The average excitation energy $\langle E_n - E_m \rangle_{\mathrm{Av}}$ for the $2s$ state of hydrogen has been calculated numerically and found to be 17.8 Ry, an amazingly high value. Using this figure and $K = mc^2$, the logarithm has the value 7.63, and we find

$$W_{ns}' = 136 \ln[K/(E_n - E_m)] = 1040 \text{ megacycles.} \qquad (12)$$

This is in excellent agreement with the observed value of 1000 megacycles.

A relativistic calculation to establish the limit K is in progress. Even without exact knowledge of K, however, the agreement is sufficiently good to give confidence in the basic theory. This shows

(1) that the level shift due to interaction with radiation is a real effect and is of finite magnitude,

(2) that the effect of the infinite electromagnetic mass of a point electron can be eliminated by proper identification of terms in the Dirac radiation theory.

(3) that an accurate experimental and theoretical investigation of the level shift may establish relativistic effects (e.g., Dirac hole theory). These effects will be of the order of unity in comparison with the logarithm in Eq. (11).

If the present theory is correct, the level shift should increase roughly as Z^4 but not quite so rapidly, because of the variation of $\langle E_n - E_m \rangle_{\mathrm{Av}}$ in the logarithm. For example, for He$^+$, the shift of the $2s$ level should be about 13 times its value for hydrogen, giving 0.43 cm^{-1}, and that of the $3s$ level about 0.13 cm^{-1}. For the x-ray levels LI and LII, this effect should be superposed upon the effect of screening which it partly compensates. An accurate theoretical calculation of the screening is being undertaken to establish this point. . . .

ooooooo

Although Bethe has given a theoretical explanation of the Lamb-Retherford effect by using a simple mathematical subtraction technique to eliminate the infinities that burden the Dirac theory, his procedure is only approximately correct and leaves the theory with all its deficiencies.

Following Bethe's work a series of papers, presented almost simultaneously by a number of authors working independently of each other, gave a systematic insight into the infinity difficulties of the theory and showed how these were to be overcome. These papers ultimately established a self-consistent mathematical scheme for using quantum electrodynamics in conjunction with the Dirac theory of the electron, to obtain correct results for phenomena involving the interaction of the electron with the electromagnetic field. The theory as it now stands, however, is by no means a complete picture of quantum electrodynamics since it can say nothing about the structure of the electron and still gives an infinite result for the self-energy of the electron. In its present form, the theory as developed by Feynman, Schwinger, Tomonaga and others, uses all the formalism that is present in quantum mechanics but organizes it in such a way that one can see where the infinities are and thus avoid them by a "renormalization" process. One group of infinities is related to the self-energy of the electron, and these can be side-stepped by incorporating them into the rest mass of the electron and then replacing the mass of the electron that appears in the Dirac equation by the experimental value of this mass. This is called "mass renormalization." The other group of infinities stems from the interaction of the electron with the sea of negative-energy states in the vacuum. This is called "vacuum polarization" because the electron, by means of its radiation field, creates momentary virtual pairs or dipoles in the vacuum (positrons and electrons), which then annihilate each other. These vacuum polarization infinities can be rendered harmless by incorporating them into the charge on the electron and then using the experimental value of the charge in the equations. This procedure is called "charge renormalization."

Although Tomonaga, Schwinger, and Feynman worked on these developments independently and almost simultaneously, their formulations differ considerably even though their conclusions are quite similar. Since the work of Tomonaga and Schwinger are similar we shall consider here only Schwinger's papers as being representative of the methods developed independently by these two physicists. Feynman's approach to this problem, however, is so radically different, at least in appearance, from that of Tomonaga and Schwinger that one must consider his discoveries separately. The Tomonaga-Schwinger procedure, which was formulated and applied to its fullest mathematical extent by Schwinger in a series of important papers, is a careful step-by-step mathematical analysis of the difficulties inherent in the original Dirac theory of the electron and an analytical reformulation of the theory. Consequently, the equations describing the interaction of an electron and a radiation field or the interaction of two electrons are free of the inconsistencies that lead to the infinities, which cannot be properly subtracted from the meaningful results in the Dirac theory. The importance of Schwinger's treatment lies in its theoretical completeness and its generality.

To see just what Schwinger accomplished in reformulating the Dirac theory of the electron we must first comprehend the difficulties that were encountered before this treatment. A simple analysis of the manner in which one has to apply the Dirac equation to the description of the state of a system (e.g., the motion of an electron) shows that although the Dirac equation is relativistically correct in that it is invariant to a Lorentz transformation, time is involved in such a way that the equation does not give a correct relativistic description of the state of the system. This is so because the Dirac equation (as does the Schroedinger equation), in spite of its relativistic form, assigns the same "instant of time" to different points of space. As a result of this the commutation relations have a nonrelativistic form even in the Dirac theory and the function that defines the state of a system depends on the time quite differently from the way it depends on space. This means, essentially, that the wave function that describes the state of a system and the commutation relations have meaning only in a particular Lorentz frame of reference. In this sense the theory is not relativistically correct in the fullest sense of this phrase.

Tomonaga was the first to point out that the theory can be made relativistically correct by recasting it in a form in which all references to a specific time for all points of space are eliminated. This means that the equations of motion of the theory must be so stated that they refer to space-time points and to world lines rather than to different points in space at a given time. In this way no particular frame of reference is singled out in which to express the commutation relations or the function that describes the state of a system. Sin-Itiro Tomonaga of Tokyo published his fundamental article in Japan in 1943, but physicists in this country were not aware of it until after the Lamb-Retherford experiment. Schwinger and Feynman had already completed most of their basic work when reports of Tomonaga's theory and English translations of his paper began to reach American physicists in the winter of 1947–1948. It is interesting that whereas Schwinger and Feynman had available the experimental results of Lamb and Retherford to inspire them, Tomonaga reached his goal on the basis of theory alone. Although Tomonaga was the first one to recast the equations into this fully relativistic form, Schwinger was the first to carry out a complete self-consistent reformulation.

As Schwinger first pointed out in his initial paper, the problem of isolating the infinities of the theory so that they can be properly subtracted from the physically meaningful results (that is, incorporated into "unobservable renormalization factors") is related to formulating the theory in a completely covariant form (that is, relativistically correct) at each stage of its development. Thus, in referring to the sidetracking of the infinities Schwinger asks "whether quantum electrodynamics can account unambiguously for the recently observed deviations from the Dirac theory of the electron, without the introduction of fundamentally new concepts?" This paper, the first in a series devoted to the above question, is occupied with the formulation of a completely covariant electrodynamics. "Manifest [that is, obvious at each stage] covariance with respect to Lorentz and gauge transformations is essential in a convergent theory since the use of a particular reference system or gauge in the course of calculation can result in a loss of covariance in view of the ambiguities that may be the concomitant of infinities."

To carry out this program and answer the above question Schwinger subjected the Dirac equation and the quantum-electrodynamic field theory to a searching analysis and showed precisely where the difficulties are to be found. He then reformulated the theory in such a way that it is now completely relativistic and it is possible with the new formalism to isolate the various singularities (that is, infinities) and to make them harmless by a renormalization procedure. The remarkable result of Schwinger's theory is that the procedure leads to an equation of motion for the electron in a radiation field in which the interaction energy alone between the field and the electron (or between two fields) determines the behavior of the system. Since this interaction energy is relativistically invariant, the theory formulated in this way contains none of the objections to which the original Dirac theory is subject. With this formulation Schwinger was able to take care of the infinities arising from the self-energy of the electron and also of those introduced into the theory by the vacuum polarization. By isolating these infinities and incorporating the first into the mass (mass renormalization) and the second into the charge (charge renormalization) he was able to calculate the measured anomalous magnetic moment of the electron to an extremely high accuracy and also to calculate very accurately the Lamb-Retherford displacement of the S and P levels of hydrogen.

Although Schwinger's solution of the infinities difficulty is the most general and theoretically complete exposition of the subject, the mathematical formalism in which it is presented and the mathematical techniques that must be used to apply it to most problems are so difficult and complex that it is seldom used. Instead the methods and techniques developed by Feynman are applied to most problems. The reason for this is that Feynman, starting from a point of view entirely different from Schwinger's, discovered a formulation of the completely covariant theory that enables one to write down the answer to most problems (if they are not too involved) almost by inspection. The beauty of the Feynman technique is that it gives a complete view (a sort of over-all survey) of all the processes that are taking place and thus enables one to write down mathematical expressions for each of these processes in turn. This procedure is still further facilitated by a diagram or graph (the famous Feynman diagrams) which gives a complete geometrical representation of the process being studied. These are space-time diagrams consisting of directed straight and curly lines (the straight lines represent the world lines of electrons and the curly lines represent the world lines of photons) which show schematically the time-space sequence in which the process being investigated unfolds. The use of world lines (that is, space-time diagrams) to represent the entire process being studied has another great advantage: it leads to a relativistically invariant treatment of the problem quite easily, since world lines are the same for all observers and hence relativistically invariant. The meeting of a straight and a curly line means either the emission (creation) by the electron of a photon or the absorption (destruction) of the photon. In these diagrams a directed solid line may point either toward the future (in the direction of increasing time) or toward the past (the direction of decreasing time) so that there is no restriction as to how the straight lines are to be drawn. This corresponds to the finding that the equations of physics are symmetrical in time and are not altered when the time in these equations is replaced by its negative. This is called time inversion or inflection. One of the beauties of the Feynman method is that it automatically takes into account time inversion, and thus introduces the positron on the same basis as the electron. As Feynman points out, the straight line directed backward in time represents the motion of a positron, so that in this theory a positron is represented as an electron moving from the future into the past. Thus, these diagrams represent the creation or the annihilation of a pair (an electron-positron pair) by the intersection at a point of a straight line directed toward the future and a straight line directed toward the past. In this way all possible interactions that contribute to a process can be represented graphically; since each of these graphs can be expressed mathematically according to certain fairly simple rules developed by Feynman, a complete mathematical expression giving the probability for the process can be written down. Thus, in principle the solution to any problem, taking into account all the interactions that contribute to it, can be written down, almost by inspection. But in practice the evaluation of the mathematical terms that occur is so complex in higher order calculations that the Feynman procedure is limited to the first few orders of approximation.

Feynman's discovery of his graphs and the methods for evaluating them evolved from an approach to quantum mechanics that departs considerably from the traditional procedure introduced by Schroedinger and is closer to the matrix mechanics of Heisenberg. The standard way of treating a problem in quantum mechanics is to set up the Hamiltonian (that is, the total energy expressed in terms of momenta and coordinates) and then to transform it to an operator (operating on the wave function or the state vector, as it is called) by replacing each component of the momentum by a differential operator with respect to the corresponding coordinate. The operator for the Hamiltonian thus obtained, operating on the wave function, is then equated to the rate at which the wave function varies with the time. This is the Schroedinger wave equation. Essentially, it says that the unfolding (or evolution in time) of the state of a system (the wave function) is determined by the differential operator that represents the total energy of the system.

One usually seeks to solve the Schroedinger differential equation by a step-by-step process in which the change in the wave function (that is the state vector) is considered step by step in short time intervals. Thus one assumes that one knows the state of the system at some initial moment and then obtains it at a very short interval later by noting that the change of the system from its initial state is just equal to the product of the small time interval and the Hamiltonian (as an operator) applied to the initial state (that is, to the initial wave function). In this way one can, at least in principle, obtain a step-by-step evolution of the state of the system from some initial moment to any desired later time. Carried out with proper regard for relativistic accuracy, this is the procedure of Schwinger.

The disadvantage of this procedure is that it involves the investigator in the analysis of details that are superfluous and, in fact meaningless as far as the over-all picture of the process is concerned. Moreover, it is difficult in this step-by-step procedure to keep track of all the various terms that may contribute to the final result in a particular problem and to make sure that these various terms are relativistically correct. These difficulties are all eliminated in the Feynman method because Feynman considers the event in its entirety and represents the evolution of the system from its initial state to its final state as one continuous space-time path that starts from the initial moment and continues in a series of connected directed straight lines to the final moment. All intermediate processes, such as the virtual emission and absorption of photons and the creation and annihilation of pairs, or the interaction of the electron with external perturbing fields, are represented on this continuous graph by sudden changes in direction (which may take one backward in time) of the directed straight line or by the appearance of curly lines that emerge from the straight lines and move off or else come back to the straight line again to form a loop (the creation and annihilation of a virtual photon). The interaction of the moving electron with an external field on this space-time diagram is shown by a kink (a sudden change in direction) of the directed straight line and may be accompanied by the sudden appearance of a curly line at the kink (the emission or absorption of a photon).

Any particular event is now represented by the sum of all possible Feynman diagrams that can be drawn from the initial space-time point to the final space-time point. Since there are very definite rules for constructing these diagrams and each line in any diagram (as well as each point where there is a kink or change of direction) has a mathematical counterpart, the complete mathematical scheme for describing any event can be written down. This procedure is particularly effective when one is involved in higher order calculations which are completely unmanageable with the traditional procedure. In the Feynman method each kink or change in direction of the directed straight line represents an additional order in the calculation. Thus, the graphic scheme representing the second-order interaction of an electron and an external field of force contains two changes in direction of the directed straight line (the world line) describing the motion of the electron.

Although the Feynman and the Schwinger methods appear quite different at first sight, they are really completely equivalent, as was first demonstrated rigorously by Freeman Dyson. It is said that Feynman, on hearing of Dyson's proof that his procedure and Schwinger's are mathematically equivalent, remarked, "Now I have been translated into hieroglyphics." This is an interesting revelation of Feynman's attitude toward the highly formalistic approach to physical problems. The essential difference between the Tomonaga-Schwinger formalism and the Feynman approach is that the former is a field theory whereas the latter deals directly with the space-time history of the particles involved; it is a carryover into quantum mechanics of "action at a distance" between particles. Feynman's method introduces a set of simple rules that enable one to calculate the physically observable quantities that, according to Feynman, are the only things that can and should be calculable from a theory. In this sense, Feynman's ideas are closer to Heisenberg's point of view than to Schroedinger's. Feynman's insistence on dealing directly and only with observable quantities has led to the growth and great importance of the "S-matrix point of view" in the study of fundamental particles today. This is a natural extension of Heisenberg's original matrix mechanics.

It should be emphasized that the discoveries of Schwinger, Feynman, Tomonaga, and Dyson have added nothing new to our picture of nature; the fundamental difficulties associated with the infinite self-energy and the structure of the electron still remain. The work of these physicists has shown, however, that the Dirac theory of the electron is more powerful and general than had been thought previously to be the case. All that is required for the application of the Dirac theory to its fullest productivity is a consistent and relativistically correct way of taking into account all the interactions that contribute to any event. This is the essential importance of the renormalization physics that has grown out of the work of Schwinger. This has been very well expressed by Professor Dyson in an article in *Science:*

Tomonaga, Schwinger, and Feynman rescued the [Dirac] theory without making any radical innovations. Their victory was a victory of conservatism. They kept the physical basis of the theory precisely as it had been laid down by Dirac, and only changed the mathematical superstructure. By polishing and refining with great skill the mathematical formalism, they were able to show that the theory does in fact give meaningful predictions for all observable quantities. The predictions are in all cases finite, unambiguous, and in agreement with experiment. The divergent and meaningless quantities are indeed present in the theory, but they appear in such a way that they automatically eliminate themselves from any quantity which is in principle observable. The exact correspondence between quantities which are unambiguously calculable and quantities which are observable becomes, in the end, the theory's most singular virtue.[2]

The renormalization techniques that give a physically reasonable answer to any question that may arise in the interaction of electrons with the electromagnetic field can also be applied to eliminate some of the infinity difficulties that occur in the interaction of nucleons via the meson fields. Here the procedure is only moderately fruitful and most of the difficulties remain even with renormalization. This is so because the coupling between nucleons and the mesonic fields is many times stronger than that between electrons and the electromagnetic field. Hence, the renormalization procedure, which is essentially a sum of an infinite number of terms in successively higher powers of the coupling constant between the particle and the field (that is, the number that measures how strong the interaction between the particle and the field is), does not converge but becomes infinitely large for the interaction between two nucleons. Hence, this procedure is not trustworthy even if one considers only first- or second-order perturbations.

ooooooo

SCHWINGER

Quantum Electrodynamics [3]

THE DEVELOPMENT OF QUANTUM MECHANics in the years 1925 and 1926 had produced rules for the description of

---

[2] *Science,* 150 (1965), 589.

[3] Schwinger, *Selected Papers in Quantum Electrodynamics* (New York: Dover, 1958), pp. vii–xvii.

systems of microscopic particles, which involved promoting the fundamental dynamical variables of a corresponding classical system into operators with specified commutators. By this means, a system, described initially in classical particle language, acquires characteristics associated with the complementary classical wave picture. It was also known that electromagnetic radiation contained in an enclosure, when considered as a classical dynamical system, was equivalent energetically to a denumerably infinite number of harmonic oscillators. With the application of the quantization process to these fictitious oscillators the classical radiation field assumed characteristics describable in the complementary classical particle language. The ensuing theory of light quantum emission and absorption by atomic systems marked the beginning of quantum electrodynamics, as the theory of the quantum dynamical system formed by the electromagnetic field in interaction with charged particles (in a narrower sense, the lightest charged particles). The quantization procedure could be transferred from the variables of the fictitious oscillators to the components of the field in three-dimensional space, based upon the classical analogy between a field specified within small spatial cells, and equivalent particle systems. When it was attempted to quantize the complete electromagnetic field, rather than the radiation field that remains after the Coulomb interaction is separated, difficulties were encountered that stem from the gauge ambiguity of the potentials that appear in the Lagrangian formulation of the Maxwell equations. The only real dynamical degrees of freedom are those of the radiation part of the field. Yet one can employ additional degrees of freedom which are suppressed finally by imposing a consistent restriction on the admissible states of the system. To make more evident the relativistic invariance of the scheme, other equivalent forms were given to the theory by introducing different time coordinates for each of a fixed number of charged particles coupled to the electromagnetic field. This formal period of quantization of the electromagnetic field was terminated by a critical analysis of the limitations in the accuracy of simultaneous measurements of two field strengths, produced by the known quantum restrictions on the simultaneous measurability of properties of material test bodies. The complete agreement of these considerations with the formal implications of the operator commutation relations indicated the necessity and consistency of applying the quantum mechanical description to all dynamical systems. The synthesis of the complementary classical particle and field languages in the concept of the quantized field, as exemplified in the treatment of the electromagnetic field, was found to be of general applicability to systems formed by arbitrary numbers of identical particles, although the rules of field quantization derived by analogy from those of particle mechanics were too restrictive, yielding only systems obeying the Bose-Einstein statistics. The replacement of commutators by anti-commutators was necessary to describe particles, like the electron, that obey the Fermi-Dirac statistics. In the latter situation there is no realizable physical limit for which the system behaves as a classical field.

But, from the origin of quantum electrodynamics in the classical theory of point charges came a legacy of difficulties. The coupling of an electron with the electromagnetic field implied an infinite energy displacement, and, indeed, an infinite shift of all spectral lines emitted by an atomic system; in the reaction of the electromagnetic field stimulated by the presence of the electron, arbitrarily short wave lengths play a disproportionate and divergent role. The phenomenon of electron-positron pair creation, which finds a natural place in the relativistic electron field theory, contributes to this situation in virtue of the fluctuating densities of charge and current that occur even in the vacuum state as the matter-field counterpart of the fluctuations in electric and magnetic field strengths. In computing the energy of a single electron relative to that of the vacuum state, it is of significance that the presence of the electron tends to suppress the charge-current fluctuations induced by the fluctuating electromagnetic field. The resulting electron energy, while still divergent in its dependence upon the contributions of arbitrarily short wave lengths, exhibits only a logarithmic infinity; the combination of quantum and relativistic effects has destroyed all correspondence with the classical theory and its strongly structure-dependent electromagnetic mass. The existence of current fluctuations in the vacuum has other implications, since the introduction of an electromagnetic field induces currents that tend to modify the initial field; the "vacuum" acts as a polarizable medium. New non-linear electromagnetic phenomena appear, such as the scattering of one light beam by another, or by an electrostatic field. But, in the calculation of the current induced by weak fields, there occur terms that depended divergently upon the contributions of high-energy electron-positron pairs. These were generally considered to be completely without physical significance, although it was noticed that the contribution to the induced charge density that is proportional to the inducing density, with a logarithmically divergent coefficient, would result in an effective reduction of all densities by a constant factor which is not observable separately under ordinary circumstances. In contrast with the divergences at infinitely high energies, another kind of divergent situation was encountered in calculating the total probability that a photon be emitted in a collision of a charged particle. Here, however, the deficiency was evidently in the approximate method of calculation; in any deflection of a charged particle it is certain that "zero" frequency quanta shall be emitted, which fact must be taken into account if meaningful questions are to be asked. The concentration on photons of very low energy permitted a sufficiently accurate treatment to be developed, in which it was recognized that the correct quantum description of a freely moving charged particle includes an electromagnetic field that accompanies the particle, as in the classical picture. It also began to be appreciated that the quantum treatment of radiation processes was inconsistent in its identification of the mass of the electron, when decoupled from the electromagnetic field, with the experimentally observed mass. Part of the effect of the electromagnetic coupling is to generate the field that accompanies the charge, and which reacts on it to produce an electromagnetic mass. This is familiar classically, where the sum of the two mass contributions appears as the effective electron mass in an equation of motion which, under ordinary conditions, no longer refers to the detailed structure of the electron. Hence, it was concluded that a classical theory of the latter type should be the correspondence basis for a quantum electrodynamics.

Further progress came only with the spur of experimental discovery. Exploiting the wartime development of electronic and microwave techniques, delicate measurements disclosed that the electron possessed an intrinsic magnetic moment slightly greater than that predicted by the relativistic quantum theory of a single particle, while another prediction of the latter theory concerning the degeneracy of states in the excited levels of hydrogen was contradicted by observing a separation of the states. (Historically, the experimental stimulus came entirely from the latter measurement; the evidence on magnetic anomalies received its proper interpretation only in conseqence of the theoretical prediction of an additional spin magnetic moment.) If these new electron properties were to be understood as electrodynamic effects, the theory had to be recast in a usable form. The parameters of mass and charge associated with the electron in the formalism of electrodynamics are not the quantities measured under ordinary conditions. A free electron is accompanied by an electromagnetic field which effectively alters the inertia of the system, and an electromagnetic field is accompanied by a current of electron-positron pairs which effectively alters the strength of the field and of all charges. Hence a process of renormalization must be carried out, in which the initial parameters are eliminated in favor of those with immediate physical significance. The simplest approximate method of accomplishing this is to compute the electrodynamic corrections to some property and then subtract the effect of the mass and charge redefinitions. While this is a possible non-relativistic procedure, it is not a satisfactory basis for relativistic calculations where the difference of two individually divergent terms is generally ambiguous. It was necessary to subject the conventional Hamiltonian electrodynamics to a transformation designed to introduce the proper description of single electron and photon states, so that the interactions among these particles would be characterized from the beginning by experimental parameters. As the result of this calculation, performed to the first significant order of approximation in the electromagnetic coupling, the electron acquired new electrodynamic properties, which were completely finite. These included an energy displacement in an external magnetic field corresponding to an additional spin magnetic moment, and a displacement of energy levels in a Coulomb field. Both predictions were in good accord with experiment, and later refinements in experiment and theory have only emphasized that agreement. However, the Coulomb calculation disclosed a serious flaw; the additional spin interaction that appeared in an electrostatic field was not that expected from the relativistic transformation properties of the supplementary spin magnetic moment, and had to be artificially corrected. Thus, a complete revision in the computational techniques of the relativistic theory could not be avoided. The electrodynamic formalism is invariant under Lorentz transformations and gauge transformations, and the concept of renormalization is in accord with these requirements. Yet, in virtue of the divergences inherent in the theory, the use of a particular coordinate system or gauge in the course of computation could result in a loss of covariance. A version of the theory was needed that manifested covariance at every stage of the calculation. The basis of such a formulation was found in the distinction between the elementary properties of the individual uncoupled fields, and the effects produced by the interaction between them. The application of these methods to the problems of vacuum polarization, electron mass, and the electromagnetic properties of single electrons now gave finite, covariant results which justified and extended the earlier calculations. Thus, to the first approximation at least, the use of a covariant renormalization technique had produced a theory that was devoid of divergences and in agreement with experience, all high energy difficulties being isolated in the renormalization constants. Yet, in one aspect of these calculations, the preservation of gauge invariance, the utmost caution was required, and the need was felt for less delicate methods of evaluation. Extreme care would not be necessary if, by some device, the various divergent integrals could be rendered convergent while maintaining their general covariant features. This can be accomplished by substituting, for the mass of the particle, a suitably weighted spectrum of masses, where all auxiliary masses eventually tend to infinity. Such a procedure has no meaning in terms of physically realizable particles. It is best understood, and replaced, by a description of the electron with the aid of an invariant proper-time parameter. Divergences appear only when one integrates over this parameter, and gauge invariant, Lorentz invariant results are automatically guaranteed merely by reserving this integration to the end of the calculation.

Throughout these developments the basic view of electromagnetism was that originated by Maxwell and Lorentz—the interaction between charges is propagated through the field by local action. In its quantum mechanical transcription it leads to formalisms in which charged particles and field appear on the same footing dynamically. But another approach is also familiar classically; the field produced by arbitrarily moving charges can be evaluated, and the dynamical problem reformulated as the purely mechanical one of particles interacting with each other, and themselves, through a propagated action at a distance. The transference of this line of thought into quantum language was accompanied by another shift in emphasis relative to the previously described work. In the latter, the effect on the particles of the coupling with the electromagnetic field was expressed by additional energy terms which could then be used to evaluate energy displacements in bound states, or to compute corrections to scattering cross-sections. Now the fundamental viewpoint was that of scattering, and in its approximate versions led to a detailed space-time description of the various interaction mechanisms. The two approaches are equivalent; the formal integration of the differential equations of one method supplying the starting point of the other. But if one excludes the consideration of bound states, it is possible to expand the elements of a scattering matrix in powers of the coupling constant, and examine the effect of charge and mass renormalization, term by term, to indefinitely high powers. It appeared that, for any process, the coefficient of each power in the renormalized coupling constant was completely finite. This highly satisfactory result did not mean, however, that the act of renormalization had, in itself, produced a more correct theory. The convergence of the power series is not established, and the series doubtless has the significance of an asymptotic expansion. Yet, for practical purposes, in which the smallness of the coupling parameter is relevant, this analysis gave assurance that calculations of arbitrary precision could be performed.

The evolutionary process by which relativistic field theory was escaping from the confines of its non-relativistic heritage culminated in a complete reconstruction of the foundations of quantum dynamics. The quantum mechanics of particles had been expressed as a set of operator prescriptions superimposed upon the structure of classical mechanics in Hamiltonian form. When extended to relativistic fields, this approach had the disadvantage of producing an unnecessarily great asymmetry between time and space, and of placing the existence of Fermi-Dirac fields on a purely empirical basis. But the Hamiltonian form is not the natural starting point of classical dynamics. Rather, this is supplied by Hamilton's action principle, and action is a relativistic invariant. Could quantum dynamics be developed independently from an action principle, which, being freed from the limitations of the correspondence principle, might automatically produce two distinct types of dynamical variables? The correspondence relation between classical action, and the quantum mechanical description of time development by a transformation function, had long been known. It had also been observed that, for infinitesimal time intervals and sufficiently simple systems, this asymptotic connection becomes sharpened into an identity of the phase of the transformation function with the classically evaluated action. The general quantum dynamical principle was found in a differential characterization of transformation functions, involving the variation of an action operator. When the action operator is chosen to produce first order differential equations of motion, or field equations, it indeed predicts the existence of two types of dynamical variables, with operator properties described by commutators and anti-commutators, respectively. Furthermore, the connection between the statistics and the spin of the particles is inferred from invariance requirements, which strengthens the previous arguments based upon properties of non-interacting particles. The practical utility of this quantum dynamical principle stems from its very nature; it supplies differential equations for the construction of the transformation functions that contain all the dynamical properties of the system. It leads in particular to a concise expression of quantum electrodynamics in the form of coupled differential equations for electron and photon propagation functions. Such functions enjoy the advantages of space-time pictorializability, combined with general applicability to bound systems or scattering situations. Among these applications has been a treatment of that most electrodynamic of systems —positronium, the metastable atom formed by a positron and an electron. The agreement between theory and experiment on the finer details of this system is another quantitative triumph of quantum electrodynamics.

The post-war developments of quantum electrodynamics have been largely dominated by questions of formalism and technique, and do not contain any fundamental improvement in the physical foundations of the theory. Such a situation is not new in the history of physics; it took the labors of more than a century to develop the methods that express fully the mechanical principles laid down by Newton. But, we may ask, is there a fatal fault in the structure of field theory? Could it not be that the divergences—apparent symptoms of malignancy—are only spurious byproducts of an invalid expansion in powers of the coupling constant and that renormalization, which can change no physical implication of the theory, simply rectifies this mathematical error? This hope disappears on recognizing that the observational basis of quantum electrodynamics is self-contradictory. The fundamental dynamical variables of the electron-positron field, for example, have meaning only as symbols of the localized creation and annihilation of charged particles, to which are ascribed a definite mass without reference to the electromagnetic field. Accordingly it should be possible, in principle, to confirm these properties by measurements, which, if they are to be uninfluenced by the coupling of the particles to the electromagnetic field, must be performed instantaneously. But there appears to be nothing in the formalism to set a standard for arbitrarily short times and, indeed, the assumption that over sufficiently small intervals the two fields behave as though free from interaction is contradicted by evaluating the supposedly small effect of the coupling. Thus, although the starting point of the theory is the independent assignment of properties to the two fields, they can never be disengaged to give those properties immediate observational significance. It seems that we have reached the limits of the quantum theory of measurement, which asserts the possibility of instantaneous observations, without reference to specific agencies. The localization of charge with indefinite precision requires for its realization a coupling with the electromagnetic field that can attain arbitrarily large magnitudes. The resulting appearance of divergences, and contradictions, serves to deny the basic measurement hypothesis. We conclude that a convergent theory cannot be formulated consistently within the framework of present space-time concepts. To limit the magnitude of interactions while retaining the customary coördinate description is contradictory, since no mechanism is provided for precisely localized measurements.

In attempting to account for the properties of electron and positron, it has been natural to use the simplified form of quantum electrodynamics in which only these charged particles are considered. Despite the apparent validity of the basic assumption that the electron-positron field experiences no appreciable interaction with fields other than electromagnetic, this physically incomplete theory suffers from a fundamental limitation. It can never explain the observed value of the dimensionless coupling constant measuring the electron charge. Indeed, since charge renormalization is a property of the electromagnetic field, and the latter is influenced by the behavior of every kind of fundamental particle with direct or indirect electromagnetic coupling, a full understanding of the electron charge can exist only when the theory of elementary particles has come to a stage of perfection that is presently unimaginable. It is not likely that future developments will change drastically the practical results of the electron theory, which gives contemporary quantum electrodynamics a certain enduring value. Yet the real significance of the work of the past decade lies in the recognition of the ultimate problems facing electrodynamics, the problems of conceptual consistency and of physical completeness. No final solution can be anticipated until physical science has met the heroic challenge to comprehend the structure of the sub-microscopic world that nuclear exploration has revealed.

On Quantum-Electrodynamics and the Magnetic Moment of the Electron [4]

ATTEMPTS TO EVALUATE RADIATIVE COR-
rections to electron phenomena have heretofore been beset by divergence
difficulties, attributable to self-energy and vacuum polarization effects.
Electrodynamics unquestionably requires revision at ultra-relativistic
energies, but is presumably accurate at moderate relativistic energies. It
would be desirable, therefore, to isolate those aspects of the current
theory that essentially involve high energies, and are subject to modification by a more satisfactory theory, from aspects that involve only moderate energies and are thus relatively trustworthy. This goal has been
achieved by transforming the Hamiltonian of current hole theory electrodynamics to exhibit explicitly the logarithmically divergent self-energy of
a free electron, which arises from the virtual emission and absorption of
light quanta. The electromagnetic self-energy of a free electron can be
ascribed to an electromagnetic mass, which must be added to the mechanical mass of the electron. Indeed, the only meaningful statements of
the theory involve this combination of masses, which is the experimental
mass of a free electron. It might appear, from this point of view, that
the divergence of the electromagnetic mass is unobjectionable, since the
individual contributions to the experimental mass are unobservable. However, the transformation of the Hamiltonian is based on the assumption of
a weak interaction between matter and radiation, which requires that the
electromagnetic mass be a small correction $(\sim (e^2/\hbar c)m_0)$ to the mechanical mass m_0.

The new Hamiltonian is superior to the original one in essentially three
ways: it involves the experimental electron mass, rather than the unobservable mechanical mass; an electron now interacts with the radiation
field only in the presence of an external field, that is, only an accelerated
electron can emit or absorb a light quantum; the interaction energy of an
electron with an external field is now subject to a *finite* radiative correction. In connection with the last point, it is important to note that the
inclusion of the electromagnetic mass with the mechanical mass does not
avoid all divergences; the polarization of the vacuum produces a logarithmically divergent term proportional to the interaction energy of the
electron in an external field. However, it has long been recognized that

---

[4] Julian Schwinger, *Physical Review,* 73 (1948), 416.

such a term is equivalent to altering the value of the electron charge by a constant factor, only the final value being properly identified with the experimental charge. Thus the interaction between matter and radiation produces a renormalization of the electron charge and mass, all divergences being contained in the renormalization factors.

The simplest example of a radiative correction is that for the energy of an electron in an external magnetic field. The detailed application of the theory shows that the radiative correction to the magnetic interaction energy corresponds to an additional magnetic moment associated with the electron spin, of magnitude $\delta\mu/\mu = (1/2\pi)e^2/\hbar c = 0.001162$. It is indeed gratifying that recently acquired experimental data confirm this prediction. Measurements on the hyperfine splitting of the ground states of atomic hydrogen and deuterium have yielded values that are definitely larger than those to be expected from the directly measured nuclear moments and an electron moment of one Bohr magneton. These discrepancies can be accounted for by a small additional electron spin magnetic moment. Recalling that the nuclear moments have been calibrated in terms of the electron moment, we find the additional moment necessary to account for the measured hydrogen and deuterium hyperfine structures to be $\delta\mu/\mu = 0.00126 \pm 0.00019$ and $\delta\mu/\mu = 0.00131 \pm 0.00025$, respectively. These values are not in disagreement with the theoretical prediction. More precise conformation is provided by measurement of the g values for the $^2S_{1/2}$, $^2P_{1/2}$ and $^2P_{3/2}$ states of sodium and gallium. To account for these results, it is necessary to ascribe the following additional spin magnetic moment to the electron, $\delta\mu/\mu = 0.00118 \pm 0.00003$.

The radiative correction to the energy of an electron in a Coulomb field will produce a shift in the energy levels of hydrogen-like atoms, and modify the scattering of electrons in a Coulomb field. Such energy level displacements have recently been observed in the fine structures of hydrogen, deuterium, and ionized helium. The values yielded by our theory differ only slightly from those conjectured by Bethe on the basis of a nonrelativistic calculation, and are, thus, in good accord with experiment. Finally, the finite radiative correction to the elastic scattering of electrons by a Coulomb field provides a satisfactory termination to a subject that has been beset with much confusion.

A paper dealing with the details of this theory and its applications is in course of preparation.

ооооооо

FEYNMAN

The Theory of Positrons [5]

INTRODUCTION

THIS IS THE FIRST OF a set of papers dealing with the solution of problems in quantum electrodynamics. The main principle is to deal directly with the solutions to the Hamiltonian differential equations rather than with these equations themselves. Here we treat simply the motion of electrons and positrons in given external potentials. In a second paper we consider the interactions of these particles, that is, quantum electrodynamics.

The problem of charges in a fixed potential is usually treated by the method of second quantization of the electron field, using the ideas of the theory of holes. Instead we show that by a suitable choice and interpretation of the solutions of Dirac's equation the problem may be equally well treated in a manner which is fundamentally no more complicated than Schrödinger's method of dealing with one or more particles. The various creation and annihilation operators in the conventional electron field view are required because the number of particles is not conserved, i.e., pairs may be created or destroyed. On the other hand charge is conserved which suggests that if we follow the charge, not the particle, the results can be simplified.

In the approximation of classical relativistic theory the creation of an electron pair (electron A, positron B) might be represented by the start of two world lines from the point of creation, 1. The world lines of the positron will then continue until it annihilates another electron, C, at a world point 2. Between the times t_1 and t_2 there are then three world lines, before and after only one. However, the world lines of C, B, and A together form one continuous line albeit the "positron part" B of this continuous line is directed backward in time. Following the charge rather than the particles corresponds to considering this continuous world line as a whole rather than breaking it up into its pieces. It is as though a bombardier flying low over a road suddenly sees three roads and it is only

---

[5] Richard P. Feynman, *Physical Review*, 76 (1949), 749–756.

when two of them come together and disappear again that he realizes that he has simply passed over a long switchback in a single road.

This over-all space-time point of view leads to considerable simplification in many problems. One can take into account at the same time processes which ordinarily would have to be considered separately. For example, when considering the scattering of an electron by a potential one automatically takes into account the effects of virtual pair productions. The same equation, Dirac's, which describes the deflection of the world line of an electron in a field, can also describe the deflection (and in just as simple a manner) when it is large enough to reverse the time-sense of the world line, and thereby correspond to pair annihilation. Quantum mechanically the direction of the world lines is replaced by the direction of propagation of waves.

This view is quite different from that of the Hamiltonian method which considers the future as developing continuously from out of the past. Here we imagine the entire space-time history laid out, and that we just become aware of increasing portions of it successively. In a scattering problem this over-all view of the complete scattering process is similar to the S-matrix viewpoint of Heisenberg. The temporal order of events during the scattering, which is analyzed in such detail by the Hamiltonian differential equation, is irrelevant. The relation of these viewpoints will be discussed much more fully in the introduction to the second paper, in which the more complicated interactions are analyzed.

The development stemmed from the idea that in non-relativistic quantum mechanics the amplitude for a given process can be considered as the sum of an amplitude for each space-time path available. In view of the fact that in classical physics positrons could be viewed as electrons proceeding along world lines toward the past the attempt was made to remove, in the relativistic case, the restriction that the paths must proceed always in one direction in time. It was discovered that the results could be even more easily understood from a more familiar physical viewpoint, that of scattered waves. This viewpoint is the one used in this paper. After the equations were worked out physically the proof of the equivalence to the second quantization theory was found.

First we discuss the relation of the Hamiltonian differential equation to its solution, using for an example the Schrödinger equation. Next we deal in an analogous way with the Dirac equation and show how the solutions may be interpreted to apply to positrons.. The interpretation seems not to be consistent unless the electrons obey the exclusion principle. (Charges obeying the Klein-Gordon equations can be described in an analogous manner, but here consistency apparently requires Bose statistics.) . . .

GREEN'S FUNCTION TREATMENT OF SCHRÖDINGER'S EQUATION

We begin by a brief discussion of the relation of the non-relativistic wave equation to its solution. The ideas will then be extended to relativistic particles, satisfying Dirac's equation, and finally in the succeeding paper to interacting relativistic particles, that is, quantum electrodynamics.

The Schrödinger equation

$$i\partial\psi/\partial t = H\psi, \tag{1}$$

describes the change in the wave function ψ in an infinitesimal time Δt as due to the operation of an operator $\exp(-iH\Delta t)$. One can ask also, if $\psi(\mathbf{x}_1, t_1)$ is the wave function at $\mathbf{x}_1$ at time t_1, what is the wave function at time $t_2 > t_1$? It can always be written as

$$\psi(\mathbf{x}_2, t_2) = \int K(\mathbf{x}_2, t_2; \mathbf{x}_1, t_1)\psi(\mathbf{x}_1, t_1)d^3\mathbf{x}_1, \tag{2}$$

where K is a Green's function for the linear Eq. (1). (We have limited ourselves to a single particle of coordinate $\mathbf{x}$, but the equations are obviously of greater generality.) If H is a constant operator having eigenvalues E_n, eigenfunctions ϕ_n so that $\psi(\mathbf{x}, t_1)$ can be expanded as $\sum_n C_n {}_n(\mathbf{x})$, then $\psi(\mathbf{x}, t_2) = \sum \exp(-iE_n (t_2 - t_1)) C_n\phi_n(\mathbf{x})$. Since $C_n = \int \phi_n{}^*(\mathbf{x}_1)\psi(\mathbf{x}_1, t_1)d^3\mathbf{x}_1$, one finds (where we write 1 for $\mathbf{x}_1, t_1$ and 2 for $\mathbf{x}_2, t_2$) in this case

$$K(2, 1) = \sum_n \phi_n(\mathbf{x}_2)\phi_n{}^*(\mathbf{x}_1) \exp(-iE_n(t_2 - t_1)), \tag{3}$$

for $t_2 > t_1$. We shall find it convenient for $t_2 < t_1$ to define $K(2, 1) = 0$ (Eq. (2) is then not valid for $t_2 < t_1$). It is then readily shown that in general K can be defined by that solution of

$$(i\partial/\partial t_2 - H_2)K(2, 1) = i\delta(2, 1), \tag{4}$$

which is zero for $t_2 < t_1$, where $\delta(2, 1) = \delta(t_2 - t_1)\delta(x_2 - x_1) \times \delta(y_2 - y_1)\delta(z_2 - z_1)$ and the subscript 2 on H_2 means that the operator acts on the variables of 2 of $K(2, 1)$. When H is not constant, (2) and (4) are valid but K is less easy to evaluate than (3).

We can call $K(2, 1)$ the total amplitude for arrival at $\mathbf{x}_2, t_2$ starting from $\mathbf{x}_1, t_1$. (It results from adding an amplitude, $\exp iS$, for each space time path between these points, where S is the action along the path. The transition amplitude for finding a particle in state $\chi(\mathbf{x}_2, t_2)$ at time t_2, if at t_1 it was in $\psi(\mathbf{x}_1, t_1)$, is

$$\int \chi^*(2) K(2, 1) \psi(1) d^3\mathbf{x}_1 d^3\mathbf{x}_2. \tag{5}$$

A quantum mechanical system is described equally well by specifying the function K, or by specifying the Hamiltonian H from which it results. For some purposes the specification in terms of K is easier to use and visualize. We desire eventually to discuss quantum electrodynamics from this point of view.

To gain a greater familiarity with the K function and the point of view it suggests, we consider a simple perturbation problem. Imagine we have a particle in a weak potential $U(\mathbf{x}, t)$, a function of position and time. We wish to calculate $K(2, 1)$ if U differs from zero only for t between t_1 and t_2. We shall expand K in increasing powers of U:

$$K(2, 1) = K_0(2, 1) + K^{(1)}(2, 1) + K^{(2)}(2, 1) + \cdots. \tag{6}$$

To zero order in U, K is that for a free particle, $K_0(2, 1)$. To study the first order correction $K^{(1)}(2, 1)$, first consider the case that U differs from zero only for the infinitesimal time interval Δt_3 between some time t_3 and $t_3 + \Delta t_3 (t_1 < t_3 < t_2)$. Then if $\psi(1)$ is the wave function at $\mathbf{x}_1, t_1$, the wave function at $\mathbf{x}_3, t_3$ is

$$\psi(3) = \int K_0(3, 1) \psi(1) d^3\mathbf{x}_1, \tag{7}$$

since from t_1 to t_3 the particle is free. For the short interval Δt_3 we solve (1) as

$$\psi(\mathbf{x}, t_3 + \Delta t_3) = \exp(-iH\Delta t_3)\psi(\mathbf{x}, t_3)$$
$$= (1 - iH_0\Delta t_3 - iU\Delta t_3)\psi(\mathbf{x}, t_3),$$

where we put $H = H_0 + U$, H_0 being the Hamiltonian of a free particle. Thus $\psi(\mathbf{x}, t_3 + \Delta t_3)$ differs from what it would be if the potential were zero (namely $(1 - iH_0\Delta t_3)\psi(\mathbf{x}, t_3)$) by the extra piece

$$\Delta\psi = -iU(\mathbf{x}_3, t_3) \cdot \psi(\mathbf{x}_3, t_3)\Delta t_3, \tag{8}$$

which we shall call the amplitude scattered by the potential. The wave function at 2 is given by

$$\psi(\mathbf{x}_2, t_2) = \int K_0(\mathbf{x}_2, t_2; \mathbf{x}_3, t_3 + \Delta t_3)\psi(\mathbf{x}_3, t_3 + \Delta t_3) d^3\mathbf{x}_3,$$

since after $t_3 + \Delta t_3$ the particle is again free. Therefore the change in the wave function at 2 brought about by the potential is (substitute (7) into (8) and (8) into the equation for $\psi(\mathbf{x}_2, t_2)$):

$$\Delta\psi(2) = -i \int K_0(2, 3) U(3) K_0(3, 1)\psi(1) d^3\mathbf{x}_1 d^3\mathbf{x}_3 \Delta t_3.$$

In the case that the potential exists for an extended time, it may be looked upon as a sum of effects from each interval Δt_3 so that the total effect is obtained by integrating over t_3 as well as $\mathbf{x}_3$. From the definition (2) of K then, we find

$$K^{(1)}(2, 1) = -i \int K_0(2, 3) U(3) K_0(3, 1) d\tau_3, \tag{9}$$

where the integral can now be extended over all space and time, $d\tau_3 = d^3\mathbf{x}_3 dt_3$. Automatically there will be no contribution if t_3 is outside the range t_1 to t_2 because of our definition, $K_0(2, 1) = 0$ for $t_2 < t_1$.

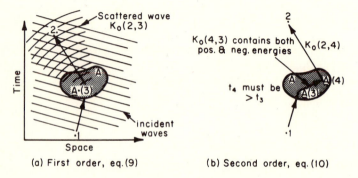

(a) First order, eq. (9)   (b) Second order, eq. (10)

Fig. 86–1. The Schroedinger (and Dirac) equation can be visualized as describing the fact that plane waves are scattered successively by a potential. Fig. 86–1 (a) illustrates the situation in first order. $K_0(2,3)$ is the amplitude for a free particle starting at point 3 to arrive at 2. The shaded region indicates the presence of the potential A which scatters at 3 with amplitude $-iA(3)$ per cm³ sec. (Eq. (9)). In (b) is illustrated the second order process (Eq. (10)), the waves scattered at 3 are scattered again at 4. However, in Dirac one-electron theory $K_0(4,3)$ would represent electrons both of positive and of negative energies proceeding from 3 to 4. This is remedied by choosing a different scattering kernel $K_+(4,3)$, Fig. 86–2.

We can understand the result (6), (9) this way. We can imagine that a particle travels as a free particle from point to point, but is scattered by the potential U. Thus the total amplitude for arrival at 2 from 1 can be considered as the sum of the amplitudes for various alternative routes. It may go directly from 1 to 2 (amplitude $K_0(2, 1)$, giving the zero order term in (6)). Or [see Fig. 86–1(a)] it may go from 1 to 3 (amplitude

$K_0(3, 1)$), get scattered there by the potential (scattering amplitude $-iU(3)$ per unit volume and time) and then go from 3 to 2 (amplitude $K_0(2, 3)$). This may occur for any point 3 so that summing over these alternatives gives (9).

Again, it may be scattered twice by the potential [Fig. 86–1(b)]. It goes from 1 to 3 ($K_0(3, 1)$), gets scattered there ($-iU(3)$) then proceeds to some other point, 4, in space time (amplitude $K_0(4, 3)$) is scattered again ($-iU(4)$) and then proceeds to 2 ($K_0(2, 4)$). Summing over all possible places and times for 3, 4, we find that the second order contribution to the total amplitude $K^{(2)}$ (2, 1) is

$$(-i)^2 \int \int K_0(2, 4) U(4) K_0(4, 3) U(3) K_0(3, 1) d\tau_3 d\tau_4. \qquad (10)$$

This can be readily verified directly from (1) just as (9) was. One can in this way obviously write down any of the terms of the expansion (6).

TREATMENT OF THE DIRAC EQUATION

We shall now extend the method of the last section to apply to the Dirac equation. All that would seem to be necessary in the previous equations is to consider H as the Dirac Hamiltonian, ψ as a symbol with four indices (for each particle). Then K_0 can still be defined by (3) or (4) and is now a 4–4 matrix which operating on the initial wave function, gives the final wave function. In (10), $U(3)$ can be generalized to $A_4(3) - \boldsymbol{\alpha} \cdot \mathbf{A}(3)$ where A_4, $\mathbf{A}$ are the scalar and vector potential (times e, the electron charge) and $\boldsymbol{\alpha}$ are Dirac matrices.

To discuss this we shall define a convenient relativistic notation. We represent four-vectors like $\mathbf{x}$, t by a symbol x_μ, where $\mu = 1, 2, 3, 4$ and $x_4 = t$ is real. Thus the vector and scalar potential (times e) $\mathbf{A}$, A_4 is A_μ. The four matrices $\beta\boldsymbol{\alpha}$, β can be considered as transforming as a four vector γ_μ (our γ_μ differs from Pauli's by a factor i for $\mu = 1, 2, 3$). We use the summation convention $a_\mu b_\mu = a_4 b_4 - a_1 b_1 - a_2 b_2 - a_3 b_3 = a \cdot b$. In particular if a_μ is any four vector (but not a matrix) we write $a = a_\mu \gamma_\mu$ so that a is a matrix associated with a vector (a will often be used in place of a_μ as a symbol for the vector). The γ_μ satisfy $\gamma_\mu \gamma_\nu + \gamma_\nu \gamma_\mu = 2\delta_{\mu\nu}$ where $\delta_{44} = +1$, $\delta_{11} = \delta_{22} = \delta_{33} = -1$, and the other $\delta_{\mu\nu}$ are zero. As a consequence of our summation convention $\delta_{\mu\nu} a_\nu = a_\mu$ and $\delta_{\mu\mu} = 4$. Note that $ab + ba = 2a \cdot b$ and that $a^2 = a_\mu a_\mu = a \cdot a$ is a pure number. The symbol $\partial/\partial x_\mu$ will mean $\partial/\partial t$ for $\mu = 4$, and $-\partial/\partial x$, $-\partial/\partial y$, $-\partial/\partial z$ for $\mu = 1, 2, 3$. Call $\nabla = \gamma_\mu \partial/\partial x_\mu = \beta \partial/\partial t + \beta \boldsymbol{\alpha} \cdot \nabla$. We shall imagine hereafter, purely for relativistic convenience, that ϕ_n^* in (3) is replaced by its adjoint $\phi_n = \overline{\phi}_n^* \beta$.

Thus the Dirac equation for a particle, mass m, in an external field $A = A_\mu \gamma_\mu$ is

$$(i\nabla - m)\psi = A\psi, \tag{11}$$

and Eq. (4) determining the propagation of a free particle becomes

$$(i\nabla_2 - m)K_+(2, 1) = i\delta(2, 1), \tag{12}$$

the index 2 on ∇_2 indicating differentiation with respect to the coordinates $x_{2\mu}$ which are represented as 2 in $K_+(2, 1)$ and $\delta(2, 1)$.

The function $K_+(2, 1)$ is defined in the absence of a field. If a potential A is acting a similar function, say $K_+^{(A)}(2, 1)$ can be defined. It differs from $K_+(2, 1)$ by a first order correction given by the analogue of (9) namely

$$K_+^{(1)}(2, 1) = -i \int K_+(2, 3)A(3)K_+(3, 1)d\tau_3, \tag{13}$$

representing the amplitude to go from 1 to 3 as a free particle, get scattered there by the potential (now the matrix $A(3)$ instead of $U(3)$) and continue to 2 as free. The second order correction, analogous to (10) is

$$K_+^{(2)}(2, 1) = -\iint K_+(2, 4)A(4)$$
$$\times K_+(4, 3)A(3)K_+(3, 1)d\tau_4 d\tau_3, \tag{14}$$

and so on. In general $K_+^{(A)}$ satisfies

$$(i\nabla_2 - A(2) - m)K_+^{(A)}(2, 1) = i\delta(2, 1), \tag{15}$$

and the successive terms (13), (14) are the power series expansion of the integral equation

$$K_+^{(A)}(2, 1) = K_+(2, 1)$$
$$-i \int K_+(2, 3)A(3)K_+^{(A)}(3, 1)d\tau_3, \tag{16}$$

which it also satisfies.

We would now expect to choose, for the special solution of (12), $K_+ = K_0$ where $K_0(2, 1)$ vanishes for $t_2 < t_1$ and for $t_2 > t_1$ is given by (3) where ϕ_n and E_n are the eigenfunctions and energy values of a particle satisfying Dirac's equation, and ϕ_n^* is replaced by ϕ_n.

The formulas arising from this choice, however, suffer from the drawback that they apply to the one electron theory of Dirac rather than to the hole theory of the positron. For example, consider as in [Fig. 86–1(a)] an electron after being scattered by a potential in a small region 3 of space time. The one electron theory says (as does (3) with $K_+ = K_0$) that the scattered amplitude at another point 2 will proceed toward positive times with both positive and negative energies, that is with both positive and negative rates of change of phase. No wave is scattered to times previous to the time of scattering. These are just the properties of $K_0(2, 3)$.

On the other hand, according to the positron theory negative energy states are not available to the electron after the scattering. Therefore the choice $K_+ = K_0$ is unsatisfactory. But there are other solutions of (12). We shall choose the solution defining $K_+(2,1)$ so that $K_+(2,1)$ *for* $t_2 > t_1$ *is the sum of* (3) *over positive energy states only.* Now this new solution must satisfy (12) for all times in order that the representation be complete. It must therefore differ from the old solution K_0 by a solution of the homogeneous Dirac equation. It is clear from the definition that the difference $K_0 - K_+$ is the sum of (3) over all negative energy states, as long as $t_2 > t_1$. But this difference must be a solution of the homogeneous Dirac equation for all times and must therefore be represented by the same sum over negative energy states also for $t_2 < t_1$. Since $K_0 = 0$ in this case, it follows that our new kernel, $K_+(2, 1)$, *for* $t_2 < t_1$ *is the negative of the sum* (3) *over negative energy states.* That is,

$$K_+(2, 1) = \Sigma_{POS\ E_n}\ \phi_n(2)\bar{\phi}_n(1)$$
$$\times \exp(-iE_n(t_2 - t_1)) \quad \text{for} \quad t_2 > t_1$$

$$(17)$$

$$= -\Sigma_{NEG\ E_n}\ \phi_n(2)\bar{\phi}_n(1)$$
$$\times \exp(-iE_n(t_2 - t_1)) \quad \text{for} \quad t_2 < t_1.$$

With this choice of K_+ our equations such as (13) and (14) will now give results equivalent to those of the positron hole theory.

That (14), for example, is the correct second order expression for finding at 2 an electron originally at 1 according to the positron theory may be seen as follows [Fig. 86–2]. Assume as a special example that $t_2 > t_1$ and that the potential vanishes except in interval $t_2 - t_1$ so that t_4 and t_3 both lie between t_1 and t_2.

First suppose $t_1 > t_3$ [Fig. 86–2(b)]. Then (since $t_3 > t_1$) the electron assumed originally in a positive energy state propagates in that state (by $K_+(3, 1)$) to position 3 where it gets scattered $(A(3))$. It then proceeds to 4, which it must do as a positive energy electron. This is correctly described by (14) for $K_+(4, 3)$ contains only positive energy components in its expansion, as $t_4 > t_3$. After being scattered at 4 it then proceeds on to 2, again necessarily in a positive energy state, as $t_2 > t_4$.

In positron theory there is an additional contribution due to the possibility of virtual pair production [Fig. 86–2(c)]. A pair could be created by the potential $A(4)$ at 4, the electron of which is that found later at 2. The positron (or rather, the hole) proceeds to 3 where it annihilates the electron which has arrived there from 1.

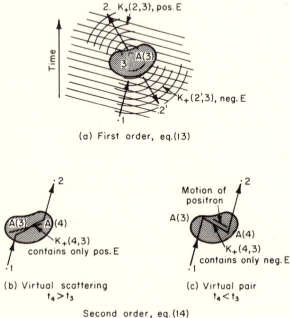

(a) First order, eq.(13)

(b) Virtual scattering
$t_4 > t_3$

(c) Virtual pair
$t_4 < t_3$

Second order, eq.(14)

Fig. 86–2. The Dirac equation permits another solution $K_+(2,1)$ if one considers that waves scattered by the potential can proceed backward in time as in Fig. 86–2(a). This is interpreted in the second order processes (b), (c), by noting that there is now the possibility (c) of virtual pair production at 4, the positron going to 3 to be annihilated. This can be pictured as similar to ordinary scattering (b) except that the electron is scattered backward in time from 3 to 3. The waves scattered from 3 to 2′ in (a) represent the possibility of a positron arriving at 3 from 2′ and annihilating the electron from 1. This view is proved equivalent to hole theory: electrons traveling backward in time are recognized as positrons.

This alternative is already included in (14) as contributions for which $t_4 < t_3$, and its study will lead us to an interpretation of $K_+(4, 3)$ for $t_4 < t_3$. The factor $K_+(2, 4)$ describes the electron (after the pair production at 4) proceeding from 4 to 2. Likewise $K_+(3, 1)$ represents the electron proceeding from 1 to 3. $K_+(4, 3)$ must therefore represent the propagation of the positron or hole from 4 to 3. That it does so is clear. The fact that in hole theory the hole proceeds in the manner of an electron of negative energy is reflected in the fact that $K_+(4, 3)$ for $t_4 < t_3$ is (minus) the sum of only negative energy components. In hole theory the real energy of these intermediate states is, of course, positive. This is true here too, since in the phases $\exp(-iE_n(t_4 - t_3))$ defining $K_+(4, 3)$ in (17), E_n is negative but so is $t_4 - t_3$. That is, the contributions vary with t_3 as $\exp(-i \mid E_n \mid (t_3 - t_4))$ as they would if the energy of the intermediate state were $\mid E_n \mid$. The fact that the entire sum is taken as negative in computing $K_+(4, 3)$ is reflected in the fact that in hole theory the amplitude has its sign reversed in accordance with the Pauli principle and the fact that the electron arriving at 2 has been exchanged with one in the sea. To this, and to higher orders, all processes involving virtual pairs are correctly described in this way.

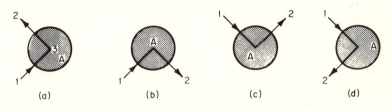

Fig. 86–3. Several different processes can be described by the same formula depending on the time relations of the variables t_2, t_1. Thus $P_v \mid K_+{}^{(A)}(2,1) \mid{}^2$ is the probability that: (a) An electron at 1 will be scattered at 2 (and no other pairs form in a vacuum). (b) Electron at 1 and positron at 2 annihilate leaving nothing. (c) A single pair at 1 and 2 is created from vacuum. (d) A positron at 2 is scattered to 1. ($K_+{}^{(A)}(2,1)$ is the sum of the effects of scattering in the potential to all orders. P_v is a normalizing constant.)

The expressions such as (14) can still be described as a passage of the electron from 1 to 3 ($K_+(3, 1)$), scattering at 3 by $A(3)$, proceeding to 4 ($K_+(4, 3)$), scattering again, $A(4)$, arriving finally at 2. The scatterings may, however, be toward both future and past times, an electron propagating backwards in time being recognized as a positron.

This therefore suggests that negative energy components created by scattering in a potential be considered as waves propagating from the scattering point toward the past, and that such waves represent the propagation of a positron annihilating the electron in the potential.

With this interpretation real pair production is also described correctly [see Fig. 86–3]. For example in (13) if $t_1 < t_3 < t_2$ the equation gives the amplitude that if at time t_1 one electron is present at 1, then at time t_2 just one electron will be present (having been scattered at 3) and it will be at 2. On the other hand if t_2 is less than t_3, for example, if $t_2 = t_1 < t_3$, the same expression gives the amplitude that a pair, electron at 1, positron at 2 will annihilate at 3, and subsequently no particles will be present. Likewise if t_2 and t_1 exceed t_3 we have (minus) the amplitude for finding a single pair, electron at 2, positron at 1 created by $A(3)$ from a vacuum. If $t_1 > t_3 > t_2$, (13) describes the scattering of a positron. All these amplitudes are relative to the amplitude that a vacuum will remain a vacuum, which is taken as unity. (This will be discussed more fully later.)

The analogue of (2) can be easily worked out. It is,

$$\psi(2) = \int K_+(2, 1)N(1)\psi(1)d^3V_1, \qquad (18)$$

where d^3V_1 is the volume element of the closed 3-dimensional surface of a region of space time containing point 2, and $N(1)$ is $N_\mu(1)\gamma_\mu$ where $N_\mu(1)$ is the *inward* drawn unit normal to the surface at the point 1. That is, the wave function $\psi(2)$ (in this case for a free particle) is determined at any point inside a four-dimensional region if its values on the surface of that region are specified.

To interpret this, consider the case that the 3-surface consists essentially of all space at some time say $t = 0$ previous to t_2, and of all space at the time $T > t_2$. The cylinder connecting these to complete the closure of the surface may be very distant from $\mathbf{x}_2$ so that it gives no appreciable contribution (as $K_+(2, 1)$ decreases exponentially in space like directions). Hence, if $\gamma_4 = \beta$, since the inward drawn normals N will be β and $-\beta$,

$$\psi(2) = \int K_+(2, 1) \, \beta\psi(1)d^3\mathbf{x}_1$$
$$- \int K_+(2, 1') \, \beta\psi(1')d^3\mathbf{x}_{1'}, \quad (19)$$

where $t_1 = 0$, $t_{1'} = T$. Only positive energy (electron) components in $\psi(1)$ contribute to the first integral and only negative energy (positron) components of $\psi(1')$ to the second. That is, the amplitude for finding a charge at 2 is determined both by the amplitude for finding an electron previous to the measurement and by the amplitude for finding a positron after the measurement. This might be interpreted as meaning that even in a problem involving but one charge the amplitude for finding the charge at 2 is not determined when the only thing known is the amplitude for finding an electron (or a positron) at an earlier time. There may have been no electron present initially but a pair was created in the measurement (or also by other external fields). The amplitude for this contingency is specified by the amplitude for finding a positron in the future.

We can also obtain expressions for transition amplitudes, like (5). For example if at $t = 0$ we have an electron present in a state with (positive energy) wave function $f(\mathbf{x})$, what is the amplitude for finding it at $t = T$ with the (positive energy) wave function $g(\mathbf{x})$? The amplitude for finding the electron anywhere after $t = 0$ is given by (19) with $\psi(1)$ replaced by $f(\mathbf{x})$, the second integral vanishing. Hence, the transition element to find it in state $g(\mathbf{x})$ is, in analogy to (5), just ($t_2 = T$, $t_1 = 0$)

$$\int \bar{g}(\mathbf{x}_2)\beta K_+(2, 1)\beta f(\mathbf{x}_1)d^3\mathbf{x}_1 d^3\mathbf{x}_2, \qquad (20)$$

since $g^* = \bar{g}\beta$.

If a potential acts somewhere in the interval between 0 and T, K_+ is replaced by $K_+^{(4)}$. Thus the first order effect on the transition amplitude is, from (13),

$$-i\int \bar{g}(\mathbf{x}_2)\beta K_+(2, 3)A(3)K_+(3, 1)\beta f(\mathbf{x}_1)d^3\mathbf{x}_1 d^3\mathbf{x}_2. \qquad (21)$$

Expressions such as this can be simplified and the 3-surface integrals, which are inconvenient for relativistic calculations, can be removed as follows. Instead of defining a state by the wave function $f(\mathbf{x})$, which it has at a given time $t_1 = 0$, we define the state by the function $f(1)$ of four variables $\mathbf{x}_1$, t_1 which is a solutioin of the free particle equation for all t_1 and is $f(\mathbf{x}_1)$ for $t_1 = 0$. The final state is likewise defined by a function $g(2)$ over-all space-time. Then our surface integrals can be performed since $\int K_+(3, 1)\beta f(\mathbf{x}_1)d^3\mathbf{x}_1 = f(3)$ and $\int \bar{g}(\mathbf{x}_2)\beta d^3\mathbf{x}_2 K_+(2, 3) = g(3)$. There results

$$-i\int \bar{g}(3)A(3)f(3)d\tau_3, \qquad (22)$$

the integral now being over-all space-time. The transition amplitude to second order (from (14)) is

$$-\int\int \bar{g}(2)A(2)K_+(2, 1)A(1)f(1)d\tau_1 d\tau_2, \qquad (23)$$

for the particle arriving at 1 with amplitude $f(1)$ is scattered ($A(1)$), progresses to 2, ($K_+(2, 1)$), and is scattered again ($A(2)$), and we then ask for the amplitude that it is in state $g(2)$. If $g(2)$ is a negative energy state we are solving a problem of annihilation of electron in $f(1)$, positron in $g(2)$, etc.

We have been emphasizing scattering problems, but obviously the motion in a fixed potential V, say in a hydrogen atom, can also be dealt with. If it is first viewed as a scattering problem we can ask for the amplitude, $\phi_k(1)$, that an electron with original free wave function was scattered k times in the potential V either forward or backward in time to arrive at 1. Then the amplitude after one more scattering is

$$\phi_{k+1}(2) = -i \int K_+(2, 1)V(1)\phi_k(1)d\tau_1. \tag{24}$$

An equation for the total amplitude

$$\psi(1) = \sum_{k=0}^{\infty} \phi_k(1)$$

for arriving at 1 either directly or after any number of scatterings is obtained by summing (24) over all k from 0 to ∞;

$$\psi(2) = \phi_0(2) -i \int K_+(2, 1)V(1)\psi(1)d\tau_1. \tag{25}$$

Viewed as a steady state problem we may wish, for example, to find that initial condition ϕ_0 (or better just the ψ) which leads to a periodic motion of ψ. This is most practically done, of course, by solving the Dirac equation,

$$(i\nabla - m)\psi(1) = V(1)\psi(1), \tag{26}$$

deduced from (25) by operating on both sides by $i\nabla_2 - m$, thereby eliminating the ϕ_0, and using (12). This illustrates the relation between the points of view.

For many problems the total potential $A + V$ may be split conveniently into a fixed one, V, and another, A, considered as a perturbation. If $K_+{}^{(V)}$ is defined as in (16) with V for A, expressions such as (23) are valid and useful with K_+ replaced by $K_+{}^{(V)}$ and the functions $f(1)$, $g(2)$ replaced by solutions for all space and time of the Dirac Eq. (26) in the potential V (rather than free particle wave functions).

PROBLEMS INVOLVING SEVERAL CHARGES

We wish next to consider the case that there are two (or more) distinct charges (in addition to pairs they may produce in virtual states). In a succeeding paper we discuss the interaction between such charges. Here we assume that they do not interact. In this case each particle behaves independently of the other. We can expect that if we have two particles a and b, the amplitude that particle a goes from x_1 at t_1, to x_3 at t_3 while b goes from x_2 at t_2 to x_4 at t_4 is the product

$$K(3, 4; 1, 2) = K_{+a}(3, 1)K_{+b}(4, 2).$$

The symbols a, b simply indicate that the matrices appearing in the K_+ apply to the Dirac four component spinors corresponding to particle a or b respectively (the wave function now having 16 indices). In a potential K_{+a} and K_{+b} become $K_{+a}^{(A)}$ and $K_{+b}^{(A)}$ where $K_{+a}^{(A)}$ is defined and calculated as for a single particle. They commute. Hereafter the a, b can be omitted; the space time variable appearing in the kernels suffice to define on what they operate.

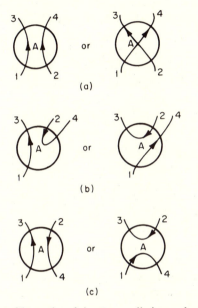

Fig. 86–4. Some problems involving two distinct charges (in addition to virtual pairs they may produce): $P_v \mid K_+^{(A)}(3,1)K_+^{(A)}(4,2) - K_+^{(A)}(4,1) K_+^{(A)}(3,2) \mid^2$ is the probability that: (a) Electrons at 1 and 2 are scattered to 3,4 (and no pairs are formed). (b) Starting with an electron at 1 a single pair is formed, positron at 2, electrons at 3,4. (c) A pair at 1,4 is found at 3,2, etc. The exclusion principle requires that the amplitudes for processes involving exchange of two electrons be subtracted.

The particles are identical however and satisfy the exclusion principle. The principle requires only that one calculate $K(3, 4; 1, 2) - K(4, 3; 1, 2)$ to get the net amplitude for arrival of charges at 3, 4. (It is normalized assuming that when an integral is performed over points 3 and 4, for example, since the electrons represented are identical, one divides by 2.) This expression is correct for positrons also [Fig. 86–4]. For example the amplitude that an electron and a positron found initially at x_1 and x_4 (say $t_1 = t_4$) are later found at x_3 and x_2 (with $t_2 = t_3 > t_1$) is given by the same expression

$$K_+^{(A)}(3, 1)K_+^{(A)}(4, 2) - K_+^{(A)}(4, 1)K_+^{(A)}(3, 2). \qquad (27)$$

The first term represents the amplitude that the electron proceeds from 1 to 3 and the positron from 4 to 2 [Fig. 86–4(c)], while the second term represents the interfering amplitude that the pair at 1, 4 annihilate and what is found at 3, 2 is a pair newly created in the potential. The generalization to several particles is clear. There is an additional factor $K_+^{(4)}$ for each particle, and anti-symmetric combinations are always taken.

No account need be taken of the exclusion principle in intermediate states. As an example consider again expression (14) for $t_2 > t_1$ and suppose $t_4 < t_3$ so that the situation represented [Fig. 86–2(c)] is that a pair is made at 4 with the electron proceeding to 2, and the positron to 3 where it annihilates the electron arriving from 1. It may be objected that if it happens that the electron created at 4 is in the same state as the one coming from 1, then the process cannot occur because of the exclusion principle and we should not have included it in our term (14). We shall see, however, that considering the exclusion principle also requires another change which reinstates the quantity.

For we are computing amplitudes relative to the amplitude that a vacuum at t_1 will still be a vacuum at t_2. We are interested in the alteration in this amplitude due to the presence of an electron at 1. Now one process that can be visualized as occurring in the vacuum is the creation of a pair at 4 followed by a re-annihilation of the *same* pair at 3 (a process which we shall call a closed loop path). But if a real electron is present in a certain state 1, those pairs for which the electron was created in state 1 in the vacuum must now be excluded. We must therefore subtract from our relative amplitude the term corresponding to this process. But this just reinstates the quantity which it was argued should not have been included in (14), the necessary minus sign coming automatically from the definition of K_+. It is obviously simpler to disregard the exclusion principle completely in the intermediate states.

All the amplitudes are relative and their squares give the relative probabilities of the various phenomena. Absolute probabilities result if one multiplies each of the probabilities by P_v, the true probability that if one has no particles present initially there will be none finally. This quantity P_v can be calculated by normalizing the relative probabilities such that the sum of the probabilities of all mutually exclusive alternatives is unity. (For example if one starts with a vacuum one can calculate the relative probability that there remains a vacuum (unity), or one pair is created, or two pairs, etc. The sum is P_v^{-1}.) Put in this form the theory is complete and there are no divergence problems. Real processes are completely independent of what goes on in the vacuum.

When we come, in the succeeding paper, to deal with interactions between charges, however, the situation is not so simple. There is the possibility that virtual electrons in the vacuum may interact electromagnetically with the real electrons. For that reason processes occurring in the vacuum are analyzed in the next section, in which an independent method of obtaining P_v is discussed.

VACUUM PROBLEMS

An alternative way of obtaining absolute amplitudes is to multiply all amplitudes by C_v, the vacuum to vacuum amplitude, that is, the absolute amplitude that there be no particles both initially and finally. We can assume $C_v = 1$ if no potential is present during the interval, and otherwise we compute it as follows. It differs from unity because, for example, a pair could be created which eventually annihilates itself again. Such a path would appear as a closed loop on a space-time diagram. The sum of the amplitudes resulting from all such single closed loops we call L. To a first approximation L is

$$L^{(1)} = -\frac{1}{2} \int \int Sp[K_+(2, 1)A(1) \times K_+(1, 2)A(2)]d\tau_1 d\tau_2. \quad (28)$$

For a pair could be created say at 1, the electron and positron could both go on to 2 and there annihilate. The spur, Sp, is taken since one has to sum over all possible spins for the pair. The factor $\frac{1}{2}$ arises from the fact that the same loop could be considered as starting at either potential, and the minus sign results since the interactors are each $-iA$. The next order term would be

$$L^{(2)} = +(i/3) \int \int \int Sp[K_+(2, 1)A(1) \times K_+(1, 3)A(3)K_+(3, 2)A(2)]d\tau_1 d\tau_2 d\tau_3,$$

etc. The sum of all such terms gives L.

In addition to these single loops we have the possibility that two independent pairs may be created and each pair may annihilate itself again. That is, there may be formed in the vacuum two closed loops, and the contribution in amplitude from this alternative is just the product of the contribution from each of the loops considered singly. The total contribution from all such pairs of loops (it is still consistent to disregard the exclusion principle for these virtual states) is $L^2/2$ for in L^2 we count every pair of loops twice. The total vacuum-vacuum amplitude is then

$$C_v = 1 - L + L^2/2 - L^3/6 + \cdots = \exp(-L), \quad (29)$$

the successive terms representing the amplitude from zero, one, two, etc., loops. The fact that the contribution to C_v of single loops is $-L$ is a consequence of the Pauli principle. For example, consider a situation in which two pairs of particles are created. Then these pairs later destroy themselves so that we have two loops. The electrons could, at a given time, be interchanged forming a kind of figure eight which is a single loop. The fact that the interchange must change the sign of the contribution requires that the terms in C_v appear with alternate signs. (The exclusion principle is also responsible in a similar way for the fact that the amplitude for a pair creation is $-K_+$ rather than $+K_+$.) Symmetrical statistics would lead to

$$C_v = 1 + L + L^2/2 = \exp(+L).$$

The quantity L has an infinite imaginary part (from $L^{(1)}$, higher orders are finite). We will discuss this in connection with vacuum polarization in the succeeding paper. This has no effect on the normalization constant for the probability that a vacuum remain vacuum is given by

$$P_v = |\,C_v\,|^2 = \exp(-2\cdot\text{real part of } L),$$

from (29). This value agrees with the one calculated directly by renormalizing probabilities. The real part of L appears to be positive as a consequence of the Dirac equation and properties of K_+ so that P_v is less than one. Bose statistics gives $C_v = \exp(+L)$ and consequently a value of P_v greater than unity which appears meaningless if the quantities are interpreted as we have done here. Our choice of K_+ apparently requires the exclusion principle.

Charges obeying the Klein-Gordon equation can be equally well treated by the methods which are discussed here for the Dirac electrons. How this is done is discussed in more detail in the succeeding paper. The real part of L comes out negative for this equation so that in this case Bose statistics appear to be required for consistency. . . .

Space-Time Approach to Quantum Electrodynamics [6]

THIS PAPER SHOULD BE CONSIDERED as a direct continuation of a preceding one.[*] (I) in which the motion of electrons, neglecting interaction, was analyzed, by dealing directly with the

[6] Feynman, *Physical Review,* 76 (1949), 769–774.
[*] R. P. Feynman, *Phys. Rev.* **76,** 749 (1949), hereafter called I.

solution of the Hamiltonian differential equations. Here the same technique is applied to include interactions and in that way to express in simple terms the solution of problems in quantum electrodynamics.

For most practical calculations in quantum electrodynamics the solution is ordinarily expressed in terms of a matrix element. The matrix is worked out as an expansion in powers of $e^2/\hbar c$, the successive terms corresponding to the inclusion of an increasing number of virtual quanta. It appears that a considerable simplification can be achieved in writing down these matrix elements for complex processes. Furthermore, each term in the expansion can be written down and understood directly from a physical point of view, similar to the space-time view in I. It is the purpose of this paper to describe how this may be done. We shall also discuss methods of handling the divergent integrals which appear in these matrix elements.

The simplification in the formulae results mainly from the fact that previous methods unnecessarily separated into individual terms processes that were closely related physically. For example, in the exchange of a quantum between two electrons there were two terms depending on which electron emitted and which absorbed the quantum. Yet, in the virtual states considered, timing relations are not significant. Only the order of operators in the matrix must be maintained. We have seen (I), that in addition, processes in which virtual pairs are produced can be combined with others in which only positive energy electrons are involved. Further, the effects of longitudinal and transverse waves can be combined together. The separations previously made were on an unrelativistic basis (reflected in the circumstance that apparently momentum but not energy is conserved in intermediate states). When the terms are combined and simplified, the relativistic invariance of the result is self-evident.

We begin by discussing the solution in space and time of the Schrödinger equation for particles interacting instantaneously. The results are immediately generalizable to delayed interactions of relativistic electrons and we represent in that way the laws of quantum electrodynamics. We can then see how the matrix element for any process can be written down directly. In particular, the self-energy expression is written down.

So far, nothing has been done other than a restatement of conventional electrodynamics in other terms. Therefore, the self-energy diverges. A modification in interaction between charges is next made, and it is shown that the self-energy is made convergent and corresponds to a correction to the electron mass. After the mass correction is made, other real processes are finite and insensitive to the "width" of the cut-off in the interaction.

Unfortunately, the modification proposed is not completely satisfactory theoretically (it leads to some difficulties of conservation of energy). It does, however, seem consistent and satisfactory to define the matrix element for all real processes as the limit of that computed here as the cut-off width goes to zero. A similar technique suggested by Pauli and by Bethe can be applied to problems of vacuum polarization (resulting in a renormalization of charge) but again a strict physical basis for the rules of convergence is not known.

After mass and charge renormalization, the limit of zero cut-off width can be taken for all real processes. The results are then equivalent to those of Schwinger who does not make explicit use of the convergence factors. The method of Schwinger is to identify the terms corresponding to corrections in mass and charge and, previous to their evaluation, to remove them from the expressions for real processes. This has the advantage of showing that the results can be strictly independent of particular cut-off methods. On the other hand, many of the properties of the integrals are analyzed using formal properties of invariant propagation functions. But one of the properties is that the integrals are infinite and it is not clear to what extent this invalidates the demonstrations. A practical advantage of the present method is that ambiguities can be more easily resolved; simply by direct calculation of the otherwise divergent integrals. Nevertheless, it is not at all clear that the convergence factors do not upset the physical consistency of the theory. Although in the limit the two methods agree, neither method appears to be thoroughly satisfactory theoretically. Nevertheless, it does appear that we now have available a complete and definite method for the calculation of physical processes to any order in quantum electrodynamics.

Since we can write down the solution to any physical problem, we have a complete theory which could stand by itself. It will be theoretically incomplete, however, in two respects. First, although each term of increasing order in e^2/hc can be written down it would be desirable to see some way of expressing things in finite form to all orders in $e^2/\hbar c$ at once. Second, although it will be physically evident that the results obtained are equivalent to those obtained by conventional electrodynamics the mathematical proof of this is not included. Both of these limitations will be removed in a subsequent paper.

Briefly the genesis of this theory was this. The conventional electrodynamics was expressed in the Lagrangian form of quantum mechanics. . . . The motion of the field oscillators could be integrated out, . . . the result being an expression of the delayed interaction of the particles. Next the modification of the delta-function interaction could be made directly from the analogy to the classical case. This was still not complete because the Lagrangian method had been worked out in detail only for particles obeying the non-relativistic Schrödinger equation. It was then modified in accordance with the requirements of the Dirac equation and the phenomenon of pair creation. This was made easier by the reinterpretation of the theory of holes (I). Finally for practical calculations the expressions were developed in a power series in $e^2/\hbar c$. It was apparent that each term in the series had a simple physical interpretation. Since the result was easier to understand than the derivation, it was thought best to publish the results first in this paper. . . .

The point of view which is taken here of the interaction of charges differs from the more usual point of view of field theory. Furthermore, the familiar Hamiltonian form of quantum mechanics must be compared to the over-all space-time view used here. The first section is, therefore, devoted to a discussion of the relations of these viewpoints.

COMPARISON WITH THE HAMILTONIAN METHOD

Electrodynamics can be looked upon in two equivalent and complementary ways. One is as the description of the behavior of a field (Maxwell's equations). The other is as a description of a direct interaction at a distance (albeit delayed in time) between charges (the solutions of Lienard and Wiechert). From the latter point of view light is considered as an interaction of the charges in the source with those in the absorber. This is an impractical point of view because many kinds of sources produce the same kind of effects. The field point of view separates these aspects into two simpler problems, production of light, and absorption of light. On the other hand, the field point of view is less practical when dealing with close collisions of particles (or their action on themselves). For here the source and absorber are not readily distinguishable, there is an intimate exchange of quanta. The fields are so closely determined by the motions of the particles that it is just as well not to separate the question into two problems but to consider the process as a direct interaction. Roughly, the field point of view is most practical for problems involving real quanta, while the interaction view is best for the discussion of the virtual quanta involved. We shall emphasize the interaction viewpoint in this paper, first because it is less familiar and therefore requires more discussion, and second because the important aspect in the problems with which we shall deal is the effect of virtual quanta.

The Hamiltonian method is not well adapted to represent the direct action at a distance between charges because that action is delayed. The Hamiltonian method represents the future as developing out of the present. If the values of a complete set of quantities are known now, their values can be computed at the next instant in time. If particles interact through a delayed interaction, however, one cannot predict the future by simply knowing the present motion of the particles. One would also have to know what the motions of the particles were in the past in view of the interaction this may have on the future motions. This is done in the Hamiltonian electrodynamics, of course, by requiring that one specify besides the present motion of the particles, the values of a host of new variables (the coordinates of the field oscillators) to keep track of that aspect of the past motions of the particles which determines their future behavior. The use of the Hamiltonian forces one to choose the field view-point rather than the interaction viewpoint.

In many problems, for example, the close collisions of particles, we are not interested in the precise temporal sequence of events. It is not of interest to be able to say how the situation would look at each instant of time during a collision and how it progresses from instant to instant. Such ideas are only useful for events taking a long time and for which we can readily obtain information during the intervening period. For collisions it is much easier to treat the process as a whole. The Møller interaction matrix for the collision of two electrons is not essentially more compli-cated than the non-relativistic Rutherford formula, yet the mathematical machinery used to obtain the former from quantum electrodynamics is vastly more complicated than Schrödinger's equation with the e^2/r_{12} inter-action needed to obtain the latter. The difference is only that in the latter the action is instantaneous so that the Hamiltonian method requires no extra variables, while in the former relativistic case it is delayed and the Hamiltonian method is very cumbersome.

We shall be discussing the solutions of equations rather than the time differential equations from which they come. We shall discover that the solutions, because of the over-all space-time view that they permit, are as easy to understand when interactions are delayed as when they are in-stantaneous.

As a further point, relativistic invariance will be self-evident. The Hamiltonian form of the equations develops the future from the instan-taneous present. But for different observers in relative motion the instan-taneous present is different, and corresponds to a different 3-dimensional cut of space-time. Thus the temporal analyses of different observers is different and their Hamiltonian equations are developing the process in different ways. These differences are irrelevant, however, for the solution is the same in any space-time frame. By forsaking the Hamiltonian method, the wedding of relativity and quantum mechanics can be accom-plished most naturally.

We illustrate these points in the next section by studying the solution of Schrödinger's equation for non-relativistic particles interacting by an instantaneous Coulomb potential (Eq. 2). When the solution is modified to include the effects of delay in the interaction and the relativistic prop-erties of the electrons we obtain an expression of the laws of quantum electrodynamics (Eq. 4).

THE INTERACTION BETWEEN CHARGES

We study by the same methods as in I, the interaction of two particles using the same notation as I. We start by considering the non-relativistic case described by the Schrödinger equation (I, Eq. 1). The wave function at a given time is a function $\psi(\mathbf{x}_a, \mathbf{x}_b, t)$ of the coordinates $\mathbf{x}_a$ and $\mathbf{x}_b$ of each particle. Thus call $K(\mathbf{x}_a, \mathbf{x}_b, t; \mathbf{x}_a', \mathbf{x}_b', t')$ the amplitude that particle a at $\mathbf{x}_a'$ at time t' will get to $\mathbf{x}_a$ at t while particle b at $\mathbf{x}_b'$ at t' gets to $\mathbf{x}_b$ at t. If the particles are free and do not interact this is

$$K(\mathbf{x}_a, \mathbf{x}_b, t; \mathbf{x}_a', \mathbf{x}_b', t') = K_{0a}(\mathbf{x}_a, t; \mathbf{x}_a', t') K_{0b}(\mathbf{x}_b, t; \mathbf{x}_b', t')$$

where K_{0a} is the K_0 function for particle a considered as free. In *this* case we can obviously define a quantity like K, but for which the time t need not be the same for particles a and b (likewise for t'); e.g.,

$$K_0(3, 4; 1, 2) = K_{0a}(3, 1) K_{0b}(4, 2) \tag{1}$$

can be thought of as the amplitude that particle a goes from $\mathbf{x}_1$ at t_1 to $\mathbf{x}_3$ at t_3 and that particle b goes from $\mathbf{x}_2$ at t_2 to $\mathbf{x}_4$ at t_4.

When the particles do interact, one can only define the quantity $K(3, 4; 1, 2)$ precisely if the interaction vanishes between t_1 and t_2 and also between t_3 and t_4. In a real physical system such is not the case. There is such an enormous advantage, however, to the concept that we shall continue to use it, imagining that we can neglect the effect of interactions between t_1 and t_2 and between t_3 and t_4. For practical problems this means choosing such long time intervals $t_3 - t_1$ and $t_4 - t_2$ that the extra interactions near the end points have small relative effects. As an example, in a scattering problem it may well be that the particles are so well separated initially and finally that the interaction at these times is negligible. Again energy values can be defined by the average rate of change of phase over such long time intervals that errors initially and finally can be neglected. Inasmuch as any physical problem can be defined in terms of scattering processes we do not lose much in a general theoretical sense by this approximation. If it is not made it is not easy to study interacting particles relativistically, for there is nothing significant in choosing $t_1 = t_3$ if $\mathbf{x}_1 \neq \mathbf{x}_3$, as absolute simultaneity of events at a distance cannot be defined invariantly. It is essentially to avoid this approximation that the complicated structure of the older quantum electrodynamics has been built up. We wish to describe electrodynamics as a delayed interaction between particles. If we can make the approximation of assuming a meaning to $K(3, 4; 1, 2)$ the results of this interaction can be expressed very simply.

To see how this may be done, imagine first that the interaction is simply that given by a Coulomb potential e^2/r where r is the distance between the particles. If this be turned on only for a very short time Δt_0 at time t_0, the first order correction to $K(3, 4; 1, 2)$ can be worked out exactly as was Eq. (9) of I by an obvious generalization to two particles:

$$K^{(1)}(3, 4; 1, 2) = -ie^2 \int\int K_{0a}(3, 5)K_{0b}(4, 6)r_{56}^{-1}$$
$$\times K_{0a}(5, 1)K_{0b}(6, 2)d^3\mathbf{x}_5 d^3\mathbf{x}_6 \Delta t_0,$$

where $t_5 = t_6 = t_0$. If now the potential were on at all times (so that strictly K is not defined unless $t_4 = t_3$ and $t_1 = t_2$), the first-order effect is obtained by integrating on t_0, which we can write as an integral over both t_5 and t_6 if we include a delta-function $\delta(t_5 - t_6)$ to insure contribution only when $t_5 = t_6$. Hence, the first-order effect of interaction is (calling $t_5 - t_6 = t_{56}$):

$$K^{(1)}(3, 4; 1, 2) = -ie^2 \int\int K_{0a}(3, 5)K_{0b}(4, 6)r_{56}^{-1}$$
$$\times \delta(t_{56})K_{0a}(5, 1)K_{0b}(6, 2)d\tau_5 d\tau_6, \quad (2)$$

where $d\tau = d^3\mathbf{x}dt$.

We know, however, in classical electrodynamics, that the Coulomb potential does not act instantaneously, but is delayed by a time r_{56}, taking the speed of light as unity. This suggests simply replacing $r_{56}^{-1}\delta(t_{56})$ in (2) by something like $r_{56}^{-1}\delta(t_{56} - r_{56})$ to represent the delay in the effect of b on a.

This turns out to be not quite right, for when this interaction is represented by photons they must be of only positive energy, while the Fourier transform of $\delta(t_{56} - r_{56})$ contains frequencies of both signs. It should instead be replaced by $\delta_+(t_{56} - r_{56})$ where

$$\delta_+(x) = \int_0^\infty e^{-i\omega x}d\omega/\pi = \lim_{\epsilon \to 0} \frac{(\pi i)^{-1}}{x - i\epsilon} = \delta(x) + (\pi i x)^{-1}. \quad (3)$$

This is to be averaged with $r_{56}^{-1}\delta_+(-t_{56} - r_{56})$ which arises when $t_5 < t_6$ and corresponds to a emitting the quantum which b receives. Since

$$(2r)^{-1}(\delta_+(t - r) + \delta_+(-t - r)) = \delta_+(t^2 - r^2),$$

this means $r_{56}^{-1}\delta(t_{56})$ is replaced by $\delta_+(s_{56}^2)$ where $s_{56}^2 = t_{56}^2 - r_{56}^2$ is the square of the relativistically invariant interval between points 5 and 6. Since in classical electrodynamics there is also an interaction through the vector potential, the complete interaction should be $(1 - (\mathbf{v}_5 \cdot \mathbf{v}_6)\delta_+$ $(s_{56}{}^2)$, or in the relativistic case,

$$(1 - \boldsymbol{\alpha}_a \cdot \boldsymbol{\alpha}_b)\delta_+(s_{56}{}^2) = \beta_a\beta_b\gamma_{a\mu}\gamma_{b\mu}\delta_+(s_{56}{}^2).$$

Hence we have for electrons obeying the Dirac equation,

$$K^{(1)}(3,4;1,2) = -ie^2 \iint K_{+a}(3,5)K_{+b}(4,6)\gamma_{a\mu}\gamma_{b\mu}$$
$$\times \delta_+(s_{56}{}^2)K_{+a}(5,1)K_{+b}(6,2)d\tau_5 d\tau_6, \qquad (4)$$

where $\gamma_{a\mu}$ and $\gamma_{b\mu}$ are the Dirac matrices applying to the spinor corresponding to particles a and b, respectively (the factor $\beta_a\beta_b$ being absorbed in the definition, I Eq. (17), of K_+).

This is our fundamental equation for electrodynamics. It describes the effect of exchange of one quantum (therefore first order in e^2) between two electrons. It will serve as a prototype enabling us to write down the corresponding quantities involving the exchange of two or more quanta between two electrons or the interaction of an electron with itself. It is a consequence of conventional electrodynamics. Relativistic invariance is clear. Since one sums over μ it contains the effects of both longitudinal and transverse waves in a relativistically symmetrical way.

We shall now interpret Eq. (4) in a manner which will permit us to write down the higher order terms. It can be understood [see Fig. 86–5] as saying that the amplitude for *"a"* to go from 1 to 3 and *"b"* to go from 2 to 4 is altered to first order because they can exchange a quantum. Thus, *"a"* can go to 5 (amplitude $K_+(5,1)$) emit a quantum (longitudinal, transverse, or scalar $\gamma_{a\mu}$) and then proceed to 3 $(K_+(3,5))$. Meantime *"b"* goes to 6 $(K_+(6,2))$, absorbs the quantum $(\gamma_{b\mu})$ and proceeds to 4 $(K_+(4,6))$. The quantum meanwhile proceeds from 5 to 6, which it does with amplitude $\delta_+(s_{56}{}^2)$. We must sum over all the possible

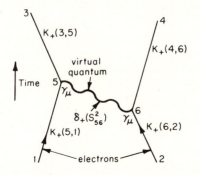

Fig. 86–5. The fundamental interaction Eq. (4). Exchange of one quantum between two electrons.

quantum polarizations μ and positions and times of emission 5, and of absorption 6. Actually if $t_5 > t_6$ it would be better to say that "a" absorbs and "b" emits but no attention need be paid to these matters, as all such alternatives are automatically contained in (4).

The correct terms of higher order in e^2 or involving larger numbers of electrons (interacting with themselves or in pairs) can be written down by the same kind of reasoning. They will be illustrated by examples as we proceed. In a succeeding paper they will all be deduced from conventional quantum electrodynamics.

Calculation, from (4), of the transition element between positive energy free electron states gives the Møller scattering of two electrons, when account is taken of the Pauli principle.

The exclusion principle for interacting charges is handled in exactly the same way as for non-interacting charges (I). For example, for two charges it requires only that one calculate $K(3, 4; 1, 2) - K(4, 3; 1, 2)$ to get the net amplitude for arrival of charges at 3 and 4. It is disregarded in intermediate states. The interference effects for scattering of electrons by positrons discussed by Bhabha will be seen to result directly in this formulation. The formulas are interpreted to apply to positrons in the manner discussed in I.

As our primary concern will be for processes in which the quanta are virtual we shall not include here the detailed analysis of processes involving real quanta in initial or final state, and shall content ourselves by only stating the rules applying to them. The result of the analysis is, as expected, that they can be included by the same line of reasoning as is used in discussing the virtual processes, provided the quantities are normalized in the usual manner to represent single quanta. For example, the amplitude that an electron in going from 1 to 2 absorbs a quantum whose vector potential, suitably normalized, is $c_\mu \exp(-ik \cdot x) = C_\mu(x)$ is just the expression (I, Eq. (13)) for scattering in a potential with $A(3)$ replaced by $C(3)$. Each quantum interacts only once (either in emission or in absorption), terms like (I, Eq. (14)) occur only when there is more than one quantum involved. The Bose statistics of the quanta can, in all cases, be disregarded in intermediate states. The only effect of the statistics is to change the weight of initial or final states. If there are among quanta, in the initial state, some n which are identical then the weight of the state is $(1/n!)$ of what it would be if these quanta were considered as different (similarly for the final state).

THE SELF-ENERGY PROBLEM

Having a term representing the mutual interaction of a pair of charges, we must include similar terms to represent the interaction of a charge with itself. For under some circumstances what appears to be two distinct electrons may, according to I, be viewed also as a single electron (namely in case one electron was created in a pair with a positron destined to annihilate the other electron). Thus to the interaction between such electrons must correspond the possibility of the action of an electron on itself.

This interaction is the heart of the self-energy problem. Consider to first order in e^2 the action of an electron on itself in an otherwise force free region. The amplitude $K(2, 1)$ for a single particle to get from 1 to 2 differs from $K_+(2, 1)$ to first order in e^2 by a term

$$K^{(1)}(2, 1) = -ie^2 \int \int K_+(2, 4)\gamma_\mu K_+(4, 3)\gamma_\mu$$
$$\times K_+(3, 1)d\tau_3 d\tau_4 \delta_+(s_{43}{}^2). \quad (5)$$

It arises because the electron instead of going from 1 directly to 2, may go [Fig. 86–6] first to 3 ($K_+(3, 1)$), emit a quantum (γ_μ), proceed to 4 ($K_+(4, 3)$), absorb it (γ_μ), and finally arrive at 2 ($K_+(2, 4)$). The quantum must go from 3 to 4 ($\delta_+(s_{43}{}^2)$).

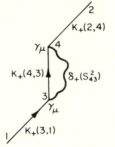

Fig. 86–6. Interaction of an electron with itself, Eq. (5).

This is related to the self-energy of a free electron in the following manner. Suppose initially, time t_1, we have an electron in state $f(1)$ which we imagine to be a positive energy solution of Dirac's equation for a free particle. After a long time $t_2 - t_1$ the perturbation will alter the wave function, which can then be looked upon as a superposition of free particle solutions (actually it only contains f). The amplitude that $g(2)$ is contained is calculated as in (I, Eq. (21)). The diagonal element ($g = f$) is therefore

$$\int \int \bar{f}(2)\beta K^{(1)}(2, 1)\beta f(1)d^3\mathbf{x}_1 d^3\mathbf{x}_2. \quad (6)$$

The time interval $T = t_2 - t_1$ (and the spatial volume V over which one integrates) must be taken very large, for the expressions are only approximate (analogous to the situation for two interacting charges). This is because, for example, we are dealing incorrectly with quanta emitted just before t_2 which would normally be reabsorbed at times after t_2.

If $K^{(1)}(2, 1)$ from (5) is actually substituted into (6) the surface integrals can be performed as was done in obtaining I, Eq. (22) resulting in

$$-ie^2 \int\int \bar{f}(4)\gamma_\mu K_+(4, 3)\gamma_\mu f(3)\delta_+(s_{43}{}^2)d\tau_3 d\tau_4. \qquad (7)$$

Putting for $f(1)$ the plane wave $u \exp(-ip \cdot x_1)$ where p_μ is the energy (p_4) and momentum of the electron $(p^2 = m^2)$, and u is a constant 4-index symbol, (7) becomes

$$-ie^2 \int\int (\bar{u}\gamma_\mu K_+(4, 3)\gamma_\mu u)$$
$$\times \exp(ip \cdot (x_4 - x_3))\delta_+(s_{43}{}^2)d\tau_3 d\tau_4,$$

the integrals extending over the volume V and time interval T. Since $K_+(4, 3)$ depends only on the difference of the coordinates of 4 and 3, $\chi_{43\mu}$, the integral on 4 gives a result (except near the surfaces of the region) independent of 3. When integrated on 3, therefore, the result is of order VT. The effect is proportional to V, for the wave functions have been normalized to unit volume. If normalized to volume V, the result would simply be proportional to T. This is expected, for if the effect were equivalent to a change in energy ΔE, the amplitude for arrival in f at t_2 is altered by a factor $\exp(-i\Delta E(t_2 - t_1))$, or to first order by the difference $-i(\Delta E)T$. Hence, we have

$$\Delta E = e^2 \int (\bar{u}\gamma_\mu K_+(4, 3)\gamma_\mu u) \exp(ip \cdot x_{43})\delta_+(s_{43}{}^2)d\tau_4, \qquad (8)$$

integrated over all space-time $d\tau_4$. This expression will be simplified presently. In interpreting (8) we have tacitly assumed that the wave functions are normalized so that $(u^*u) = (\bar{u}\gamma_4 u) = 1$. The equation may therefore be made independent of the normalization by writing the left side as $(\Delta E)(\bar{u}\gamma_4 u)$, or since $(\bar{u}\gamma_4 u) = (E/m)(\bar{u}u)$ and $m\Delta m = E\Delta E$, as Δm $(\bar{u}u)$ where Δm is an equivalent change in mass of the electron. In this form invariance is obvious.

One can likewise obtain an expression for the energy shift for an electron in a hydrogen atom. Simply replace K_+ in (7), by $K_+{}^{(V)}$, the exact kernel for an electron in the potential, $V = \beta e^2/r$, of the atom, and f by a wave function (of space and time) for an atomic state. In general the ΔE which results is not real. The imaginary part is negative and in $\exp(-i\Delta ET)$ produces an exponentially decreasing amplitude with time. This is because we are asking for the amplitude that an atom initially with no photon in the field, will still appear after time T with no photon. If the atom is in a state which can radiate, this amplitude must decay with time. The imaginary part of ΔE when calculated does indeed give the correct rate of radiation from atomic states. It is zero for the ground state and for a free electron.

In the non-relativistic region the expression for ΔE can be worked out as has been done by Bethe. In the relativistic region (points 4 and 3 as close together as a Compton wave-length) the $K_+^{(V)}$ which should appear in (7) can be replaced to first order in V by K_+ plus $K_+^{(1)}(2, 1)$ given in I, Eq. (13). The problem is then very similar to the radiationless scattering problem. . . .

THE NUCLEAR SHELL

ooooooooooo

Johannes Daniel Jensen (b. 1906)

Johannes Daniel Jensen was born on June 28, 1906. He obtained his doctorate from Hamburg University in 1932 and was a member of the faculty of that university from 1936 to 1941. In 1941, he became Professor of Physics at the Hannover Institute of Technology, spending eight years there until called to a professorship at Heidelberg in 1949, where he is now the director of the Institute of Theoretical Physics. Frequently a visitor in the United States, he published in 1955 with Prof. Maria Goeppert-Mayer of the University of California the "Elementary Theory of Nuclear Shell Structure." It was for shell structure theory of the nucleus that he shared the 1963 Nobel Prize with Professor Mayer and Prof. Eugene Wigner of Princeton University.

In 1950, Professor Jensen became co-editor (with Prof. Otto Haxel) of the *Zeitschrift für Physik*. Professor Jensen makes his home in Heidelberg.

Jensen's Nobel address, which follows, is a lucid and entertaining account of the history of nuclear theory as well as of his unique contributions to physics. For those who are not acquainted with the concepts of the shell model of the nucleus, a few words explaining some of the concepts used by Jensen are worthwhile. The concept of the shell model stems from the arrangement of electrons in the outer regions of an atom. We know that as we go to heavier atoms, the electrons arrange themselves in closed concentric shells. Every time that we come to an atom in which all the shells are closed (that is, each shell contains as many electrons as it possibly can) we obtain one of the noble gases (helium, neon, etc.)— an inert and extremely stable atom. The electronic shells in the atom are the K shell with 2 electrons, the L shell with 8 electrons, the M shell with

18 electrons, and so on. We may therefore call the numbers 2, 8, 18, etc. the "magic" numbers of atomic structure. Now we know that these arrangements of electrons in the outer region of the atom are due to the Pauli exclusion principle as discussed in Chapter 59 and to the fact that the electrons have a half unit of spin. An additional factor in this electronic shell structure is that each electron has its own orbital angular momentum and, to a very good approximation, moves independently of the other electrons. The empirical evidence for the electronic shell structure is, of course, the periodic table of elements.

Since protons and neutrons also have half units of spin and are governed by the Pauli exclusion principle, one is immediately led to the idea of a nuclear shell structure. But there is one argument against this: nuclear forces between individual nucleons are extremely large so that one may not picture them as moving in orbits independently of one another as is true for electrons. However, suppose that, to a first approximation, we could picture each nucleon (neutron or proton) as moving in its own orbit in a kind of nuclear force field, independently of the motions of the other nucleons. We could then assign an orbital angular momentum as well as spin to each nucleon so that each nucleon would have its own distinct quantum numbers. The Pauli exclusion principle could then be applied to the nucleus, and the nucleons would arrange themselves in shells. A closed nuclear shell would then manifest itself as an extremely stable (a very large binding energy or mass defect) nucleus. Such nuclei would also be more abundant than others. Observations show that such nuclei occur.

We find that when the number of neutrons or protons inside a nucleus has one of the values 2, 8, 20, 28, 50, 82, 126 that nucleus is unusually abundant and extremely stable; these numbers are called the "magic numbers." Jensen and Maria Goeppert-Mayer's contribution was to show how these numbers can be explained in terms of a shell structure. Eugene Wigner developed the mathematical techniques, in the form of group theory that were needed to analyze nuclear structure.

ㅇㅇㅇㅇㅇㅇㅇㅇ

JENSEN

The History of the Theory of Structure of the Atomic Nucleus [1]

I HAVE HAD OCCASION DURING recent weeks to think of my teachers. One man who had a decisive influence on my early attempts to gain some understanding of nuclei stands out among them: he was Niels Bohr. Thus it seems appropriate today to look back and to examine the background from which our concepts of nuclear structure emerged.

I shall devote only a few sentences to the time preceding Chadwick's discovery of the neutron (1932). At that time our information regarding the nucleus was very sparse. All we had was a chart of stable isotopes with nuclear masses which were not very accurate, a few nuclear spins, an estimate of nuclear radius of about $1.4 \times 10^{-13} A^{\frac{1}{3}}$ centimeter, the phenomenon of natural radioactivity, and a few nuclear reactions. Ideas on nuclear structure were still dominated by Prout's hypothesis of 1815; this was that electrons and protons, the only elementary particles known at the time, were bound together in a nucleus in such a way that A protons and $A-Z$ electrons formed a nucleus of charge Z. But from the point of view of quantum mechanics this picture led to a great puzzle. Consider the deuteron as the simplest example today. According to this picture, the deuteron contains two protons and one electron, just like the ion of the hydrogen molecule. Yet in the deuteron these particles occupy 10^{-5} times less space in linear dimensions than in the hydrogen molecule. According to the uncertainty principle, very strong forces must be present in order to confine electrons to such a small space. These new forces should then show up in the hydrogen spectrum and change the Balmer formula; in particular, they should give rise to a much larger splitting than that discovered later by Lamb. Because of lack of time I cannot go into other difficulties arising from this picture.

In view of these conflicts many physicists including Niels Bohr were

---

[1] J. Hans D. Jensen, *Science,* 147 (1965), 1419–1422. 1954 Nobel address.

inclined to expect far-reaching changes in our basic physical concepts as well as in quantum mechanics.

At the same time there was an attempt to postulate that alpha particles form the basic building blocks of nuclei. One warning by Schroedinger still persists in my mind from those days. During the late '20's he accused the participants in a Berlin seminar of lack of imagination. In his temperamental manner he said, "Just because you see alpha particles coming out of the nucleus, you should not necessarily conclude that they exist inside it in the same form!" And he used a highly illustrative example to demonstrate how this reasoning can lead to a completely erroneous conclusion.

It is very remarkable how little information could be obtained at that time about the nucleus from the study of alpha decay. Max von Laue described this very clearly in a letter to Gamow in 1926; he congratulated Gamow on his explanation of the Geiger-Nuttal formula in terms of the tunneling effect and then went on: "However, if then the phenomenon of alpha decay occurs predominantly in the region outside the nucleus because of quantum mechanics, it is obvious that we cannot learn a great deal about nuclear structure from it." Gamow tells that at first he was quite perplexed after reading these lines, but after he had thought about it he decided that von Laue was right. The situation that very little insight into the structure of the nucleus could be gained from this oldest nuclear phenomenon persisted for a long time. Only about 6 years ago was some progress made when Mang applied the shell model to the problem of alpha decay. It seems to me that Mang's results completely confirm Schroedinger's skepticism; obviously the alpha particles really first appear during emergence from the nucleus.

The discovery of free neutrons completely changed the situation. Now it became possible to divorce the grave difficulties of "the localization of electrons in the nucleus," to which I shall return later, from the specific problem of nuclear structure. Thus in spite of Schroedinger's warning (this time, of course, regarding the neutrons) one could propose the hypothesis that protons and neutrons are the fundamental building blocks of the nucleus. (Rutherford had already proposed this in a conversation before Chadwick's discovery, and Harkins had published the suggestion.) The specific nuclear forces which act between them must be responsible for binding the nucleus. Heisenberg was the first to point out the consequences of this hypothesis and to arrive at important formulations and results in his series of noteworthy papers in *Zeitschrift fuer Physik* (1932–33).

These ideas can be separated into two stages. First, the saturation phenomenon is accepted as an empirical fact, that is, the approximate proportionality of nuclear binding energy (showing up as mass defect) to the particle number A, as well as the proportionality of the nuclear volume to A—roughly as $V = A \cdot r^3 (4\pi/3)$, where $r = 1.4 \times 10^{-13}$ centimeter. The numerical value of r was simply a gross estimate at that time; now we know from Stanford experiments that it is about 20 percent smaller. These facts as well as the results of scattering experiments led us to the conclusion that nuclear forces must have a short range. In spite of this shortness of range, Heisenberg in one of his papers considered the nucleus as a superposition of two Fermi gases (a neutron gas and a proton gas) which freely permeate each other and which are confined to the volume given above by an averaged potential. The basic fact that the stable nuclei have about the same number of neutrons and protons, $Z \approx A/2$, is explained on this basis as a consequence of Pauli's principle. In addition, one gets the right order of magnitude for the curvature of the parabola obtained by taking an $A = $ const. cross section through the surface of binding energies of stable nuclei. The opening of the parabola is too large by a factor of about two; with the new nuclear radius obtained by Hofstadter the agreement is even better. Similarly, the decrease in the ratio $Z : A$ with increasing mass number results as a natural consequence of the interplay between the accumulating Coulomb interaction and the consequences of Pauli's principle.

Thus the basic idea of the shell model was expressed for the first time, that is, the idea of free motion of individual nucleons in an average potential. Every further development was an almost necessary extension of these ideas to a system with a finite number of particles. At the same time the Leipzig school as well as Wigner and his co-workers devoted themselves to the study of light nuclei, mainly on the basis of the shell model. The particular stability of the nuclei, $_2\text{He}_2^4$, $_8\text{O}_8^{16}$, and $_{20}\text{Ca}_{20}^{40}$, was not the only thing explained in this way. For example, Wigner and his co-workers came to a quantitative conclusion that the unknown nuclei, $_{16}\text{S}_{20}^{36}$ and $_{20}\text{Ca}_{28}^{48}$, should be even more stable; later these were in fact observed in mass spectrometers as natural isotopes with very small abundance. While this was somewhat a matter of luck in view of insufficient knowledge of the forces, it was nevertheless one of the first predictions of nuclear theory to be verified experimentally. In addition, around the same time (1937) Hund and Wigner, independently of each other, developed the concept of supermultiplets that played such an important part in classifying nuclides and in the systematics of beta decay. This concept was based on the specific charge and spin independence of nuclear forces. In the notable work of Bethe and Bacher in *Reviews of Modern Physics* (1936), which soon became known as "Bethe's bible," very convincing arguments were presented to show that nuclear forces in fact show a very weak spin dependence; in particular the spin-orbit coupling should be very weak.

In the years immediately following the discovery of neutrons vigorous development of experimental nuclear physics began. This was partially due to the possibility of performing experiments with neutrons; partially to the completion of the first accelerators and to great improvements in measuring and counting techniques. For me these were the years of my first encounters with both Copenhagen and Niels Bohr; in Copenhagen I was privileged to witness attempts at theoretical interpretation of the rapidly accumulating experimental data.

Two new phenomena were particularly important for the development of our concepts of nuclear structure. They were: relatively high effective cross sections for the nucleon-nucleon scattering, and the sharp, closely spaced resonances discovered by Fermi, Amaldi, and co-workers in slow-neutron scattering and capture. The latter phenomenon could be explained not at all in terms of the picture in which the neutron is moving in an average potential. Thus Niels Bohr's concept of the "compound nucleus" came into being. In this picture, the state of the nucleus is characterized by intimate coupling of all nucleons to each other; this description does not allow us to speak of the motion of a single nucleon independently of the simultaneous state of motion of all the other nucleons. However, this intuitive, semi-classical picture of Niels Bohr had to be brought into agreement with the postulates of quantum mechanics. To this day the golden bridge has been the Breit-Wigner formula; this originated outside Copenhagen, but, after being seen on every blackboard of the Copenhagen institute at all hours, naturally it received appropriate space in the above-mentioned "Bethe bible." Probably every theoretician pondered long and often about its interpretation and even about its proof; and it occupies many minds even today.

The ground state of a nucleus also was mainly described in terms of Bohr's picture. A concept of nuclear matter was formed in which this nuclear matter is packed to saturation density and has binding energy proportional to its volume; for real nuclei it has surface tension with surface energy proportional to its surface. The "Bethe bible" also contains an excellent discussion of the basis of these assumptions. The greatest success of this model was the description of nuclear fission by Bohr and Wheeler (1939), which contains almost everything that is understood to date (1936) about this phenomenon.

Schroedinger's remark, that one should not necessarily assume that the particles observed emerging as free particles from the nucleus during nuclear transformations must exist in the same form inside the nucleus, was heavily emphasized by Fermi's papers on beta decay (1933–34). In these papers the above-mentioned dilemma, which arises from the concept of "electrons inside the nucleus," was literally dissolved into nothingness. Fermi drew radically important consequences from the idea that the proton and the neutron are two quantum states of a single fundamental particle, the nucleon. Between these two states quantum transitions can take place (Fermi used Heisenberg's version of the isospin formalism in his theory). Such a quantum transition is accompanied by the creation of an electron and a neutrino. Today's young physicist, who already as a student juggles creation and annihilation operators on the blackboard, can hardly get the feeling of what a conceptual breakthrough was contained in Fermi's formulation. As an illustration, let me quote from a historical letter by Pauli in December 1930 in which he proposed for the first time his neutrino hypothesis to his befriended colleagues: "I came to a desperate conclusion . . . namely, it seems possible that *inside the nucleus* there can *exist* electrically neutral particles which I shall call neutrinos. . . . The continuous beta spectrum becomes understandable if one assumes that, during beta decay, emission of an electron is accompanied by *emission* of a neutrino." I emphasize the words *exist inside the nucleus* and *emission*. Pauli certainly did not choose these words simply to make his ideas more digestible to his experimenting colleagues, but because the words represented the physical ideas of those days. This is even more remarkable in view of the fact that the concepts and techniques of particle creation used by Fermi had been available long before in the so-called second quantization of Jordan, Klein, and Wigner. However, two years later, in his *Handbuch* article Pauli himself regarded it only as a mathematical trick; Fermi's work finally convinced him that there was real physics in it.

Yukawa's work also occurred in that half of the decade. He showed that the forces between nucleons are transmitted by a field which must show retardation effects and quanta associated with these retardation effects, the mesons. The latter are perhaps of secondary importance in the nuclear structure problems since it was practically established in Heisenberg's investigations that in the nucleus the nucleons move so slowly that one may hope to understand the essential features of nuclear structure by using nonrelativistic quantum mechanics. However, the strong coupling of the Yukawa field to its source is extremely important; its strength, $g^2/\hbar c$, is of the order of magnitude of ten (in contrast with the Sommerfeld constant $e^2/\hbar c = \frac{1}{137}$ in electrodynamics). This led Niels Bohr to an idea on nuclear matter, which, to my knowledge, he never wrote down; but it is permanently inscribed in my memory from our conversations. This idea was as follows: Since the field is strongly coupled to its source, the hitherto existing picture of the "compound nucleus" may be much too naïve. Perhaps, the only sensible concept is to consider the whole nucleus as a field which is highly nonlinear because of strong coupling; when this field is quantized it gives, in addition to other conserved quantities like angular momentum, integral charges Z, and energies (that is, masses) that form a spectrum with values close to the integral numbers A on which the "excitation energy" bands are superimposed. The assumption that in the nucleus there exist Z protons and $(A–Z)$ neutrons such as we encounter as free particles in appropriate experiments would make almost no sense.

Naturally, the skepticism of Schroedinger (mentioned at the beginning) would thus be formulated in its extreme. However, Niels Bohr conceived a picture of the nucleus which closely resembles our current concepts in high-energy physics on elementary particles and "resonances" (for example, such as ρ-, ω-, and η-mesons). Certainly, one should not lose sight of this point of view in nuclear physics either, although it has been shown since that it is possible to speak of the existence of individual nucleons in a nucleus as a useful approximation.

The picture of the nucleus just described is in accord with the fact that just by glancing at the table of stable isotopes we can see that the nuclear properties are continuous functions of A and Z. To be sure, there were indications of discontinuities and windings in the valley of the energy surface. I have already pointed out the exceptional cases of the nuclei with Z and $N = 2$, 8, 20. It also seems strange that the alpha energy does not increase uniformly as one goes further away from alpha-stable nuclei in the mass valley; instead it is largest right at the polonium isotopes. This indicates that special exceptions occur for $Z = 82$. Similarly, in the diagram in which alpha energies are plotted against Z and N, we see curves with steep slopes from $N = 128$ to $N = 126$; Gamow called this figure the "Heisen-Berg." The work of Seaborg and collaborators made the profile of these "hills" even more striking. Elsasser, Guggenheim, Ivanenko, and others attempted to explain these and other phenomena in terms of the shell model; however, it seemed impossible to accommodate the groups of numbers Z and $N = 2$, 8, 20, on the one hand and $Z = 82$, $N = 126$ on the other, under the same roof. But, mainly because of the success of Bohr's compound-nucleus model, there was a tendency to consider these phenomena as curiosities of little significance to the fundamental question of nuclear structure.

The war years and the first few years thereafter put physicists in Germany into oppressive isolation, but at the same time, remarkably enough, these years provided some leisure to pursue many a question, even perhaps some problem seemingly leading nowhere in particular. At that time I held frequent discussions with Haxel in Berlin and Göttingen and with Suess in Hamburg of the empirical facts which single out the above-mentioned numbers. Suess paid more and more attention to them, primarily in his cosmo-chemical studies: he found that in the interval between the known numbers, additionally the numbers Z and $N = 50$ and $N = 82$ were clearly prominent. Haxel, at first quite independently, encountered the same numbers from other nuclear data.

Although my two colleagues wanted to convince me that these numbers held the key to nuclear structure, I did not know what to make of it at first; I thought the name "magic numbers," whose origin was unknown to me, to be very appropriate. Then, a few years after the war I had the luck to return to Copenhagen for the first time. There in a recent issue of the *Physical Review* I found the work of Maria Goeppert-Mayer, "On closed shells in nuclei," where she too collected the empirical evidence for the remarkable features associated with these numbers. That gave me courage to talk about this work, along with our results, in a theoretical seminar. I shall never forget this seminar. Niels Bohr listened very carefully and threw in questions which became more and more lively. Once he said: "But that is not in Mrs. Mayer's papers!"; Bohr evidently had carefully read, and thought about, this work. The seminar turned into a long, lively discussion. I was very much impressed by the intensity with which Niels Bohr received, weighed, and compared these empirical facts, facts that did not at all fit into his own picture of nuclear structure. It was only from that hour on that I began to consider seriously the possibility of a "demagification" of the "magic numbers."

At first I tried to remain as much as possible within the old framework. To begin with, I considered only the spin of the whole nucleus, since there appeared to exist a simple correlation between the magic nucleon numbers and the sequence of nuclear spins and their multiplicities. I first thought of the single-particle model with strong spin-orbit coupling during an exciting discussion with Haxel and Suess, in which we tried to include all the possible empirical facts in this scheme. As we did this it turned out that because of the spin-orbit coupling the number 28 should be something like a magic number. I remember how we looked for some experimental indication of this, and I remember being pleased when we found some indication of it among the still-meager data that were available at that time.

Nevertheless, I did not feel very happy about the whole picture, and I was not really surprised when a serious journal refused to publish our first letter on the ground that "It is not really physics but only playing with numbers." It was only because of the lively interest in the magic numbers displayed by Niels Bohr that I then sent the same letter to Weisskopf who forwarded it to the *Physical Review*. But it was not until later, after I had presented our ideas in a Copenhagen seminar and been able to discuss them with Niels Bohr, that I finally gained some confidence. One of the first comments of Bohr seems remarkable to me: "Now I understand why nuclei do not show rotational bands in their spectra." With the accuracy of measurement available at that time one could look for such spectra only in lighter nuclei, which according to the liquid drop or a similar model should have relatively small moments of inertia and therefore widely separated rotational levels. As we know today, these lighter nuclei as well as most of the others show in fact no rotational bands; Bohr's argument was that, of course in a picture in which single particles move independently in an average spherically symmetric potential, there can no longer be any place for a superimposed rotation of a nucleus as a whole, just as in the system of electrons in an atomic shell.

Even though the shell model finally proved to be more than just a convenient language with which the experimentalists could compare their results and which perhaps brought to light a few fundamental features of nuclear structure, during the following years I still had to agree with Robert Oppenheimer when he told me: "Maria [Goeppert-Mayer] and you are explaining magic by miracles." Only recently in his lecture at Oak Ridge, Wigner said a similar thing, carefully choosing, however, his own words.

From the start it was clear to me as well as to Mrs. Goeppert-Mayer that apparently the shell model could approximately describe only the ground state and the low-excited states of nuclei. While the consequences of the Pauli principle for nucleon-nucleon interactions could possibly guarantee the self-consistency of this picture, the Pauli principle becomes less and less stringent as the excitation energies become higher, and the nucleon-nucleon correlations arising from nuclear forces become increasingly important; in an exact description such correlations are, of course, present in the ground state as well.

Therefore, during my next visit to Cophenhagen it gave me a certain satisfaction when, questioned about news on the shell model, I could instead talk of the ideas which then occupied my namesake Peter Jensen and me as well as Steinwedel and Danos. Following a suggestion by Goldhaber and Teller, we tried to provide a semiclassical explanation for the recently discovered large dipole absorption in the nuclear photoeffect at 15 to 20 Mev; that is, we described it as an excited state of nuclear matter in which all nucleons are in the state of motion such that strict phase relations exist among *all* of them. In this way the frequency of the absorption maximum, as well as its dependence on the nuclear mass number, could be related to the symmetry energy and to the nuclear radius in a satisfactory way. The width of the "giant resonance" provided a measure of the rate at which such phase relations disappear. Niels Bohr understood immediately why the study of this particular type of "collective motion" (as one puts it today in the jargon of specialists) was especially close to my heart. One had to establish at which excitation energies the correlations enforced by the nucleon-nucleon interactions become dominant over the effect of the averaged forces, even if importance of the correlations is kept down in the ground state by Pauli's principle.

In the following years much work was devoted to the study of such correlations. First of all, a most remarkable feature of current nuclear physics came to light as a consequence of the work of Kurath and of the former Harwell group (Flowers, Elliot, and others) on the one hand, and of the work of the young Copenhagen school (Aage Ben Bohr, Mottelson, Nilsson, and others) on the other. This feature is the fact that, even though the two pictures start from complementary, each-other limiting, points of view, their quantitative results seem immediately to meet and to overlap.

When one considers all these questions as a whole—the problems of nuclear structure, nuclear forces, as well as the problems of elementary particles—in spite of all the successes perhaps a verse of Rilke may be appropriate. In the early days of quantum mechanics my late teacher, Wilhelm Lenz, brought this verse to my attention. Rilke speaks in it of his feelings at the turn of the century, which he depicts as a large book in which one page is turned over; he concludes:

> "The lustre of the new-turned page one senses,
> Where everything may yet unfold;
> The silent powers measure their expanses;
> Each other darkly they behold."

88

ooooooooooo

RADIOCARBON DATING

ooooooooooo

Willard Frank Libby (b. 1908)

The discovery of the transformation of the radioactive elements, one into another through the step-by-step disintegration process, soon led to information on the half-lives of these unstable substances. The recognition of the long half-lives of uranium and thorium, of the order respectively of one billion and ten billion years, suggested that these elements, together with some of their disintegration products, might serve as accurate clocks yielding the time of their formation and of the earth itself. Over the intervening years this hope has been realized. It would seem, now, that our planet originated some 4.5 billion years ago.

Until rather recently no radioactive substance was known whose properties and half-life were such that it could be used to date substances in the organic, as opposed to the inorganic, world. The dating of ancient events and civilizations through organic artifacts, refuse, or through animal or even human remains, could supply much valuable information to the historical record if a precise means and the right radioactive element were available. Fortunately, after World War II through the discovery of the radioactive isotope, C^{14}, with a half-life of 5,568 years, a highly useful dating technique was developed. The isolation of this isotope, the investigation of its properties, and the refinement of its use in dating are all owed to Willard F. Libby and his associates.

Recorded history extends back only some five thousand years; in that interval there are many gaps because of the lack of written records. But man's culture is older by many thousands of years than his written records. C^{14}'s clock ticks on in the artifacts, refuse, animal remains, and even the burned-out campfires of those ancient times. From radiocarbon, we have learned that the cave drawings in the Lascaux caves of France can be assigned to men of skull and skeletal structures similar to modern Euro-

1593

peans and that they flourished about 15,000 years ago. An even earlier dating from the Aurignacian period of some 27,000 years ago indicates that *Homo sapiens* was then already fully differentiated as a species.

The appearance of early man in North America has generally been linked to the maximum advance of the ice sheet in the most recent glaciation. Previously assumed to have occurred about 25,000 years ago, this most southerly advance of the ice sheet has now been placed by radiocarbon analysis of wood samples from the Two Creeks forest bed in Wisconsin in the more recent past of 11,000 years ago. Evidences of early habitation on this continent when analyzed give dates of the order of 10,000 years, corroborating the appearance of man in North America with the maximum of the last glaciation; the time of these events, though, is much more recent than previously supposed. The value of this method to the construction of an accurate archaeology is thus apparent.

The following article, which describes the physical basis of the dating technique, is taken from Libby's monograph "Radiocarbon Dating." [1] Briefly, the method depends upon the fact that C^{14} is being continually formed in the upper atmosphere by the interaction of the incoming primary cosmic radiation with air atoms. This reaction produces neutrons that, entering the nuclei of nitrogen atoms in the air, result in the formation of C^{14} atoms. Such atoms quickly combine with oxygen in the air to form molecules of carbon dioxide, and these molecules soon become homogeneously mixed with molecules of stable CO_2 by the churning of the atmosphere. Thus, all samples of atmospheric carbon dioxide will be found to be radioactive and consequently all plants, since plants grow by incorporating this substance. In the same way, since all animals ultimately subsist on plants, all animals and all humans are radioactive.

Present evidence leads to the conclusion that there has been a constant rate of production of radiocarbon in the atmosphere for at least the past ten thousand years and this production has been in equilibrium with its decay. This balance has been a characteristic over that time of all living carbonaceous material. During the lifetime of any plant or animal, the radiocarbon assimilated from food will be in exact balance with the radiocarbon disintegrating in the tissues. When death occurs, the balance immediately ceases, and the radiocarbon atoms present become fewer and fewer as time goes on. The mean number of disintegrations per minute per gram of carbon atoms from living material is 15.3; from a knowledge of the half-life of C^{14} we know that the same carbon 5,568 years after the death of the material would show an average of 7.65 disintegrations.

Radioactive C^{14} atoms decay by emitting a β particle, that is, an electron. To determine the age of a once-living substance such as wood, the

---

[1] Willard F. Libby, *Radiocarbon Dating* (Chicago: University of Chicago Press, 1952).

sample must be very carefully reduced to pure carbon, taking care that all other material is excluded. If the activity is determined from the pure carbon itself the material must be so disposed that all β particles released by the disintegrating atoms will be counted. Alternatively, the carbon may be reacted into a gaseous form such as carbon dioxide or acetylene. Whether gas or solid, the carbon is introduced into a sensitive Geiger counter and its activity determined. The measured disintegrations per gram per minute are then substituted for I in equation (5) of the paper from which the desired value of t, the age of the material (in years), is found.

Willard Frank Libby was born at Grand View, Colorado, on December 17, 1908. He completed his undergraduate studies at the University of California at Berkeley in 1931 and received his Ph. D. at the same institution in 1933. He was then appointed instructor in chemistry and in 1938, assistant professor. In 1941 he was awarded a Guggenheim Fellowship which he held at Princeton University. He later transferred to Columbia University, Division of War Research, serving during the period of the war, 1941–1945, on the uranium isotope separation project. After the war he was appointed professor of chemistry at the Institute of Nuclear Studies and the University of Chicago. It was during this time at Chicago that he carried on the C^{14} research and developed the dating techniques that are presented in the selection which follows. In 1954, Libby was appointed a member of the U. S. Atomic Energy Commission; he served for five years, resigning in 1959 to become professor of chemistry at the University of California at Los Angeles, his present position. The recipient of many awards, medals, and prizes for his distinguished contributions to chemistry, he was honored by the Nobel Prize in chemistry for 1960 for his development of the C^{14} dating techniques.

9329999

LIBBY

Radiocarbon Dating [2]

PRINCIPLES

THE DISCOVERY OF COSMIC RADIATION by V. F. Hess in 1911 led to repeated conjectures as to possible permanent effects this radiation might have on the surface of the earth. The energy

---

[2] Willard F. Libby, *Radiocarbon Dating* (Chicago: University of Chicago Press, 1952), pp. 1–10.

received by the earth in the form of cosmic radiation is commensurate with that received as starlight. It is therefore really quite small in terms of the solar energy. The specific energy, that is, the energy per constituent particle, is very much higher than for any other type of radiation, averaging several billions of electron volts (1 electron volt is 1.6×10^{-12} ergs, which is the average energy of motion of a gas molecule at 10,000° C.). It is conceivable, therefore, that the cosmic radiation will alter the earth's atmosphere in detectable ways.

It was discovered shortly after the neutron itself had been discovered that neutrons were present in the higher layers of the atmosphere probably as secondary radiations produced by the primary cosmic rays. Measurements by cosmic-ray physicists have clearly established that the population in the atmosphere rises with altitude to a maximum somewhat above 40,000 feet and then falls. This proves the secondary character of the radiation—that it is not incident on the earth from interstellar space but is a product of the impact of the true primary radiation on the earth's atmosphere. A corroborating point in this connection is the recent demonstration that the neutron is truly radioactive with a lifetime of about 12 minutes, which of course removes any possibility of the neutrons having time to travel any considerable distance in interstellar space, though the trip from the sun could be made without complete decay to hydrogen.

Consideration of possible nuclear transmutations which the cosmic rays might effect leads one immediately to consider what the neutrons, known to be produced by the cosmic rays, might be expected to do to the earth's atmosphere. In the laboratory many studies have been made of the effects of neutrons of various energies on all the ordinary elements and especially on nitrogen and oxygen, the constituents of the air. In general, the results are that oxygen is extraordinarily inert but that nitrogen is reactive. It appears certain that, of the two nitrogen isotopes, N^{14}, of 99.62 per cent abundance, and N^{15}, of 0.038 per cent abundance, N^{14} is the more reactive. With neutrons of thermal velocity the reaction

$$N^{14} + n = C^{14} + H^1 \qquad\qquad (1)$$

is dominant, the cross-section [3] of the N^{14} atom for a room temperature thermal neutron being in the vicinity of 1.7×10^{-24} cm.², whereas the thermal neutron cross-section for reaction with O^{16} is of the order of 0.1 per cent of this. It is therefore quite certain that thermal neutrons introduced into ordinary air will react according to Equation (1) to form the radiocarbon isotope of mass 14 and half-life of 5568 ± 30 years.

---

[3] "Cross-section" for the capture of a neutron by a nucleus means the area surrounding a nucleus (like a target area) which a neutron must hit, on the average, if it is to be captured. The larger the cross-section (expressed in square centimeters), the greater is the probability that the neutron will be captured.

The neutrons in the air being formed by the energetic cosmic rays possess energy themselves, probably of the order of 5–10 mev (million electron volts) on the average when first formed. After birth they then collide with the air molecules and lose their energy by collision, either elastic or inelastic, either reacting in one of these collisions and so being absorbed or finally attaining thermal energies where they are quite certain to be absorbed to form radiocarbon by Reaction (1). Laboratory studies of the effects of energetic neutrons on air again indicate that the nitrogen is the more reactive constituent. Reaction (1) is still dominant, though a second reaction,

$$N^{14} + n = B^{11} + He^4, \tag{2}$$

occurs. The latter reaction becomes dominant at energies above 1 mev but even at the most favored energies attains cross-sections of only 10 per cent of that of nitrogen for thermal energies. Reaction (1), on the other hand, goes with considerable probability in the region of 0.4–1.6 mev.

A third type of reaction of high-energy neutrons with nitrogen,

$$N^{14} + n = C^{12} + H^3, \tag{3}$$

has been reported in the laboratory. The nature of the laboratory experiment was such that it was difficult to estimate the cross-section for the reaction, but the reported value was 10^{-26} cm.², to an accuracy of about a factor of 5. It is certain from the masses of the atoms involved in Reaction (3) that neutrons of not less than 4 mev are involved, since the reaction is endothermic to this extent. The hydrogen isotope in Reaction (3) is the radioactive hydrogen called tritium, of 12.46 years half-life, which decays to form the stable isotope of helium, He^3, which occurs in atmospheric helium in an abundance of 1.2×10^{-6} parts He^3 per ordinary helium in atmospheric air. It is thought that this value is accurate to about 30 per cent. The abundance of He^3 in ordinary helium from terrestrial sources varies widely from undetectably small values in uranium ores, where an excessively large amount of He^4 is found, to the values of 12×10^{-6} parts for certain Canadian rocks. In general, however, the He^3 content of helium from the earth's crust is not over one-tenth as large as that of atmospheric helium. Since tritium produced by Reaction (3) lasts such a short time, one knows that any tritium produced by Reaction (3) will introduce an equivalent amount of He^3 into the earth's atmosphere, so that one possible effect of the cosmic-ray bombardment of the earth's atmosphere could be the introduction of He^3 into the atmospheric helium. It is seen that this may be the case, since it is observed that atmospheric helium is richer in He^3 than terrestrial helium.

Summarizing the three most probable reactions, only the first and third lead to radioactive isotopes. It is therefore to be expected that the neutrons produced by the cosmic radiation may produce these radioactive materials in the earth's atmosphere. After these points were made, a search in nature for both radioactivities was instituted. Both have since been found in amounts and concentrations corresponding roughly to those expected.

Therefore, we now have more confidence in the basic postulates made in the arguments outlined above—that the behavior of the cosmic-ray neutrons in the air is predictable from the observed behavior of laboratory neutrons on nitrogen and oxygen and that the possibility of the neutrons having higher energy than laboratory neutrons appears not to confuse the issue appreciably.

The prediction of the expected amounts of radiocarbon and tritium can be made only on the basis of some information about the relative probabilities of Reactions (1), (2), and (3). Reaction (1) is so much more probable, however, that it is clear that the yield of radiocarbon will be nearly equal to the total number of neutrons generated by the cosmic rays, a number which we shall call Q in units of number per square centimeter per second. The tritium yield, due to Reaction (3) only, is taken to be of the order of the ratio of these cross-sections, or about 1 per cent of Q. The latter will be considerably more uncertain than the yield of radiocarbon, since the cross-section for Reaction (3) is much more uncertain than that for Reaction (1) and more specifically than the dominance of Reaction (1). If we integrate the data for the neutron intensity as a function of altitude from sea-level to the top of the atmosphere, to obtain the total number of neutrons, Q, produced per square centimeter per second, and average this over the earth's surface according to the observed variation of neutron intensity with latitude, we obtain a figure for Q, the average number of neutrons generated per square centimeter of the earth's surface per second by the incidence of cosmic radiation. If we further assume that the cosmic-ray production of radiocarbon is an ancient phenomenon in terms of the 5600-year half-life of radiocarbon (i.e., the cosmic rays have remained at essentially their present intensity over the last 10,000 or 20,000 years), we can conclude that there is, some place on earth, enough radiocarbon to guarantee that its rate of disintegration is just equal to its rate of formation. Evaluation of Q from the experimental data available gives 2.6 as a most likely value. Since the earth's surface has 5.1×10^{18} cm.^{2}, the radiocarbon inventory must be such that 1.3×10^{19} beta disintegrations occur per second.

$$C^{14} = \beta^- + N^{14+}. \tag{4}$$

Since laboratory measurement of the specific disintegration rate of radiocarbon gives 1.6×10^{11} disintegrations per second per gram, dividing we obtain 8.1×10^7 grams, or 81 metric tons, as the predicted inventory for radiocarbon on earth. This is equivalent to 365 million curies (1 curie is that quantity of radioactivity which gives a disintegration rate of 3.7×10^{10} per second). Reasoning similarly, we predict a tritium inventory of about 3 million curies in nature.

The question remains as to where the radiocarbon will occur. A moment's thought answers this, however. We consider the problem of the ultimate fate of a carbon atom introduced into the air at a height of some 5 or 6 miles. It seems certain that within a few minutes or hours the carbon atom will have been burned to [a] carbon dioxide molecule. It is true that there are points of interest to discuss in the question of the kinetics of combustion of atomic carbon in the air, and research is necessary to supply definite answers for the many questions which would arise in such a discussion. It seems probable, however, that the carbon will not long remain in any condition other than carbon dioxide. Postulating that this is so (i.e., the absorption of cosmic ray neutrons by nitrogen of the air is equivalent to the production of radioactive carbon dioxide), we can proceed to an immediate answer to the question as to where natural radiocarbon should occur on earth. Radioactive carbon dioxide will certainly mix with considerable speed with the atmospheric carbon dioxide, and so we conclude that all atmospheric carbon dioxide is rendered radioactive by the cosmic radiation. Since plants live off the carbon dioxide, all plants will be radioactive; since the animals on earth live off the plants, all animals will be radioactive. Thus we conclude that all living things will be rendered radioactive by the cosmic radiation. In addition, there is another carbon reservoir for the natural radiocarbon, and this is the inorganic carbon in the sea present as dissolved carbon dioxide, bicarbonate and carbonate, for it is known that an exchange reaction occurs between carbon dioxide and dissolved bicarbonate and carbonate ions. The time for radioactive carbon dioxide in the air to distribute itself through this reservoir probably is not in excess of 500 years. This is the so-called "turn-over" time for the life-cycle which has been widely discussed by geochemists. The estimates vary quite widely, but it does seem that this time can hardly exceed 1000 years. Since this is a time short as compared to the lifetime of radiocarbon, we conclude that any given radiocarbon atom will make the round trip several times in its lifetime, and we therefore predict that the distribution of radiocarbon throughout the reservoir will be quite uniform, there being little vertical or latitudinal or longitudinal gradients left. One has some cause to suspect that there might be variations in intensity over the earth's surface, for the reason that it is known that the cosmic-ray neutron component varies by a factor of about 3.5^9 between equatorial and polar regions, the intensity being greater in the polar regions.

As expected, however, on the basis of the probable brevity of the turn-over time as compared to the lifetime of radiocarbon, it has been found that the distribution is uniform. Materials have been selected from various points on the earth's surface and from various altitudes, and the specific radioactivity has been found to be identical within the error of measurement, which amounts to some 3–5 per cent.

In order to predict the specific radioactivity of living carbon, the amount of carbon in the exchange reservoir must be estimated. Careful consideration of the complex biochemical questions involved leads us to the numbers given in [Table 88–1].

TABLE 88-1. *Carbon Inventory*

Source	Amount (gm/cm^2)
Ocean "carbonate"	7.25
Ocean, dissolved organic	0.59
Biosphere	0.33
Atmosphere	0.12
Total	8.3

The dominance of the inorganic material dissolved in the sea is obvious from these numbers. This has the immediate consequence that variations in living conditions which will lead to variations in the amount of living matter on earth will not appreciably affect the total carbon in the reservoir. Or, conceivably, the only possible significant variations of the quantity of carbon in the reservoir must involve changes in the volume, the temperature, or the acidity (pH) of the oceans. This probably means that the reservoir has not changed significantly in the last few tens of thousands of years, though there is the point to consider of the effect of the glaciation on both the volume and the mean temperature of the oceans. If the numbers in [Table 88–1] are correct, there are some 8.3 grams of carbon in exchange equilibrium with the atmospheric carbon dioxide for each square centimeter of the earth's surface, on the average, and since there are some 2.6 neutrons incident per square centimeter per second, we must expect that these 8.3 grams of carbon will possess a specific radioactivity of 2.6/8.3 disintegrations per second per gram, or 2.6 $\times$ 60/8.3 disintegrations per minute per gram. This number, 18.8, is to be compared with the experimentally observed value of 16.1 $\pm$ 0.5. The agreement seems to be sufficiently within the experimental errors involved, so that we have reason for confidence in the theoretical picture set forth above.

The agreement between these two numbers bears on another point of real importance—the constancy in intensity of the cosmic radiation over the past several thousand years. If one were to imagine that the cosmic radiation had been turned off until a short while ago, the enormous amount of radiocarbon necessary to the equilibrium state would not have been manufactured and the specific radioactivity of living matter would be much less than the rate of production calculated from the neutron intensity. Or, conversely, if one were to imagine that the intensity had been much higher in the past until very recently, the specific radioactivity would greatly exceed that calculated from the observed neutron intensity. Since 5568 ± 30 years will be required to bring the inventory halfway to any new equilibrium state demanded by the change in cosmic-ray intensity, we find some evidence in the agreement between these numbers that the cosmic-ray intensity has remained essentially constant for the last 5000–10,000 years. This does not mean that it could not exhibit hourly, daily, or even annual fluctuations. It does mean, however, that the intensity averaged over 1000 years or so has not changed. There is the slight possibility that an approximately compensating change in the carbon inventory has occurred, but for the reasons mentioned above the buffering action of the great reservoir in the sea makes this very remote.

A further point of interest in connection with the inventory and the observed specific assay is that the carbon isotopes apparently are fractionated in being incorporated into the biosphere from the inorganic world. This effect was discovered some time ago for the isotope C^{13}, which has a mean abundance of 1.1 per cent in ordinary carbon. It was found that the ratio of the abundance of C^{13} in inorganic carbon to that in biological carbon is 1.03. On the basis of this, one would expect a value of 1.06 for the analogous ratio for C^{14}, radiocarbon. Since the mass spectrographic measurements of the C^{13} abundance are quite accurate and the theory on which one calculates the 1.06 ratio from the observed 1.03 ratio for C^{13} is quite rigorous, we are inclined to multiply our assay of biological material by 1.06 rather than to take the mean value of the small number of measurements we have made on inorganic carbon. The mean of the biological assay is 15.3 ± 0.1. Multiplying by 1.06, we obtain 16.2 for inorganic carbon; then, averaging according to the weight factors given in [Table 88–1], we derive the average 16.1 for the carbon inventory as a whole. One must remember, however, that wood or other biological material will present an assay of 15.3 and that modern seashell will present an assay of 16.2.

If the cosmic radiation has remained at its present intensity for 20,000 or 30,000 years, and if the carbon reservoir has not changed appreciably in this time, then there exists at the present time a complete balance between the rate of disintegration of radiocarbon atoms and the rate of assimilation of new radiocarbon atoms for all material in the life-cycle. For example, a tree, or any other living organism, is in a state of equilibrium between the cosmic radiation and the natural rate of disintegration of radiocarbon so long as it is alive. In other words, during the lifetime the radiocarbon assimilated from food will just balance the radiocarbon disintegrating in the tissues. When death occurs, however, the assimilation process is abruptly halted, and only the disintegration process remains.

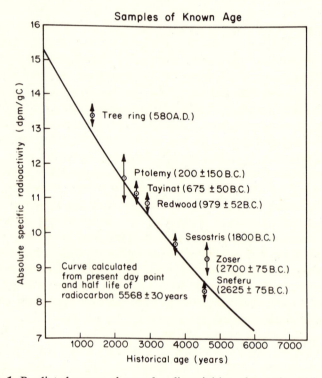

Fig. 88–1. Predicted versus observed radioactivities of samples of known age.

It has been known for many years that the rate of disintegration of radioactive bodies is extraordinarily immutable, being independent of the nature of the chemical compound in which the radioactive body resides and of the temperature, pressure, and other physical characteristics of its environment. The reason for this is that the transformation is a nuclear phenomenon involving energies very much larger than those corresponding to the chemical bonds and to the various physical influences to which matter might conceivably be subjected. Therefore, we conclude that the rate of disappearance of radioactivity following death corresponds to the exponential decay law for radiocarbon as represented by the solid curve in [Fig. 88–1], in which the world-wide assay of 15.3 for biological materials corresponds to zero time, and the predicted specific radioactivities for various times thereafter are given by the curve. The equation for the curve is

$$I = 15.3 \exp\left(-0.693\,\frac{t}{5568}\right) \tag{5}$$

or

$$I = 15.3 \times 2^{(t/5568)}, \tag{5'}$$

in which t is the age of the organic material in years, age being defined as the time elapsed since death occurred. The experimental points shown in [Fig. 88–1] are the observed assays for various samples of known age. . . . In so far as the points fit the curve, we have reason to believe that the method is sound and gives the correct ages. The errors indicated on the experimental points are standard deviations, and it appears that the results are favorable as judged statistically.

It is obvious that we must be careful in selecting samples to choose materials that contain the original carbon atoms present at the time death occurred. In other words, samples must not have been preserved with organic materials containing carbon of age different from that of the sample. Care must also be taken that chemical changes have not led to replacement of the carbon atoms. In a general way, organic materials consisting mainly of large molecules, such as cellulose and charcoal, are favored. An example of questionable material is shell, for it is quite conceivable that shell which is powdery and chalky in appearance has had its carbonate atoms replaced.

XV

ooooooooooo

NUCLEAR REACTIONS AND
NUCLEAR ENERGY

ooooooooooo

89

○○○○○○○○○○

NUCLEAR THEORY

○○○○○○○○○○○

Werner Karl Heisenberg (b. 1901)

Once the neutron was discovered, nuclear physics developed with great speed both experimentally and theoretically. Since the experimental physicists, such as those in the Fermi school at Rome, were collecting vast amounts of data, it was necessary for the theoreticians to collate these data and construct a rational model of the nucleus that could explain the evidence and indicate the direction for new research. The theoretical problem in nuclear research differs in one very important respect from that encountered in the structure of the outer regions of the atom. In ordinary atomic physics one deals with a swarm of electrons surrounding a nucleus; each electron has a mass that is negligible compared with the mass of the nucleus. This means that one can treat the problem as a central force (the Coulomb force) problem, so that a fairly simple perturbation procedure can be applied. Since the mass of each electron is negligible compared to the mass of the nucleus and since the positive electric charge is concentrated in the nucleus, whereas the negative charge is distributed over the various individual electrons, we may neglect the interactions among the individual electrons to a first approximation.

But this is not the case inside the nucleus. There, each nucleon (neutron or proton) is of equal status. There is no single concentration of nuclear matter from which we may depict the emanation of the nuclear forces that keep the nucleus together. Hence, a simple perturbation procedure is not applicable, and we must treat the nucleus as a whole without being able to separate it into two more or less distinct parts.

Another difficulty arises in nuclear physics because the exact nature of the nuclear forces is not known. We do not have such a straightforward situation as in the case of the Coulomb force between two charged particles. For that reason nuclear physics developed along semiempirical lines, with little commitment to any particular type of nuclear force. Fortunately, it soon became clear that many properties of the nucleus can be discussed and understood without making specific assumptions about the exact mathematical form of the law of interaction between two nucleons. The reason for this is in the very nature of the nuclear forces; they are of such short range that it hardly matters how one specifies them over such a small distance as long as sufficiently large magnitudes are chosen to agree with the data.

Even without penetrating into the nucleus and determining its detailed structure we can derive certain of its properties from the empirical data, and then use these properties to draw conclusions about the structure. Thus, we have very accurate experimental data concerning the masses of the various nuclei. From this we can obtain the binding energies of the different nuclei, on the assumption that all nuclei are constructed of protons and neutrons; this then permits us to analyze the stability of these nuclei. As we have stated in our discussion of Fermi's work in nuclear physics, the binding energy of a nucleus is equal to the work that is needed to separate (to large distances) all the protons and neutrons from each other, that is, to disrupt the nucleus entirely. Put differently, it is the energy that is released (in the form of γ rays, electrons, neutrinos, and positrons) when all the neutrons and protons come together to form a nucleus. If the total energy of a group of nucleons when they come very close together (within nuclear distances) is negative, these particles form a stable nucleus; if this energy is not negative, no stable nucleus is formed. The more negative this energy is (potential energy is negative and kinetic energy is positive), the more stable will be the nucleus that is formed.

To calculate the binding energies of nuclei one need only have accurate values for their masses and compare them with the sum of the masses of the individual nucleons of which they are composed. If the mass of the nucleus is smaller than the sum of a comparable number of free protons and neutrons, the nucleus is stable, otherwise it is not stable. This follows from Einstein's famous discovery of the equivalence of mass and energy, $E = mc^2$.

If one now has a fairly accurate picture of the binding energies of the various nuclei, particularly in relationship to their atomic weights, one can see how these binding energies increase as the atomic weight increases, and one can make important deductions about the over-all nature of nuclear forces and the way in which the nucleons are distributed inside the nucleus of an atom. These points are very beautifully and clearly explained in the excerpt from Heisenberg's book *Nuclear Physics* that follows. Thus, from the fact that the binding energy per nucleon remains the same as we go to heavier nuclei, Heisenberg points out that one may assume that the nucleons inside a nucleus interact (to a very good approximation) only with their nearest neighbors. This is generally referred to as the saturation of nuclear forces. Moreover, since the volume of the nucleus is proportional to the number of nucleons, one may further conclude that the nucleons are spread out uniformly throughout the nucleus. This leads to the famous liquid drop model of the nucleus, first introduced by Bohr, which has proved so useful in explaining nuclear fission and nuclear transformations in general.

ᴏᴏᴏᴏᴏᴏᴏ

HEISENBERG

The Normal States of Atomic Nuclei [1]

THE BINDING ENERGY OF THE NUCLEI

OF THE QUESTIONS MENTIONED AT the conclusion of the previous lecture, let us discuss first the one concerning the forces which are operative between the building blocks of the nucleus and hold these particles together. This question may be formulated as follows: What physical magnitude or what property of the atom determines its stability? One might be inclined to think, at first, that this question is a difficult one, and that in order to answer it, we must be familiar with the entire mechanical system represented by an atomic nucleus, in all its details. However, fortunately, this is not the case. There are a few fundamental laws which enable us to discuss the stability and other general properties of a system even though we may be ignorant of the nature of the forces acting within it, as well as of the details of its structure. These are the well-known laws of the conservation of mass, energy, etc., which state that these things can neither be created out of nothing nor be annihilated. Those laws which are of primary significance here, are the laws of the conservation of energy, of electric charge, and of angular momentum.

We shall begin with the law of the conservation of energy. Let us assume that it is possible to employ certain forces so as actually to remove a particle from a nucleus (which latter consists of protons and neutrons). We may make this theoretically possible by the naïve assumption that we can actually seize this particle and transport it to a point far away from

---

[1] Werner Heisenberg, *Nuclear Physics* (New York: Philosophical Library, 1953), pp. 66–80, 90–103.

the nucleus. Since the particle was originally firmly bound to the nucleus, it is now attracted by it, so that a certain amount of work is required in order to remove it; in other words, energy must be introduced into the system. Now, according to the energy laws, this work, this imported energy, is quite independent of the method employed to remove the particle. Therefore it follows that every particle is bound within the nucleus by a definite quantity of energy, and this quantity of energy can be calculated if it is somehow possible to ascertain the quantity of energy of the system before and after the removal of the particle. Let us now proceed to define the concept of the *binding energy* of a nucleus. This term stands for that change in nuclear energy which takes place when the constituent parts of the nucleus—originally far away from each other—are combined to form that nucleus. Since the reverse of this process, the breaking up of the nucleus, requires an expenditure of energy—in other words, energy must be applied to the nucleus—the nucleus must lose energy in the process of its formation. Therefore, the binding energy of an atomic nucleus is always a negative quantity, by definition. Naturally, the more stable a nucleus is, the more difficult it is to split it into its constituent parts, and the greater is the quantity of work that is necessary for this purpose. Therefore, stability increases with the absolute magnitude of the (negative) binding energy, and thus, strictly mathematically, the smaller the binding energy, the greater is the stability of the nucleus. For this reason, when speaking of a greater or smaller binding energy of a nucleus, we usually refer to its absolute magnitude. In this sense, the greater is the binding energy of a nucleus, the greater is its stability.

Since we are still unfamiliar with the details of nuclear structure, we are unable to calculate the binding energies from the nuclear properties. We must therefore attempt, conversely, to ascertain the magnitudes of binding energies by other methods, in order to use them as a basis for drawing conclusions about the properties of the nucleus.

The simplest example of a nucleus containing more than one particle is the deuteron, the hydrogen nucleus of mass number 2 which consists of 1 proton and 1 neutron. When such a nucleus is formed from these two component parts, the same quantity of energy must be liberated which would be necessary to break it up. Thus we start out from a state in which the proton and the neutron are still in a state of rest, far away from each other, and exert practically no force on each other. Let the quantity of energy present, under these conditions, within the system constituted by these two particles, be called 0. (The choice of zero for the potential energy of a system is arbitrary, and this choice may always be made in the most expedient manner.) As soon as the particles have combined in a deuteron, the energy of the system has decreased by the absolute magnitude of its binding energy. If we manage to measure in some way the energy content of a deuteron, we can ascertain the magnitude of its binding energy from the difference in energy before and after the joining of its constituent parts, and we can use it as a basis for reaching a conclusion concerning the stability of this nucleus.

We can proceed by the same method and add, let us say, another proton. This gives us the binding energy of the helium nucleus $_2He^3$. And we could continue in the same manner, step by step, to ascertain the magnitude of the binding energy of every nucleus.

The physicist customarily measures energy in *ergs* (the erg is a unit of the centimetre-gramme-second system), whereas the engineer measures it in foot-pounds or, e.g. kilowatt-hours. For thermal energies he uses the *calorie* as a unit. Thus, the different branches of physics and technical science use those units, which are most suitable for the field in question because they are designed for the orders of magnitude of energy generally encountered in that particular field, so that the energy units are neither so small nor so big as to be unwieldy or inconvenient to work with. The same principle applies to atomic physics. Atomic physicists often make use of charged particles, electrons, accelerated by high voltage, in order to measure the binding energies of electrons. Therefore, in this case the unit of energy is that quantity of energy which is gained by an electron—or in general, by any particle which carries one elementary quantum of electric charge—in passing through a potential drop of 1 volt. This energy unit is called the *electron-volt* (*ev*). It is a very convenient unit to use when dealing with extranuclear atomic structure, for it is more or less of the same order of magnitude as the binding energies of the structure. But the binding energy of the nuclear particles is about one million times greater. Therefore, in nuclear physics it is customary to use a million times this unit—1 million ev = 1 *Mev*. One Mev is the energy which a particle carrying one elementary quantum of electricity gains on dropping through a potential difference of 1 million volts. However, it is still a very small quantity when compared with 1 erg, viz:

$$1 \, \text{Mev} = 1 \cdot 6 \cdot 10^{-6} \, \text{erg}.$$

We have just mentioned the energy which is liberated when a proton and a neutron combine in a deuteron. As a matter of fact, it is possible to measure this energy very well by actually producing this phenomenon. A source of neutrons is required for this purpose. Modern experimental physics has such sources available. Of course, it is true that during the process of their production, neutrons move at very high velocities and must first be slowed down in order to be brought nearly to rest, so as to be capable of combining with hydrogen atoms from this state of rest. We therefore shoot them through some substance which contains hydrogen.

The neutrons collide with very many hydrogen atoms, and as a result of these collisions, they gradually lose most of their kinetic energy, except for a very small quantity which corresponds to the temperature of that particular substance. They end up with a so-called thermal velocity. In this state they are caused to combine with protons.

In this process, the binding energy of the deuteron is liberated, and in conformity with the law of the conservation of energy, it must still exist somewhere—in other words, it must go somewhere, in some form. The most logical assumption is that it leaves in the form of an electromagnetic radiation, namely, as gamma radiation of an extremely short wavelength. It is therefore to be expected that the formation of each deuteron, from one proton and one neutron, is associated with the emission of a gamma-ray photon very rich in energy. The relationship of the energy E of this photon to its frequency v is determined by Planck's formula, $E = hv$, where h is Planck's constant. The energy E is thus identical with the amount of the binding energy of the deuteron. This gamma radiation can actually be observed. Since we know how to measure the frequency v, it is actually possible to measure the binding energy of a deuteron. It amounts to $2 \cdot 3$ Mev. One might surmise that this energy is radiated in the form of several photons, rather than as a single one. However, it can be proved that such a process is actually far more improbable than the emission of one single photon.

There is, however, another, simpler method available for acquiring knowledge concerning the binding energy of atomic nuclei. According to Einstein's theory of relativity, there is a simple relationship between the mass of a body and its energy content. A relationship of this kind was known, in a special form, in pre-relativistic days, too; it follows from the electro-dynamics of moving objects. Hasenöhrl had already pointed out that the radiation enclosed in a cavity had a seemingly inert mass m, proportional to the energy of the system, m being proportional to E/c^2, where c is the velocity of light. But he failed to compute the proportionality factor correctly. The relationship between energy and mass was made clear by the theory of relativity, which—this is the decisive point—raised it to the status of a universal natural law, applicable not only to the theory of radiation, but to every other branch of physics as well. In other words, the following relation is true universally:

$$m = \frac{E}{c^2}$$

The meaning of this equation is: Any system having the energy content E has a mass m commensurate with this energy content, and the quantity of this mass is E/c^2. This conclusion has rather strange consequences. For instance, when a clock is being wound, it must become slightly heavier because energy is being stored in its spring. But the quantities of energy in this case are so small as to make the increase in the mass of the clock too minute to be capable of being demonstrated. The mass E/c^2 is much too small in comparison with the mass of the clock itself.

But this relationship between energy and mass can be put to practical use in nuclear physics, where the stored-up energy is of appreciable magnitude compared with nuclear masses. Expressed in the form $E = mc^2$, this relationship enables us to calculate the energy content, E, of a system from its mass, m. The velocity of light is known; it is almost exactly 300,000 km. per second, i.e. 3×10^{10} cm. per second. In atomic nuclei, the orders of magnitude are totally different from those met with in the above example of winding up a clock. It is true that the binding energies of nuclei are very small, but so are their masses too. Therefore, the mass $m = E/c^2$ is no longer negligibly small in comparison with the masses of the nuclei themselves. Consequently, any change taking place in the nuclei as a result of changes in energy content can be measured with a considerable degree of accuracy. The application of the above formula to atomic nuclei confirms at the same time the important relationship it expresses.

Since energy is liberated when a deuteron is formed from a proton and a neutron, the mass of the deuteron must be less than the sum total of the masses of the proton and the neutron while these two particles still had a separate existence. This must apply to every nucleus composed of N neutrons and Z protons. This statement can be expressed in the form of an equation as follows:

$$M_{nucleus} = Nm_{neutron} + Zm_{proton} - \frac{|E|}{c^2}$$

where $|E|$ is the binding energy, taken as a positive magnitude, of the nucleus, which in the case of the deuteron is liberated in the form of a photon.

It is convenient to use the above equation in a slightly modified form, referring it to the neutral atom, i.e. to the nucleus plus the extranuclear atomic structure, as a whole, instead of the nucleus alone. In this case, the hydrogen atom of mass number 1, with its one electron, must be substituted for the proton. As a result, the masses appearing on both sides of [the] equation increase by the mass of the Z electrons possessed by the entire atom, on the one hand, and by the Z protons, on the other. The equation then will read:

$$M_{atom} = Nm_{neutron} + Zm_{H \, atom} - \frac{|E|}{c^2}$$

From this equation we can compute the binding energy of a nucleus if we know exactly the mass of the atom in question, the mass of the neutron and the mass of the hydrogen atom.

The mass of an atom is thus always $|E|/c^2$ less than the sum of the masses of its component parts. This difference in mass is called the *mass defect* of the nucleus. It equals $|E|/c^2$, and therefore:

$$mass\ defect = \frac{|E|}{c^2} = Nm_{\ neutron} + Zm_{\ H\ atom} - M_{\ atom}$$

Atomic masses are usually expressed in terms of the standard physical atomic mass unit (*a.m.u.*) which is approximately equal to the mass of a hydrogen atom, or of a neutron; it is exactly $\frac{1}{16}$ of the mass of the oxygen isotope $_8O^{16}$. The mass defects are of the order of magnitude of $\frac{1}{1,000}$ a.m.u., and therefore it is customary to express them in units of $\frac{1}{1,000}$ a.m.u. (a.m.u.$^{-3}$). The energy equivalent of 1 a.m.u.$^{-3}$, i.e. 1 a.m.u.$^{-3} \times c^2$, happens to differ only slightly from the energy unit 1 Mev. To be exact:

1 a.m.u.$^{-3}$ is the equivalent of $0 \cdot 93$ Mev.

Accordingly, the binding energies of nuclei are also of the order of magnitude of 1 Mev.

Thus the physicist has two completely independent processes available for determining the binding energies: He can measure them directly, or can compute them from the mass defects. In the latter case, it is essential, of course, to be able to determine the masses of the atoms to a high degree of accuracy, in order to deduce the binding energy from them, for we are dealing with minute differences, measurable in $\frac{1}{1,000}$ths of the masses only. Let it suffice here to say that this is accomplished with the aid of the *mass spectrograph*, an apparatus first developed by Aston. In the mass spectrograph, charged atoms are caused to pass through electric and magnetic fields, where they are deflected. As we have already seen, the extent of their deflections depends on the ratio of their charge e to their mass m, as well as on their velocity. The mass spectrograph is designed so that only particles having a certain velocity are singled out and become the objects of observation. The ratio e/m can then be determined, and since the charge e of the particles is known, their mass m can be computed— or, to be more exact, their mass, m, can be compared with the mass of the oxygen isotope $_8O^{16}$, which is exactly $16 \cdot 000$ a.m.u. by definition. For the calculation of the binding energies, we need also the exact masses of the hydrogen atom and the neutron. The mass of the hydrogen atom is $1 \cdot 00813$ a.m.u., the mass of the neutron is $1 \cdot 00895$ a.m.u.

Let us now consider, quantitatively, the changes in mass when a deuterium atom is formed. Before the formation of this atom, there was an individual hydrogen atom, $_1H^1$, and an individual neutron, $_0n^1$; after the combination of these two, there is a deuterium atom, $_1D^2$, and a free photon, hv. This finding can be expressed by the following formula:

$$_1H^1 + {}_0n^1 \rightarrow {}_1D^2 + hv$$

Now the mass of a deuterium atom is $2 \cdot 0147$ a.m.u., whereas the sum of the masses of the hydrogen atom and the neutron amounts to $1 \cdot 00813 + 1 \cdot 00895 = 2 \cdot 0171$ a.m.u. The mass of the deuterium atom is actually smaller than the sum of the masses of its component parts, and this difference is the mass defect, which amounts to $0 \cdot 0024$ a.m.u. ($2 \cdot 4$ a.m.u.$^{-3}$). But expressed in terms of its energy equivalent, this mass defect represents a binding energy of about $2 \cdot 2$ Mev, which is exactly the energy released in the form of a photon, as we have already pointed out. Thus we see that there are two totally independent methods for the calculation of the binding energy, and both methods yield the same answer, and therefore provide the best possible proof of the truth of the principle of the equivalence of mass and energy. This is an especially important fact, for here we are not dealing with electric fields, with reference to which this principle was well known even in pre-relativistic times, but with fields of a totally different nature.

The findings just discussed show also why the atomic weights of the elements are not integral multiples of a basic unit, as Prout had conjectured. In the first place, the mass of the proton and the mass of the neutron differ slightly from each other. Furthermore, when they combine, a fraction of the sum total of their masses disappears; this fraction corresponds to their binding energy. So even if the mass of the proton were exactly equal to the mass of the neutron, the atomic weights of the elements would still not be integral multiples of a basic unit. This explains the slight deviations from integral numbers in the atomic weights of the lighter elements. But the very considerable deviations of the atomic weights of the heavier elements must be explained in another way. These deviations are more apparent than real and are due to the fact that the natural elements are, mostly, mixtures of various isotopes. Each isotope consists of atoms with a nucleus of a specific type, the mass number of which is almost exactly an integer. But the average mass number of this mixture of isotopes is not an integer.

Thus we have established the desired criterion for the stability of a nucleus. A nucleus holds together because an amount of work would be required in order to break it up into its component parts. The work required is a measure of the binding energy, which, in turn, is equal to the mass defect of the nucleus, expressed in terms of energy. A nucleus would not be stable if it were possible to break it up without doing any work. We must, however, add that the other conservation laws must be taken into consideration too. According to the law of the conservation of electric charge, an atom cannot undergo any change that would alter the total charge present in the system. Hence, the change of a proton into a neutron, or of a neutron into a proton, cannot take place in the nucleus without compensation. Otherwise, many atoms which are actually considered stable would have to be unstable. There is, for instance, a boron nucleus having the (not exact) mass number 12, and also a carbon nucleus having the mass number 12. The boron nucleus consists of 7 neutrons and 5 protons, whereas the carbon nucleus has 6 protons and 6 neutrons. Their respective symbols are $_5B^{13}$ and $_6C^{13}$. The mass of the boron nucleus, however, is slightly greater than that of the carbon nucleus. The difference is $0 \cdot 013$ a.m.u., and consequently, the difference in binding energy is about 12 Mev. The carbon nucleus has a greater mass defect than the boron nucleus, so that its component parts are bound together more tightly than those of the boron nucleus. We can assume, therefore, that the boron nucleus is unstable and changes spontaneously into a carbon nucleus. This transmutation would liberate energy to the extent of 12 Mev. But this process can occur only when a neutron of the boron nucleus changes into a proton. However, by virtue of the law of conservation of electric charge, such a process is possible only if the newly formed elementary quantum of positive electricity is compensated for by the simultaneous formation of an elementary quantum of negative electricity and the latter removed from the nucleus. This could take place through the emission of an electron simultaneously with the change of the neutron into a proton. Actually, this boron nucleus is not a stable structure, but a radioactive one. It emits electrons—in other words, negative beta rays —and changes into a carbon nucleus.

Nevertheless, this transformation would not be possible if the law of the conservation of angular momentum did not hold. As we have mentioned before, the angular momentum, or *spin,* of both a proton and a neutron is $\hbar/2$, to be considered positive or negative according to the spatial orientation of the axis of rotation. Therefore, the angular momentum of a nucleus composed of an even number of particles is always an even multiple of $\hbar/2$. Both the carbon nucleus and the boron nucleus consist of 12 particles; consequently, the nuclear spin of each must be an integer multiple of h. But pursuant to the law of the conservation of electric charge, an electron must be emitted during the transmutation process, and this electron, too, has an angular momentum (electronic spin) of $\hbar/2$. Therefore, the resulting carbon nucleus would retain an angular momentum (nuclear spin), the value of which is an odd multiple of $\hbar/2$. In this case, therefore, the angular momenta involved would not balance. But in this predicament we must remember that when we studied natural beta radiation, we found that similar difficulties of balancing the energies furnished us with a clue to the existence of the neutrino, ejected simultaneously with the emission of the electron. The neutrino, obviously, accounts for the conservation of the angular momentum. The electrons emitted by the boron nucleus display a continuous series of energy values; this fact leads us to the assumption that a neutrino is emitted simultaneously in this case, too. The facts that the boron nucleus is really unstable and that it eventually changes into a carbon nucleus through the emission of an electron and a neutrino, point to the conclusion that the neutrino also has an angular momentum or spin value of $\hbar/2$, opposite in direction, or mathematical sign, to that of the electron, so that it compensates for the electron.

We have now gained a general view of the conclusions which can be drawn from the three conservation laws with respect to the stability of the nucleus. Our findings may be summed up briefly as follows: The nucleus of an atom will always change spontaneously into another nucleus if this process, firstly liberates energy, and secondly, is compatible with the laws of conservation of charge and angular momentum. It is true, of course, that this spontaneous transformation may occur after the lapse of a considerable period of time only, in other words, that its probability may be very small. But if either one of the conditions just mentioned is not given, the nucleus in question is a stable one.

NUCLEAR STRUCTURE

The conservation laws have enabled us to reach far-reaching conclusions concerning the stability of atoms, without resorting to any hypothesis about the conditions within the nucleus or the forces operative in it. Now let us attempt to formulate conclusions concerning the internal structure of the nucleus, on the ground of experiments, independently of specific assumptions about these internal forces. How are the protons and neutrons distributed within the nucleus? Can we compare a nucleus with, say, a drop of liquid, in which the molecules are packed with uniform density? Or should the nucleus be compared rather to a globular star cluster, in the centre of which the stars are extremely close to one another, but more widely separated with greater distances from the centre?

In this connection, the mass defects render a very important service. From them we can calculate the binding energy, and we find that when reckoned for individual particles within the atom, the binding energy is approximately the same in all atoms. The lighter atoms—up to about aluminium—where the absolute magnitude is smaller, are an exception to this rule. In other atoms, the binding energy of each nuclear particle is always between 6 and 9 Mev. It seems, therefore, that all nuclear particles are bound more or less equally firmly.

We may draw a further conclusion from the size of the nucleus. We can determine, approximately, the diameter of a nucleus from the deflection of alpha particles in the substance in question, by ascertaining what fraction of them shows so strong a deflection that it cannot be accounted for by the effects of the external electric field of the nucleus, but can only be explained by direct collisions with the nucleus. The larger the nucleus, the more frequently will such collisions occur. These experiments have shown, for instance, that the diameter of a uranium nucleus consisting of 238 particles is about four times as large as that of the helium nucleus which consists of 4 particles. Their respective volumes are, therefore, as 1 to 4^3, in other words, the volume of the uranium nucleus is about sixty-four times the volume of the helium nucleus. However, the uranium nucleus has about sixty times as many component particles as the helium nucleus.

These two facts—the approximate equality of the binding energies of the individual particles, and the approximate proportionality of the number of particles to the volume of the nucleus—warrant the conclusion that the protons and neutrons are distributed approximately uniformly throughout the nucleus, because if this were not the case, their binding energies would show considerable differences, both in individual parts of a nucleus and in different nuclear types. Moreover, this fact, in conjunction with the proportionality of the number of particles and the volume, indicates that this density distribution is the same in all nuclei, except, again, for the very lightest atoms. Therefore, we may speak of a homogeneous nuclear substance in all nuclei, which consists of a mixture of protons and neutrons packed with an approximately constant density. There is a slight difference here between different atomic species, with respect to the ratio of the number of neutrons to the number of protons.

Therefore, we obtain a very accurate model of a nucleus by likening it to a drop of liquid. Just as water droplets of different sizes can form from water molecules, so drops of nuclear matter of different sizes—the different atomic nuclei—can form from protons and neutrons. This liquid-drop model has exactly the properties which can be observed in an atomic nucleus. For the molecules are packed with equal density of distribution throughout a drop of liquid, and all the molecules are bound together in it by the same quantity of energy. The knowledge of the existence of a universal, homogeneous nuclear substance facilitates greatly our understanding of nuclear structure.

But this liquid drop has also other, still more subtle characteristics, and now we must investigate whether these have their analogies in the nucleus. Actually, in a liquid drop, not all molecules are bound together equally firmly. The molecules on the surface are linked with the others on one side only, and therefore, on the whole they are less tightly bound than the others. This explains the phenomenon of *surface tension*. Certain considerations concerning energy, which are absolutely analogous to those which we have already applied to atomic nuclei, explain the fact that this surface tension causes these drops to assume a spherical shape. For the surface energy of a drop is proportional to the area of the surface, and it consequently tends to make the surface area as small as possible. We must assume the presence of such surface tension in atomic nuclei, too. As a result of the lesser cohesion of the particles situated on the surface, this surface tension must produce a decrease of the total binding energy, and consequently, of the average energy per particle as well. Just as in a liquid drop, the surface tension is the cause of the spherical shape of atomic nuclei, too.

There is, however, one essential difference between nuclear matter and a liquid. The liquid consists of molecules which are electrically neutral, whereas the nuclear matter contains not only neutrons but electrically charged protons, too. Therefore, our analogy must be one between nuclei and liquid drops containing electrically charged molecules with forces of repulsion operating between them. There is also an electric force of repulsion present in the nuclei of atoms. . . .

The Nuclear Forces

GENERAL PROPERTIES OF THE NUCLEAR FIELD

THE COHESION OF PROTONS AND neutrons within the atomic nucleus is ensured by forces, to which we have referred as *nuclear forces,* although we have not yet discussed their nature. The electric forces of repulsion, which are also operative in the nucleus, exert a purely disruptive effect. What can we learn today from the experiments on the nature of these nuclear forces? Let us first study briefly the form which an answer to this question must take. Assuming that we did not as yet know what electric forces were, how could we begin to explain their nature? We could begin by stating that electric charges mutually repel each other, with a force which decreases inversely as the square of the distance between them. According to the knowledge gained in the early part of the nineteenth century, we could add that a fundamental relationship exists between electric and magnetic forces—e.g.: varying electric forces always generate magnetic forces, and vice versa. Moreover, we might add that the phenomena of light, which used to be regarded as something of a special nature, are among these electromagnetic phenomena, and are simply nothing but electromagnetic waves. The next step would be to note that in certain experiments light appears not as a wave, but as flying particles, in other words, in the shape of photons, and thus we would discover a relationship between the electromagnetic field and these photons. A truly exhaustive description of electromagnetic forces can, however, be given solely with the aid of mathematical equations, expressing how electromagnetic forces change and spread. A complete picture of the "nature" of these phenomena is supplied only by Maxwell's equations in combination with the equations of the quantum theory.

But as for the nuclear forces we have not got to them yet. Nevertheless, we can already form a picture of them, which is correct qualitatively at least and includes as many details as the picture of the electromagnetic forces—except for the exact mathematical formulae.

The first question to arise here is: How does the force operating between two particles in the atomic nucleus depend on their distance from each other? Is it perhaps also in inverse proportion to the square of this distance? The simplest object available for the study of this problem is the deuteron; we inquire about the force which binds a proton and a neutron in a deuteron. Once this force is known, we have a good prospect of comprehending the cohesion of other nuclei. The force in question cannot possibly be electrical in character, if for no other reason than that the neutron carries no electric charge. Furthermore, electric forces would be much too weak to account for the considerable energies which result from the mass defects.

We have already pointed out that when a deuteron is formed out of a proton and a neutron, the binding energy is liberated as a photon, with an energy of $2 \cdot 2$ Mev.—in other words, as electromagnetic energy. This means that a process is taking place in which energy is converted from one form to another—the non-electromagnetic energy of the nuclear field into the electromagnetic energy of radiation. Therefore, it follows that in common with all other types of energy, the energy of the nuclear field possesses the capacity of being transformed into other forms of energy.

We can gain some insight into the dependence of nuclear forces on the distance by observing the deflection of flying neutrons when they pass near a proton [Fig. 89–1]. Modern physics has access to sources of neutrons. All that is necessary is simply to send the neutrons through a hydrogen-containing substance, for example, a hydrocarbon, such as paraffin, or water, to cause them to be deflected from their straight paths. The magnitude of the deflection of a neutron depends, naturally, on the distance of its path from the proton. This distance is more frequently a greater than a smaller one. Instances of neutrons passing close to a proton are very rare. If the forces decrease relatively slowly with the distance— as, for instance, in the case of electric charges—even though the distance may be considerable, the neutrons will still be deflected a little. It would indeed be observed that a very large number of neutrons are deflected, but the deflection is always very slight. As a matter of fact, large deflections are seldom observed. If, on the other hand, the force diminishes rapidly with the distance, the majority of the neutrons are not deflected at all. In the case of the deflected neutrons—those few which pass sufficiently close to the proton—both small and large deflections may be observed to occur with comparable frequency.

P—Proton
N—Neutron

Fig. 89–1. Deflection of a neutron in the neighborhood of a proton.

Such experiments have demonstrated that the force between neutron and proton diminishes with the distance more rapidly than is the case with electric forces of attraction and repulsion. The degree of accuracy of the measurements does not as yet permit us to formulate exactly the law of distance. Nevertheless, we can state that the force is becoming already very small at a distance of 5×10^{-13} cm. This means that the force between proton and neutron has an extremely short range, and in this respect it is very different from an electric force.

Instead of studying the force, we may base our considerations on the potential energy which a neutron has within the field of a proton (or vice versa). When the distance is a very large one, we arbitrarily assign to this energy the magnitude 0. At finite distances, it has a negative magnitude. Due to the limited range, the potential energy is practically 0 for any but a very small distance. [Fig. 89–2] shows an approximate curve of the potential energy as a function of the distance r. This energy increases rapidly from high negative magnitudes until it reaches the vicinity of 0, which it then approaches asymptotically. Dealing with small distances, the potential energy curve can be computed indirectly from the mass defect of the deuteron. In addition to its potential energy, the system has also a kinetic energy, since the proton and neutron reciprocally vibrate with reference to each other, with a continuous transformation of kinetic energy into potential energy, and vice versa. The sum total of these energies always equals the binding energy, $2 \cdot 2$ Mev., which is shown in [Fig. 89–2] as a horizontal line. The average magnitude of the kinetic energy can be estimated, for instance, in accordance with the uncertainty principle, from the diameter of the deuteron. The accuracy of our knowledge of the exact location of this object of finite diameter goes hand in hand with a proportionate inaccuracy of our knowledge of its velocity, and the squared velocity times one-half the mass gives us the magnitude of the average kinetic energy. Once we know both the kinetic energy and the total energy, we can calculate from them the potential energy. [Fig. 89–2] is the result of considerations of this nature.

Short-range forces are known to exist in nature elsewhere, too; the most important example is exhibited by the chemical forces, the so-called *valences* (unless we are dealing with what is called a *polar* combination), in other words, the forces, which, for instance, bind two hydrogen atoms

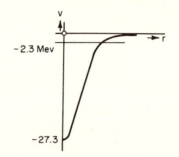

Fig. 89–2. Potential of the force between neutron and proton.

to one oxygen atom in a water molecule. These, too, are short-range forces which are operative actually only when the atoms are in direct contact, but become infinitesimally small as soon as the distance between the atoms increases.

It is due to this extremely short range that in heavier, macroscopic structures we can perceive neither the chemical nor the nuclear forces, whereas electric or magnetic forces are perceptible without any difficulty. The force between two magnetic poles is felt directly by the hand in which a magnet is held, and your hair stands on end as you approach an electrical high-tension apparatus. But chemical forces can never be perceived in this direct fashion, for they are operative over molecular distances only. The same applies to nuclear forces; they cannot be perceived anywhere except in the nuclear phenomena themselves.

This has already supplied us with a certain general view of the nature of the force operative between a proton and a neutron. But what about the force between two protons?

One might surmise, to start with, that electric repulsion only is operative between them, since the force between protons and neutrons would be sufficient in itself to explain both nuclear cohesion and the fact that nuclear matter in a stable state consists of an approximately equal number of protons and neutrons. For if some force were operative between protons and neutrons only, the symmetry would already be guaranteed, to begin with. But experience concerning the deflection of protons by protons proves that forces of attraction are acting between particles of the same kind—in other words, not only between protons but between neutrons, too—which forces of attraction are approximately equal to those acting between protons and neutrons. In the case of two protons the situation is more complicated, because the electric force of repulsion is super-

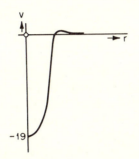

Fig. 89–3. Potential of the force between proton and proton.

imposed on the nuclear force of attraction. But when dealing with very short distances, the force of repulsion is much weaker than the nuclear force, so that in this case, practically, only the latter is operative. However, due to its long range, the electric force continues to be perceptible long after the nuclear force has ceased to be operative. If we draw a diagram of the potential energy of a proton at various distances from another proton, it will look more or less like the one reproduced in [Fig. 89–3]. In fact, up to a distance of the order of 5×10^{-13} cm., the picture is practically identical with the one shown in [Fig. 89–2]. From that point on, however, the potential energy does not approach 0 asymptotically, but passes through 0, rises to positive magnitudes, and only then does it drop asymptotically towards 0. Between two protons there exists what we call a *potential barrier,* a specimen of which will be discussed repeatedly later on.

According to all this, one might surmise that there exists a state in which two individual protons are bound to each other, namely, when their distances from each other are so small that the nuclear force of attraction overcomes the electric force of repulsion. But this is probably never the case. As pointed out before, two particles bound to each other vibrate constantly in relation to each other, even in their normal or ground state, the state of least energy. This "zero-point vibration" is probably so powerful that it makes it impossible for any permanent bond to exist between two individual protons. But the attraction between protons is certain to play an important part in the more complex nuclei.

So now we have obtained our first overall view of nuclear forces. The most important of these is the force of attraction between neutron and proton. There is, furthermore, a force of a similar order of magnitude acting between two protons or two neutrons. The operative range of these nuclear forces diminishes rapidly with the distance, and in this respect they resemble the chemical valency forces, which likewise possess a very short range only.

THE NUCLEAR FORCES AS EXCHANGE FORCES

Let us now continue to formulate our queries in the same way as we did when dealing with the electric forces. Thus our first question will be: Does there exist any analogy permitting us to link nuclear forces with particles in a way similar to that in which we link electric forces with photons? . . . The building blocks of the extranuclear structure of the atom are the electrons which are bound to the nucleus by the electric field. The electric field, in turn, is linked with the photons emitted by the atom when certain changes occur in this extranuclear structure. The building blocks of the nucleus are the neutrons and protons, which are held together by the nuclear field, while in this case the electric field is not a binding but a disruptive factor. Here, too, there are particles emitted by the nucleus as a result of changes in state, and in this case, we must distinguish between different kinds of particles. First, there are the gamma rays or photons. Analogously to the photons originating in the extranuclear atomic structure, these photons are linked to the electric field in the nucleus. In addition to these, there are the electrons and positrons, emitted in nuclear transmutations, and the neutrinos which always accompany them. The latter are similar to photons in many respects. The only difference is that neutrinos have a spin or angular momentum of $\hbar/2$, whereas that of a photon is either 0 or $\hbar$.

It seems logical here to assume that the emission of these particles is linked up with the nuclear force field, somewhat in the same way as is the emission of photons with the electric field in the extranuclear atomic structure. But such an analogy would mean that the force between neutron and proton is transmitted because of the electrons, positrons and neutrinos. A similar linking of certain particles to a field must not be misinterpreted as meaning that the field is composed of such particles. The expression "composed of" always suggests that the field might be conceived, to be, as it were, replaced by such particles. Actually, however, field and particles are, so to speak, merely different aspects of the very same concept, as was discussed earlier, in connection with the extra-nuclear structure of the atom.

The most correct way of expressing the situation is: There is a nuclear field, and in stationary states this nuclear field takes on the aspect of a short-range field, continually diminishing in intensity away from its centre, while in non-stationary processes it takes on the aspect of a wave radiation. The latter can be observed either as a wave radiation or as particles, according to the method of observation employed. We shall attempt to explain this by comparison with the more familiar electric field, by describing the force exerted by one electron upon another in two languages —first, in the language of waves, and then in the language of particles.

We can say, first, that an electron produces an electric field around itself, and that this electric field spreads in conformity with Maxwell's equations. It may act on another electron and create a force on the latter. The corresponding description in terms of the other aspect is: One electron produces a particle, a photon, and this photon is subsequently absorbed by another electron. Thus in the first phrasing we speak of a "production of a field," and in the other of a "production of a particle"; in the first statement, we refer to an "action of a field," in the second one to an "absorption of a photon by a particle." This state of affairs can be expressed schematically as follows:

Wave Aspect: Electron creates field; field acts on another electron.

Particle Aspect: Electron emits photon; photon is absorbed by another electron.

Both statements describe the same event. The first version is familiar to everybody who has ever had any dealings with electric fields. The second one is unfamiliar to most people, because in technical science as well as in macroscopic physics it is always unnecessary to conceive of an electric field as linked to photons. Under atomic conditions, however, this very frequently proves to be a useful expedient. With reference to atomic radiation, it is often more convenient to speak of photons than of spherical waves.

Now let us apply exactly the same type of phraseology to the forces operative between protons and neutrons. First, we can say: The neutron produces a nuclear field, and this field acts on the proton. This is the description in terms of the wave aspect. In the terminology of the particle aspect, our description will be: The neutron produces particles, and these particles are absorbed by the proton. Let us again express this schematically, as follows:

Wave Aspect: Neutron creates field; field acts on proton.

Particle Aspect: Neutron emits electron plus neutrino; electron and neutrino are absorbed by proton.

Interpreting in this manner the force operative between neutron and proton, we see that an exchange of charge is linked with the action of the force. Namely, if in order to exert this force, the neutron must emit an electron and a neutrino, its charge is altered; it changes into a proton. And conversely, a proton changes into a neutron, due to the absorption of an electron and a neutrino. An exactly analogous conversion may occur also when a proton emits a positron and a neutrino, which are then absorbed by the neutron.

Thus, the nuclear forces are associated with an exchange of charged particles, and for this reason, forces of this kind are called *exchange forces*. They are of a very peculiar character, and it is their characteristic feature that their action is linked with an exchange of roles between the two partners. In this respect, therefore, they are totally different from the electric forces. But a close relationship with chemical forces is again evident. Quantum theory has already shown that chemical forces may also

Fig. 89–4. Ion of hydrogen molecule.

be regarded in general as exchange forces. For a similar exchange of charges occurs in the case of chemical forces, too. The simplest example of this is the hydrogen molecule ion, which consists of a hydrogen atom and a hydrogen nucleus [Fig. 89–4]. It is therefore actually a structure composed of two protons with an electron circling around them. This ion is a truly stable structure, and the force which holds it together owes its existence to the circumstance that the one electron revolves at times around one proton, at times around the other one. This means that in this case, too, we find that the force is linked with an exchange of charge—the shift of the electron from one proton to the other.

The concept of "exchange force" can be comprehended most easily on the ground of the following experiment, carried out with the big Lawrence cyclotron in California in 1948. Neutrons of great energy are hurled against protons in a cloud chamber. The paths of the protons after collision become visible in the cloud chamber. In the case of an ordinary force, one would expect the great majority of the neutrons to be deflected to a very slight extent only (since they would not hit the proton exactly in the centre), while the protons would be hurled aside, with a relatively low velocity, at an angle of 90 deg. to the path of the neutrons. But in the case of an exchange force, the neutrons and protons must exchange roles after the collision; in the majority of collisions, the protons must continue along the paths of the oncoming neutrons (since the neutrons have actually been changed into protons) while the neutron is hurled aside at an angle of approximately 90 deg. This is exactly what we actually see in the cloud chamber. . . .

The situation is, however, not quite so simple as we have made it appear. If the analogy of nuclear and electric forces were as we have been supposing, we would be in a position to determine the frequency of the occurrence of beta decay in a manner similar to that employed to determine the frequency of the occurrence of the emission of a photon in the extranuclear structure of the atom. When an extranuclear atomic structure is in an excited state, there exists in it at any given moment a certain probability of the emission of a light ray. By "certain probability" we mean the following: In the wave aspect, the continuous movement of electrons causes a wave radiation to issue forth. In the particle aspect, there exists at any given moment a certain probability of the emission of a photon. These two views of the situation are linked to each other by the fact that the probability of radiation is given by the intensity of the emitted wave. The stronger is the wave, the greater is the probability of radiation, and the shorter-lived is the excited state. The duration of the excited state depends, therefore, on the amplitude of the vibration of the electrons.

The lifetime of a beta-unstable nucleus thus depends on the intensity of the wave radiation issuing forth from it. But if we carry out this computation on the ground of the considerations outlined above, we arrive at lifetimes much shorter than those actually observed. There still exists a discrepancy at this point, and this realization led the Japanese scientist Yukawa to a somewhat modified theory.

Yukawa assumes that between the nuclear field and the electrons, positrons and neutrinos there is still another species of particle, which may be called *Yukawa particle* for the time being. These Yukawa particles are assumed to have a mass several hundred times that of an electron, and to be capable of disintegrating into electrons, positrons and neutrinos, directly or eventually through other decay processes. So, according to Yukawa's theory in nuclear transmutations, such a Yukawa particle should actually be emitted. However, this does not happen, because the Yukawa particle has such a great rest mass that the energy, mc^2, necessary for its formation is not available. But the Yukawa particle can break up (directly, or indirectly through other processes) into electrons and neutrinos, and this happens, in a certain sense, in the moment of its formation, so that on the whole, it is sufficient to provide the energy required for the formation of the light particles, the electron and neutrino. This theory thus regards the process of nuclear transmutation as occurring in several steps. First, the Yukawa particle is formed from the nuclear field —or more correctly, the nuclear field itself is identical with the Yukawa particle, which for lack of sufficient energy for its formation cannot manifest itself as a real particle. Instead, no sooner is it formed than it breaks up into electrons and neutrinos, which then actually leave the nucleus.

If we accept this theory as a working hypothesis—and there is much in it to make it plausible—there arises the question whether the Yukawa particles are perhaps identical with a certain species of particle already observed in cosmic radiation. Actually, the most recent experiments make it extremely probable that the role of the Yukawa particles is played—in part, at any rate—by the heavy mesons (or "π particles") observed by Powell; for in cases of nuclear fission of very high energy, these π particles have been observed to be hurled forth from the nuclei. The π particles . . . are about 275 times as heavy as an electron. According to Powell's observations, they first break up into a light meson and a neutral particle (the latter is probably simply a neutrino). This light meson (its mass is about 213 times the mass of an electron) then breaks up further into an electron and probably two neutral particles. It is recognized here that the emission of electrons and neutrinos can occur by very roundabout ways only, possibly due somehow to the fact that the probability of the occurrence of a beta decay is extraordinarily small compared with the probability of other nuclear changes.

These considerations show also that the problem of the relationship between nuclear forces and the elementary particles regarded as being linked with them is a very complex one, which cannot be solved for many more years to come. At this moment, the only thing we know for certain is that the nuclear forces are, to a considerable extent at any rate, exchange forces, and that there exist unstable elementary particles, the mass of which is between the mass of an electron and the mass of a proton, and which are associated somehow with these nuclear forces. Any further clarification will become possible only when the very high energy nuclear disintegration processes have been investigated much more thoroughly than they have been up to now. . . .

90

ENERGY PRODUCTION
IN STARS

Hans A. Bethe (b. 1906)

Bethe was an international figure in physics when he left Germany as a young man in the early 1930's to teach and work in England, but his most brilliant work was done in the United States after he became professor of physics at Cornell University. At just about that time, 1934, the neutron was discovered, and there began the feverish work in neutron and nuclear physics that dominated all the major laboratories of the world. Bethe at once entered this field with his usual comprehensive approach. His work, theoretical in nature, dealt with the analysis of nuclear forces and the construction of models of light nuclei. One of the first problems he considered (in collaboration with Peierls) was the interaction of a neutron and a proton. Since a neutron-proton pair is the simplest type of compound nucleus that can exist, it plays a generic role in nuclear physics similar to that played by the hydrogen atom in atomic physics, so that its theoretical treatment was therefore very important. Many questions had to be answered before nuclear theory could give a coherent picture of the structure of the nucleus. It was essential to know whether one could use quantum mechanics to describe the behavior of nucleons inside the nucleus just as one uses quantum mechanics outside the nucleus. The neutron-proton complex was the ideal system for studying this problem.

Bethe and Peierls treated this system theoretically by using the usual quantum-mechanical rules and assuming that the neutron and proton interaction can be represented by a simple law. This law was set forth as follows: As long as the neutron and the proton are separated by more than a critical distance (of the order of 10^{-13} cm) they have no influence on each other; if they are closer, there is a constant but very large pull between them. This type of interaction is known as the "rectangular well" and permits a very simple treatment of the problem. In spite of its simplicity, however, this model gives very good results. As Bethe and others have shown, changing the type of interaction (as long as one keeps it very short range and very strong) does not significantly affect the final results. Bethe and Peierls solved the two-body nuclear problem with quantum mechanics and showed that the two-body nuclear system (now known as the deuteron, an isotope of hydrogen) is stable. Many of the properties of the deuteron were derived by Bethe theoretically; this stimulated experimental work by others. In addition, by showing that quantum mechanics is applicable inside the nucleus he opened a new field for theoretical physics.

Although Bethe was not directly interested in astronomy during the decade from 1930 to 1940, his work led to the discovery of the nuclear reactions that generate the radiation of stars similar to the sun. It had been known for a long time that the energy radiated from stars cannot come from ordinary chemical reactions such as ordinary combustion, nor can it be accounted for in most cases by a mechanical process such as a slow but steady gravitational contraction. To begin with, the temperatures inside stars are much too high for the existence of stable molecules, so that molecular reactions such as burning cannot occur. Actually, the amount of combustible material would be so meager that a star could not continue radiating for more than a few thousand years. Second, the release of gravitational energy, at a sufficiently high rate to account for the luminosity of the stars, could have gone on only for a few million years in the past; in the case of the sun, about 30,000,000 years, and in the case of the very luminous stars, such as Capella, a few hundred thousand years. It was therefore necessary to look for some unusual source of energy, and it was clear to every physicist and astronomer, years before the neutron has been discovered and before much was known about the nucleus, that the stellar release of radiant energy involves some kind of subatomic or nuclear process.

In his famous book *The Internal Constitution of the Stars,* which was the first systematic treatment of modern astrophysics, the great British astronomer Sir Arthur Stanley Eddington states:

> It is now generally agreed that the main source of a star's energy is sub-atomic. There appears to be no escape from this conclusion; but since the hypothesis presents many difficulties when we study the details, it is incumbent upon us to examine carefully all alternatives. . . .
>
> In seeking a source of energy other than contraction [gravitational] the first question is whether the energy to be radiated in the future is hidden in the star or whether it is being picked up continuously from outside. Sug-

gestions have been made that the impact of meteoric matter provides the heat or that there is some subtle radiation traversing space which the star picks up. Strong objections may be urged against these hypotheses individually; but it is unnecessary to consider them in detail because they have arisen through a misunderstanding of the nature of the problem. *No source of energy is of any avail unless it liberates energy in the deep interior of the star.*

It is not enough to provide for the external radiation of the star. We must provide for the maintenance of the high internal temperature without which the star would collapse.[1]

In his book Eddington considered various types of subatomic processes and concluded that although energy can be released by the breakdown of the nuclei of atoms as in radioactive decay, the only process that can properly account for the great quantities of energy released by the stars and for their long lives as energy radiators is one in which nuclei are built up from less massive constituents. In this analysis, one can use the Einsteinian principle that mass and energy are equivalent and that when mass is destroyed an equivalent amount of energy is released whose quantity equals the mass destroyed multiplied by the square of the speed of light ($E = mc^2$). Eddington pointed out that if four protons combined or coalesced to form a helium nucleus, energy would be released because the mass of the helium nucleus is about 1 per cent less than the mass of the four free protons.

With the discovery of the neutron it soon became clear to physicists and astronomers alike that the helium nucleus is, indeed, built up from four protons, but just how the process is initiated or maintained inside the stars was not clear until Bethe in the United States and Weizsäcker in Germany began a series of independent investigations. Both of these investigators considered a series of reactions starting with the coalescence of two protons to form a deuteron and then a subsequent set of reactions ending in the formation of helium, after two other protons had been captured. This series of reactions is now known as the proton-proton chain and has been thoroughly and accurately investigated by various physicists and astronomers. The first complete analysis of the proton-proton chain was made in 1938 by Bethe and C. Critchfield, one of his students. In this paper they laid down the general procedure for an analysis of this type of reaction. The experimental data for certain physical parameters at that time were still in considerable error, and Bethe concluded that the proton-proton chain can account for only a small amount of the energy emitted by a star like the sun (the prototype of what astronomers call main se-

---

[1] Arthur S. Eddington, *The Internal Constitution of the Stars* (New York: Dover, 1930), pp. 288.

quence stars). He therefore sought other types of nuclear reactions that can account for the total energy generation.

Bethe found a solution of this intriguing and important problem after attending a meeting of the American Physical Society in Washington, part of which was devoted to the problem of stellar energy. Returning home on the train from this meeting, he analyzed all the interactions of the light nuclei with protons that can occur at the high temperatures found in stars, starting with helium and advancing to, but excluding, carbon. He was immediately struck by the speed with which all such nuclei interact with protons and ultimately end up as ordinary helium. This could mean only one thing. These light nuclei could not be the source of stellar energy because they are changed into helium so fast that stars could not exist for more than a few thousand years.

But, the situation with carbon proved quite different. Although the carbon nucleus, like lighter nuclei, combines with a proton at temperatures found in stellar interiors in a relatively short time, astronomically speaking, this is only the first step in a cycle of six nuclear reactions involving three other protons in which the carbon nucleus finally reappears and the four protons are coalesced into a helium nucleus. This is the famous carbon cycle, discovered by Bethe, which he described in 1938 in a short note to the *Physical Review*. The note follows this commentary.

At that time, the difficulty in accounting for stellar energy generation in terms of nuclear reactions lay in explaining how positively charged protons can be absorbed by the positively charged nuclei. Even in the case of light nuclei, such as lithium, beryllium, boron, and carbon, the charge on the nuclei is sufficiently large to repel free protons very strongly. This repulsion can, of course, be overcome if the protons hit the nuclei with sufficient kinetic energy. But even when the temperature inside the stars is many millions of degrees, the average speed of the free protons relative to the nuclei is too small for this to happen. However, because of the statistical distribution of the proton velocities about the average, there are always some moving with very high speeds, and hence with enough kinetic energy to penetrate into the nucleus. In stellar interiors like the sun, such high-speed protons are few in number, and energy released in this way would be inadequate to account for stellar radiation, except for considerations introduced by quantum mechanics and the wave properties of particles such as protons.

It had already been shown by G. Gamow in his quantum-mechanical explanation of the emission of α particles from radioactive nuclei, and also by Atkinson and Houtermans, that the wave properties of protons enable them to penetrate into charged nuclei even when these protons do not have enough kinetic energy to overcome the nuclear Coulomb repulsion. Bethe used this wave picture to calculate the probability for protons to penetrate into the various nuclei that take part in the carbon cycle. In this way he obtained a formula for the rate at which the carbon cycle proceeds in stellar interiors and showed that at the temperatures to be expected near the center of stars like the sun, the carbon cycle should be responsible for the generation of most of the energy. In fact, with the aid of the carbon cycle, Bethe and his collaborators obtained a theoretical model of the sun that corresponds fairly well with what one might expect the interior conditions to be.

This was done before World War II when some of the nuclear data were not very accurate. With the advances of postwar nuclear techniques, it became clear that the formula both for the carbon cycle and for the proton-proton chain had to be revised. The proton-proton chain is now known to be far more effective in releasing energy in stars like the sun than the carbon cycle. However, both the carbon cycle and the proton-proton chain operate simultaneously in stellar interiors; the latter is the dominant process in stars that are as luminous or less luminous than the sun and the former plays the major role in the stars that are hotter and more luminous than the sun. In any case, Bethe's pioneering work with the proton-proton chain and the carbon cycle laid the foundation for the great advances that have occurred in the last two decades in our knowledge of the structure and the evolution of stars.

There is an interesting point in connection with this work that Bethe mentions in the last paragraph of the short paper that follows. He notes that all the reactions of the light nuclei with protons ultimately lead to the end product helium. Since helium itself does not react with protons, the relative abundances of heavier elements above helium cannot change inside the stars on the main sequence. From this he concluded that the so-called *Aufbau* hypothesis, which had been advanced by many physicists and astronomers, and which proposes the idea that all the heavy elements are built up in successive stages from protons, must be discarded. Bethe reasoned at that time that there was no stable nucleus of atomic weight 5, so that there was no way to jump the gap from ordinary helium to lithium, and other heavier elements, by proton capture. We now know that when enough hydrogen (about 12 per cent) has been transformed into helium in the center core of stars like the sun, the helium core begins to contract to such an extent that the core temperature rises very rapidly until a temperature close to 100,000,000 degrees is reached. At this high temperature a new type of nuclear reaction (first described and analyzed by E. Salpeter) takes place. Three helium nuclei (α particles) coalesce to form an ordinary carbon nucleus. From then on, as the temperature in the core of the star increases, nuclear reactions involving helium nuclei and heavier nuclei occur, and increasingly heavy nuclei are formed, thus vindicating the *Aufbau* hypothesis.

oooooooo

BETHE

Energy Production in Stars [2]

IN SEVERAL RECENT PAPERS, THE present author has been quoted for investigations on the nuclear reactions responsible for the energy production in stars. As the publication of this work which was carried out last spring has been unduly delayed, it seems worth while to publish a short account of the principal results.

The most important source of stellar energy appears to be the reaction cycle:

$$C^{12} + H^1 = N^{13} \ (a), N^{13} = C^{13} + \epsilon^+ \ (b)$$
$$C^{13} + H^1 = N^{14} \ (c)$$
$$N^{14} + H^1 = O^{15} \ (d), O^{15} = N^{15} + \epsilon^+ \ (e) \tag{1}$$
$$N^{15} + H^1 = C^{12} + He^4 \ (f).$$

In this cycle, four protons are combined into one α-particle (plus two positrons which will be annihilated by two electrons). The carbon and nitrogen isotopes serve as catalysts for this combination. There are no alternative reactions between protons and the nuclei $C^{12}C^{13}N^{14}$; with N^{15}, there is the alternative process

$$N^{15} + H^1 = O^{16},$$

but this radiative capture may be expected to be about 10,000 times less probable than the particle reaction (f). Thus practically no carbon and nitrogen will be consumed and the energy production will continue until all protons in the star are used up. At the present rate of energy production, the hydrogen content of the sun (35 percent by weight) would suffice for 3.5×10^{10} years.

The reaction cycle (1) is preferred before all other nuclear reactions. Any element *lighter* than carbon, when reacting with protons, is destroyed

---

[2] H. A. Bethe, *Physical Review*, 55 (1938), 103.

permanently and will not be replaced. E.g., Be^9 would react in the following way:

$$Be^9 + H^1 = Li^6 + He^4$$
$$Li^6 + H^1 = Be^7$$
$$Be^7 + \epsilon^- = Li^7$$
$$Li^7 + H^1 = 2He^4.$$

Therefore, even if the star contained an appreciable amount of Li, Be or B when it was first formed, these elements would have been consumed in the early history of the star. This agrees with the extremely low abundance of these elements (if any) in the present stars. These considerations apply also to the heavy hydrogen isotopes H^2 and H^3.

The only abundant and very light elements are H^1 and He^4. Of these, He^4 will not react with protons at all because Li^5 is unstable, and the reaction between two protons, while possible, is rather slow and will therefore be much less important in ordinary stars than the cycle (1).

Elements heavier than nitrogen may be left out of consideration entirely because they will react more slowly with protons than carbon and nitrogen, even at temperatures much higher than those prevailing in stars. For the same reason, reactions between α-particles and other nuclei are of no importance.

T A B L E   9 0 – 1 .   *Energy Production in the Sun for Several Nuclear Reactions*

Reaction	Average Energy Production ϵ(erg/ g sec.)
$H^1 + H^1 = H^2 + \epsilon^+ + f.$*	0.2
$H^2 + H^1 = He^3$	3×10^{16}
$Li^7 + H^1 = 2He^4$	4×10^{14}
$B^{10} + H^1 = C^{11} + f.$	3×10^5
$B^{11} + H^1 = 3He^4$	10^{10}
$N^{14} + H^1 = O^{15} + f.$	3
$O^{16} + H^1 = F^{17} + f.$	10^{-4}

* "$+ f.$" means that the energy production in the reactions following the one listed, is included. E.g. the figure for the $N^{14} + H^1$ includes the complete chain (1).

To test the theory, we have calculated [Table 90–1] the energy production in the sun for several nuclear reactions, making the following assumptions:

(1) The temperature at the center of the sun is 2×10^7 degrees. This

value follows from the integration of the Eddington equations with any reasonable "star model." The "point source model" with a convective core which is a very good approximation to reality gives 2.03×10^7 degrees. The same calculation gives 50.2 for the density at the center of the sun. The central temperature is probably correct to within 10 percent.

(2) The concentration of hydrogen is assumed to be 35 percent by weight, that of the other reacting element 10 percent. In the reaction chain (1), the concentration of N^{14} was assumed to be 10 percent.

(3) The ratio of the average energy production to the production at the center was calculated from the temperature-density dependence of the nuclear reaction and the temperature-density distribution in the star.

It is evident from [Table 90–1] that only the nitrogen reaction gives agreement with the observed energy production of 2 ergs/g sec. All the reactions with lighter elements would give energy productions which are too large by many orders of magnitude if they were abundant enough, whereas the next heavier element, O^{16}, already gives more than 10,000 times too small a value. In view of the extremely strong dependence on the atomic number, the agreement of the nitrogen-carbon cycle with observation is excellent.

The nitrogen-carbon reactions also explain correctly the dependence of mass on luminosity for main sequence stars. In this connection, the strong dependence of the reaction rate on temperature ($\sim T^{18}$) is important, because massive stars have much greater luminosities with only slightly higher central temperatures (e.g., Y Cygni has $T = 3.2 \times 10^7$ and $\epsilon = 1200$ ergs/g sec.).

With the assumed reaction chain, there will be no appreciable change in the abundance of elements heavier than helium during the evolution of the star but only a transmutation of hydrogen into helium. This result which is more general than the reaction chain (1) is in contrast to the commonly accepted "Aufbauhypothese."

A detailed account of these investigations will be published soon.

ooooooooooo

FISSION

ooooooooooo

Lise Meitner (b. 1878)

Otto R. Frisch (b. 1904)

Niels Bohr (1885-1962)

In 1919, when Lord Rutherford first used α particles to disrupt atomic nuclei, very few people or even physicists believed that this was more than a scientific curiosity and that nuclear physics would ever have any practical use. The very fact that a vast amount of energy (the so-called binding energy of the nucleus) must be poured into a nucleus to disrupt it or even to tear out one of its nucleons, seemed to indicate to physicists that no energy could ever be obtained by tearing a nucleus apart. And yet, just twenty years after Rutherford first disrupted a nucleus by bombarding it with very energetic α particles, uranium fission was discovered by Hahn and Strassmann and the world was thrust into the era of atomic energy and atomic bombs.

How can energy be obtained from the disintegration of a nucleus—even though the nucleus is a stable structure, which apparently must absorb energy in order to undergo fission? Let us consider the formation of the simplest compound nucleus (the deuteron or heavy hydrogen), consisting of a proton and a neutron. If these two particles are initially at rest with respect to each other and are not very close together (that is, if they are separated by more than a trillionth of a centimeter), we can say that they are in a state of zero energy with respect to one another (zero kinetic energy because they are at rest, and zero potential energy because the interaction between them is zero). Of course each particle has its mass energy mc^2 according to Einstein's formula, but this does not play a primary role in nuclear formation.

Suppose now that we bring the neutron and proton closer and closer together until they are within the range of their mutual nuclear attraction. At this point they suddenly rush violently together, losing energy while they do so, because they are attracted to each other. Because this attraction does work on each particle they acquire kinetic energy. But since they lose more potential energy by coming close together than the kinetic energy they thus acquire, their total store of energy is reduced. The total store of energy at any given moment is the total mass of the system times the square of the speed of light—Einstein's famous relationship $E = mc^2$. Thus, the mass of the deuteron is smaller than the sum of the masses of the proton and the neutron. This difference in mass appears as a burst of energy in the form of a γ ray when the proton and neutron combine to form the deuteron.

We may represent this process by the following crude picture. Consider a deep but narrow crater with steeply slanting walls, surrounded by a flat, smooth terrain on which there is a black (the proton) and a red (the neutron) ball. As long as the balls are on the flat surface, they are not attracted to each other and they remain at rest. If the two balls now are brought to opposite points on the crater's edge (so that they start rolling down the slope of the crater), they will move toward each other very rapidly as they roll down the slope. Of course, this is due to the gravitational pull on each ball, but to pursue our analogy with the neutron and the proton, we may imagine that the balls move toward each other because of an attraction that arises when they are separated only by the diameter of the crater. If there were no friction along the slope of the crater, the two balls would roll down to the bottom and then right back up to the top again, and we would not have a compound system. But because of the friction along the slope, the balls reach the bottom with less mechanical energy than they had at the top. Their energy at the top is all potential (which we may take to be zero), but as they roll toward the bottom, they lose potential and gain kinetic energy. However, their net gain in kinetic energy is not equal to their loss in potential, because some of the initial potential energy was dissipated by the friction and flowed into the ground as heat. This is analogous to the emission of a γ ray when the neutron and the proton combine to form the deuteron.

Now suppose that below a certain level in the crater the walls are perfectly smooth so that the spheres generate no heat as they roll from that level to the bottom. It is clear then, that after a few large oscillations back and forth in the crater, the spheres will reach an equilibrium configuration, moving around forever with a fixed amount of mechanical energy in the frictionless part of the crater. Thus the two spheres form a stable dynamical system inside the crater because they lost some of their mechanical energy as they rolled down the wall of the crater. We can disrupt this system only if we supply mechanical energy in some form to the spheres. Of course, we must supply at least as much mechanical energy as the spheres lost by friction.

If we pursue this picture further, we note that we can send as many red spheres into the crater as we wish (assuming that each sphere takes up but a small amount of space). This is equivalent to adding more and more neutrons to the deuteron and thus building up more and more massive isotopes of hydrogen. Offhand, there appears to be no objection to this, because all neutrons pull upon each other as strongly as they pull upon protons, and consequently each neutron is like another sphere rolling into the crater. But there are definite quantum rules that prevent this. Since all neutrons are identical and have a half unit of spin (like the electron) they obey the Pauli exclusion principle. This means that only one neutron can occupy the lowest energy state in the deuteron (only one red ball can move around in the frictionless region). Another neutron can still enter into a threefold combination with the proton and the other neutron by aligning its spin opposite to that of the neutron already in the deuteron, since the Pauli exclusion principle allows two identical particles to move in very nearly similar orbits if their spins are antiparallel.

The Pauli exclusion principle prevents our carrying the analogy much further. Although we can send any number of red spheres into the crater, no more than two neutrons can form a stable structure with one proton. A third neutron is prevented, by the Pauli exclusion principle, from getting close enough to the other two to form a stable nucleus. How, then, can we get stable nuclei with more than three nucleons in combination? Only by adding more protons. Since protons are different from neutrons, they are not prevented by the Pauli principle from getting close to the neutrons already in the nucleus. With more protons in the nucleus, more neutrons can also be added. But adding a proton to a nucleus presents another problem. Protons repel each other electrostatically; hence, we cannot simply add them to nuclei the way we might roll spheres along a level surface into a crater. The protons already in the nucleus repel any new ones trying to get in. However, we can still carry out the analogy for protons if we picture the crater as surrounded by a very steep hill that rises above the level ground to a fairly high ridge and then falls off gently on all sides as we move away from the crater. It would resemble a lunar crater, with sloping outside walls. Before we can get a sphere into such a crater, we must first push it up the hill. Once the ball is at the top of the hill, we can let it go and watch it fall into the crater. It is more difficult to get it out now than previously, because we must bring it from the bottom of the crater up to the top of the hill again. (Note that in this imaginary crater the red sphere, the neutron, must be pictured as being able to go through the hill with no resistance. A neutron has no charge and hence suffers no electrostatic repulsion.)

From this analogy, it becomes evident that it is not so easy to build up heavier and heavier nuclei. The more neutrons we add, the more protons we must add. The hill, because of the increased nuclear charge, gets steeper with each additional proton. But if the hill got steeper with additional protons, with no change in the manner in which the nucleons arranged themselves once they fell into the nuclear crater, they would all fall deep down into the crater. Energy could never be obtained by disrupting such a nucleus, since as much energy would have to be used to accomplish this as would be obtained when the nucleus was disrupted.

But something else happens when we go to heavier and heavier nuclei. The Pauli principle applies to protons just as it does to neutrons. The black and red spheres (protons and neutrons) do not all fall to the bottom of the crater because the bottom is filled up when two black and two red spheres (2 protons and 2 neutrons) are present to form the helium nucleus or α particle. The other spheres must now find their places closer to the top of the crater and as more and more spheres are added, they lie closer and closer to the top of the crater. We can now see how a great deal more energy can be obtained from a fission process than is supplied to the nucleus to induce the fission. Again we use the analogy with the crater, but this time we place our crater (which we make quite shallow, rather than deep, to take into account the spheres already inside it) on top of a very high peak (like the crater of a volcano). To get a black sphere (proton) into this crater we must first roll it up the side of the crater (do work on it, or give it energy). It then drops into the crater by itself. But since the crater is very shallow, the sphere remains close to the top of the peak, and it takes only a small amount of energy to bring it back to the top and let it roll down to the outside again.

Thus by supplying only a small amount of energy to the spheres, in the shallow crater on top of the peak, we can bring them to the edge. They then, in rolling down the side, acquire a lot more energy than is needed to lift them out of the shallow crater. To carry through an analogy with the volcano, if the lava in the volcano begins to boil violently some of the lava can overflow and move down the slopes of the crater, acquiring vastly more energy than it had while boiling.

We must apply this type of reasoning to understand the source of the vast amount of energy that is released in uranium fission, even though the fission has been induced by a neutron with only a small amount of energy. This is best analyzed by picturing the uranium nucleus as a liquid drop, discussed in detail in our commentary on Bohr's paper on uranium fission. Suppose now that we observe a drop of water suspended from a faucet which is high above the ground (the height being equivalent to the hill surrounding our crater). The drop is held to the faucet by the surface tension forces in the liquid. By blowing gently on the drop or tapping the faucet gently, we can dislodge the drop (it tears away), and once dislodged it acquires a great deal of energy while falling from its height above the ground. In the same way, the gentle disturbance that a slowly moving neutron communicates to a uranium nucleus separates the latter into halves, which were only loosely held together initially. However, the Coulomb repulsion between the two halves (like the pull of gravity on the drop of liquid) pushes them away from one another at very high speeds. Lise Meitner and O. R. Frisch were among the first to analyze the experimental data correctly. After Hahn and Strassmann had demonstrated that one of the by-products of their bombardment of uranium with neutrons was barium (or its isotopes) Meitner and Frisch pointed out how such a splitting of uranium can occur. In a letter sent to *Nature* in 1939, which follows this commentary, they used the liquid-drop model to show how fission can occur under the appropriate conditions.

Lise Meitner, who, together with Frisch, originated the idea of nuclear fission, was born in Vienna, Austria, on November 7, 1878. One of eight children (three girls and five boys), she was brought up in Vienna and obtained her doctorate from the University of Vienna in 1906. The following year, she studied in Berlin with Planck and soon began research in radioactivity in collaboration with Otto Hahn. From 1912–1915, she was assistant to Planck at the Institute for Theoretical Physics at the University of Berlin. In 1917, she was appointed head of the Physics Department in the Kaiser Wilhelm Institute for Chemistry. At that time, she and Hahn began studies of β decay. Later, she and Von Beyer discovered homogeneous groups in the β emission from radioactive elements. She continued in β- and γ-ray spectra until 1938, when Hitler's persecution of the Jews forced her to flee to Sweden. There she joined the staff of the Nobel Institute in Stockholm. At the end of 1938, she received a description from Hahn of his experiments on the interaction of neutrons with uranium. Meitner suspected from the results that the uranium nucleus was split approximately into equal parts; a subsequent discussion with Frisch led to their joint proposal of fission that appeared as a letter in *Nature,* entitled "A New Type of Nuclear Reaction."

For her discovery, Lise Meitner has received numerous awards and prizes and has been elected a foreign member of most of the scientific academies of Europe. She makes her home in Cambridge, England.

Otto Robert Frisch was born in Vienna, Austria, on October 1, 1904. His father, Dr. Justinian Frisch, was in the printing business; his mother,

Auguste Meitner Frisch, was a pianist. Lise Meitner, with whom he collaborated, is his aunt. Frisch received his doctor's degree from the University of Vienna in 1926. He then carried on research in Berlin; in Hamburg he spent the years 1930–1933 with Otto Stern working on molecular beams, moving from there to London to work with Blackett in 1933–1934. The next five years he spent in Bohr's institute in Copenhagen. It was at the end of his stay here that he and Meitner advanced the idea of nuclear fission. In 1939, he moved to England, first Birmingham, then Liverpool and Oxford. In 1943, he went to the Los Alamos Laboratory in New Mexico as a member of the British team working on the Atomic Energy Project. On returning to England he went first to the British Atomic Energy Research Establishment at Harwell and then to Cambridge, where in 1947 he succeeded Sir John Douglas Cockcroft as Jacksonian Professor of Natural Philosophy. The following year, he was elected a Fellow of the Royal Society. In 1951, he married Ursula Blau. The couple have a son and a daughter and make their home in Cambridge.

ଠଠଠଠଠଠଠ

MEITNER and *FRISCH*

Disintegration of Uranium by Neutrons: A New Type of Nuclear Reaction [1]

ON BOMBARDING URANIUM WITH NEUTRONS, Fermi and collaborators found that at least four radioactive substances were produced, to two of which atomic numbers larger than 92 were ascribed. Further investigations demonstrated the existence of at least nine radioactive periods, six of which were assigned to elements beyond uranium, and nuclear isomerism had to be assumed in order to account for their chemical behavior together with their genetic relations.

In making chemical assignments, it was always assumed that these radioactive bodies had atomic numbers near that of the element bombarded, since only particles with one or two charges were known to be emitted from nuclei. A body, for example, with similar properties to those of osmium was assumed to be eka-osmium ($Z = 94$) rather than osmium ($Z = 76$) or ruthenium ($Z = 44$).

---

[1] Lise Meitner and O. R. Frisch, *Nature,* 143 (1939), 239 f.

Following up an observation of Curie and Savitch, Hahn and Strassmann found that a group of at least three radioactive bodies, formed
from uranium under neutron bombardment, were chemically similar to
barium and, therefore, presumably isotopic with radium. Further investigation, however, showed that it was impossible to separate these bodies
from barium (although mesothorium, an isotope of radium, was readily
separated in the same experiment), so that Hahn and Strassmann were
forced to conclude that *isotopes of barium* $(Z = 56)$ *are formed as a
consequence of the bombardment of uranium* $(Z = 92)$ *with neutrons.*

At first sight this result seems very hard to understand. The formation
of elements much below uranium has been considered before, but was
always rejected for physical reasons, so long as the chemical evidence was
not entirely clear cut. The emission, within a short time, of a large number of charged particles may be regarded as excluded by the small penetrability of the "Coulomb barrier," indicated by Gamow's theory of alpha
decay.

On the basis, however, of present ideas about the behaviour of heavy
nuclei, an entirely different and essentially classical picture of these new
disintegration processes suggests itself. On account of their close packing
and strong energy exchange, the particles in a heavy nucleus would be
expected to move in a collective way which has some resemblance to the
movement of a liquid drop. If the movement is made sufficiently violent
by adding energy, such a drop may divide itself into two smaller drops.

In the discussion of the energies involved in the deformation of nuclei,
the concept of surface tension of nuclear matter has been used and its
value has been estimated from simple considerations regarding nuclear
forces. It must be remembered, however, that the surface tension of a
charged droplet is diminished by its charge, and a rough estimate shows
that the surface tension of nuclei, decreasing with increasing nuclear
charge, may become zero for atomic numbers of the order of 100.

It seems therefore possible that the uranium nucleus has only small
stability of form and may, after neutron capture, divide itself into two
nuclei of roughly equal size (the precise ratio of sizes depending on finer
structural features and perhaps partly on chance). These two nuclei will
repel each other and should gain a total kinetic energy of *c.* 200 Mev., as
calculated from nuclear radius and charge. This amount of energy may
actually be expected to be available from the difference in packing fraction between uranium and the elements in the middle of the periodic
system. The whole "fission" process can thus be described in an essentially
classical way, without having to consider quantum-mechanical "tunnel
effects," which would actually be extremely small, on account of the large
masses involved.

After division, the high neutron/proton ratio of uranium will tend to
readjust itself by beta decay to the lower value suitable for lighter ele-

ments. Probably each part will thus give rise to a chain of disintegrations. If one of the parts is an isotope of barium the other will be krypton ($Z = 92 - 56$), which might decay through rubidium, strontium and yttrium to zirconium. Perhaps one or two of the supposed barium-lanthanum-cerium chains are then actually strontium-yttrium-zirconium chains.

It is possible, and seems to us rather probable, that the periods which have been ascribed to elements beyond uranium are also due to light elements. From the chemical evidence, the two short periods (10 sec. and 40 sec.) so far ascribed to ^{239}U might be masurium isotopes ($Z = 43$) decaying through ruthenium, rhodium, palladium and silver into cadmium.

In all these cases it might not be necessary to assume nuclear isomerism; but the different radioactive periods belonging to the same chemical element may then be attributed to different isotopes of this element, since varying proportions of neutrons may be given to the two parts of the uranium nucleus.

By bombarding thorium with neutrons, activities are obtained which have been ascribed to radium and actinium isotopes. Some of these periods are approximately equal to periods of barium and lanthanum isotopes resulting from the bombardment of uranium. We should therefore like to suggest that these periods are due to a "fission" of thorium which is like that of uranium and results partly in the same products. Of course it would be especially interesting if one could obtain one of these products from a light element, for example, by means of neutron capture.

It might be mentioned that the body with half-life 24 min. which was chemically identified with uranium is probably really ^{239}U, and goes over into an eka-rhenium which appears inactive but may decay slowly, probably with emission of alpha particles. (From inspection of the natural radioactive elements, ^{239}U cannot be expected to give more than one or two beta decays; the long chain of observed decays has always puzzled us.) The formation of this body is a typical resonance process; the compound state must have a life-time a million times longer than the time it would take the nucleus to divide itself. Perhaps this state corresponds to some highly symmetrical type of motion of nuclear matter which does not favour "fission" of the nucleus.

ooooooo

The discovery of nuclear fission by Hahn and Strassmann and the analysis of the energetic relations in the case of uranium fission by Lise Meitner in 1939 came at one of the most critical periods in the history of the world. World War II was about to erupt; the persecutions of scientists in Germany and to a lesser extent in Italy had brought many of the out-standing European physicists to this country. When news of uranium fission was announced, Enrico Fermi was already a permanent member of the Columbia University physics department; most of his Rome group had left Italy to work in the Western democracies, many of them in the United States. In a sense this was also a critical period for physics. Neu-tron research seemed to have reached a plateau, and many of the top physicists were turning their attention to other fields. With the discovery of fission, however, a tremendous impetus was given to neutron and nuclear research, and such leaders as Fermi were soon deeply involved in nuclear-fission problems, aided by the development of the cyclotron and the new electronic techniques that were being rapidly introduced into physical research.

The most important problem that arose in connection with uranium fission dealt with the emission of secondary neutrons by the fission frag-ments. After Meitner and Frisch had pointed out that the discovery of Hahn and Strassman of a radioactive barium isotope in the fission frag-ments meant that a new type of nuclear reaction was taking place, Fermi realized that secondary neutrons would be emitted and that a chain reac-tion was possible. What was most puzzling was the absence of a natural chain reaction involving fission of the uranium in the earth and resulting in one vast atomic explosion. That this does not happen indicates that either not enough secondary neutrons are emitted during each fission process to sustain a chain reaction (for each fission more than one secondary neu-tron must be emitted for a chain reaction to occur) or that not ordinary uranium 238 but one of its rare isotopes undergoes fission—or both state-ments are true. It was demonstrated experimentally by Fermi and his col-laborators that enough secondary neutrons are emitted for a chain reac-tion to occur. But it also became clear that under normal conditions, with low-energy neutrons, it is not uranium 238 but one of its less massive isotopes that undergoes fission.

The theories of nuclear forces and nuclear models had been developed sufficiently to enable physicists to analyze the fission process theoretically. In the forefront of this work was Niels Bohr. To account for certain properties of the nucleus, particularly what is known as the saturation of the density of the nucleus and the saturation of nuclear forces, Bohr in-troduced what is now known as the liquid-drop model of the nucleus (see Chapter 45).

Recalling the mass defect of the nucleus (that the total mass of the nucleus is smaller than the sum of the masses of its constituent neutrons and protons) and Einstein's theory of the equivalence of mass and energy ($E = mc^2$), it is apparent that the mass defect is in fact the measure of the amount of energy released in the formation of the nucleus. The mass defect multiplied by the square of the speed of light gives us the binding energy of the nucleus—the amount of energy needed to break down the nucleus into its component protons and neutrons. It was known that the binding energy per particle inside the nucleus, that is, the total binding energy divided by the total number of neutrons and protons inside the nucleus, is approximately the same for all nuclei. It thus appears that all nuclei are bound with about the same cohesiveness. In other words, there is a kind of saturation of the binding force in the sense that the neutrons and protons in the nucleus only interact with their immediate neighbors (at least to a very good approximation).

It was also known that the density of the nuclear material is fairly uniform as we go from one nucleus to the other. This can be seen from the sizes of the nuclei. By bombarding nuclei with α particles and protons we can calculate the diameters and hence the volumes of the various nuclei, starting from the lightest and going to the heaviest. We find that the volume of a nucleus increases approximately as the number of particles in the nucleus increases. For example, the nucleus of uranium contains about sixty times as many particles as the helium nucleus does; but the volume of the uranium nucleus is about sixty times larger than that of the helium nucleus. Thus, the density of the nuclear material in both nuclei is about the same.

It follows, then, that the nuclear material is a kind of homogeneous substance spread out in a uniform manner in all nuclei. The substance in any nucleus consists of approximately equal numbers of neutrons and protons packed together at a constant density. In other words, the nuclear material is distributed in a nucleus just the way the material is distributed in a liquid drop. This liquid-drop model, first introduced by Bohr, can account very nicely for most of the observed properties of the nucleus. It is easy to see that just as we can have liquid drops of various sizes but with the same binding energy per molecule (no matter how large a drop is, it takes the same amount of energy to rip out a molecule, say, by evaporation), we can have nuclei of various sizes. The liquid-drop model leads to some other interesting characteristics that have been verified experimentally. The nuclear drop has surface-tension forces at its surface that keep the nucleus spherical in shape just as the surface tension tends to keep a drop of water or a soap bubble round. Moreover, just as a liquid drop can be broken into two or more drops if it is set vibrating properly, so, too, can a nucleus; this is an important phenomenon in nuclear fission. In the short paper that follows, Bohr used the liquid-drop model to determine which isotope of uranium undergoes fission when it absorbs a slow neutron. He attacks the problem by means of an analogy with what occurs when molecules are evaporated from a liquid drop. With this model Bohr pictures the fission as occurring in two steps.

In the first step, when the neutron is absorbed, a new compound nucleus is formed that has more internal energy than the original uranium nucleus; this energy is stored in the compound nucleus the way heat is stored in a drop. The second step, according to Bohr's analysis, depends on what happens to the energy introduced into the nucleus by the neutron. If all or most of the energy is concentrated on a single particle, such as a neutron, proton, or α particle, near the surface of the nucleus, the usual type of nuclear reaction occurs; the compound nucleus emits one of these particles and settles down to become a new stable nucleus. However, if the energy brought by the absorbed neutron is transformed into mechanical vibrations of the whole nucleus, the nucleus undergoes deformations that may shatter it into two equal or very nearly equal parts—and fission takes place.

Fission occurs when the short-range, strong nuclear forces that keep the neutrons and protons bound together are overcome by the long-range, repulsive electrostatic forces that are disruptive. As long as the nuclear matter is kept close together, the short-range forces prevail and the nucleus remains unaffected when the neutron enters. But if the energy of the neutron causes the nucleus to vibrate so that it becomes elongated in one direction, the nuclear forces in that direction may be reduced sufficiently below the repulsive forces, which are scarcely affected by the elongation; then fission occurs.

As Bohr points out in his paper, the energy necessary to bring about the necessary deformation of the nucleus decreases with increasing nuclear charge (the repulsive forces become bigger and therefore help the deformation get started); a point is reached for a given atomic number when the energy for deformation is comparable with the energy needed for the emission of a single particle. The probability for fission is then of the same order of magnitude as the probability for particle emission.

Bohr then considers how to determine which of the uranium or thorium isotopes undergo fission. For neutrons moving with energies of about 25 electron volts and hence considerably faster than thermal neutrons (thermal neutrons move about as fast as molecules in the atmosphere under ordinary conditions; they are also called slow neutrons), there is a strong increase in the absorption by uranium 238 (clearly a resonance phenomenon) without an accompanying increase of the fission process. It follows that the ordinary abundant isotope of uranium does not account for the observed fission. In other words for both ordinary uranium and thorium the probability for emission of a single particle after fast neutron absorption is much greater than the probability for fission; consequently these nuclei are stable against fission.

But the situation is quite different for thermal or slow neutrons. Uranium displays more fission after slow neutron absorption than thorium.

Uranium, then, would seem to be the active element in fission; but it must be some isotope of uranium other than 238—Bohr then points out that it is very probably the rare isotope 235. His reasoning is as follows: Since the excitation energy and hence the energy available for deformation increases with the energy of the absorbed neutron, the probability for fission should increase with the energy of the absorbed neutron. But since there is hardly any such increase of fission in uranium 238, another isotope must be involved. The situation as far as slow neutrons go is then the following: Since uranium 238 is not involved, we look to the isotope 235 and find that symmetry plays a role. When U^{235} absorbs a neutron, it becomes a nucleus of mass 236 (an increase in one unit of mass) and has an even number of neutrons and protons. Nuclear theory states that in an even-numbered nucleus the protons and neutrons are more tightly bound together than in an odd-numbered nucleus. Consequently, when 235 absorbs a neutron to become 236, the neutron gives up much more of its mass in the binding process than it does when 238 absorbs it to become the odd nucleus 239. Thus the slow neutrons give up much more excitation energy to uranium 235, really to uranium 236, than they do to uranium 238 and this causes 235 (actually uranium 236) to split.

Because U^{235} is very scarce (only one gram of 235 is present in each 140 grams of uranium) fission occurs only rarely under ordinary conditions. This was an important factor in the development of the atomic bomb, since it was imperative to isolate a sufficient amount of 235 to ensure a chain reaction. This problem is discussed in Chapter 92.

ооооооо

B O H R

Resonance in Uranium and Thorium Disintegrations and the Phenomenon of Nuclear Fission [2]

THE STUDY OF THE NUCLEAR transmutations by neutron bombardment in uranium and thorium, initiated by Fermi and his collaborators, and followed up by Meitner, Hahn and Strassmann, and by Curie and Savitch, has brought to light a number of most inter-

[2] Niels Bohr, *Physical Review*, 55 (1939), 418 f.

esting phenomena. Above all, as pointed out by Meitner and Frisch, the recent discovery of Hahn and Strassmann of the appearance of a radioactive barium isotope as the product of such transmutations offers evidence of a new type of nuclear reaction in which the nucleus divides into two nuclei of smaller charges and masses with release of an energy of more than a hundred million electron volts. The direct proof of the occurrence of this so-called nuclear fission was given by Frisch for thorium as well as for uranium by the observation of the very intense ionization produced in a gas by the high speed nuclear fragments.

In a recent note commenting on the ingenious suggestions put forward for the explanation of the fission phenomenon by Meitner and Frisch, the writer has stressed that the course of the new type of reactions, just as that of ordinary nuclear reactions, may be assumed to take place in two well-separated stages. The first of these is the formation of a compound nucleus, in which the energy is stored in a way resembling that of the heat motion of a liquid or solid body; the second consists either in the release of this energy in the form of radiation or in its conversion into a form suited to produce the disintegration of the compound nucleus. In the case of ordinary reactions, resulting in the emission of a proton, neutron or α-particle from this nucleus, we have to do with a concentration of a considerable part of the excitation energy on some particle at the nuclear surface, sufficient for its escape, which resembles the evaporation of a molecule from a liquid drop. In the case of the fission phenomena, the energy has to be largely converted into some special type of motion of the whole nucleus causing a deformation of the nuclear surface sufficiently large to lead to a rupture of the nucleus comparable to the division of a liquid drop into two droplets. From considerations of statistical mechanics analogous to those applied to the evaporation-like nuclear disintegrations, it follows indeed that the probability of occurrence of fission becomes comparable to that of ordinary nuclear reactions when, with increasing nuclear charge, the deformation energy concerned has decreased to values of the same order of magnitude as that demanded for the escape of a single particle.

Here I should like to show how such considerations would seem to offer a simple interpretation of the peculiar variation with neutron velocity of the cross sections of the different transmutation processes of uranium and thorium observed by Meitner, Hahn and Strassmann. In the light of the new discoveries, the great variety of processes obtained, which could not be disentangled on the ordinary ideas of nuclear disintegrations, would seem, according to Meitner and Frisch, to be reduced to only two types of transmutations. Of these the one consists in an ordinary radiative capture of the incident neutron, resulting in the formation of the normal state of the compound nucleus, which is subsequently transmuted by β-ray emission into a stable nucleus. The other consists in the fission of the excited compound nucleus, which may take place in a large number of different ways, in which a wide range of mass and charge numbers of the fragments may occur. This last point, which makes it impossible without a closer study of the statistical distribution of the fragments to trace a product of given chemical properties and radioactive period back to its origin from some particular isotope of the original element, is, as we shall see, of especial importance for the understanding of certain striking peculiarities in the case of uranium.

For the capture processes, which lead to the radioactive uranium and thorium isotopes of periods 24 and 33 minutes, respectively, Meitner, Hahn and Strassmann found evidence of resonance phenomena for neutrons of comparatively small velocities. In uranium, where the phenomenon was more completely investigated, they found for neutron energies of about 25 volts a capture cross section at least 30 times larger than that for thermal neutrons. Since in this resonance region the cross section amounts to about 10^{-21} cm², it is, as they pointed out, obviously necessary from simple arguments of dispersion theory to ascribe the phenomenon to the abundant uranium isotope of mass number 238. From the fact that neither for uranium nor thorium is the resonance capture accompanied by any large increase of the cross section for the fission processes, we may further conclude that the probability of radiation by the compound nucleus in the excited states concerned is considerably larger than the fission probability, and that the normal states of these nuclei, apart from their β-ray radioactivity, are essentially stable.

As regards all other transmutation processes, which are now to be ascribed to fission, marked differences between uranium and thorium were found in the investigations of Meitner, Hahn and Strassmann as well as in the direct experiments of Frisch. With fast neutrons, fission cross sections of the same order of magnitude were found for uranium and thorium, but with neutrons of thermal velocities a large increase of the fission cross section was observed for uranium and not for thorium. The results for fast neutrons are simply explained on the basis of the general picture of nuclear processes outlined above, according to which we should expect the fission probability to increase much more rapidly with excitation than the radiation probability, and to become considerably larger than the latter for the high excitations of the compound nucleus concerned. The peculiar effect in uranium for slow neutrons could obviously, however, not be reconciled with the above considerations if it were to be attributed to the formation of the compound nucleus of mass number 239; but since, as already indicated, the periods of the most frequent radioactive fragments should be independent of the isotope undergoing fission, we have the possibility of attributing the effect concerned to a fission of the excited nucleus of mass 236 formed by the impact of the neutrons on the rare isotope of mass 235.

From the fact that the binding energy of a neutron in a nucleus of even charge number should be appreciably larger if the mass number is even than if it is odd, we should actually expect for a given neutron velocity a higher excitation energy for the compound nucleus 236 than for 239, and accordingly a much denser distribution of resonance levels and a much larger probability of fission in the former than in the latter case. Even for excitations produced by impacts of slow neutrons, we may therefore expect that the probability of fission of the nucleus 236 will be larger than that of radiative capture; and due to the corresponding broadening of the levels, the level distribution of 236 in this region might even be continuous. In any case, provided the fission probability is high enough, we shall expect for small neutron energies cross sections inversely proportional to the velocity, allowing us to account both for the observed yields of the process concerned for thermal neutrons and for the absence of any appreciable effect for neutrons of somewhat higher velocities. For fast neutrons the cross sections can, of course, never exceed nuclear dimensions, and because of the scarcity of the isotope concerned the fission yields will be much smaller than those obtained from neutron impacts on the abundant isotope.

It would thus seem that all the known experimental facts receive a simple explanation without any assumption of peculiarities of special levels. Such assumptions as have hitherto been thought necessary to account for these phenomena would in fact seem difficult to reconcile with general ideas of nuclear excitation. In a forthcoming paper in collaboration with Professor John A. Wheeler, a closer discussion will be given of the fission mechanism and of the stability of heavy nuclei in their normal and excited states.

92

ooooooooooo

CHAIN-REACTING PILE

ooooooooooo

Enrico Fermi (1901-1954)

Shortly after Fermi had accepted a professorship of physics at Columbia University in 1939 word reached this country via Bohr that Hahn and Strassmann in Germany had produced nuclear fission by bombarding the uranium nucleus with neutrons. This caused great excitement in nuclear laboratories all over the world, and soon experimental nuclear physicists everywhere were busy splitting uranium nuclei, and theoretical physicists were equally busy trying to interpret and explain the results.

It was only natural that Fermi, by consensus the top nuclear physicist of the age, should take a major part in this activity. Soon he was involved in nuclear fission experiments at the Pupin physics laboratories at Columbia. Working with him at the time was the Hungarian-born physicist, the late Leo Szilard. Envisioning the implications of these experiments for the security of the world against the aggression of the axis powers, Szilard initiated the steps that led to Einstein's famous letter to President Roosevelt. Both Fermi and Szilard were quick to see that if there were some neutrons among the fission products, they could, in turn, induce additional fissions, and a chain reaction might result.

A number of questions had to be answered in connection with this phenomenon and certain technical problems had to be solved. To begin with, which particular isotope of uranium undergoes fission most readily? Thanks to the theoretical analysis of Niels Bohr and J. A. Wheeler, it was known that the isotope is U^{235}, and not the abundant isotope U^{238}, although the latter also suffers fission to a small extent. This is in agreement with the observations that indicated that fission—under ordinary conditions—is a very rare phenomenon, about as rare as the isotope U^{235} as compared to U^{238}.

Second, one had to know the speed of the neutrons emitted during fis-

1652

sion, for it was known that U^{235} fission is caused by slow neutrons. Hence, if the neutrons emitted during fission were fast, they would first have to be slowed down if a chain reaction were to be achieved.

Third, one would have to determine how many neutrons were emitted in each fission process. This number must be bigger than one if a chain reaction is to result. If only one neutron were emitted per fission, there could be no geometric growth of the fission process, and the whole thing would die out very quickly. On the other hand, if each fission process gave birth to two neutrons, these could then split two nuclei, giving rise to four neutrons, and so on. This is what we mean by a "chain reaction," a geometric increase in the number of neutrons that can cause additional splitting of nuclei.

The emission of more than one neutron during each fission is in itself not sufficient to ensure a chain reaction, for these neutrons might be wasted by being used up in absorption processes that compete with the fission process. The important point is that there must be more than one neutron per fission after the neutrons initially emitted in a fission are slowed down. This factor, called the reproductive factor, must be larger than one. A chain reaction can then occur since we have a situation similar to the growth of money in compound interest.

Finally, one would have to see whether the product neutrons (that is, those emitted during fission) could be kept within the uranium to cause additional fission. This depends on what is called the mean free path of the neutron. This is the average distance that a neutron travels before it is absorbed by a uranium nucleus. It is desirable for this distance to be short, for then a neutron cannot get very far (or escape from the uranium) before inducing fission. But even if the mean free path were long, one could still obtain a chain reaction by piling up (hence the name atomic pile) enough uranium so that the neutrons would ultimately have to be absorbed because of the great amount of uranium surrounding them on all sides.

These are the questions that Fermi set out to answer when Einstein's letter convinced President Roosevelt to assign a few thousand dollars to what ultimately was to become the Manhattan Project.

In the early stages of this work at Columbia University Fermi had already obtained some evidence that a chain reaction was possible. It was then decided to carry on the project at the University of Chicago; it was there that the first chain-reacting pile was constructed and successfully operated.

This momentous event was announced to the President in a code telegram stating that "the Italian navigator had reached shore safely and found the natives friendly."

Before we discuss Fermi's papers we may note that a nuclear reactor or a "pile," as the latter name implies, consists of slugs of pure uranium metal arranged in a space lattice embedded in a matrix of graphite. In present reactors the uranium slugs are generally situated at regular intervals on "fuel rods." In addition there are cylindrical openings in the pile for inserting control rods made of neutron-absorbing materials. The uranium is, of course, the fuel and the source of the neutron flux. The graphite is present to slow down the neutrons and thus prepare them to carry on the fission. The control rods, usually of boron steel, are used to control the rate of the chain reaction by absorbing neutrons and thus reducing the neutron flux.

The first of the two papers is a historical document. Except for minor editorial revisions it is Fermi's official report of the first experimental production of a divergent chain reaction. It took place in a temporary laboratory, a squash court under the west stands of the stadium at the University of Chicago on December 2, 1942. The reactor described is thus the prototype of all the power production reactors that have followed it. Because of the straightforward descriptive nature of this paper, little comment in the way of introduction seems necessary. An appendix by Fermi's colleagues giving the details of the construction of the pile is included. A second appendix published with the original paper and dealing with the control of the pile is omitted.

The second of the two papers gives the elementary theory of the chain-reacting pile. To make this paper more understandable, we explain a few of the terms that he uses. We first note that to produce a chain reaction or a self-sustaining pile a game of slowing down and catching neutrons must be played. The neutrons that are emitted during a fission process can have energies up to one million electron-volts, and must be slowed down before they are lost in some fashion or other. This is the whole trick, but it is not a trick that can be mastered easily because there are so many hazards in the paths of the neutrons.

We first note that not all neutrons emitted as fission products come out with the same energy because the total energy released in the fission process is divided among all the products some of which are heavy nuclei. The amount of energy that any particular neutron gets (and hence its speed) is a matter of chance. Fermi then states that the fast neutrons are slowed down by "elastic collisions with the atoms of carbon and with inelastic collisions with the uranium atoms." By "elastic collisions" the physicist means that the total amount of kinetic energy after the collision is the same as before, but is distributed differently. Thus, when a neutron hits a carbon nucleus elastically, the neutron loses some of its kinetic energy and the kinetic energy of the carbon nucleus increases exactly by this amount; this occurs when the neutron collides with a nucleus whose mass is not very much greater than that of the neutron.

When a neutron hits a very massive nucleus elastically, it just bounces off, losing none of its kinetic energy. Hence, atoms of small atomic weight like carbon are used in a pile for slowing down neutrons. When a fast neutron hits a uranium nucleus, it can lose some of its kinetic energy by exciting the nucleus itself (stirring up the protons and neutrons inside the nucleus to greater activity). This is called an inelastic collision, but this is only moderately effective in slowing down neutrons.

Fermi then goes on to speak of "thermal energies." This simply means the kinetic energy of a neutron when it is moving with the average energy of molecules in a gas at room temperature. This is the final result of the slowing-down process; "thermal neutrons" are what we want for fission. As Fermi points out, it takes about 15 collisions of a neutron with carbon atoms to reduce the neutron kinetic energy by a factor of 10. This means that about 110 such collisions are required to bring a 1,000,000-volt neutron down to thermal energy, which is $\frac{1}{40}$ of a volt.

A number of things can happen to the neutron to end its life as an independent and, therefore, a fission-producing particle before it reaches thermal energy. Fermi discusses these neutron-capturing processes in terms of the "cross-section" for the process. To understand this idea, let us suppose that bullets are being fired at a target. We can imagine that this target has only a certain effective area for the occurrence of some event, which is triggered only when the bullet strikes this effective area. We would then call this area the "collision cross-section" for the event. We may now further imagine that each nucleus carries a target area with it for each type of event or process that can occur. Only if a neutron strikes within this area does the particular event take place that is associated with that area or cross-section. The larger the cross-section for an event, that is, a collision, the more probable that event is. Cross-sections, like all areas, are expressed as squares of lengths, that is, square centimeters.

A few examples will illustrate this concept. Both cadmium and boron capture neutrons very readily; we say that they have a large neutron-capture cross-section. This cross-section is of the order of 10^{-24} square centimeters, which, though in itself a very small number, is very large for a nuclear cross-section. In fact, a boron or a cadmium nucleus captures neutrons so easily that physicists referred to it as easy as "hitting a barn." Hence 10^{-24} square centimeters is referred to as a "barn" and taken as a unit of cross-section.

The cross-section for the capture of a neutron by a carbon nucleus is only five thousandths of a barn. In general, the absorption cross-section for neutrons follows the inverse velocity law. This simply means that the smaller the velocity of the neutron, the larger is the capture cross-section, and vice versa. We can see why this is so if we recall that the De Broglie wavelength of a particle gets bigger as its speed gets smaller. In other words, as the neutron slows down, it spreads out and hence can contact nuclei over a wider area.

Fermi now analyzes the various accidents that can happen to the neutron before it is slowed down. It can be absorbed by the carbon. He dismisses this because the cross-section for this process is very small. There then remains the absorption by the uranium itself. This can either result in the emission of a γ-ray with a new isotope of uranium being formed or in fission. The first of these capture processes is called "resonance capture" and reduces the number of neutrons that are available for fission. Finally, some neutrons will be lost by escaping from the pile entirely. All of these losses must be considered in calculating the chain reaction.

If ν fast neutrons are produced in a single fission, the number of neutrons available for further fission, and hence for reproduction of new neutrons, is smaller than ν by a factor that is measured by or is proportional to the probability that these neutrons are absorbed in a fission process. Thus, if we start out with one neutron which produces one fission and hence ν fast neutrons, the number of neutrons available for fission in the second generation will be $P\nu$ where P is the probability that a fast neutron is ultimately absorbed in a fission process. The product $P\nu$ is called the "reproduction factor"; it is clear that this must be larger than one for a self-sustaining chain reaction. The problem then in building a chain-reacting atomic pile lies in making the factor P, "the probability that a fast neutron is ultimately absorbed by the fission process," as large as possible. This means reducing all the factors, such as resonance absorption, absorption by carbon, and so on, as much as possible and increasing the fission absorption as much as possible. This presents a difficulty since, in general, one cannot increase the favorable factors without at the same time increasing the unfavorable ones.

Thus, to slow down the fast neutrons as much as possible and thereby make them fission-producing neutrons, one should use large quantities of carbon, but this increases the chance that neutrons will be lost by carbon capture. On the other hand, if one uses large quantities of uranium to increase the probability of fission, one also increases the loss of neutrons by uranium resonance capture before the neutrons are slowed down. This difficulty can be partly overcome by concentrating the uranium in lumps and distributing these lumps in the carbon matrix like stones in earth.

To see how this reduces losses by resonance absorption before the neutron is slowed down as compared to an arrangement in which the uranium and carbon atoms are distributed homogeneously we need merely consider a fast neutron that has an energy close to the energy for resonance capture. Resonance capture is defined as capture that occurs only if the neutron is moving at a very definite speed. When the carbon and uranium are uniformly distributed the neutron will not have far to go before meeting a uranium nucleus and being absorbed, because, on the average, every second nucleus it meets will be a uranium nucleus. But if the uranium is distributed in lumps, the neutron will meet very many carbon atoms before coming to a uranium lump; by that time it will have lost much of its energy and will not be near resonance. If, however, some neutrons with resonance energy do strike a lump of uranium, they will be absorbed by the uranium atoms on the surface of the lump and the interior nuclei will scarcely be affected.

Thus, by clever geometry and a proper distribution of the uranium atoms relative to the carbon atoms, Fermi and his co-workers achieved a chain reaction. To illustrate the reproduction factor under reasonable conditions Fermi gives a table showing what happens in the second generation if two fast neutrons are produced per fission. He assumes that 3 per cent of these are immediately recaptured in a fast fission process, 10 per cent are resonance-absorbed, 10 per cent are absorbed by carbon, and 77 per cent end up as thermal neutrons, some of which give rise to fission and some of which are resonance absorbed. By adding up all the neutrons emitted in these processes, Fermi gets the reproduction factor and shows that for this case a chain reaction is possible only if at least 1.22 of the original two neutrons become thermal neutrons and give rise to fission.

This commentary gives only a brief outline of the problems involved. In Fermi's papers each of the points that enter into the final absorption of the neutrons is considered in detail and the actual operation and physical properties of the pile are analyzed and described.

ּ◌◌◌◌◌◌◌

F E R M I

Experimental Production of a Divergent Chain Reaction [1]

THIS REPORT GIVES A DESCRIPTION of the construction and operation of a chain reacting pile. The pile was constructed in

---

[1] Enrico Fermi. *American Journal of Physics,* 20 (1952), 536–541.

the West Stands Laboratory during the months of October and November 1942 and was operated for the first time on December 2, 1942.

It will appear from its description that an experiment of this kind requires the collaboration of a large number of physicists.

The two groups of Zinn and Anderson took charge of the preparation of the materials and of the actual construction of the pile; the group of Wilson prepared the measuring equipment and the automatic controls.

A large share of the credit for the experiment goes also to all the services of the Metallurgical Laboratory and in particular to the groups responsible for the development of the production and the testing of the materials. The exceptionally high purity requirements of graphite and uranium which were needed in very large amounts probably made the procurement of suitable materials the greatest single difficulty in all the development.

GENERAL DESCRIPTION OF THE PILE

The pile consists essentially of a lattice of lumps, partly of uranium metal and partly of uranium oxide imbedded in graphite. Except for a small fraction near the surface of the pile the lattice cell is a cube of 8.25 inches side.

Since only a relatively small amount of metal (about six tons) was available and since our graphite was of various brands of different purity it had been planned originally to construct the pile in an approximately spherical shape, putting the best materials as near as possible to the center. It happened actually that the critical conditions were reached before the sphere was completed and construction was interrupted about one layer above the critical dimensions. For the same reason the top layers of the pile were made appreciably smaller than would correspond to the spherical shape originally planned. The present structure may be roughly described as a flattened rotational ellipsoid having the polar radius 309 cm and the equatorial radius 388 cm [see Fig. 92–1].

The graphite is supported on a wooden structure and rests on the floor on its lowest point.

The original plan foresaw the possibility that it might have been necessary to evacuate the structure in order to reach the critical conditions. For this reason the pile was constructed inside a tent of rubberized balloon fabric that in case of need could have been sealed and evacuated.

Since the amount of metal available was only about 6 tons, the metal-bearing part of the lattice was designed for best utilization of the metal rather than for best reproduction factor. The metal lumps used weighed 6 pounds and consisted of metals of various origins (Westinghouse, Metal Hydrides, and Ames). An exponential experiment performed on the metal lattice had given for it a reproduction factor of 1.067 and $\nabla^2 = 101.7 \times 10^{-6} \, \text{cm}^{-2}$.* The use of heavier metal lumps of seven or eight pounds would have given a better reproduction factor. Since, however, heavier metal lumps would have reduced the volume of the metal-bearing part of the lattice, it was deemed advisable to use lumps somewhat undersize.

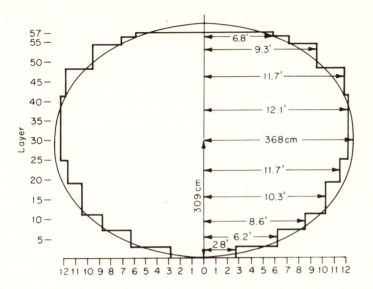

Fig. 92–1. Vertical cross section of the pile, showing the equivalent ellipsoid.

The greatest part of the volume was occupied by a lattice having the same cell side of 8¼ inches with lumps of pressed UO_2 weighing about 2140 g. The reproduction factor for this lattice had been measured in a previous exponential experiment and had been found to be 1.039 with a $\nabla^2 = 59 \times 10^{-6} \, \text{cm}^{-2}$.

MEASUREMENTS PERFORMED DURING THE CONSTRUCTION

A series of measurements was performed while the pile was being assembled in order to make sure that the critical dimensions could not be reached inadvertently without taking the proper precautions. These meas-

---

* The neutron density n varies approximately according to the equation $\nabla^2 n = an$, where a is a constant depending on the physical and geometrical structure of the lattice. The value of a is called the Laplacian of the lattice and is denoted by ∇^2. Larger values of ∇^2 correspond to a better structure.

urements had also the purpose of checking the neutron multiplication properties of the structure while it was being assembled so as to permit the determination of the critical point before actually reaching it.

The measurements were performed using two types of detectors. A BF$_3$ counter was inserted in a slot about 43 inches from the ground and its readings were taken at frequent intervals of time. In addition an indium foil was irradiated every night in a position as close as possible to the effective center of the structure and its induced activity was measured the following morning and compared with the readings of the BF$_3$ counter. For these measurements the natural neutrons spontaneously emitted by uranium are a perfectly adequate source and no other source of neutrons was added.

TABLE 92–1. *Measurements on the Pile during Construction*

Layer	A	R_{eff}(cm)	R^2_{eff}/A
15	42	128	390
19	78	158	320
23	119	187	294
25	148	200	270
29	221	225	229
33	345	248	178
36	470	265	149
41	350	288	98
45	1360	308	70
47	1940	317	52
51	4400	332	25
54	12400	344	9.5
57	divergent	356	—

Typical results of these measurements are collected in [Table 92–1]. The first column indicates the height of the structure expressed in number of layers (each layer approximately 4⅛ in.). The second column gives the intensity *A* expressed in counts per minute of a standard indium foil, induced by the natural neutrons when the foil is placed at a central place inside the structure where the neutron intensity is a maximum. Actually, the foils were placed as close as possible to the best position and a small correction was applied in order to account for the fact that the foil was not exactly at the optimal position.

In a spherical structure having the reproduction factor 1 for infinite dimensions the activation of a detector placed at the center due to the natural neutrons is proportional to the square of the radius. For an ellipsoid a similar property holds, the intensity at the center being proportional to the square of an effective radius R_{eff} given by the formula

$$\frac{3}{R^2_{\text{eff}}} = \frac{1}{a^2} + \frac{1}{b^2} + \frac{1}{c^2}, \qquad (1)$$

where a, b, and c are the semi-axes of the ellipsoid. For the case of spherical sectors such as were the shapes of our structure at various stages of its construction, it clearly would be a major mathematical task to determine exactly R_{eff}. It proves, however, rather easy and not too arbitrary to determine graphically for any height of the spherical sector an equivalent flattened ellipsoid [see Fig. 92–1]. The effective radius can then be calculated with formula (1). The values listed in the third column of [Table 92–1] are calculated in this way.

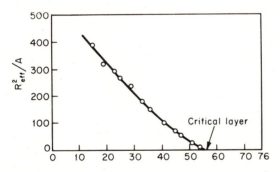

Fig. 92–2. Plot showing the approach to the critical size during construction.

If the reproduction factor were 1 for our lattice the expression given in the fourth column of the table should be a constant. It is seen instead that the values listed in column four decrease steadily and converge to zero at about the 56th layer. This is the point where the critical conditions are attained and where the intensity due to the natural neutrons would become infinitely large. The values of R^2_{eff}/A are plotted in [Fig. 92–2]. The critical layer is at the intersection of the curve with the x axis.

During the construction as a matter of precaution, appreciably before reaching this critical layer, some cadmium strips were inserted in suitable slots. They were removed once every day with the proper precautions in order to check the approach to the critical conditions. The actual construction was carried in this way to the 57th layer, about one layer beyond the critical dimensions. When all the cadmium is removed the effective reproduction factor of the structure is about 1.0006.

MEASURING EQUIPMENT AND CONTROLS

Any detector of neutrons or of gamma-radiation can be used for measuring the intensity of the reaction. Neutron detectors are somewhat preferable since they give a more immediate response to the intensity of the reaction and are not affected by the radiations emitted by the fission products after shut-down of the reaction.

Actually used for determining the intensity of the reaction were several such neutron detectors, namely, two BF_3 proportional counters placed on the outside of the pile and several ionization chambers filled with BF_3 and placed near one of the walls of the pile. These chambers were connected to suitable amplifying systems, and the amplified current was used to operate recording instruments and the automatic controls and safety devices.

The controlling of the reaction was obtained by inserting in the pile some strips of neutron absorbing materials (cadmium and, in one case, boron steel).

When the pile is not in operation, several such cadmium strips are inserted in a number of slots so as to bring the effective reproduction factor considerably below 1. It was actually found that any one of the cadmium strips is alone sufficient to bring the pile below the critical conditions. Besides a number of cadmium strips that can be used for manual operation of the pile, the pile is provided also with two safety rods and one automatic control rod. The safety rods are normally out of the pile during operation. They are kept outside of the pile by a catch operated by a magnet and they are connected to a suitable system of weights so that they are drawn inside the pile by the weights if the catch is released. The magnets are energized by an amplifying system in such a way that they are automatically released if the intensity of the neutrons emitted by the pile rises about a specified limit.

The automatic control rod may be pushed inside and outside the pile by two electric motors and may be operated either by hand or by an amplifying system in such a way that the rod is pushed inside if the intensity of the reaction increases above the desired level, and is pulled outside if the intensity is below the desired level. . . .

OPERATION OF THE PILE

In order to operate the pile, all the cadmium strips except one are first taken out of the pile. The last rod is then slowly pulled out of the pile. As the critical conditions are approached, the intensity of the neutrons emitted by the pile begins to increase rapidly. It should be noticed, however, that when this last strip of cadmium is so far inside the pile that the effective reproduction factor is just below 1, it takes a rather long time for the intensity to reach the saturation value. In a similar way, if the cadmium strip is so far outside of the pile that the reproduction factor is greater than 1, the intensity rises at a rather slow rate. Indeed, for our pile, when all the cadmium is completely outside of the pile, the intensity rises approximately at the rate of a factor of 2 every minute. When the cadmium strip is close to the critical position, these relaxation times become exceedingly long. It has been found, for example, that for one of our controlling strips, the relaxation time is given by: 230 minutes/x, where x is the distance of the rod from the critical position expressed in cm. This means that if the rod is only 1 cm off the critical position, the relaxation time is about 4 hours. For the automatic control rod the corresponding constant is 180 minutes. These long relaxation times which are due to the existence of a small percentage of delayed neutrons emitted in the fission process make it rather easy to keep the pile operating at a constant level of intensity even without the use of automatic regulation. Indeed, to operate the pile at the desired level of intensity, one can usually proceed as follows:

First, the last strip of cadmium is pulled completely outside of the pile and the intensity as indicated by the various measuring devices begins to rise slowly. Since in these conditions, the relaxation time is about two minutes, the desired level of intensity is usually reached in a few minutes. As soon as the meters indicate that the desired level has been attained, the rod is pushed inside the pile to about the critical position. The measuring instruments indicate immediately a steadying of the intensity at about the desired level. In order to keep the level constant, it is sufficient to push the rod one or two cm in or out every once in a while so as to compensate for the small variations in the reproduction factor due primarily to changes of atmospheric pressure.

. . . During the first operation of the pile . . . the intensity was permitted to increase up to a value corresponding to an energy production of about ½ watt. At this point, the automatic safety device operated, and the safety rods were pulled inside the pile and the reaction interrupted. . . .

A higher intensity test was made on December 12 when the pile was operated to an energy production of approximately 200 watts. The test was not run to a higher intensity on account of the limitations imposed by the necessity of keeping the radiation outside of the building well below the physiological tolerance dose. During the operation at high intensity which lasted about 45 minutes, some records of the intensity in various rooms inside the building and on the street outside were taken with standard R-meters and with BF_3 counters and indium foils to detect the neutron intensity. Typical values obtained in this survey are shown in [Table 92–2].

TABLE 92-2. *Radiation Survey in the Vicinity of the Pile*

	Milliroentgen per Minute	Counts per Minute of a Standard Indium Foil at Saturation
Near pile	50	8×10^6
Inside pile room far from pile	6	10^6
Corridors on side of pile room	2	2×10^5
Tower room	0.0005	negligible
Sidewalk of Ellis Street nearest to pile	0.05	6000
Sidewalk of Ellis Street farthest from pile	0.01	2700
Control	0.001	—

COMPARISON OF EXPECTED AND OBSERVED CRITICAL DIMENSIONS

In spite of the fact that the shape of the pile and its internal structure are far from regular, some conclusions may be obtained as to the actual reproduction factors of the various lattices used in the pile and their comparison with the reproduction factors expected from the results of exponential experiments.

We have already indicated [see Fig. 92–1] that the outline of the structure is not far from that of a flattened rotation ellipsoid with a polar semi-axis of 309 cm and an equatorial semi-axis of 388 cm. Formula (1) gives then as effective radius of the structure,

$$R = 355 \text{ cm.}$$

This value of the radius corresponds to a ∇^2 of 78.3×10^{-6} cm^{-2} and to an average reproduction factor of about 1.054.

Since various lattices have been used at various places inside the structure, such values are only mean values for the various lattices used, and they can be compared with the individual values only if the statistical weight pertaining to each kind of lattice is known.

One can prove easily that the statistical weight of each component lattice is in first approximation proportional to its volume multiplied by the mean square density of neutrons over the volume occupied by the given lattice type. An attempt has been made to calculate in this way the statistical weight of the various lattices represented in our structure. The results of this calculation are given in [Table 92–3].

The first column of the table gives the type of lattice. For the sake of simplicity, lattice types having presumably a rather similar reproduction factor have been grouped together under the denomination of Speer. The second column gives the statistical weight of each kind of lattice expressed in percent. The third column gives the values of ∇^2 as obtained from exponential experiments. The weighted average of ∇^2 is 73.4 instead of the value of 78.3 as estimated from the critical dimensions.

This is an indication that the values of ∇^2 and of the reproduction factors as calculated from exponential experiments have been slightly

TABLE 92–3.   *Statistical Weight of Various Lattices in the Pile*

Type of Lattice	Statistical Weight	$\nabla^2 \times 10^6$ from Exponential Experiments
Metal	39.2%	+102
AGOT Brown AGOT	53.5	+ 59
Speer	6.6	+ 45
U. S. Live	0.5	− 10
Dead	0.2	−520
	Weighted average	73.4

underestimated, the correct values being probably about 0.003 or 0.004 higher than the published values.

ENERGY EMITTED BY THE PILE

The number of neutrons emitted by the pile, the number of fissions and the energy produced can be estimated in terms of the activity of standard indium foils placed inside the pile. The standardization of these indium foils has indicated that the following relationship exists between the resonance actvity, A_{Res} expressed in counts/minute at saturation with the foil screened by cadmium, and the slowing down density of neutrons in graphite

$$q = 0.00156 \times A_{\text{Res}}. \qquad (2)$$

The cadmium ratio in the greatest fraction of the volume of our structure is about 6.6; this means that if an activity of A counts/minute at saturation is recorded when the indium foil is not screened by cadmium, the activity with cadmium would be

$$A_{\text{Res}} = A/6.6$$

and consequently,

$$q = 0.00156 \times A/6.6 = 0.000236 \times A.$$

The total number of neutrons that are slowed down inside the pile from above to below indium resonance energy is given, therefore, by:

$$0.000236 \times \overline{A}V,$$

where $\overline{A}$ is the mean value of activity and V is the volume of the pile. We have assumed

$$V = 1.95 \times 10^8 \text{ cc.}$$

On the other hand, one can estimate that $\overline{A}$ is equal to about $0.3 \times$ the activity A_0 at the center of the pile. It follows that the total number of neutrons slowed down in the pile from above to below indium resonance is

$$1.4 \times 10^4 \times A_0.$$

The total number of neutrons produced in the pile is about 13 percent higher, since some of the fast neutrons produced are absorbed at resonance before reaching indium resonance energy and a small fraction escapes from the pile. The total number of neutrons produced is given, therefore, by

$$1.6 \times 10^4 \times A_0. \tag{3}$$

If we assume that 2.2 neutrons per fission are emitted, we obtain from this the number of fissions per second expressed by the formula

$$F = 7200A_0.$$

Assuming that the energy produced per fission is 200 Mev, equivalent to 3.2×10^{-4} erg, the power output of the pile is given by

$$2.3A_0 \text{ erg/sec} = 2.3 \times 10^{-7} \times A_0 \text{ watts.}$$

This formula has been used in the estimates of the power output already given.

୦୦୦୦୦୦୦

ANDERSON, GRAVES, KOONTZ, SEREN, WATTENBERG, WEIL, and ZINN

Construction of the Chain-Reacting Pile [2]

IN THE PREVIOUS SECTIONS OF this report some discussion of the general structural features of the chain-reacting pile is given. In this section the detailed plan of the graphite-uranium system is set forth, together with a brief description of the preparation and testing of the special materials. This work, which occupied a period of three months, required that very careful physical measurements be made on rather large quantities of material. Our indebtedness to the Research Assistants, H. Agnew, D. L. Hill, H. Lichtenberger, G. Miller, R. Nobles, W. Nyer, H. Kubitshek, L. Sayvetz, and W. Strum, upon whom the main burden for carrying out these measurements fell, is here acknowledged.

Two types of measurements on the materials with which it is proposed to build a chain reaction must be made. First, the reproduction factor for the particular graphite-uranium system being used must be determined and, secondly, reasonably large samples of the actual materials of construction must be checked in order to insure that the reproduction factor will not be lowered by the introduction of inferior batches of uranium or graphite. In this instance the problem was somewhat complicated by the fact that in the first chain-reacting pile three different types of graphite-uranium systems had to be used.

DETERMINATION OF THE REPRODUCTION FACTOR

The exponential pile experiment is designed to determine the reproduction factor k of an infinite lattice of uranium lumps in graphite without the necessity of constructing piles of very large dimensions. From such

---

[2] H. L. Anderson *et al., American Journal of Physics,* 20 (1952), 541–550.

pile experiments the optimum cell constants have been determined for pressed UO_2 (density = 6.1 g/cm^3) and cast uranium metal (density = 18 g/cm^3), together with the values of k associated with these optimum lattices in graphite of poorer quality than that available for the chain-reacting pile. For the purpose of designing the chain-reacting pile it was necessary to determine the value of k for the three components (cast uranium metal in AGOT graphite—pressed UO_2 in AGOT graphite—pressed UO_2 in Speer graphite) of its structure. The measurements and results of the exponential piles which were constructed to test these components will be given in this section.

Briefly, the theory of exponential pile measurements is as follows:

If one considers a uranium-graphite lattice structure of square cross section with side equal to a, and semi-infinite height, with a source of fast neutrons at the center of the base, then, at points sufficiently far removed from the source, the neutron intensity will be given by an equation of the form

$$n = \sum_{ij} B_{ij} e^{-x/b_{ij}} \cos \frac{i\pi y}{a} \cos \frac{j\pi z}{a}, \qquad (1a)$$

where the x axis is taken along the vertical axis of the pile, and the $x = 0$ plane coinciding with the base of the pile. Thus, for points on the axis, each harmonic of the neutron intensity decreases exponentially,

$$n = B_{ij} \exp(-x/b_{ij}), \qquad (2a)$$

with a relaxation distance equal to b_{ij}. At a sufficiently large distance from the source the first harmonic only is important. The relaxation length $b(b_{11})$ is related to the reproduction factor k through the following equation:

$$K = \left[1 - \frac{\lambda \Lambda}{3} \left(\frac{1}{b^2} - \frac{2\pi^2}{a^2} \right) \times \exp \left\{ \frac{r_0^2}{4} \left(\frac{1}{b^2} - \frac{2\pi^2}{a^2} \right) \right\} \right], \qquad (3a)$$

where λ = mean free path of thermal neutrons in graphite, Λ = mean free path for absorption collision, and $r_0^2/4$ = the age of nascent thermal neutrons. The quantity

$$\left(\frac{1}{b^2} - \frac{2\pi^2}{a^2} \right) = \frac{1}{c^2},$$

where c is the diffusion length. For the case that k is close to unity, c is very large and $1/c^2$ small so that one can write

$$K = \left[1 - \left(\frac{\lambda \Lambda}{3} + \frac{r_0^2}{4} \right) \left(\frac{1}{b^2} - \frac{2\pi^2}{a^2} \right) \right] \qquad (4a)$$

or

$$K = \left(1 - \frac{L^2}{c^2}\right), \text{ where } L^2 = \left(\frac{\lambda\Lambda}{3} + \frac{r_0^2}{4}\right). \tag{5a}$$

Thus, if L, the migration length, is known, a measurement of the relaxation distance b, associated with the first harmonic of the neutron intensity, will determine the reproduction factor corresponding to a lattice of infinite dimensions similar to the one being tested.

Because of the finite height (124 in.) of an actual exponential pile, two corrections must be applied to the neutron intensity measurements. First, a "harmonic correction" due to the presence of higher harmonics at points near the source; and second, an "end-correction" due to the proximity of the top of a pile to the measuring positions.

To determine the relaxation distance b, indium foils (0.0924 g/cm^2) are placed at positions along the axis of the pile, and the induced 54-minute activity measured on G-M counters. For these measurements the foil is held in a nickel holder; thus, the activation (A_{ni}) is due to both thermal and indium resonance neutrons. (All measurements are corrected to give the activities that would be observed for infinite times of irradiation.) The emission of neutrons by spontaneous fission of the uranium in the pile produces a "background" which must be subtracted from the intensity measurements. Finally, after making the harmonic and end corrections, one calculates b from the relation

$$b = \frac{D}{\ln\{(A_{ni})2/(A_{ni})1\}}, \tag{6a}$$

where D is the distance between the two positions at which (A_{ni}) is measured.

The length of a side a to be used in calculating k from Eq. (4a) must be that value for which the neutron intensity actually becomes equal to 0. (Because of the finite length of the mean free path λ compared to the dimensions of the pile, the effective side is larger than the physical side.) From neutron intensity measurements near the edge of the pile one can estimate the effective value of a.

The migration length L (Eq. (5a)) can be calculated from the graphite density and the cadmium ratio. The cadmium ratio (A_{ni})/(A_{cd}) is the ratio of the activity of a foil with nickel holder (A_{ni}) and the activity (A_{cd}) at the same position when the foil is covered with cadmium. Activation in the latter case is due only to indium resonance neutrons.

The three piles with which we are concerned had the following general features in common. A pile was constructed on a base (AGX graphite), 16 in. high, in the top layer of which a source channel was placed. Four

(Ra + Be) fast neutron sources, each of approximately 0.5 g, were used, and these were divided into two closely equivalent 1 g sources. Each was placed in the channel at positions approximately halfway from the center to the edges of the pile. This arrangement, through cancellation of odd harmonics of the neutron intensity at points along the pile axis, considerably reduced the harmonic correction to be applied to the measurements. The lattice structure measured 99 in. × 99 in. × 123¾ in., and consisted of 15 layers (each 4⅛ in. high) of graphite bearing uranium, alternating with 15 layers of solid graphite. Measuring slots extending to the center of the pile were inserted in horizontal sections corresponding to the even-numbered graphite layers.

In order to eliminate errors caused by slow neutrons being scattered back into the pile from the surroundings, the top and sides of the piles were covered with cadmium sheet.

In specifying the positions at which measurements were made, the following coordinate system and unit of length are used. The origin is taken at the center of the base of the lattice; the x coordinate along the pile axis, the y coordinate in the direction of the line joining the sources, and the z coordinate in the direction of the measuring slots. The fundamental lattice constant (also equal to the distance between two layers of the pile) is taken as the unit of length, and in the piles to be described, is equal to 8.25 in.

Pile No. 18

The structure of this pile consisted of a cubic lattice of pressed UO_2 (Mallinckrodt ether purified) pseudo-spheres (average weight 2143 g) in Speer graphite. The lattice spacing was 8.25 inches, and the ratio of the weight of graphite to that of uranium per cell was 6.4.

A summary of the measurements is given in [Table 92–4].

T A B L E   9 2 – 4 .   *Measurements on Pile No. 18*

Position	Average Intensities [a]			
	With Source		Without Source	Net Intensity
x, y, z	A_{ni}	A_{cd}	A_{ni}	A_{ni}
4, 0, 0	33569		75	33494
6, 0, 0	17373	2747	82	17291
10, 0, 0	4513		70	4443

[a] Counts per minute.

In [Table 92–5] are given the correction factors and corrected intensities together with a least square analysis of the results.

TABLE 92–5. *Analysis of Results of Measurements upon Pile No. 18*

Position x, y, z	Net Intensity from Table 93–4	Harmonic Correction	End Correction	Corrected Intensities	Log l	Least Square Value 5.11350 .14525x
4, 0, 0	33494	1.0193	1.0006	34161	4.5445	4.5325
6, 0, 0	17291	1.0039	1.0022	17396	4.2403	4.2420
10, 0, 0	4443	1.0002	1.0323	4587	3.6615	3.6610

With the distance between positions 4 and 10 equal to 125.8 cm, we obtain for the exponential relaxation distance (Eq. (6a)) $b = 62.74$ cm. The effective side of the pile was estimated to be $a = 256.9$ cm. With this value, and that for b, we calculate

$$\frac{1}{c^2} = \frac{2\pi^2}{a^2} - \frac{1}{b^2} = 45 \times 10^{-6}\,\text{cm}^{-2}$$

and $c = 149$ cm.

From [Table 92–4] we obtain a cadmium ratio equal to 6.32. The value of the migration length, L (Eq. (5a)), can be estimated knowing the graphite density (1.54) and the cadmium ratio. For this pile $L^2 = 712$ cm^2.

From Eq. (5a) we obtain for the reproduction factor

$$k = 1.032.$$

[Comparable data for two other piles listed as No. 27 and No. 29 are omitted—Editors.]

GRAPHITE CROSS-SECTION MEASUREMENTS

. . . Accurate determination of the neutron capture cross section of the graphite to be used in a reacting pile is necessary for two reasons. First, if there is too much absorption in the graphite a chain reaction may be impossible or may require dimensions too large to be practical, and secondly, since the effect of the absorption is proportional to the square of neutron density the use of low cross-section material near the center will reduce the size of the structure. For these reasons cross-section measurements were made on each brand of graphite used in the structure. These were AGX (National Carbon Company), US (U. S. Graphite Company), Speer (Speer Graphite Company), and nine different lots of AGOT (National Carbon Company) graphite. For these measurements a series of σ cross-section piles, described in the following section, were constructed.

Description of σ-Piles

Most of these piles were built on a base of Speer graphite approximately 5×5 ft and about 3 ft high. A source slot through the center of the center layer of this base parallel to one edge measured about 10×10 cm. $\frac{1}{4} \times \frac{1}{4}$-in. graphite strips were fastened to the top of this base in parallel rows 12 in. apart. On these strips a layer of Speer or AGX graphite was laid leaving a $\frac{1}{4}$-in. gap into which cadmium could be inserted. In general, this layer was different from the graphite being measured and was used only because long pieces were available to bridge the ¼-in. gap. Above this layer 15 layers of the material to be tested were laid with detector slots at the top of layers 3, 6, and 9. These slots, numbered 1, 2, and 3, respectively, passed through the vertical axis of the pile perpendicular to the source slot in order that small inaccuracies in placing the foils would have a minimum effect on the measurement and in order to reduce as much as possible the radiation absorbed by operators handling the foils. The entire pile above the gap was covered with cadmium in order to reduce to a minimum the number of thermal neutrons entering the pile from the room.

In those piles built to measure σ for AGX, US, and Speer 1 graphite the dimensions of this top portion were very nearly $5 \times 5 \times 5$ ft. The remaining Speer piles and the AGOT piles were about 168×157 cm and 157 cm high.

THEORY

The thermal neutron density n in a graphite structure containing a source is described by the following differential equation:

$$D\Delta n - (1/t)n + q = 0, \qquad (1b)$$

where D is the diffusion coefficient $= \lambda V/3$, λ is the mean free path for scattering, V is the neutron velocity, t is the mean life of a thermal neutron, and q is the nascent thermal density. If measurements are made with cadmium in the gap and without cadmium in the gap we will have two such equations for the two neutron densities n_1 and n_2. Subtracting these two equations and writing $n = n_2 - n_1$, we have

$$D\Delta n - (1/t)n = 0, \qquad (2b)$$

or

$$L^2\Delta n - n = 0,$$

where L is the diffusion length $(= Dt)$.

We will give the solution of this equation for a rectangular pile whose sides are $(a - 2\lambda/\sqrt{3})$, $(b - 2\lambda/\sqrt{3})$, and $(Z - \lambda/\sqrt{3})$ parallel to the x, y, and z axis, respectively. For boundary conditions we will assume that $n = 0$ when $x = \pm a/2$, $y = \pm b/2$ and $z = Z$. The solution is

$$n = \sum_{lm} B_{lm} \cos \frac{l\pi x}{a} \cos \frac{m\pi y}{b} \left(e^{-z/b_{lm}} - e^{-(2Z-z)/b_{lm}} \right). \qquad (3b)$$

Here b_{lm}, the distance for the intensity of the lm harmonic to decrease by a factor of $1/e$ in a pile of infinite length is related to L by the following equation:

$$\frac{1}{L^2} = \frac{1}{b_{lm}^2} - \pi^2 \left(\frac{l^2}{a^2} + \frac{m^2}{b^2} \right). \tag{4b}$$

Along the vertical axis of the pile the first harmonic of neutron density is proportional to

$$e^{-z/b_{11}} - e^{-(2Z-z)/b_{11}}.$$

The second term of this expression is a reflection from the top of the pile and would not be present in an infinitely tall pile. Hence to correct for the finite height of a pile all intensities along the axis are multiplied by

$$\frac{1}{1 - e^{-2(Z-z)/b_{11}}}, \tag{5b}$$

the so-called end correction.

Equation (4b) gives a means of determining L. One either measures b_{11} far from the source where the higher harmonics are small or corrects the measured intensities for these harmonics and obtains b_{11} closer to the source where the intensity is easier to measure.

This is done as follows: Assuming a value of L, Eq. (4b) permits a calculation of the relaxation length of each harmonic. Writing Eq. (3b) for the z axis we have

$$n = \sum_{lm} B_{lm}(e^{-z/b_{lm}} - e^{-(2Z-z)/b_{lm}}).$$

If two equal sources are used at $x = \pm a/4$, two such solutions must be added and a factor of $\cos l\pi/4$ appears. This causes the 1,3 harmonic to cancel the 3,1 harmonic and the 1,5 to cancel the 5,1 along the Z axis. The 3,3 harmonic is the first to appear and is negative.

To a good approximation we can write

$$n = B_{11}(e^{-z/b_{11}} - e^{-(2Z-z)/b_{11}})$$
$$- B_{33}(e^{-z/b_{33}} - e^{-(2Z-z)/b_{33}}) + \cdots.$$

The harmonic correction factor is therefore

$$\frac{B_{11}}{n} (e^{-z/b_{11}} - e^{-(2Z-z)/b_{11}}).$$

MEASUREMENTS

. . . Measurements were made with indium foils of 26 cm² area weighing 92.4 mg/cm^{-2}. Two counters were used and each determined the activity of three foils from each of the three slots when there was cadmium in the slot and again when the slot was empty. Irradiation times were adjusted to keep the initial counting rates below 1500 counts per minute. The count was started three minutes after the foils were removed from the pile and continued for most measurements until more than 20,000 counts had been recorded. Assuming a half-life of 54 minutes for indium the initial activity after infinite irradiation was calculated. Since the sensitivities of the two counters were not the same, the activities measured on one counter were multiplied by the ratio of sensitivities as determined from measurements on a number of piles. The mean activities at slots 1 and 3 were corrected for harmonics and end effects as explained in the preceding section. Then if these corrected activities are called I_1 and I_3, respectively, b_{11} was obtained from the formula

$$b_{11} = Z_{13}/(\ln_e I_1/I_3),$$

where Z_{13} is the distance between slots 1 and 3. Equation (4b) of the preceding section was used to calculate the diffusion length. These values are given in [Table 92–6], Column 2, for each of the garphites measured.

TABLE 92–6. *Diffusion Lengths and Cross Sections for Various Graphites*

Graphite	L	$L_{1.6}$	$\sigma_a \times 10^{24}$
SP 1	49.53	48.35	0.00549
SP 2	49.77	47.93	0.00563
SP 2′	50.53	48.63	0.00541
TO 1	50.32	50.64	0.00499
TO 0, 2, 3, 4, 5, 6	48.95	49.71	0.00518
TO 8, 9, 13	49.74	50.49	0.00502
T 10	50.83	51.40	0.00484
T 11	51.16	51.70	0.00479
T 12	49.86	50.42	0.00504
T 14	50.14	50.67	0.00499
T 15	49.71	50.96	0.00493
AGX	43.25	43.79	0.00668
U. S.	44.57	44.79	0.00638

Column 1 gives the name of the graphite as stamped on each piece. GX 2 refers to the shipment of AGX cut to $4 \times 4 \times 30$ in. SP 1 refers to the shipment of Speer graphite cut to 10×10 cm cross section. SP 2 and SP 2' refer to Speer graphite cut to $4\frac{1}{8} \times 4\frac{1}{8} \times 16\frac{1}{2}$ in. The prime denotes graphite taken from the ends of the furnace. This graphite was not stamped. TO 1 refers to the 1st lot of AGOT graphite; TO 2 refers to the second lot, and similarly for other lots up to lot 15. Column 3 gives the diffusion length corrected to a density of 1.600 grams/cc, and Column 4 gives the cross section calculated from the formula

$$\sigma_a = \frac{12.8 \times 10^{-24}}{L_{1.6}^2}.$$

It will be noted that the best graphites measured were T 10 and T 11. These lots and some T 14 were used for the core of the pile. The rest of the AGOT formed a rough sphere around this. SP 2 and SP 2' graphite was placed outside this. At the very outside of the pile US and GX 2 graphite was used interchangeably.

PRESSING OF URANIUM OXIDE

The greater part of the pile contains uranium dioxide lumps which were fabricated by compressing loose dry UO_2 powder in a die with a hydraulic press. The chief problem here was the design of the die. . . . It is essential that the die be made of a good quality tool steel, hardened and ground and polished since the powder has a considerable abrasive action. The force used in making the briquettes was in the range of 150 to 175 tons. Lubrication of the die proved to be important and it was found that a dilute solution (0.5 percent by weight) of stearic acid in acetone was quite satisfactory. A small amount of a wetting agent (ethylene glycol) was added to the lubricant so that when it was brushed on the polished surface of the die it would spread evenly. After some experience in handling the dies had been obtained it was possible to fabricate with one press 400 to 500 briquettes in an 8-hour working day.

MACHINING OF GRAPHITE

The graphite is received from the manufacturer in bars of $4\frac{1}{4} \times 4\frac{1}{4}$-in. cross section and in lengths from 17 in. to 50 in. The surfaces are quite rough and therefore it is necessary that they be made smooth and that bricks of a standard length be cut.

For this work ordinary wood-working machines were used. Two surfaces are first made plane and accurately perpendicular to each other in a jointer and the remaining two surfaces are finished by a planer. A swing-saw was used for cutting to length. The surfaces were held to ± 0.005 inch and the length to ± 0.020 inch. The only departure from this was a slight rippling which appeared occasionally as the result of dull blades or improper manipulation of the work on the machines. Molybdenum steel cutting blades were used in these machines and resharpening, although a constant chore, was not so frequent as to cause any real difficulty. About 14 tons of material could be prepared in this way per 8-hour working day. In all 40,000 bricks were required.

A further graphite machining operation was the drilling of the $3\frac{1}{4}$-in. diameter holes with shaped bottoms, which were required to permit the insertion of the UO_2 briquettes into the graphite. These holes were drilled in a single operation by mounting a spade bit in the head stock of a heavy lathe and forcing the brick up to the tool with the lathe carriage. Due care had to be given to the design of the cutting tool, and to the alignment and centering of the bit.

These tools required frequent resharpening and, in fact, this proved to be the only difficulty in this operation. Carballoy bits showed the longest life but were rejected because of the greater effort required in preparing them. Bits ground from old files proved to be most satisfactory; about 60 holes could be drilled without resharpening. Actual drilling of the hole required about 20 seconds and from 60 to 100 holes per hour was the usual rate for the whole operation. A total of 22,000 holes were drilled.

CONSTRUCTION OF THE PILE

The unit cell of the graphite-uranium lattice has a side of $8\frac{1}{4}$ in. and a volume of 0.324 cu ft. In order to achieve this lattice the graphite bricks were machined to a cross section of $4\frac{1}{8} \times 4\frac{1}{8}$ in. and were cut to a length of $16\frac{1}{2}$ in. The structure was planned as a sphere of maximum radius of 13 ft; the choice of a sphere being necessary because of the fact that probably not sufficient material would be available for any other shape which would be chain reacting. The decision to build a sphere necessitated two important additions to the structure. The first of these was a wooden framework in which the sphere was inscribed, and secondly, a graphite pier which supports the side of the sphere through which the control rods pass. It was believed to be entirely possible that after the structure was erected that the wood might warp or shrink and cause some displacement of the graphite above it. Since this would be undesirable from the point of view of passing control rods into the pile, that part of the pile through which the rods pass is entirely supported by this graphite pier. Originally it had been intended to evacuate the pile and, therefore, considerable pains were taken to see that the wooden framework fitted the graphite securely and that it presented a smooth continuous surface to the surrounding balloon cloth envelope. It turned out, however, that evacuation was not necessary and, therefore, these details are unimportant.

The cube in which the sphere is inscribed has a side of 24 ft 2 in. From this it follows that a part of the 26-ft diameter sphere is cut off on the sides; these parts represent a rather small percentage of the total volume of the sphere. As planned the sphere was to have a shell 1 in. thick on the outside made up of graphite without uranium or so-called dead graphite. The graphite-uranium lattice was expected to occupy a sphere of 12-ft radius and have a total volume of 7200 cu ft and hence about 22,300 cells were expected to be included in the structure.

As has been indicated earlier not all of the material available was of uniform quality and in order to use this material most efficiently that of highest quality was placed at the center with the less reactive types arranged in concentric shells; the quality decreasing outward from the center. The 26-ft diameter sphere would have required that about 75 layers of the $4\frac{1}{8}$-in. thick bricks would be piled up; however, the chain-reacting condition was reached at the 57th layer. The actual amount of graphite in the pile is indicated in [Table 92–7] in which also the amounts of each brand are given.

TABLE 92–7. *Graphite in Pile*

Source	Brand	Lbs
National Carbon Co.	AGOT	510,000
Speer Graphite Co.		145,000
U. S. Graphite Co.	U. S.	32,000
National Carbon Co.	AGX	60,000
AGX + Speer (Pier only)		24,000
		771,000 = 385.5 tons

The US and AGX brands had dimensions somewhat different than the majority of the graphite and since they are of lower quality they were mostly used in the outer shell of dead graphite.

In [Table 92–8] the details of the uranium lumps are given. Column 1 gives the geometrical form of the lump.

The designation $3\frac{1}{4}$-in. pseudosphere indicates pressings which were cylinders of $3\frac{1}{4}$ in. diameter and $3\frac{1}{4}$ in. height, but which had the edges cut off at 45° so that they were roughly spherical. The designation 3-in. cylinder means a cylinder of height and diameter of 3 in. Since five varieties of uranium lumps and four brands of graphite were used a considerable variation in the combination making up the cell was possible.

TABLE 92–8. *Uranium in Pile*

Geometrical Shape	Compound	Weight	Density g/cm³	Number	Total Weight in Pile
2¼-in. cylinder	Metal	6.0 lb	18	2060	12,400 lb
3¼-in. pseudosphere	UO₂	4.72	6.10	14,840	70,000
3¼-in. pseudosphere	U₃O₈	3.99	5.17	1200	4790
3-in. cylinder	UO₂	4.56	6.14	540	2460
3-in. cylinder	U₃O₈	3.97	5.20	840	3340
				19,480	92,990 = 46.5 tons

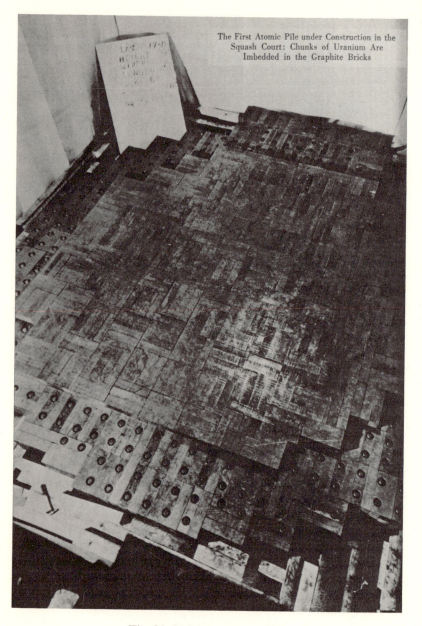

The First Atomic Pile under Construction in the Squash Court: Chunks of Uranium Are Imbedded in the Graphite Bricks

Fig. 92–3. A layer of the pile.

Metal—AGOT. Uranium metal cylinders combined with the highest quality AGOT graphite.

AGOT Br + AGOT. $3\frac{1}{4}$-in. pseudosphere of UO_2 inserted in an AGOT graphite brick and combined with undrilled AGOT bricks to make up the lattice.

Sp. Br + Sp. $3\frac{1}{4}$-in. pseudosphere of UO_2 inserted in a Speer graphite brick and combined with undrilled Speer bricks to make up the lattice.

AGOT Bl + Sp. $3\frac{1}{4}$-in. pseudosphere of U_3O_8 inserted in a drilled brick of AGOT graphite and combined with undrilled Speer bricks to make up the lattice.

[Figure 92–3] is a photograph of the 19th and 18th layers. The roughly spherical form of the structure is shown and also some of the supporting wood frame work. The lattice is maintained in the vertical direction by inserting between two oxide bearing layers a layer of dead graphite. Layer 19 as shown in the photograph is only partially completed.

A total of 10 slots passing completely through the pile were provided. Three of these near the center are used for the control and safety rods, the remainder being available for experimental purposes. In addition one row of bricks carrying uranium lumps and passing very close to the center of the pile is arranged so that it can be pushed completely out of the pile. This construction permits the removal of samples from the pile and is useful for experimental purposes.

ㅇㅇㅇㅇㅇㅇㅇㅇ

F E R M I

Elementary Theory of the Chain-Reacting Pile [3]

ABSORPTION AND PRODUCTION OF NEUTRONS IN A PILE

WE CONSIDER A MASS, ''THE pile,'' containing uranium spread in some suitable arrangement throughout a block of graphite. Whenever a fission takes place in this system, an average number (v) of neutrons is emitted with a continuous distribution of energy of the order of magnitude of 1,000,000 EV. After a neutron is emitted, its energy decreases by elastic collisions with the atoms of carbon and to

---

[3] Fermi, *Science*, 105 (1947), 27–32.

some extent also by inelastic collisions with the uranium atoms. In the majority of cases the neutrons will be slowed down to thermal energies. This process requires about 100 collisions with carbon atoms. After the energy of the neutron is reduced to thermal value, the neutron keeps on diffusing until it is finally absorbed. In several cases, however, it will happen that the neutron is absorbed before the slowing-down process is completed.

The neutron may be absorbed by either the carbon or the uranium. The absorption cross-section of carbon for neutrons of thermal energy is quite small, its value being approximately .005 $\times$ 10^{-24} cm.^{2} For graphite of density 1.6, this corresponds to a mean free path for absorption of about 25 m. It is believed that the absorption cross-section follows the 1/v law, and consequently the absorption cross-section, which is already quite small at thermal energies, becomes practically negligible for neutrons of higher energy. It is therefore a sufficiently good approximation to assume that absorption by carbon during the slowing-down process can be neglected.

The absorption of a neutron by uranium may lead either to fission or to absorption by a (n, γ) process. We shall refer to this last possibility as the process of resonance absorption. The relative importance of fission and resonance absorption in the different energy intervals is not the same. In this respect we can consider roughly three intervals:

(1) Neutrons with energy above the fission threshold of U^{238}—We can call these conventionally "fast neutrons." For fast neutrons the most important absorption process is fission, which normally takes place in the abundant isotope U^{238}. Resonance absorption is smaller but not negligible.

(2) Neutrons of energy below the fission threshold of U^{238} and above thermal energy—We shall refer to these neutrons as "epithermal neutrons." For epithermal neutrons the most important absorption process is the resonance capture. The cross-section for this process as a function of energy is quite irregular and presents a large number of resonance maxima that can be fairly well represented by the Breit-Wigner theory. In practical cases the resonance absorption becomes important for neutron energy below about 10,000 EV and increases as the energy of the neutrons decreases.

(3) Neutrons having thermal agitation energy or "thermal neutrons" —For thermal neutrons both the resonance and fission absorption processes are important. In this energy range both cross-sections follow approximately the 1/v law, and therefore their relative importance becomes practically independent of the energy. Let σ_f and σ_r be the cross-sections for fission and resonance absorption for neutrons of energy kT, and η be the average number of neutrons emitted when a thermal neutron is absorbed by uranium. Then η differs from v, since only the fraction

$\sigma_f/(\sigma_\nu + \sigma_f)$ of all the thermal neutrons absorbed by uranium produces a fission. It is, therefore,

$$\eta = \nu\sigma_f/(\sigma_f + \sigma_\nu). \tag{1}$$

The preceding discussion leads one to conclude that only a fraction of the original fast neutrons produced will end up by producing a fission process. For systems of finite size, further losses of neutrons will be expected by leakage outside the pile.

Limiting ourselves for the present to systems of practically infinite dimensions, we shall call P the probability that a fast neutron ultimately is absorbed by the fission process. The average number of neutrons produced in the "second generation" by the first neutron will then be

$$k = P\nu. \tag{2}$$

Usually, k is called the "reproduction factor" of the system. A self-sustaining chain reaction evidently is possible only when $k > 1$. If this is the case, the reaction actually will take place provided the leakage loss of neutrons is sufficiently small. This, of course, can always be achieved if the size of the pile is large enough.

LIFE HISTORY OF A NEUTRON

When a fast neutron is first emitted in our pile, the following events may take place:

(1) There is a small probability that the neutron will be absorbed by uranium before its energy has been appreciably decreased. If this is the case, the absorption leads often to fission of U^{238}. The probability of such fast fissions, however, is usually only a few per cent. Indeed, if the system contains little uranium and a large amount of carbon, the elastic collisions with carbon tend to reduce the energy very rapidly to a value below the fission threshold of U^{238}. If, on the other hand, the system is very rich in uranium, the inelastic collision processes become very probable and rapidly reduce the energy of the original fast neutron to a fairly low value before it has a chance to produce a fission in U^{238}.

(2) In the large majority of the cases, therefore, the neutron is not absorbed as a fast neutron and rapidly loses its energy, mostly due to collision against the carbon atoms. One can prove in an elementary way that it takes about 6.3 collisions against the carbon atoms to reduce the energy by an average factor of e. Consequently, it will take about 14.6 collisions in order to reduce the energy by a factor of 10, and about 110 collisions to reduce the energy from 1,000,000 EV to the thermal energy value of

$\frac{1}{40}$ v. While this slowing-down process is in progress, the neutron may be absorbed by the resonance process in uranium. We shall call p the probability that a neutron is not absorbed before reaching thermal energy. One of the most important factors in designing a pile consists in trying to minimize the probability that neutrons are removed from the system by resonance absorption during the slowing down.

(3) If the neutron is not absorbed during the slowing-down process, it eventually reaches thermal energy and ultimately will be absorbed by either uranium or carbon. If uranium and carbon were mixed uniformly, the probability for these two events would be in the ratio of the absorption cross-sections of uranium and carbon for thermal neutrons multiplied by the atomic concentrations of the two elements. Since actually the mixture is not uniform, this is only approximately true. We shall call f the probability that a thermal neutron is absorbed by uranium. In designing a chain-reacting pile one will normally try to adjust things so as to have both f and p as large as possible. Unfortunately, the two requirements are contradictory, because in order to make f large, one shall try to build a system very rich in uranium in order to reduce the probability of absorption of thermal neutrons by carbon. On the other hand, in a system containing a relatively small amount of carbon the slowing-down process will be relatively slow, and consequently the probability of resonance absorption during the slowing down will be large.

It is clear, therefore, that one shall have to conciliate two opposite requirements by finding an optimum value for the ratio of uranium to carbon.

In a homogeneous mixture of uranium and carbon the values of f and p depend only on the relative concentrations of the two elements. If we do not restrict ourselves, however, to homogeneous mixtures only, one can try to obtain a more favorable situation by proper arrangement of the geometrical distribution of the two components. This actually is possible to a considerable extent, because of the following circumstances. The resonance absorption which is responsible for the loss of neutrons during the slowing down has very sharp cross-section maxima of the Breit-Wigner type. Therefore, if the uranium, instead of being spread through the graphite mass, is concentrated in rather sizable lumps, we will expect that the uranium in the interior of a lump will be shielded by a thin surface layer from the action of neutrons with energy close to a resonance maximum. Therefore, the resonance absorption of a uranium atom inside the lump will be much less than it would be for an isolated atom. Of course, self-absorption in a lump reduces not only the resonance absorption but also the thermal absorption of uranium. One can expect theoretically, however, and experiment has confirmed, that at least up to a certain size of lumps the gain obtained by reducing the resonance loss of neutrons overbalances by a considerable amount the loss due to a lesser absorption of thermal neutrons.

The typical structure of a pile is a lattice of uranium lumps embedded in a matrix of graphite. The lattice may be, for example, a cubic lattice of lumps or a lattice of rods of uranium. This latter arrangement is slightly less efficient from the point of view of the neutron absorption balance but often presents some practical advantages, since it makes easier the removal of the heat produced by the pile. In the present discussion we shall consider only lattices of lumps.

TABLE 92-9.

Probability (%)	Type of Process	Neutrons Produced per Neutron Absorbed	Neutrons per Generation by One Neutron
3	Fast fission	2	.06
10	Resonance absorption	0	0
10	Absorption by carbon	0	0
77	Absorption by uranium at thermal energies	η	.77 η

It is useful to give some typical figures for the probabilities of the various absorption processes. These probabilities, of course, are not constant but depend on the details of the structure of the lattice. Average figures for a good lattice will be given as an example. When a neutron is first produced by a fission taking place in a lump of uranium, it may have a probability of the order of 3 per cent of being absorbed, giving rise to fission before losing any appreciable amount of energy. In 97 per cent of the cases when this does not happen the neutron will initiate its slowing-down process, and it may either be absorbed by the resonance process during the slowing down or reach thermal energy. The probability of resonance absorption during the slowing down may be of the order of 10 per cent, so that 87 per cent of the original neutrons will be slowed down to thermal energies. Of these, perhaps 10 per cent may be absorbed by carbon and the remaining 77 per cent by uranium. If we assume for the purpose of example that $v = 2$, we shall have in one generation the processes summarized in [Table 92–9]. For the example given, the reproduction factor will be, therefore,

$$k = .06 + .77\eta. \qquad (3)$$

Consequently, a lattice of the type described would have a reproduction factor larger than 1, provided η is larger than 1.22.

In order to evaluate the reproduction factor one must be able to calculate the probabilities for the various processes mentioned. Some points of view which may be used in the practical calculation will be indicated briefly.

PROBABILITY OF FISSION BEFORE SLOWING DOWN

The value of this quantity is very easily calculable for a very small lump of uranium. In this case it is obviously given by

$$P_F = \sigma_F \, nd, \qquad (4)$$

where σ_F is the average value of the fission cross-section for fission neutrons; n is the concentration of uranium atoms in the lump; and d is the average value of the distance that the neutron produced in the lump must travel before reaching the surface of the lump. The case of a lump of larger size is more complicated, since then multiple collision processes become important and both elastic and inelastic scattering play a considerable role. In particular, the last process for a lump of large size effectively slows down the neutrons before the fission threshold of U^{238} and brings them down to an energy level in which they are readily absorbed by the resonance process.

RESONANCE ABSORPTION

If we had a single atom of uranium in a graphite medium where fast neutrons are produced and slowed down to thermal energy, the probability per unit time of a resonance absorption process of neutrons with energy larger than thermal energy would be given by the following expression:

$$\frac{q\lambda}{.158} \int \sigma(E) \, \frac{dE}{E}, \qquad (5)$$

where q is the number of fast neutrons entering the system per unit time and unit volume, λ is the mean free path, and $\sigma(E)$ is the resonance absorption cross-section at energy E. The integral must be taken between a low limit just above thermal energy and an upper limit equal to the average energy of the fission neutrons. One will expect that the largest contribution to the integral will be due to the Breit-Wigner peaks of $\sigma(E)$.

The above formula would be very much in error in the case of a lattice of lumps. As already indicated, this is due to the fact that inside a lump there is an important self-screening effect that reduces very considerably the density of neutrons having energy close to a resonance maximum.

The best approach to a practical solution to the problem is therefore a direct measurement of the number of neutrons absorbed by resonance in lumps of uranium of various sizes.

Measurements of this type have been performed first at Princeton University, and the results have been summarized in practical formulas that are used in the calculations.

PROBABILITY OF ABSORPTION AT THERMAL ENERGIES

If uranium and carbon were uniformly mixed, a thermal neutron would have a probability

$$\frac{N_U \sigma_U}{N_C \sigma_C + N_U \sigma_U} \tag{6}$$

to be absorbed by uranium. In this formula N_C and N_U represent the numbers of atoms of carbon and of uranium per unit volume, and σ_C and σ_U represent the cross-sections of carbon and uranium for thermal neutrons.

More complicated is the case of a lattice distribution of lumps of uranium in graphite, since the density of thermal neutrons throughout the system is not uniform but is large at the places far from the uranium lumps and smaller near and inside the uranium lumps, due to the fact that the absorption of thermal neutrons is much greater in uranium than in graphite. Let $\overline{n_C}$ and $\overline{n_U}$ be the average densities of thermal neutrons in the graphite and in the uranium lumps. The number of thermal neutrons absorbed by uranium and by carbon will be proportional to $N_U \, \sigma_U \, \overline{n_U}$ and $N_C \, \sigma_C \, \overline{n_C}$, and we will have, therefore, instead of Equation (6), the corrected formula,

$$f = \frac{N_U \, \sigma_U \, \overline{n_U}}{N_U \, \sigma_U \, \overline{n_U} + N_C \, \sigma_C \, \overline{n_C}}. \tag{7}$$

For practical purposes it is usually sufficiently accurate to calculate $\overline{n_C}$ and $\overline{n_U}$, using the diffusion theory. The approximation is made to substitute the lattice cell by a spherical cell having volume equal to that of the actual cell, with the boundary condition that the radial derivative of the density of neutrons vanishes at the surface of the sphere. It is also assumed that the number of neutrons that are slowed down to thermal energies per unit time and unit volume is constant throughout the graphite part of the cell. This approximation is fairly correct, provided the dimensions of the cell are not too large. With these assumptions one finds the following formula for the probability, f, that thermal neutrons be absorbed by uranium:

$$f = \frac{3\alpha^2}{\alpha^3 - \beta^3} \cdot \frac{(1-\alpha)(1+\beta)e^{-\beta+\alpha} - (1+\alpha)(1-\beta)e^{\beta-\alpha}}{(\alpha+s-s\alpha)(1+\beta)e^{-\beta+\alpha} - (\alpha+s+s\alpha)e^{\beta-\alpha}} \quad (8)$$

where α and β represent the radius of the lump and the radius of the cell expressed taking the diffusion length in graphite, $1 = \sqrt{\lambda\Lambda/3}$, as unit of length. It is further

$$s = \frac{\lambda}{\sqrt{3}} \frac{1+\gamma}{1-\gamma}, \quad (9)$$

where γ is the reflection coefficient of the lump for thermal neutrons.

LATTICE CONTAINING A LARGE NUMBER OF CELLS

The density of neutrons of any given energy in a lattice containing a large number of cells is a function of the position in the lattice. One can arrive at a simple mathematical description of the behavior of such a system by neglecting in first approximation the local variation of such functions due to the periodic structure of the lattice and substituting for the actually inhomogeneous system an equivalent homogeneous system. In this section we shall accordingly simplify the problem by substituting for all densities of neutrons values obtained by averaging the actual values over the volume of the cell. The densities will then be represented by smooth functions such as one would expect in a homogeneous uranium-graphite mixture.

Let $Q(x, y, z)$ be the number of fast neutrons produced per unit time and unit volume at each position in the lattice. These neutrons diffuse through the mass and are slowed down. During this process some of the neutrons are absorbed at resonance. Let $q(x, y, z)$ be the number of neutrons per unit time and unit volume which become thermal at the position x, y, z—q is called the "density of the nascent thermal neutrons."

We shall assume that if an original fast neutron is generated at a point, 0, the probability that it becomes thermal at a given place has a Gaussian distribution around 0. This assumption may be justified by considering that the diffusion process of slowing down consists of very many free paths. Experimentally one finds that the distribution curve of the nascent thermal neutrons around a point source of fast neutrons is represented only approximately by a Gaussian distribution, and formulas have been used in which the actual distribution is described as a superposition of two or three Gaussian curves with different ranges. For the purpose of the present discussion, however, we shall take only one. For each fast neutron produced only p neutrons reach thermal energy. The distribution of nascent thermal neutrons produced by a source of strength 1, placed at the origin of the coordinate, shall then be represented by

$$q_1 = \frac{p}{\pi^{3/2} r_0^3} e^{-r^2/r_0^2}. \tag{10}$$

For graphite of density 1.6 the range, r_0, is of the order of 35 cm. The density of nascent thermal neutrons at point P can be expressed in terms of Q by adding up the contribution of all the infinitesimal sources, $Q(P')d\tau'$ ($d\tau'$ represents the volume element around the point, P'). We obtain in this way

$$q(P) = \frac{p}{\pi^{3/2} r_0^3} \int Q(P') e^{-((P'-P)^2/r_0^2)} 2\tau'. \tag{11}$$

The density, $n(x, y, z)$, of the thermal neutrons is connected to q by the differential equation,

$$\frac{\lambda v}{3} \Delta n - \frac{v}{\Lambda} n + q = 0, \tag{12}$$

where λ is the collision mean free path of thermal neutrons, v is their velocity, and Λ is the mean free path for absorption of a thermal neutron. Equation (12) is obtained by expressing a local balancing of all processes whereby the number of thermal neutrons at each place tends to increase or decrease. The first term represents the increase in number of neutrons due to diffusion ($\lambda v/3$ is the diffusion coefficient of thermal neutrons); the second, the loss of neutrons due to absorption; and the third, the effect of the nascent thermal neutrons.

It should be noted that the absorption mean free path Λ in Equation (12) is much shorter than the corresponding quantity, Λ_0, in pure graphite. Indeed, the absorption in the lattice is due mostly to the uranium. In first approximation Λ is given by

$$\Lambda = (1 - f)\Lambda_0. \tag{13}$$

In practical cases Λ may be of the order of magnitude of 300 cm., whereas Λ_0 in graphite without uranium is about 2,500 cm.

When a thermal neutron is absorbed by uranium, η new neutrons are produced by fission. This number should be increased by a few per cent in order to take into account the effect of the small probability of fast fission. Let $\epsilon\eta$ be the total number of fast neutrons so corrected.

The number of thermal neutrons absorbed per unit volume and unit time is $\frac{V\eta}{\Lambda}$. Of these, the fraction f is absorbed by uranium. We have, therefore,

$$Q = f\eta \, \epsilon \, \frac{V}{\Lambda} n + Q_0, \qquad (14)$$

where $f\eta\epsilon \, \frac{V}{\Lambda}$ represents the number of fast neutrons produced in the chain reaction process, and Q_0 represents the number of fast neutrons produced by an outside source if one is present. In most cases, of course, Q_0 will be equal to 0. From Equations (11), (12), and (14) we can eliminate all unknowns except n, and we find

$$\frac{3}{\lambda\Lambda} n - \Delta n = \frac{3p \, \epsilon \, \eta f}{\pi^{3/2} r_0^3 \Lambda \lambda} \int n(P') e^{-(P'-P)^2/r_0^2} \, d\tau'$$

$$\qquad (15)$$

$$+ \frac{3p}{\pi^{3/2} r_0^3 \lambda v} \int Q_0(P') e^{-(P'-P)^2/r_0^2} \, d\tau'.$$

A solution of this equation is obtained readily by developing both Q_0 and n in a Fourier series. The general term of this development, corresponding to Q_0 of the form $Q_0 \sin \omega_1 x \sin \omega_2 y \sin \omega_3 z$, is:

$$n = \frac{(\Lambda p Q_0/v) \sin \omega_1 x \sin \omega_2 y \sin \omega_3 z}{\left(1 + \frac{\lambda\Lambda}{3} \omega^2\right) e^{\omega^2 r_0^2/4} - \epsilon \, pf\eta}, \qquad (16)$$

where $\omega^2 = \omega_1^2 + \omega_2^2 + \omega_3^2$.

When the dimensions of the pile are finite but very large compared with mean free path, the boundary condition is that all densities must vanish at the surface. If the pile, for example, is a cube of side a and the origin of the coordinates is taken in one of the corners, it is:

$$\omega_1 = \frac{\pi n_1}{a}; \quad \omega_2 = \frac{\pi n_2}{a}; \quad \omega_3 = \frac{\pi n_3}{a}, \qquad (17)$$

where n_1, n_2, n_3 are positive integral numbers that define the various Fourier components. The critical dimensions of the system are such that the denominator of Equation (16) vanishes for the 1, 1, 1 harmonic, since in this case the density of the neutrons becomes infinitely large. The critical condition can be expressed, therefore, by the equation:

$$\left(1 + \frac{3\pi^2}{a^2}\frac{\lambda\Lambda}{3}\right)e^{3\pi^2/a^2r_0^2/4} = \epsilon\, pf\eta. \tag{18}$$

The right-hand side in this formula is the reproduction factor, *k*, for a system of infinite size. We can therefore write the critical condition as follows:

$$k = \left(1 + \frac{3\pi^2}{a^2}\frac{\lambda\Lambda}{3}\right)e^{3\pi^2/a^2r_0^2/4}. \tag{19}$$

In most cases both the exponent of *e* and the term added to 1 in the parentheses are small compared with 1, and so the previous expression can be simplified to:

$$k = 1 + \frac{3\pi^2}{a^2}\left(\frac{\lambda\Lambda}{3} + \frac{r_0^2}{4}\right). \tag{20}$$

This formula can be used in order to calculate the critical side of a pile of cubical shape. If, for example, we assume for a special lattice numerical values of $\lambda = 2.6$ cm., $\Lambda = 350$ cm., $r_0^2 = 1,200$ cm.^{2}, and $k = 1.06$, we find for the critical side of a cubical pile, a = 584 cm. Naturally, these constants are merely hypothetical, and though included within the possible range, are in practical cases strongly dependent on the details of the lattice structure.

It is useful to derive an approximate relationship between the power produced by a pile and the intensity of thermal neutrons inside it. Roughly 50 per cent of the thermal neutrons absorbed in a pile give rise to fission, and the energy released per fission is of the order of 200 MEV. This corresponds to about 1.6×10^{-4} ergs per thermal neutron absorbed. Since the number of thermal neutrons absorbed per unit volume is vn/Λ, the energy produced is approximately

$$\frac{vn}{\Lambda}\, 1.6 \times 10^{-4} \cong 4.6 \times 10^{-7}\, vn\ \text{ergs/cm.}^3\ \text{sec.} \tag{21}$$

Naturally, the power is not produced uniformly throughout the pile because *n* is a maximum at the center and decreases to 0 at the edge of the pile. For a cubical pile *n* is represented approximately by

$$n = n_0 \sin\frac{\pi x}{a} \sin\frac{\pi y}{a} \sin\frac{\pi z}{a}, \tag{22}$$

where n_0 is the density of neutrons at the center of the pile. Integrating the previous expression (21) over all the volume of the pile, one obtains the following formula for the power:

$$W = \frac{8}{\pi^3}\, 4.6 \times 10^{-7}\, nv\, a^3 = 1.2 \times 10^{-7}\, n_0\, v\, a^3. \qquad (23)$$

If, again, we take as an example a pile with a side of 584 cm., we find $W = 24\, n_0\, v$ ergs/ sec. When the pile is operating at a power of 1 kw., the flux of thermal neutrons at the center is therefore about $n_0 v = 4 \times 10^8$ neutrons/cm.^{2} sec. . . .

93

ooooooooooo

POWER FROM FUSION

ooooooooooo

Ernest William Titterton (b. 1914)

The preceding chapter contains Fermi's account of the construction of the first "pile" or nuclear reactor together with his elementary theory of its operation. This great achievement was effected under Fermi's direction by a group of able scientists working under the stress of wartime conditions to develop a means of producing plutonium and the super-bomb that could be realized with its use. But it was also clear that the controlled release of fission energy would provide a new power source that in the years to come would compete with fossil fuels and then out-distance them as a prime source of power. Less than a quarter century has gone by since the initial operation of Fermi's reactor, but already power reactors are in use for generating electricity in countries all around the world. Areas in which it was impracticable to operate conventional generating stations now have the advantages and convenience of electricity; for example, experimental power reactors are in operation on the Antarctic continent and in northern Greenland. But this great advance also carries with it problems that will assume larger and larger proportions as time goes on. For purposes of this discussion and to avoid complexity, we shall limit ourselves only to the problems connected with power generation and with the uranium-graphite reactor.

The fission process itself produces a number of radioactive nuclei; this energy, resident in the fission products, amounts to about 5 per cent of the total energy released. Although the initial decay of fission radio-activity is rapid, significant long-lived activities remain. The half-life of the latter is about 30 years. The fission products remain in the cylindrical slugs of uranium metal spaced in a lattice structure in the moderator matrix of the reactor. As the products accumulate they reduce the probability of fission and the efficiency of the reactor decreases. Eventually, the slugs must be replaced as more and more of the uranium is "burned up" and the proportion of "ash" increases. But the metal removed from the reactor is highly radioactive. Until the short-lived activity has decayed sufficiently the slugs are stored under water, which serves as a radiation shield. They are then subjected to chemical treatment to reclaim the plutonium produced and the residual uranium. The liquid waste containing the radioactive ash must then be disposed of.

With few fission plants in operation this problem, although difficult, is not large. But it has been estimated that if the world's power were generated with fission reactors, about 10^9 curies per year of activity would require disposal. This is such an enormous activity that if it were dispersed uniformly in the Atlantic Ocean it would significantly raise the activity of the water. In any event, to dump radioactive wastes in the ocean could cause damaging world-wide biological changes that could persist for years. Alternatively, the dumping of liquid wastes into the earth is accompanied by seepage hazards that appear insupportable. The safest procedure appears to consist of fixing the waste in certain clay materials, in concrete blocks, or incorporating it in glass which is highly resistant to solution or leaching. Disposal of these solids in abandoned dry mines or in the desert appears feasible.

It will be apparent even from this brief review that the disposal of radioactive waste products from fission reactors poses an increasingly urgent, world-wide biological and health problem that should be regulated by international agreement. To produce nuclear power without generating such a hazard would indeed be a highly desirable goal. Is there any possibility that it may be achieved? Fortunately, the *possibility* exists through the use of nuclear *fusion* instead of fission. Fission involves the splitting of heavy atoms located at the end of the periodic table; fusion involves the building of light atoms from hydrogen at the beginning of the periodic table. Interestingly enough, the production of huge amounts of power by nuclear fusion is a natural process and goes on throughout the universe. It is the process by which our sun generates the heat by which all the stars radiate. Nuclear fusion as a source of stellar radiation was first investigated in a theoretical paper by Atkinson and Houtermans in 1929. Very little was added to their work until about ten years later when Bethe discovered the specific nuclear reactions that take place to produce this energy (see Chapter 90). Unfortunately, to produce fusion artificially is a task of much greater magnitude than to produce fission. A brief analysis will show why.

In order to make two atoms stick together after a collision and produce a new nucleus it is necessary for their nuclei to approach each other closely enough so that the short-range nuclear forces can act to make them coalesce. But such a close approach requires relatively enormous energy in order to overcome the long-range Coulomb force of repulsion arising from the like charges of the nuclei. It appears that the simplest way to endow atoms with the requisite high speeds for fusion, consistent with allowing them repeated opportunities for collision, is to heat the atoms concerned as a gas. The thermal motion of the gas atoms thus provides the continual collisions. But gas temperatures in the millions of degrees are required for fusion and no container exists that will withstand such temperatures. There is, however, the possibility of creating an electrical discharge with the desired atoms—hydrogen, in this instance—and containing the moving ions by means of an impressed magnetic field. The ions therefore are essentially in a magnetic "bottle." Fifteen years of research have been expended on this method and considerable progress has been made, but a successful fusion reactor still appears far away. An account of the way in which fusion comes about and how this process proceeds naturally in the stars is lucidly explained in the following excerpt from E. W. Titterton's book *Facing the Atomic Future*.

Ernest William Titterton, a native of England, was born on March 4, 1914. He received his early education at the Queen Elizabeth School in Tamworth, Staffordshire, and went from there to the University of Birmingham where he obtained his bachelor's, master's and doctoral degrees. Upon finishing his doctorate in 1939, he became a research officer in the Admiralty and from 1943 to 1947 was a member of the British Scientific Mission to the United States on atomic bomb development. He was engaged in the first atomic bomb test at Alamagordo, New Mexico, in 1945 and was advisor on instrumentation at the Bikini atomic weapons test the following year. During 1946–1947 he was head of the Electronics Division at the Los Alamos Laboratory in New Mexico and for the following three years he directed atomic research at the British Atomic Energy Research Establishment (AERE) at Harwell. Since 1950 he has been professor of nuclear physics at the Australian National University at Canberra. He has been a member of the Australian Atomic Weapons Safety Committee since 1955 and its chairman since 1957; he also serves as a member of the Australian Defense Research and Development Policy Commission. He resides with his family in Canberra, Australia.

oooooooo

TITTERTON

Power from Fusion? [1]

BY FAR THE MOST ABUNDANT element in the universe is the lightest—hydrogen. As one progresses to heavier elements there is a steady decrease in abundance until for elements in the neighbourhood of silver and upwards to the heaviest element on earth, uranium, the abundance is roughly constant. It has long been known that, if light elements could be made to react ("fuse") together to form heavier elements, energy would be released, and it is natural to enquire whether, by such means, a new power source could be achieved based on raw materials which are far more plentiful than the uranium and thorium found in the earth's crust. Earlier we discussed the reaction which occurs when lithium metal is bombarded with protons:

$$Li^7 + H^1 = He^4 + He^4 + energy$$

and showed that, although a large energy gain results in an individual reaction, it can be produced only by using an accelerating machine to generate high-speed protons, a process which consumes far more power than is produced from the nuclear reactions. The reason, it will be recalled, is that most of the accelerated particles fail to make nuclear reactions—most frequently the bombarding particle is slowed down and stopped by the electron shells surrounding the atoms of the target material long before it "hits" a nucleus. Even when a particle does collide with a nucleus the nuclear reaction does not always occur, because the charge of the bombarding particle interacts with that of the target nucleus and the forces tend to keep the two particles apart. Unless they come into intimate "contact" the very short-range nuclear forces do not come into play and the particle is scattered without a nuclear reaction occurring. Neutrons do not suffer from either of these difficulties, and it is because of this that it is possible

---

[1] Ernest W. Titterton, *Facing the Atomic Future* (New York: Macmillan, 1956), pp. 154–164.

to produce an efficient chain reaction and obtain atomic power from uranium and thorium isotopes.

To overcome the difficulty of the poor efficiency of man-made laboratory accelerating machines we might consider means which nature provided for us. If we take a closed box and examine the motions of the gas atoms within it, the particles are found to be rushing around in all directions, moving quite at random. Sometimes two atoms of the gas will undergo head-on collisions, sometimes they make glancing collisions, and at other times a faster atom can overtake and crash into another from the rear; in fact every conceivable type of collision is occurring. Under the normal conditions of temperature and pressure encountered on earth the collisions are not sufficiently violent—the particles are not moving fast enough—for nuclear reactions to occur; the electron shells surrounding the nuclei are strong enough to prevent them from coming into contact. If now the gas is heated to raise its temperature, the thermal agitation of the gas particles becomes more violent and they move with higher speed. Ultimately a point will be reached where the "shells" of electrons around the nuclei are insufficiently strong to prevent the nuclei from coming into contact and then nuclear reactions will begin to take place. Such reactions, produced by applying heat to increase the thermal motions of the atoms, are called "thermonuclear" reactions. Only a tiny fraction of the particles in the gas volume will react at any given time, and those involved in "head-on" collisions will most likely be effective. Although the chance of a nuclear reaction in any given collision is small, collisions occur continuously as long as the temperature is maintained and, as a result, the number of nuclear reactions occurring in a given time remains the same.

This all sounds remarkably easy—all that is required is a closed box in which the elements to be fused into heavier ones are placed and heat is applied until the nuclear reaction begins to occur. However, we have to enquire what is the temperature at which motions of the particles of the gas become sufficiently violent for the nuclei to react. Here arises the difficulty; the temperature needed depends on the atoms it is desired to fuse, but even in the most favourable case is in the region of a million degrees C. When it is remembered that the most heat-resistant metal out of which the box could be made is tungsten, and this melts at 3,370° C., it is immediately apparent that an experiment of the simple type discussed above can never be done on earth. The box would melt long before a temperature was reached at which a thermonuclear reaction could take place. The chances of obtaining cheap and copious power from hydrogen, or other light elements, therefore, would appear to be slender. However, the problem is an exciting one and further consideration of the factors involved is justified.

THE HEAT MOTION OF ATOMS IN A GAS

If the motion of the atoms of the gas confined in the box is analysed it is found that, at a given temperature, they are not all moving at the same speed. There are atoms of a wide variety of speeds present in our box; the actual distribution of speeds is as shown in [Fig. 93–1] and was calculated by the Englishman, Clerk Maxwell, in the last century. If the gas in the box is heated and held at a higher temperature, the average speed is increased but the distribution remains very broad. Thus one temperature is distinguished from another by a difference in the mean speed of the

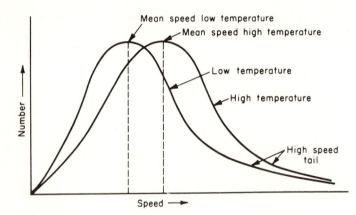

Fig. 93–1. Maxwellian distribution of speeds of atoms in a gas.

atoms in the box. From earlier remarks it is clear that the atoms most likely to take part in the thermonuclear reactions are those travelling at the highest speed, that is, those in the "tail" of the distribution. Although at any temperature there are always some high-speed, energetic particles present, they are few compared with slower particles. Increasing the temperature increases the number of fast particles and hence makes it more probable that nuclear interactions occur. The second factor preventing charged nuclei from coming into contact to make nuclear reactions is the electrical forces between them which constitute a kind of barrier; this is discussed in the next section.

THE NUCLEAR BARRIER AND QUANTUM LEAKAGE

The effect of the electrical barrier between charged particles can be illustrated by a game analogy. Suppose we have a nicely shaped hill which has a hole in its top, as indicated in [Fig. 93–2], and are given a number of balls which we desire to roll into the hole on the top of the hill. Getting the ball into the hole is considered as making a nuclear reaction, the prize being the energy released in the process. Now suppose our aim is not good and the first ball rolled goes along the path AB. It will climb the hill partially, but will be pushed away by the contour and deflected along the path CD. If the aim is good but the speed with which the ball is rolled too low, it starts to climb the hill along the trajectory EF, but comes to rest before reaching the top and rolls back along its own path. In this case, to make the "nuclear reaction" the barrier of the hill must be surmounted and the incoming ball requires a minimum speed (energy) as well as correct direction before it can drop into the hole at the top.

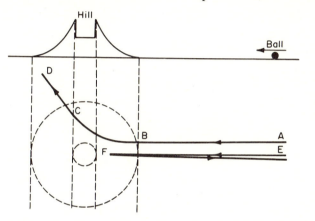

Fig. 93–2. Illustration of a "potential barrier"—ball and conical hill analogy.

This simple mechanical model illustrates the effect of a barrier, shows how bombarding particles can be deflected without producing reactions and that particles of very low speed (low energy) cannot achieve the objective. Like most analogies, this one is not completely satisfactory to describe the problem under consideration. In the case of the barrier of electrical force surrounding an atomic nucleus, it is *not* necessary for the bombarding particle to climb over the barrier in order to "drop into" the nucleus. Whatever point is reached on the barrier, there is always a chance that the particle can "leak" through it into the nucleus by virtue of a peculiar quantum phenomenon which we shall not try to explain here. The phenomenon is known as "quantum leakage" and, because of it, there is always a possibility that a particle with speed too low for it to go over the top of the barrier can be sucked into the nucleus and give rise to a nuclear reaction. The chance of this happening increases the higher up the barrier the particle is able to penetrate, that is, the higher the energy of the particle and the nearer it comes to the target nucleus.

THE RATE OF THERMONUCLEAR REACTIONS

The two factors just discussed—the wide distribution in speed of particles of a hot gas and the possibility of leakage through nuclear barriers—determine the number of nuclear reactions which occur in a given interval of time. A formula for the rate of power production from thermonuclear reactions was worked out, using these ideas, in 1929 by the Englishman, R. Atkinson, and the German, F. Houtermans. The situation is as illustrated in [Fig. 93–3], which is drawn for the case where the atoms of the

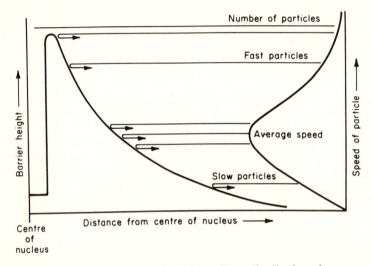

Fig. 93–3. The fast particles of the Maxwellian distribution drawn on the right penetrate high up the barrier, the average speed particles only part of the way, while the slow particles can never come very near to the nucleus.

gas have average speeds which are too small to allow them to reach the top of the barrier. The very fast particles of the Maxwell distribution can pass over the top of the barrier to make nuclear reactions. However, the large majority of the particles have speeds near to the average and only climb part of the way up the barrier. Most are turned back, but a few "leak" through and produce nuclear reactions. The slow particles climb only a small way up the barrier and the probability for making nuclear reactions is small although, occasionally, even one of these may "leak" through to the nucleus to produce a reaction. Physicists talk of the "penetrability" of the barrier, and this increases as the speed of the bombarding particles is raised. The situation can be summarised as in [Fig. 93–4], where curves for speed distribution of the particles and the penetrability of a particle of a given speed are plotted together. The number of nuclear reactions which occur is given approximately by multiplying the number of particles with a given speed and the corresponding penetrability for a particle of this speed, and the result of this manipulation is indicated by the shaded curve. It will be seen that maximum effect is produced by a group of particles having sufficient speed to result in a high penetrability, the speed being not so high as to make them too few in number in the Maxwell distribution.

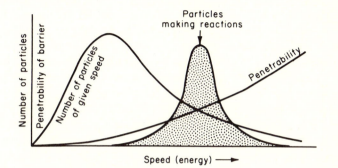

Fig. 93–4. The energy distribution and the barrier penetrability determine the energy range in which the majority of reactions occur.

This discussion shows that, for a given temperature, greatest success will be achieved in nuclear reactions where the barrier is lowest and thinnest. The barrier results from the repulsion between the electric charges of the two colliding nuclei and is smallest when the charges are least. It follows, therefore, that the best nuclear reaction would be expected to be that between hydrogen nuclei, as these have the smallest charge—unity. Ordinary hydrogen (mass 1 and charge 1) occurring in nature is not suitable, as the reaction rate is very low, but heavy hydrogen, deuterium (mass 2 and charge 1), is most suitable, and the reaction

$$H^2 + H^2 = n^1 + He^3 + \text{energy}$$

has a high rate and has been studied intensively in nuclear physics laboratories. By substituting numerical data obtained from the laboratory measurements into the theoretical formula for the rate of the reaction it is possible to predict precisely what will happen in this case. The rate of reaction varies very rapidly with temperature, as is shown by the fact that, below 500,000° C. very little energy is released, but in going from 500,000 to 1,000,000° C. the energy output increases by a million times. In fact, at 1,000,000° C. one pound of deuterium would release about 20 MW. of power, enough to supply the needs of a good-sized town. Of course, the hotter we make the deuterium the greater the energy released and the shorter the time the reaction can continue before all the deuterium is fused to helium-3. By pushing the rate of burning to the limit and flashing the temperature to a very high value, a fantastic energy release can be obtained in a very short time, and this is a thermonuclear explosion. Since 1952 we have known that such thermonuclear explosions can be achieved, and nature, once again, has posed mankind a major problem—the destructive capability of fusion nuclear reactions appears far easier to achieve than the peaceful application as a steady power source.

The fact that a mass of deuterium would have to be held at a steady temperature of between a half and one million degrees C. in order for it to become a power source makes it seem unlikely that this source will be tapped by mankind. The difficulty of constructing furnaces which would not vaporise long before the required temperature is attained seems to be insuperable. However, all over the world scientists are challenged by this problem and are considering ways and means of surmounting the difficulty by one trick or another. The usual approach is to try to achieve high temperatures using electric arc discharges, often in the presence of strong magnetic fields. Temperatures as high as $50,000°$ C. can be obtained in this way but, so far, even at this temperature the fraction of nuclei colliding violently enough to interact is too small to be observable.

The reaction described is not the only one which will give energy rapidly. The third isotope of hydrogen, tritium (mass 3 and charge 1), is also a good material, especially when used with deuterium in the reaction

$$H^2 + H^3 = He^4 + n^1 + \text{energy}$$

It is believed that this reaction will also proceed at "low" temperatures of between a half and one million degrees C. It would be a foolish man indeed who would say that the problem is insoluble, but on the other hand it would be equally foolish at this stage to bank on a solution being forthcoming.

Actually all life on earth depends on thermonuclear energy brought to us in the form of the sunlight, and this chapter will conclude with a discussion of the processes going on in the sun which provide this energy.

THERMONUCLEAR REACTIONS
IN THE STARS

For some hundreds of years it has been clear to scientists that the sun must contain a rather unusual source of energy, for it has been radiating unchanged throughout the whole of recorded history. Early computations showed that the energy could not be of a chemical type due to the burning of chemical materials or the sun would have been consumed completely within a few thousand years. A more reasonable suggestion, offered about a hundred years ago, was that the sun's energy is derived from a steady shrinking of its volume. Such a steady contraction of the sun could provide radiation at the present rate for a period of some 20 million years— considerably longer than the chemical energy hypothesis. Even so, this is not long enough; from other data we know that at least 1,000 million years is required to explain the evolution of life on the surface of the earth.

During the early part of this century it began to be realised that the sun and the stars are very large spheres of exceedingly hot gas, the gas being mainly hydrogen with smaller admixtures of other light elements. Although the surface of the sun has a temperature which can be measured on earth as being in the neighbourhood of 6,000° C., it can be shown by calculation that the interior is much hotter. In fact, if one could move gradually into the body of the sun the temperature and pressure would be found to rise slowly until, at the centre, they are 20 million degrees C. and 160,000 million atmospheres respectively.

A mass of gas held at an exceedingly high temperature and pressure is just what is needed to produce thermonuclear reactions and, in 1929, Atkinson and Houtermans made the suggestion that the sun's energy was derived from such reactions. The state of knowledge at the time did not permit them to say which nuclear reactions were the ones responsible, and it was ten years before the study of nuclear physics advanced to the point where Hans Bethe could suggest appropriate reactions, compatible with the known compositions of the sun, the rate of production of energy and the conditions within the sun which have been determined by the astronomers. Bethe showed that a series of nuclear reactions were involved which converted hydrogen to helium through a process known as the carbon-nitrogen cycle. To see how the processes work, suppose the cycle starts with a carbon atom. This is rushing about inside the large body of the sun, colliding with other nuclei from time to time. In due course it collides with a fast hydrogen atom, fusing with it to become a nitrogen isotope of mass 13 according to the equation

$$C^{12} + H^1 = N^{13} + \text{energy}$$

This is a process which can be observed directly in nuclear physics laboratories on earth. It is found that the nucleus of nitrogen-13 is radioactive and emits a positive electron with a half-life of about ten minutes, transforming into a stable, but rare, isotope of carbon-13 according to the equation

$$N^{13} = C^{13} + \beta^+ + \text{energy}$$

The stable carbon-13 so formed undergoes random heat motion within the sun until later on it collides with a hydrogen nucleus, coalescing to form a stable nucleus of nitrogen according to the equation

$$C^{13} + H^1 = N^{14} + energy$$

The nitrogen nucleus moves off and, after a while, picks up a third proton to become oxygen-15, thus:

$$N^{14} + H^1 = O^{15} + energy$$

The O^{15} nucleus, like C^{13}, is unstable and emits a positive electron with a half-life rather less than two minutes, becoming nitrogen-15, a stable nucleus:

$$O^{15} = N^{15} + \beta^+ + energy$$

This third nucleus of nitrogen continues on its wanderings and eventually is struck by yet another proton, when it disintegrates into a carbon-12 nucleus and a helium nucleus:

$$N^{15} + H^1 = C^{12} + He^4 + energy$$

The net result of this cycle of reactions is that we start with a carbon-12 nucleus and absorb four protons, ending with another carbon-12 nucleus (not the same) and a helium nucleus. The process, therefore, does not use up the carbon but converts four protons into one alpha particle with a release of about 28,000,000 volts of energy. The carbon nucleus is essential to the cycle of reactions, but it is not used up; it acts as an agent to enable the four atoms of hydrogen to combine to form a single atom of helium. It is the hydrogen which is being used by being slowly converted to helium, and the reaction can go on for as long as there is any hydrogen left in the sun. The rate of consumption of hydrogen is extremely small, and, since the beginning of time, only a few per cent. of it has been used. At the present rate of energy generation the hydrogen supply of the sun will last for some 10,000 million years, so there need be no fear on this account. Today it is believed that the stellar universe runs exclusively on atomic energy sources. In addition to the reaction cycle proposed by Bethe, there is another involving hydrogen directly which is thought to be of major consequence. It is:

$$H^1 + H^1 = H^2 + \beta^+$$
$$H^2 + H^1 = H^3 + \gamma$$
$$He^3 + He^3 = He^4 + H^1 + H^1$$

Again it will be seen that the reaction amounts to the converting of four hydrogen nuclei into an alpha particle.

These two reaction cycles are the main processes which provide energy during the greater part of the life of a star. In the very early stages, however, other reactions do occur; for example, the reaction between lithium and protons discussed earlier in this chapter, but these are fast reactions and the materials are burned up quickly, providing energy only for a very short period at the temperatures and pressures of a stellar interior. For this reason light elements such as lithium, beryllium and boron are burned up exceedingly rapidly in the early stages of energy generation. When the supply of hydrogen in a star begins to be exhausted, the temperature has to rise to enable new and more complicated nuclear reactions to take over the task of making energy available. The history of a star from its early formation to its final death is a fascinating story and is not yet completely understood. The key to its solution was found when it was realised that the energy coming from the stars is of thermonuclear origin. Without energy derived from thermonuclear reactions in the sun there would be no wind, water power, coal or oil on the earth. The very food we eat is, in the end, derived from sunlight and so from thermonuclear energy. It is a strange paradox that mankind can exist only because thermonuclear reactions going on in the sun and stars provide energy but yet, through the development of hydrogen weapons on earth, thermonuclear reactions threaten extinction.

PART XVI

HIGH-ENERGY PHYSICS

○○○○○○○○○○

ᴏᴏᴏᴏᴏᴏᴏᴏᴏᴏ

PARITY AND ITS ILL
FORTUNE

ᴏᴏᴏᴏᴏᴏᴏᴏᴏᴏ

C. N. Yang (b. 1922)
T. D. Lee (b. 1926)

Among the many features of nature that have suggested to man-kind a universe governed by a well-ordered system of laws, the ubiquity of symmetries has been perhaps the most cogent. The structure of the cell, the morphology of higher organisms, the geometrical patterns of crystals, all lead to the conviction that the laws of nature must be inti-mately related to symmetry. Until the beginning of this century, sym-metries observed in nature were used empirically to discover new and unusual properties of matter without looking for any deeper significance. The symmetry that Mendeleev discovered in the properties of the chemi-cal elements led him to classify the elements into families, although no attempt was made to relate this symmetry to any fundamental law of nature.

Einstein took the first important step in relating the laws of nature to symmetry in his formulation of the special theory of relativity, in 1905, when he based his derivation of the Lorentz transformation equations on the equivalence of space-time for all observers in inertial coordinate sys-tems. Einstein's work was fundamental to the understanding of any re-lationship between symmetry and the laws of nature. Time and space, ac-cording to Einstein, must be treated together. Although there are certain purely spatial symmetry relationships that are valid for all observers, the most profound conclusions are to be derived from symmetry properties

only if space and time are merged into a single entity. His work emphasized the need for a discussion of symmetry in terms of coordinate systems, with the expectation that the symmetry properties most significant
for the fundamental laws of nature would be those revealed in moving
systems. Finally, and of greatest importance, is Einstein's introduction of
the concept of invariance and the delineation of its relationship to space-
time symmetries.

The principle of invariance is related to symmetry in Einstein's treatment of the space-time interval, which is the basis of the special theory
of relativity. Furthermore, symmetry, or invariance, is related to conservation principles. Before Einstein's introduction of the space-time concept,
the spatial separation of events and the time intervals between them were
treated separately in the belief that they were the same for all observers.
Then Einstein insisted that one must treat the space-time interval as the
invariant quantity when one transforms from one Galilean coordinate system (intertial frame of reference) to another. In other words, since space-
time is symmetrical with respect to all observers, the space-time interval
must be invariant. Thus symmetry and invariance are equivalent. But the
invariance of the space-time interval signifies that a certain quantity associated with a system (for example, a moving particle) must be the same
for all observers and hence conserved. Thus symmetry and invariance are
related to conservation principles. The quantity so conserved for a moving
particle and that corresponds to the invariance of the space-time interval
is the square of the momentum of the particle minus the square of its
energy divided by the square of the speed of light. This is essentially the
rest mass of the particle. Thus, the invariance of the space-time interval,
or the proper time of the moving particle, is equivalent to the conservation of rest mass. From this we may conclude that a particular type of
symmetry in nature implies the existence of a conservation law. We shall
see that this assumption has played a major role in the development of
the physics of the atom, the nucleus, and of elementary particles.

Einstein developed the general theory of relativity by using still another
example of symmetry, namely, that the space-time interval must be the
same for all observers, whether they are in inertial frames of reference or
in accelerated coordinate systems. This is the substance of the principle
of equivalence, which states that all the effects that can be observed
within a small region of a gravitational field can be duplicated by an
appropriately accelerated system. In other words, inertial forces cannot
be distinguished from gravitational forces in small regions of space.

Although the remarkable relationship between symmetry (invariance)
and conservation principles first became apparent in the theory of relativity, the most fruitful application of this relationship is found in quantum mechanics. Because quantum mechanics is essentially an algebra of

mathematical operators, many of the properties of atoms, nuclei, and fundamental particles can be derived merely from a mathematical analysis of the symmetry properties of the quantum-mechanical operators that correspond to the physical observables of the motion or state of these particles. Thus the symmetry of the operator that corresponds to the energy (that is, the Hamiltonian) of the system is of particular importance. Because of these symmetries, its invariance to particular types of transformations must embody conservation principles. If the Hamiltonian is symmetrical with respect to the spatial coordinates (that is, if a translation of the origin of the coordinate system used to describe the motion of a particle does not alter the Hamiltonian), the momentum of the particle is conserved. In the same way, if the Hamiltonian is unaltered when the time is changed, the energy of the system is conserved. Finally, if the Hamiltonian is spherically symmetric, so that a rotation of the coordinate system leaves it unaltered, the angular momentum of the system is conserved. Each of these conservation principles leads to a particular quantum number, hence, the existence of quantum numbers is, in a sense, a consequence of the symmetries in nature.

We must now consider another aspect of the symmetry properties of a system in the quantum-mechanical scheme. The description of the system in quantum mechanics is given by its wave function, or, more generally, its state vector. The state of the system is described mathematically by a function of space and time (which may be treated as a vector in an abstract function space) that changes from moment to moment as the system interacts with external force fields. Each of the observable quantities associated with the system (for example, its energy, momentum, or angular momentum) is treated as a mathematical operator influencing the state vector of the system. These operators determine how this state vector changes with passing time. Thus the Hamiltonian energy operator, applied to the state vector, represents the change of the state vector with time; a rotation operator, applied to the state vector, represents a change in the orientation of the system, and so on. The symmetry properties of the system may therefore be investigated by considering the symmetry properties of the wave function or state vector of the system. Thus if the Hamiltonian of the system has the kind of symmetry which implies that a certain physical quantity is invariant when the system is subjected to the physical operation corresponding to the mathematical operator, the wave function describing the state of the system must at the same time change to another state function in a definite way. This is referred to as a transformation (or a rotation) of the state vector in the abstract mathematical function space (also called Hilbert space in honor of the great German mathematician David Hilbert who discovered the principle laws of abstract function spaces many years before quantum mechanics was discovered) in which the state vector is represented. In other words, the symmetries of the system being considered must be evident in the mathematical symmetries of the state vector.

We now consider an important type of symmetry which we did not discuss in the previous paragraphs. The analysis of this symmetry as it relates to the decay of certain types of mesons (the theta- and tau-mesons) led to the important discovery that right- and left-handedness in nature are not indistinguishable. Not all phenomena in nature can be described with equal correctness as being either right handed or left handed. In other words, right- and left-handedness are intrinsic properties of certain systems. Nature does not mix up the right- and left-handedness in the construction of such systems.

A decade ago, had we asked a physicist, we should have been told that there was no experiment involving any of the known laws of nature that could provide an operational definition of left and right. Were we to attempt to communicate the meaning of left and right to intelligent beings on, let us say, a distant planet, there would have been no way to do this without turning their attention toward some particular asymmetric structure—possibly a constellation of stars—that both we and they could observe in common. Nature, at the level at which forces operate, seemed to have no preferred directions or orientations. Left, right, north, south, or any other direction—all would seem conventions that had meaning only in the macroscopic world where man could observe temporary asymmetries. Nature itself was thought to be always and everywhere governed by symmetry. We shall see that this can now be done experimentally for certain systems.

Before discussing the discovery of the intrinsic character of the "handedness" of certain systems in nature, we consider the symmetry of some material system (for example, an atom or a nucleus), when the coordinate system in which the motion of the system is described is changed from what is called a right-handed coordinate system to a left-handed one. We describe a right-handed coordinate system as one with its three mutually perpendicular spatial axes (X, Y, Z) pointing in such a way that if the forefinger of the right hand points in the direction of the X axis, and the second finger of the right hand points in the direction of the Y axis, then the thumb of the right hand, held at right angles to the two fingers, points in the direction of the Z axis. This means that if a right-handed coordinate system is rotated so that the X axis moves toward the Y axis, then the Z axis must point in the direction that a right-handed screw would advance if it were rotated in the direction from X to Y (that is, in a clockwise direction). A left-handed coordinate system is one in which the three mutually perpendicular axes, $X, Y,$ and $Z,$ point respectively in the directions of the forefinger, second finger, and thumb of the left hand if these are held in mutually perpendicular directions to one another.

What then is the nature of the operation that transforms a right-handed coordinate system to a left-handed one? We know what this means physically, for we obtain such a transformation by using a mirror. As just described, if we hold the forefinger, the second finger, and thumb of the right hand so that one of the fingers points directly toward a mirror, the image in the mirror is exactly the same as the arrangement of the three fingers on the left hand. In other words, the passage or transformation from a left-handed to a right-handed system, and vice versa, is equivalent to the reflection of the coordinate system in a plane mirror. This type of transformation of a coordinate system is called a spatial reflection or inversion. Now suppose that the Hamiltonian describing the state of a system remains unaltered when we pass from a right-handed to a left-handed coordinate system (in other words, the Hamiltonian is invariant to a spatial reflection of the coordinate system). What does this mean physically? Since the Hamiltonian represents the evolution of the state of the system in time, this means that if we watch the system in a mirror, the events as they are revealed are as valid a description of nature as the events that are actually happening in real space. We may express this important statement somewhat differently: If the Hamiltonian that describes the dynamic properties of a system is invariant to a reflection of the coordinate system, then the mirror image of any dynamic process that the system may undergo is also a possible and equally probable physical process that the system can experience. Thus, it is immaterial whether we look at the world directly or through a mirror: There is no way of distinguishing between left-handed and right-handed events since they are both equally probable; if suddenly right-handedness and left-handedness were interchanged, no observable difference would occur in the world. Of course, this is on the assumption that the Hamiltonian describing any part of the universe or the whole of it is symmetrical with respect to reflections.

For a long time this was thought to be the case for all physical events. To see what this means from the quantum-mechanical point of view we must understand what a reflection of coordinates does to the wave function or state vector of a system, and for this we must define what a reflection of the spatial coordinate system means mathematically. It is easy to see that we obtain such a transformation (that is, a reflection or the mirror image of a given coordinate system) if we replace X, Y, and Z (the coordinates of all points) by $-X$, $-Y$, and $-Z$. In other words, if we replace all the coordinates of a system by their negative values, we obtain the description of the system in the mirror-image coordinate system.

From this we learn at once what happens to the wave function, or state vector, of a system when we change the description from a right-handed to a left-handed coordinate system. We may treat this change of coordinate system as though it were a transformation of the state vector resulting from an operator (the reflection operator) applied to this state vector. If, after applying this operator once to the state vector, we then apply it again (that is, view the system through two mirrors), we obtain the original state vector since the second reflection cancels the effect of the first one.

We view this double operation quantum mechanically as follows: If R is the operator that describes the first reflection, then the two successive reflections are represented by R^2. The quantity R^2 must equal 1, since the effect of R^2 gives us the original state vector again. Hence, the numerical representation of the operator R itself must be either $+1$ or -1, since the square of either of these numbers is 1. In the reflected coordinate system, therefore, the wave function must either remain unchanged or change its sign. Events in nature may, according to this point of view, be divided into two groups: those for which the state vector remains the same when the "handedness" of the coordinate system is changed, and those for which the state vector changes its sign in such a transformation. We may refer to these as even and odd events, respectively, and we shall see that there appears to be a rule in nature about such events. Odd events were thought always to remain odd and even events always to remain even. This phenomenon, or law, called the conservation of parity, corresponds to the conservation of a physical quantity, the parity of a system. Parity is a property of the wave function or state vector, and one speaks of odd parity if the wave function changes sign on reflection of the coordinate system, and of even parity if the wave function does not change sign.

It can be shown that the parity of the wave function of a particle is determined by the orbital angular momentum of the particle. If the orbital angular-momentum quantum number (that is, the azimuthal quantum number) of the particle is l, the wave function of the particle is multiplied by $(-1)^l$ as the result of a reflection of the coordinate system (inversion, as it is called). The parity of the particle is thus even or odd depending upon whether the orbital angular-momentum quantum number of the particle is even or odd. The importance of parity and its conservation in ordinary atomic processes was first pointed out by O. Laporte in 1924. He showed that all the energy levels in the atom can be divided into odd and even levels. When a photon is emitted by the transition of an electron in the atom, the electron must always go from an odd to an even, or from an even to an odd level. In other words, during a transition the orbital angular momentum quantum number must change by plus or minus 1. This constitutes what is known as a selection rule, since it limits the types of transition that can occur inside an atom and therefore reduces the total number of spectral lines that can be emitted by an atom.

To see how this selection rule or the change in the sign of the wave function of the electron during a transition is related to the principle of the conservation of parity we note that after the transition, if the emission of a photon is involved, there are two particles to be considered, the electron and the emitted photon (for a transition involving absorption we start with two particles and finish with one). Thus, a knowledge of the total parity of the system after emission must take into account both the parity of the electron and the parity of the photon. Every particle in quantum mechanics is assigned a parity. Since, as can be shown, the parity of the photon is always odd, the parity of the final state is the same as the parity of the initial state only if the parity of the electron changes from odd to even or vice versa during a transition. Note that the parity of any state is obtained from the parities of the individual particles in that state by multiplying the individual parities of the particles. The product of an odd and even parity is odd and the product of two odd or two even parity particles is even.

Laporte's discovery of the conservation of parity for atomic systems led physicists to accept this principle as a general law of nature and to discard any Hamiltonian that does not have the kind of symmetry that would leave it invariant to a reflection of the coordinate system. No one had any reason to object to this in the early years of quantum mechanics since it seemed eminently reasonable to insist that there be no distinction between the universe and its mirror image and to insist that the mathematical formulation of the laws of physics take this equivalence of right- and left-handedness into account. These assumptions seemed valid until the discovery of the famous theta-tau-meson puzzle or paradox, which was first recognized in 1953. It was found then that these two K-mesons, which seem to have identical masses and lifetimes, decay in different schemes with different parities. The theta-meson decays into two pi-mesons, the tau-meson decays into three pi-mesons. Since the pi-meson has odd parity, this would mean that the parent theta- and tau-mesons must differ in parity (if parity is conserved in this decay process as it is in electromagnetic processes). Thus, the conservation of parity, applied to this decay process, led to the assumption that these were two different K-mesons, even though they were alike in all other respects.

Lee and Yang, on examining this situation, discovered that the principle of conservation of parity had never been experimentally verified for certain types of interaction or phenomena known as weak interactions. In the physics of elementary particles, one divides phenomena into two types (excluding electromagnetic and gravitational phenomena): those involving strong interactions between particles, and those involving weak interactions. Weak interactions involve the decay of mesons and, in general, any reactions in which neutrinos or antineutrinos are emitted. Lee and Yang therefore proposed that the conservation of parity be discarded in any reactions involving neutrinos and in weak interactions in general. The decay of the K-mesons is itself a weak interaction so that according to Lee and Yang this decay need not obey the principle of the conservation of parity. Hence the tau- and the theta-meson are the same kind of meson, which can decay either by conserving parity or not.

Since this suggestion was extremely revolutionary, it was necessary to test it in a way that nobody could question. Lee and Yang suggested that the simplest and most conclusive test could be carried out by examining some particular β-decay process and its mirror image, since such processes involve neutrinos and should therefore not necessarily conserve parity. If parity is conserved, the actual process and its mirror image should occur with equal probability, but if parity is not conserved, the mirror-image process and the actual process should occur at different rates.

Such an experiment was carried out by C. S. Wu and her collaborators. They studied the electrons emitted in the β decay of cobalt 60. If all the cobalt nuclei are lined up in a magnetic field so that their intrinsic spins are parallel, as many electrons should be emitted in a direction parallel to the cobalt spin as in the direction opposite to the cobalt spin if parity is indeed conserved. This symmetry would be observed if the emission of electrons from the cobalt nuclei were viewed in a mirror, for the conservation of parity requires that the actual emission of electrons and the image of this process be the same. But if the emissions in the cobalt spin direction were different from those in the opposite direction, the mirror image of this process would show just the opposite situation so that parity would not be conserved. This was exactly what the experiments of Wu and others showed.

The results of these experiments can be understood if, as suggested by Lee and Yang, the neutrino be considered as a spiral structure with a left-handed helicity. According to this picture, the direction of motion of the neutrino and the direction of its intrinsic spin are opposite to each other so that the neutrino spins and advances like a left-handed screw. It follows that when the cobalt atoms undergo β decay, they emit their neutrinos in the direction opposite to their lined-up spins and not in the direction of these spins. This is so because the neutrino leaves the cobalt nucleus with its spin parallel to that of the cobalt nucleus; hence, since it has the helicity of a left-handed screw, it must move off in the opposite direction. Since the theory of β decay shows that there is a greater probability for electrons to be emitted in the same direction as the neutrinos in β decay, more electrons are emitted with direction opposite to the cobalt spin than in the same direction. But this disagrees with classical assumptions about mirror-image events; hence, it follows that parity is not conserved in this β-decay process. Today we know that parity is not conserved in any interaction involving the emission of neutrinos or antineutrinos, the particles that are emitted, together with positrons, in β-decay processes.

Although the principle of the conservation of parity does not apply to weak interactions, a more general conservation principle does apply if we consider the general asymmetry of charged particles in the universe. Our universe consists of massive positively charged particles, protons, and very light negatively charged particles, electrons, so that there is a lack of symmetry between charge and mass. However, the discovery of the positron (antielectron) and the antiproton shows us that a universe could just as well be constructed with massive negatively charged particles, antiprotons, and light positrons. If then we had a cobalt atom consisting of these antiprotons, it would emit positrons and these would leave the anticobalt nuclei in a preferential direction opposite to that of the electrons from ordinary cobalt. In other words, the mirror image of the ordinary cobalt β-decay process is not really impossible; it exists in the world of antimatter. This means that, if we transform from a right- to a left-handed coordinate system and at the same time replace all the particles by their antiparticle numbers (called charge conjugation), the Hamiltonian describing the system remains invariant. Thus charge conjugation and reflection together form a higher type of symmetry in the universe.

The spirality of the neutrino requires that this particle (and the antineutrino) move with speed of light and have no rest mass. In this respect it behaves like a photon. If a neutrino moved with less than the speed of light, it could have no definite spirality, for it would always be possible to find a coordinate system (namely, one moving faster than the neutrino) in which its spirality would appear opposite to the spirality as seen by an observer in a coordinate system moving with a speed less than that of the neutrino. In both cases, if the direction of motion of the neutrino is taken parallel to that of the two observers, the direction of spin of the neutrino is the same, while the directions of motion as seen by the two observers are different. To one observer the neutrino would look like a right-handed screw; to the other, like a left-handed one. Hence, if the neutrino is to have the same handedness for all observers, it must move with the speed of light so that no observer can overtake it and thus see it recede. Since the neutrino moves with the speed of light, it can have no rest mass, for its moving mass, and hence its energy, would be infinite by the Einstein relationship between the mass and the speed of a body.

Chen Ning (Franklin) Yang was born in Hofei, Anwhei, China, on September 22, 1922, and spent his early years on the campus of Tsinghua University, near Peiping, where his father, Ke Chuan Yang, was a professor of mathematics. He was the first of five children in a household devoted to cultural and intellectual pursuits.

On completing his secondary-school education, Yang matriculated at the National Southwest Associated University in Kunming, China, and received his B.Sc. degree in 1942. By that time, the Tsinghua University had moved to Kunming because of the Sino-Japanese War; Yang received his M.Sc. degree there in 1944. At the end of the war in 1946 he went to the University of Chicago on a Tsinghua University Fellowship to do graduate work in nuclear physics under the direction of Edward Teller. He received his Ph.D. from the university in 1948 and remained there as an instructor for one year. In 1949 he went to the Institute for Advanced Study at Princeton, where he began his work on elementary particles and weak interactions that led to the discovery of the nonconservation of parity. In 1955 Yang became a professor at the Institute and held that post until 1965, when he accepted an endowed chair of physics at the Stoney Brook, L.I., division of the University of the State of New York.

Like Dr. Lee, with whom he collaborated in the parity work, Dr. Yang has devoted a great deal of his research efforts to the fields of statistical mechanics and symmetry principles. Although he was greatly influenced by Enrico Fermi while at the University of Chicago, his interest in symmetry principles goes back to his undergraduate days when he wrote a baccalaureate thesis, "Group Theory and Molecular Spectra." His M.Sc. thesis, "Contributions to the Statistical Theory of Order-Disorder Transformations," stemmed from his interest in statistical mechanics. This early work, including his Ph.D. thesis, led to many subsidiary problems in which the principle of the conservation of parity had to be dealt with and analyzed. Quite naturally, Dr. Yang became involved in parity work. In one of his first papers in this field, he proved in a very ingenious manner that the parity of the pi-meson is odd, that is $= -1$, and that its intrinsic angular momentum (span) is zero. The knowledge of the parity of the pi-mesons was very important in analyzing the so-called theta-tau puzzle, namely, that these two K-mesons, similar in all other observable features, decay by different modes, one breaking down into two pi-mesons and the other into three pi-mesons.

Dr. Yang has written extensively, not only for the professional physicist, but also for the layman and for scientists in other fields who were interested in a simplified review of modern developments in physics. As can be seen from his Nobel Prize address, his writing and lecturing are marked by simplicity and charm. His ideas are so presented and developed that the physics rather than the formalism is emphasized and always easy to follow. In spite of his great achievements, he is always modest, self-effacing, and easily approachable, and in his discussions with others he is affable, patient, and understanding.

Professor Yang is a fellow of the American Physical Society, and of the Academia Sinica. He is also a member of the National Academy of Sciences. In 1957 he received the Albert Einstein Commemorative Award and in 1958 he received an honorary D.Sc. degree from Princeton.

Dr. Yang is married to Chih Li Tu, whom he met while he was teaching mathematics at her high school in China. They have two sons and a daughter.

Tsung Dao Lee, the son of Tsing Kong Lee, a Shanghai merchant, and Ming Chang Chang, was born on November 24, 1926. After graduating from the Kiangsi Middle School in Kanchow in 1943, he matriculated at the National Checkiang University in Kweichow Province. He was unable to complete his college education there because of the Japanese invasion and was forced to flee to Kunming, Yunnan, where he attended the National Southwest University. There he met Chen Ning Yang, who was to become his collaborator in the discovery of the nonconservation of parity and was to share the Nobel Prize with him in 1957.

The Chinese government recognized Lee's great talents in physics and awarded him a scholarship in 1946 that brought him to the University of Chicago, where he studied with Fermi. Being then greatly interested in the properties of very dense (degenerate) matter and in the structure of very dense stars (the white dwarfs), he wrote his Ph.D. thesis on the "Hydrogen Content of White Dwarfs" in 1950.

After spending some months at the Yerkes Observatory of the University of Chicago as a research associate, he went to the University of California in Berkeley as a lecturer and research associate. At the end of 1951, he went to the Institute of Advanced Study in Princeton as a fellow and remained there as a staff member until 1953. There he renewed his friendship with Dr. Yang and began working with him on various basic problems in elementary particle physics.

During his residence at the Institute, Lee published papers on various basic problems in statistical mechanics and in nuclear and elementary particle physics, which soon led to his recognition as one of the most talented of the younger theoretical physicists. His approach to problems was always a nontraditional one, marked by great ingenuity and deep physical insight.

In 1953, Lee left Princeton to become assistant professor of physics at Columbia University and in three years was promoted to a full professorship, thus becoming at the age of twenty-nine the youngest full professor on the Columbia University faculty. This three-year period was marked by great scientific activity; Lee generally spent his weekends commuting to Princeton to work with Dr. Yang. This collaboration finally led to a joint paper, published in the *Physical Review* in 1956, which questioned the universal validity of the principle of the conservation of parity and proposed an experiment to test it. The confirmation of their analysis brought them the Nobel Prize. Lee is the second youngest scientist ever to have received the Nobel Prize, the youngest having been Sir Lawrence Bragg, who received it in 1915 at the age of twenty-five.

After receiving the Nobel Prize, Lee continued working on fundamental particle theory and field theories in collaboration with Yang and others. He remained at his academic post at Columbia for a number of years, lecturing on various phases of theoretical physics, and then went to the Institute of Advanced Study as a professor. After residing at Princeton for a few years, he returned to Columbia University to become its first Enrico Fermi professor of physics.

Dr. Lee has received many honors, among which are the Albert Einstein Commemorative Award of Yeshiva University in 1957 and the Science Award of the Newspaper Guild of New York. He is a member of the National Academy of Sciences, a fellow of the American Physical Society and the Academia Sinica. In 1958 he was awarded an honorary D.Sc. degree by Princeton University.

In 1950 he married a former graduate student, Hui Chung Chin. They have two sons, James and Stephen.

ooooooo

YANG

Law of Parity Conservation and Other Symmetry Laws [1]

IT IS A PLEASURE AND a great privilege to have this opportunity to discuss the question of parity conservation and other symmetry laws. We shall be concerned first with the general aspects of the role of the symmetry laws in physics, second, with the development that led to the disproof of parity conservation, and last, with a discussion of some other symmetry laws which physicists have learned through experience but which do not yet together form an integral and conceptually simple pattern. The interesting and very exciting developments since parity conservation was disproved will be covered by T. D. Lee in his lecture.

SYMMETRY PRINCIPLES

The existence of symmetry laws is in full accordance with our daily experience. The simplest of these symmetries, the isotropy and homogeneity of space, are concepts that date back to the early history of human

---

[1] C. N. Yang, *Science*, 127 (1958), 563–568. 1957 Nobel address.

thought. The invariance of mechanical laws under a coordinate transformation of uniform velocity, also known as the invariance under Galilean transformations, is a more sophisticated symmetry that was early recognized and that formed one of the cornerstones of Newtonian mechanics. The consequences of these symmetry principles were greatly exploited by physicists of past centuries and gave rise to many important results. A good example in this direction is the theorem that in an isotropic solid there are only two elastic constants.

Another type of consequences of the symmetry laws relates to the conservation laws. It is common knowledge today that, in general, a symmetry principle (or, equivalently, an invariance principle) generates a

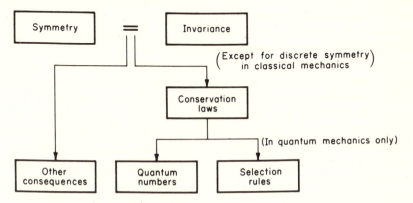

Fig. 94–1. Relationship between conservation laws and symmetry laws.

conservation law. For example, the invariance of physical laws under space displacement has as a consequence the conservation of momentum, and the invariance under space rotation has as a consequence the conservation of angular momentum. While the importance of these conservation laws was fully understood, their close relationship with the symmetry laws does not seem to have been clearly recognized until the beginning of the 20th century [see Fig. 94–1].

With the advent of special and general relativity, the symmetry laws gained new importance: Their connection with the dynamical laws of physics took on a much more integrated and interdependent relationship than in classical mechanics, where, logically, the symmetry laws were only consequences of the dynamical laws that, by chance, possess the symmetries. Also in the relativity theories the realm of the symmetry laws was greatly enriched to include invariances that were by no means apparent from daily experience. Their validity, rather, was deduced from or was later confirmed by complicated experimentation. Let me emphasize that the conceptual simplicity and intrinsic beauty of the symmetries that so evolve from complex experiments are, for the physicists, great sources of encouragement. One learns to hope that nature possesses an order that one may aspire to comprehend.

It was not, however, until the development of quantum mechanics that the use of the symmetry principles began to permeate into the very language of physics. The quantum numbers that designate the states of a system are often identical with those that represent the symmetries of the system. It indeed is scarcely possible to overemphasize the role played by the symmetry principles in quantum mechanics. To quote two examples: The general structure of the periodic table is essentially a direct consequence of the isotropy of Coulomb's laws. The existence of the antiparticles—namely, the positron, the antiproton, and the antineutron— were theoretically anticipated as consequences of the symmetry of physical laws with respect to Lorentz transformations. In both cases nature seems to take advantage of the simple mathematical representations of the symmetry laws. When one pauses to consider the elegance and the beautiful perfection of the mathematical reasoning involved and contrast it with the complex and far-reaching physical consequences, a deep sense of respect for the power of the symmetry laws never fails to develop.

One of the symmetry principles—the symmetry between the left and the right—is as old as human civilization. The question whether nature exhibits such symmetry was debated at length by philosophers in the past. Of course, in daily life, left and right are quite distinct from each other. Our hearts, for example, are always on our left sides. The language that people use, both in the Orient and the Occident, carries even a connotation that right is good and left is evil. However, the laws of physics have always shown complete symmetry between the left and the right, the symmetry in daily life being attributed to the accidental asymmetry of the environment, or to the initial conditions in organic life. To illustrate the point, I might mention that if there existed a mirror-image man with his heart on his right side, his internal organs reversed as compared with ours, and in fact his body molecules (for example sugar molecules) the mirror image of ours, and if he ate the mirror image of the food that we eat, then according to the laws of physics, he should function as well as we do.

The law of right-left symmetry was used in classical physics but was not of any great practical importance there. One reason for this derives from the fact that right-left symmetry is a discrete symmetry, unlike rotational symmetry which is continuous. Whereas, in classical mechanics, the continuous symmetries always led to conservation laws, a discrete symmetry does not. With the introduction of quantum mechanics, however, this difference between the discrete and continuous symmetries disappears. The law of right-left symmetry then leads also to a conservation law: the conservation of parity.

The discovery of this conservation law dates back to 1924, when Laporte found that energy levels in complex atoms can be classified into *"gestri-*

chene" and *"ungestrichene"* types, or, in more recent language, even and odd levels. In transitions between these levels during which one photon is emitted or absorbed, Laporte found that the level always changes from even to odd or vice versa. Anticipating later developments, we remark that the evenness or oddness of the levels was later referred to as the parity of the levels. The even levels are defined as having parity $+1$, the odd levels, parity -1. One also defines the photon emitted or absorbed in the usual atomic transitions as having odd parity. Laporte's rule can then be formulated as the statement that, in an atomic transition, with the emission of a photon, the parity of the initial state is equal to the total parity of the final state—that is, the product of the parities of the final atomic state and the photon emitted. In other words, parity is conserved, or unchanged, in the transition.

In 1927 Wigner took the critical and profound step of proving that the empirical rule of Laporte is a consequence of the reflection invariance, or right-left symmetry, of the electromagnetic forces in the atom. This fundamental idea was rapidly absorbed into the language of physics. Since right-left symmetry was unquestioned also in other interactions, the idea was further taken over into new domains as the subject matter of physics extended into nuclear reactions, β-decay, meson interactions, and strange particle physics. One became accustomed to the idea of nuclear parities as well as to that of atomic parities, and one discusses and measures the intrinsic parities of the mesons. Throughout these developments, the concept of parity and the law of parity conservation proved to be extremely fruitful, and the success was, in turn, taken as a support for the validity of right-left symmetry.

THETA-TAU PUZZLE

Against such a background the so-called θ–τ puzzle developed in the last few years. Before I explain the meaning of this puzzle it is best to go a little into a classification of the forces that act between subatomic particles, a classification which the physicists have learned through experience to use in the last 50 years. The four classes of interactions, together with their strengths, are listed in [Table 94–1].

TABLE 94–1. *Classes and Strengths of Interactions.*

CLASS	STRENGTH
1. Nuclear forces	1
2. Electromagnetic forces	10^{-2}
3. Weak forces (decay interactions)	10^{-13}
4. Gravitational forces	10^{-38}

The strongest interactions are the nuclear interactions, which include the forces that bind nuclei together and the interactions between the nuclei and the π mesons. These also include the interactions that give rise to the observed strange particle production. The interactions of the second class are the electromagnetic interactions, about which physicists know a great deal. In fact, the crowning achievement of the physicists of the 19th century was a detailed understanding of the electromagnetic forces. With the advent of quantum mechanics, our understanding of electromagnetic forces gave, in principle, an accurate, integral, and detailed description of practically all the physical and chemical phenomena of our daily experience. The third class of forces, the weak interactions, was first discovered around the beginning of this century in the β-radioactivity of nuclei—a phenomenon which, especially in the last few years, has been extensively studied experimentally. With the discovery of π-μ, μ-e decays and μ capture, it was noticed independently by Klein, by Tiomno and Wheeler, and by Lee, Rosenbluth, and me that these interactions have roughly the same strengths as β-interactions. They are called weak interactions, and in the last few years their rank has been constantly added to through the discovery of many other weak interactions responsible for the decay of the strange particles. The consistent and striking pattern of their almost uniform strength remains today one of the most tantalizing phenomena—a topic which we shall come back to later. About the last class of forces, the gravitational forces, we need only mention that in atomic and nuclear interactions they are so weak as to be completely negligible in all observations made with existing techniques.

Now to return to the θ–τ puzzle. In 1953 Dalitz and Fabri pointed out that, in the decay of the θ and τ mesons,

$$\theta \rightarrow \pi + \pi$$
$$\tau \rightarrow \pi + \pi + \pi$$

some information about the spins and parities of the τ and θ mesons can be obtained. The argument is, very roughly, as follows. It has previously been determined that the parity of a π meson is odd (that is, equals -1). Let us first neglect the effects due to the relative motion of the π-mesons. To conserve parity in the decays, the θ meson must have the total parity or, in other words, the product parity, of two π-mesons, which is even (that is, equals $+1$). Similarly, the τ meson must have the total parity of three π-mesons, which is odd. Actually, because of the relative motion of the π-mesons, the argument was not as simple and unambiguous as here set forth. To render the argument conclusive and definitive, it was necessary to study experimentally the momentum and angular distribution of the π-mesons. Such studies were made in many laboratories, and by the spring of 1956 the accumulated experimental data seemed to indicate unambiguously, along the lines of reasoning discussed above, that θ and τ do not have the same parity and, consequently, that they are not the same particle. This conclusion, however, was in marked contradiction to other experimental results which also became definite at about the same time. The contradiction was known as the "$\theta-\tau$ puzzle" and was widely discussed. To recapture the atmosphere of that time, I shall quote a paragraph concerning the conclusion that θ and τ are not the same particle from a report, entitled "Present knowledge about the new particles," which I gave at the International Conference on Theoretical Physics in Seattle, Washington, in September 1956:

"However it will not do to jump to hasty conclusions. This is because experimentally the K mesons [that is, τ and θ] seem all to have the same masses and the same lifetimes. The masses are known to an accuracy of, say, from 2 to 10 electron masses, or a fraction of a percent, and the lifetimes are known to an accuracy of, say, 20 percent. Since particles which have different spin and parity values, and which have strong interactions with the nucleons and pions, are not expected to have identical masses and lifetimes, one is forced to keep the question open whether the inference mentioned above that the τ and θ are not the same particle is conclusive. *Parenthetically, I might add that the inference would certainly have been regarded as conclusive, and in fact more well founded than many inferences in physics, had it not been for the anomaly of mass and lifetime degeneracies.*"

The situation that the physicist found himself in at that time has been likened to that of a man in a dark room groping for an outlet. He is aware of the fact that in some direction there must be a door which would lead him out of his predicament. But in which direction?

That direction, it turned out, lay in the faultiness of the law of parity conservation for the weak interactions. But to uproot an accepted concept one must first demonstrate why the previous evidences in its favor are insufficient. T. D. Lee and I examined this question in detail, and in May 1956 we came to the following conclusions. (i) Past experiments on the weak interactions had actually no bearing on the question of parity conservation. (ii) In the strong interactions—that is, interactions of class 1 and 2 [Table 94–1]—there were indeed many experiments that established parity conservation to a high degree of accuracy, but not to a sufficiently high degree to be able to reveal the effects of a lack of parity conservation in weak interactions.

The fact that it was believed for so long, without experimental support, that the law of parity conservation held good for the weak interactions, was very startling. But what was more startling was the prospect that a space-time symmetry law, which the physicists have learned so well, may be violated. This prospect did not exactly appeal to us. Rather, we were, so to speak, driven to it through frustration in the various other efforts at understanding the θ–τ puzzle that had been made.

As I shall mention later, there is known in physics a conservation law —the conservation of isotopic spin—that holds for interactions of class 1 but breaks down when weaker interactions are introduced. Such a possibility of an approximate symmetry law was, however, not expected of the symmetries related to space and time. In fact, one is tempted to speculate, now that parity conservation has been found to be violated in the weak interactions, whether in the description of the weak interactions the usual concept of space and time is adequate. At the end of this discussion I shall have occasion to come back to a closely related topic.

Why was it the case that among the multitude of experiments on β-decay—the most exhaustively studied of all the weak interactions—there was no information on the conservation of parity in the weak interactions? The answer derives from a combination of two reasons. First, the fact that the neutrino does not have a measurable mass introduces an ambiguity that rules out indirect information on parity conservation from such simple experiments as the spectrum of β-decay. Second, to study directly parity conservation in β-decay, it is not enough to discuss nuclear parities, as one had always done. One must study parity conservation of the *whole* decay process. In other words, one must design an experiment that tests right-left symmetry in the decay. Such experiments had not been made.

TEST OF PARITY CONSERVATION IN THE WEAK INTERACTIONS

Once these points were understood, it was easy to point out what were the experiments that would unambiguously test the previously untested assumption of parity conservation in the weak interactions. T. D. Lee and I proposed, in the summer of 1956, a number of such tests concerning β-decay, π-μ, μ-e and strange particle decays. The basic principles involved in these experiments are all the same: *One constructs two sets of experimental arrangements which are mirror images of each other, and which contain weak interactions. One then examines whether the two arrangements always give the same results in terms of the readings of their meters* (or counters). If the results are not the same, one has an unequivocal proof that right-left symmetry, as we usually understand it, breaks down. The idea is illustrated in [Fig. 94–2], which shows the experiment proposed to test parity conservation in β-decay.

This experiment was first performed in the latter half of 1956, and was finished early in 1957, by Wu, Ambler, Hayward, Hoppes, and Hudson. The actual experimental setup was very involved, because to eliminate disturbing outside influences, the experiment had to be made at very low temperatures. The technique of combining a measurement of β-decay with low-temperature apparatus had not been known before and constituted a major difficulty, which was successfully solved by these authors. To their courage and their skill physicists owe the exciting and clarifying developments of the past year concerning parity conservation.

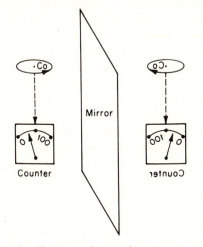

Fig. 94–2. Schematic diagram of experiment to test parity conservation in β-decay.

As a result of their experiment, Wu, Ambler, and their collaborators found that there is a very large difference in the readings of the two meters illustrated schematically in [Fig. 94–2]. Since the behavior of the other parts of their apparatus observes right-left symmetry, the asymmetry that was found must be attributed to the β-decay of cobalt. Very rapidly after these results were made known, many experiments were performed which further demonstrated the violation of parity conservation in various weak interactions.

DISCUSSION

The breakdown of parity conservation brings into focus a number of questions concerning symmetry laws in physics which I shall now briefly discuss in general terms:

1) The experiment of Wu, Ambler, and their collaborators also proves that charge conjugation invariance is violated for β-decay. Another symmetry, called time-reversal invariance, is at the present moment still being experimentally studied for the weak interactions.

The three discrete invariances—reflection invariance, charge conjugation invariance, and time-reversal invariance—are connected by an important theorem, called the CPT theorem. Through the use of this theorem one can prove a number of general results concerning the experimental manifestations of the possible violations of the three symmetries in the weak interactions.

Of particular interest is the possibility that time-reversal invariance in the weak interactions may turn out to be intact. If this is the case, it follows from the CPT theorem that, although parity conservation breaks down, right-left symmetry will still hold if one switches all particles into antiparticles in taking a mirror image. In terms of [Fig. 94–2], this means that if one changes *all* the matter that composes the apparatus at the right into antimatter, the meter reading would become the same for the two sides if time-reversal invariance holds. It is important to notice that, in the usual definition of reflection, the electric field is a vector and the magnetic field a pseudovector, while in this changed definition their transformation properties are switched. The transformation properties of the electric charge and the magnetic charge are also interchanged. It would be interesting to speculate on the possible relationship between the nonconservation of parity and the symmetrical or unsymmetrical role played by the electric and magnetic fields.

The question of the validity of the continuous space-time symmetry laws has been discussed to some extent in the past year. There is good evidence that these symmetry laws do not break down in the weak interactions.

2) Another symmetry law that has been widely discussed is that giving rise to the conservation of isotopic spin. In recent years the use of this symmetry law has produced a remarkable empirical order among the phenomena concerning the strange particles. It is, however, certainly the least understood of all the symmetry laws. Unlike Lorentz invariance or reflection invariance, it is not a "geometrical" symmetry law relating to space-time invariance properties. Unlike charge conjugation invariance it does not seem to originate from the algebraic property of the complex numbers that occur in quantum mechanics. In these respects it resembles the conservation laws of charge and heavy particles. The latter laws, however, are exact, while the conservation of isotopic spin is violated upon the introduction of electromagnetic interactions and weak interactions. An understanding of the origin of the conservation of isotopic spin and how to integrate it with the other symmetry laws is undoubtedly one of the outstanding problems in high-energy physics today.

3) I have mentioned before that all the different varieties of weak interactions share the property of having very nearly identical strengths. The experimental work on parity nonconservation in the past year reveals that they very probably also share the property of not respecting parity

conservation and charge conjugation invariance. They therefore serve to differentiate between right and left once one fixes one's definition of matter versus antimatter. One could also use the weak interactions to differentiate between matter and antimatter once one chooses a definition of right versus left. If time-reversal invariance is violated, the weak interactions may even serve to differentiate simultaneously right from left and matter from antimatter. One senses herein that the origin of the weak interactions may be intimately tied in with the question of the differentiability of left from right and of matter from antimatter.

ooooooo

L E E

Weak Interactions and Nonconservation of Parity [2]

IN THE PREVIOUS LECTURE C. N. Yang has outlined the position of our understandings concerning the various symmetry principles in physics prior to the end of 1956. Since then, in the short period of one year, the proper roles of these principles in various physical processes have been greatly clarified. This remarkably rapid development was made possible only through the efforts and ingenuities of many physicists in various laboratories all over the world. To have a proper perspective and understanding of these new experimental results, it may be desirable to review very briefly our knowledge about elementary particles and their interactions.

ELEMENTARY PARTICLES AND THEIR INTERACTIONS

The family of elementary particles that we know today consists of numerous members. Each member is characterized, among other properties, by its mass, charge, and spin. These members are separated into two main groups, the "heavy-particle" group and the "light-particle" group. The well-known examples of heavy particles are protons and neutrons, of light particles, photons and electrons. Apart from the obvious

[2] T. D. Lee, *Science,* 127 (1958), 569–573.

implication that a heavy particle is heavier than a light particle, this classification stems from the observation that a single heavy particle cannot disintegrate into light particles even if such disintegration should be compatible with the conservation laws of charge, energy, momentum, and angular momentum. This fact is more precisely formulated as the "law of conservation of heavy particles," which states that if to each heavy particle we assign a heavy particle number $+1$, to each antiheavy particle a heavy particle number -1, and to each light particle a corresponding number 0, then in all known physical processes the algebraic sum of the heavy particle numbers is absolutely conserved. One of the simplest evidences of the validity of this law is the fact that we, or our galaxy, have not disintegrated into radiation and other light particles.

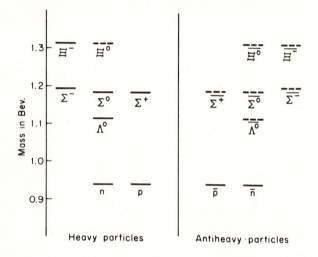

Fig. 94–3. Masses and charges of heavy particles and antiheavy particles.

[Fig. 94–3] shows all the known heavy particles (and antiheavy particles). All heavy particles except the nucleons are called hyperons and are labeled by capital Greek letters. The solid lines represent particles that have already been observed, while the dotted lines represent particles that are expected to exist from general theoretical arguments. All known heavy particles have half-integral spins. [Fig. 94–4] shows all the known light particles. Among these, the $e^{\pm}$, $\mu^{\pm}$ and ν, $\bar{\nu}$ have half-integral spins. They are called leptons. The rest—photons, pions, and K-mesons—have integral spins.

The interactions (not including the gravitational forces) between these particles can be classified into three distinct groups.

1) *Strong interactions.* This group is responsible for the production

and the scattering of nucleons, pions, hyperons (that is, Λ°, Σ^{-}, and so forth), and K-mesons. It is characterized by a coupling constant $f^2/\hbar c \cong 1$.

2) *Electromagnetic interactions.* The electromagnetic coupling constant is $e^2/\hbar c = 1/137$.

3) *Weak interactions.* This group includes all known nonelectromagnetic decay interactions of these elementary particles and the recently observed absorption process of neutrinos by nucleons. These interactions are characterized by coupling constants $g^2/hc \cong 10^{-14}$.

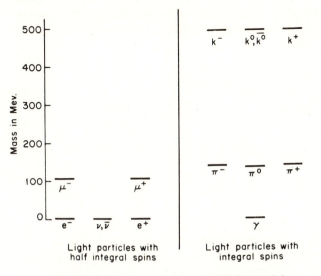

Fig. 94–4. Masses and charges of light particles.

The law of conservation parity is valid for both the strong and the electromagnetic interactions but is not valid for the weak interactions. This discussion will be mainly concerned with the recently observed effects of nonconservation of parity in the various weak interactions.

NONINVARIANCE UNDER MIRROR REFLECTION AND CHARGE CONJUGATION

The weak interactions cover a large variety of reactions. At present there are about twenty known phenomenologically independent reactions ranging from the decay of various hyperons to the decay of light particles. Within the last year, many critical experiments have been performed to test the validity of the law of conservation of parity in these reactions. We shall first summarize the experimental results together with their direct theoretical implications. Next, we shall discuss some further possible consequences and theoretical considerations.

β-Decay. The first experiment that conclusively established the non-conservation of parity was that on β-angular distribution from polarized cobalt-60 nuclei [Fig. 94–5]. The cobalt-60 nuclei are polarized by a magnetic field at very low temperatures. Indeed, in this experiment, the circular direction of the electric current in the solenoid that produces the polarizing magnetic field, together with the preferential direction of the β-ray emitted, differentiates in a very direct way a right-handed system from a left-handed system. Thus the nonconservation of parity or the noninvariance under a mirror reflection can be established without reference to any theory.

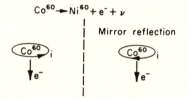

Fig. 94–5. β-decay from polarized cobalt-60 nucleus.

Furthermore, from the large amount of angular asymmetry observed, it can also be established that the β-decay interaction is not invariant under a charge conjugation operation. That this can be concluded without performing the extremely difficult (in fact, almost impossible) experiment using anticobalt-60 is based on certain theoretical deductions under the general framework of local field theory. In the following we shall try to sketch this type of reasoning.

Let us consider the β-decay process, say,

$$n \rightarrow p + e^- + \nu, \tag{1}$$

in which each particle is described by a quantized wave equation. In particular the neutrino is described by the Dirac equation

$$\sum_{\mu=1}^{4} \gamma_\mu \frac{\partial}{\partial x_\mu} \psi_\nu = 0, \tag{2}$$

where γ_1, γ_2, γ_3, γ_4 are the four (4×4) anticommuting Dirac matrices and x_1, x_2, x_3, $x_4 = ict$ are the four space-time coordinates. For each given momentum there exist two spin states for the neutrino and two spin states for the antineutrino. These may be denoted by ν_R, ν_L, $\bar{\nu}_R$, $\bar{\nu}_L$. We define the helicity $\mathcal{H}$ to be

$$\mathcal{H} \equiv \vec{\sigma} \cdot \hat{p}, \tag{3}$$

with $\vec{\sigma}$ as the spin operator and $\hat{p}$ the unit vector along the momentum direction, then these four states have, respectively, helicities equal to $+1$, -1, -1 and $+1$ [Fig. 94–6]. Mathematically, this decomposition of

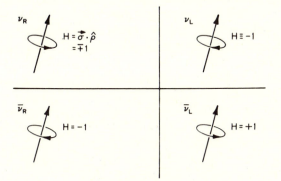

Fig. 94–6. Helicities of a four-component neutrino.

states corresponds to a separation of ψ_ν into a right-handed part ψ_R and a left-handed part ψ_L with

$$\psi_\nu = \psi_R + \psi_L, \tag{4}$$

where

$$\psi_R = \tfrac{1}{2}(1 - \gamma_5)\psi_\nu, \tag{5}$$
$$\psi_L = \tfrac{1}{2}(1 + \gamma_5)\psi_\nu, \tag{6}$$

and

$$\gamma_5 = \gamma_1\gamma_2\gamma_3\gamma_4$$

It is easy to see that both ψ_R and ψ_L separately satisfy the Dirac equation (Eq. 2). With this decomposition the β process of a nucleus A can be represented schematically as

$$A \to B + e^- + \begin{cases} C_i{}^R\nu_R & (\mathcal{H} = +1) \\ C_i{}^L\nu_L & (\mathcal{H} = -1) \end{cases} \begin{matrix} (7) \\ (8) \end{matrix}$$

with C_i^R and C_i^L as the various probability amplitudes for emission of ν_R and ν_L, respectively. The suffix i represents the various possible channels for such emissions. If the theory is invariant under proper Lorentz transformation, then there are five such channels: namely scalar S, tensor T, vector V, pseudoscalar P and axial-vector term A. According to the general rules of quantum field theory with any interaction term representing the decay of a particle, there exists a corresponding hermitian conjugate term which represents the decay of the antiparticle. Thus, the decay of the antinucleus $\overline{A}$ can be schematically represented by

$$\overline{A} \to \overline{B} + e^+ + \begin{cases} C_i^{R*}\overline{\nu}_R & (\mathfrak{K} = -1) & (7') \\ C_i^{L*}\overline{\nu}_L & (\mathfrak{K} = +1) & (8') \end{cases}$$

with C_i^{R*} and C_i^{L*} as the corresponding amplitudes for emission of $\overline{\nu}_R$ and $\overline{\nu}_L$. Under the charge conjugation operator we change a particle to its antiparticle but we do not change its spatial or spin wave functions. Consequently, it must have the same helicity. Thus, if the β-decay process is invariant under the charge conjugation operator, then we should expect process 7 to proceed with the same amplitude as process 8'. The condition for invariance under charge conjugation is, then,

$$C_i^R = C_i^{L*} \tag{9}$$

for all $i = $ S, T, V, P, A.

In the decay of cobalt-60, because there is a difference of spin values between cobalt-60 and nickel-60, only the terms $i = $ T and $i = $ A contribute. From the large angular asymmetry observed it can be safely concluded that for both $i = $ T, A

$$|C_i^R| \neq |C_i^L|$$

which contradicts Eq. 9 and proves the noninvariance of β-interaction under charge conjugation. In the above, for illustration purposes, we assume the neutrino to be described by a four-component theory and, further, we assume that in the β-decay process only a neutrino is emitted. Actually, the same conclusion concerning the noninvariance property under charge conjugation can be obtained even if the neutrino should be described by a, say, eight-component theory, or, if in addition to the β-process that a neutrino is produced an antineutrino may also be emitted.

Recently many more experiments have been performed on the longitudinal polarization of electrons and positrons, the β-γ correlation together with the circular polarization of the γ radiation and the β-angular distribution with various polarized nuclei other than cobalt-60. The results of all these experiments confirm the main conclusions of the first cobalt-60 experiment, that neither the parity operator nor the charge conjugation operator is conserved in β-decay processes.

Another interesting question is whether the β-decay interaction is invariant under the product operation of (charge conjugation $\times$ mirror reflection). Under such an operation we should compare the decay of A with that of $\overline{A}$ but with opposite helicities. Thus, if β-decay is invariant under the joint operation of (charge conjugation $\times$ mirror reflection) we should expect process 7 to proceed with the same amplitude as process 7′ and similarly for processes 8 and 8′. The corresponding conditions are then

$$C_i^R = C_i^{R*},$$

and

$$C_i^L = C_i^{L*}. \tag{10}$$

Although experiments have been performed to test the validity of these conditions, at present these experiments have not reached a conclusive stage and we still do not know the answer to this important question.

π-μ-e Decay. The $\pi^{\pm}$-meson decays into a $\mu^{\pm}$-meson and a neutrino. The $\mu^{\pm}$-meson, in turn, decays into an $e^{\pm}$ and two neutrinos (or antineutrinos). If parity is not conserved in π-decay, the μ-meson emitted could be longitudinally polarized. If in the subsequent μ-decay parity is also not conserved, the electron (or positron) emitted from such a μ-meson at rest would in general exhibit a forward and backward angular asymmetry with respect to the polarization of the μ-meson [Fig. 94–7].

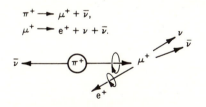

$$\pi^+ \longrightarrow \mu^+ + \bar{\nu},$$
$$\mu^+ \longrightarrow e^+ + \nu + \bar{\nu}.$$

Fig. 94–7. π-μ-e decay.

Consequently, in the π-μ-e decay sequence we may observe an angular correlation between the momentum of a $\mu^{\pm}$-meson measured in the rest system of a π-meson and the momentum of $e^{\pm}$ measured in the rest system of $\mu^{\pm}$. If this angular correlation shows a forward-backward asymmetry, then parity must be nonconserved in both π-decay and μ-decay. The experimental results on these angular correlations appeared within a few days after the results on β-decay were known. These results showed conclusively that not only is parity not conserved but that the charge conjugation operator is also not conserved in π-decay as well as in μ-decay.

Later, direct measurements on the longitudinal polarization of the positron from μ^+-decay were made and established the same conclusion concerning μ-decay.

K-μ-e Decay. In this case we have instead of the π-meson the heavier K-meson which decays into a μ-meson and a neutrino [Fig. 94–8]. An experiment on the angular correlation between the μ^+ momentum from

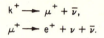

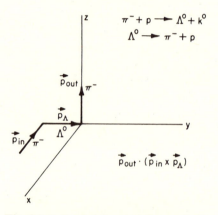

Fig. 94–8. *K-μ-e* decay.

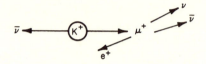

Fig. 94–9. Production and decay of Λ^0.

the decay of a K$^+$-meson and the positron momentum from the μ^+-decay established that in K-decay the parity as well as the charge conjugation operator is not conserved.

Λ^0 *Decay.* The Λ^0 particle can be produced by colliding an energetic π^- on a proton. The Λ^0 subsequently decays into a proton plus a π^- [Fig. 94–9]. The observation of an asymmetrical distribution with respect to the sign of the product $\vec{p}_{out} \cdot (\vec{p}_{in} \times \vec{p}_\Lambda)$ formed from the momentum of the incoming pion $\vec{p}_{in}$, the momentum of the lambda particle, $\vec{p}_\Lambda$, and that of the decay pion $\vec{p}_{out}$ would constitute an unequivocal proof that parity is not conserved in this decay. Recent experiments on these reactions demonstrate that in these reactions there is indeed such an angular correlation between $\vec{p}_{\text{out}}$ and $(\vec{p}_{\text{in}} \times \vec{p}_\Lambda)$. Furthermore, from the amount of the large up-down asymmetry, it can be concluded that the Λ°-decay interaction is also not invariant under the charge conjugation operation.

From all these results it appears that the property of nonconservation of parity in the various weak interactions and that the noninvariance property of these interactions under charge conjugation are well established. In connection with these properties we find an entirely new and rich domain of natural phenomena which, in turn, give us new tools to probe further into the structure of our physical world. These weak interactions offer us natural ways to polarize and to analyze the spins of various elementary particles. Thus, for example, the magnetic moment of the μ-meson can now be measured to an extremely high degree of accuracy which, otherwise, would be unattainable; the spins of some hyperons now may perhaps be determined unambiguously through the observed angular asymmetries in their decays; new aspects of the electromagnetic fields of various gas, liquid, and solid materials can now be studied by using these unstable, polarized particles. However, perhaps the most significant consequences are the openings of new possibilities and the reexamination of our old concepts concerning the structure of elementary particles. We shall next discuss two such considerations—the two-component theory of the neutrino and the possible existence of a law of conservation of leptons.

TWO-COMPONENT THEORY OF NEUTRINO AND LAW OF CONSERVATION OF LEPTONS

Before the recent developments on nonconservation of parity, it was customary to describe the neutrino by a four-component theory in which, as mentioned before, to each definite momentum there are the two spin states of the neutrino ν_R and ν_L, plus the two spin states of the antineutrino $\bar{\nu}_R$ and $\bar{\nu}_L$. In the two-component theory, however, we assume that two of these states, say ν_L and $\bar{\nu}_L$, simply do not exist in nature. The spin of the neutrino is then always parallel to its momentum, while the spin of the antineutrino is always antiparallel to its momentum. Thus, in the two-component theory we have only half of the degrees of freedom that we have in the four-component theory. Graphically, we may represent the spin and the velocity of the neutrino by the spiral motion of a right-handed screw and that of the antineutrino by the motion of a left-handed screw [Fig. 94–10].

The possibility of a two-component relativistic theory of a spin ½ particle was first discussed by H. Weyl as early as 1929. However, in the past, because parity is not manifestly conserved in the Weyl formalism, it has always been rejected. With the recent discoveries such an objection becomes completely invalid.

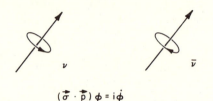

$$(\vec{\sigma} \cdot \vec{p})\, \phi = i\dot{\phi}$$

Fig. 94–10. Two-component neutrino.

To appreciate the simplicity of this two-component theory in the present situation, it is best if we assume further the existence of a conservation law for leptons. This law is in close analogy with the corresponding conservation law for the heavy particles. We assign to each lepton a leptonic number l equal to $+1$ or -1 and to any other particle the leptonic number zero. The leptonic number for a lepton must be the negative of that for its antiparticle. The law of conservation of leptons then states that, "in all physical processes the algebraic sum of leptonic numbers must be conserved."

Some simple consequences follow immediately if we assume that this law is valid and that the neutrino is described by the two-component theory.

1) The [rest] mass of the neutrino and the antineutrino must be zero. This is true for the physical mass even with the inclusion of all interactions. To see this let us consider a neutrino moving with a finite momentum. From the two-component theory the spin of this neutrino must be parallel to its momentum. Suppose now it has a nonvanishing physical mass. Then, we can always send an observer traveling along the same direction as the neutrino but with a velocity faster than that of the neutrino. From this observer's point of view this "neutrino" now becomes a particle with the spin along its original direction but the direction of momentum reversed—that is, it becomes an "antineutrino." However, since the leptonic number for the neutrino is different from that of the antineutrino, these two particles cannot be transformed into each other by a Lorentz transformation. Consequently, the physical mass of a neutrino must be zero.

2) The theory is not invariant under the parity operator P which by definition inverts all spatial coordinates but does not change a particle

into its antiparticle state. Under such an operation one inverts the momentum of a particle but not its spin direction. Since in this theory these two are always parallel for a neutrino, the parity operator P, when it is applied to a neutrino state, leads the neutrino to a nonexisting state. Consequently, the theory is not invariant under the parity operation.

3) Similarly, one can show that the theory is not invariant under the charge conjugation operation which changes a particle into its antiparticle but not its spin direction or its momentum.

To test the complete validity of the conservation law of leptons and the two-component theory, we have to investigate in detail all the neutrino processes. For example, in β-decay we must have either

$$n \to p + e^- + \nu \qquad (\mathcal{H}\nu = +1),$$

or

$$n \to p + e^- + \bar{\nu} \qquad (\mathcal{H}_\nu = -1).$$

This can be determined by measuring the spin and the momentum of the neutral lepton—to see whether it is a neutrino (right-handed helicity) or an antineutrino (left-handed helicity). Through the law of conservation of angular momentum, measurements on polarizations and angular distributions of the nucleus and the electrons can lead to determination of the spin states of the neutrino. Similarly, through recoil momentum measurements, we can find out information about the linear momentum of the neutrino. In the same way we can use not only β-decay but π-decay, μ-decay and K-decay to test the validity of either the two-component theory or the law of conservation of leptons. At present, these measurements have not yet reached a definitive stage. Much of our future theory may depend on the results of these experiments.

REMARKS

The progress of science has always been the result of a close interplay between our concepts of the universe and our observations of nature. The former can only evolve out of the latter, and yet the latter is also conditioned greatly by the former. Thus, in our exploration of nature, the interplay between our concepts and our observations may sometimes lead to totally unexpected aspects among already familiar phenomena. As in the present case, these hidden properties are usually revealed only through a fundamental change in our basic concept concerning the principles that underlie natural phenomena. While all this is well known, it is nevertheless an extremely rich and memorable experience to be able to watch at a close distance in a single instance the mutual influence and the subsequent growth of these two factors—the concept and the observation. It is, indeed, a privilege that I have this opportunity to tell you part of this experience in the recent developments concerning the nonconservation of parity and the weak interactions.

ooooooo

R O D B E R G   and   *W E I S S K O P F*

Fall of Parity [3]

A NUMBER OF RECENT EXPERIMENTS in nuclear physics have revealed that some of the very basic properties of nature seem to be different from what we believed them to be. It is rare in the history of physics that the results of only a few experiments force upon us a change in our fundamental principles. This is just what has happened now, and this essay tries to explain the situation.

Before describing the experiments themselves, we will discuss the basic principle which is attacked by their results. It is the *principle of parity*. This principle can be stated in the following form: any process which occurs in nature can also occur as it is seen reflected in a mirror. Thus nature is mirror-symmetric. The mirror image of any object is also a possible object in nature; the motion of any object as seen in a mirror is also a motion which would be permitted by the laws of nature. Any experiment made in a laboratory can also be made in the way it appears as seen in a mirror, and any resulting effect will be then the mirror image of the actual effect. In more elegant language, the laws of nature are invariant under reflection.

As an example, take a perfectly uniform bar supported in the middle by a pivot, as in [Fig. 94–11]. We all know that it will not tip, but let us prove this using mirror symmetry, or the principle of parity. There are three possibilities: (i) the bar could tip clockwise, (ii) it could tip counterclockwise, or (iii) it could remain horizontal. Suppose we place a mirror as in [Fig. 94–12] (the dotted line represents the mirror). The mirror image of the bar and its support is identical with the object. However, if motion (*a*) were the correct one, the mirror image would show

[3] L. S. Rodberg and V. F. Weisskopf, *Science*, 125 (1957), 627–632.

motion (*b*) and not the correct motion i; hence, we have a contradiction to the principle of parity. Only the possibility iii is identical with its reflection and thus must be the correct one since the object itself is identical with its reflection.

Now we suppose the pivot to be frictionless and rotate the bar around the axis *AA'* [Fig. 94–13]. The situation is unchanged since this rotation appears unchanged in the mirror. Then this rotation will not cause the bar to tilt.

Fig. 94–11. Uniform bar pivoted in the middle.

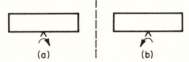

(a)   (b)

Fig. 94–12. Mirror image of bar. This illustrates the lack of mirror symmetry if the bar should rotate.

Fig. 94–13. Rotating bar viewed in mirror. The sense of rotation is unchanged by reflection.

ELECTROMAGNETIC RADIATION

Let us now look at a more sophisticated example. We will examine the radiation from an electric dipole. Such a dipole can be pictured, for example, as a charge which oscillates up and down in the *z*-direction [Fig. 94–14]. We see, first of all, that the radiation pattern will be symmetric around the *z*-axis. This is because the electric dipole exhibits a cylindrical symmetry about this axis.

We will now use mirror symmetry to show that the intensity is the same above and below the *x*-*y*-plane. In [Fig. 94–15] we illustrate the two cases. The mirror image of the oscillating dipole is identical with the object, apart from a phase shift of half a period. When the object moves up, the image moves down. However, the radiation intensity pattern is constant in time, and therefore it is not affected by this shift in time. We see that the mirror image of the radiation pattern labeled "right" is exactly like the actual one, as it should be, while the pattern labeled "wrong" is inverted: the object has a stronger field downward, while the image has a stronger field upward. They cannot both be right.

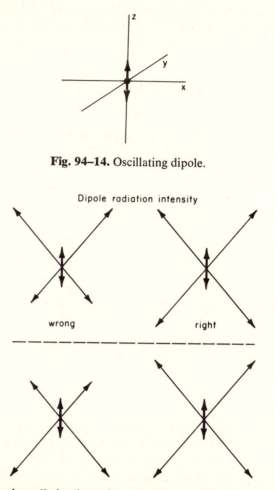

Fig. 94–14. Oscillating dipole.

Dipole radiation intensity

wrong   right

Fig. 94–15. Dipole radiation-intensity patterns and their mirror images. The pattern marked "right" emits the same intensities into the upper and lower hemispheres; the pattern marked "wrong" emits more into the upper hemisphere than into the lower.

Let us now look at the electromagnetic field associated with this radiation. Here we examine the instantaneous position of the moving charge, and of the electric field, since we know that after each half period the direction of the dipole and also the direction of the field strength change their sign. Let us suppose that the charge is moving upward. We know that the electric field must be perpendicular to the direction of propagation, and we would like only to decide the question of the relative directions of the electric field in two beams, one going upward and the other downward. In fact, we want to decide between the two possibilities marked "wrong" and "right" in [Fig. 94–16]. Using mirror symmetry, we can rule out the possibility marked "wrong." This situation cannot hold, for the dipole is turned around in reflection, while the electric field is not. (Alter-

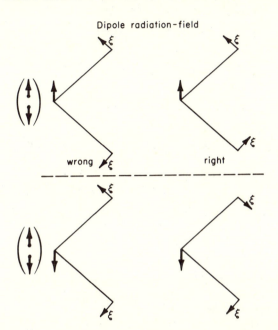

Fig. 94–16. The electric field distribution of a dipole radiation and its mirror image. The little arrows marked $[\varepsilon]$ represent the direction of the electric field at a given time in the wave emitted in the direction shown. The heavy arrow in the center shows the displacement of the dipole at that time. The two heavy arrows in parentheses symbolize a quadrupole source.

natively, if we wait half a period, the mirror-dipole will point upward again, but the electric field will have reversed its direction.) On the other hand, in the situation marked "right," the electric field has "followed" the dipole upon reflection. (Here, if we wait half a period, the mirror dipole and electric field will reverse, reproducing the present actual dipole and electric field.) Then the situation marked "right" must be the true one.

On the other hand, a quadrupole consists of two dipoles opposite each other. It is thus unchanged when it is reflected in a mirror, so that we have the reversed case; the electric field of quadrupole radiation must be invariant upon reflection in a mirror, and the case marked "wrong" in [Fig. 94–16] would be the correct one. We say that dipole radiation has an "odd" parity since E has changed direction; quadrupole radiation has an "even" parity, since E is unchanged.

We have used the electric field in this discussion since it alone specifies a direction (the direction of the force on a positive charge). This direction becomes the reflected direction when seen in a mirror. The magnetic field does not specify a direction, but only a sense of rotation (for example, the sense of rotation of a moving charged particle which produced it). However, the sense of rotation is unchanged under reflection. It is important to remember here that the "direction" of the magnetic field is usually

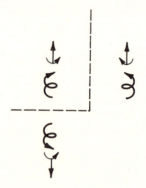

Fig. 94–17. A spiral and its mirror changes. The horizontal mirror changes the direction but not the sense of rotation. The vertical one changes the sense of rotation, but not the direction.

defined in terms of an arbitrarily chosen "right-handed screw." That is, we associate the magnetic field with a screw, which arbitrarily ascribes a direction to a sense of rotation in order to express it by a vector. This situation is usually described by saying that the electric field is described by a polar vector which changes direction under reflection, while the magnetic field is described by an axial vector, which does not change direction under reflection.

Let us now consider an object such as a screw which has a "spirality"— that is, a direction of motion associated with a sense of rotation [Fig. 94–17]. Its mirror image has the opposite spirality and must also exist in nature, by our principle of parity. Thus, in [Fig. 94–17], we see that we may place our testing mirror in two positions, one of which reflects the direction of motion but leaves the sense of rotation unchanged, while the other has the reverse effect. In either case, the spirality is changed.

An example is the tetrahedral molecule of [Fig. 94–18]. We see that the reflected molecule cannot, by any rotation, be made to be identical with the original molecules (just as we cannot turn our left hand in such a position that it looks like our right hand). Thus these are distinct molecules which, by the principle of parity, must both exist in nature. An example of this situation is the quartz crystal, composed of many of these molecules. This crystal illustrates on a large scale this "handedness." The principle of parity requires that both types of crystals be found in nature.

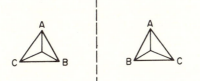

Fig. 94–18. An asymmetric tetrahedral molecule viewed in a mirror.

A well-known example is the fact that sugar occurs in two varieties. However, it is only the right-handed kind, glucose, which is found in living matter. As physicists, we do not believe that this indicates an inherent handedness of nature; rather, we believe that it can be attributed to an accident which occurred at the origin of life. Life could just as well have developed by using levulose instead of glucose.

BETA DECAY

We now proceed to consider the actual experiments which have shed new light on this principle of parity, in particular, experiments on beta decay. All we need to know here is that there are atomic nuclei which emit electrons along with neutral, massless particles known as neutrinos. For instance, the isotope of cobalt known as cobalt-60 becomes nickel-60 and emits an electron (e^-) and a neutrino (ν)

$$Co^{60} \to Ni^{60} + e^- + \nu$$

The cobalt nucleus has a spin—that is, it is rotating with a well-defined angular momentum when it is in its normal state. Now we ask: In what directions will the electrons emerge? In a normal piece of cobalt, electrons will emerge in all directions because nuclei are oriented in all directions because of the heat motion.

Suppose we orient the nuclei—that is, force all the nuclei to align their axes of rotation parallel to a given direction and have them rotate in the same sense. This is the difficult part of the experiment since it is so hard to "get hold of" the nucleus. The only way is through the magnetic moment arising from the spin. The spin can be forced into a given direction by an external magnetic field if we can reach temperatures of less than 0.1 °K. Then it is possible to orient the nuclei.

What do we now expect? The nuclei are all rotating in the same sense. Let us apply the principle of parity. In a mirror [Fig. 94–19] they rotate the same, but the direction of the electrons is reversed. Thus the situation marked "wrong," in which more electrons emerge in one direction than

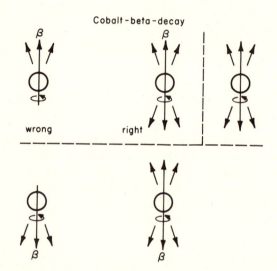

Fig. 94–19. Cobalt β decay. Possible electron decay patterns and their mirror images. Only the choice which is mirror-symmetric should occur if the principle of parity is valid.

in the other, violates the principle of parity: the mirror image contradicts the actual situation. Since the parity principle requires both to be right, we must exclude this case. Hence, we expect the same number of electrons to emerge in each direction.

This now sets the scene for the experiment. It was performed at the National Bureau of Standards in Washington, D.C., where the cryogenic equipment was available for experimenting at very low temperatures. The physicists who did it were C. S. Wu from Columbia University and E. Ambler, R. W. Hayward, D. D. Hoppes, and R. P. Hudson of the National Bureau of Standards. They oriented the rotation of cobalt nuclei and compared the electron intensities in the two opposite directions along the axis of rotation.

There are several remarkable features about this experiment. It is one of those experiments which only a few people would perform because the result "obviously" follows from mirror symmetry. Great discoveries are always made when one doubts the "obvious." In this case, it was the insistence of two theoretical physicists, T. D. Lee of Columbia and C. N. Yang of the Institute for Advanced Study, which prompted the experimenters to look for the effect. Lee and Yang suspected that the principle of parity may be invalid for certain weak interactions like beta decay.

Another remarkable feature of this experiment is the size of the effect which was measured. The intensity of electrons in one direction along the axis of rotation was found to be 40 percent larger than it was in the other. It is very rare in the history of physics that the failure of an established principle shows up with such large effects in the first experiment. Usually the first doubts are based on small deviations which hardly exceed the limits of error, and only after the passing of time and the application of great effort by many people are effects as large as 40 percent found.

In view of the historic importance of this experiment, it is perhaps worth while to show the actual curves as measured. They are reproduced in [Fig. 94–20]. The scale labeled "time" is actually a scale of temperature. The cobalt sample is cooled to a temperature at which its nuclei are aligned, and then it slowly warms up in the course of time. The curve labeled "gamma anisotropy" really tells us the fraction of nuclei which are oriented. For a large anisotropy, most of the nuclei are aligned. As the cobalt warms up, the heat motion causes the alignment to become more random, and the gamma anisotropy decreases.

The curve labeled "β-asymmetry" is the significant one. This tells us the number of electrons emerging in the direction of the magnetic field, and the number emerging in the opposite direction. We see that there are more in one direction than in the other, that the electrons go up when the spin is turning one way and down when the spin is turning the other way. This shows that the principle of parity does not hold in this experiment. Remember that the spin of the nucleus tells only a sense of rotation. And yet the electron emerges in a preferred *direction*. This is the mark of the parity violation. The fact that there is a direction associated with a sense of rotation shows that there is a definite "handedness" exhibited in the beta decay of cobalt-60. The mirror image of the decaying cobalt nucleus would have the opposite handedness and seemingly does *not* occur in nature.

The same experiment has also been done with cobalt-58, which is a *positron* emitter. It goes over into iron-58 and emits a positron (e^+) and an antineutrino

$$Co^{58} \rightarrow Fe^{58} + e^+ + \bar{\nu}$$

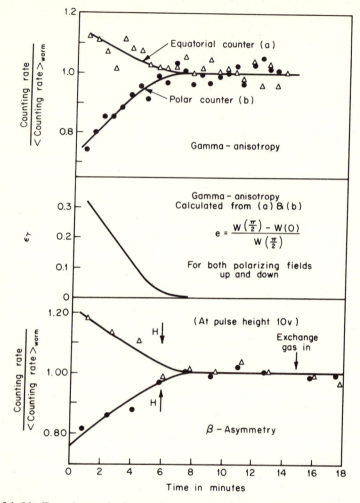

Fig. 94–20. Experimental observations on β-decay of cobalt-60. The gamma anisotropy measures the orientation of the nuclei. The β-asymmetry measures the number of electrons which emerge parallel, and antiparallel, to the magnetic field.

where $\bar{\nu}$ denotes the antineutrino. Whenever a negative electron is emitted in a beta decay, as in cobalt-60, it is accompanied by a neutrino, and whenever a positron is emitted, it goes with an antineutrino. Most significantly, the same group of physicists have found the opposite handedness in the positron case. For the same rotational sense of the nucleus, negative electrons seem to emerge in one direction and positrons in the other.

SPIRALITY

A possible explanation of these new phenomena has been proposed by Lee and Yang, and independently by L. Landau in Moscow and by A. Salam in England. They suggest that the spirality is associated with the neutrino, since all other phenomena in nuclear physics, which involve no neutrinos, exhibit perfect mirror symmetry. With this hypothesis, the difficulty is isolated from the rest of physics. It "minimizes the damage" and puts this strange property on the neutrino, which is already a strange particle.

Lee, Yang, Landau, and Salam argue that the neutrino is a spiral. Its sense of rotation and its direction of propagation are connected such that they form, say, a left-handed screw. The neutrino has the property that its spin (its rotation) must be such that its axis is parallel to its motion and its sense such as to form a left-handed screw. The antineutrino is supposed to have the opposite properties. It forms a right-handed screw.

It is interesting to note that particles with such properties must always move with the velocity of light c and, therefore, necessarily have a zero rest mass. If they would move with a velocity v less than c, they would reverse their spirality for an observer moving faster than v in the same

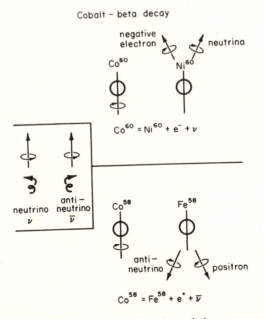

Fig. 94–21. The Lee-Yang-Landau explanation of the asymmetric beta decay of cobalt-60 and cobalt-58.

direction. Hence, their spirality would be dependent on the observer and could not be an intrinsic property.

With these helical neutrinos, the observed effects can indeed be explained [Fig. 94–21]. The emitted particles must take along some of the spin of the emitting nucleus. Hence, the sense of rotation of the neutrino will be the same as the one of the cobalt nucleus. Its direction of emission must then be such that a left-handed screw is formed. Hence, the neutrino will be emitted only in one direction—namely, the one which forms a left-handed screw with its sense of rotation. The electrons are emitted mostly in the same direction as the neutrino. Thus, we get a preferred direction of emission for the electrons, as observed.

A good support for this explanation is found in the experiment with cobalt-58, in which the emitted particles are a positron and an antineutrino. If the hypothesis is correct, the preferred direction of the positrons must be opposite here to the preferred direction of the electrons in cobalt-60, for the antineutrino has the opposite spirality. In fact, that is just what the experiment has shown!

EXPERIMENTS ON MESONS

There is a second kind of experiments in which a similar violation of the parity law has been observed. These experiments have to do with some of the newly discovered short-lived particles, the mesons. The most important meson is the π-meson, which is probably the "quantum" of the nuclear force field. It is responsible for the binding forces in the nucleus. It occurs in three varieties, positive, negative, and neutral; it has a mass 265 times that of an electron, and it is known to have no intrinsic spin. When it is in free motion, the charged π-meson has a very short lifetime of only 10^{-8} second and decays into a μ-meson and a neutrino. The μ-meson is a particle very similar to an electron. It has a charge (positive or negative) and a spin of $\frac{1}{2}\hbar$ just like the electron, but its mass is 250 times larger. It too is unstable and decays after 10^{-6} second into an electron and two neutrinos. This double decay chain

$$\pi \rightarrow \mu + \nu \rightarrow e + 2\nu + \nu$$

is a very interesting phenomenon and has been studied in detail.

[Fig. 94–22] shows a bubble chamber photograph of such processes, made recently by I. Pless, R. Williams, and co-workers. What one sees in such a picture are the charged particles only and not the neutrinos. One observes π-meson tracks coming from above which end when the π-mesons come to rest. They then decay, and one sees a (short) μ-meson track emerge from the end point of the π-meson track. At the end of this track a third track emerges which is the track of the electron. The last track is longer again and is not very straight because the light-weight electron can easily be deviated from its path. A careful observer will find in [Fig. 94–22] that in five out of the six decay chains the electron is emitted

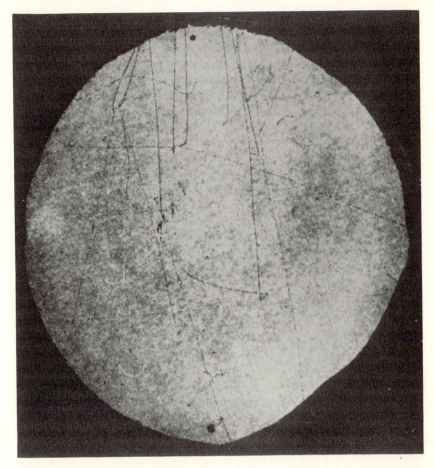

Fig. 94–22. Bubble chamber photograph of the π-μ-e decay chain. Dark tracks entering the chamber from above are π-mesons. Short dark tracks at ends of the π-meson tracks are μ-mesons produced in the decay of the π-mesons. The long light tracks are electrons produced in the decay of the μ-mesons. The electron tracks emerge in a predominantly backward direction relative to the direction of the μ-meson tracks.

"backward" in reference to the motion of the μ-meson. This effect has been established by more careful experiments, at Columbia University by Garwin, Lederman, and Weinrich, at the University of Chicago by Friedman and Telegdi.

Why are the electrons emitted backward? Again, this is an example of the breakdown of the parity rule. When the μ-meson comes to a rest at the end of its short track, the only motion left to it is its rotation. How can a rotation determine a preferential direction of decay? Only by defining a preferential "handedness" or screw sense. This, of course, is a violation of the parity law, for the mirror image of the process would show the opposite preference.

The Yang-Lee hypothesis, ascribing a spirality only to the neutrino, would also explain these meson experiments. This is shown schematically in [Fig. 94–23]. The π-meson decays into a μ-meson and a neutrino. The

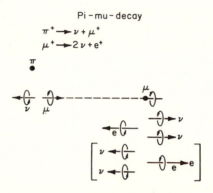

Fig. 94–23. π-μ-e decay. The neutrino is a spiral (here shown as left-handed). The μ-meson produced in π-μ decay must possess the same spirality. When the μ-meson decays, two neutrinos are emitted in a direction opposite that of a high-energy electron. Because of the inherent spirality of the neutrinos, the relative directions must be as shown. The mirror image of this decay process is shown in brackets. By the parity principle, this should also be a possible decay process; experiment shows that it is not.

spin of the neutrino is always supposed to form a left-handed screw with its direction of propagation. From this it follows directly that in this decay the μ-meson also must form a left-handed screw with its rotation and its velocity since the spin and motion of the π-meson before decay was zero, and, consequently, the spin and motion of the two decay particles must be opposed. (In general, the spin of the μ-meson is not fixed relative to its direction of motion; Yang and Lee assume such coupling to be compulsory only for neutrinos. However, in this case its spin axis is parallel to its motion, and its sense of rotation is left handed.)

Now we look at the second decay in the chain, the decay of the μ-meson into two neutrinos and an electron. The conservation of momentum requires, for those cases in which the electron obtains large energies, that the two neutrinos be emitted in one direction and the electron in the opposite one. The two neutrinos are necessarily emitted in the direction of the μ-meson motion because of the fact that their sense of rotation will coincide with the one of the μ-meson (conservation of spin) and because of the necessity of forming a left-handed screw. Hence, the electron will be emitted mostly backward, as observed.

NOVELTY OF THE PHENOMENON

Let us now discuss two experiments which in all probability cannot actually be performed. A discussion of them is instructive, however, because it illustrates the essential novelty of the phenomenon.

We first return to the pivoted bar with which we began this discussion. Suppose it is made of cobalt-60, and suppose we rotate it about the axis AA' [Fig. 94–24]. (This example was suggested by E. M. Purcell.) As

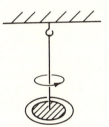

Fig. 94–24. Aluminum disk suspended by a thin wire. If the disk is coated on top with cobalt-60, it will spontaneously rotate as shown.

it rotates, the nuclear spins align themselves and the bar becomes very slightly magnetic. (This is the Barnett effect.) The electrons will then be emitted in a given direction; they will be absorbed in the bar, and one end will contain more energy than the other. (Actually, under normal conditions, this effect is so small that it cannot be observed at all.) Since the theory of relativity tells us that energy and mass are related, one end will be heavier than the other. Then, theoretically at least, the bar *will* tilt. Thus, a microscopic process (beta decay) which violates the principle of parity could lead in principle to a macroscopic observation of its violation.

An even more dramatic experiment has been suggested by J. R. Zacharias. Suppose a small round disk of aluminum is coated on the top with a thin film of cobalt-60 and suspended in a horizontal position by a thin wire attached to its center, as shown in [Fig. 94–24]. The disk will begin to rotate! And, if the experiment is repeated, it will always rotate in the same direction! This can be understood from our previous discussion of beta decay, if we observe that the electrons which are emitted downward will be stopped in the aluminum, while those which are emitted upward will escape (the neutrinos escape in either case). One can think of the electrons which are stopped as transmitting their spirality to the block, which then begins to rotate. If the cobalt coating were on the lower side, the rotation would be in the other direction.

ANTIMATTER

It is very suggestive to consider the violation of the principle of parity in connection with another somewhat better known asymmetry in our physical world. This is the asymmetry with respect to electric charge. The massive atomic nuclei are all positively charged, and the light electrons are negative. Physicists began to suspect that this asymmetry was only apparent after the discovery of the positive electron, the positron, in the early 1930's. It was shown that one can produce an electron pair, a negative and a positive electron, with light quanta of sufficient energy. The positron is in all respects the exact opposite of the negative electron; it is its so-called "antiparticle." If a positron hits an ordinary electron, the two particles annihilate each other (the opposite process of pair creation), and their masses are transformed into light energy. The question of charge symmetry was completely cleared up after the discovery last year of the antiproton and the antineutron. The antiproton is a negative proton; it is antiparticle to the ordinary proton. It was produced with the very high energies now available from the large accelerators. The antineutron is the antiparticle of the ordinary neutron; it is just as neutral in respect to charge, of course, but it is opposite to the neutron in all respects. For example, it has the opposite magnetic moment, and it will annihilate into γ-rays or other forms of field energy with any neutron it meets, just as the negative proton will when it encounters a positive proton.

Hence, it seems that the charge asymmetry of matter is only apparent. One could also build up "antimatter," as it were, by using antiprotons and antineutrons for nuclei and positrons around them instead of electrons. Such antimatter would be the exact replica of our matter, with opposite charge: negative nuclei and positive electrons. It just so happens that our world is made of one type of matter. Some distant galaxies might be made of the other type.

We do not know much about the properties of antimatter, but it is highly plausible that there exists an interesting reciprocity in respect to the parity problem. We have mentioned that cobalt-58, which is a positron emitter, has shown the opposite spirality to the negatron emitter, cobalt-60. Cobalt-58 emits antineutrinos, which are the antiparticles to the neutrinos emitted by cobalt-60. Hence, antiparticles seem to have the spirality opposite to that of the particles. Thus, it is most probable that "anticobalt-60" would emit its positrons in the opposite direction to cobalt-60. If this is so, the violation of the mirror symmetry appears in a new light: we argued before that the mirror image of cobalt-60 decay does not correspond to any possible process in nature. Now we see that this mirror image might be just the decay of "anticobalt-60"! By bringing together the two asymmetries in nature, the charge asymmetry and the mirror asymmetry, we might be at the threshold of the discovery of a new and higher *symmetry,* which Landau has called the Combined Parity Principle. This principle says that the mirror image of any process in nature is also a possible process, but only if all charges are replaced by their opposite charges or if matter is replaced by antimatter. Since matter and antimatter are completely equivalent, the mirror symmetry of nature would be reestablished in a new and more interesting form.

We have seen in these developments how the increase in our knowledge of the properties of nature sometimes rocks the foundations of our understanding and forces us to a greater awareness of unsolved problems. The more the island of knowledge expands in the sea of ignorance, the larger its boundary to the unknown.

95

ooooooooooo

NUCLEI AND NUCLEONS

ooooooooooo

Robert Hofstadter (b. 1915)

On December 10, 1961, Robert Hofstadter was awarded the Nobel Prize in physics, a prize that he shared with Rudolf Mössbauer, for detailed investigations into the structure of matter. Hofstadter, who is professor of physics at Stanford University, conducted his research by extending the technique of previous electron-scattering studies to higher energies. The scattering technique had been familiar to physicists for nearly half a century, ever since the experiments of Ernest Rutherford at Manchester. But never had it yielded such precise knowledge. Hofstadter discovered that nucleons (protons and neutrons) consist of charged mesonic clouds. The same charged heavy mesonic clouds were shown to appear in both the neutron and the proton. In the proton, these clouds appeared to add to the effect of their charges; in the neutron the clouds seemed to cancel one another.

Thus, the proton and neutron, once assured a place as elementary particles in their own right, were seen to be complex bodies of constituent mesons. "What will happen from [this] point on?" asks Hofstadter at the close of his Nobel address, which we reproduce here. "One can only guess," he answers, ". . . but my personal conviction is that the search for ever-smaller and ever-more fundamental particles will go on as long as man retains the curiosity he has always demonstrated."

Two methods have been used traditionally by physicists to investigate the structure of atoms and nuclei: the scattering and absorption by these systems of bombarding particles and the emission of radiation or material particles from such systems. Most of our knowledge about the electronic structure and the energy levels of the atom has come from an analysis of the photons (spectral lines) emitted by excited atoms. The electronic structure of the atom lends itself quite naturally to this type of analysis because the electrons in an atom can be excited to higher levels quite easily in ordinary flames, discharge tubes, and in sparks. The scattering of low-energy electrons, as in the Franck-Hertz experiments, can also be used for this purpose since the electronic configuration in an atom is quite distended, rather than being highly concentrated, so that the electronic atomic dimensions are of the same order of magnitude as the De Broglie wavelengths of low-speed electrons.

But our knowledge of the structure of the nucleus of the atom has come almost entirely from scattering experiments since the nucleus is a small, very tightly bound structure which can be excited only with great difficulty. In other words, we have hardly any nuclear spectroscopy—certainly nothing comparable to atomic spectroscopy—so that we are forced to investigate the nucleus by means of scattering experiments. The earliest such experiments were performed by Rutherford with α particles. These led to the discovery of the nucleus itself and to the first artificial transmutation of nuclei. However, using α particles to obtain a detailed picture of the structure of the nucleus itself, that is, of the distribution of the electric charge and magnetic moments inside the nucleus, is not feasible because of the large Coulomb repulsion suffered by an α particle as it approaches the nucleus and because only a small range of α-particle energies is available.

With the development of high-energy particle accelerators, high-speed protons became available and the scattering of these from light nuclei revealed many features of nuclear forces and nuclear structure. With the discovery of the neutron a new era began in nuclear theory, and in the hands of physicists like Fermi the neutron became a powerful analytical tool.

Hofstadter's method of probing nuclei and nucleons (protons and neutrons) by particle scattering differs from the previous methods in his use of light particles (electrons) rather than massive particles. It may appear at first that the electron is the natural particle to be used for probing nuclei since it is negatively charged and therefore is not electrically repelled by nuclei. This would, indeed, be the case if the electron were a classical particle. But the electron has wave properties and these interfere with its ability to get close to a nucleus under ordinary conditions. The De Broglie wavelength of a particle varies inversely as the product of the mass and speed of a particle. Thus, because of the small mass of the electron, its De Broglie wavelength at ordinary speeds is much larger than the diameter of a nucleus. In a sense, then, such an electron does not "see" the fine details of the nucleus any more than we can see the fine details of a molecule with radio waves. Because of its large wavelength, such an electron suffers a centrifugal repulsion that prevents it from coming close to the nucleus.

It was clear to all physicists that electrons could be used as nuclear probes if one could impart high speeds to them such that their De Broglie wavelengths were reduced below the diameters of nuclei, that is, a few ten-trillionths of a centimeter. This meant imparting energies of the order of one billion volts to electrons. Although the technical difficulties in doing this appeared forbidding, Hofstadter undertook this work when he went to Stanford University in 1950, where a linear accelerator capable of supplying the required electron energies had been constructed.

To understand the nature of the experiment we note that when an electron penetrates a nucleus it suffers electric and magnetic forces which deviate it from its original path. This deviation depends on the initial speed of the electron and on the structure of the nucleus. If one now separates the electrons, after they have been scattered by a nucleus, into groups according to velocity, one can use the quantum mechanical laws of scattering to analyze the structure of the nucleus. In a sense this is nothing more than a very high resolving power electron microscope. The actual charge density in the nucleus is determined in terms of what is called a "form factor," which depends on the size of the nucleus and the charge distribution inside it. A simple analogy with the motion of a comet in the gravitational field of the sun will illustrate the principles involved.

When a comet comes from a great distance into the neighborhood of the sun the gravitational pull of the sun causes it to move in a very elongated orbit. An analysis of this orbit gives us the mass of the sun. We do not obtain the actual distribution of mass within the sun because the sun behaves like a gravitational point as far as the comet is concerned, and a point has no structure. But suppose, now, that the comet came very close to the sun or actually penetrated it. Then, the details of the mass distribution would play an important role in the motion of the comet and its orbit would give some idea of this distribution. Thus, if the comet passed right through the sun, but at a definite distance from the sun's center, the scattering action would be smaller than if the sun were concentrated in a single point because, in the former case, only part of the sun's mass affects the comet's motion, whereas in the latter case the entire mass of the sun plays a role in the process.

A similar situation arises in the scattering of electrons by nuclei. If a nucleus were just a point charge, one could calculate the scattering effect of the nucleus on the electrons by a straightforward application of the Dirac theory and quantum electrodynamics. When combined with the "Born approximation," this leads to a fairly simple expression for the scattering cross-section, that is, the target area around a nucleus that the electron must hit to be deviated through a certain angle from its original direction of motion. But the nucleus is not a point charge and its finite size must be taken into account in analyzing the electron scattering. This can be done by simply multiplying the scattering cross-section for a point charge by a "form factor" or "structure factor." This factor depends only on the amount of momentum transferred by the scattered electron to the nucleus. Since the "form factor" is always smaller than one, the effect of the finite size of the nucleus is to reduce the scattering cross-section below its value for a point charge.

The analysis of the charge distribution inside a nucleus by this scattering technique proceeds as follows. Using a fairly wide range of electron energies, one measures the scattering cross-sections for these incident electrons and compares these cross-sections with the cross-section for a point charge. The difference between this quantity and the observed cross-section gives us the "form factor" for some particular value of the momentum transfer. If one knows the values of the form factor for a large enough range of momentum transfers one can use a simple mathematical device to calculate the charge distribution inside the nucleus.

Hofstadter first began working with nuclei and then went on to the analysis of the structure of the proton and the neutron. His work with nuclei showed quite clearly that every nucleus has a core of electric charge surrounded by a thin skin in which the charge falls off to zero quite quickly. In this nuclear core the charge density is constant. The size of this core is different for different nuclei but is equal to about one ten-trillionth of a centimeter multiplied by the cube root of the number of neutrons and protons in the nucleus. Thus, for a nucleus with an atomic weight 64 the core has a radius of about four ten-trillionths of a centimeter. The thickness of the nuclear skin is the same for all nuclei and is equal to about two and a half ten-trillionths of a centimeter.

After this basic work in the analysis of nuclear structure Hofstadter applied these electron-scattering techniques to the study of the structure of nucleons. Until Hofstadter did this work, there was no evidence that the proton or the neutron had a structure or a finite size, although it was already known that the proton does not obey the Dirac equation because its magnetic moment is not equal to that predicted by the Dirac theory. Hofstadter's experiments show conclusively that the proton is not a point but that it has a fairly large size. Its radius is about seven tenths of a ten-trillionth of a centimeter.

In discussing the size and structure of the proton, we must consider two different form factors because the proton has a magnetic moment as well as a charge distribution and both play a role in the scattering of electrons. When an electron approaches a proton, the two particles interact electrostatically because of their charges, but they also interact magnetically because they both behave like small magnets. The scattering formula must therefore take into account the interaction between the magnetic moments of the proton and electron. This introduces another form factor which shows that the magnetic moment of the proton, like its electric charge, is distributed over a finite radius and is not concentrated in a point. Hofstadter applied the same electron-scattering techniques to study the structure of the neutron and demonstrated that, like the proton, the neutron is not a point but is distributed over a finite volume. Since the neutron has no charge distribution, its structure must be expressed in terms of its magnetic moment, which is distributed the way the magnetic moment of the proton is.

On the basis of Hofstadter's work, physicists now believe that both the proton and the neutron consist of cores surrounded by clouds of mesons that so arrange themselves as to give the correct magnetic moment in both cases. According to this model of the nucleon, the value of the magnetic moment that is actually measured arises because the nucleon oscillates between its two possible states. Thus, the neutron, for a fraction of its lifetime, behaves as though it were a proton and a pi meson and the proton oscillate between being a proton, a neutron, and a pi meson.

Following Hofstadter's Nobel address, we have included an excellent survey by Prof. L. L. Foldy, of the Case Institute of Technology, of the most recent developments in our knowledge of the structure of the nucleon and how this structure is related to the hierarchy of elementary particles discovered in recent years. For definitions of some of the terms, such as "isospin," used by Foldy, see Chapter 96.

Robert Hofstadter was born in New York City on February 5, 1915, to a family with a long tradition of learning and culture. His father was Louis Hofstadter and his mother the former Henrietta Koenigsberg. He received his elementary and secondary school education in the New York City public schools and attended the College of the City of New York for his higher education. He graduated from CCNY in 1935 with the B.S. degree, magna cum laude, and he was awarded the Kenyon Prize for excellence in mathematics and physics.

Later in 1935, on receiving the Coffin Fellowship from the General Electric Company, he entered Princeton University as a graduate student in physics and was awarded both the M.A. and the Ph.D. degrees in 1938. His doctoral thesis dealt with the infra-red spectrum of organic molecules and with the general problem of the hydrogen bond in molecular structure. After receiving his doctorate, he continued doing research work at Princeton as a Proctor Fellow. The work he pursued during this period—the photoconductivity in willemite crystals—aroused his interest in the use of crystals as electron detectors and in the general problem of scintillation counters. This was important for his later work because accurate electron detectors are essential in high-energy electron scattering experiments. In 1939, Hofstadter received the Harrison Fellowship from the University of Pennsylvania, where he went to work on the large Van de Graaff machine that was being built there. This work stimulated his interest in nuclear physics, but the outbreak of the war interrupted his career in pure research, and he went on to industrial scientific work arising from military needs.

In the early years of the war, he worked at the Bureau of Standards, but then went on to the Norden Corporation where he remained until the end of the war. He then went back to Princeton as assistant professor of physics and continued the work on crystal conduction counters that he had started before the war. He applied his detection techniques to Compton effect experiments and, in the process of improving his detectors, discovered that sodium iodide, activated by thallium, makes an excellent scintillation counter. The counters that he developed in this work, which were made from very well-formed crystals of sodium iodide doped with thallium, proved to be excellent energy measuring devices for gamma rays and energetic charged particles, such as electrons. In addition to being very efficient particle counters, they could also be used as spectrometers to measure the energies of particles. Thus they were just the kind of instrument that was needed for Hofstadter's later work.

In 1950 Hofstadter left Princeton to become an associate professor of physics at Stanford University where a high energy accelerator was to be made available for the kind of electron scattering experiments that he was interested in doing. Since the accelerator was still under construction when Hofstadter came to Stanford, he devoted most of his time to building the kind of equipment that he would need for the scattering experiments, but he also improved his scintillation counters and, in the process, developed new detectors for neutrons and X-rays. When the accelerator was completed, Hofstadter dedicated himself completely to the high-energy electron scattering experiments which finally led to his discovery of the charge and magnetic moment distributions in nucleons. Most of the results for which he won the Nobel Prize in 1961 were obtained in the years from 1954 to 1957. Since 1957 he has been concerned with improving the accuracy of his results and obtaining more precise form factors—the mathematical quantities that give the distributions of charge in the nucleons.

Hofstadter, now a full professor at Stanford, is a member of the National Academy of Sciences, a Fellow of the American Physical Society, and a member of the Council of the American Physical Society. In 1959 he was named California Scientist of the Year and in 1958–1959 was a Guggenheim Fellow. In 1942 he married Nancy Givan of Baltimore, Maryland. They have a son, Douglas, and two daughters, Laura and Mary.

ᴑᴑᴑᴑᴑᴑᴑᴑ

HOFSTADTER

Structure of Nuclei and Nucleons [1]

I AM VERY CONSCIOUS OF the high honor that has been conferred on me, and I wish to thank the Swedish Academy of Science sincerely for this recognition. It is a privilege and a pleasure to review the work which has brought me here and which concerns a very old and interesting problem.

Over a period of time of at least 2000 years man has puzzled over and sought an understanding of the composition of matter. It is no wonder that his interest has been aroused in this deep question, because all objects he experiences, including even his own body, are in a most basic sense special configurations of matter. The history of physics shows that whenever experimental techniques advance to the extent that matter, as then known, can be analyzed by reliable and proven methods into its "elemental" parts, newer and more powerful studies subsequently show that the "elementary particles" have a structure themselves. Indeed this structure may be quite complex, so that the elegant idea of elementarity must be abandoned. This observation provides the theme of my lecture.

In recent times the structure of matter has been shown to arise from various combinations of the "atoms" of the periodic system. The picture of the now-familiar atom was first sketched by Rutherford, Bohr, Pauli, and others and later developed in great detail by many of their colleagues. The efforts of these scientists have led to an understanding of the cloud of electrons which surrounds the dense center of the atoms, the so-called nucleus. In the nucleus practically all the mass of the atom resides in an extremely concentrated form. The nucleus itself was an invention of the aforementioned physicists, and in the year 1919 the first vague ideas concerning the sizes of nuclei were worked out. By studying the deviations from Coulomb scattering of alpha particles, Rutherford showed that a nuclear radius was of the order of 10^5 times smaller than an atomic radius. Subsequently other investigators demonstrated, by means of studies

---

[1] R. Hofstadter, *Science*, 136 (1962), 1013–1022. 1961 Nobel address.

of alpha-particle radioactivity, neutron-capture cross sections, and comparisons of the energy of decay of mirror nuclei, that consistent values for nuclear size parameters could be obtained. All useful methods showed that if a nucleus could be represented by a model of a uniformly charged sphere, the radius R of the sphere would be given by the relation

$$R \cong 1.40 \times 10^{-13} A^{1/3} \text{ cm} \tag{1}$$

where A is the mass number of the nucleus.

This is the point from which the present studies began. Although much of what I wish to say concerns nucleon structure (a nucleon is a proton or a neutron), the method of investigation that my co-workers and I have employed had its origins in the study of larger nuclei. Consequently, a historical approach beginning with the larger nuclei not only seems natural but also may be didactically sound. I shall therefore review briefly the method used in studying nuclear sizes and shall at the same time give some of the results, which may not be without interest themselves.

METHOD OF HIGH-ENERGY ELECTRON SCATTERING

We have used the method of high-energy electron scattering. In essence the method is similar to the Rutherford scattering technique, but in the case of electrons it is presently believed that only a "simple" and well-understood interaction—the electromagnetic or Coulomb interaction—is involved between the incident electron and the nucleus investigated. Under these conditions quantum electrodynamics and Dirac theory teach us how to calculate a differential elastic-scattering cross section. It can be shown that the differential cross section corresponding to a beam of electrons scattering against a point nucleus of small charge Ze, lacking spin and magnetic moment, is calculable by the Born approximation and takes the following form:

$$\frac{d\sigma}{d\Omega} = \left(\frac{Ze^2}{2E}\right)^2 \frac{\cos^2(\theta/2)}{\sin^4(\theta/2)} \frac{1}{1 + \dfrac{2E}{Mc^2} \sin^2(\theta/2)} = \sigma_{NS} \tag{2}$$

in the laboratory system of coordinates. This is the "Mott" scattering cross section, where E is the incident energy, θ is the scattering angle, and M is the mass of the struck nucleus. Other symbols in Eq. 2 have their usual meanings. If a nucleus has a finite size, and is thus not merely a point, the scattering cross section is decreased below the value of the scattering from a point. The decrease can be described in terms of a factor, represented by F, which is called the "form factor" or "structure factor." Thus, in the Born approximation,

$$\frac{d\sigma}{d\Omega} = \sigma_{NS} F^2(q) \tag{3}$$

and this is the elastic-scattering cross section for a finite nucleus (2). Here q is the momentum-energy transfer, defined by the relation

$$q = \frac{(2E/\hbar c)\sin(\theta/2)}{[1 + (2E/Mc^2)\sin^2(\theta/2)]^{1/2}} \tag{4}$$

The parameter q is relativistically invariant and is a very important quantity in electron-scattering studies. The form factor F takes account of the interference between scattered wavelets arising from different parts of the same, finite nucleus and therefore is responsible for diffraction effects observed in the angular distribution. The quantity F is actually given by

$$F = \frac{4\pi}{q} \int_0^\infty \rho(r)\,(\sin qr)\,r\,dr \tag{5}$$

in the event that the nucleus exhibits spherical symmetry. The quantity $\rho(r)$ is the electric charge density function, in which r represents the distance from the center of the nucleus to the volume element where ρ is measured. A mathematical inversion of Eq. 5 allows one to deduce the form of $\rho(r)$ if $F(q)$ is known over a large range of values of q.

Of course, since we used the Born approximation and therefore specified small values of the atomic number, the foregoing description of the basic formulas of the electron-scattering process is only an approximate one. More exact methods of finding the scattering cross section have been developed by many authors. These calculations of more precise types employ the "phase-shift" methods and are applicable to heavy nuclei as well as light ones. The qualitative physical ideas involved in the determination of nuclear structure can be adequately described by the Born approximation method (Eq. 3). Nevertheless, quantitative results definitely require the more elaborate phase-shift methods, and simple—and in this case, closed—formulas cannot be given to describe the scattering cross section.

Early electron-scattering experiments were carried out at the University of Illinois in 1951 at an incident electron energy of about 15.7 Mev. Such experiments showed that nuclear radii obeyed an approximate relationship of the type given in Eq. 1. However, few details of nuclear shape or size could be discerned because the energy of the electrons was relatively low and the corresponding de Broglie wavelength of the electrons was larger than the typical size of the nucleus.

In 1953 higher-energy electrons became available at Stanford University and at the University of Michigan, and experiments on various nuclei were carried out. Phase-shift interpretations of the Stanford experiments showed that the rule expressed in Eq. 1 was approximately true, but that in reality the nuclear charge density distribution could not be described in terms of a single size parameter R. If one attempted so to describe it, at

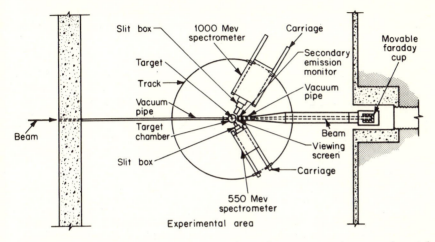

Fig. 95–1. Schematic diagram of a modern electron-scattering experimental area. The track on which the spectrometers roll has a radius of approximately 13.5 feet.

the expense of an inferior fit between experiment and theory, the resulting R would have to be made 20 percent smaller than the value of the radius in Eq. 1. Mu-mesonic atom studies showed, a bit earlier, that a similar conclusion was required for a one-parameter description of the size of the nucleus. Two parameters could not be determined from the mu-mesonic atom investigations. . . . The type of geometry employed in a modern electron-scattering experimental area is shown in [Fig. 95–1]. . . .

CHARGE DENSITY DISTRIBUTIONS IN NUCLEI

The electron-scattering method was employed in the manner I have described and resulted in the determination of two-parameter descriptions of nuclear charge density distributions. Studies of the charge density distributions in various nuclei culminated in the evolution of a simple scheme of construction of most spherical nuclei. Such nuclei could be represented by a charge density function of the type shown in [Fig. 95–2]. The exact

1766   HIGH-ENERGY PHYSICS

shape of this density function is not of overriding importance; rather, the distance c from the center of the nucleus to the 50-percent point and the interval t between the 90-percent and 10-percent ordinates are the two important parameters that determine the behavior of the scattering cross sections. A trapezoidal distribution with the same values of the two parameters would also suffice to describe the experimental results in the medium and heavier nuclei when the fitting procedure is limited by the accuracy obtained in the experiments. Higher accuracy will probably distinguish between these possibilities but such studies are only beginning now.

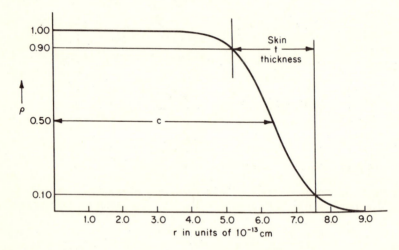

Fig. 93–2. The shape and parameters which describe an approximate model of the gold nucleus. This type is called the Fermi model.

The results of many of these experiments covered a large range of nuclei and demonstrated that two simple rules can be used to summarize the scheme of construction of spherical nuclei:

$$c = (1.07 \pm 0.02) \times 10^{-13} A^{1/3} \text{ cm}$$
$$t = (2.4 \pm 0.3) \times 10^{-13} \text{ cm} = \text{constant} \tag{6}$$

The first equation gives the principal parameter governing the size of a nucleus and describes the behavior with increasing A of a kind of "mean" nuclear radius. The second equation states that the thickness of the nuclear skin is constant. The second rule implies that there is some property of nuclear matter that causes the outer nuclear regions to develop an essentially constant surface thickness. The two rules together are responsible for the approximate constancy of the central charge density of nuclei. . . .

FORM FACTORS OF THE PROTON

The results obtained with heavier nuclei indicated that the electron-scattering method could also be applied to the very light nuclei and even to the proton itself. Accordingly, in early 1954 experiments were initiated on hydrogen and helium. The first targets employed high-pressure, thin-wall gas chambers and were designed by the late Eva Wiener. In the latter

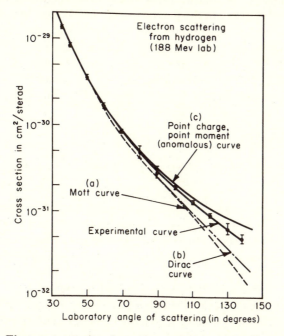

Fig. 95–3. Electron scattering from the proton at an incident energy of 188 Mev. *a*, The theoretical Mott curve for a spinless point proton; *b*, the theoretical curve for a point proton with a Dirac magnetic moment alone; *c*, the theoretical behavior of a point proton having the anomalous Pauli contribution in addition to the Dirac value of the magnetic moment. The deviation from *c* of the experimental curve represents the effect of form factors for the proton and indicates structure within the proton. The best fit in this figure indicates a root-mean-square radius close to 0.7×10^{-13} centimeter.

part of 1954 it was first realized that the experiments on hydrogen demonstrated that the proton was an object of finite size and not merely a point object. In fact, the size was found to be surprisingly large and could be described in terms of a root-mean-square radius of value $(0.74 \pm 0.24) \times 10^{-13}$ centimeter. It is an interesting fact that more recent determinations of the root-mean-square proton charge radius appear to converge on a value of $(0.79 \pm 0.08) \times 10^{-13}$ centimeter. [Fig. 95–3] shows the first evidence of finite size in the proton; it has been drawn from Hofstadter and McAllister. The first experiments leading to these conclusions were carried out at relatively low energies ($\sim$ 190 Mev).

Now the proton is known to have a spin and a magnetic moment. The magnetic moment will affect the scattering behavior appreciably at values of $\hbar q$ (Eq. 4) in the range equal to or larger than about 0.2 Mc, where M is the mass of a nucleon. The magnetic type of scattering causes a leveling off in the decrease of the elastic cross section as a function of the scattering angle at high energies of the incident electrons. As may be seen in [Fig. 95–3], the experimental data fell below the theoretica curve for a proton possessing a point charge and a point magnetic moment. This behavior can be understood in terms of the theoretical scattering law developed by M. Rosenbluth in 1950. This law described the composite effect of charge and magnetic moment scattering and is given by the following equation:

$$\frac{d\sigma}{d\Omega} = \sigma_{NS} \left\{ F_1{}^2 + \frac{\hbar^2 q^2}{4M^2 c^2} \times \left[2(F_1 + KF_2)^2 \tan^2 (\theta/2) + K^2 F_2{}^2 \right] \right\} \quad (7)$$

where σ_{NS} is taken from Eq. 2 with $Z = 1$. In the Rosenbluth equation the quantity $F_1(q)$ is the Dirac form factor, representing the proton's charge and its associated Dirac magnetic moment. The quantity $F_2(q)$ is the Pauli form factor and represents the anomalous magnetic moment of the proton. K in Eq. 7 indicates the static value (1.79) of the anomalous magnetic moment in units of the nuclear magneton.

Although one may speak qualitatively of size and shape factors of the proton in the low-energy limit, it is more consistent and more desirable, from a quantitative point of view, to discuss only the two phenomenological form factors $F_1(q)$ and $F_2(q)$. Actually, all the electromagnetic structure of the proton is, in principle, described by the behavior of these quantities as functions of q. Note that for the proton, $F_1(0) = F_2(0) = 1.00$. Meson theory should be able to make definite assertions about F_1 and F_2, starting from the foregoing values.

In our subsequent discussion we shall concentrate on determining the two phenomenological quantities (F_1, F_2) from the experimental data, so that the form factors can be compared with theory. Experimental determination of the form factors can be accomplished, for example, by using the method of intersecting ellipses or by other, equivalent methods based on the relativistic idea that each F is a function *only* of q, and not of E or θ separately.

The early work on the proton was confirmed by subsequent studies at higher energies ($\sim$ 600 Mev), but these energies were still low enough so that the assumption $F_1 \cong F_2$ could be employed. It was noted in the latter experiments that F_1 was slightly greater than F_2 at values of $q^2 = 4f^{-2}$, where $f = \text{fermi} = 10^{-13}$ centimeter. The value of one fermi corresponds to $(197 \text{ Mev})^{-1}$.

Recently the extension of the experimental measurements to higher energies (~ 1.0 Bev) showed that indeed $F_1 > F_2$. The appropriate

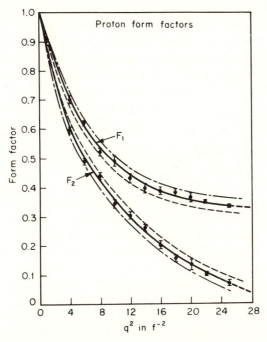

Fig. 95–4. The most recent Stanford experimental data on the form factors of the proton. There are two dashed curves lying between the central-value experimental curves (solid lines). If the error limits are correlated so that they move in opposite directions, as indicated by the dashed lines, the corresponding cross sections will remain consistent with experiment. A similar statement holds for the two curves of long and short dashed lines, lying outside F_1 and F_2, the central-value experimental curves. The question of correlated error needs additional study, but the dashed inner and outer curves are thought to give reasonable error limits of F_1 and F_2.

detailed behavior is shown in [Fig. 95–4] and represents the most recent Stanford experimental data on this subject. I will describe the possible theoretical significance of these results after brief discussions of, first, some tests of the Rosenbluth equation and, second, the experimental determinations of the form factors of the neutron.

Various tests of the validity of the Rosenbluth equation were made in these experiments by examining whether F_1 and F_2 are really functions of q alone. In all cases studied for which q^2 was less than $25f^{-2}$, complete consistency in F_1, F_2 values at different energies and angles was observed; thus, the Rosenbluth equation was checked and found to be valid below $q^2 = 25f^{-2}$. At the highest values reached in these experiments—namely $q^2 \cong 31f^{-2}$—the Stanford cross sections could not be combined with the cross sections at the same value of q in recently reported Cornell experiments to give *real* values of F_1 and F_2. If this observation can be confirmed, the possibility exists that quantum electrodynamics may fail at high momentum transfers, or that two-photon exchange processes, heretofore neglected, are needed to correct the Rosenbluth equation, or that some other fundamental aspect of the scattering theory needs improvement. This is an interesting question for the future to decide.

FORM FACTORS OF THE NEUTRON

Let us now turn to the question of the neutron. According to relativistic quantum electrodynamics the neutron possesses Dirac and Pauli form factors. Proton and neutron form factors may be referred to, respectively, as F_{1p}, F_{2p}, F_{1n}, F_{2n}. Static values of the neutron form factors are known to be $F_{1n}(0) = 0$, $F_{2n}(0) = 1.00$. F_{1n} is also known, from early neutron scattering experiments, to vary as q^4 at small values of q in an expansion of F_{1n} as a function of q^2. This relationship is commonly expressed by saying that within experimental error, the root-mean-square radius of the neutron is zero. Thus, the neutron is not only a neutral body from the point of view of electric charge but has a power expansion of F_{1n} that starts off as a function of q^2 with zero slope! Consequently, it is most difficult to determine F_{1n} (and also F_{2n}) of the neutron. The difficulty is compounded by the experimental fact that neutron targets are obtained only by using the deuteron as a neutron carrier, for free neutrons in large numbers are unobtainable in confined spaces. A neutron is in vigorous motion in the deuteron, and this additional complication must be taken into account somehow. It is necessary at this point to introduce a relativistic theory of the deuteron to allow properly for the effects of the motion of the bound neutron. Of course, at the present stage of development of relativity theory, the deuteron problem can be solved only in an approximate way. Hence we can see that the experimental elucidation and determination of the form factors of the neutron present formidable difficulties.

Many of these difficulties were overcome in work that Yearian and I did in which we used a difference method to compare the scattering from the deuteron and from the proton. We first showed that the neutron could not be represented as a point nucleon and that its magnetic moment was distributed in a manner similar to that of the proton. In [Fig. 95–5] are shown data of the type from which such conclusions were drawn. The spread-out deuteron peak shows the effect of the motion of the proton and neutron in the deuteron, and this wide peak may be compared with the sharp peak of the free proton. In the work in which the finite size of the neutron was discovered, the neutron form factor F_{1n} was assumed to be approximately zero and F_{2n} had the behavior described earlier.

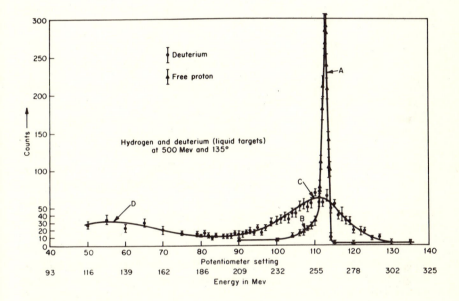

Fig. 95–5. Experimental comparison of the scattering from the moving proton and neutron in the deuteron (curve C) and the scattering associated with free protons (curve A). Region B, The bremsstrahlung tail of the proton curve. At D are electrons which have been scattered after producing pions in deuterium, and also other low-energy electrons. From the scattering data near C the form factors of the neutron can be obtained. The proton peak is used for comparison measurements. No correction has been applied in the figure for the difference in density of liquid deuterium and liquid hydrogen.

It may be noted parenthetically that it was on the basis of the foregoing results that Nambu postulated the existence of a new heavy neutral meson, now known as ω-meson. Events of the past year have brilliantly confirmed the existence of this meson. A pion-pion resonance (ρ-meson) responsible for the magnetic behavior of the nucleon form factors was also postulated, by Frazer and Fulco, on the basis of these experiments. This resonance was also found recently.

The foregoing conclusions about the behavior of the neutron, and also the assumption that $F_{1n} \cong 0$, have been confirmed recently. More detailed studies, as yet unpublished, support this description of the neutron form factors. These results are shown in [Fig. 95–6]. In work reported, F_{1n} was

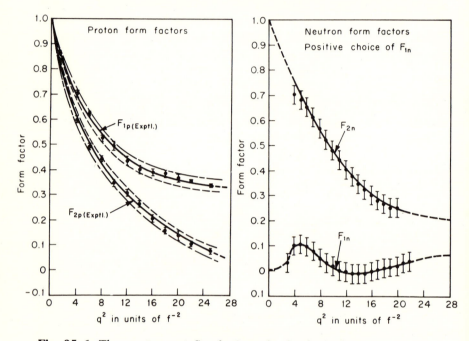

Fig. 95–6. The most recent Stanford results for both the neutron and the proton for positive values of F_{1n}. The regularity of the neutron curves arises from the fact that the experimental deuteron curves were smoothed before the corresponding data were put into the theoretical formulas from which the form factors are deduced. The four curves of this figure can be fit approximately with dispersion-theory or Clementel-Villi curves corresponding to the newly discovered heavy mesons. It is interesting to note that the newer neutron data agree very well with older results and that many of the present conclusions could have been drawn in 1958.

found to be small and positive. However, Durand has recently shown that the theory of the deuteron used in the early work to derive the values of the neutron form factors can be improved. When the improved formula is employed, the slightly positive values of the form factor F_{1n} are relatively unaffected in the low q^2 region, but in the range $6f^{-2} < q^2 < 20f^{-2}$ the values of F_{1n} are reduced to approximately zero, within experimental error. Because the neutron measurements are so fraught with both experimental and theoretical difficulties we must still regard these new, more accurate results, particularly for F_{1n}, as preliminary.

RECENT RESULTS ON NUCLEONS

[Fig. 95–6] shows the most recent Stanford results for both the proton and the neutron. An ambiguity exists in the choice of sign of F_{1n}. [Fig. 95–6] shows data for the positive F_{1n} values and the corresponding F_{2n} values. [Fig. 95–7] shows the neutron data for the negative F_{1n} values and

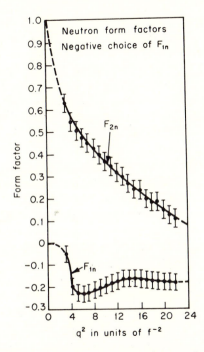

Fig. 95–7. Graph similar to Fig. 95–6. It gives the set of values of F_{1n} and F_{2n} for the negative choice of F_{1n}. At present the curves of Fig. 95–6 appear to fit the Clementel-Villi curves better than those of Fig. 95–7 do.

the corresponding values of F_{2n}. Theoreticians prefer the choice of the positive F_{1n} values, but as a purely experimental problem the negative F_{1n} values must be considered possible until proved untenable. The dashed parts of the curve in [Fig. 95–6] refer to probable behavior at low q^2, and the steep fall of F_{2n} that corresponds to the negative F_{1n} values would be very surprising and is not expected.

If the choice of positive values of F_{1n} is made—and these values seem more likely—an understanding of all the proton and neutron data can be obtained along the lines of the heavy-meson or pion-resonance theory of Bergia *et al.* or the equivalent interpretation by Herman and me of the early data in terms of Clementel-Villi form factors, using Yukawa clouds of different ranges and delta functions. These initial and approximate theoretical interpretations are probably correct in principle but incomplete in detail, and it now seems likely that it is necessary to add to them the effects on the form factors of a third heavy meson (η-meson). Such a particle has recently been discovered by A. Pevsner *et al.* Its existence was also predicted by Sakurai.

Attempts are now being made to fit the data of [Fig. 95–6] in terms of the heavy meson theory in a way similar to that reported [earlier] but with three mesons (ρ, ω, η) instead of two. I hesitate to show the results of the studies since the exact mass values of the heavy mesons are not yet definite and small variations of these values affect the relative importance of the mesons in the form factor equations in a sensitive way. Furthermore, it would not be surprising if new heavy mesons are discovered in the near future, and these might also contribute to the form factors. Suffice it to say that approximate agreement with the data of [Fig. 95–6] can be obtained with the set of three mesons (ρ, ω, η).

If we now attempt to summarize the recent progress in nucleon structure determinations and in their interpretation, we may say that the proton and neutron are two different aspects of a single entity—the nucleon. The third component of isotopic spin distinguishes between the two particles. Isotopic form factors can be developed in a well-known way from the proton and neutron form factors. A phenomenological and qualitative interpretation of the nucleon form factors then shows that the same charged mesonic clouds appear in both the neutron and the proton. In the proton the clouds add together, and in the neutron the clouds cancel.

It is a bit too early to give the final and definitive details of the mesonic clouds or of their heavy-meson compositions, since, as already indicated, such details are now being worked out. However, it is possible, and even likely, that the next year or so should witness a crystallization of the "final" values of the nucleon structure parameters in terms of the models afforded by the new heavy-meson picture of the proton and neutron. The fact that new research is needed in order to clarify this picture is symptomatic of the general problem of the structure of elementary particles.

CONCLUSION

In concluding this discussion it may be appropriate to return to the theme introduced earlier and raise the question once again of the deeper, and possibly philosophical, meaning of the term "elementary" particle. As we have seen, the proton and neutron, which were once thought to be elementary particles, are now seen to be highly complex bodies. It is almost certain that physicists will subsequently investigate the constituent parts of the proton and neutron—the mesons of one sort or another. What will happen from that point on? One can only guess at future problems and future progress, but my personal conviction is that the search for ever-smaller and ever-more-fundamental particles will go on as long as man retains the curiosity he has always demonstrated.

ooooooo

F O L D Y

The Structure of Nucleons [2]

THE URGE TO REDUCE THE seemingly infinite variety and complexity of the visible world to some aesthetically satisfactory order has been a part of man's intellectual life since ancient times. In ancient philosophy and in modern science the natural orientation of this drive has been in the direction of understanding this variety and complexity as the natural outcome of the enormous number of combinatorial possibilities available to even a small number of basic entities subject to fixed laws of behavior. The search for these basic entities and for the strict formulation of the laws which govern them is still very much the essential fabric of physics today.

The history of this intellectual pursuit has revealed an aspect which probably was not anticipated by the ancient philosophical school which first proposed an atomistic character of the visible universe—namely, that the familiar objects and phenomena of everyday experience are not the direct and immediate consequence of the organization of the basic entities which they envisaged, but represent instead one rank in a hierarchy of organized structures, each level of the hierarchy being characterized by a degree of internal logical structure of its own, in part independent of the hierarchies lying above and below. To illustrate: the mechanics of the solar system could be understood in terms of a continuous distribution of matter characterized by mass density alone with its behavior governed by Newton's laws of motion and gravitation. At the next lower level, where

---

[2] L. L. Foldy, *Physics Today,* 18 (1965), 26–44.

internal but macroscopic properties of gross matter are examined, we have, on the one hand, the description of its elastic, thermal, electrical, and optical properties in terms of appropriate coefficients and, on the other, the achievements of chemistry in reducing the variety of substances with different physical properties—first, to mixtures of pure chemical substances, and then further to appropriate combinations of the ninety-odd chemical elements. The chemical laws of combination, in turn, suggested the first indications of a physical reality to an atomistic concept of material structure by revealing that a natural explanation of the regularities observed could be achieved in terms of elementary atoms of each chemical element when combined with rules (of then unknown origin) respecting the affinity of these atoms in forming chemical bonds. Statistical mechanics and kinetic theory gave further support to such an atomistic concept in showing how the elastic, thermal, and other physical properties of gross matter could be understood directly from such an atomistic viewpoint.

But as the atomic structure of gross matter was becoming incontrovertible, the first evidences that atoms themselves were not irreducible, and indeed possessed structure of their own, were making their appearance. The unraveling of atomic structure and its role in determining the previously arbitrary elements involved in chemical affinity and in the coefficients describing the intrinsic properties of matter on a macroscopic level—first through the discovery of the electron, the proton, and the atomic nucleus, and then through the development of quantum mechanics —was accompanied by the discovery of internal structure of the nucleus itself. The discovery of the neutron and the positron set the stage for examining this new level of material structure. Here something new was required: the nuclear glue which bound the nucleus together, something different from the familiar forces of gravitation and electromagnetism which had sufficed for the atom and the hierarchies of structure which lay above. When, in 1937, Yukawa proposed the meson theory of nuclear forces as the solution to this problem, the state was laid for the subject of this article. For once one admits the basic correctness of the meson theory of nuclear forces, the laws of quantum mechanics allow no alternative but that there should exist some minimum of internal structure to the neutron and proton. More of this later, but first it is necessary to mention some other developments which play an important role in what follows.

DISCOVERIES AND SPECULATIONS

In Dirac's theory of the positron, Fermi's theory of beta decay involving the then hypothetical neutrino, and in Yukawa's theory of nuclear forces, there entered a new conception, an implementation of an aspect of Einstein's theory of relativity: namely, that particles (other than the photon) could be created out of energy directly, and hence that at least some of the entities found emerging from atoms (or, more specifically, their nuclei), such as positrons, electrons, and mesons, were not actually permanent constituents of the atom, but like photons were brought into existence through the conversion of available energy. The importance of this concept for the purposes of this exposition lies in the fact that, whereas the atom, and in large measure the atomic nucleus itself, could (to a good approximation) be considered to be composed of electrons, neutrons, and protons as essentially *permanent* constituents, at the next level, the internal structure of protons and neutrons, one is forced to admit the existence of a new kind of structural entity—"virtual particles" of only transitory existence, created and destroyed through the same agency which is responsible for the interactions between the particles themselves as a direct consequence of the basic quantum fluctuation phenomena associated with the Heisenberg uncertainty principle. This represents a somewhat radical revision in the very concept of material structure from what had prevailed or been envisaged earlier.

Two other developments of some importance for this subject require mention. The first is the discovery of the mu meson, which for a while masqueraded as the meson of Yukawa's theory of nuclear forces. Its significance lies not in this comedy of errors, but in the realization that here is the first particle which seems to play no significant role in the behavior of matter on a macroscopic scale. Electrons, protons, and neutrons are essential to the structure of macroscopic matter; photons and pions (the actual Yukawa particles) supply the essential forces between them; neutrinos, in their role in beta decay, determine at least the stabilities of some of the elements; positrons, antiprotons, and antineutrons provide a relativistic rounding-out of the theory of the "necessary" particles; but muons seem to play only a superficial role. Yet their symmetrical involvement with neutrinos and electrons in the theory of weak interactions suggests that they are not a minor nuisance but are involved in some essential way in the scheme of things.

The second development is the discovery in the past decade of a host of new strongly interacting particles of transitory existence whose connection with the macroscopic world is equally mysterious. The very number of such new particles, together with the evidences of their involvement in systematic symmetries with the more familiar proton, neutron, and pion, suggest strongly that what we have become used to calling "elementary particles" are not necessarily the basic structural entities of the universe but another level in the hierarchy or organization of matter. Physics is now deeply immersed in the clarification of the systematics of material organization at this level and as new unities are uncovered these must add dimension to one's views of the structure of the neutron and proton. Conversely, what is discovered about the structure of the proton and neutron has implications for the structure of this host of particles. As to the next lower level in the material hierarchy, if one exists, one can only speculate; but some of these speculations are already of such potential interest for the subject at hand as to deserve some mention below.

In brief summary, with the examination of the structure of the proton and neutron one is investigating a new hierarchical level in the material organization of the physical universe, related to, but underlying, the now substantially explored level of atomic and nuclear structure. At this level, the proton and neutron are just two examples of a variety of entities which seem to be closely related and which by custom are called "elementary particles." From this point of view these two particles are not outstanding because they are fundamentally simpler than the other objects, but rather because they have been more accessible to experimental observation. That another hierarchy in the structure of matter may underlie the "elementary particles" is strongly urged by the desire for greater economy in the number of truly fundamental entities and by indications of sufficient symmetries to make such an underlying structural basis an attractive possibility. Thus, while the experimental results emerging from the study of neutron and proton will have some degree of permanence, their physical interpretation will likely be subject to revisions of a character which cannot at this time be foretold.

THE MEANING OF STRUCTURE

To turn now to our principal topic, the structure of the neutron and proton, it is perhaps appropriate to dwell for a moment on the question, "What constitutes structure?" One may have intuitive notions concerning this, but when encountering something new one cannot be certain that intuitive ideas are adequate to the situation. Thus one might immediately think in terms of a structural situation extended in space or in space-time; it is perhaps justifiable, but the possibility cannot be overlooked that there exists internal structure which is not of this character.

The internal symmetries of particles such as those associated with isospin or SU (3) invariance, for example, have not yet been identified as possessing a spatio-temporal connection. To postulate an isospin for a nucleon such that in pointing "up" in a hypothetical isospin space it represents a proton and pointing "down" a neutron is simply a semantic device; to discover that nuclear forces are independent of this orientation, however, would appear to endow this device with some physical reality but does not require that it has a spatio-temporal counterpart in the nucleon itself. Nevertheless, leaving such possibilities in abeyance for the moment, one can ask about the evidence for, say, spatial extension in the neutron and proton. If we find such evidence we can then inquire whether this spatial extension is of a purely static character, reflecting only a "geometrical shape" of these particles, or whether it is associated with an internal dynamics. In other words, do there exist internal degrees of freedom having some kind of analog with the internal degrees of freedom associated with an atom as a result of its being constituted of electrons? If the latter is the case it is to be expected that the system would then exhibit various internal states associated with different internal configurations; excited quantum states, in other words. One could also inquire as to the nature of the basic elements to which the dynamics has reference, the constituents of the nucleon, so to speak, and as to whether they have a permanent or transitory existence as mentioned earlier.

Straightforward as the questions appear, there are substantial conceptual difficulties in asking that experiments provide straightforward answers to them. Consider the simplest question: do protons and neutrons have spatial extension? In classical relativity there is a theorem that any system which has angular momentum must have a certain minimal spatial extension; applied to the neutron or proton this would predict a minimal spatial extension of the order of the Compton wavelength of the particle. When relativity and quantum mechanics are combined, a new difficulty arises. It does not seem possible to associate with a quantum system in a relativistic way a concept of localization which carries with it all the implications of classical localizability. There are two (at least) concepts of localizability or of associated position that can be used. One, the Dirac position concept, has the disadvantage that the process of measurement to establish this kind of localizability would immediately create other particles so one would not be localizing a single particle. The other, the Newton-Wigner position concept, has the difficulty that, if the particle is considered localized at a point in one Lorentz frame, it will not be localized in another Lorentz frame. The ambiguity in the concept of position here involved is measured by a quantity of the order of the Compton wavelength of the particle. Since the structural details of the elementary particles are, in fact, distributed over distances of just this magnitude, there will necessarily be some ambiguity in forming a space-time picture of this structure. We emphasize that the difficulty is a conceptual one: either type of position concept is internally self-consistent and can serve as an appropriate medium for expressing physical results, and once these have been formulated in one picture they are immediately transformable into the other.

Next, one may ask what qualities of a nucleon exhibit this spatial extension and to what extent are the spatial distributions of such qualities the same or different. Thus one could ask about the spatial distribution of energy density in a particle (which, in principle, but not yet in practice, could be determined from the behavior of the particle in sufficiently rapidly varying gravitational fields), or the distribution of electrical charge and current which can be determined from the particle's response to electromagnetic fields, or a host of other densities which measure the response of the particle to various other "force fields". Experimentally, of course, one would like a complete categorization of these "quality densities" in order to have a comprehensive description of the structure of a particle. In fact, one would like to extend the idea of these densities to "transition densities" associated with a change in state or nature of a particle, such as the change of neutron to proton in the case of beta decay. At a higher level still, one would be interested in polarizability effects—that is, the changes in internal density distributions induced by external influences which are sufficiently strong that higher order effects must be taken into account.

ELECTROMAGNETIC STRUCTURE

To approach these questions in their most familiar and experimentally best-explored aspect, let us consider first the case of charge and magnetization density. Historically, the first indication that the electromagnetic organization of the proton and neutron was more complex than that of the electron was the fact that the magnetic moments of these particles deviated very considerably from the values predicted by the simple Dirac theory of particles of spin $\frac{1}{2}$. In the simple Dirac theory a charged particle has attributed to it a point charge only (from the viewpoint of the Dirac position concept). Nevertheless, the particle shows a magnetic moment and spatial charge distribution in interaction with electromagnetic fields through the characteristic kinematical feature of relativistic quantum theory, Zitterbewegung, which is intimately connected to the dualistic concept of position mentioned earlier. Even for a free particle of zero momentum, the Dirac position coordinate carries out a complicated random motion over a region of dimensions of its Compton wavelength, giving rise to a charge and current distribution over such dimensions. In the Newton-Wigner picture, the position of such a particle is stationary, but the nonlocal character of its electromagnetic interaction in this picture yields essentially the same charge and current distribution as above. It is this current distribution which gives rise to the "normal" or Dirac moment of a charged particle. A deviation of the magnetic moment from this value, therefore, may be conceived of as arising from specifically dynamical effects reflecting further structure. Such an additional moment is what is called an anomalous or Pauli moment.

A natural source of the anomalous moment of proton and neutron is provided by the Yukawa theory of nucleonic interactions. According to this theory, the internucleonic force arises from the exchange of quanta (mesons) of a new type of field (the meson field) for which the quanta have finite rest mass. The exchanged particle can be charged, giving rise to the "exchange" character of nuclear forces: a neutron changes into a proton by emission of a negatively charged meson which is then absorbed by a proton, converting it into a neutron; in the process, momentum and charge are exchanged between the two particles. The exchanged mesons are "virtual particles" in that they arise from quantum fluctuations which fail to conserve energy during the time required for the exchange, insufficient energy being available to create a "real" meson. But the same quantum fluctuations which make the above process possible require that an isolated neutron, for example, be continually dissociating into a proton and negative meson and reassociating into a neutron. Similarly, an isolated proton would be dissociating into a neutron and positive meson and reassociating. The electromagnetic structure of these particles will reflect the charge and current distributions associated with this virtual decomposition. Since the fraction of the time that a nucleon is dissociated is dependent on the strength of the interaction, and since this interaction must be strong to describe the strong nuclear forces, one would expect in particular a large anomalous moment for these particles, as observed. One would also expect the charge and current associated with the particles to be distributed over spatial regions which are of the order of the meson Compton wavelength, but even this semiquantitative prediction could be modified by strong interactions between mesons.

To confirm such a picture of the electromagnetic structure of nucleons one would like to verify the spatial distribution of charge and current which it predicts, and in particular, to show that the former differs from that expected on the basis of the Dirac theory. The natural way to do this is by the means used by Rutherford to delineate the nature of the distribution of charge in the atom, namely by studying the scattering of charged particles by such an electromagnetic structure. A first attempt in this direction was made in 1948 by groups at Columbia (under Rabi) and Chicago (under Fermi) who sought to detect an interaction of an electrostatic character between slow neutrons and electrons. Some evidence of an effect was obtained and more quantitative determinations have since been made. Unfortunately, the evidence obtained in this way was not decisive, since it was later shown that the observed result was consistent with a point magnetic moment (Pauli moment) for a particle in the Dirac picture, the electrostatic effect arising again from the combined effect of this moment and the kinematical feature of Zitterbewegung. Thus there was no evidence from this experiment that the neutron has an intrinsic charge distribution. Although the neutron does have an intrinsic current distribution as evidenced by its magnetic moment, the magnitude of the latter gives no indication of the spatial extent of these currents. Actually, what the neutron-electron interaction experiment shows is that the second radial moment of the charge density distribution is very small, not that the charge density in the neutron is identically zero.

The natural way to look further for information about charge and current distributions by the Rutherford technique is to go to higher resolution methods afforded by scattering energetic charged particles from nucleons. In the case of a fixed charge and current distribution, the scattering amplitude associated with a given momentum transfer between the charge distribution and the scattered particle is a direct measure of the space Fourier transforms of these distributions for the wavelength associated with the momentum transfer. With more energetic charged particles, larger momentum transfers and hence shorter wavelengths are accessible, and more detail can be seen in the associated distributions. For an unambiguous interpretation of such scattering data, however, one must be certain that the only important interaction between the charged particle used as a probe and the particle whose charge and current distribution are being explored is the electromagnetic one, and further that the probe have no electromagnetic structure itself, or at least have its electromagnetic structure known. In addition, the electromagnetic interaction should be weak enough that higher order (polarizability) effects should not be important. Since the electromagnetic interaction between probe and explored particle can always be represented as the exchange of virtual photons between the two, this last condition is equivalent to saying that the scattering process is dominated by the exchange of a single photon. These conditions are satisfied (up to quite high energies, at least) by electrons and muons as probe particles.

The construction of a high-energy linear electron accelerator at Stanford finally permitted a decisive attack on this problem. In 1955 Hofstadter and his co-workers were able to demonstrate unambiguously that the charge and current distributions in the proton were indeed spatially extended over distances of the order of 10^{-13} cm. They were able to do this by showing that the ratio of the observed scattering of electrons by protons to what would be expected on the basis of the Dirac equation for a proton carrying a point charge and point Pauli moment was a rapidly decreasing function of increasing momentum transfer; this is exactly what one would expect from an extended charge and current distribution; the rate of decrease gives a measure of the actual distribution size. These and further experiments at Stanford, together with later experiments at Cornell and at the Cambridge (Massachusetts) Electron Accelerator, have yielded a quantitative determination of the essential structure functions for the proton up to momenta transfers q of the order of 2 BeV/c. These structure functions, or form factors as they are also called, represent in essence the Fourier transforms of the charge and magnetization distributions in the proton. Corresponding to the two position concepts available (the Dirac and the Newton-Wigner) there are two ways of presenting the form-factor data. The form factors which are called F_1 and F_2 are roughly speaking the Fourier transforms of the charge and magnetization respectively using the Dirac position concept, while the function called G_E and G_M are the corresponding factors for the Newton-Wigner position concept.

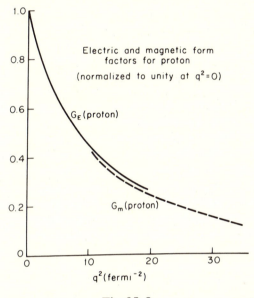

Fig. 95–8.

The two sets are related by simple linear equations so that knowing one set is equivalent to knowing the other. The G-functions are directly accessible to experiment. We show a plot of the G-functions for the proton in [Fig. 95–8]. A rough characterization of the results in physical terms may be expressed as follows:

(1) The shape of the curves is such that they represent a spatial charge and magnetization distribution which is roughly exponential in character with a (root-mean-square) radius of about 0.8×10^{-13} cm.

(2) The size and shape of the charge distribution is quite similar to that of the magnetization distribution.

(3) The fact that the curves seem to approach zero smoothly suggests that there is no "hard core" of charge (or current) inside the proton, but that all the charge and current is smoothly distributed.

Corresponding information about the neutron is not as satisfactory, but this reflects only the fact that free neutrons are not available as targets for electron scattering. By using deuterons as targets it is possible to obtain relatively clear-cut information on the magnetic form factor G_M for the neutron, but information on the electric form factor G_E is still quite uncertain. Available information concerning the magnetic form factor G_M for the neutron shows it to be essentially the same as that for the proton. It is more difficult to say anything definite about the electric form factor G_E for the neutron. Electron-scattering results from different laboratories are inconsistent and in some cases such results only determine G_E^2 so that even the sign is uncertain. The fact that the neutron has zero net charge means that G_E is zero at zero momentum transfer, while the low-energy neutron-electron interaction results indicate that it should be positive at small momentum transfers, with a definite slope. There may exist some difficulty in reconciling this low momentum transfer information with even the quite uncertain results at high momentum transfer obtained from high-energy electron scattering.

Let us turn now to the question of the kind of physical picture required to understand these results. In [Fig. 95–9(a)] we have represented a Feynman diagram for the scattering of electrons by protons in the center-of-mass system. The wavy line represents the virtual photon exchanged between the electron and the proton. It carries a momentum q which changes the momentum of the proton from p to $p + q$. It also carries some angular momentum and isospin. The "blob" where it joins the proton line represents the charge and current distribution which is a "source" or "sink" for the photon. We are interested in the structure of this blob. If the proton were a structureless particle, it would be represented by a simple point charge which could absorb the photon as shown in [Fig. 95–9(b)]. If the proton is sometimes virtually dissociated into a pion and neutron, then we have in addition a contribution to the blob like that shown in [Fig. 95–9(c)], where the photon is absorbed by the virtual meson; such a process is reflected in a spatial extension of the charge and current distribution in the proton. The diagram is drawn with no representation of any interaction between the two mesons into which the photon is "converted" in the process of being absorbed. Calculations on a simple model of this type have not succeeded in quantitatively describing the observed form factors. If, however, there is a strong interaction between the mesons as schematically indicated by the cross-hatching shown in [Fig. 95–9(d)], it is possible for a resonance in the pion-pion scattering to occur such that the conversion of a photon into a pair of pions takes place primarily to this resonant state. The energy at which such a resonant state occurs will have a strong effect on the rate at which form factors fall off with increasing momentum transfer. Such two-pion states contribute only to the so-called isovector part of the form factors, which means they give equal and opposite contributions to proton and neutron form factors. The isoscalar contribution which gives like-signed contributions to both proton and neutron contributions will arise from processes like that shown in [Fig. 95–9(e)] where a photon converts into three mesons. Here too, interactions between the pions of the type indicated there can lead to resonance states which seem again to be of dominant importance. Through close analysis, it was discovered that the shapes of the observed form factors could be reasonably well described if such resonances occurred in both the two-meson and three-meson exchanges at an energy corresponding to a mass of the resonant states of approximately five pion masses. This

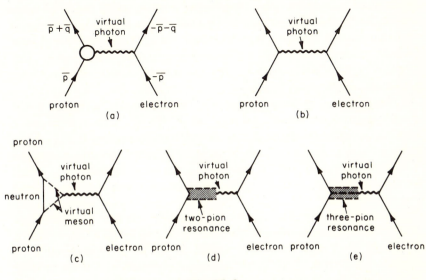

Fig. 95–9.

formed the basis for a *prediction* of such pion resonances, which was strikingly confirmed experimentally by the discovery of the ρ, ω, and ϕ vector mesons, of which two have a mass in the neighborhood of $5\frac{1}{2}$ pion masses and the third a mass in the neighborhood of $7\frac{1}{2}$ pion masses. There is considerable present interest in seeing how quantitatively the available experimental information can be explained in terms of the "known" vector mesons (or resonances) which can couple the photon line to the nucleon line, but a detailed analysis of these attempts is beyond the scope of this article and we summarize the situation by indicating that such analyses give promise of success. . . .

Rather, let us return to some more general theoretical considerations concerning the type of nucleon structure which is schematically indicated by the sketches in [Fig. 95–10]. We have indicated some of the elements which contribute to the blob where the photon line joins the proton line. A general analysis according to dispersion theory indicates that one will have additive contributions to the form factors of nucleons arising from every conceivable system into which a photon can (virtually) convert and which in turn can be absorbed by a nucleon. Besides the particular meson contributions we have indicated, there will be such structures as a nucleon-antinucleon pair or similar pairs of strange particles (hyperons). (To some extent these are already included in our vector meson exchanges, for by the same quantum fluctuation process outlined earlier, such mesons have a definite probability of being virtually decomposed into baryon-antibaryon pairs.) The form of each contribution depends on the mass of the system which couples the photon line to the baryon line and on the "strength" with which each such system is itself coupled to the two lines it connects. To apply dispersion theory to the problem at hand

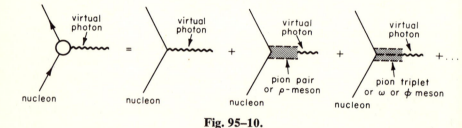

Fig. 95–10.

one must assume that the strengths decrease generally with increasing mass so that the form factors are dominated by the contributions of the lowest mass systems which can form the requisite bridge between nucleon and photon. The vector mesons we have described are then the principal contributors. From this point of view, the "inside" of a nucleon is a complex of complicated configurations of various mesons, meson complexes, baryon pairs, baryon resonances, etc., which come into (virtual) existence and disappear again as a result of quantum fluctuations; each makes some contribution, large or small, to the charge and current density of the object we call a nucleon. This is far from the relatively simple picture of the structure of the atom, where the charge and current distribution is associated with permanent and essentially stable constituents—electrons, protons, and neutrons.

Before leaving the subject of the electromagnetic structure of the nucleon we mention another source of experimental information. If we turn the diagrams in [Fig. 95–9] "on their side" we have a representation of a different physical process, namely the annihilation of a proton-antiproton pair into a virtual photon which decomposes into an electron-positron pair. This differs from the electron-scattering process in that the square of the (invariant) momentum transfer is now negative instead of positive. The amplitude for this process is expressible also in terms of the form factors described earlier, but we are now dealing with analytic continuations of these functions to values of q^2 which are negative and less than $-4M^2$ where M is the proton mass. The "integrity" of analytic functions, that is, the fact that their value in one region of the complex plane is connected with their values everywhere, means that such information is also useful in fixing the form of the charge and current distributions in the proton. Experiments of this type are in their initial stages, but eventually they should considerably enhance our information about the electromagnetic structure of the nucleon. Muon scattering and hyperfine structure in the atomic spectrum of hydrogen represent additional potential sources of information.

GRAVITATIONAL AND WEAK INTERACTIONS

We have remarked earlier that one is also interested in the distribution of other physical quantities of the nature of densities inside nucleons. The energy (and momentum) density distribution, while in principle determinable, is far from being accessible experimentally at the present time. In analogy with the electromagnetic case one would like to explore scattering in which a single gravitational quantum is exchanged between the nucleon and the probe particle. Unfortunately there do not seem to exist particles for use as probes in which some other kind of quantum exchange would not dominate the scattering process, and if such did exist, the weakness of their interactions would appear to pose problems for their detection. The prospects for obtaining information of this kind are therefore grim. We mention this process here only to illustrate a general principle: Electric charge and current densities are sources and sinks for electromagnetic quanta (photons) and can be explored by examining processes in which a single photon is exchanged, as indicated earlier. The energy-momentum density tensor is a source and sink for gravitational waves, and hence its spatial distribution could be explored by processes in which single gravitational quanta are exchanged. Generalizing this idea, we see that we can examine the source and sink density for any field by an analogous process. Therefore, let us look at other situations where a corresponding interpretation is possible.

The question of ensuring that only single quantum exchange takes place in a scattering process is simpler in those situations where the interactions mediated by the quanta of the field are relatively weak. This immediately brings to mind the so-called "weak interactions" which are responsible for such processes as beta-decay, muon-decay, muon-capture, etc. Consider, for example, the process illustrated in [Fig. 95–11(a)] in which an antineutrino interacts with a proton to yield a neutron and a positron. It has been proposed that this interaction is actually mediated by a vector meson field as shown in [Fig. 95–11(b)], but there is no direct evidence for its existence at the present time. If such a meson field exists, its quanta (the so-called W mesons) must have a mass considerably greater than the mass of the proton. Whether or not it exists it is conceptually possible to visualize the interaction to take place as shown in [Fig. 95–11(b)], since the W meson serves essentially to transfer momentum, and in this case electric charge as well, between the leptons and the nucleons. The sources and sinks of this meson field will be "currents" associated with the leptons on the one hand and the nucleons on the other.

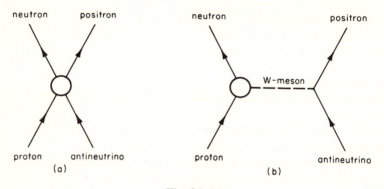

Fig. 95–11.

If no W mesons exist we have a direct interaction between these "weak currents," as they are called, but we can explore their structure just as well by the same techniques that would be applicable in the case W mesons do exist, and these techniques would be in close analogy to those used in the electromagnetic case. What we need to do is to determine how the amplitude for the process described depends on the momentum transfer involved in the process. Describing these by appropriate form factors, the Fourier transforms of the latter would be related to the spatial distributions of these "weak currents."

Let us first note some differences between the present case and the electromagnetic case. First, there is a charge transfer in the process which means that the nucleon must change its isospin in the process of emitting a W meson. This means in turn that the associated weak current here involved will now have only an isovector part rather than an isoscalar part as well as in the electromagnetic case, or stating the result more conservatively, only the isovector part of the current plays a role in this process. Furthermore, we know from various sources that there are two basic kinds of weak interactions, the vector and the axial vector. This means there will be two kinds of weak currents, one of a vector character and one of an axial vector character. Feynman and Gell-Mann have proposed that the vector currents are conserved currents of the same character as the electromagnetic current, and that they are in fact just the "charged components" of the isovector current of which the "neutral component" is the ordinary electromagnetic current. By charged and neutral components is meant here that the currents are associated with a change in charge or no change in charge of the nucleon. This proposal has been strikingly confirmed in beta-decay experiments and by the relationship between beta-decay and muon-decay. In these experiments only relatively low momenta transfers are involved between the participating nucleons and leptons. If the Feynman–Gell-Mann scheme is indeed correct, the form factors associated with the vector weak currents should be the same as the electromagnetic form factors even for large momentum transfers. A detailed confirmation of this would be a striking triumph for the Feynman–Gell-Mann hypothesis and would suggest that there exists only one vector current associated with elementary particles to which all vector fields are coupled, though with different strengths. On the other hand there is no electromagnetic analog to the axial vector currents involved in the weak interactions. These currents are also described by form factors whose momentum-transfer dependence it would be of interest to determine. Unfortunately, the neutrino experiments which have been carried out so far at Brookhaven and CERN are not yet of the character to shed direct information on these questions. One can look forward hopefully, however, to the day when the structure of the weak currents in nucleons will be studied with neutrino beams in much the same way as the electromagnetic structure is currently being probed with electrons.

On the theoretical side we may remark further that if the Feynman–Gell-Mann picture of the weak vector current is correct and its physical extension in space corresponds to that of the electromagnetic current, then again this extension arises primarily from pion pairs, or more explicitly the pion resonance called the ρ meson, (only isotopic spin-1 mesons can now contribute so that the ω and ϕ would not contribute), as the bridge between the nucleon and the hypothetical W meson. Thus the physical picture of the nucleon which would emerge from determining these form factors would not be essentially different from that described above as revealed by the electromagnetic structure.

STRONG INTERACTIONS

Having remarked on the electromagnetic, the "gravitational," and the weak-interaction structure of the nucleon, we must turn now to the only remaining class of known interactions—the so-called strong interactions.

Here the problem is complicated by the fact that these interactions are so strong that it is not easy to see how to isolate contributions to scattering or interaction processes associated with the exchange of a single quantum or particle. What makes it possible to attempt some kind of analysis is the fact that the range of the interaction associated with the exchange of a particle or system of particles between the interacting systems is inversely proportional to the mass of the exchanged system. Thus the longest-ranged interaction is that associated with the lightest exchanged systems. In the case of nucleon-nucleon scattering, for example, the lightest system of strongly interacting character is a single pion and its exchange should then dominate the interaction at large impact parameters. At somewhat smaller impact parameters the exchange of two pions would become important. The existence of the strong interaction between two pions which give rise to the meson resonance we call the ρ meson, means that two-pion exchange contributions tend to take place in these resonant states, corresponding to single ρ meson exchange. Since the mass of these is about four times the pion mass, there exists a substantial range of impact parameters where only the single pion exchange should be important. The problem is then to isolate these large impact parameter collisions from the close collisions. In general, this means that it must be possible to construct wave packets representing the colliding particles whose spatial extent is substantially smaller than a pion Compton wavelength. This in turn requires the examination of sufficiently high energy collisions. Even at high energies there will be close encounters as well as distant encounters. To isolate the distant encounters attention must be focused on those collisions in which the orbital angular momentum is sufficiently large for a given incident energy that close encounters are no longer possible. In cases where the energy is sufficiently high that the total scattering amplitude involves so many angular momentum states that the contribution of the few small angular momentum states which involve the effect of close encounters is relatively small, we may effectively accomplish the same result. Thus, by this means one can effectively study the strong interaction structure of the outer fringes of particles like nucleons, their periphery so to speak, whence, the name "peripheralism" for the general study of such processes.

Consider first in more detail the nucleon-nucleon elastic scattering process as shown in [Fig. 95–12(a)]. The momentum transfer involved in the scattering will take place through the exchange of systems like a single pion, a ρ meson, etc. We would like to isolate the one-pion contribution exhibited in [Fig. 95–12(b)]. The blobs at the vertices in this figure now represent the structure or distribution of source strength for absorption or emission of a pion by the nucleon, and determines the "strength" of the interaction associated with a given momentum transfer, or a form factor in the same sense as in the electromagnetic case that we discussed earlier. The difference is that we are now examining a "pseudoscalar" source function or current rather than a vector current from the point of view of relativistic transformation properties. If we consider scattering at energies up to a few hundred MeV, then one can make a phase shift analysis of the scattering amplitude. The phase shifts for higher angular momentum states will be dominated by the single-pion exchange contributions to the force and therefore will give us some information about these blobs. At these energies, however, about all we can determine is the total strength of the source, that is the form factor for small momentum transfer, which is effectively what we call the pion-nucleon coupling constant g; it plays the same role for meson emission and absorption as the total charge e does for photon emission and absorption.

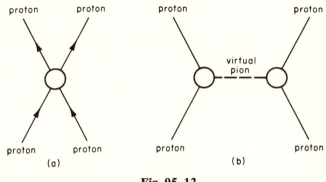

Fig. 95–12.

To find out something about the momentum transfer dependence of the form factor one would have to go to higher energies where larger momenta transfers are possible. Here one encounters a difficulty which has limited the effectiveness of "peripheralism" in yielding results free of ambiguity. This is the onset of a substantial cross section for inelastic processes even in peripheral collisions—processes like pion production or production of strange particles. Whenever such inelastic processes occur they react back on the elastic processes to yield an imaginary part of the scattering amplitude. This imaginary part cannot arise from single pion exchange but requires at least two pion exchanges for its description. The fact that the imaginary part of the amplitude becomes comparable to its real part indicates then that the basic assumption of the peripheralism approach is breaking down.

This problem appears somewhat less severe if one applies the peripheralism approach to an inelastic process such as that illustrated in [Fig.

95–13] where we have the conversion of a pion into a ρ meson through a collision with a proton. One conjectures that the required momentum transfer in the process arises from the exchange of a single pion. In this case, however, there are two unknown blobs whose structure in terms of form factors is involved in the amplitude for the process. Furthermore, the reactions of other inelastic processes on this inelastic channel are still quite substantial in reducing the probability that this particular process can occur. Thus a decrease of the cross section for this inelastic process with increasing momentum transfer will reflect not only the drop in the form factors associated with the two vertices where the exchange pion is emitted and absorbed but also the distortion of the waves representing the incident and emitted particles as a result of absorption produced by competing inelastic processes. While the peripheralism approach to high energy reactions is substantially increasing our insight into the essential elements that make up these processes, it still suffers from strong limita-

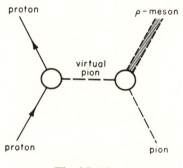

Fig. 95–13.

tions insofar as allowing one to analyze quantitatively each element that enters, as for example, the momentum-transfer dependence of the form factors for pion emission or absorption. There exists, in fact, a close similarity between the methods of peripheralism in elementary particle physics and the study of direct interactions in nuclear physics and a substantial similarity between the nature and quantitative accuracy of the conclusions which can be drawn in the two cases.

To summarize, then, the type of nucleon structure analysis we have been discussing is the determination of the spatial distribution of source functions for various types of fields which may be coupled to a nucleon— or, in more general terms, the form factors which characterize a vertex like that shown in [Fig. 95–14]. Here the two full lines represent a nucleon (more generally, any baryon) entering and emerging from the vertex "on the mass shell" (which means that the relation between the momentum and energy of the baryon is that of a free particle). The dashed line entering the vertex represents a virtual quantum of some field which transfers the requisite energy and momentum to the baryon along with charge, isospin, strangeness, etc., as selection rules may demand. For each fixed set of quantum numbers required to characterize the incoming and outgoing baryon states, the dependence of the associated vertex function on the invariant momentum transfer to the baryon represents a form factor which can be interpreted as a Fourier transform of the source function for the field with which the virtual quantum is associated. In the case where the virtual quantum is a photon, one has now a fair determination of this source function for nucleons except for the case of the charge distribution in the neutron. For the "weak currents" which are the sources of the hypothetical W mesons which mediate the weak interactions, and for the source functions of the strongly interacting meson fields, there remains much to be done experimentally and theoretically, but in general many of the means are at hand for the vigorous prosecution of such a program.

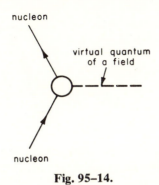

Fig. 95–14.

On the conceptual side, the picture of a nucleon which must be associated with such form factors is not easy to visualize. As a consequence of quantum fluctuations, the physical nucleon must be pictured as passing through a disorderly sequence of virtual states in which it is dissociated into those various combinations of strongly interacting particles which selection rules allow, each of these possible states making its contribution, large or small, to the form factors. The transitory existence of these "virtual particles" and their considerable variety then yields a picture far more complex than the relatively orderly picture presented by the electronic structure of the atom.

The proliferation of the number of particles which we have become habituated to terming elementary—the nucleons, hyperons, baryon resonances, mesons, and meson resonances of various characters—has raised the question whether there may exist an underlying dynamical structure for them, a lower hierarchical level in the structure of matter in which the observed "elementary particles" are composites of even simpler entities. Such speculations have been greatly strengthened by the recent uncovering of remarkable symmetries between these particles. The famous SU (3) symmetry of Gell-Mann and Ne'eman, allow the grouping of the nucleons together with the Σ and Λ particles into an octet of particles related to each other in a way analogous to that in which the neutron and proton have been related in nuclear physics. Ten of the baryon resonances allow a similar grouping into a "decuplet". The pseudoscalar mesons can be similarly grouped into an octet, while the vector mesons constitute an octet and a singlet under this symmetry. The even more recently studied SU (6) symmetry allows the octet and decuplet of baryons to be combined into a single grouping and all of the aforementioned mesons to be similarly combined. What is most intriguing is that the group-theoretical structure of these multiplets is such as to allow these baryons and baryon resonances to be considered as composites of one (or perhaps several) triplets of more fundamental particles which are variously called quarks, aces, fundamental triplets, etc. The particles of an elementary triplet would be the basic carriers of the entities which we call charge, baryon numbers, isospin, and strangeness and would carry half-integral spin. The baryons of the octet and decuplet would then be composites of three such basic triplets, their differing isospins, strangeness, and spin arising from the various combinations of these quantities which can be formed from the different combinations of triplet particles that can be assembled with like spatial symmetry. The mesons, both vector and pseudoscalar, would similarly be constructed from a member of a basic triplet bound to an antiparticle of a basic triplet.

This is not the place to go into details of such schemes, and some of what is known has been ably summarized by other authors. What is pertinent to our particular subject is the light that is thrown on the question of the source functions or form factors for the particles which we presently call elementary, including the nucleons. It has been found that the electromagnetic currents fall neatly into the classification scheme afforded by these symmetry properties, and that the same is true of the "weak currents" and also of the "strong currents" which are the sources of the vector mesons. This suggests that the structure of these currents has a form which is similar to (but not necessarily identical with!) the superposition of currents associated individually with the basic triplet particles themselves. If in fact such a superposition held, at least approximately, then the form factors of all these particles could be related to the form factors associated with the basic triplets themselves. Such simplicity is perhaps too much to hope for, but in any case the relations between different particles illuminated by these underlying symmetries are reflected in corresponding relations among their form factors; this could greatly reduce the amount of experimental work which needs to be done in order to obtain a comprehensive picture of the internal structure of elementary particles.

A striking example of the power of these symmetry ideas is the following: In the proposed SU(6) symmetry scheme, the simplest assumption about the transformation properties of the electromagnetic currents yields the prediction that the static magnetic moment of the neutron is minus two thirds that of the proton, a result confirmed by the experimental values to a few percent. From a straightforward extension of this assumption, the identity of the magnetic form factors for proton and neutron, as observed, also follows. The magnetic moment of the lambda particle is also predicted and is consistent with the crude experimental results presently available. Many other predictions concerning the various form factors of the members of the baryon octet and decuplet can be made which are currently beyond the range of experimental verification.

There seems little doubt that approximate symmetries among the elementary particles exist and probably have some significance. Whether the attractive picture of basic triplets as the underlying basis of these approximate symmetries will survive depends in part on the actual observation of the triplets. Since their masses are necessarily large, it is possible that we must await a new generation of high-energy accelerators before we can transmute this theoretical speculation into substantial experimental fact, or perhaps the cosmic rays will again serve us.

ᴓᴓᴓᴓᴓᴓᴓᴓ

H. A. Bethe Discusses High Energy Physics [3]

HIGH ENERGY PHYSICS IS UNDOUBTEDLY today the frontier of physics. The discoveries in this field of study contribute most of the advance of our fundamental understanding of nature.

When I began my career as a physicist the frontier of the subject was in atomic physics. In 1926–30, most problems of atomic physics were solved by the application of quantum mechanics. It was astonishing how quickly the subject developed, and how every problem yielded to theoretical treatment. Physicists were spoiled by this period of amazing success of a single theoretical approach. The same approach gave us in addition the theory of the chemical bond, and an understanding of the solid state. Solid state theory is still a very fruitful field, giving many important advances and new insights into the working of the nonrelativistic

---

[3] Bethe, *Science,* 147 (1965), 1551 f.

Schrödinger equation for complicated systems. However, one could hardly claim that it advances our *fundamental* understanding of nature.

The 1930's and '40s were characterized by the advance of nuclear physics. There the task was to find the force between nucleons, and the quantum states of nuclei under the influence of this force. Neither of these tasks is completed, and much interesting work remains to be done.

Particle physics, or high energy physics, is different from atomic and nuclear physics in being far removed from our daily experience. It is easy to justify work in atomic physics: The subject has direct intellectual appeal because it explains so much of the world in which we live. Moreover, its applications in chemistry and solid state physics are of great technical importance, as are some direct applications of atomic physics such as lasers. Because of these many practical applications, much of the progress in the field is now being made by industry. In nuclear physics, the practical application of nuclear power and atomic weapons is too well known to need discussion.

No such practical application has appeared, or is likely to appear, for particle physics. Indeed the processes observed in particle physics may not occur in nature outside the lab to any important extent. (They do of course occur when cosmic rays interact with matter, and may conceivably take place in those distant astronomical objects which emit energy far beyond the usual amount for a galaxy.)

There are at least three reasons for the fascination of particle physics. One is the conviction that this is indeed the most basic field of knowledge in the physical world. We want to know and to understand, and no other field will give us such deep understanding. The second reason is that particle physics will give us the basis for the theoretical treatment of another field, nuclear physics, which *is* related to the world as we know it. To find the nuclear force we must know the interaction of subnuclear particles with nucleons.

The third reason is just the very difficulty of the theory. In contrast to atomic physics which yielded to one single theoretical approach, the Schrödinger equation, it has been necessary to try many different approaches to particle physics which supplement each other. One of the difficulties is the great strength of the forces which makes approximation methods inapplicable—and approximation methods were the key to success of most of atomic theory. Secondly, we do not have any differential or integral equation in closed form, a fact closely related with the possibility of creating any number of additional particles in the interaction of two high energy particles. A third difficulty is the essential involvement of relativity theory together with the presence of many particles. Interesting theoretical methods have however been developed for dealing with some of these problems, such as dispersion theory, Regge pole theory and many others. But because of the many difficulties of the theory, it is very hard to deduce the fundamental interactions from a given experimental result, such as the cross section of a certain process.

The difficulty of the theory puts greater demands on the experimenter. His experiments must allow a simple interpretation without involving complicated and therefore doubtful theoretical steps. A good example is the Brookhaven neutrino experiment which showed directly the existence of two different neutrinos, associated respectively with the electron and the μ meson. In the field of strong interactions, recent work has concentrated on finding resonances and their properties (charge, angular momentum, parity, etc.), rather than just to measure cross sections. This demand to get easily interpretable results is combined with the difficulty of experimentation—extremely large apparatus, small number of events, often many particles in one event, some of which are neutral and therefore invisible, etc.

In spite of these difficulties, both theoretical and experimental, particle physics has already given results of great beauty. While at first sight there seems to be a confusing and overwhelming multitude of different particles, there appears to be a great amount of symmetry in their properties. Gell-Mann and others have shown that the particles can be grouped into families of 8 or 10 (perhaps in some cases more). The particles in each family have close resemblance, and the structure of the various families is either analogous or closely related.

This beautiful theory, known as SU3 symmetry, could be developed only after hundreds of painstaking experimental papers, and dozens of unsuccessful theoretical attempts at clarification. In addition to classifying the then-known particles, the theory predicted a new particle, the Ω^-, which was discovered at Brookhaven early in 1964. Both the theory and the experimental work have been written up in very good articles in the *Scientific American*. The SU3 theory is probably not the last word in particle physics. It leaves many problems unexplained, in particular it gives a very incomplete account of particle masses and reaction cross sections.

Frequently the study of particle physics has given unexpected insights into the earlier branches of physics. For instance, the study of the decay of K mesons made it likely that in this process parity was not conserved. This led Lee and Yang to conjecture that the same might be true in other weak interactions, particularly in the beta decay of nuclei. Although beta decay had been studied for at least 25 years before, it was only after this suggestion that the violation of parity in this process was experimentally found. As a more recent example, in 1964 Fitch *et al.* discovered that in at least one decay mode of a K meson, even the reversibility of time may not be satisfied. Thus particle physics touches the most fundamental concepts of space and time.

It is no surprise that particle physics has attracted the most ambitious, and the best brains among the young physicists. It would be wrong to support this branch to the exclusion of others. There are challenging problems in nuclear physics, solid state physics, and other branches. I myself have devoted the last ten years of my research to low energy nuclear physics. But I believe that particle physics deserves the greatest support among all the branches of our science because it gives the most fundamental insights. . . .

96

○○○○○○○○○○○

ELEMENTARY PARTICLES

○○○○○○○○○○○

Henry A. Boorse

Lloyd Motz

HISTORICAL SURVEY

Until recently physicists were able to explain the structure of complex systems in what appeared to be increasingly simple terms. Thus, the properties of matter were reduced to the behavior of molecules, which, in turn, were pictured as consisting of atoms, and so on; indeed, it was this search for simplicity that prompted many early scientists and philosophers to accept the Greek atomic concept of matter. What can be simpler than a universe consisting of aggregations of a single kind of indivisible particle? To solve the riddle of matter it was merely necessary to discover the nature of the forces between these primordial particles, for then the great variety in the properties of bulk matter would be accounted for by the countless number of ways these atoms could combine.

The discovery of two kinds of electric charge and Faraday's electrolytic experiments destroyed this naïve atomic picture, but left most scientists with the hope that only two fundamental particles would be needed to account for the chemical and physical properties of matter. The discovery of the electron as the basic unit of negative electric charge and the proton as the basic unit of positive charge seemed to justify this hope, since it appeared that one could now construct all kinds of matter by combining equal numbers of protons and electrons, with the electrostatic forces between these particles keeping things in equilibrium. The discovery of the photon complicated the picture somewhat. If the photon were to be treated as a particle in its own right, it would have to be in a category quite different from that of the electron and proton. However, it could

1799

play no role in the actual structure of matter since it could never be brought to rest to occupy some particular position in a structural model. The difference between the photon and the electron and proton may be presented most forcefully by noting that the latter both have nonzero rest masses, whereas the photon's rest mass must be zero. Looked at from this point of view, the photon offered no problem since it was not necessary to assign any role to it. One simply assumed that the photon was destroyed when it was absorbed by an electron or proton and came into existence when emitted by them. The photon is thus a transitory particle existing only from the moment that it is emitted to the moment that it is absorbed. In a sense, we might say that a photon is emitted only to be absorbed. On the other hand, from the point of view of modern quantum electrodynamics, the photon is the building block or fundamental particle of the electromagnetic field. The electromagnetic interaction between charged particles and the electromagnetic field occurs by the emission and absorption of photons.

With the photon assigned to this intermediary role—the carrier of the electromagnetic interaction between charged particles—it appeared that the structure of matter might be completely accounted for by just the two charged particles, the electron and the proton. The protons would contribute most of the mass of the atom and the electrons would supply the necessary negative charge to make the atom as a whole electrically neutral and to hold it together. Although this was a very appealing picture and seemed to supply all the essentials, it ran into serious trouble with the discovery of the Rutherford planetary atom. According to this proposed model of the atom (which is now firmly established) all the protons are concentrated into a tiny nucleus that occupies only one-thousand trillionth of the volume of the entire atom. This presented an immediate problem because it indicated that, in addition to the electrostatic repulsion between protons, which would, if uncompensated, cause the nucleus to fly apart, there must be some kind of attractive forces inside the nucleus. At first this need for attractive forces seemed to offer no difficulty because protons, like all matter, exert attractive gravitational forces on each other so that gravitation appeared to provide such attractive forces in the nucleus. Moreover, since the gravitational force increases as the distances between protons get smaller and smaller, it appeared that the force inside the nucleus should be just large enough to keep it together, but simple calculation showed that this is not so. In fact, the gravitational force is many orders of magnitude too small for this task, being the weakest of the known forces in nature. This immediately implied that the proton is a much more complex particle than had been assumed initially. Not only do electrostatic and gravitational fields surround it, but other force fields must emanate from it to keep the nucleus together.

The simple picture of matter consisting of only electrons and protons was given another blow when the wave properties of the electron were discovered; their existence implied that electrons have too large a wave structure to permit containment inside the nucleus. Moreover, the predicted spin and statistical characteristics of nuclei would not agree with observation if nuclei contained electrons. On the other hand, in the 1920's it was thought that electrons must be inside nuclei to account for the net charge on the nucleus. Furthermore, the emission of β rays (electrons) from certain types of radioactive nuclei seemed to require the presence of electrons.

Nothing much could be done about these difficulties as long as electrons and protons were the only fundamental particles known. But suddenly, almost as though physicists had stepped across a threshold, new particles began to appear in bewildering numbers. Whereas some of them were warmly welcomed by the theoretical physicists intent on constructing a model of the atom and the nucleus, most of them were at first accepted the way Job might have accepted his tribulations—things one had to live with but without any rhyme or reason.

The first new particle to appear on the scene after the discovery of the electron, proton, and photon did not show itself directly; its existence was inferred because it was demanded by certain conservation principles. The existence of this particle, the neutrino, was postulated by Pauli as early as 1927 to account for the apparent discrepancy in the energy balance when β-rays are emitted by radioactive nuclei. Later, when the neutron was discovered, its decay into a proton and electron also required the emission of a neutrino (actually, as we shall see, an antineutrino), not only to maintain the energy balance, but also to balance the spins before and after the decay of the neutron.

CONSERVATION PRINCIPLES

Since a sensible picture of all the new particles that have been found can be constructed only with the aid of conservation principles, we must consider these principles briefly before discussing the new particles themselves. First of all, we have the conservation of momentum, which simply states that if there are no external forces acting on a system—a collection of interacting particles—the total momentum of the system must remain constant, regardless of how the constituent particles move about or interact with each other. Thus, if a particle, like a neutron, decays into a collection of other particles, the momentum of the particle before its decay must equal the total momentum (the sum of the individual momenta) of all the decay particles. This principle is very useful in helping the particle physicist identify and classify the decay products of any reaction.

Closely associated with the conservation of momentum is conservation of energy. Indeed, the theory of relativity tells us that energy and momentum of a system are not conserved separately for all observers, but that a single quantity, called the energy-momentum 4-vector, is conserved. In the calculation of the momentum and energy of a system, the energy and the momentum of each photon must be included and the energy corresponding to the mass of each particle must also be taken into account. The conservation of energy simply ensures that no process will occur if not enough energy is available for the process. If enough energy is available, a process will occur spontaneously, unless some other conservation principles prohibit it. Since the total energy of the system (the total measured mass times the square of the speed of light plus the energy of each photon) before the spontaneous process occurs is the same as after the process, what do we mean by "enough energy" available? Why should a process go in one direction rather than in the reverse direction if the total energy must be the same at each step of the process? To answer this question we must consider the masses alone. If the total mass of a system is larger than its total mass after the process, the process will occur spontaneously. In other words, the "energy available" for a spontaneous process is the difference between the total mass (the sum of the masses of all the particles in the system) of the system before and after the process. Thus, since the mass of the neutron is somewhat larger than the mass of a proton plus an electron, the neutron spontaneously decays into a proton and an electron. The total energy after the decay is the same as before, but not all of it appears in the form of mass. Some of the original energy appears as kinetic energy of the newly formed particles: the proton, electron, and neutrino.

In addition to conservation of momentum and energy, we also have conservation of angular momentum or rotational motion. The total rotational motion of an isolated system before and after a process must be equal. Rotational motion, in general, consists of two parts: one part arising from the orbital motions of the particles in the system, and the other from the spin of each particle. The total rotational motion or angular momentum is obtained by summing the orbital and spinning motions for all the particles. In discussing the properties and behavior of elementary particles, we do not deal with orbital motions, and the only thing that concerns us here is the spin of each particle. The conservation of angular momentum then tells us that, in any process involving the transformation of one group of "elementary" particles into another, the total spin (the spins of all particles added together) before and after the process must be the same.

Here we must be careful because spin is a vector (that is, a directed quantity) and adding such quantities is unlike the usual process of addition. We overcome this difficulty by always considering the components of the spin in a particular direction and adding them together. The spins of particles occur in integer and half-integer multiples on a basic unit, which is Planck's constant h divided by 2π, and is written as $\hbar$. In terms of this unit, the spin of both the electron and the proton is $\frac{1}{2}$ and the spin of the photon is 1. Like the electron and the proton, the neutrino also has a spin of $\frac{1}{2}$.

Are there any other conservation principles that must be taken into account in our analysis of the fundamental particles of which matter is constructed? There are a few other important ones. One of these deals with electric charge. The total charge in the universe is constant, at least as far as all evidence indicates; charge can neither be created nor destroyed. Therefore, the total charge of a system must be the same before and after the process occurs. If a new, positively charged particle suddenly appears during a process, a new, negatively charged particle must appear at the same time to compensate for the positive charge. Charge occurs in integer multiples (positive and negative) of a basic unit, which is the charge on the proton. As far as is known, only three values of this unit of charge occur on fundamental particles: -1, 0, $+1$. Examples are the electron (-1), the neutrino (0), and the proton $(+1)$. The charge on the photon is also 0.

Another conservation principle deals with the total number of heavy particles or nucleons (protons and neutrons) in the universe. Since no experimental evidence has ever been adduced for the destruction or creation of a heavy particle, we must assume that the total number of heavy particles (protons plus neutrons or any other particles that finally become protons or neutrons) in the universe is conserved. This number must therefore be the same before and after any process. Thus, a neutron decays into a proton and two light particles (electron and neutrino) so that we start with one heavy particle (neutron) and end with another one (proton). Light particles like electrons, photons, and neutrinos are not conserved, as is clear from the β-decay process (e.g., the decay of the neutron) and from processes involving the emission and absorption of photons. Note, however, that the total lepton number, where by leptons we mean electrons, neutrinos, and muons (and their antiparticle counterparts), is conserved. This follows because a lepton always appears or disappears with an antilepton, so that the total number, counting antileptons as negative, remains constant.

There are two more conservation principles that have guided physicists and are still important in the classification of particles: the conservation of parity, which we have already discussed in the commentary preceding the article by Lee and Yang, and the "conservation of strangeness," an entirely new kind of quantity that had to be introduced to understand the way certain heavy particles decay. It is proper that these two principles should be grouped together because they are not universally valid, but are obeyed only in processes in which no neutrinos are emitted or absorbed. Later, we shall classify processes according to the strength of the interactions, that is, the forces, involved. The weakest interactions are those involving the gravitational force. They play no role in particle processes. Next in increasing order of strength come the so-called "weak interactions" involving neutrino emission and absorption, for example, β-decay processes. These are also called "Fermi interactions," since Fermi developed a theory of β-decay based on such interactions. Then come electromagnetic interactions, involving the absorption and emission of photons, which are about a trillion times stronger than the "weak interaction." Finally, we have the "strong interactions," an example of which is the interaction between two nucleons, that is, the nuclear force. These are about 137 times stronger than the electromagnetic interactions and hence about one hundred trillion times stronger than the "weak interactions." Conservation of parity and of "strangeness" is not valid for weak interactions but holds for electromagnetic and strong interactions.

At this point we discuss only parity; we shall return to the subject of "strangeness" later. By conservation of parity, we refer to the behavior of the wave properties of a particle. Since every particle is described by a wave amplitude, which depends on (that is, is a function of) the coordinates of the particle, we can classify particles according to how their wave amplitudes or "wave functions" behave when the coordinates of the particles are replaced by their negative values. This simply means comparing the behavior of a particle in the real world with its behavior as seen through a mirror. If such a reflection leaves the wave amplitude unchanged, we say that the particle has even parity, but if the wave amplitude changes its sign when viewed through a mirror, we say that the parity is odd. Thus, parity can have only two values: $+1$ (even parity) and -1 (odd parity). Conservation of parity means that the total parity of a system (obtained by multiplying together the parities of the individual particles in the system) is the same before and after a process occurs. As was first predicted by Lee and Yang in 1957, this principle is violated in weak interactions. For a further discussion of this see the commentary on the work of Lee and Yang (Chapter 94).

Before returning to our history of fundamental particles we must introduce one more principle that governs the classification of these particles: the Pauli exclusion principle and the statistics of particles, which we have discussed in detail in earlier chapters of this book. We have seen that particles can be classified into two different groups according to the kind of statistics they obey. If particles are governed by the Pauli exclusion principle, they obey the Fermi-Dirac statistics and are called fermions; particles to which the Pauli principle does not apply obey the Bose-Einstein statistics and are called bosons. In general, particles with half a unit of spin are fermions and those with zero or one unit of spin are bosons. Thus, electrons, nucleons (protons and neutrons), and neutrinos are fermions, whereas photons are bosons. A fermion can never change into a boson, and vice versa. However, a boson can break up into other bosons or into an even number of fermions plus additional bosons, and an even number of fermions (plus additional bosons when needed) can combine to form a boson. A fermion can only break up into an odd number of fermions plus bosons in any process.

CONSERVATION PRINCIPLES AND SYMMETRY

Before leaving these general principles, which govern the over-all behavior of particles, it is instructive to regard them from a somewhat different point of view that has a bearing on the classification of these particles. As indicated in our commentary on symmetries (the work of Lee and Yang), a conservation principle is generally associated with some kind of symmetry in the dynamic properties of a system of particles and this, in turn, means that there are quantities associated with the system which are invariant to certain changes, and hence are related to quantum numbers. Thus one should be able to describe particle properties by introducing the quantum numbers that are associated with the various symmetries and then arranging the particles into groups according to the numerical values of these numbers. To see how this works specifically, we note that the conservation of momentum means that the dynamic structure of the system must be such that the structure is not altered when the system is shifted from one point to another in space. The conservation of energy implies that in a system left to itself the total dynamic properties do not change from moment to moment. The conservation of angular momentum means that the dynamic properties are not altered if the system is rotated in any way; hence, the system has symmetry about the axis of rotation. A quantum number is associated with each of these invariances; the rotational quantum number is of particular importance in analyzing atomic and molecular spectra.

The conservation of parity means the system is symmetrical with respect to a reflection; its dynamic properties are not altered when viewed through a mirror. The conservation of charge is associated with a quantity called gauge and implies that the dynamic symmetry of a system is such that its properties do not change when the gauge is changed. A change of gauge occurs when the wave amplitude of the system is multiplied by a factor. Conservation of charge means then that multiplying the wave function (or wave amplitude) by such a factor does not alter the state of the system. One can therefore introduce a quantum number, the so-called isotopic spin or isospin quantum number to represent charge just as we introduce a quantum number for angular momentum. In the same way, the conservation of "strangeness" and nucleon number is related to a symmetry that is of a mathematical rather than a physical nature, and cannot be expressed in terms of spatial relationships in the way rotational symmetry or the reflection symmetry can. Nevertheless, these mathematical symmetries must be incorporated in our over-all mathematical representation of particles and used in their classification. The conservation of strangeness and nucleon number means that quantum numbers must be assigned to represent these conserved quantities. Actually, as we shall see, the conservation of charge, of nucleon or heavy particle number, and of strangeness are related so that they are governed by a single type of symmetry in some kind of hypothetical space. The Pauli principle and the statistical properties of a system of particles are related to the invariance in the structure when two of the particles of the system are interchanged. This last type of symmetry is present because two identical particles, e.g., electrons, cannot be distinguished.

SYMMETRIES AND GROUP THERAPY

Now that we have traced the relationship between conservation principles and symmetries, let us consider how these symmetries are investigated and are related to the dynamic properties of a system. This is done by a mathematical technique called "group theory," the application of which to the analysis of the spectra of complex atoms and molecules was developed in its most productive form by E. Wigner, who was awarded the Nobel Prize in 1963 for his contributions to symmetry principles in physics. Where the dynamic symmetry properties of a system can be found by inspection, group theory does not have to be applied, but where the spatial symmetries are complex, as in the many electron atoms and in molecules, or are in a hypothetical space and are of a purely mathematical form with no apparent spatial counterpart, only group theory can lead to a complete analysis. There is another advantage to the group-theory approach. Mathematicians have been studying groups of all kinds for years, so that their properties are well known. One can therefore carry over these mathematical developments to physics, with the hope that the group properties uncovered by the mathematicians will reveal all the conservation principles and symmetries of the elementary particles in nature.

We can best illustrate the group-theory method by some simple examples. Suppose we have a system of particles and we shift it along a line by a small amount. This is called a translation and can be represented mathematically by changing the coordinate of each particle by this small amount. This means that the wave function of the system is altered in some way by this process since the wave function depends on the co-ordinates. This change in the wave function is represented in quantum mechanics by a mathematical operator applied to the wave function—in this case, the momentum operator. Consider now all possible translations of the system along the given line. Each such translation is represented by an operator and all of these operators—an infinite number in this case—constitute a mathematical group. A collection or set of operators is called a group if (1) the product of any two of the operators, that is, the application of one operator followed by another, is itself a member of the set; and if (2) for each operator in the set the inverse operator is also present so that the application of an operator followed by the application of its inverse operator leaves the wave function and hence the state of the system unaltered.

To see how the analysis of a group can give us insight into the physical structure of a system, we briefly consider the group of rotations about an axis. Because the dynamic structure of the system does not change when the system is rotated, the mathematical representation—in this case, a certain type of matrix—of the rotation group must have a structure such that when it is applied as an operator to the wave function of the system before rotation, we obtain the wave function (or wave amplitude) of the rotated system. For this to be true, the matrix representing the rotation, that is, the mathematical form of the group of rotations, must have a definite structure that can be derived from the mathematical properties of the group. The importance of this for physics is that the structural elements of the matrix representing the rotation group can be related to the various multiplets of the spectrum of the system. Thus, group theory can be used to analyze spectra. It is hoped that symmetry groups can be used in the same way to classify particles.

We now summarize briefly the procedure that is used in classifying particles and arranging them into a structural scheme. One first finds all the conservation principles applicable to the system of particles and assigns quantum numbers to these. One then relates these quantum numbers to symmetries—spatial or purely mathematical—and seeks the group representations of these symmetries. The mathematical structures of these groups then allow one to arrange the particles into multiplets in analogy with the spectral lines.

ANTIPARTICLES AND MESONS

Let us return to our story of the discovery of the various particles and how they fit into the structural scheme of things. The first real break in the electron-proton picture of the universe, disregarding for the moment the postulated neutrino, came with the discovery of the positron, whose existence had already been predicted by the Dirac theory. Since the Dirac theory applies not only to the electron but also to protons, neutrons, and neutrinos, the existence of the positron, or, as we shall now call it, the antielectron, implies by analogy the existence of the antiproton, the antineutron, and the antineutrino. In fact, all particles must have their anticounterparts. The photon is its own antiparticle, but the antiparticles of spin $\frac{1}{2}$ particles are the mirror images of these particles. The introduction of antiparticles has in a sense saved the principle of the conservation of parity if this principle is enlarged to include charge. Thus, if the signs of all the charges in a system are changed while at the same time the system is viewed through a mirror, its dynamic structure must remain unchanged. Even in weak interaction processes, reflections do not destroy the structural invariance provided each particle is replaced by its antiparticle. This is called charge conjugation, so that we may say that our system must remain invariant to charge conjugation and reflection acting at the same time. This is generally referred to as CP (charge-parity) invariance. We thus see that the existence of antiparticles is demanded by the charge-parity symmetry in nature. This important property of antiparticles was not known when the positron was discovered, but became apparent later.

The next great step away from the simple electron-proton dualism came with the discovery of the neutron, which proved its usefulness at once by fitting nicely into a consistent scheme for the nucleus, and thus eliminating all the difficulties that would stem from a nucleus consisting of protons and electrons. In addition to simplifying nuclear structure, the neutron gave the first clue as to the nature of nuclear forces, that is, the force between nucleons (neutrons and protons) that keep the nucleus together. By analogy with the emission and absorption of photons, which accounts for electromagnetic forces between charged particles, Yukawa postulated the emission and absorption of heavy particles, now called mesons, to account for the strong forces between nucleons. The mesons would thus be the quanta of a nuclear force field just as the zero rest-mass photons are the quanta of the electromagnetic field. These nuclear field quanta, now called pi mesons or pions, were discovered about ten years after Yukawa's prediction and after physicists had been misled by the discovery of the mu meson or muon, which is not a field quantum at all, but a particle in its own right that seems to have no reason at all for existing. Today the muon is not referred to as a meson at all, the word "meson" being reserved for the quanta of the nuclear field and their excited states.

The pion has a mass of about 270 times the electron mass, a spin of zero units, obeys the Bose-Einstein statistics, and possesses three different electrical charges: positive, negative, and zero. Each of the charged pions decays into a muon and neutrino in about three one-hundred millionths of a second; the neutral pion decays into two γ-rays in about a thousand trillionth of a second. The positive pion is the antiparticle of the negative pion and the neutral pion is its own antiparticle. We shall presently see how the pion can be classified into a group-theoretical scheme, but for the moment let us examine the nucleon more carefully.

When the neutron was first discovered, it was treated as a fundamental particle in its own right—quite different from, but on a par with, the proton—except that it was not stable, being about 1.5 electron masses heavier than a proton and an electron, and hence decaying into a proton, electron, and antineutrino when left to itself. Then experimental evidence showed that the nuclear force between two protons is equal to that between two neutrons, or between a neutron and a proton. In other words, the strong interaction is charge-independent, so that, as far as it is concerned, the neutron and the proton appear to be identical particles. If there were no electromagnetic interaction, one could not distinguish between a proton and neutron on the basis of their mutual nuclear interactions alone. We may therefore say that the proton and the neutron are a "charge doublet," being two different energy states of a single particle, the nucleon.

THE CHARGE DOUBLET AND ISOTOPIC SPIN

This idea of a particle doublet led Heisenberg to introduce a new designation in analogy with the doublet spin states of an electron in a magnetic field. All electrons have $\frac{1}{2}$ a unit of spin, but this spin does not become apparent until a magnetic field is switched on: two electrons with opposite spins are identical when no magnetic field is present. When the electrons are in a magnetic field their spins line up either parallel to the field or antiparallel to it; those with parallel spin have a slightly different energy from those with antiparallel spins, so that one group of electrons can then be distinguished from the other. Thus, the electron is a magnetic doublet because of its spin. The reason the electron has only two magnetic states of energy is that its spin is $\frac{1}{2}$. If its spin were 0 it would have one magnetic state (singlet); if its spin were 1, it would have three magnetic states (triplet), and so on. In analogy with this idea, and because the proton and neutron cannot be distinguished when no electromagnetic interactions are present, Heisenberg suggested that the nucleon be assigned a new quantum number, $\frac{1}{2}$, called "isotopic spin," which can have the components $+\frac{1}{2}$ or $-\frac{1}{2}$ (parallel or antiparallel) relative to some direction in an "isotopic spin space," just the way the spin of the electron can have the components $+\frac{1}{2}$ or $-\frac{1}{2}$ along some chosen direction in actual space.

The following convention has been adopted for isotopic spin: a nucleon whose isotopic spin component is $+\frac{1}{2}$ is a proton; if its isotopic spin component is $-\frac{1}{2}$, it is a neutron. The charge independence of nuclear forces can now be expressed as the conservation of isotopic spin; when nucleons interact, the total isotopic spin is conserved if electromagnetic forces are disregarded.

Although isotopic spin was introduced at first as a purely mathematical device to express the charge independence of nuclear forces, physicists soon realized that it also presented a technique for expressing some of the symmetry properties of the new particles that were being so rapidly discovered. It also showed that group-theoretic methods could be applied to the classification of particle multiplets just as groups are used to classify spectral line multiplets. Mathematicians had, for many years, been studying what are called "unitary unimodular groups," which can be represented by matrices of a given number of rows and columns. Now the two-dimensional unitary unimodular group, called SU(2), can be represented by the three 2×2 Pauli spin matrices; hence, the ordinary spin multiplets of particles such as electrons can be derived from the structure of the SU(2) group. Heisenberg therefore suggested that a representation of the SU(2) groups also be used to describe the neutron-proton charge doublet. The three matrices would now represent the x, y, z components of isospin, that is, of charge, but they would be governed by the same mathematical rules as the spin matrices.

This idea opened up a whole range of new possibilities, for if we can have charge doublets, why not higher charge multiplets, for example, a charge triplet. One would then describe such a triplet of particles by assigning to it the isotopic spin 1. This is in complete analogy with ordinary spin, where a particle having a spin 1 can have three different states of energy in a magnetic field. Its spin can orient itself in only three ways in a magnetic field: parallel, perpendicular, and antiparallel to the field. If there were no magnetic field, these three states would be identical. In the same way, a charge triplet with isotopic spin 1 would represent three particles with $+1$, 0, and -1 units of electric charge, but otherwise identical. All the members of this charge triplet should behave exactly the same way in processes involving strong interactions, but differently in electromagnetic interactions. The British physicist N. Kemmer was the first one to point out that the three pions, π^-, π^0, π^+ are precisely such a charge triplet, and that these three pions are indistinguishable in strong interactions. They differ only in an electromagnetic field and in their decay modes, which involve weak and electromagnetic interactions. The existence of a pion charge triplet is required by the conservation of isotopic spin, that is, the charge independence of nuclear forces. The nuclear force (disregarding the Coulomb repulsion) between two protons or between two neutrons can equal that between a proton and a neutron only if a neutral pion with very nearly the same mass as that of the two charged pions exists. Two protons or two neutrons can then interact via the virtual emission and absorption of these neutral pions.

Kemmer's application of the isotopic spin concept to pions gave the first indication of how powerful symmetry principles might be in classifying "elementary particles." Before we consider the most recently discovered particles and where they fit into the scheme of things, let us see what additional sense we can make of the particles already discussed. If, for the moment, we neglect the muon and the neutrino, there are two general groups of particles: those that are permanent like the electron and nucleon and those like the photons and mesons, which are the quanta of the electromagnetic and nuclear force fields, respectively. We now note that all the "permanent particles" (electrons and nucleons) have a half unit of spin, whereas the photons and mesons have zero spin. This means that the statistics of permanent particles are different from those of quanta. All known quanta (photons and mesons) are bosons, but the permanent particles are fermions.

Having separated particles into bosons and fermions, we can also separate the fermions into light and heavy particles. The light particles, like the electrons, are called leptons, and the heavy particles are called baryons or hyperons. Thus far we have discussed only two baryons—the proton and neutron—which are really different states of a single charge doublet—the nucleon—but we shall presently consider many more baryons. In addition to the electron, we must count the neutrino and the muon as leptons. The muons are a complete mystery to physicists at the present time and seem to play no role in any structural scheme of matter. Except for their mass—about 208 electron masses—they are identical with electrons and positrons. They are fermions (spin $\frac{1}{2}$) and occur as particle μ^- and as antiparticle μ^+. Today physicists consider the muon a heavy electron, and possibly an excited state of the ordinary electron or the positron. The neutrino is a permanent particle with zero charge, zero rest mass, and spin $\frac{1}{2}$ (a fermion), and is involved in all weak interaction processes. Recently, M. Schwartz, L. Lederman, and J. Steinberger demonstrated experimentally that there are two different neutrinos: one associated with the electron, and the other with the muon. These two neutrinos are identical in all respects except that one always appears together with the electron in weak interaction, e.g., β-decay processes, and the other appears together with the muon in weak interaction, e.g., the decay of the pion to a muon and a neutrino. Some physicists consider the electron-neutrino as the zero charge state of the electron and the muon-neutrino as the zero charge state of the muon. This idea recommends itself if we consider the decay of a proton into a neutron, a positron and a neutrino. Since an outgoing positron is equivalent to an incoming electron, we may describe the decay of a proton as an encounter between a proton and an electron in which an exchange of charge occurs. The electron gives up its charge to the proton, or vice versa, and in the process the proton becomes a neutron. At the same time, the electron reverts to its uncharged state—the neutrino.

THE DISCOVERY OF STRANGE PARTICLES

Now that we have divided particles into fermions and bosons—the carriers of the field—and the fermions into leptons and baryons, we consider the baryons and the heavy mesons in more detail. The simple picture of the nucleon doublet and the pion triplet had to be discarded in 1950 when a whole range of new particles suddenly appeared in cosmic-ray tracks. The most striking of these was what we now call the lambda or Λ-particle. This is a neutral particle that is associated with so-called V-shaped tracks as shown in figs. 96–1 to 96–3. The two visible tracks forming the V shape can be analyzed and be shown to arise either from the motion of a proton and negative pion or from a negative and positive pion. Clearly these two particles cannot be created from nothing, so that this kind of V-shaped event means that some neutral particle—more massive than a proton and pion combined—must have decayed at the point where the tracks of the proton and pion meet. That this particle is neutral is indicated by the absence of any track leading to the V event. This Λ^0-particle was shown to have a mass of 2182 electron mass and to decay either into a proton and negative pion or into a neutron and neutral pion. We write this as follows:

$$\Lambda^0 \to p + \pi^-$$
$$\to n + \pi^0.$$

Since the Λ^0-particle decays into a fermion and a boson, it must itself be a fermion with spin $\frac{1}{2}$. We now know also that Λ^0 is a neutral particle and hence a charge singlet with isotopic spin 0. However, when the Λ^0 was first discovered, its isotopic spin was not known, but assumed to be $\frac{1}{2}$, even though no positively charged Λ^0 was found. This led to a certain difficulty which we shall discuss in a moment. Since the Λ^0 decays into a nucleon it must be included among the baryons. Its lifetime, that is, the time in which it decays, is about three ten-billionths of a second, and this, too, led to difficulties which are related to its isotopic spin. In addition to the Λ^0 we also have the antilambda or $\bar{\Lambda}^0$. The bar over a symbol indicates the antiparticle.

At the same time that the V tracks arising from Λ particles were discovered, other kinds of V tracks were also found. These were shown to arise from a π^+ and a π^- moving away from the point where the two

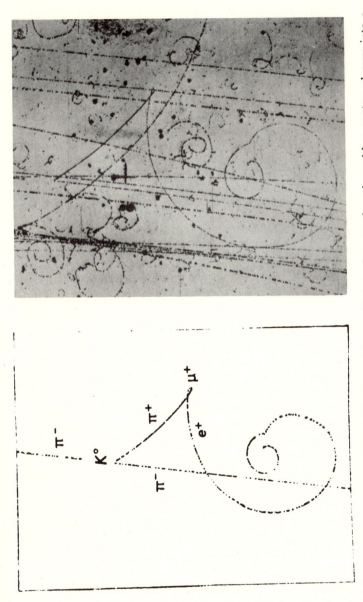

Fig. 96–1. (a) Neutral K particle, formed in a collision of a negative pion with a proton, decays into a pair of oppositely charged pions, as outlined in the drawing. The event is recorded in this photograph as a series of bubbles produced by charged particles in a chamber of liquid propane. The positive pion decays further to a muon and a neutrino, which leaves no bubble track. Finally, the muon decays to a positron and two invisible neutrinos. A neutral lambda was presumably made together with the K, but if so it left the chamber without decaying to charged particles and made no track. The incoming pion was produced in the Cosmotron at Brookhaven National Laboratory. (After M. Gell-Mann & E. P. Rosenbaum, *Scientific American,* 197(1957), 73.)

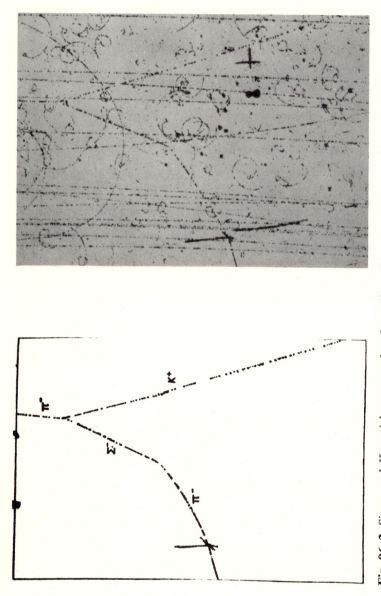

Fig. 96-2. Sigma and K particles are produced together when a pion hits a proton in the bubble chamber. The sigma decays to a pion and an invisible neutron. The pion then hits a carbon nucleus and makes a "star." The experiments shown here and in Fig. 96-1 were performed by J. H. Steinberger, N. P. Samios, R. J. Plano, F. R. Eisler, and M. Schwartz, all of Columbia University. (After M. Gell-Mann and E. P. Rosenbaum, *Scientific American*, 197(1957), 74.)

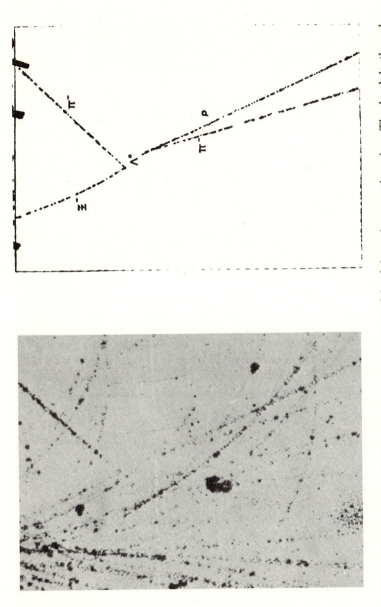

Fig. 96–3. Negative xi particle decays into a neutral lambda and a negative pion. The lambda then decays into a proton and a second negative pion. The xi was produced by the collision of a high-energy cosmic ray with a nucleus in a lead plate. This photograph, which shows tracks in a cloud chamber below the plate, was made by E. W. Cowan of the California Institute of Technology. (From M. Gell-Mann and E. P. Rosenbaum, *Scientific American,* 197 (1957), 74.

tracks begin. Again we must conclude that some neutral particle must have decayed into a π^+ and π^- at this point since pions cannot come out of nothing. These neutral particles were called K^0-mesons; since they decay into bosons they must themselves be bosons with zero spin and are thus properly classified as mesons. Later positive K^+- and negative K^--mesons were also found with masses close to the mass of the K^0-meson—about 966 electron masses. This prompted physicists to classify the K-meson as a charge triplet with isotopic spin 1 just like the pions, and this led to difficulties of the same kind as those stemming from the $\bar{\Lambda}^0$ particle. The lifetimes of the K-mesons range from about one ten-billionth of a second to about a millionth of a second.

We now consider the difficulties that were encountered when the Λ and K particles were first discovered and how these difficulties were cleared up at about the same time by M. Gell-Mann and K. Nishijima, working independently and starting from a suggestion by A. Pais. The difficulty with these particles first became evident from their lifetimes, which are much longer than one would expect when considered in connection with their strong interactions and the way they must be produced. All processes involving strong interactions occur very rapidly—in about one trillion-trillionths of a second—the time it takes light to move across a nucleon, provided enough energy is available for the process. Now we know from the great abundance of V events found in cosmic rays that both Λ and K particles are very numerous and must therefore be produced very rapidly, that is, by strong interactions. One would, therefore, by the principle of reversibility, expect these particles to decay by strong interactions and thus have lifetimes of the order of 10^{-23} seconds. But they behave quite differently; their lifetimes are about a hundred trillion times longer than this and hence are the result of weak interactions and probably related to β-decay. Even though the Λ^0 decays into what appears to be a strong reaction scheme—a proton plus a negative pion—the process is really a weak reaction. The puzzling question is why this is so. Because of this unexpected behavior when these particles decay, physicists referred to Λ and K particles as "strange" or "queer."

We must now describe how the difficulty associated with the difference between the way the strange particles are created and the way they decay was cleared up. To do this we consider an analogy with electrons and positrons. Suppose we allow a very energetic beam of γ rays to impinge upon heavy nuclei. This beam would create electron-positron pairs in great abundance. The positrons would be destroyed quickly and we would detect only large numbers of electrons left over. If we did not know that positrons are created together with electrons we would be quite puzzled on finding that the electrons formed by the γ rays do not decay, but last practically forever. For by the process of reversibility we would expect the electrons to decay as quickly into γ rays as they are created by the γ rays. But knowing that electrons are negatively charged particles and that charge must be conserved in all processes, we realize that every time an electron is created a positron is also created to keep the total charge zero, just as it was before the creation of the pair. We see then that an electron cannot decay into γ rays by itself—it can only do so together with a positron. Thus charge conservation keeps the electrons alive when no positrons are around.

It occurred to A. Pais, then at the Institute for Advanced Study at Princeton and now Professor of Physics at Rockefeller University, that the same kind of thing applies to the creation and decay of strange particles. Suppose that in addition to electric charge there is still another kind of charge in nature that is not found on electrons, nucleons, or pions; let us call this charge "strangeness." Suppose, moreover, that this kind of charge is conserved in all strong interactions, but need not be conserved in weak interactions. If strangeness now occurs in integer units—both positive and negative—we can, following Pais, clear up the lifetime difficulty described above as follows: We proceed in analogy with positron-electron pair creation which conserves electric charge. We assume that strangeness is conserved in all strong interactions so that two or more strange particles with opposite strangeness charges must be created simultaneously in a strong reaction. Pais did not call this pair production but "associated production" and we see that this idea eliminates the lifetime difficulty. All we need do is assume Λ^0 and K^0 particles have opposite strangeness and that whenever a Λ^0 is produced in a strong reaction a K^0 must be produced. This conserves strangeness. But once a K^0 and Λ^0 are created in such a reaction, they move away from each other and neither one of them has any way of decaying alone without violating the conservation of strangeness. This means that neither one can decay by a strong reaction, that is, in the very short time (about 10^{-23} seconds) associated with strong interactions. But after a long enough time (about a hundred millionth of a second) they decay through a weak interaction for which strangeness conservation is not required. This, as we see, eliminates the difficulty.

THE STRANGENESS QUANTUM NUMBER

We now come to the important contribution of Gell-Mann and Nishijima to this particle game. They were the first to introduce a quantum number for strangeness, and to show how it is to be calculated for a particle. They then used the concept of strangeness to organize elementary particles into a reasonable scheme, and to analyze particle reactions. To see how strangeness is defined we separate the particles into baryons and mesons, and consider baryons first. As we have already indicated, any particle that decays into, or can be formed from, one or more nucleons is a baryon. We assign to each such particle a baryon number B or nucleonic charge equal to the number of nucleons "hidden" in it or, put differently, to the number of protons that ultimately appear in its final decay. Thus a nucleon (proton or neutron) has a nucleonic charge or baryon number B = 1 and a Λ^0 particle also has B = 1, and so on. All antibaryons have negative baryon numbers. Thus antinucleons and anti-lambda particles have B = −1. To obtain the total baryon number in a system of particles, we add all the B's together (taking positive values for baryons and negative values for antibaryons). Thus, a system consisting of a proton, neutron, and Λ^0 has B = 3, whereas B = 0 for a system with one proton and one antilambda, and so on. The baryon number is conserved in all processes, and is zero for all leptons and mesons.

We consider now the electric charge or isotopic spin of baryons. We have seen that we can group baryons into charge multiplets. Since the two nucleons form a charge doublet with isotopic spin $\frac{1}{2}$, it was assumed that all higher baryons would be charge doublets of the same kind; when the Λ^0 particle was first discovered, it was thought that its isotopic spin was $\frac{1}{2}$ and that a Λ^+ would also be found sooner or later. This conclusion was based on analogy with the neutron-proton charge doublet and the fact that Λ^0 has a baryon number B = 1. It was felt that Λ particles ought to be charge doublets like the nucleons since they are members of the baryon family. But one day Gell-Mann, in discussing the heavy strange particles, referred to them inadvertently as particles of isotopic spin 1. He quickly corrected himself, saying he had meant $\frac{1}{2}$, not 1, but later, after thinking about this slip of the tongue, he had the brilliant notion that his first statement might be the correct one and that Λ particles are strange precisely because they are *not* charge doublets. If they were not doublets they must then either be charge triplets with isotopic spin 1, or charge singlets with isotopic spin 0. Gell-Mann decided to pursue this idea. If, following Gell-Mann, we suppose that normal baryons—like the nucleon—are only those charge multiplets whose average charge (obtained by adding the charges of all the members of the multiplet and dividing by the multiplet number) equals $\frac{1}{2}$, then strange baryons are those whose average charge does not equal $\frac{1}{2}$. The strangeness would then be measured by how much the average charge of the strange charge multiplet differs from $\frac{1}{2}$.

Gell-Mann then reasoned that one should be able to arrange the strange particles into some kind of orderly scheme by assigning a strangeness quantum number S to each hyperon charge multiplet and imposing the condition that S be conserved in all strong interactions. Gell-Mann and Nishijima independently defined S as equal to twice the average charge of a charge multiplet minus its baryon number. The formula for S is thus $S = 2q - B$, where q is the average charge. From this it immediately follows that $S = 0$ for nucleons—$q = \frac{1}{2}$ and $B = 1$ for the neutron-proton doublet—as it should be since nucleons are normal baryons. On the other hand, since Λ^0 is a charge singlet with zero average charge, and with $B = 1$, it has a strangeness of $S = 0 - 1 = -1$. One can show from this definition that the strangeness of an antibaryon multiplet is the negative of the corresponding baryon multiplet, since the baryon number B changes sign when we go from baryon to antibaryon.

We now consider the strange mesons like the K particles. Since the pions π^-, π^0, π^+ with an average charge of zero constitute the normal meson triplet, we may define strange mesons as meson charge doublets or, in fact, meson charge multiplets whose average charge is not zero. In other words, whereas the departure from an average charge value of $\frac{1}{2}$ is a measure of the strangeness of baryons, the strangeness of mesons is measured by the difference between their average charge value and zero. Since the baryon number of any meson is zero, we see that the strangeness quantum number S of a meson charge multiplet can still be defined as it is for baryons. From the previous formula we will then have $S = 2q$ for mesons, since $B = 0$. This formula shows us that the pion triplet has zero strangeness, which is just what we want. What about the K-mesons? If the K-mesons formed a charge triplet, with K^+ the antiparticle of the group—as one might be inclined to suppose in analogy with the pions, because K^-, K^0, and K^+ are all known to exist—their strangeness would be zero by definition. But we know from the slowness of their decay that they must be strange particles with S different from zero. Hence they cannot be a charge triplet but must form two charge doublets, that is, a doublet and an antidoublet. Thus K^+ and K^0 form one doublet and $\overline{K}^-$ and $\overline{K}^0$ the antidoublet. This means that there must be two neutral K's, one being the antiparticle of the other. This is indeed the case, and one of the brilliant successes of the strangeness theory was its prediction of two kinds of neutral K's, called K_1^0 and K_2^0, with quite different lifetimes. This has been experimentally verified.

Consider now the doublet K^+, K^0. Its average charge q is $\frac{1}{2}$. Hence, from the formula $S = 2q$ we see that its strangeness is $+1$. The strangeness of the antidoublet $\overline{K}^-$, $\overline{K}^0$ is, of course, -1. We see now that the principle of conservation of strangeness requires that either a K^+ or a K^0 must be formed simultaneously with a Λ^0 in a strong interaction (e.g., the collision of two very energetic nucleons or a nucleon and a pion), since $S = -1$ for Λ^0 and $S = +1$ for K^+, K^0. Whether the K^+ or the K^0 is formed is determined by charge conservation. Strangeness conservation has thus saved the day and explained why strange particles must decay slowly.

We come now to some remarkable predictions stemming from the strangeness theory. First, of course, there must be an antilambda, $\overline{\Lambda}^0$, with strangeness equal to $+1$. Such a particle is formed together with either $\overline{K}^-$ or $\overline{K}^0$, as has been experimentally verified. Suppose now that a baryon triplet existed with isotopic spin 1. Its average charge q would be zero, and its baryon number would be 1. Hence, from the formula $S = 2q - B$, its strangeness quantum number S would equal -1. Such a triplet called Σ^-, Σ^0, Σ^+ with all three members having very nearly the same mass, was found after its existence had been predicted. In addition, the antibaryon triplet $\overline{\Sigma}^-$, $\overline{\Sigma}^0$ and $\overline{\Sigma}^+$ also exists.

In addition to strange baryon triplets there are also strange baryon doublets. Consider a charge doublet of isotopic spin $\frac{1}{2}$ but, unlike the nucleon, consisting of a pair of particles with charge -1 and 0. The average charge q of such a doublet is $-\frac{1}{2}$ and its baryon number is $B = 1$. Hence its strangeness is $S = -1 - 1 = -2$. This doublet called the xi doublet (Ξ^-, Ξ^0) has been found. Its anticounterpart $\overline{\Xi}^0$, $\overline{\Xi}^+$ also exists.

In Table 96–1 the isotopic spins, the strangeness quantum numbers, and the charges of the known strange multiplets are given. White circles are particles and black circles are antiparticles. In Table 96–2 the life-times, spins, masses and decay modes of known particles are given.

THE CLASSIFICATION OF PARTICLES BY SYMMETRY GROUPS

Although the introduction of the concept of strangeness led to a simplification of particle classification, the situation was quite unsatisfactory from the point of view of a single basic principle from which the mass spectrum of the various families of particles could be deduced. Nor could one understand the occurrence of the various particles in terms of any single dynamic principle that would relate the massive baryons to the nucleon and the massive mesons to the pions. It was therefore necessary to uncover some universal principle or some all-encompassing symmetry from which all else can be derived. The two ideas that were then current and still are being investigated are the following: (1) The "bootstrap" theory as developed by G. F. Chew, S. Frautschi, and others, which starts from the premise that none of the strongly interacting particles (that is, baryons and mesons)—called "hadrons" as a group—are fundamental particles but that each one is a dynamic bound state of various combinations of all hadrons *including itself*. One then seeks to obtain a self-consistent way of describing all strongly interacting particles in terms of combinations of what are essentially force fields. This is closely related to Bohr's idea that the nucleus should not be treated as a collection of

TABLE 96-1. *Some Strange Particles. (From M. Gell-Mann and E. P. Rosenbaum,* Scientific American, *197(1957), 85.)*

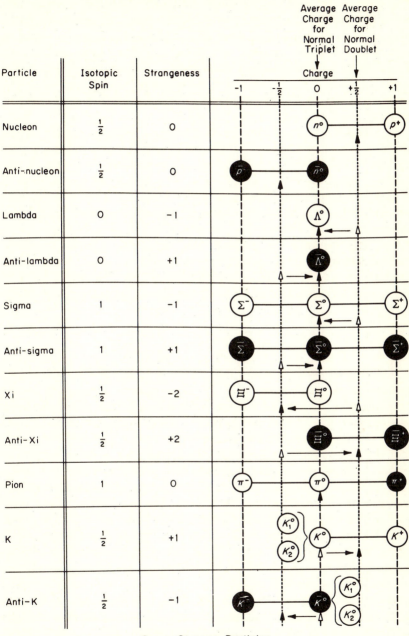

Some Strange Particles

Arrows to the right and left show the displacement of strange particles from normal position.

TABLE 96–2. *The Fundamental Particles*

Particle		Spin	Strangeness	I	I_z	Mass, Mev	Lifetime, sec	Decay mode
Graviton	g	2				0	Stable	
Photon	γ	1				0	Stable	
Leptons	e^-	½				0.510976 ± 0.000007	Stable	$e^- + \nu + \nu$
	μ^-	½				105.70 ± 0.06	$2.212 \pm 0.001 \times 10^{-6}$	$e^- + \gamma$
								$e^- + e^+ + e^-$
	ν^*	½				0	Stable	$e^- + \nu + \nu + e^+ + e^-$
Mesons	$\pi\pm$	0	0	1	± 1	139.63 ± 0.06	$(2.56 \pm 0.005) \times 10^{-8}$	$\mu^\pm + \left\{ \begin{matrix} \nu \\ \nu \end{matrix} \right\}$
								$e^\pm + \left\{ \begin{matrix} \nu \\ \nu \end{matrix} \right\}$
	π°	0	0	1	0	135.04 ± 0.16	$< 4 \times 10^{-16}$	2γ
	K^+	0	1	½	½	494.0 ± 0.2	$(1.224 \pm 0.013) \times 10^{-8}$	$\pi^+ + \pi^- + \pi^+$
								$\pi^+ + \pi^\circ + \pi^\circ$
								$\pi^+ + \pi^\circ$
								$\mu^+ + \nu + \pi^\circ$
								$e^+ + \nu + \pi^\circ$
								$\mu^+ + \nu$
	K°	0	1	½	$-½$	497.9 ± 0.6	$K_1^\circ: (1.00 \pm 0.038) \times 10^{-10}$	$\pi^\circ + \pi^\circ$
								$\pi^+ + \pi^-$
							$K_2^\circ: 6.1 \begin{smallmatrix} 1.6 \\ -1.1 \end{smallmatrix} \times 10^{-8}$	$\pi^\circ + \pi^\circ + \pi^\circ$
								$\pi^\circ + \pi^+ + \pi^-$

TABLE 96–2. (*Continued*)

Particle	Spin	Strangeness	I	I_z	Mass, Mev	Lifetime, sec	Decay mode
							$\mu^\pm + \left\{{\nu \atop \nu}\right\} + \pi^\mp$
							$e^\pm + \left\{{\nu \atop \nu}\right\} + \pi^\mp$
Baryons p	½	0	½	½	938.213 ± 0.01	Stable	
n	½	0	½	-½	939.506 ± 0.01	(1.04 ± 0.13) × 10³	$p + e^- + \nu$
Λ	½	-1	0	0	1115.36 ± 0.14	(2.505 ± 0.086) × 10^{-10}	$p + \pi^-$; $n + \pi^0$; $p + \epsilon^- + \nu$; $p + \mu^- + \nu$
Σ⁺	½	-1	1	1	1189.40 ± 0.20	(0.81 ± 0.06) × 10^{-10}	$n + \pi^+$; $p + \pi^0$; $n + e^+ + \nu$; $n + \mu^+ + \nu$; Λ + leptons
Σ°	½	-1	1	0	1191.5 ± 0.5	< 0.1 × 10^{-10}	$\Lambda + \gamma$
Σ⁻	½	-1	1	-1	1196.0 ± 0.3	(1.61 ± 0.1) × 10^{-10}	$n + \pi^-$; $p + e^- + \nu$; $p + \mu^- + \nu$; Λ + leptons
Ξ°	Fermion	-2	½	½	1311 ± 8.0	1.5 × 10^{-10} (1 event)	$\Lambda + \pi^0$
Ξ⁻	Fermion	-2	½	-½	1318.4 ± 1.2	1.28 ± 0.35 × 10^{-10}	$\Lambda + \pi^-$

* ν = neutrino.

nucleons, but rather as a system of interacting force fields. (2) A fundamental set of particles and fields does exist and all other particles can be considered as excited states or "resonances" of these basic particles. This would go back to the Democritus atomistic concept and seek to explain all known particles as constructed of these basic particles.

The first attempts (outside the two schemes listed above) at explaining the baryon mass spectrum in terms of an over-all symmetry—called "global symmetry"—were made independently by Gell-Mann and Schwinger in 1957. The idea behind global symmetry, which is not a very clearly defined concept, is that all baryons are identical particles as far as interactions via the pion field are concerned, but show mass differences when they interact via K-mesons. Thus the π-meson field was treated as the source of very strong baryon interactions and hence highly (globally) symmetrical, whereas the K field was treated as only moderately strong and hence of an unsymmetrical nature. It was hoped that the baryon mass spectrum could be derived from the "broken symmetry" introduced by the K field, just as the electromagnetic field breaks the mass symmetry between a neutron and a proton, which otherwise are identical (charge independence of nuclear forces). This hope was dashed, however, when A. Salam demonstrated in 1959 that the observed scattering of pions by nucleons is different from their scattering by hyperons (baryons other than nucleons) in disagreement with the global idea, which requires that pions interact equally with all baryons.

After the global symmetry theory was discarded, particle physicists still continued their search for a basic underlying symmetry that could lead to a single classification scheme for all particles. Although one cannot say at present that such a basic symmetry has been found, some remarkable successes have been achieved in this field. Again the basic motive in all of this work is, first of all, to establish a universal symmetry for all particles, and then to show that the mass spectrum of these particles can be explained in terms of some kind of symmetry-breaking effect. A symmetry breaking effect means a weak force field that upsets the symmetry imposed by the strong force. Since symmetries mean that certain quantities remain invariant when operators are applied to the dynamic structure of a system and these operators can be arranged into mathematical groups, particle physicists reverted to group theories to find basic groups whose structure would give the desired results. The work that has been done in this field is associated with M. Gell-Mann, Y. Ne'eman, A. Pais, A. Salam, F. Gürsey, T. Sakurai, J. Schwinger, N. Cabibbo, S. Okubo, R. Feynman, R. Marshak, and S. Glashow, among others. It has been variously designated as the "Eightfold Way," the "Octet Unitary Symmetry Model," and the "SU(3) Model," and has been developed as an extension of the SU(2) symmetry model applied to nucleons.

We first indicate briefly how the higher group symmetry was introduced as an extension of the SU(2) group and then see how this type of group-theoretical approach leads to a simple classification scheme. To begin with, since there were just eight known baryons when this search for symmetry was begun—two nucleons, one lambda, three sigmas, and two xi's—it was argued that these should form a supermultiplet, an octet which would then break up into separate isotopic spin, that is, charge, multiplets as the result of a symmetry-breaking effect like the electromagnetic field. Thus, the SU(2) symmetry group, which gives the charge or isotopic spin multiplets, should be contained in a larger symmetry group. The baryons would then correspond naturally to an eight-dimensional irreducible representation of this enlarged unitary group, and the familiar charge multiplets would appear when mass differences were introduced. Thus by a simple generalization of charge independence, that is, SU(2) symmetry, one would obtain the enlarged unitary symmetry that would give the desired result.

Since the SU(2) group is represented by all unitary 2×2 matrices—and there are just three such independent ones, which give the three components of isotopic spin—one is led to the SU(3) group as a natural extension of SU(2). The SU(3) group is represented by all unitary 3×3, that is, 3 rows and 3 columns, matrices. It can be shown that there are just eight independent such matrices and that these can be arranged to correspond to isotopic spin, baryon number—or rather, hypercharge Y, which is defined as baryon number plus strangeness—and to strangeness. The first three of the eight matrices are just the components of isotopic spin, four others are related to strangeness, and the eighth is proportional to hypercharge Y. Thus this "unitary spin" group has an eight-dimensional representation (hence the designation "eightfold way"), which corresponds to the baryon supermultiplet. When the symmetry of this group is broken, isotopic spin and hypercharge (baryon number and strangeness) are still conserved, but the four quantities associated with the remaining four matrices are not conserved and the baryons split into four groups: Ξ, Λ, Σ, and N. Here N stands for nucleon. The electromagnetic field partially destroys the conservation of isotopic spin so that these groups break up into charge multiplets. Finally, weak interaction breaks the symmetry associated with hypercharge or strangeness, and only conservation of baryon number and of electric charge remains as absolute.

The SU(3) group immediately led to an important prediction when applied to mesons. If these also form an octet, then, in addition to the pion triplet and the two K doublets, there must be a singlet of zero strangeness and zero isotopic spin. This meson—called χ by Gell-Mann and $\pi^{0\prime}$ by Ne'eman—now called η was discovered in 1962. Still another meson octet

of larger mass—a charge triplet ρ, a singlet, ω, and two doublets K*, $\overline{\text{K}}$*—
were also predicted and then discovered. Finally, another singlet ϕ was
predicted and discovered. The ρ triplet is related to the pion triplet, K*
and $\overline{\text{K}}$* are related to K and $\overline{\text{K}}$, and ω and ϕ are related to η.

Two other important results were derived from the SU(3) symmetry.
To begin with, one obtains a sum rule that relates the masses of the four
charge multiplets in an octet. In this type of sum rule no distinction is
made between the masses of the baryons in any one charge multiplet,
since these mass differences are quite small. For the baryon octet Gell-
Mann gives the following first-order formula for the masses:

$$(½)(m_N + m_\Xi) = (¼)(3m_\Lambda + m_\Sigma).$$

This agrees with observation to within a few million electron volts. A
similar formula applies to a meson octet, if instead of the masses we use
the squares of the masses. Okubo has generalized this formula to apply
to any supermultiplet and not just to an octet. If I is the isotopic spin of
any member of such a multiplet and S is its strangeness, then the mass M
of this member is

$$M = M_N + aS + b[I(I+1) - S^2/4]$$

where M_N is the nucleon mass and a and b are constants. This reduces to
the previous formula for an octet.

Recently the SU(3) symmetry group was extended to an SU(6) symmetry by combining isotopic spin and strangeness—which together give
the fundamental triplet of SU(3)—with ordinary spin. Since angular spin
can have two orientations in space, this immediately doubles the multiplicity of the symmetry and leads to an SU(6) group of operators. The
results of this wider symmetry are in remarkably good agreement with
observation, and one of its most notable successes is that it gives the
value ⅔ for the ratio of the magnetic moment of the neutron to that of
the proton. This is the first time that a theory has succeeded in explaining
this ratio.

PARTICLE MULTIPLETS AND THEIR MASS SPECTRUM

We can most easily represent the various multiplets of the SU(6)
symmetry group by a particle graph in which the mass is plotted along
the ordinate and the strangeness is plotted along the abscissa, as shown
in Fig. 96–5. We first consider the baryon spectrum. According to this
representation the various particles in this graph are to be looked upon

as "resonances" or "excited states" of the nucleon. This simply means that all of these short-lived states can be reached by supplying the appropriate amount of energy to the nucleon. But these excited states, in general, differ from the ground state (nucleon) not only in energy, that is, mass, but also in ordinary spin, in charge, and in strangeness or hypercharge. These excited states or resonances decay to the ground state in one or more steps with the emission of pions, K-mesons, leptons, or photons. The particular type of particle that is emitted in a transition from the excited to the ground state is determined by the difference in quantum numbers between the two states and the mass difference. If the two states have the same strangeness, pions are emitted, but if they differ in strangeness, K-mesons must be emitted since these mesons are the carriers of strangeness.

Ultimately, the factor that determines the kind of boson that can be emitted when a system goes from one state to another is conservation of energy. A transition will not occur unless a boson with a mass equal to the energy difference between the two states can be created. Thus, to take the simplest and best known case, that of electronic transitions in excited atoms, the only bosons that can be emitted are photons—by electromagnetic coupling—because the energy differences between the excited states of atoms are much too small for the emission of lepton pairs (electron-neutrino pairs) or for meson emission, even though the electron in its excited state is coupled to the meson and lepton fields in addition to the electromagnetic field. In the transitions between the excited states of an atomic nucleus not only are photons emitted, but there is also enough energy for electron-neutrino pair emission by weak interaction coupling to the lepton field. But there is not enough energy for meson emission. Note that an electron-neutrino pair may be treated as a boson since it consists of two fermions. In transitions between the excited states of the nucleon (hyperons or resonances) enough energy is available for the emission of all three types of bosons—photons, lepton pairs, and mesons. Note, however, that K emission can occur only between the highly excited hyperon states and the lower states because of the very large mass of the K-meson. Conservation of energy forbids the de-excitation of the Λ, Σ and Ξ states by the emission of K-mesons even though this would be allowed if enough energy were available since these states differ in strangeness from the ground state (nucleon). If strangeness were absolutely conserved, the Λ, Σ, and Ξ states would thus never decay. But since there is enough energy for the emission of pions and lepton pairs through weak interactions, and since strangeness does not have to be conserved in such interactions, these states do decay by such emissions. In Fig. 96–4 the transitions between the $I = \frac{3}{2}$, $j = \frac{3}{2}^+$ excited states and the ground state of the baryon by π-emission are shown (I is the isotopic spin and j is the ordinary spin). The plus sign above and to the right of the $3/2$ is the parity of the state.

In Fig. 96–5 the various excited states of the baryon spectrum, as given by Weisskopf, are shown. The masses—plotted along the ordinate—are given in units of billion electron volts (Gev) and the various SU(6)

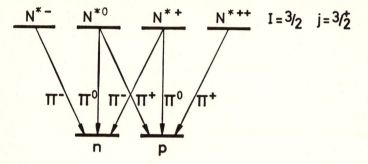

Fig. 96–4. Transitions between the $(3/2, 3/2)$ state and the ground state of the baryon. I, isotopic spin; j, ordinary spin. (From V. Weisskopf, *Science*, 149(1965).)

BARYON SPECTRUM

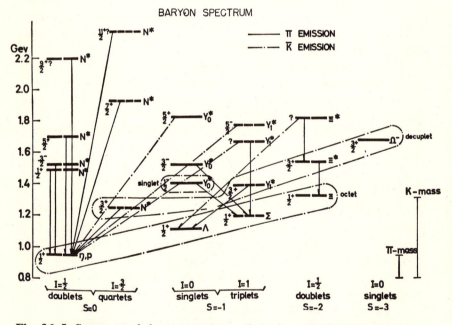

Fig. 96–5. Spectrum of the energy states of the baryon. The isotopic spin I and the strangeness S are given at the bottom, the angular spin and parity are given at the left of the level, the symbol at the right. The isotopic multiplicity, the transitions by meson emission, and some SU(3) multiplets are indicated. (After V. Weisskopf, *Science,* 149(1965), 1180.)

multiplets are encircled. Thus, in addition to the octet (which we have already discussed), there is a singlet Y_0^* and a decuplet consisting of 10 members. The strangeness, plotted along the abscissa, ranges from 0 to -3, and for each value of the strangeness there are different isotopic or charge multiplets. $I = 0$ gives a charge singlet, $I = \frac{1}{2}$ gives a charge doublet, $I = 1$ gives a charge triplet, $I = \frac{3}{2}$ gives a quartet, and so on. The ordinary spin of each state is shown by the number (e.g., $\frac{1}{2}$, $\frac{3}{2}$, and so on) to the left of it. A plus sign at the upper right of this number means that the parity of the state is positive and a minus sign means that it is negative. The letter to the right of each state is the symbol by which it is known. Thus, Ω^- is a baryon singlet of even parity, of spin $\frac{3}{2}$, and of strangeness -3. It has a mass of 1.6 billion electron volts and is a member of a decuplet. Note that all the baryons belonging to the same SU(6) multiplet have the same ordinary spin and the same parity. Thus the octet members all have positive parity and spin $\frac{1}{2}$, whereas all the members of the decuplet have positive parity and spin $\frac{3}{2}$. The emission of a pion in a de-excitation transition is shown by a solid line and the emission

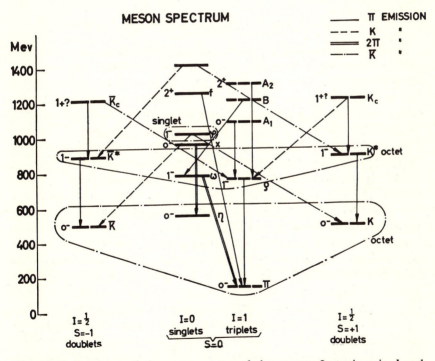

Fig. 96–6. Spectrum of the energy states of the meson. Isotopic spin I and strangeness S are given at the bottom, angular spin and parity at the left of the level, the symbol at the right. The isotopic multiplicity, the transitions by meson emission, and some SU(3) multiplets are indicated.

of a K-meson by a broken line going from the higher to the lower state. The masses of the pion and the K-meson in Gev are shown by the vertical lines to the right of the graph.

In Fig. 96–6 the spectrum of the excited states of the meson or heavy boson is shown as given by V. Weisskopf. Note that in this graph the masses are plotted in units of million electron volts (Mev) rather than in Gev. All other designations are the same as in Fig. 96–3. Two super-multiplets of the SU(6) group and a singlet are shown. The two multiplets are both octets; the lower one is of negative parity and zero spin and the upper one is of negative parity and spin 1. The η meson is shown as a member of the lower octet and the ρ and ω mesons as members of the higher octet. Just as for excited baryons, the excited states of the bosons decay by the emission of pions or K-mesons provided enough energy is present. The ground state of this spectrum—the π mesons—is not a true ground state but only approximately so because pions decay by weak interactions. Note that all boson states have a baryon number B = 0, whereas B = 1 for all baryon states.

THE FUNDAMENTAL TRIPLET: QUARKS

Thus far almost everything that we have described is not much more than very sophisticated classification; we have said very little about attempts—very meager at best—that have been made to explain the baryon and meson spectrums in terms of a dynamic picture, that is, by means of some kind of internal structure of hyperons. The question is whether all of these hadrons (baryons and mesons) can be explained in terms of some basic entities that we might call "elementary" and which therefore have a permanence. Looked at from this point of view the baryons are essentially different from the mesons; baryons cannot disappear, whereas mesons can and do disintegrate. This seems to indicate that there is a real difference between these two types of particles. This also seems to be borne out by the work of Hofstadter, which shows that the nucleons consist of a core surrounded by a pulsating cloud of mesons. In terms of such a picture any baryon may be described as some excited state of the nucleon combined with a few mesons. However, from another point of view, if we consider the properties of baryons and antibaryons, any meson may be pictured as a combination of baryons, antibaryons, and some mesons. Thus, by cleverly manipulating things we can to some extent consider all hyperon states as combinations of each other. This idea is the basis of the "bootstrap" procedure that we have already discussed.

Since bootstrap physics leaves much to be desired and cannot point to very many successes, we must look for other avenues for some kind of insight into the "structure" of hadrons. Here the concept of strangeness may be of great help because the supermultiplets of SU(6) are divided into submultiplets according to the value of the strangeness. It appears, then, that strangeness is related to some kind of symmetry in the dynamics of hadron structure and we might now try to see if we can relate this new symmetry to basic structural elements. To see how this might be done we first consider how the introduction of strangeness enlarges the symmetry properties of hadrons. If there were no strangeness, the basic symmetry of our particles would be the twofold isotopic spin or charge symmetry, and its multiplet structure would be described by the SU(2) symmetry group, which has a basic doublet structure. To see how a doublet symmetry group can be used to construct complex systems, we consider the proton and the neutron which are the two members of the isotopic

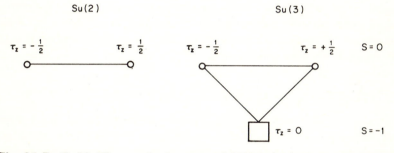

Fig. 96–7. (Left) The two basic states of SU(2) having a z-component of the isotopic spin $\tau_z = \frac{1}{2}$ and $-\frac{1}{2}$. (Right) The three basic states of SU(3) consisting of a basic SU(2) pair and a third state with $S = -1$ and $\tau_z = 0$. (From V. Weisskopf, *Science,* 149(1965).)

doublet $I = \frac{1}{2}$. By combining protons and neutrons in different ways we can obtain the known isotopes of the nuclei. Thus a system of two nucleons gives us either a singlet with isotopic spin 0 (the isotopic spins of the two nucleons are antiparallel) or a triplet with isotopic spin 1 (the two individual isotopic spins are parallel). Three nucleons give us isotopic doublets (total isotopic spin $\frac{1}{2}$) and quartets (total isotopic spin $\frac{3}{2}$). We thus see from the example just given that the SU(2) multiplets in general are derived by combining two basic units, which we may take as the two possible projections along a hypothetical z axis of the isotopic spin $\frac{1}{2}$, as shown on the left of Fig. 96–7. The only possibilities for such a projection for $I = \frac{1}{2}$ are $I_z = \frac{1}{2}$ and $I_z = -\frac{1}{2}$.

Suppose now that to these two basic structural elements we add a third entity with $I_z = 0$ but with $S = -1$. If we now assign the value $S = 0$ to the two entities with $I_z = \pm \frac{1}{2}$, we then get a basic triplet of the sort shown on the right side of Fig. 96–7. The idea now is to see if, by combining these three basic elements (which have been named "quarks") in various ways, we can obtain the observed baryons. That this can, indeed, be done is evident from the material in Fig. 96–8 where various quark combinations are shown to correspond to known hadrons. The two quarks with $I = \frac{1}{2}$ and with $S = 0$ are indicated as circles and the quark with $I = 0$ and $S = -1$ is represented as a square. We now picture each baryon as consisting of exactly three quarks, which may be chosen from among the three basic quarks in any way that may be desired. Expressed

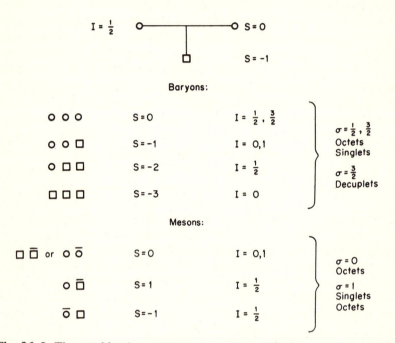

Fig. 96–8. The combinations of three basic "quark" states and the combinations of a pair of quark-antiquark states. The resulting strangeness S, isotopic spin I, the angular spin σ are indicated. (From V. Weisskopf, *Science*, 159 (1965), 1187.)

pictorially, every baryon is to consist of circles and squares combined in groups of three. If we choose all circles, we must have $S = 0$, but we can have $I = \frac{1}{2}$ or $I = \frac{3}{2}$, in other words, charge doublets and triplets. By combining two round quarks and one square quark we get $S = -1$, with $I = 0$ or $I = 1$, that is, charge singlets and triplets. By combining one round quark and two square ones we get $S = -2$ (note that the strangeness quantum numbers are just added algebraically) and $I = \frac{1}{2}$—a charge doublet. Finally, by combining three square quarks we obtain $S = -3$ and $I = 0$—a singlet. We see that these states of isotopic spin and strangeness are just those given by the multiplets of the SU(3) group. The introduction of strangeness has thus enlarged the symmetry group from $SU(2)$ to $SU(3)$ and has led to a basic triplet.

One can now enlarge the $SU(3)$ to an $SU(6)$ symmetry group by including ordinary spin. If we assume that each quark has an angular spin of $\frac{1}{2}$, so that it can have just two orientations in space, we obtain six basic quark states, which, of course, leads to the $SU(6)$ group. Note that if ordinary (angular) spin is not taken into account, the isotopic spin and strangeness lead to 13 quark states: 2 for $I = \frac{1}{2}$, 4 for $I = \frac{3}{2}$, 1 for $I = 0$, and so on. If we now include ordinary spin we obtain twice this number of 26 states. These can be divided into two octets and one decuplet as shown in Fig. 96–5. The octets are associated with angular spin $\sigma = \frac{1}{2}$, $\frac{3}{2}$, and the decuplet is associated with spin $\frac{3}{2}$. There is also a singlet in this scheme with negative parity and spin $\frac{1}{2}$ whose existence can be derived from a quantitative analysis of the $SU(6)$ group.

One can derive the meson supermultiplets from quarks by picturing each meson as consisting of one quark and one antiquark. The strangeness of an antiquark is the opposite of that of the quark. The round antiquark has strangeness 0 and the square antiquark has strangeness $+1$. If all possible combinations of two such quarks are made from the $S = 0$ (round) and $S = -1$ (square) quarks and from their anticounterparts (circles and squares with bars), as shown in the lower half of Fig. 96–6, we obtain the meson supermultiplets. This quark-antiquark combination for mesons is forced on us by the following properties of mesons: Each supermultiplet contains both mesons and their antiparticles with opposite strangeness; triplets with $S = 0$ consist of mesons and their own antiparticles; mesons with $I = \frac{1}{2}$ have strangeness numerically, that is, regardless of sign, equal to 1. It is easy to see from these three properties that only a quark-antiquark combination can give mesons. If ordinary spin is included, the meson spectrum breaks up into two octets: one with spin σ equal to 0 and the other with spin equal to 1. Just as in the baryon spectrum there is also a singlet state ϕ with negative parity and spin 1.

If the three types of quarks (and antiquarks) were identical in mass, all the members of a supermultiplet would have the same mass; of course, this is not so. This would correspond to complete symmetry. There must therefore be some weak force field between the quarks that breaks this symmetry and gives rise to mass differences among the members of a supermultiplet. We may represent this asymmetry by allowing the mass of the $S = -1$ quark to be somewhat larger than the mass of the other two quarks. This means that the supermultiplet would break up into strangeness submultiplets of different masses. Since the more square (strangeness-carrying) quarks we include in a hadron the more massive it is under these conditions, the mass of a hadron should increase with increasing numerical value of the strangeness. Our baryon and meson spectrum graphs show that this is, indeed, the case. The differences in the masses of the members belonging to the same submultiplet of given strangeness arise from the electric charge differences within the sub-multiplet. Put differently, the coupling to the electromagnetic field breaks the symmetry of the supermultiplet still further, thus leading to mass variations within each strangeness submultiplet.

When the basic "quark triplet" was introduced, no baryons of strangeness $S = -3$ were known. The possible quark combination □ □ □ indicates, however, that a baryon with $S = -3$ should exist if the triplet picture is correct. This baryon, the Ω, was subsequently discovered and thus lent considerable support to the SU(6) theory.

SUMMARY

In spite of the many successes quarkists have enjoyed in presenting an orderly and understandable picture of the hadron spectrum, there is no experimental evidence at all that the quarks are anything more than convenient mathematical fictions for expressing the known symmetries. We are certainly not justified at this point in concluding that a nucleon consists of three physical entities having the properties described above simply because the baryon spectrum can be explained in terms of such a model. This, in a sense, would be equivalent to concluding that the photon is composed of an electron-positron pair because the unit spin and the zero charge of the photon can be derived from such a model. We are thus left with a tantalizing and incomplete picture in which the observations are arranged in a very orderly scheme based upon symmetry principles but which gives us no real understanding of what these symmetries mean as far as the dynamic structure of the baryon goes. We may, indeed, have only begun to scratch the surface of the baryon states that can be excited if enough energy is available, and it may well be that only by going to very high energies can we solve the problem of baryon structure.

The baryon spectrum itself seems to tell us this, for the existence in this spectrum of many different resonances lying relatively close together (the masses of all the hadrons lie within about a billion electron volts of each other) means that these, taken all together, are but the fine structure of a single ground state and that higher states at much greater energies are still to be found. This implies that there are perhaps two different kinds of strong forces at work: one extremely strong and the other moderately strong. The very strong force is responsible for the over-all symmetry and it keeps the dynamical structure of the hadron invariant to the SU(6) group of operators. If this very strong force were the only force at work, we would observe no supermultiplets since the masses of all the baryons thus far observed would be equal. But the moderately strong force breaks the SU(6) symmetry and gives rise to the observed supermultiplets. This is similar to the fine structure of the spectral lines of an atom. If there were no electromagnetic interaction among the outer electrons of an atom, the rotational symmetry imposed on the atom by central force arising from the nucleus would give rise to well-separated spectral lines with no multiplet structure. But the electronic interactions destroy this symmetry and cause each of the lines to break up into multiplets. If we apply this same reasoning to baryons, we see that we are simply observing the effects of the moderately strong force and the excited states associated with the very strong force will only be observed when we use excitation energies many times larger (billions of electron volts) than the energy differences between the baryons now observed.

In our search for the hadron structure we must not forget that what is perhaps the most fundamental and simplest question of all still remains unanswered: What is the structure of the electron and why does it have its observed properties? Although the quantum electrodynamics has given us a way of calculating the interaction of the electron with the electromagnetic field to an amazing accuracy, it has done so at the expense of denying us any insight into the origin of the mass or the electric charge of the electron. The values for these quantities are to be accepted as preordained; they are shrouded in the mystery of renormalization—a scheme that relieves us of the mathematical burden of having to work with infinities, but burdens us with a deep sense of incompleteness. Added to the problem of the electron is the problem of the muon and the two neutrinos. Possibly, in analogy with the picture of the nucleon as a core surrounded by a cloud of mesons, we may picture the electron as a core surrounded by a cloud of photons, but how such a structure can maintain itself against very rapid decay is difficult to see, unless we introduce enormously large attractive force fields inside the electron itself.

We conclude this book with the introduction (an excerpt from Newtons *Optiks*) and the summary from an address given by Victor F. Weisskopf to the American Physical Society meeting in Washington, D. C., on April 23, 1965. Weisskopf, who is now Director-General of the European Organization of Nuclear Research (CERN), is ranked as one of the leading physicists today. The many original papers that he published have played an important role in bringing physics to its present exciting position.

ᴑᴑᴑᴑᴑᴑᴑᴑ

WEISSKOPF

Quantum Theory and Elementary Particles [1]

ALL THESE THINGS BEING CONSIDERED, it seems probable to me that God in the beginning formed Matter in solid, massy, hard, impenetrable, moveable Particles, of such Sizes and Figures, and with such other Properties, and in such Proportion to Space, as most conduced to the End for which he formed them; and that these primitive Particles being Solids, are incomparably harder than any porous Bodies compounded of them; even so very hard, as never to wear or break in pieces; no ordinary Power being able to divide what God himself made in the first Creation. While the Particles continue entire, they may compose Bodies of one and the same Nature and Texture in all Ages: But should they wear away, or break in pieces, the Nature of Things depending on them would be changed. Water and Earth, composed of old worn Particles and Fragments of Particles, would not be of the same Nature and Texture now, with Water and Earth composed of entire Particles in the Beginning. And therefore, that Nature may be lasting, the Changes of corporeal Things are to be placed only in the various Separations and new Associations and Motions of these permanent Particles.[2]

SUMMARY

Let us try to summarize what we can answer today to Newton's question for the reasons of the unchanging properties of nature. The characteristic and well-defined structures of atoms and nuclei are based upon the symmetry of quantum states of these composite units. But the stability of their constituents is still poorly understood. There are two types of entities which we encounter here: they go under the names leptons and hadrons. The leptons include the two electrons in their charged and uncharged form, and the hadrons include all baryons and mesons. To our knowledge, these entities are subject to mutual interactions of four different types

---

[1] Victor F. Weisskopf, *Science,* 149 (1965), 1181, 1189.
[2] Isaac Newton, *Opticks* (I. B. Cohen, ed.) (New York: Dover, 1952), p. 400.

TABLE 95-3. *The Four Interactions and Their Symmetries*

Interaction	Translation and Rotation	Charge⎫ Baryon⎬ Conservation	Parity Conservation	Strangeness Conservation	Isotopic Spin Conservation	SU(6)
					Symmetry	
Weak	X	X				
Electromagnetism	X	X	X	X	X	
Strong	X	X	X	X	X	
Very strong	X	X	X	X	X	X

which we enumerate in the order of their strength: gravity, weak interactions, electromagnetism, and strong interactions (see Table 95–3). We leave out gravity from our considerations since its role in the world of elementary particles is completely unknown.

Weak interactions exist between all of these entities, leptons and hadrons alike; electromagnetic interactions are found between all particles carrying charges or magnetic moments; strong interactions exist only in the case of hadrons. Today we do not know whether the hadrons have an internal structure; hence it is not clear whether the strong interactions should be considered as acting between hadrons or as acting between the constituents of hadrons.

The symmetries of these interactions determine many of the properties of the units and therefore are the essential shape-giving factors. It is most interesting that the number of symmetries increases with the strength of interaction. All of the interactions are subject to the translational and rotational symmetry of the space in which they are imbedded. This is a symmetry which appears to us as quite natural. The laws of conservation of energy, momentum, and angular momentum are a direct consequence of these symmetries. All interactions are subject also to two further conservation laws, which are not so well understood at present: the charge conservation, and the conservation of baryon and lepton number. Parity and strangeness, however, are not conserved by the weak interactions; they are conserved only by the electromagnetic interaction, and those stronger than it; isotopic spin conservation holds only for the strong interactions; SU(6) symmetry is valid for the strong interactions, but there exists a relatively weaker part of these interactions which violates it [see Table 96–1].

The stronger the interaction, the more symmetries exist. Is this remarkable fact significant for the ultimate explanation of the existence of elementary particles? It may be, for instance, that a certain number of symmetry principles imposes a unique dynamics, which then determines the properties of its fundamental units. It may also be that hadrons and leptons are not the ultimate structures at all; the hadrons may be composite structures of particles such as the quarks. If this were the case, the proton and the neutron would be a sort of "molecule" made up of fundamental particles; the nuclear force between the nucleons would be a kind of Van de Waals force, an indirect effect of much stronger interactions within the "molecule." Then the fundamental problem of elementary particles would reappear at a higher level when it is asked: why do quarks exist? Most probably, however, the actual solution of the problem will take a new and wholly unexpected form.

It is fit to close these remarks with another prophetic statement of Newton, the timeliness of which is almost uncanny:

Now the smallest Particles of Matter may cohere by the strongest Attractions, and compose bigger Particles of weaker Virtue; and many of these may cohere and compose bigger Particles whose Virtue is still weaker, and so on for divers Successions, until the Progression end in the biggest Particles on which the Operations in Chymistry, and the Colours of natural Bodies depend, and which by cohering compose Bodies of a sensible Magnitude.

There are therefore Agents in Nature able to make the Particles of Bodies stick together by very strong Attractions. And it is the Business of experimental Philosophy to find them out.[3]

---

[3] *Ibid.*, p. 394.

NAME INDEX

SUBJECT INDEX